P9-CKB-350

Concrete
Design
Handbook

THIRD EDITION

Cement Association of Canada
Association Canadienne du Ciment

60 QUEEN STREET, OTTAWA, ONTARIO, CANADA K1P 5Y7

Copyright © 2006

by

Cement Association of Canada

All rights reserved.

With the exception of the CSA A23.3 Standard, this book or any part thereof is the exclusive property of the Cement Association of Canada and must not be reproduced in any form without the written permission of the Cement Association of Canada.

All material in *A23.3-04 Design of Concrete Structures Standard*, and all copyrights, ownership and other rights are the sole and exclusive property of the Canadian Standards Association. Reproduction of this material in any form is prohibited without the written permission of the Canadian Standards Association.

Third Edition
First Printing January 2006

ISBN 1-896553-20-6

Printed in Canada

CAC Concrete Design Handbook

Table of Contents

Chapter 4 — Shear and Torsion

Chapter 5 — Slabs

Chapter 6 — Deflections

Chapter 7 — Short Columns

Chapter 8 — Slender Columns

Chapter 9 — Foundations

Chapter 10 — Prestressed Concrete

Chapter 11 — Seismic Design

Chapter 12 — Anchorage

Chapter 13 — Tilt-up Concrete Wall Panels

GUIDE TO CHAPTERS

Part I

CSA Standard A23.3-04 - Design of Concrete Structures

Explanatory Notes on CSA Standard A23.3-04

Part II

Chapter Design Aid

1 - General

2 – Design for Flexure

3 - Development and Splices of Reinforcement

4 - Shear and Torsion

5 - Slabs

6 - Deflections

7 - Short Columns

8 - Slender Columns

9 - Foundations

10 - Prestressed Concrete

11 - Seismic Design

12 - Anchorage

13 - Tilt-up Concrete Wall Panels

Préface

L'Association canadienne du ciment a décidé de refaire son manuel de calcul des structures de béton, suite à la publication de la norme CSA A23.3-04.

Le manuel contient la norme avec notes explicatives en partie I, suivie des 13 chapitres de la partie II. Chacun de ces chapitres contient des textes explicatifs, des exemples et des graphiques et tableaux couvrant une vaste gamme d'applications pratiques, le tout tenant compte des commentaires reçus de la part des utilisateurs de la version précédente.

Étant donné l'ampleur et la nature de ce document qui est sujet à de fréquentes modifications, et dû au fait que différents auteurs participent à sa rédaction, l'Association canadienne du ciment a donné priorité à d'autres documents dans son programme de traduction.

L'association peut toutefois, grâce à son personnel technique, répondre à toutes les questions qui lui seront posées et cela dans les deux langues officielles.

FOREWORD

This Handbook supersedes the second edition of the Concrete Design Handbook, published by the Association in 1995.

The Concrete design Handbook addresses analysis and design of reinforced concrete structural elements in accordance with CSA Standard A23.3-04, Design of Concrete Structures. This Standard, henceforth referred to as "CSA Standard A23.3", contains significant revisions to the content of the previous edition. These include:

- A reorganization of material, relocating the Symbols and Definitions to the front of the Standard.

- New revised shear design provisions, merging the Simplified and General Methods for shear design and the elimination of iterative calculation procedures.

- Significantly revised seismic design provisions corresponding to the seismic design changes in the 2005 NBCC.

- A complete new Annex "D" on Anchorage, providing anchorage design provisions in accordance with the new Concrete Capacity Design Method.

- New design specifications for piles and pile caps in Clause 15.

- The inclusion of design provision for Slab Band systems new to this edition of the A23.3 Standard, and a general reorganization of Clause 13.

Material explaining the intent and application of these revisions is included in this Handbook.

A reproduction of the Standard appears in the Handbook, together with explanatory notes on its provisions. This material is followed by a total of thirteen chapters covering many aspects of the structural design of conventionally reinforced and prestressed concrete buildings. Basic information on design for fire resistance and design recommendations for structures which will be exposed to corrosive environments are also included.

The format of this Handbook was selected to aid designers in a systematic manner.

Following the CSA Standard and its explanatory notes, each chapter contains informative text and background information on its subject. Design aids covering a broad range of practical applications are provided for design efficiency. Chapters have been prepared by different authors and therefore differ somewhat in the style of presentation. Some authors emphasize reviews of design requirements or trace the background of new provisions, while others concentrate on numerical examples to illustrate applications. Every effort has been made to ensure that a chapter format which best illustrates practical use of the material under consideration has been adopted in all cases. In all example problems, unless otherwise noted, reference to a 'section', 'table', or 'figure' is an implied reference to the Handbook. A reference to a "clause" is an implied reference to CSA Standard A23.3.

NOTE

This publication has been prepared by the Cement Association of Canada to aid in the design of reinforced concrete building structures. It has been the intent of CAC to present information in a manner which will serve as an extension to CSA Standard A23.3-04, Design of Concrete Structures, and the other documents referenced herein. While every attempt has been made to present information that is factual and in a useable format, none of the references to the CSA Standard or the National Building Code should be construed as an endorsement of the material appearing in the Handbook by the agencies responsible for the referenced material.

This publication is intended SOLELY for the use of PROFESSIONAL PERSONNEL who are competent to evaluate the significance and limitations of the information provided herein, and who will accept total responsibility for the application of this information. The authors and the Cement Association of Canada disclaim any and all RESPONSIBILITY and LIABILITY for the application of the stated principles and for the accuracy of any of the material contained in this publication to the full extent permitted by law.

ACKNOWLEDGEMENT

This Handbook was prepared by a team of authors, many of whom are members of the CSA Technical Committee on Reinforced Concrete Design.

Authors involved in the preparation and review of this publication are:

P. Adebar	University of British Columbia
A. Abdel-Akher	Consultant
S. Alexander	UMA Engineering Ltd
M. Bartlett	University of Western Ontario
E.C. Bentz	University of Toronto
M. P. Collins	University of Toronto
W. Dilger	University of Calgary
N. J. Gardner	University of Ottawa
W. Kassian	Kassian Dyck and Associates
T. Kokai	Halcrow Yolles
R. E. Loov	University of Calgary
R. J. McGrath	Cement Association of Canada
D. Mitchell	McGill University
J. Mutrie	Jones ● Kwong ● Kishi
P. Paultre	Université de Sherbrooke
M. Saatcioglu	University of Ottawa
A. Scanlon	The Pennsylvania State University
G. Weiler	Weiler, Smith, Bowers Consultants

The material in Chapter 1 is based on the second edition, and has been updated for the new CSA A23.3-04 Standard and 2005 NBCC requirements. The first edition of this Chapter was written by S. Cumming, M. Saatcioglu and J.G. MacGregor.

Chapter 10 was originally written by P. Breeze, W. Dilger and B. Loov, T. I. Campbell and J. Fowler. The listed authors have updated this Chapter to reflect current CSA A23.3 requirements.

The following people also contributed to the development of Chapter 5 Slabs. Mehmet Aydin, Dennis Bremault, Liwu Guo, Chunglong Li, Yingqing Ling, Joshua Little, Cara Dawn Nash, Grant Ormberg, and Michael Swanson.

Additional support was received from Vivek Anand in the development of Chapter 12.

Permission has kindly been granted by the Canadian Standards Association to reproduce in this Handbook CSA Standard A23.3-04, Design of Concrete Structures.

The permission of the Canadian Commission on Building and Fire Codes to reproduce portions of Appendix "D", Fire Performance Ratings of the National Building Code of Canada 2005, and other selected extracts from the National Building Code of Canada 2005, is gratefully acknowledged.

PART I

CSA STANDARD A23.3-04

Explanatory Notes
on
CSA Standard A23.3-04

With the permission of the Canadian Standards Association, material is reproduced from CSA Standard A23.3-04 Design of Concrete Structures, which is copyrighted by CSA and copies of which may be purchased from CSA, 1560 Spectrum Way Suite 100, Mississauga Ontario, L4W 5N6

Included in this section are Explanatory Notes on the above standard.
The explanatory notes are copyrighted by the Cement Association of Canada.

Note:

This copy of the CSA A23.3 Standard will not be updated to reflect amendments made to the original content by CSA. For up-to-date information, see the current edition of the CSA catalogue of standards, or visit the CSA website at www.csa.ca.

Design of concrete structures

Legal Notice for Standards

Canadian Standards Association (CSA) standards are developed through a consensus standards development process approved by the Standards Council of Canada. This process brings together volunteers representing varied viewpoints and interests to achieve consensus and develop a standard. Although CSA administers the process and establishes rules to promote fairness in achieving consensus, it does not independently test, evaluate, or verify the content of standards.

Disclaimer and exclusion of liability

This document is provided without any representations, warranties, or conditions of any kind, express or implied, including, without limitation, implied warranties or conditions concerning this document's fitness for a particular purpose or use, its merchantability, or its non-infringement of any third party's intellectual property rights. CSA does not warrant the accuracy, completeness, or currency of any of the information published in this document. CSA makes no representations or warranties regarding this document's compliance with any applicable statute, rule, or regulation.

IN NO EVENT SHALL CSA, ITS VOLUNTEERS, MEMBERS, SUBSIDIARIES, OR AFFILIATED COMPANIES, OR THEIR EMPLOYEES, DIRECTORS, OR OFFICERS, BE LIABLE FOR ANY DIRECT, INDIRECT, OR INCIDENTAL DAMAGES, INJURY, LOSS, COSTS, OR EXPENSES, HOWSOEVER CAUSED, INCLUDING BUT NOT LIMITED TO SPECIAL OR CONSEQUENTIAL DAMAGES, LOST REVENUE, BUSINESS INTERRUPTION, LOST OR DAMAGED DATA, OR ANY OTHER COMMERCIAL OR ECONOMIC LOSS, WHETHER BASED IN CONTRACT, TORT (INCLUDING NEGLIGENCE), OR ANY OTHER THEORY OF LIABILITY, ARISING OUT OF OR RESULTING FROM ACCESS TO OR POSSESSION OR USE OF THIS DOCUMENT, EVEN IF CSA HAS BEEN ADVISED OF THE POSSIBILITY OF SUCH DAMAGES, INJURY, LOSS, COSTS, OR EXPENSES.

In publishing and making this document available, CSA is not undertaking to render professional or other services for or on behalf of any person or entity or to perform any duty owed by any person or entity to another person or entity. The information in this document is directed to those who have the appropriate degree of experience to use and apply its contents, and CSA accepts no responsibility whatsoever arising in any way from any and all use of or reliance on the information contained in this document.

CSA is a private not-for-profit company that publishes voluntary standards and related documents. CSA has no power, nor does it undertake, to enforce compliance with the contents of the standards or other documents it publishes.

Intellectual property rights and ownership

As between CSA and the users of this document (whether it be in printed or electronic form), CSA is the owner of all works contained herein that are protected by copyright, all trade-marks (except as otherwise noted to the contrary), and all inventions and trade secrets that may be contained in this document, whether or not such inventions and trade secrets are protected by patents and applications for patents. The unauthorized use, modification, copying, or disclosure of this document may violate laws that protect CSA's intellectual property and may give rise to a right in CSA to seek legal redress for such use, modification, copying, or disclosure. CSA reserves all intellectual property rights in this document.

Authorized use of this document

This document is being provided by CSA for informational and non-commercial use only. The user of this document is authorized to do only the following:

If this document is in electronic form:
• load this document onto a computer for the sole purpose of reviewing it;
• search and browse this document; and
• print this document.

Limited copies of this document in print or paper form may be distributed only to persons who are authorized by CSA to have such copies, and only if this Legal Notice appears on each such copy.

In addition, users may not and may not permit others to
• alter this document in any way or remove this Legal Notice from the attached standard;
• sell this document without authorization from CSA; or
• make an electronic copy of this document.

If you do not agree with any of the terms and conditions contained in this Legal Notice, you may not load or use this document or make any copies of the contents hereof, and if you do make such copies, you are required to destroy them immediately. Use of this document constitutes your acceptance of the terms and conditions of this Legal Notice.

CANADIAN STANDARDS
ASSOCIATION

CSA Standards Update Service

A23.3-04
December 2004

Title: *Design of concrete structures*
Pagination: 232 pages (xviii preliminary and 214 text), each dated **December 2004**

Automatic notifications about any updates to this publication are available.

- To register for e-mail notifications, and/or to download any existing updates in PDF, enter the Online Store at **www.ShopCSA.ca** and click on **My Account** on the navigation bar.

  The **List ID** for this document is **2015962**.

- To receive printed updates, please complete and return the attached card.

✂--

Name _____

Organization _____

Address _____

City _____

Province/State _____

Country _____ Postal/Zip Code _____

E-mail _____

I consent to CSA collecting and using the above information to send me updates relating to this publication.

Visit CSA's policy on privacy at www.csagroup.org/legal to find out how we protect your personal information.

A23.3-04

Affranchir
suffisamment

Place
Stamp Here

ASSOCIATION CANADIENNE DE NORMALISATION
BUREAU CENTRAL DE L'INFORMATION
5060, SPECTRUM WAY, BUREAU 100
MISSISSAUGA ON L4W 5N6
CANADA

CANADIAN STANDARDS ASSOCIATION
CONSOLIDATED MAILING LIST
5060 SPECTRUM WAY, SUITE 100
MISSISSAUGA ON L4W 5N6
CANADA

CSA Standard

A23.3-04
Design of concrete structures

**CANADIAN STANDARDS
ASSOCIATION**

®*Registered trade-mark of Canadian Standards Association*

*Published in December 2004 by Canadian Standards Association
A not-for-profit private sector organization
5060 Spectrum Way, Suite 100, Mississauga, Ontario, Canada L4W 5N6
1-800-463-6727 • 416-747-4044*

Visit our Online Store at www.ShopCSA.ca

ISBN 1-55397-559-6
Technical Editor: Muktha Tumkur

© Canadian Standards Association — 2004

All rights reserved. No part of this publication may be reproduced in any form whatsoever without the prior permission of the publisher.

Contents

Technical Committee on Reinforced Concrete Design

D. Mitchell	McGill University, Montréal, Québec	*Chair*
R.J. McGrath	Cement Association of Canada, Ottawa, Ontario	*Vice-Chair*
P. Paultre	Université de Sherbrooke, Sherbrooke, Québec	*Secretary*
C.M. Allen	Adjeleian Allen Rubeli Limited, Ottawa, Ontario	
F.M. Bartlett	University of Western Ontario, London, Ontario	
W.J. Clark	Morrison Hershfield Limited, Toronto, Ontario	
M.P. Collins	University of Toronto, Toronto, Ontario	
W.H. Dilger	University of Calgary, Calgary, Alberta	
R. Dozzi	Harris Rebar, Stoney Creek, Ontario	
J.R. Fowler	Canadian Precast/Prestressed Concrete Institute, Ottawa, Ontario	
W. Kassian	Kassian Dyck and Associates, Calgary, Alberta	
F. Knoll	Nicolet Chartrand Knoll Limitée, Montréal, Québec	
T. Kokai	Yolles Partnership Inc., Toronto, Ontario	
T. Loo	Omicron Consulting Group, Vancouver, British Columbia	
R.E. Loov	University of Calgary, Calgary, Alberta	
J.G. MacGregor	J.G. MacGregor Engineering Ltd., Halfmoon Bay, British Columbia	
J.G. Mutrie	Jones Kwong Kishi Consulting Engineers, North Vancouver, British Columbia	

J.A. Patrick	Alberta Infrastructure, Edmonton, Alberta	
A. Perry	CBCL Limited, Halifax, Nova Scotia	
C. Taraschuk	Institute for Research in Construction, National Research Council Canada, Ottawa, Ontario	
C.M. Wang	Bantrel Co., Calgary, Alberta	*Associate*
M. Tumkur	CSA, Mississauga, Ontario	*Project Manager*

In addition to the members of the Committee, the following people contributed to the development and publication of this Standard:

P. Adebar	University of British Columbia, Vancouver, British Columbia
S.D.B. Alexander	UMA Engineering Ltd., Edmonton, Alberta
E.C. Bentz	University of Toronto, Toronto, Ontario
W.D. Cook	McGill University, Montréal, Québec
R.H. DeVall	Read Jones Christoffersen Ltd., Vancouver, British Columbia
L. Gartley	Hilti Canada Ltd., Burlington, Ontario
W. Janzen	Bogdonov Pao Associates Ltd., Vancouver, British Columbia
G. Kirkham	Bogdonov Pao Associates Ltd., Vancouver, British Columbia
Y.W.P. Lam	CWMM Consulting Engineers Ltd., Vancouver, British Columbia
J. Markulin	John Bryson and Partners, Vancouver, British Columbia
A. Metten	Bush Bohlman & Partners, Vancouver, British Columbia
S.H. Simmonds	University of Alberta, Edmonton, Alberta

R. Simpson   Glotman Simpson Consulting Engineers,
                        Vancouver, British Columbia

G. Smith   Weiler Smith Bowers Consultants,
                        Burnaby, British Columbia

G. Weiler   Weiler Smith Bowers Consultants,
                        Burnaby, British Columbia

Preface

This is the fifth edition of CSA A23.3, *Design of concrete structures*. It supersedes the previous editions published in 1994, 1984, 1977 (metric) and 1973 (imperial), and 1959.

   This Standard is intended for use in the design of concrete structures for buildings in conjunction with CSA A23.1-04/A23.2-04, *Concrete materials and methods of concrete construction/Methods of test and standard practices for concrete,* and CSA A23.4, *Precast concrete — Materials and construction* (under preparation).

   Changes in this edition include the following:

(a)   This Standard is now based on the load factors and load combinations specified in the *National Building Code of Canada*, 2005 (see Annex C).

(b)   Clause 2.2 contains new definitions for different types of walls; these depend on the level of axial load and the primary loading on the wall.

(c)   In Clause 8.4.2, the resistance factor for concrete, ϕ_c, has been increased from 0.60 to 0.65.

(d)   Clause 10 on flexure and axial loads contains a revised alternative expression for calculating the flexural stiffness, *EI*, for slenderness effects.

(e)   Clause 11 on shear and torsion contains new design provisions for members such as slabs, footings, joists, and wide shallow beams. Clause 11.3.6.3 provides a new, simplified method for shear design. Clause 11.3.6.4 contains revised design provisions for the general method. These revised design provisions are based on the modified compression field theory.

(f)   Clause 13 on two-way slab systems has been revised to provide different distribution factors for factored moments in column strips. New requirements for slab band construction are also specified.

(g)   Clause 14 contains new provisions for reinforcement details for walls, including requirements for concentrated reinforcement and ties for vertical reinforcement. A new clause (Clause 14.4) on the structural design of shear walls has been added. It includes requirements for compression flanges for assemblies of interconnected walls.

(h)   Clause 15 on foundations includes new clauses on the design requirements for pile caps and piles.

(i)   In Clause 16 on precast concrete, the resistance factor for concrete, ϕ_c, has been increased from 0.65 to 0.70 for the design of elements produced in CSA-certified manufacturing plants.

(j)   Clause 18 on prestressed concrete has a modified expression for the stress in unbonded prestressing tendons at factored resistance.

(k)   Clause 21 on special provisions for seismic design specifies requirements that conform to the new categories for seismic force resisting systems in the *National Building Code of Canada*, 2005. Provisions for determining member stiffnesses have been added. The requirements for checking that the columns are stronger than the beams have been changed for the design of ductile frames and frames with moderate ductility. In Clause 21.4.4, the requirements for confinement reinforcement for columns have been changed to include the effects of axial load level as well as the arrangement of transverse reinforcement and longitudinal bars. Maximum spacing limits for transverse reinforcement in columns of ductile frames have been changed. New ductility requirements have been added in Clause 21.6 for individual walls, coupled walls, partially coupled walls, and coupling beams. In Clause 21.6.9 on shear strength of ductile walls, the method for determining the factored shear resistance has been changed. New requirements for the design of squat walls have been added in Clause 21.7.4. A new clause (Clause 21.8) on conventional construction ($R_d = 1.5$) has been added. Clause 21.9 provides new requirements for ductile moment resisting frames, ductile shear walls, and moderately ductile shear walls constructed using precast concrete. New requirements for the design of structural diaphragms have been added in Clause 21.10. Clause 21.11 provides new requirements for foundations, including footings, foundation mats, pile caps, grade beams, slabs on grade, piles, piers, and caissons. Revised requirements for the design of frame members not considered part of the seismic force resisting system are specified in Clause 21.12.

(l)   Clause 22 on plain concrete contains a new clause (Clause 22.8) on the design of deep foundations.

(m) There is a new Annex D on anchorage based on the requirements specified in Appendix D of ACI (American Concrete Institute) 318M-02/318RM-02, *Building Code Requirements for Structural Concrete and Commentary*. Annex D deals with anchors cast into the concrete or post-installed into hardened concrete. It covers anchors used to transmit applied loads, including straight bolts, hooked bolts, headed studs, expansion anchors, undercut anchors, and inserts.

This Standard was prepared by the Technical Committee on Reinforced Concrete Design, under the jurisdiction of the Strategic Steering Committee on Structures (Design), and has been formally approved by the Technical Committee. It will be submitted to the Standards Council of Canada for approval as a National Standard of Canada.

December 2004

Notes:
(1) *Use of the singular does not exclude the plural (and vice versa) when the sense allows.*
(2) *Although the intended primary application of this Standard is stated in its Scope, it is important to note that it remains the responsibility of the users of the Standard to judge its suitability for their particular purpose.*
(3) *This publication was developed by consensus, which is defined by CSA Policy governing standardization — Code of good practice for standardization as "substantial agreement. Consensus implies much more than a simple majority, but not necessarily unanimity". It is consistent with this definition that a member may be included in the Technical Committee list and yet not be in full agreement with all clauses of this publication.*
(4) *CSA Standards are subject to periodic review, and suggestions for their improvement will be referred to the appropriate committee.*
(5) *All enquiries regarding this Standard, including requests for interpretation, should be addressed to Canadian Standards Association, 5060 Spectrum Way, Suite 100, Mississauga, Ontario, Canada L4W 5N6.*
   Requests for interpretation should
   (a) define the problem, making reference to the specific clause, and, where appropriate, include an illustrative sketch;
   (b) provide an explanation of circumstances surrounding the actual field condition; and
   (c) be phrased where possible to permit a specific "yes" or "no" answer.
   Committee interpretations are processed in accordance with the CSA Directives and guidelines governing standardization and are published in CSA's periodical Info Update, which is available on the CSA Web site at www.csa.ca.

A23.3-04
Design of concrete structures

1 Scope

1.1 General
This Standard specifies requirements, in accordance with the *National Building Code of Canada,* for the design and strength evaluation of
(a) structures of reinforced and prestressed concrete;
(b) plain concrete elements; and
(c) special structures such as parking structures, arches, tanks, reservoirs, bins and silos, towers, water towers, blast-resistant structures, and chimneys.
Note: *Special requirements for parking structures are specified in CAN/CSA-S413.*

1.2 Fire resistance
This Standard requires designs to be carried out in accordance with the fire resistance requirements of the applicable building code (see Clause 8.1.2).

1.3 Alternative design procedures
Designs that use procedures which are not covered by this Standard but are carried out by a person qualified in the methods applied and provide a level of safety and performance equivalent to designs complying with this Standard are acceptable if carried out by one of the following methods:
(a) analysis based on generally established theory;
(b) evaluation of a full-scale structure or a prototype by a loading test; or
(c) studies of model analogues.

1.4 Terminology
In CSA Standards, "shall" is used to express a requirement, i.e., a provision that the user is obliged to satisfy in order to comply with the standard; "should" is used to express a recommendation or that which is advised but not required; "may" is used to express an option or that which is permissible within the limits of the standard; and "can" is used to express possibility or capability. Notes accompanying clauses do not include requirements or alternative requirements; the purpose of a note accompanying a clause is to separate from the text explanatory or informative material. Notes to tables and figures are considered part of the table or figure and may be written as requirements. Annexes are designated normative (mandatory) or informative (non-mandatory) to define their application.

1.5 Units of measurement
Equations appearing in this Standard are compatible with the following units:
(a) area: mm^2 (square millimetres);
(b) force: N (newtons);
(c) length: mm (millimetres);
(d) moment: N•mm (newton millimetres); and
(e) stress: MPa (megapascals).
Whenever the square root of the concrete strength is determined, the concrete strength and the square root of the concrete strength are both expressed in megapascals.
Other dimensionally consistent combinations of units may be used, provided that appropriate adjustments are made to constants in non-homogeneous equations.
Note: *Some examples of non-homogeneous equations are found in Clauses 12.2.2 and 12.8.*

2 Reference publications, definitions, symbols, and standard notation and calculations

2.1 Reference publications

This Standard refers to the following publications, and where such reference is made, it shall be to the edition listed below, including all amendments published thereto.

CSA (Canadian Standards Association)
A23.1-04/A23.2-04
Concrete materials and methods of concrete construction/Methods of test and standard practices for concrete
Note: *Excerpts from this Standard are presented in Annex A.*

A23.4 (under preparation)
Precast concrete — Materials and construction

CAN/CSA-G30.18-M92 (R2002)
Billet-steel bars for concrete reinforcement

G40.20-04/G40.21-04
General requirements for rolled or welded structural quality steel/Structural quality steel

CAN/CSA-S16-01
Limit states design of steel structures

CAN/CSA-S413-94 (R2000)
Parking structures

W59-03
Welded steel construction (metal arc welding)

W186-M1990 (R2002)
Welding of reinforcing bars in reinforced concrete construction

ACI (American Concrete Institute)
318M-02/318RM-02
Metric Building Code Requirements for Structural Concrete and Commentary

336.3R-93
Design and Construction of Drilled Piers

55.2-04/355.2R-04
alification of Post-Installed Mechanical Anchors in Concrete and Commentary

2-97
of Slabs on Grade

/T1.1R-01
ce Criteria for Moment Frames Based on Structural Testing

ernational (American Society for Testing and Materials)

cification for Steel Welded Wire Reinforcement, Plain, for Concrete

A 307-04
Standard Specification for Carbon Steel Bolts and Studs, 60 000 PSI Tensile Strength

A 416/A 416M-02
Standard Specification for Steel Strand, Uncoated Seven-Wire for Prestressed Concrete

A 421/A 421M-02
Standard Specification for Uncoated Stress-Relieved Steel Wire for Prestressed Concrete

A 496-02
Standard Specification for Steel Wire, Deformed, for Concrete Reinforcement

A 497/A 497M-02
Standard Specification for Steel Welded Wire Reinforcement, Deformed, for Concrete

A 722/A 722M-98 (2003)
Standard Specification for Uncoated High-Strength Steel Bar for Prestressing Concrete

C 330-04
Standard Specification for Lightweight Aggregates for Structural Concrete

AWS (American Welding Society)
D1.1/D1.1M:2004
Structural Welding Code — Steel

NRCC (National Research Council Canada)
National Building Code of Canada, 2005

User's Guide — NBC 2005: Structural Commentaries (Part 4)

Other publications
ACI-ASCE Committee 550. 1993. Design recommendations for precast concrete structures. *ACI structural journal.* 90:115–121.

Canadian Precast/Prestressed Concrete Institute. 2005. *Design manual: Precast and prestressed concrete.* 4th ed. Ottawa: Canadian Precast/Prestressed Concrete Institute.

Cement Association of Canada. 2005. *Concrete design handbook.* 3rd ed. Ottawa: Cement Association of Canada.

Precast/Prestressed Concrete Institute. 1999. *PCI design handbook: Precast and prestressed concrete.* 5th ed. Chicago: Precast/Prestressed Concrete Institute.

2.2 Definitions
The following definitions apply in this Standard:

Auxiliary member — a rib or edge beam that serves to strengthen, stiffen, or support the shell. Auxiliary members usually act jointly with the shell.

Base (of a structure) — the level at which earthquake motions are assumed to be imparted to a structure. This level does not necessarily coincide with the ground level.

Beam — an element subjected primarily to loads and forces producing flexure.

Bell — an enlargement at the bottom of a pre-drilled cast-in-place concrete pile.

Bonded tendon — a prestressing tendon that is bonded to concrete either directly or through grouting.

Boundary elements — portions of a wall, typically at the ends, that are reinforced by vertical reinforcement and can contain transverse reinforcement. Boundary elements do not necessarily require an increase in wall thickness.

Buckling prevention ties — ties that meet the requirements of Clause 21.6.6.9 and are intended to prevent buckling of the longitudinal reinforcement under reverse cyclic loading.

Collector — an element that serves to transfer forces within a structural diaphragm to members of the seismic force resisting system.

Column — a member that has a ratio of height to least lateral dimension of 3 or greater and is used primarily to support axial compressive load.

Column capital — an enlargement of the column adjacent to the underside of a slab to improve the shear strength of the slab.
Note: *The dimensions c_1 and c_2 and the clear span ℓ_n are based on an effective support area defined by the intersection of the bottom surface of the slab, or of the drop panel if there is one, with the largest right circular cone, right pyramid, or tapered wedge whose surfaces are located within the column and capital or bracket and are oriented not more than 45° to the axis of the column.*

Column strip — that portion of the design strip with a width on each side of a column centreline equal to $0.25\ell_2$ or $0.25\ell_1$, whichever is less. The column strip includes beams, if any.

Composite concrete flexural members — concrete flexural members of precast or cast-in-place concrete elements, or both, constructed in separate placements but interconnected so that all elements respond to loads as a unit.

Concrete —

Plain concrete — concrete that contains no reinforcing or prestressing steel or less reinforcing or prestressing steel than the specified minimum for reinforced concrete.

Reinforced concrete — concrete that is reinforced with not less than the minimum amount of reinforcement required by Clauses 7 to 21 and 23 and is designed on the assumption that the two materials act together in resisting forces.

Structural low-density concrete — concrete having a 28 day compressive strength not less than 20 MPa and an air-dry density not exceeding 1850 kg/m^3.

Structural semi-low-density concrete — concrete having a 28 day compressive strength not less than 20 MPa and an air-dry density between 1850 and 2150 kg/m^3.

Concrete cover — the distance from the concrete surface to the nearest surface of reinforcement or prestressing tendon.

Confinement ties — ties that meet the requirements of Clauses 21.4.4.2 to 21.4.4.4 and are intended to provide confinement to the enclosed concrete.

Connection — a region that joins two or more members, of which one or more is precast.

Ductile connection — a connection that experiences yielding as a result of the design displacement.

Strong connection — a connection that remains elastic while adjoining members experience yielding as a result of the design displacement.

Core — that part of the member cross-section confined by the perimeter of the transverse reinforcement measured from out-to-out of the transverse reinforcement.

Cover — see **Concrete cover**.

Critical section — a section where a plastic hinge can start to form under earthquake loading.

Crosstie — a reinforcing bar that passes through the core and is anchored around reinforcing bars on opposite sides of a member.

Curvature friction — friction resulting from bends or curves in the specified prestressing tendon profile.

Deep foundation — a structural element that transfers loads from the superstructure to the deeper bearing soil or rock strata by end bearing, friction, or both. Examples of deep foundations include driven piles, drilled cast-in-place piles, and slurry walls.

Deformed reinforcement — deformed reinforcing bars, deformed wire, welded smooth wire fabric, and welded deformed wire fabric complying with Clause 3.1.3.

Design cross-section — the representative panel cross-section at the maximum moment and deflection locations of the panel for which the design forces and deflections are determined and from which the resistance and stiffness are calculated.

Design displacement — the total lateral displacement expected for the design basis earthquake calculated in accordance with Clause 4.1.8 of the *National Building Code of Canada*.

Designer — the person responsible for the design.

Design strip — the portion of a slab system that includes beams and supports along a column line and is bound by the centreline of the panels on each side.

Design width — the width of a tilt-up panel to be reinforced to withstand the factored loads tributary to it.

Development length — the length of embedded reinforcement required to develop the design strength of reinforcement.

Development length for a bar with a standard hook in tension — the length measured from the critical section to the outside end of the hook (the straight embedment length between the critical section and the start of the hook [point of tangency] plus the radius of the bend and one bar diameter).

Drilled pile — a pile cast-in-place in a pre-drilled hole.

Driven pile — a reinforced concrete, prestressed concrete, structural steel, timber, or composite pile driven into the ground.

Drop panel — thickening of the slab in the area adjacent to a column for deflection control, extra shear strength, or extra flexural depth.

Ductile coupled shear wall — a shear wall system that complies with Clauses 21.2 and 21.6 and has ductile shear walls connected by ductile coupling beam(s) where at least 66% of the base overturning moment resisted by the wall system is carried by axial tension and compression forces resulting from shear in the coupling beam(s). This structural system qualifies for a force modification factor, R_d, of 4.0 in the *National Building Code of Canada*.

Ductile coupling beam — a coupling beam that complies with Clauses 21.2 and 21.6.8 and is designed to dissipate energy.

Ductile moment-resisting frame — a moment-resisting frame that complies with Clauses 21.2 and 21.5, resists seismic forces, and dissipates energy through beam flexural yielding. This structural system qualifies for a force modification factor, R_d, of 4.0 in the *National Building Code of Canada*.

Ductile partially coupled shear wall — a shear wall system that complies with Clauses 21.2 and 21.6 and has ductile shear walls connected by ductile coupling beam(s) where less than 66% of the base overturning moment resisted by the wall system is carried by axial tension and compression forces resulting from shears in the coupling beam(s). This structural system qualifies for a force modification factor, R_d, of 3.5 in the *National Building Code of Canada*.

Ductile shear wall — a shear wall that complies with Clauses 21.2, 21.6.1 to 21.6.7, and 21.6.9, resists seismic forces, and dissipates energy through flexural yielding at a plastic hinge. This structural system qualifies for a force modification factor, R_d, of 3.5 in the *National Building Code of Canada*.

Effective depth of section — the distance measured from the extreme compression fibre to the centroid of the tension reinforcement.

Effective prestress — the stress remaining in prestressing tendons after all losses have occurred.

Elastic analysis — an analysis of deformations and internal forces based on equilibrium, compatibility of strains, and assumed elastic behaviour.

Embedment length — the length of embedded reinforcement provided beyond a critical section.

Experimental analysis — an analysis based on measuring deformations and strains of a structure or its model. It is based on either elastic or inelastic behaviour.

Factored load effect — the effect of factored load combinations specified in Clause 8.3 (including earthquake load effects determined in accordance with Clause 4.1.8 of the *National Building Code of Canada*).

Flat plate — a flat slab without drop panels.

Folded plate — a special class of shell structures formed by joining flat, thin slabs along their edges to create a three-dimensional spatial structure.

Footing — a shallow structural element that transfers loads from the superstructure to the bearing strata (soil or rock).

Headed bar — a bar with a welded or forged head at one or both ends, with the head dimensioned to be capable of developing the nominal tensile strength of the reinforcing bar at the head-bar interface without failure of the head or crushing failure of the concrete under the head.

Helical tie — a continuously wound reinforcement in the form of a cylindrical helix enclosing longitudinal reinforcement.

Hoop — a closed tie or continuously wound tie. A closed tie can be made up of several reinforcing elements with seismic hooks at each end. A continuously wound tie should also have seismic hooks at each end.

Jacking force — a temporary force exerted by the device that introduces tension into prestressing tendons.

Lifting stresses — stresses in a tilt-up panel during lifting.

Limit states — those conditions of a structure at which it ceases to fulfill the function for which it was designed.

Load —

> **Dead load** — a specified dead load as defined in the *National Building Code of Canada*.

> **Factored load** — the product of a specified load and its load factor.

> **Live load** — a specified live load as defined in the *National Building Code of Canada*.

> **Specified load** — a load specified by the *National Building Code of Canada* without load factors.

> **Sustained load** — the specified dead load plus that portion of the specified live load expected to act over a period of time sufficient to cause significant long-term deflection.

Load factor — a factor applied to a specified load that, for the limit state under consideration, takes into account the variability of the loads and load patterns and analysis of their effects.

Low-density aggregate — aggregate that complies with ASTM C 330.

Middle strip — that portion of the design strip bounded by two column strips.

Moderately ductile moment-resisting frame — a moment-resisting frame that complies with Clauses 21.2 and 21.7.2, that resists seismic forces, and that dissipates energy through beam flexural yielding. This structural system qualifies for a force modification factor, R_d, of 2.5 in the *National Building Code of Canada*.

Moderately ductile shear wall — a shear wall that complies with Clauses 21.2 and 21.7.3, that resists seismic forces, and that dissipates energy through flexural yielding at a plastic hinge or through one of the two mechanisms specified in Clause 21.7.4.2. This structural system qualifies for a force modification factor, R_d, of 2.0 in the *National Building Code of Canada*.

Modulus of rupture of concrete — the flexural strength of concrete determined using the third-point loading test method specified in CSA A23.2.

Moment-resisting frame — a frame in which columns, beams, and joints resist forces through flexure, shear, and compression.

Panel — a slab area bounded by column, beam, or wall centrelines on all sides.

Partial prestressing — prestressing such that the calculated tensile stresses under specified loads exceed the limits specified in Clause 18.3.2(c).

Pedestal — an upright compression member with a ratio of unsupported height to least lateral dimension of less than 3.

Pile — an elongated structural element drilled or driven into the ground for supporting loads by end bearing, friction, or both.

Pile cap — a reinforced concrete element connected to the top of a pile or pile group that transfers loads from the superstructure to the pile or pile group.

Pile casing — a steel tube or liner used for pre-drilled cast-in-place concrete pile construction.

Pile shaft — that portion of the pile from the pile toe to the pile top, excluding any bell or cap.

Pile toe — the bottom of the pile.

Plain reinforcement — reinforcement that does not conform to the definition of deformed reinforcement.

Plastic hinge — a region of a member where inelastic flexural curvatures occur.

Post-tensioning — a method of prestressing in which the tendons are tensioned after the concrete has hardened.

Precast concrete — concrete elements cast in a location other than their final position in service.

Prestressed concrete — concrete in which internal stresses have been initially introduced so that the subsequent stresses resulting from dead load and superimposed loads are counteracted to a desired degree. This can be accomplished by post-tensioning or pretensioning.

Pretensioning — a method of prestressing in which the tendons are tensioned before the concrete is placed.

Probable moment resistance — the moment resistance of a section calculated using axial loads P_s and P_p, where applicable; $1.25f_y$ as the stress in the tension reinforcing; and the specified values of f'_c, with ϕ_c and ϕ_s taken as 1.0.

Regular two-way slab system — a slab system consisting of approximately rectangular panels and supporting primarily uniform gravity loading. Such systems meet the following geometric limitations:
(a) within a panel, the ratio of longer to shorter span, centre-to-centre of supports, is not greater than 2.0;
(b) for slab systems with beams between supports, the relative effective stiffness of beams in the two directions $(\alpha_1 \ell_2^2)/(\alpha_2 \ell_1^2)$ is not less than 0.2 or greater than 5.0;
(c) column offsets are not greater than 20% of the span (in the direction of offset) from either axis between centrelines of successive columns; and
(d) the reinforcement is placed in an orthogonal grid.

Reinforcement — non-prestressed steel that complies with Clauses 3.1.2 and 3.1.3.

Resistance —

   Factored resistance — the resistance of a member, connection, or cross-section calculated in accordance with this Standard, including the application of appropriate resistance factors.

   Nominal resistance — the resistance of a member, connection, or cross-section calculated in accordance with this Standard, without including resistance factors.

Resistance factor — the factor, specified in Clause 8.4 and applied to a specified material property or to the resistance of a member for the limit state under consideration, which takes into account the variability of dimensions, material properties, quality of work, type of failure, and uncertainty in the prediction of resistance.

Ribbed shell — a spatial structure with material placed primarily along certain preferred rib lines, with the areas between the ribs filled with thin slabs or left open.

Sandwich panel — a panel consisting of two concrete layers or wythes separated by a layer of insulation.

Seismic crosstie — a single bar having a seismic hook at one end and a hook not less than 90° with at least a six-bar-diameter extension at the other end. The hooks engage peripheral longitudinal bars. The 90° hooks of successive crossties engaging the same longitudinal bar are alternated end for end.

Seismic force resisting system — that part of the structural system that has been considered in the design to provide the required resistance to the earthquake forces and effects in accordance with Clause 4.1.8 of the *National Building Code of Canada*.

Seismic hook — a hook with at least a 135° bend with a six-bar-diameter extension (but not less than 100 mm) that engages the longitudinal reinforcement and is anchored in the confined core.

Slab band — a continuous extension of a drop panel between supports or between a support and another slab band.

Specified strength of concrete — the compressive strength of concrete used in the design and evaluated in accordance with Clause 4.

Spiral — a helical tie complying with Clauses 7.6.4 and 10.9.4.

Spiral column — a column in which the longitudinal reinforcement is enclosed by a spiral.

Stirrup — reinforcement used to resist shear and torsion stresses in a structural member.
Note: *The term "stirrups" is usually applied to lateral reinforcement in flexural members and the term "ties" to lateral reinforcement in compression members.*

Structural diaphragm — a structural member, such as a floor or roof slab, that transmits forces to or between lateral-force-resisting members.

Tendon — a steel element such as a wire, bar, or strand, or a bundle of such elements, that is used to impart prestress to concrete and complies with Clause 3.1.4.

Thin shell — a three-dimensional spatial structure made up of one or more curved slabs or folded plates whose thicknesses are small compared to their other dimensions.
Note: *Thin shells are characterized by their three-dimensional load-carrying behaviour, which is determined by the geometry of their form, the manner in which they are supported, and the nature of the applied load.*

Tie — a loop of reinforcing bar or wire enclosing longitudinal reinforcement. See also **Stirrup**.

Tilt-up wall panel — a reinforced concrete panel that is site-cast on a horizontal surface and subsequently tilted to a vertical orientation to form a vertical- and lateral-load-resisting building element.

Transfer — the act of transferring force in prestressing tendons from jacks or the pretensioning anchorage to the concrete member.

Tributary width — the width of a panel attracting vertical and horizontal loads that the design width must support.

Wall — a vertical element in which the horizontal length, ℓ_w, is at least six times the thickness, t, and at least one-third the clear height of the element.

> **Bearing wall** — a wall that supports
> (a) factored in-plane vertical loads exceeding 0.10 $f'_c A_g$;
> (b) weak axis moments about a horizontal axis in the plane of the wall; and
> (c) the shear forces necessary to equilibrate the moments specified in Item (b).
>
> **Flexural shear wall** — a shear wall that resists in-plane lateral loads by flexural action. Flexural shear walls have a height, h_w, above the section of maximum moment in the walls that is greater than $2\ell_w$.
>
> **Non-bearing wall** — a wall that supports factored in-plane vertical loads less than or equal to 0.10 $f'_c A_g$ and, in some cases, moments about a horizontal axis in the plane of the wall and the shear forces necessary to equilibrate those moments.
>
> **Shear wall** — a wall or an assembly of interconnected walls considered to be part of the lateral-load-resisting system of a building or structure. Shear walls support
> (a) vertical loads;
> (b) moments about horizontal axes perpendicular to the plane of the wall (strong axis bending); and
> (c) shear forces acting parallel to the plane of the wall.
> Weak axis bending can also be present.
>
> **Squat shear wall** — a shear wall with a height, h_w, above the section of maximum moment in the wall that does not exceed $2\ell_w$.

Wobble friction — friction caused by the unintended deviation of prestressing sheath or duct from its specified profile.

Yield strength — the specified minimum yield strength or yield point of reinforcement.

2.3 Symbols
The following symbols apply in this Standard:

a = depth of equivalent rectangular stress block

a_g = specified nominal maximum size of coarse aggregate

A = area of that part of cross-section between flexural tension face and centroid of gross section (see Clause 18)

= effective tension area of concrete surrounding the flexural tension reinforcement and extending from the extreme tension fibre to the centroid of the flexural tension reinforcement and an equal distance past that centroid, divided by the number of bars or wires. When the flexural reinforcement consists of different bar or wire sizes, the number of bars or wires used to compute A is to be taken as the total area of reinforcement divided by the area of the largest bar or wire used (see Clause 10)

A_b = area of an individual bar

A_c = area enclosed by outside perimeter of concrete cross-section, including area of holes (if any) (see Clause 11)

= area of core of spirally reinforced compression member measured to outside diameter of spiral (see Clause 10)

A_{ch} = cross-sectional area of core of a structural member

A_{cs} = area of concrete in strips along exposed side faces of beams (see Clause 10)

      = effective cross-sectional area of concrete compressive strut (see Clause 11)

A_{ct} = area of concrete on flexural tension side of member (see Figure 11.2)

A_{cv} = area of concrete section resisting shear transfer (see Clause 11)

      = net area of concrete section bounded by web thickness and length of section in the direction of lateral forces considered (see Clause 21)

A_f = area of flange

A_g = gross area of section

A_{gb} = gross area of a boundary element

A_j = minimum cross-sectional area within a joint in a plane parallel to the axis of the reinforcement generating the shear in the joint, equal to the lesser of A_g of the column or $2b_w h_{col}$

A_o = area enclosed by shear flow path, including area of holes (if any)

A_{oh} = area enclosed by centreline of exterior closed transverse torsion reinforcement, including area of holes (if any)

A_p = area of prestressing tendons (see Clause 10)

      = area of prestressing tendons in tension zone (see Clause 18)

      = area of tendons on the flexural tension side of the member (see Clause 11)

A_s = area of longitudinal reinforcement on the flexural tension side of the member (see Clause 11)

      = area of non-prestressed tension reinforcement (see Clauses 12, 13, 18, and 23)

A_s' = area of compression reinforcement

A_{sb} = minimum area of bottom reinforcement crossing one face of the periphery of a column and connecting the slab to the column or support to provide structural integrity

$A_{s,eff}$ = effective area of tension reinforcement

A_{sh} = total cross-sectional area of transverse reinforcement (including crossties) within spacing s and perpendicular to dimension h_c

$A_{s,min}$ = minimum area of tension reinforcement

A_{ss} = area of reinforcement in compression strut

A_{st} = area of reinforcement in tension tie (see Clause 11)

      = total area of longitudinal reinforcement (see Clause 10)

A_t = area of one leg of closed transverse torsion reinforcement (see Clause 11)

      = area of structural steel shape, pipe, or tubing in a composite section (see Clause 10)

A_{tr} = total cross-sectional area of reinforcement that is within spacing s and crosses the potential plane of bond splitting through the reinforcement being developed

A_v = area of shear reinforcement within a distance s

A_{ve} = effective shear cross-section area of coupling beam to be used for analysis

A_{vf} = area of shear-friction reinforcement

A_{vs} = cross-sectional area of headed shear reinforcement on a line parallel to the perimeter of the column

A_w = area of an individual wire to be developed or spliced

A_{xe} = effective axial cross-section area to be used for analysis

A_1 = loaded area

A_2 = area of the lower base of the largest frustum of a pyramid, cone, or tapered wedge contained wholly within the support, having for its upper base the loaded area and having side slopes of 1 vertical to 2 horizontal

b = width of compression face of member (see Clauses 9, 10, and 21)

      = width of compression face of panel within design width (see Clause 23)

      = width of member (see Clause 22)

b_b = band width of reinforced concrete slab extending a distance $1.5h_d$ or $1.5h_s$ past the sides of the column or column capital (see Clauses 13 and 21)

= bearing width for concentrated load (see Figure 23.2)

b_d = design width (see Figure 23.2)

b_f = width of flange

b_o = perimeter of critical section for shear in slabs and footings

b_s = width of support reaction (see Figure 23.2)

b_t = tributary width (see Clause 23)

= width of tension zone of section (see Clause 10)

b_v = width of cross-section at contact surface being investigated for longitudinal shear

b_w = beam web width or diameter of circular section or wall thickness (see Clause 21)

= minimum effective web width (see Clause 11)

= width of web (see Clause 10)

b_1 = width of the critical section for shear (see Clause 13) measured in the direction of the span for which moments are determined

b_2 = width of the critical section for shear (see Clause 13) measured in the direction perpendicular to b_1

c = cohesion stress (see Clause 11)

= depth of the neutral axis, with the axial loads P_n, P_{ns}, and P_s measured from the compression edge of a wall section (see Clause 21)

= distance from extreme compression fibre to neutral axis (see Clauses 9 and 10)

= distance from extreme compression fibre to neutral axis calculated using factored material strengths and assuming a tendon force of $\phi_p A_p f_{pr}$ (see Clause 18)

= distance from extreme compression fibre to neutral axis computed for the cracked transformed section (see Clause 23)

c_t = dimension equal to the distance from the interior face of the edge column to the slab edge measured parallel to c_1, but not exceeding c_1

c_y = distance from extreme compression fibre to neutral axis calculated using factored material strengths and assuming a tendon force of $\phi_p A_p f_{py}$

c_1 = size of rectangular or equivalent rectangular column, capital, or bracket measured in the direction of the span for which moments are being determined

c_2 = size of rectangular or equivalent rectangular column, capital, or bracket measured in the direction perpendicular to c_1

C = cross-sectional constant used in the definition of torsional properties

C_m = factor relating actual moment diagram to an equivalent uniform moment diagram

d = distance from extreme compression fibre to centroid of longitudinal tension reinforcement, but need not be less than $0.8h$ for prestressed members and circular sections (see Clauses 11 and 18)

= distance from extreme compression fibre to centroid of tension reinforcement (see Clauses 9, 10, 12, 13, 21, and 23)

= distance from extreme compression fibre to centroid of tension reinforcement for entire composite section (see Clause 17)

d_a = depth of compression strut (see Figure 11.3)

d_b = diameter of bar, wire, or prestressing strand

d_c = distance from extreme tension fibre to centre of the longitudinal bar or wire located closest to it

d_{cs} = the smaller of
  (a) the distance from the closest concrete surface to the centre of the bar being developed; or
  (b) two-thirds of the centre-to-centre spacing of the bars being developed

d_p = pile shaft diameter (see Clauses 15 and 22)

= distance from extreme compression fibre to centroid of the prestressing tendons (see Clause 18)

d_v = effective shear depth, taken as the greater of $0.9d$ or $0.72h$

e = distance from centroid of section for critical shear to point where shear stress is being calculated (see Clause 13)

= eccentricity of P_{tf} parallel to axis measured from the centroid of the section (see Clause 23)

E_c = modulus of elasticity of concrete

E_p = modulus of elasticity of prestressing tendons

E_s = modulus of elasticity of non-prestressed reinforcement

EI = flexural stiffness of compression member

f_c' = specified compressive strength of concrete

f_{cc}' = specified compressive strength of concrete in columns

f_{ce} = compression stress in the concrete due to effective prestress only (after allowance for all prestress losses) at the extreme fibre of a section where tensile stresses are caused by applied loads

f_{ce}' = effective compressive strength of concrete in columns

f_{ci}' = compressive strength of concrete at time of prestress transfer

f_{cp} = average compressive stress in concrete due to effective prestress force only (after allowance for all prestress losses). For slabs and footings, f_{cp} is the average of f_{cp} for the two directions (see Clause 18)

= compressive stress in concrete (after allowance for all prestress losses) at the centroid of the cross-section resisting externally applied loads or at the junction of the web and flange when the centroid lies within the flange (in a composite member, f_{cp} is the resultant compressive stress at the centroid of the composite section or at the junction of the web and flange when the centroid lies within the flange, due to both prestress and moments being resisted by the precast member acting alone) (see Clause 11)

f_{cs}' = specified compressive strength of concrete in slab

f_{cu} = limiting compressive stress in concrete strut

f_{cw}' = specified compressive strength of concrete in the wall

f_{pe} = effective stress in prestressing tendons after allowance for all prestress losses

f_{po} = stress in prestressing tendons when strain in the surrounding concrete is zero (may be taken as $0.7f_{pu}$ for bonded tendons outside the transfer length and f_{pe} for unbonded tendons)

f_{pr} = stress in prestressing tendons at factored resistance

f_{pu} = specified tensile strength of prestressing tendons

f_{py} = yield strength of prestressing tendons

f_r = modulus of rupture of concrete

f_s = calculated stress in reinforcement at specified loads

f_y = specified yield strength of non-prestressed reinforcement or anchor steel

f_y' = specified yield strength of compression non-prestressed reinforcement

f_{yh} = specified yield strength of hoop reinforcement

f_{yt} = specified yield strength of transverse reinforcement

f_{yv} = specified yield strength of headed shear reinforcement

F_a = acceleration-based site coefficient, as specified in the *National Building Code of Canada*

F_{lc}	=	required tension force in longitudinal reinforcement on flexural compression side of member
F_{lt}	=	required tension force in longitudinal reinforcement on flexural tension side of member
F_y	=	specified yield strength of structural steel section
h	=	overall thickness or height of member
h_a	=	height of effective embedment of tension tie (see Figure 11.3)
h_b	=	distance from soffit of supporting beam to soffit of supported beam (see Figure 11.1)
h_c	=	clear vertical distance between successive floor slabs attached to the shear wall assembly (see Clause 14)
	=	dimension of concrete core of rectangular section measured perpendicular to the direction of the hoop bars to outside of peripheral hoop (see Clause 21)
h_{col}	=	column dimension parallel to shear force in the joint
h_d	=	overall thickness at a drop panel
h_s	=	overall thickness of slab; for slabs with drop panels, the overall thickness of the slab away from the drop panel
h_u	=	unsupported vertical height of wall between horizontal supports
h_w	=	vertical height of wall (see Clause 21)
	=	vertical height of wall above the section of maximum moment in the wall (see Clause 14)
h_x	=	maximum horizontal centre-to-centre spacing between longitudinal bars on all faces of the column that are laterally supported by seismic hoops or crosstie legs
h_1	=	overall height of supporting beam (see Figure 11.1)
h_2	=	overall height of supported beam (see Figure 11.1)
I	=	moment of inertia of section about centroidal axis
I_b	=	moment of inertia about centroidal axis of gross section of beam
I_{cr}	=	moment of inertia of cracked section transformed to concrete
I_e	=	effective moment of inertia
I_{ec}	=	value of I_e at continuous end
I_{em}	=	value of I_e at midspan
I_{e1}	=	value of I_e at end 1 of a continuous beam span
I_{e2}	=	value of I_e at end 2 of a continuous beam span
I_g	=	moment of inertia of gross concrete section about centroidal axis, neglecting reinforcement
I_s	=	moment of inertia about centroidal axis of gross section of slab, equal to $\ell_{2a} h_s^3 / 12$
I_{st}	=	moment of inertia of reinforcement about centroidal axis of member cross-section
I_t	=	moment of inertia of structural steel shape, pipe, or tubing about centroidal axis of composite member cross-section
I_E	=	earthquake importance factor of the structure, as specified in the National Building Code of Canada
J	=	property of the critical shear section analogous to the polar moment of inertia
k	=	effective length factor
k_n	=	factor accounting for the number of longitudinal reinforcing bars in a column
k_p	=	factor accounting for compression on column or wall (see Clause 21)
	=	factor for type of prestressing in Equation (18-1)
k_1	=	bar location factor
k_2	=	coating factor
k_3	=	concrete density factor
k_4	=	bar size factor
k_5	=	welded deformed wire fabric factor

14

K_{bf}	=	panel bending stiffness at factored loads
K_{bs}	=	panel bending stiffness at service loads
K_c	=	flexural stiffness of column; moment per unit rotation
K_{ec}	=	flexural stiffness of equivalent column; moment per unit rotation
K_t	=	torsional stiffness of member; moment per unit rotation
K_{tr}	=	transverse reinforcement index
ℓ	=	effective panel height
ℓ_a	=	additional embedment length at support or at point of inflection (see Clause 12)
	=	length of effective bearing area for strut anchored by reinforcement (see Figure 11.3)
ℓ_b	=	length of bearing (see Figure 11.3)
ℓ_c	=	length of a compression member in a frame, measured from centre-to-centre of the joints in the frame (see Clause 10)
	=	length of the outermost compression segment of a coupled wall (see Clause 21)
	=	the lesser of h_c and w_c (see Clause 14)
	=	vertical clear distance between supports or unsupported length of the drilled pile (see Clause 22)
ℓ_{cg}	=	horizontal distance between centroids of walls on either side of coupling beam
ℓ_d	=	development length of reinforcement
ℓ_{db}	=	basic development length
ℓ_{dh}	=	development length of standard hook in tension, measured from critical section to outside end of hook (straight embedment length between critical section and start of hook [point of tangency] plus radius of bend and one bar diameter) (see Clauses 12 and 21)
ℓ_{hb}	=	basic development length of standard hook in tension
ℓ_j	=	dimension of joint in the direction of reinforcement passing through the joint
ℓ_n	=	clear span (see Clauses 9 and 16)
	=	length of clear span in the direction that moments are being determined, measured face-to-face of supports (see Clause 13)
ℓ_o	=	minimum length measured from the face of the joint along the axis of the structural member, over which transverse reinforcement needs to be provided (see Clause 21)
	=	overall length of tendon between anchors (see Clause 18)
ℓ_t	=	length of attached torsional member, equal to the smaller of ℓ_{1a} or ℓ_{2a} of spans adjacent to the joint
ℓ_u	=	clear span or unsupported length between floors or other effective horizontal lines of lateral support (see Clause 21)
	=	unsupported length of compression member (see Clause 10)
ℓ_w	=	horizontal length of wall
ℓ_1	=	length of span in the direction that moments are being determined, measured centre-to-centre of supports
ℓ_{1a}	=	average ℓ_1 for spans adjacent to a column
ℓ_2	=	length of span transverse to ℓ_1, measured centre-to-centre of supports
ℓ_{2a}	=	average ℓ_2 for the adjacent spans transverse to ℓ_1
	=	distance from edge to panel centreline for spans along an edge
L	=	variable load due to intended use and occupancy, including loads due to cranes, pressure of liquids in containers, or related moments or forces
m_x	=	bending moment per unit length on section perpendicular to the x-axis
	=	total design moment per unit length on section perpendicular to the x-axis
m_{xy}	=	torsional moment per unit length on section

m_y	=	bending moment per unit length on section perpendicular to the y-axis
	=	total design moment per unit length on section perpendicular to the y-axis
M_a	=	maximum moment in member at load stage at which deflection is computed or at any previous load stage
M_b	=	maximum factored moment in panel at load stage at which deflection is computed, not including P-Δ effects
M_{bs}	=	maximum moment in panel due to service loads at load stage at which deflection is computed, not including P-Δ effects
M_c	=	magnified factored moment to be used for design of compression member
M_{cr}	=	cracking moment
M_{dc}	=	decompression moment, equal to the moment when the compressive stress on the tensile face of a prestressed member is zero
M_f	=	factored moment at interior support resisted by elements above and below the slab (see Equation (13-24))
	=	factored moment, including P-Δ effects (see Clause 23)
	=	moment due to factored loads (see Clauses 10, 11, 18, and 20)
	=	unbalanced moment about the centroid of the critical shear section (see Equation (13-9))
M_{fs}	=	factored strong axis moment acting on a shear wall
M_{fw}	=	factored weak axis moment acting on a shear wall
M_{nc}	=	nominal flexural resistance of a column
M_o	=	total factored static moment
M_{pb}	=	probable flexural resistance of a beam
M_r	=	factored moment resistance
M_s	=	factored end moment on a compression member due to loads that result in appreciable sway, calculated using a first-order elastic frame analysis (see Clause 10)
	=	maximum moment due to service loads, including P-Δ effects (see Clause 23)
	=	moment due to specified loads (see Clause 18)
	=	portion of slab moment balanced by support moment (see Clause 21)
M_1	=	smaller factored end moment on a compression member associated with the same loading case as M_2 (positive if member is bent in single curvature, negative if bent in double curvature)
M_{1ns}	=	factored end moment on a compression member at the end at which M_1 acts, due to loads that cause no appreciable sway, calculated using a first-order elastic frame analysis
M_{1s}	=	factored end moment on a compression member at the end at which M_1 acts, due to loads that cause appreciable sway, calculated using a first-order elastic frame analysis
M_2	=	larger factored end moment on a compression member (always positive)
M_{2ns}	=	factored end moment on a compression member at the end at which M_2 acts, due to loads that cause no appreciable sway, calculated using a first-order elastic frame analysis
M_{2s}	=	factored end moment on a compression member at the end at which M_2 acts, due to loads that cause appreciable sway, calculated using a first-order elastic frame analysis
n	=	number of bars or wires being spliced or developed along the potential plane of bond splitting
n_ℓ	=	total number of longitudinal bars in the column cross-section that are laterally supported by the corner of hoops or by hooks of seismic crossties
N	=	unfactored permanent compressive load perpendicular to the shear plane (see Clause 11)
N_c	=	tensile force in concrete
N_f	=	factored axial load normal to the cross-section occurring simultaneously with V_f, including effects of tension due to creep and shrinkage (taken as positive for tension and negative for compression)

N_r = factored resistance in tension

p_c = outside perimeter of the concrete cross-section

p_h = perimeter of the centreline of the closed transverse torsion reinforcement

P_c = critical axial load

P_f = factored axial load (see Clauses 10 and 20)

     = factored load at mid-height of panel (see Clause 23)

     = maximum factored axial load for earthquake loading cases (see Clause 21)

P_n = earthquake-induced transfer force resulting from interaction between elements of a linked or coupled wall system, taken as the sum of the end shears corresponding to the nominal flexural resistance in the coupling beams above the section

P_{ns} = nominal net force on a cross-section for the direction being considered due to yielding in tension or compression of concentrated and distributed reinforcement during plastic hinge formation (positive for tension)

P_o = nominal axial resistance at zero eccentricity

P_p = earthquake-induced transfer force resulting from interaction between elements of a linked or coupled wall system, taken as the sum of the end shears corresponding to the probable flexural resistance in the coupling beams above the section

P_r = factored axial load resistance of wall

$P_{r,max}$ = maximum axial load resistance calculated using Equations (10-8) and (10-9)

P_{ro} = factored axial load resistance at zero eccentricity

P_s = axial force at section resulting from factored dead load plus factored live load using earthquake load factors (see Clause 21)

     = service load at mid-height of panel (see Clause 23)

P_{tf} = factored load from tributary roof or floor area

P_{ts} = service load from tributary roof or floor area

P_{wf} = factored weight of panel tributary to and above design section

P_{ws} = unfactored weight of panel tributary to and above design section

Q = stability index for a storey

r = radius of gyration of cross-section of a compression member

R_d = ductility-related force modification factor, as specified in the *National Building Code of Canada*

R_o = overstrength-related force modification factor, as specified in the *National Building Code of Canada*

R_E = reduction factor on two-way shear stress as a function of interstorey deflection

s = factor for creep deflections under sustained loads (see Clause 9)

     = maximum centre-to-centre spacing of transverse reinforcement within ℓ_d (see Clause 12)

     = spacing of headed shear reinforcement or stirrups measured perpendicular to b_o (see Clause 13)

     = spacing of shear or torsion reinforcement measured parallel to the longitudinal axis of the member (see Clause 11)

     = spacing of transverse reinforcement measured along the longitudinal axis of the structural member (see Clause 21)

s_w = spacing of wire to be developed or spliced

s_x = longitudinal spacing of transverse reinforcement

s_z = crack spacing parameter dependent on crack control characteristics of longitudinal reinforcement (see Figure 11.2)

s_{ze} = equivalent value of s_z that allows for influence of aggregate size

S = variable loads due to ice, rain, and snow (including associated rain)

$S_a(0.2)$ = damped spectral response acceleration for a period of 0.2 s, as specified in the *National Building Code of Canada*

S_p = moment, shear, or axial force at connection corresponding to development of probable strength at intended yield locations, based on the governing mechanism of inelastic lateral deformation, considering both gravity and earthquake load effects

S_r = factored flexural, shear, or axial resistance of a connection

t = wall thickness (see Clauses 14 and 22)

= wall thickness of box section (see Clause 11)

T = effects of imposed deformations due to moisture changes, shrinkage, creep, temperature, and ground settlement or combinations thereof

T_{cr} = pure torsional cracking resistance

T_f = factored torsional moment

T_r = factored torsional resistance provided by circulatory shear flow

v_c = factored shear stress resistance provided by the concrete

v_f = factored shear stress

v_r = factored shear stress resistance (see Clauses 13 and 18)

= factored shear stress resistance of shear plane (see Clause 11)

v_s = factored shear stress resistance provided by shear reinforcement

V_c = shear resistance attributed to the concrete factored by ϕ_c

V_f = factored horizontal shear in a storey (see Clause 10)

= factored shear force (see Clauses 11, 12, 13, 17, 20, and 22)

V_{fb} = factored shear force through a beam-column joint acting parallel to beam bars

V_p = component in the direction of the applied shear of the effective prestressing force factored by ϕ_p; for variable depth members, the sum of the component of the effective prestressing force and the components of flexural compression and tension in the direction of the applied shear, positive if resisting applied shear, factored by ϕ_p

V_r = factored shear resistance

$V_{r\ell}$ = factored longitudinal shear resistance

$V_{r,max}$ = maximum possible factored shear resistance

V_s = shear resistance provided by shear reinforcement factored by ϕ_s

V_{se} = shear transmitted to column or column capital due to specified loads, but not less than the shear corresponding to twice the self-weight of the slab

w_b = width of a bearing for a concentrated vertical load acting on a wall

w_c = clear horizontal distance between adjacent shear wall webs, if webs are present

w_{df} = factored dead load per unit area

w_f = factored load per unit area (see Clause 13)

= factored load per unit length of beam or per unit area of slab (see Clause 9)

= factored uniformly distributed lateral load (see Clause 23)

w_{lf} = factored live load per unit area

w_s = service uniformly distributed lateral load

x = anchorage length of tension tie (see Clause 11)

= centroidal x-axis of a critical section (see Clause 13)

= direction of coordinates in elastic plate theory (see Clause 13.6.4)

= shorter overall dimension of rectangular part of cross-section (see Clause 13)

x_d = dimension from face of column to edge of drop panel (see Figure 13.1)

CSA Standard A23.3-04

y	=	centroidal y-axis of a critical section (see Clause 13.3.5.5)
	=	direction perpendicular to coordinate x in elastic plate theory (see Clause 13.6.4)
	=	longer overall dimension of rectangular part of cross-section (see Clause 13.8.2.9)
y_t	=	distance from centroidal axis of gross section, neglecting reinforcement, to extreme fibre in tension (see Clause 9)
	=	distance from centroidal axis of section to extreme fibre in tension (see Clause 18)
z	=	quantity limiting distribution of flexural reinforcement
α	=	angle between inclined stirrups or bent-up bars and the longitudinal axis of the member (see Clause 11)
	=	ratio of moment of inertia of beam section to moment of inertia of a width of slab bounded laterally by centrelines of adjacent panels (if any) on each side of the beam, equal to I_b/I_s (see Clause 13)
α_c	=	section property reduction factor used for column effective stiffness properties
α_f	=	angle between shear friction reinforcement and shear plane
α_m	=	average value of α for beams on the four sides of a panel
α_s	=	factor that adjusts v_c for support dimensions
α_w	=	section property reduction factor used for wall effective stiffness properties
α_1	=	ratio of average stress in rectangular compression block to the specified concrete strength (see Clause 10)
	=	α in direction of ℓ_1 (see Clause 13)
α_2	=	α in direction of ℓ_2
β	=	factor accounting for shear resistance of cracked concrete (see Clauses 11 and 21)
	=	ratio of clear spans in long to short directions (see Clause 13)
	=	ratio of long side to the short side of footing (see Clause 15)
β_b	=	ratio of area of cut-off reinforcement to total area of tension reinforcement at section
β_c	=	ratio of long side to short side of concentrated load or reaction area
β_d	=	for non-sway frames and for strength and stability checks of sway frames carried out in accordance with Clauses 10.16.4 and 10.16.5, the ratio of the maximum factored sustained axial load to the maximum factored axial load associated with the same load combination
	=	for sway frames, except as required by Clauses 10.16.4 and 10.16.5, the ratio of the maximum factored sustained shear within a storey to the maximum factored shear in that storey
β_p	=	shear stress factor (see Clause 18)
β_1	=	ratio of depth of rectangular compression block to depth to the neutral axis
γ_c	=	density of concrete
γ_f	=	fraction of unbalanced moment transferred by flexure at slab-column connections
γ_v	=	fraction of unbalanced moment transferred by eccentricity of shear at slab-column connections
γ_w	=	wall overstrength factor equal to the ratio of the load corresponding to nominal moment resistance of the wall system to the factored load on the wall system, but need not be taken as less than 1.3
Δ_f	=	deflection of the top of a wall due to the effects of factored loads
Δ_h	=	additional thickness of the drop panel below the soffit of the slab
Δ_o	=	initial panel out-of-straightness (see Clause 23)
	=	relative deflection of the top and bottom of a storey, computed in accordance with Clause 10
Δ_s	=	panel mid-height deflection under service lateral and vertical loads
δ_b	=	moment magnification factor to reflect the $P\text{-}\Delta$ effect at factored loads
δ_{bs}	=	moment magnification factor to reflect the $P\text{-}\Delta$ effect at service loads
δ_i	=	interstorey deflection calculated in accordance with the *National Building Code of Canada*

δ_s	=	moment magnification factor accounting for second-order effects of vertical load acting on a structure in a laterally displaced configuration
ε_{cu}	=	maximum strain at the extreme concrete compression fibre at ultimate
ε_s	=	strain in reinforcement (see Clause 8)
	=	tensile strain in tensile tie reinforcement due to factored loads (see Clause 11)
ε_x	=	longitudinal strain at mid-depth of the member due to factored loads (positive when tensile)
ε_1	=	principal tensile strain in cracked concrete due to factored loads
ζ_s	=	deflection multiplier for sustained loads
θ	=	angle of inclination of diagonal compressive stresses to the longitudinal axis of the member
θ_{ic}	=	wall or coupling beam inelastic rotational capacity
θ_{id}	=	wall or coupling beam inelastic rotational demand
θ_s	=	smallest angle between compressive strut and adjoining tensile ties
λ	=	factor to account for low-density concrete
μ	=	coefficient of friction
ρ	=	ratio of non-prestressed tension reinforcement, equal to A_s/bd
ρ'	=	reinforcement ratio for compression reinforcement, equal to A_s'/bd
ρ_h	=	ratio of area of horizontal distributed reinforcement to gross concrete area perpendicular to this reinforcement
ρ_n	=	ratio of area of distributed reinforcement parallel to the plane to A_{cv} to gross concrete area perpendicular to that reinforcement
ρ_s	=	ratio of volume of spiral reinforcement to total volume of core (out-to-out of spirals) of a spirally reinforced compression member
ρ_{sk}	=	ratio of area of skin reinforcement to A_{cs}
ρ_t	=	ratio of total area of reinforcing steel to gross concrete section
ρ_v	=	ratio of shear friction reinforcement
σ	=	effective normal stress
ϕ	=	resistance factor applied to a specified material property or to the resistance of a member, connection, or structure, which for the limit state under consideration takes into account the variability of dimensions and material properties, quality of work, type of failure, and uncertainty in the prediction of resistance
ϕ_a	=	resistance factor for structural steel
ϕ_c	=	resistance factor for concrete
ϕ_m	=	member resistance factor
ϕ_p	=	resistance factor for prestressing tendons
ϕ_s	=	resistance factor for non-prestressed reinforcing bars
ψ	=	adjustment factor for moment of inertia for prismatic modelling of columns
ω	=	flange buckling factor

2.4 Standard notation and calculations

2.4.1 Standard notation for loads and resistances
In this Standard, the subscript f denotes a load effect based on factored loads and the subscript r denotes a resistance calculated using factored material strengths.

2.4.2 Standard notation for reinforcing bars
In this Standard, the standard notation for metric reinforcing bars is the bar designation number followed by the letter M.

2.4.3 Bar diameter for calculations
Except for calculations involving bar areas, the diameter, d_b, of metric reinforcing bars may be taken as the bar designation number.

3 Materials

3.1 Reinforcement

3.1.1
Reinforcement and prestressing tendons shall comply with Clause 6 of CSA A23.1.

Notes:
(1) *See also Clause 8.5.*
(2) *Pretensioned epoxy-coated strands should not be used in building structures because, in the event of a fire, heat will soften the coating and reduce bond.*

3.1.2
All reinforcement shall be deformed bars, except that plain bars may be used for spirals and plain bars smaller than 10 mm in diameter may be used for stirrups or ties.

3.1.3
Deformed reinforcement shall include
(a) reinforcing bars having deformations and complying with CAN/CSA-G30.18;
(b) welded wire fabric complying with ASTM A 185, with welded intersections not farther apart than 200 mm in the direction of the principal reinforcement, and with crosswires having a cross-sectional area of not less than 35% of that of the principal reinforcement (see also Clause 11.2.4(b));
(c) welded wire fabric complying with ASTM A 497/A497M, with welded intersections not farther apart than 400 mm in the direction of the principal reinforcement, and with crosswires having a cross-sectional area of not less than 35% of that of the principal reinforcement (see also Clause 11.2.4(b)); and
(d) deformed wire for concrete reinforcement complying with ASTM A 496, and not smaller than size MD25.

3.1.4
Prestressing tendons shall comply with the applicable requirements of ASTM A 416/A 416M, ASTM A421/A 421M, and ASTM A 722/A 722M.

3.2 Concrete and other materials

3.2.1
Cast-in-place concrete and constituent materials shall comply with CSA A23.1.

3.2.2
Precast concrete and constituent materials shall comply with CSA A23.4, except as specified in Clause 16.2.2.

4 Concrete quality, mixing, and placement

4.1 Quality

4.1.1
Concrete shall be proportioned and produced in accordance with CSA A23.1 or CSA A23.4, as applicable.

4.1.2
The compressive strength of concrete, f'_c, shall be determined by testing as specified in CSA A23.1, CSA A23.2, or CSA A23.4, as applicable.

4.1.3
Unless otherwise specified, f'_c shall be based on 28 day tests.

4.2 Mixing and placement
Concrete shall be mixed, placed, and cured in accordance with CSA A23.1 or CSA A23.4, as applicable.

5 Drawings and related documents
In addition to the information required by the applicable building codes, the drawings and related documents for structures designed in accordance with this Standard shall include
(a) the size and location of all structural elements, reinforcement, and prestressing tendons;
(b) provision for dimensional changes resulting from prestress, creep, shrinkage, and temperature;
(c) the locations and details of expansion or contraction joints and permissible locations and details for construction joints;
(d) the magnitude and location of prestressing forces;
(e) the specified strength of concrete in various parts of the structure at stated ages or stages of construction and the nominal maximum size and type of aggregate;
(f) the required cover;
(g) identification of the applicable reinforcing steel Standard and the specified type and grade of reinforcement;
(h) the anchorage length and the location and length of lap splices;
(i) the type and location of welded splices and mechanical connections of reinforcement;
(j) the type and grade of prestressing steel; and
(k) identification of the protective coatings for reinforcement, prestressing tendons, and hardware.

6 Formwork, falsework, embedded pipes, and construction joints

6.1 General
Formwork, falsework, construction joints, and the placement of embedded pipes and hardware shall be as specified in CSA A23.1 or CSA A23.4, as applicable.

6.2 Embedded pipes and openings
Embedded pipes and openings for mechanical and other services shall be located so as to have a negligible impact on the strength of the construction or their effects on member strength shall be considered in the design.

6.3 Construction joints

Provision shall be made for the transfer of shear and other forces through construction joints.

Note: *Construction joints in floors should generally be located near the midspan of slabs, beams, or girders unless a beam intersects a girder in that location. In such cases, the joint in the girder should be offset a distance at least equal to the depth of the beam.*

7 Details of reinforcement

Note: *The clauses of CSA A23.1 referred to in this Clause are reproduced in Annex A.*

7.1 Hooks, bends, and headed bars

7.1.1 General

Standard hooks and bends shall comply with Clause 6.6.2 of CSA A23.1. Non-standard hooks or bends shall be detailed on the drawings.

7.1.2 Stirrups and ties

Stirrups and ties shall be anchored by standard stirrup and tie hooks or by heads of headed bars. The standard stirrup and tie hooks shall have a bend of at least 135° unless the concrete cover surrounding the hook is restrained against spalling, in which case a bend of at least 90° shall be permitted. Standard tie hooks with a bend of at least 90° shall be permitted for ties in columns having a specified concrete compressive strength equal to or less than 50 MPa. Stirrups and ties of size 20M and 25M shall have inside bend diameters in accordance with Table 16 of CSA A23.1.

7.1.3 Crossties

Crossties shall be anchored by standard tie hooks or by heads of headed bars. The standard tie hooks shall have a bend of at least 135° at one end and a standard tie hook with a bend of at least 90° at the other end. The hooks shall engage peripheral longitudinal bars. The 90° hooks of successive crossties engaging the same longitudinal bar shall be alternated end for end.

7.1.4 Headed bars and studs

Headed bars and studs with a head of an area equal to ten times the bar area shall be deemed capable of developing the tensile strength of the bar without crushing of the concrete under the head provided that the specified concrete compressive strength is equal to or greater than 25 MPa and the yield strength of the bar used in the design does not exceed 500 MPa.

7.2 Placing of reinforcement

7.2.1 General

Placing of reinforcement shall be shown on the drawings and shall be as specified in CSA A23.1 or CSA A23.4, as applicable.

7.2.2 Draped fabric

When welded wire fabric with wire of 6 mm diameter or less is used for slab reinforcement in slabs not exceeding 3 m in span, the reinforcement may be curved from a point near the top of the slab over the support to a point near the bottom of the slab at midspan, provided that such reinforcement is either continuous over or securely anchored at the support.

7.3 Tolerances

7.3.1
The tolerances for placing of reinforcement shall comply with CSA A23.1 or CSA A23.4, as applicable.

7.3.2
When design requirements necessitate closer tolerances than those specified in Clause 7.3.1, such tolerances shall be clearly indicated on the construction drawings.

7.4 Spacing of reinforcement and tendons

7.4.1 Bars

7.4.1.1
The minimum clear distance between parallel bars shall comply with CSA A23.1.

7.4.1.2
In walls and one-way slabs other than concrete joist construction, the principal reinforcement shall be spaced not farther apart than the smaller of three times the wall or slab thickness or 500 mm.

7.4.1.3
The clear distance between adjacent longitudinal reinforcing bars in compression members shall not be greater than 500 mm.

7.4.2 Bundled bars

7.4.2.1
Groups of parallel reinforcing bars bundled in contact to act as a unit shall be limited to four bars in any one bundle. Bundled bars shall be tied, wired, or otherwise fastened together to ensure that they remain in position.

7.4.2.2
Bars larger than 35M shall not be bundled in beams or girders.

7.4.2.3
Individual bars in a bundle cut off within the span of flexural members shall terminate at different points at least 40 bar diameters apart.

7.4.2.4
Where spacing limitations and clear concrete cover are based on bar size, a unit of bundled bars shall be treated as a single bar of a diameter derived from the equivalent total area.

7.4.3 Pretensioning tendons

7.4.3.1
The clear distance between pretensioning wires or strands at each end of the member shall be not less than $4d_b$ for wire and not less than $3d_b$ for strands. Closer vertical spacing and bundling of strands may be used in the middle portion of the span.

7.4.3.2

The minimum clear space between groups of bundled strands shall be not less than 1.3 times the nominal maximum size of the coarse aggregate.

7.4.4 Post-tensioning tendons

The minimum clear distance between post-tensioning tendons and the requirements for bundling of post-tensioning tendons shall comply with CSA A23.1.

7.5 Special details for columns and walls

7.5.1 Offset bars

7.5.1.1

Where offset bent bars are used, the slope of the inclined portion of the bar with respect to the axis of the column shall not exceed 1:6, and the portions of the bar above and below the offset shall be parallel to the axis of the column. These details shall be shown on the drawings.

7.5.1.2

Adequate horizontal support at the offset bends shall be treated as a design matter and shall be provided by ties, spirals, or parts of the floor construction. Horizontal thrust to be resisted shall be taken as 1.5 times the horizontal component of the factored resistance in the inclined portion of the bar. Ties or spirals, if used, shall be placed not more than 150 mm from the point of the bend.

7.5.1.3

Where a column or wall face is offset by more than 75 mm, longitudinal bars shall not be offset bent.

7.5.2 Splices and load transfer in metal cores

In composite columns,
(a) splices of structural steel cores shall be made as specified in CAN/CSA-S16; and
(b) provision shall be made at column bases to transfer the loads to the footings as specified in Clause 15.9.

7.6 Transverse reinforcement

7.6.1 General

Transverse reinforcement shall comply with Clauses 7.6.2 to 7.6.6 and, where shear or torsion reinforcement is required, with Clause 11.

7.6.2 Composite columns

Transverse reinforcement in composite columns shall comply with Clauses 10.18 and 10.19.

7.6.3 Prestressing tendons

Transverse reinforcement for prestressing tendons shall comply with Clause 18.13.

7.6.4 Spirals for compression members

7.6.4.1

Spiral reinforcement for compression members shall comply with Clause 10.9.4 and, with respect to construction and spacers, with CSA A23.1.

7.6.4.2
Spiral reinforcement shall have a minimum diameter of 6 mm.

7.6.4.3
The pitch or distance between turns of the spirals shall not exceed 1/6 of the core diameter.

7.6.4.4
The clear spacing between successive turns of a spiral shall not be less than 25 mm or greater than 75 mm.

7.6.5 Ties for compression members

7.6.5.1
In compression members, all non-prestressed longitudinal bars of sizes 30M or smaller shall be enclosed by ties having a diameter of at least 30% of that of the largest longitudinal bar. All non-prestressed longitudinal bars of sizes 35M, 45M, and 55M, and all bundled bars, shall be enclosed by ties of at least size 10M. Deformed wire or welded wire fabric of equivalent area may be used.

7.6.5.2
Tie spacing shall not exceed the smallest of
(a)   16 times the diameter of the smallest longitudinal bars or the smallest bar in a bundle;
(b)   48 tie diameters;
(c)   the least dimension of the compression member; and
(d)   300 mm in compression members containing bundled bars.
For specified concrete compressive strengths exceeding 50 MPa, the tie spacing determined in accordance with Items (a) to (d) shall be multiplied by 0.75.

7.6.5.3
Ties shall be located not more than one-half of a tie spacing above the slab or footing and shall be spaced as specified in Clause 7.6.5.2 to not more than one-half of a tie spacing below the lowest reinforcement in the slab or drop panel above.

7.6.5.4
Where beams or brackets frame into a column from four directions, the ties may be terminated not more than 75 mm below the lowest reinforcement in the shallowest of such beams or brackets. (See also Clause 7.7.)

7.6.5.5
Ties shall be arranged so that every corner and alternate longitudinal bar shall have lateral support provided by the corner of a tie having an included angle of not more than 135°, and no bar shall be farther than 150 mm clear on either side from such a laterally supported bar.

7.6.5.6
Where the bars are located around the periphery of a circle, a complete circular tie may be used, provided that the ends of the ties are lap welded or bent at least 135° around a longitudinal bar or otherwise anchored within the core of the column.

7.6.5.7
Welded wire fabric of equivalent area may be used if spliced in accordance with Clauses 12.18 and 12.19. The required splice lengths shall be shown on the drawings.

7.6.5.8
Where anchor bolts are placed in the tops of columns or pedestals, they shall be enclosed by lateral reinforcement that also surrounds at least four vertical bars of the column or pedestal. The lateral reinforcement shall be distributed within 125 mm of the top of the column or pedestal and shall consist of at least two 10M bars.

7.6.6 Beams and girders — Transverse reinforcement

7.6.6.1
Compression reinforcement in beams and girders shall be enclosed by ties or stirrups satisfying the size and spacing requirements of Clauses 7.6.5.1 and 7.6.5.2 or by welded wire fabric of an equivalent area. Such ties or stirrups shall be provided along the length where compression reinforcement is required.

7.6.6.2
Transverse reinforcement for flexural framing members subject to stress reversals or to torsion at supports shall consist of closed stirrups or spirals extending completely around all main reinforcement.

7.6.6.3
Closed ties or stirrups shall be
(a) formed in one piece by overlapping standard stirrup or tie end hooks around a longitudinal bar;
(b) formed in one or two pieces spliced in accordance with the requirements for a Class B splice having a lap of $1.3\ell_d$; or
(c) anchored as specified in Clause 12.13.

7.7 Special details for beam-column connections

7.7.1
At connections of principal framing elements, such as beams and columns, an enclosure shall be provided for end anchorage of reinforcement terminating in such connections.

7.7.2
The enclosure specified in Clause 7.7.1 may consist of transverse framing members, internal closed ties, spirals, or stirrups.

7.7.3
When gravity load, wind, or other lateral forces cause the transfer of moments from beams to columns, transverse reinforcement (ties) not less than that required by Equation (11-1) shall be provided within connections of framing elements to columns. Except for connections that are part of a primary seismic force resisting system, this requirement may be waived if the connection is restrained on four sides by beams or slabs of approximately equal depth. (See also Clause 12.11.2.)

7.8 Minimum reinforcement in slabs

7.8.1
A minimum area of reinforcement of $0.002A_g$ shall be provided in each direction.

7.8.2
For exposure conditions where crack control is essential, reinforcement exceeding that required by Clause 7.8.1 shall be provided.

7.8.3

Minimum reinforcement shall not be spaced farther apart than the smaller of five times the slab thickness or 500 mm.

7.8.4

At all sections where it is required, minimum reinforcement shall be developed in tension for its specified yield strength in compliance with Clause 12.

7.8.5

Prestressing tendons used as minimum reinforcement shall comply with Clause 18.12.6.

7.9 Concrete protection for reinforcement

Concrete cover for reinforcement shall comply with the cover requirements of CSA A23.1, CSA A23.4, or CAN/CSA-S413, as applicable, unless special conditions dictate otherwise. In all cases, concrete cover shall be indicated on the drawings.

8 Design — Limit states, load combinations, and material properties

8.1 Limit states

8.1.1 Durability

Concrete structures shall satisfy the durability requirements of CSA A23.1, CSA A23.4, or CAN/CSA-S413, as applicable, for the intended use and exposure conditions.

8.1.2 Fire resistance

Concrete structures shall satisfy the fire resistance requirements of the applicable building code.

8.1.3 Ultimate limit states

Structures, structural members, and connections shall be designed such that factored resistance is greater than or equal to the effect of factored loads, with the effect of factored loads being determined as specified in Clauses 8.2 and 8.3 and the factored resistance being determined as specified in Clause 8.4.

8.1.4 Serviceability limit states

8.1.4.1 Deflections

Structures and structural members shall be designed to satisfy the deflection control requirements of Clauses 9.8 and 13.2.7, with loadings as specified in Clause 8.3.3.

8.1.4.2 Local damage and cracking

Structural members and connections shall be designed to meet the minimum reinforcement area and maximum reinforcement spacing requirements of this Standard as well as the requirements of Clauses 10.6 and 18.1 to 18.4, with loadings as specified in Clause 8.3.3.

Note: *This Standard does not specifically limit crack widths.*

8.1.4.3 Vibrations

In the design of structures and structural members, consideration shall be given to controlling vibrations within acceptable limits for the intended use.

8.1.5 Structural integrity

Consideration shall be given to the robustness of the overall structural system to minimize the likelihood of a progressive type of collapse.

Notes:

(1) *Provisions for structural integrity are required for two-way slabs (Clause 13.10.6), precast concrete structures (Clause 16.5), and tilt-up structures (Clause 23.2.9).*

(2) *The requirements in this Standard generally provide a satisfactory level of structural integrity for most concrete structures for buildings. It is possible that supplementary provisions for structural integrity will be needed for mixed or unusual structural systems or for structures exposed to severe loads such as vehicle impacts or explosions. For further guidance, refer to Commentary B in the NRCC's User's Guide to Part 4 of the* National Building Code of Canada.

8.2 Loading

8.2.1 General

Loads shall be determined in accordance with the requirements of the applicable building code.

8.2.2 Imposed deformations

8.2.2.1 General

The short-term and long-term forces and effects resulting from the interaction of the stiffness of the structure and imposed deformations such as differential settlement, non-uniform or restrained temperature changes, and restraint of shrinkage and creep shall be considered.

Notes:

(1) *Imposed deformations produce self-equilibrating moments, reactions, and stresses.*

(2) *Imposed deformations can require considerable redistribution of internal forces, which can lead to excessive cracking at service load or to brittle failure.*

(3) *Estimates of differential settlement, creep, shrinkage, or temperature change should be based on realistic assessments of such effects occurring in service. The magnitude of the internal forces and the effects of imposed deformations depend on the magnitude of the deformation, the stiffness of the structure (cracked or uncracked) resisting the deformations, and the time necessary for the deformations to occur.*

8.2.2.2 Load factor for T-loads

When deemed necessary by the designer, imposed deformations, *T*, shall be included in the appropriate load combinations, with the load factor specified in the applicable building code.

8.2.3 Prestress

In statically indeterminate structures, prestress normally causes secondary moments and reactions. These shall be included in ultimate limit state design calculations, with the load factor specified in the applicable building code.

8.3 Load combinations and load factors

Note: *See Annex C.*

8.3.1 General

Structures, structural members, and connections shall be designed to resist the bending moments, axial loads, shear forces, and torsions computed from the factored loads and load combinations specified in Clauses 8.3.2 and 8.3.3 and the applicable building code.

8.3.2 Load combinations for ultimate limit states

The effect of factored loads acting on structures, structural members, and connections shall be determined in accordance with the factored load combinations specified in the applicable building code.

Note: *See Table C.1.*

8.3.3 Load combinations for serviceability limit states

A building and its structural components shall be checked for the applicable serviceability limit states specified in Clause 8.1.4 under the effects of the service loads. The applicable load combination shall be taken as the one that results in the most unfavourable effect for the limit state under consideration.

8.4 Factored resistance

Note: *See Note (3) of the preliminary Notes to Annex C.*

8.4.1 General

The factored resistance of a member, its cross-sections, and its connections shall be taken as the resistance calculated as specified in this Standard, using the material resistance factors specified in Clauses 8.4.2 and 8.4.3.

Notes:

(1) *Member resistance factors are used in Clauses 10.15.3, 10.16.3.2, and 23.3.1.3.*

(2) *In a few cases the member rigidity, EI, is multiplied by a member resistance factor, ϕ_m, specified in the applicable clauses.*

8.4.2 Factored concrete strength

The factored concrete compressive strengths used in checking ultimate limit states shall be taken as $\phi_c f_c'$. The factored concrete tensile strengths used in checking ultimate limit states are given in terms of $\phi_c \sqrt{f_c'}$, where $\phi_c = 0.65$, except as specified in Clause 16.1.3.

8.4.3 Factored reinforcement and tendon force

The factored force in reinforcing bars, tendons, and structural shapes shall be taken as the product of the appropriate resistance factor, ϕ, and the respective steel force as specified in the applicable clause of this Standard, where

(a) ϕ_s = 0.85 for reinforcing bars and embedded steel anchors;

(b) ϕ_p = 0.90 for prestressing tendons; and

(c) ϕ_a = 0.90 for structural steel.

8.5 Reinforcement and tendon properties for design

8.5.1 Design strength for reinforcement

Design calculations shall be based on the specified yield strength of reinforcement, f_y, which shall not exceed 500 MPa except for prestressing tendons.

8.5.2 Compression reinforcement

For compression reinforcement having a specified yield strength exceeding 400 MPa, the value of f_y assumed in design calculations shall not exceed the stress corresponding to a strain of 0.35%.

Note: *CAN/CSA-G30.18 defines the yield strength of Grade 500 reinforcement at a strain of 0.35%.*

8.5.3 Stress-strain curve for reinforcement

8.5.3.1 Reinforcement and tendon stress-strain curve

The force in the reinforcement shall be calculated as ϕ_s for reinforcing bars and ϕ_p for prestressing tendons, multiplied by the force determined from strain compatibility based on a stress-strain curve representative of the steel.

8.5.3.2 Simplified reinforcement stress-strain curve

For reinforcement with a specified yield strength of 500 MPa or less, the following assumptions may be used:

(a) for strains, ε_s, less than the yield strain, f_y / E_s, the force in the reinforcement shall be taken as $\phi_s A_s E_s \varepsilon_s$; and

(b) for strains, ε_s, greater than the yield strain, the force in the reinforcement shall be taken as $\phi_s A_s f_y$.

8.5.4 Modulus of elasticity of reinforcement

8.5.4.1

The modulus of elasticity of reinforcing bars, E_s, shall be taken as 200 000 MPa.

8.5.4.2

The modulus of elasticity for tendons, E_p, shall be determined by tests or supplied by the manufacturer.
Note: *Typical values of E_p range from* 190 000 *to* 200 000 MPa.

8.5.5 Coefficient of thermal expansion of reinforcement

The coefficient of thermal expansion may be taken as $10 \times 10^{-6} / \,°C$.

8.6 Concrete properties for design

8.6.1 Design strength of concrete

8.6.1.1

Specified concrete compressive strengths used in design shall not be less than 20 MPa or more than 80 MPa, except as allowed by Clauses 8.6.1.2, 8.6.1.3, and 22.1.1 or restricted by Clauses 11.3.6.3, 12.1.2, 18.12.3.3, and 21.2.6.
Note: *Designers planning to use specified concrete strengths exceeding 50 MPa should determine whether the appropriate concretes are available. Higher strengths can require prequalification of concrete suppliers and contractors and special construction techniques.*

8.6.1.2

The upper limit on the specified concrete compressive strength specified in Clause 8.6.1.1 may be waived if the structural properties and detailing requirements of reinforced concretes having a strength exceeding 80 MPa are established for concretes similar to those to be used.
Note: *High-strength concretes vary in their brittleness and need for confinement.*

8.6.1.3

Strengths lower than those specified in Clause 8.6.1.1 may be used for mass concrete, plain concrete, or strength evaluation of existing structures.

8.6.2 Modulus of elasticity

8.6.2.1

The modulus of elasticity of concrete in compression, E_c, used in design shall be taken as the average secant modulus for a stress of $0.40\ f_c'$ determined for similar concrete in accordance with ASTM C 469. If the modulus of elasticity is critical to the design, a minimum value of E_c shall be specified and shown on the drawings.
Note: *If the modulus of elasticity is critical to the design, the designer should establish whether such concrete can be produced.*

8.6.2.2

In lieu of results from tests of similar concrete, the modulus of elasticity, E_c, for concrete with γ_c between 1500 and 2500 kg/m^3 may be taken as

$$E_c = (3300\sqrt{f'_c} + 6900)\left(\frac{\gamma_c}{2300}\right)^{1.5}$$ (8-1)

8.6.2.3

In lieu of Clauses 8.6.2.1 and 8.6.2.2, the modulus of elasticity, E_c, of normal density concrete with compressive strength between 20 and 40 MPa may be taken as

$$E_c = 4500\sqrt{f'_c}$$ (8-2)

Note: *The value of E_c is affected by the aggregate fraction in the mix, the modulus of elasticity of the aggregates, and the loading rate. The modulus of elasticity of Canadian concretes will generally be between 80 and 120% of the values specified in Clauses 8.6.2.2 and 8.6.2.3.*

8.6.3 Concrete stress-strain relationship

The concrete compressive stress-strain relationship used in design shall conform to Clause 10.1.6.

8.6.4 Modulus of rupture of concrete

The modulus of rupture, f_r, shall be taken as

$$f_r = 0.6\lambda\sqrt{f'_c}$$ (8-3)

8.6.5 Modification factors for concrete density

The effect of low-density aggregates on tensile strength and other related properties shall be accounted for by the factor λ, where
(a) $\lambda = 1.00$ for normal density concrete;
(b) $\lambda = 0.85$ for structural semi-low-density concrete in which all the fine aggregate is natural sand; and
(c) $\lambda = 0.75$ for structural low-density concrete in which none of the fine aggregate is natural sand.
Linear interpolation may be applied based on the fraction of natural sand in the mix.

8.6.6 Coefficient of thermal expansion of concrete

For the purpose of structural analysis, the coefficient of thermal expansion of concrete may be taken as 10×10^{-6} / °C.
Note: *The value of the coefficient of thermal expansion depends on the type of aggregates, the moisture state of the concrete, and the temperature of the concrete. It can vary between approximately 6×10^{-6} / °C to 13×10^{-6} / °C for concrete at temperatures between 0 and 80 °C.*

9 Structural analysis and computation of deflections

9.1 Methods of analysis

9.1.1

All members of frames or continuous construction shall be designed for the maximum effects of the factored loads as determined by an analysis carried out in accordance with one of the methods of analysis specified in Clauses 9.2 to 9.7.

9.1.2

All structural analyses shall satisfy equilibrium conditions.

CSA Standard A23.3-04

9.2 Elastic frame analysis
Load effects may be determined by elastic analysis based on the assumptions specified in Clauses 9.2.1 to 9.2.4.

9.2.1 Stiffness

9.2.1.1
Assumptions for computing the relative flexural and torsional stiffnesses of columns, walls, floors, and roof systems shall be consistent throughout the analysis.

9.2.1.2
Member stiffnesses used in analyses of the lateral deflections of frames or in second-order frame analyses shall be representative of the degree of member cracking and inelastic action at the loading stage for which the analysis is being carried out.

9.2.1.3
The effect of variable cross-sections shall be considered both in determining bending moments and in the design of the members.

9.2.2 Span length

9.2.2.1
For determining moments in continuous frames, the span length shall be taken as the distance from centre-to-centre of supports.

9.2.2.2
For beams or one-way slabs built integrally with their supports, or for columns in continuous frames, moments at the faces of the joints may be used for design.

9.2.2.3
The span length of a member that is not built integrally with its supports shall be taken as the clear span plus, at each end, half of its depth, but need not exceed the distance between centres of supports.

9.2.2.4
In the analysis of frames containing shear walls, the effect of the width of the wall on the stiffness of the beams framing into the wall shall be considered.

9.2.3 Arrangement of loads

9.2.3.1 Continuous beams and one-way slabs
For continuous beams and one-way slabs, the arrangements of live and dead loads may be limited to combinations of
(a) factored dead load of the structure and factored permanent superimposed dead load on all spans, with factored partition load and factored live load on two adjacent spans;
(b) factored dead load of the structure and factored permanent superimposed dead load on all spans, with factored partition load and factored live load on alternate spans; and
(c) factored dead and factored live load on all spans.
Note: *The superimposed dead load can (but need not) be patterned, depending on the circumstances.*

9.2.3.2 Two-way slabs

Two-way slabs analyzed using the elastic frame method shall be analyzed for the loading patterns specified in Clause 13.8.4.

9.2.4 Redistribution of moments in continuous flexural members

Except when approximate values for bending moments are used, the negative moments at the supports of continuous flexural members calculated by elastic analysis for any assumed loading arrangement may each be increased or decreased by not more than $(30 - 50c/d)$%, but not more than 20%, and the modified negative moments shall be used for calculating the moments at sections within the spans.

9.3 Approximate frame analysis

9.3.1 General

Except for prestressed concrete, approximate methods of frame analysis may be used for buildings having typical spans, storey heights, and types of construction.

9.3.2 Floor and roof loads

The moments due to floor and roof loads may be computed using an elastic analysis of a portion of the frame consisting of the floor or roof in question, with the columns above and below the floor assumed fixed at their far ends.

9.3.3 Moment and shear coefficients

In lieu of a more accurate method of frame analysis, the approximate moments and shears specified in Table 9.1 may be used in the design of continuous beams and one-way slabs, provided that
(a) there are two or more spans;
(b) the spans are approximately equal, with the longer of two adjacent spans not greater than the shorter by more than 20%;
(c) the loads are uniformly distributed;
(d) the factored live load does not exceed twice the factored dead load; and
(e) the members are prismatic.
For calculating negative moments at interior supports, ℓ_n shall be taken as the average of the adjacent clear span lengths.

Table 9.1
Approximate moments and shears
(See Clause 9.3.3.)

(Handwritten note: USE THIS FOR MOMENT COEF'S, with sketch of moment coefficients: $\frac{1}{16}$, $-\frac{1}{10}$, $-\frac{1}{11}$, and below $\frac{1}{14}$, $\frac{1}{16}$, $\frac{1}{16}$, $\frac{1}{14}$)

Moment or shear	Value
Positive moments	
End spans	
Discontinuous end unrestrained	$w_f \ell_n^2/11$
Discontinuous end integral with support	$w_f \ell_n^2/14$
Interior spans	$w_f \ell_n^2/16$
Negative moments	
Negative moment at exterior face of first interior support	
Two spans	$w_f \ell_n^2/9$
More than two spans	$w_f \ell_n^2/10$
Negative moment at other faces of interior supports	$w_f \ell_n^2/11$
Negative moment at interior face of exterior support for members built integrally with supports	
Where the support is a spandrel beam or girder	$w_f \ell_n^2/24$
Where the support is a column	$w_f \ell_n^2/16$
Shear	
Shear in end members at face of first interior support	$1.15 w_f \ell_n/2$
Shear at faces of all other supports	$w_f \ell_n/2$

9.4 Analysis by strut-and-tie models

Strut-and-tie models satisfying the requirements of Clause 11.4 may be used to determine the internal force effects, proportion the reinforcement, and confirm the concrete dimensions.
Note: *Such models are particularly appropriate in regions where plane sections do not remain plane.*

9.5 Finite element analysis

9.5.1
Finite element analysis or other numerical techniques may be used to determine load effects, provided that the differences between the behaviour of the structure and the behaviour assumed in the analysis are accounted for.
Note: *The analysis should account for the effects of cracking. If the effects of cracking are not included, the redistribution of stresses due to the anticipated cracking and the effects of this redistribution on the reinforcement layout should be explicitly considered in the design of the reinforcement.*

9.5.2
Mesh patterns and boundary conditions shall be consistent with geometry, loading, and restraint conditions. Alternative loading cases shall be considered where applicable. Care shall be taken to ensure realistic modelling of the size and stiffness of supporting elements.

9.5.3

Principal reinforcement may be concentrated in bands or tension ties. Anchorage of the reinforcement shall be explicitly considered.

9.5.4

The analysis shall be checked using independent techniques satisfying equilibrium.

9.5.5

Crack control and deflections shall be considered.

9.6 Elastic plate analysis

Analysis of planar structural elements may be based on elastic plate theory (see Clause 13.6).

9.7 Plastic analysis

9.7.1

A plastic analysis shall satisfy either the upper bound theorem or the lower bound theorem of plasticity.

9.7.2

A plastic analysis may assume either a rigid-plastic or an elastic-plastic behaviour.

9.7.3

Hinging sections shall be detailed to provide the rotational capacity assumed in the analysis.

9.7.4

Plastic analyses shall not be used for sway frames.

9.8 Control of deflections

9.8.1 General

Reinforced concrete members subject to flexure shall be designed to have adequate stiffness to limit deflections or any deformations that could adversely affect the strength or serviceability of the structure.

9.8.2 One-way construction (non-prestressed)

9.8.2.1 Minimum thickness

The minimum thickness specified in Table 9.2 shall apply to one-way construction not supporting or attached to partitions or other construction likely to be damaged by large deflections, unless computation of deflection indicates a lesser thickness can be used without adverse effects.

Note: *It is possible that Table 9.2 will not apply to members that have high ratios of superimposed dead or live loads to the self weight.*

Table 9.2
Thicknesses below which deflections are to be computed for non-prestressed beams or one-way slabs not supporting or attached to partitions or other construction likely to be damaged by large deflections

(See Clauses 9.8.2.1, 9.8.5.1, 9.8.5.2, and 13.2.6.)

	Minimum thickness, h			
	Simply supported	One end continuous	Both ends continuous	Cantilever
Solid one-way slabs	$\ell_n/20$	$\ell_n/24$	$\ell_n/28$	$\ell_n/10$
Beams or ribbed one-way slabs	$\ell_n/16$	$\ell_n/18$	$\ell_n/21$	$\ell_n/8$

Note: *The values specified in this Table shall be used directly for members with normal-density concrete where $\gamma_c > 2150$ kg/m^3 and the reinforcement is Grade 400. For other conditions, the values shall be modified as follows:*

(a) *for structural low-density concrete and structural semi-low-density concrete, the values shall be multiplied by $(1.65 - 0.0003\gamma_c)$, but not less than 1.0, where γ_c is the density in kilograms per cubic metre; and*

(b) *for f_y other than 400 MPa, the values shall be multiplied by $(0.4 + f_y/670)$.*

9.8.2.2 Immediate deflections

When deflections are to be computed, deflections that occur immediately on application of load shall be computed by methods or formulas for elastic deflections, taking into consideration the effects of cracking and reinforcement on member stiffness.

Note: *Deflections may be calculated using formulas for elastic deflections based on effective moments of inertia as specified in Clauses 9.8.2.3 to 9.8.2.5, or by methods based on the integration of curvatures at sections along the span.*

9.8.2.3 E_c and I_e

Unless deflections are determined by a more comprehensive analysis, immediate deflection shall be computed using elastic deflection equations; a modulus of elasticity, E_c, for concrete as specified in Clause 8.6.2; and the effective moment of inertia, as follows:

$$I_e = I_{cr} + \left(I_g - I_{cr}\right)\left(\frac{M_{cr}}{M_a}\right)^3 \le I_g \tag{9-1}$$

where

$$M_{cr} = \frac{f_r I_g}{y_t} \tag{9-2}$$

and f_r is as given in Clause 8.6.4, except for two-way slabs (see Clause 13.2.7).

Note: *Construction loading may govern the determination of M_a.*

9.8.2.4 Moment of inertia for continuous spans

For continuous prismatic members, the effective moment of inertia may be taken as the weighted average of the values obtained from Equation (9-1) for the critical positive and negative moment sections, as follows:

(a) two ends continuous:

$$I_{e,avg} = 0.7 I_{em} + 0.15 \left(I_{e1} + I_{e2}\right) \tag{9-3}$$

CSA Standard A23.3-04

(b) one end continuous:

$$l_{e,avg} = 0.85l_{em} + 0.15l_{ec}$$ **(9-4)**

9.8.2.5 Sustained load deflections

Unless values are obtained by a more comprehensive analysis, the total immediate plus long-term deflection for flexural members shall be obtained by multiplying the immediate deflection caused by the sustained load considered by the factor ζ_s, as follows:

$$\zeta_s = \left(1 + \frac{s}{1 + 50\rho'}\right)$$ **(9-5)**

where
ρ' = the value at midspan for simple and continuous spans and at the support for cantilevers
The time dependent factor, s, for sustained loads shall be taken to be equal to the following values:

For loads sustained for five years or more	2.0
For loads sustained for 12 months	1.4
For loads sustained for six months	1.2
For loads sustained for three months	1.0

9.8.2.6 Deflection limits
The deflection computed in accordance with Clauses 9.8.2.2 to 9.8.2.5 shall not exceed the limits specified in Table 9.3.

9.8.3 Two-way construction (non-prestressed)
Deflection control of two-way slab systems shall be checked using Clause 13.2.

9.8.4 Prestressed concrete construction

9.8.4.1 Immediate deflection
For flexural members designed in accordance with Clause 18, immediate deflection shall be computed by methods or formulas for elastic deflection.

9.8.4.2 Moment of inertia
The moment of inertia of the gross concrete section may be used for sections that are uncracked at service loads.

9.8.4.3 Partially prestressed members
For partially prestressed members (i.e., members not satisfying Clause 18.3.2(c)), the reduction in sectional stiffness caused by cracking shall be taken into account.

9.8.4.4 Sustained load deflections
The additional long-term deflection of prestressed concrete members shall be computed by taking into account stresses in concrete and steel under sustained load, including effects of creep and shrinkage of concrete and relaxation of steel.

9.8.4.5 Deflection limits

The computed deflection shall not exceed the limits specified in Table 9.3.

9.8.5 Composite construction

9.8.5.1 Shored construction

If composite flexural members are supported during construction so that after removal of temporary supports the dead load is resisted by the full composite section, the composite member may be considered equivalent to a monolithically cast member for the computation of deflection. For non-prestressed composite members containing more than one type of concrete, the portion of the member in compression shall determine whether the values specified in Table 9.2 for normal density or low-density concrete shall apply. If deflection is computed, account shall be taken of curvatures resulting from differential shrinkage of precast and cast-in-place components and of axial creep effects in a prestressed concrete member.

9.8.5.2 Unshored construction

If the thickness of a non-prestressed precast flexural member meets the requirements of Table 9.2, deflection need not be computed. If the thickness of a non-prestressed composite member meets the requirements of Table 9.2, deflection occurring after the member becomes composite need not be computed, but the long-term deflection of the precast member should be investigated for magnitude and duration of load before the beginning of effective composite action.

9.8.5.3 Deflection limits

Deflection computed in accordance with Clauses 9.8.5.1 and 9.8.5.2 shall not exceed the limits specified in Table 9.3.

Table 9.3
Maximum permissible computed deflections
(See Clauses 9.8.2.6, 9.8.4.5, 9.8.5.3, 13.2.2, and 13.2.7.)

Type of member	Deflection to be considered	Deflection limitation
Flat roofs not supporting or attached to non-structural elements likely to be damaged by large deflections	Immediate deflection due to specified live load, L, or snow load, S	$\ell_n/180$*
Floors not supporting or attached to non-structural elements likely to be damaged by large deflections	Immediate deflection due to specified live load, L	$\ell_n/360$
Roof or floor construction supporting or attached to non-structural elements likely to be damaged by large deflections	That part of the total deflection occurring after attachment of non-structural elements (sum of the long-term deflection due to all sustained loads and the immediate deflection due to any additional live load)†	$\ell_n/480$‡
Roof or floor construction supporting or attached to non-structural elements not likely to be damaged by large deflections	That part of the total deflection occurring after attachment of non-structural elements (sum of the long-term deflection due to all sustained loads and the immediate deflection due to any additional live load)†	$\ell_n/240$§

*This limit is not intended to guard against ponding. Ponding should be checked by suitable calculations of deflection, including added deflections due to ponded water, and the long-term effects of all sustained loads, camber, construction tolerances, and reliability of provisions for drainage should be taken into consideration.
†Long-term deflections shall be determined in accordance with Clause 9.8.2.5 or 9.8.4.4, but may be reduced by the amount of deflection calculated to occur before the attachment of non-structural elements.
‡This limit may be exceeded if adequate measures are taken to prevent damage to supported or attached elements.
§This limit shall not be greater than the tolerance provided for non-structural elements. It may be exceeded if camber is provided so that total deflection minus camber does not exceed the limit.
Note: For two-way slab construction, ℓ_n shall be taken as the clear span in the long direction, measured face-to-face of supports in slabs without beams and face-to-face of beams or other supports in other cases.

10 Flexure and axial loads

10.1 General principles

10.1.1 General
The factored moment and axial load resistance of members shall be based on strain compatibility and equilibrium using material resistance factors and material properties specified in Clause 8 and the additional assumptions specified in Clauses 10.1.2 to 10.1.7.

10.1.2 Plane sections assumption

The strain in reinforcement and concrete shall be assumed to be directly proportional to the distance from the neutral axis, except for unbonded tendons, deep flexural members (see Clause 10.7), and regions of discontinuities.

10.1.3 Maximum concrete strain

The maximum strain at the extreme concrete compression fibre shall be assumed to be 0.0035.

10.1.4 Balanced strain conditions

Balanced strain conditions shall exist at a cross-section when the tension reinforcement reaches its yield strain just as the concrete in compression reaches its maximum strain of 0.0035.

10.1.5 Tensile strength of concrete

The tensile strength of concrete shall be neglected in the calculation of the factored flexural resistance of reinforced and prestressed concrete members.

10.1.6 Concrete stress-strain relationship

The relationship between the compressive stress and concrete strain may be based on stress-strain curves or assumed to be any shape that results in a prediction of strength in substantial agreement with the results of comprehensive tests.

Note: *To account for differences between the in-place strength and the strength of standard cylinders, stress blocks should be based on stress-strain curves with a peak stress not greater than 0.9 f'_c. The equations in Clause 10.1.7 include this factor.*

10.1.7 Equivalent rectangular concrete stress distribution

The requirements of Clause 10.1.6 may be satisfied by an equivalent rectangular concrete stress distribution defined by the following:

(a) a concrete stress of $\alpha_1 \phi_c f'_c$ shall be assumed to be uniformly distributed over an equivalent compression zone bounded by edges of the cross-section and a straight line located parallel to the neutral axis at a distance $a = \beta_1 c$ from the fibre of maximum compressive strain;

(b) the distance c shall be measured in a direction perpendicular to that axis; and

(c) the factors α_1 and β_1 shall be taken as follows:

$$\alpha_1 = 0.85 - 0.0015\ f'_c \text{ (but not less than 0.67)} \tag{10-1}$$

$$\beta_1 = 0.97 - 0.0025\ f'_c \text{ (but not less than 0.67)} \tag{10-2}$$

10.2 Flexural members — Distance between lateral supports

10.2.1

Unless a stability analysis, including the effects of torsional loading, is carried out, beams shall comply with the limits specified in Clauses 10.2.2 and 10.2.3.

10.2.2

For a simply supported or continuous beam, the distance between points at which lateral support is provided shall not exceed the smaller of $50b$ or $200b^2/d$.

10.2.3

For a cantilever beam having lateral restraint at the support, the distance between the face of the support and the end of the cantilever shall not exceed the smaller of $25b$ or $100b^2/d$.

10.3 Flexural members — T-beams

10.3.1
In T-beams, the flange and web shall be built integrally or otherwise effectively bonded together.

10.3.2
A floor topping shall not be included as part of a structural member unless it is placed monolithically with the floor slab or designed in accordance with Clause 17.

10.3.3
The effective flange width of T-beams shall be based on overhanging flange widths on each side of the web, which shall not exceed the smallest of
(a) one-fifth of the span length for a simply supported beam;
(b) one-tenth of the span length for a continuous beam;
(c) 12 times the flange thickness; or
(d) one-half of the clear distance to the next web.

10.3.4
For beams with a slab on one side only, the effective overhanging flange width shall not exceed the smallest of
(a) 1/12 of the span length of the beam;
(b) six times the flange thickness; or
(c) one-half of the clear distance to the next web.

10.4 Flexural members — Joist construction

10.4.1
Joist construction shall consist of a monolithic combination of regularly spaced ribs and a top slab arranged to span in one direction or two orthogonal directions. Joist construction shall meet the following limits:

Minimum rib width	100 mm
Maximum rib depth	3.5 times the minimum width of rib
Maximum clear distance between ribs	800 mm
Minimum slab thickness	1/12 of the clear distance between ribs, but not less than 50 mm

10.4.2
Construction not meeting the limitations of Clause 10.4.1 shall be designed as slabs and beams.

10.5 Flexural members — Reinforcement

10.5.1 Minimum reinforcement

10.5.1.1
At every section of a flexural member where tensile reinforcement is required by analysis, minimum reinforcement shall be proportioned so that

$$M_r \geq 1.2\, M_{cr} \tag{10-3}$$

where the cracking moment, M_{cr}, is calculated using the modulus of rupture, f_r, specified in Clause 8.6.4.

10.5.1.2
In lieu of Clause 10.5.1.1, minimum reinforcement may be determined as follows:
(a) for slabs and footings, as specified in Clause 7.8; and
(b) for other flexural members, as follows:

$$A_{s,min} = \frac{0.2\sqrt{f_c'}}{f_y} b_t h \tag{10-4}$$

where
b_t = the width of the tension zone of the section considered

For T-beams with the flange in tension, b_t need not exceed $1.5b_w$ for beams with a flange on one side of the web or $2.5b_w$ for beams with a flange on both sides of the web.

10.5.1.3
The requirements of Clauses 10.5.1.1 and 10.5.1.2 may be waived if the factored moment resistance, M_r, is at least one-third greater than the factored moment, M_f.

10.5.2 Limit of c/d for yielding of tension reinforcement
The tension reinforcement in flexural members shall not be assumed to reach yield unless

$$\frac{c}{d} \leq \frac{700}{700 + f_y} \tag{10-5}$$

For flexural members without axial loads, the area of tension reinforcement shall be limited such that Equation (10-5) is satisfied. In columns or walls, when c/d exceeds this limit the stress in the tension reinforcement shall be computed based on strain compatibility.

10.5.3 Reinforcement in T-beam flanges

10.5.3.1 Flexural tension reinforcement
Where flanges are in tension, part of the flexural tension reinforcement shall be distributed over an overhanging flange width equal to 1/20 of the beam span, or the width specified in Clause 10.3, whichever is smaller. The area of this reinforcement shall be not less than 0.004 times the gross area of the overhanging flange.

10.5.3.2 Transverse reinforcement
Where the principal reinforcement in the slab forming a T-beam flange is parallel to the beam, transverse reinforcement meeting the requirement of Equation (10-4) shall extend past the face of the web a distance of 0.3 times the clear distance between the webs of the T-beams and shall extend at least to the outer bars of the flexural tension reinforcement required by Clause 10.5.3.1.

10.6 Beams and one-way slabs — Crack control

10.6.1 Crack control parameter
Bars in flexural tension zones shall be spaced so that the quantity z given by

$$z = f_s(d_c A)^{1/3} \tag{10-6}$$

does not exceed 30 000 N/mm for interior exposure and 25 000 N/mm for exterior exposure. The calculated stress in reinforcement at specified load, f_s, shall be computed as the moment divided by the product of the steel area and the internal moment arm. In lieu of such computations, f_s may be taken as 60% of the specified yield strength f_y. In calculating d_c and A, the effective clear concrete cover need not be taken to be greater than 50 mm. If epoxy-coated reinforcement is used, the value of z given by Equation (10-6) shall be multiplied by a factor of 1.2.

Note: *It is possible that the requirements of this Clause will not be sufficient for structures subject to very aggressive exposure or designed to be watertight.*

10.6.2 Skin reinforcement
For reinforced members with an overall depth, h, exceeding 750 mm, longitudinal skin reinforcement shall be uniformly distributed along the exposed side faces of the member for a distance $0.5h - 2(h-d)$ nearest the principal reinforcement. The total area of such reinforcement shall be $\rho_{sk} A_{cs}$, where A_{cs} is the sum of the area of concrete in strips along each exposed side face, each strip having a height of $0.5h - 2(h-d)$ and a width of twice the distance from the side face to the centre of the skin reinforcement (but not more than half the web width), and where $\rho_{sk} = 0.008$ for interior exposure and 0.010 for exterior exposure.

The maximum spacing of the skin reinforcement shall be 200 mm. Such skin reinforcement may be included in strength calculations if a strain compatibility analysis is conducted to determine the stresses in individual bars.

10.7 Deep flexural members

10.7.1
Flexural members with clear span to overall depth ratios less than 2 shall be designed as deep flexural members, taking into account non-linear distribution of strain, lateral buckling, and the increased anchorage requirements in such members. In lieu of more accurate procedures, the strut-and-tie model of Clause 11.4 may be used. (See also Clause 12.10.5.)

10.7.2
Minimum horizontal and vertical reinforcement in the side faces of deep flexural members shall satisfy the requirements of Clauses 10.6.2 and 11.4.5.

10.8 Design of bearing zones

10.8.1
The factored bearing resistance of concrete, other than at post-tensioning anchorages, shall not exceed $0.85\phi_c f_c' A_1$, except that when the supporting surface is wider on all sides than the loaded area, the bearing resistance on the loaded area may be multiplied by $\sqrt{A_2/A_1}$, but not more than 2.

10.8.2
Reinforcement shall be provided where required in bearing zones to resist bursting, splitting, and spalling forces.

Note: *Guidance can be found in chapter 3 of the* Design manual *published by the Canadian Precast/Prestressed Concrete Institute.*

10.9 Columns — Reinforcement limits

10.9.1
The area of longitudinal bars for compression members shall be not less than 0.01 times the gross area, A_g, of the section, except as permitted by Clause 10.10.5.

10.9.2

The area of longitudinal bars for compression members, including regions containing lap splices, shall not exceed 0.08 times the gross area of the section (see Clause 12.17.2).

Note: *The use of more than 4% of reinforcement in a column outside of the region of lap splices can involve serious practical difficulties in placing and compacting the concrete, and in placing reinforcement in beam column joints.*

10.9.3

The minimum number of longitudinal reinforcing bars in compression members shall be four for bars within rectangular or circular ties, three for bars within triangular ties, and six for bars enclosed by spirals complying with Clause 10.9.4.

10.9.4

The ratio of spiral reinforcement shall be not less than the value given by

$$\rho_s = 0.45 \left(\frac{A_g}{A_c} - 1 \right) \frac{f_c'}{f_y}$$ (10-7)

where
f_y = the specified yield strength of spiral reinforcement (not to be taken more than 500 MPa)

10.10 Columns — Resistance

10.10.1

Columns shall be designed to have adequate factored resistance under the combinations of factored axial load and moment giving the maximum and minimum ratios of moment to axial load.

10.10.2

Columns supporting two-way slabs shall be designed to meet the additional requirements of Clause 13.

10.10.3

Slender compression members shall be designed for moments magnified in accordance with Clauses 10.13 to 10.16.

10.10.4

The maximum factored axial load resistance, $P_{r,max}$, of compression members shall be
(a) for spirally reinforced columns:

$$P_{r,max} = 0.85\, P_{ro}$$ (10-8)

(b) for tied columns:

$$P_{r,max} = 0.80\, P_{ro}$$ (10-9)

where

$$P_{ro} = \alpha_1 \phi_c f_c'(A_g - A_{st} - A_t - A_p) + \phi_s f_y A_{st} + \phi_a F_y A_t - f_{pr} A_p$$ (10-10)

10.10.5

Columns with ρ_t smaller than 0.01 but larger than 0.005 may be used, provided that the factored axial and flexural resistances are multiplied by the ratio 0.5 $(1 + \rho_t/0.01)$.

10.11 Columns — Design dimensions

10.11.1 Equivalent circular column
In lieu of using the full gross area in resistance calculations, a compression member with a square, octagonal, or other regular polygonal cross-section may be considered a circular section with a diameter equal to the least lateral dimension of the actual shape. The gross area considered, the required percentage of reinforcement, and the resistance shall be based on that circular section.

10.11.2 Column built monolithically with wall
The outer limits of the effective cross-section of a spirally reinforced or tied reinforced compression member, built monolithically with a concrete wall or pier, shall not extend a distance greater than the specified concrete cover outside of the spiral or tie reinforcement.

10.11.3 Isolated column with interlocking spirals
The outer limits of the effective cross-section of a compression member with two or more interlocking spirals shall not extend a distance greater than the specified concrete cover outside of the extreme limits of the spirals.

10.12 Columns — Transmission of loads through floor system

10.12.1
When the specified compressive strength of concrete in a column is greater than that specified for a floor system, transmission of load through the floor system shall be as specified in Clause 10.12.2 or 10.12.3.

10.12.2
Concrete of the strength specified for the column, f'_{cc}, shall be placed in the floor at the column location. The top surface of the column concrete placed in the floor shall extend at least 500 mm into the floor from the face of the column. The column concrete shall be well integrated with the floor concrete.

10.12.3
The resistance of the column in the joint region shall be based on an effective concrete compressive strength, f'_{ce}, equal to
(a) for interior columns:

$$f'_{ce} = 1.05f'_{cs} + 0.25f'_{cc} \le f'_{cc} \qquad \text{(10-11)}$$

(b) for edge columns:

$$f'_{ce} = 1.4f'_{cs} \le f'_{cc} \qquad \text{(10-12)}$$

(c) for corner columns:

$$f'_{ce} = f'_{cs} \qquad \text{(10-13)}$$

Vertical dowels, spirals, or hoops may be added to increase the effective strength of the joint region.

10.13 Slenderness effects — General

10.13.1
Except as allowed by Clause 10.13.2, the design of compression members, restraining beams, and other supporting members shall be based on the factored forces and moments from a second-order analysis that considers material non-linearity and cracking as well as the effects of member curvature and lateral drift, the duration of the loads, shrinkage and creep, and interaction with the supporting

CSA Standard A23.3-04

foundation. The dimensions of the cross-sections shown on the design drawings shall be within ± 10% of the dimensions used in the analysis. The analysis procedure shall have been shown to result in predictions of strength in substantial agreement with the results of comprehensive tests of columns in indeterminate reinforced concrete structures.

10.13.2

In lieu of the procedure specified in Clause 10.13.1, the design of compression members, restraining beams, and other supporting members may be based on axial forces and moments from the analyses specified in Clauses 10.14 to 10.16, provided that $k\ell_u/r$ for all compression members is not greater than 100.

10.14 Member properties for computation of slenderness effects

10.14.1 General

10.14.1.1

The factored axial forces, P_f; the factored moments, M_1 and M_2, at the ends of the column; and, where required, the first-order lateral storey deflection, Δ_o, shall be computed using an elastic first-order frame analysis with the section properties calculated by taking into account the influence of axial loads, the presence of cracked regions along the length of the member, and the effects of duration of the loads.

10.14.1.2

The following properties may be used to determine the section properties specified in Clause 10.14.1.1:

Modulus of elasticity	E_c from Clause 8.6.2		
Moment of inertia		*Strength*	*servicability*
Beams	$0.35I_g$	6.5 Ig	
Columns	$0.70I_g$	1.0 Ig	
Walls — uncracked	$0.70I_g$	1.0 Ig	
Walls — cracked	$0.35I_g$	0.5 Ig	
Flat plates and flat slabs	$0.25I_g$	0.36 Ig	
Area	A_g		

10.14.1.3

For computation of Δ_o and $\delta_s M_s$, flexural stiffness determined from Clause 10.14.1.2 shall be divided by $(1 + \beta_d)$ to account for creep due to sustained loads.

  β_d shall be based on
(a) sustained axial loads (for Clauses 10.16.4 and 10.16.5); and
(b) sustained shear (for Clauses 10.14.4 and 10.16.3).

10.14.2 Radius of gyration

The radius of gyration, r, may be taken equal to $0.30h$ for rectangular compression members and 0.25 times the diameter for circular compression members. For other shapes, the radius of gyration may be computed using the gross concrete section.

10.14.3 Unsupported length of compression members

10.14.3.1
The unsupported length, ℓ_u, of a compression member shall be taken as the clear distance between floor slabs, beams, or other members capable of providing lateral support in the direction being considered.

10.14.3.2
Where column capitals or haunches are present, the unsupported length shall be measured to the lower extremity of the capital or haunch in the plane considered.

10.14.4 Designation as non-sway
Storeys in structures shall be designated non-sway if $Q \le 0.05$ where

$$Q = \frac{\Sigma P_f \Delta_o}{V_f \ell_c}$$ (10-14)

where
ΣP_f = the total factored vertical load in the storey in question
Δ_o = the first-order relative deflection of the top and bottom of that storey due to V_f
V_f = the factored storey shear in the storey in question
    The deflection, Δ_o, shall be determined using the flexural stiffness determined from Clause 10.14.1.2, except as required by Clause 10.16.4.

10.14.5 Columns in non-sway frames or storeys
The design of columns in non-sway frames or storeys shall be based on the analysis specified in Clause 10.15.

10.14.6 Columns in sway frames or storeys
The design of columns in sway frames or storeys shall be based on the analysis specified in Clause 10.16.
Note: *If the value of Q exceeds 0.2, a more rigid structure can be required to provide stability.*

10.15 Slenderness effects — Non-sway frames

10.15.1 Effective length factor
For compression members in non-sway frames, the effective length factor, k, shall be taken as 1.0 unless analysis shows that a lower value is justified. The calculation of k shall be based on the properties specified in Clause 10.14.1.2.

10.15.2 Non-sway frames
In non-sway frames, slenderness effects may be ignored for compression members that satisfy the following equation:

$$\frac{k\ell_u}{r} \le \frac{25 - 10\,(M_1/M_2)}{\sqrt{P_f/(f'_c A_g)}}$$ (10-15)

where M_1/M_2 is not taken less than -0.5. M_1/M_2 shall be taken as positive if the column is bent in single curvature.

10.15.3 Member stability effect

10.15.3.1

Compression members shall be designed for the factored axial load, P_f, and the moment amplified for the effects of member curvature, M_c, as follows:

$$M_c = \frac{C_m M_2}{1 - \frac{P_f}{\phi_m P_c}} \geq M_2 \qquad \text{(10-16)}$$

where
$\phi_m = 0.75$

$$P_c = \frac{\pi^2 EI}{(k\ell_u)^2} \qquad \text{(10-17)}$$

where

$$EI = \frac{0.2E_c I_g + E_s I_{st}}{1 + \beta_d} \qquad \text{(10-18)}$$

or

$$EI = \frac{0.4E_c I_g}{1 + \beta_d} \qquad \text{(10-19)}$$

M_2 in Equation (10-16) shall not be taken as less than $P_f(15 + 0.03h)$ about each axis separately. β_d in Equations (10-18) and (10-19) shall be based on the sustained axial load, except when used as specified in Clause 10.16.3.

10.15.3.2

For members without transverse loads between supports, C_m shall be taken as

$$C_m = 0.6 + 0.4 \frac{M_1}{M_2} \geq 0.4 \qquad \text{(10-20)}$$

10.15.3.3

For members with transverse loads between supports, C_m shall be taken as 1.0.

10.15.3.4

For compression members subject to bending about both principal axes, the moment about each axis shall be magnified separately based on the conditions of restraint corresponding to that axis.

10.16 Slenderness effects — Sway frames

10.16.1 Effective length factor

For compression members not braced against sway, the effective length factor, k, shall be determined based on the properties specified in Clause 10.14.1.2 and shall be greater than 1.0.

10.16.2 End moments

The moments, M_1 and M_2, at the ends of an individual compression member shall be taken as

$$M_1 = M_{1ns} + \delta_s M_{1s} \qquad \text{(10-21)}$$

$$M_2 = M_{2ns} + \delta_s M_{2s} \qquad \text{(10-22)}$$

where $\delta_s M_{1s}$ and $\delta_s M_{2s}$ shall be computed as specified in Clause 10.16.3.

10.16.3　Calculation of $\delta_s M_s$

10.16.3.1
The magnified sway moments, $\delta_s M_s$, shall be taken as the column end moments calculated using a second-order analysis based on the member stiffnesses specified in Clause 10.14.1.3.

10.16.3.2
δ_s may be calculated as follows:

$$\delta_s = \frac{1}{1 - \dfrac{\sum P_f}{\phi_m \sum P_c}} \qquad \text{(10-23)}$$

where
$\sum P_f$ = the summation for all vertical loads in a storey
$\sum P_c$ = the summation for all sway-resisting columns in a storey

P_c shall be computed from Equation (10-17) using k from Clause 10.16.1 and EI from Equation (10-18) or (10-19), with β_d based on the sustained shear.

10.16.3.3
If $Q \le 1/3$, δ_s may be computed as

$$\delta_s = \frac{1}{1 - Q} \qquad \text{(10-24)}$$

10.16.4　Slenderness limit
If an individual compression member has

$$\frac{\ell_u}{r} > \frac{35}{\sqrt{P_f /(f_c' A_g)}} \qquad \text{(10-25)}$$

it shall also be designed for the factored axial load, P_f, and the moment, M_c, computed using Clause 10.15.3, in which M_1 and M_2 are computed as specified in Clause 10.16.2. β_d shall be based on the sustained axial load evaluated for the factored load combination used to compute P_f, with k in Equation (10-17) as specified in Clause 10.15.1.

10.16.5　Strength and stability checks
In addition to load cases involving lateral loads, the strength and stability of the structure as a whole under factored gravity loads shall be considered using the following criteria, with β_d based on the sustained axial load:
(a) When $\delta_s M_s$ is computed as specified in Clause 10.16.3.1, the ratio of second-order lateral deflections to first-order lateral deflections under factored gravity loads plus a lateral load applied to each storey equal to 0.005 multiplied by the factored gravity load on that storey shall not exceed 2.5.
(b) When δ_s is computed as specified in Clause 10.16.3.2, δ_s computed using $\sum P_f$ and $\sum P_c$ under factored gravity load shall be positive and shall not exceed 2.5.

10.16.6　Moment magnification for flexural members
Flexural members in sway frames shall be designed for the total magnified end moments of the compression members at the joint.

10.17 Composite columns — General

10.17.1
Composite compression members shall include all such members reinforced longitudinally with bars and structural steel shapes, pipes, or hollow structural sections (HSS).

10.17.2
The resistance of a composite member shall be computed for the same limiting conditions applicable to ordinary reinforced concrete members.

10.17.3
In the calculation of factored capacity, the ends of a composite column shall be assumed to be hinged unless definite provisions are made to resist moment at the ends.

10.17.4
Longitudinal reinforcement shall comply with Clauses 10.9.1 and 10.9.2.

10.17.5
The total cross-section area of the metal core and reinforcement shall not exceed 20% of the gross area of the column.

10.17.6
The yield strength of the structural steel core used in the design shall be the specified minimum yield strength for the grade of structural steel used but shall not exceed 350 MPa.

10.17.7
The surface of the structural steel member in contact with concrete shall be unpainted.

10.17.8
The axial load resistance assigned to the concrete of a composite member shall be transferred to the concrete by direct bearing or shear.

10.17.9
The axial load resistance not assigned to the concrete of a composite member shall be developed by direct connection to the structural steel.

10.17.10
The structural steel elements shall be designed in accordance with CAN/CSA-S16 for any construction or other load applied before attainment of composite action.

10.17.11
The design of composite columns with a concrete core encased by structural steel shall be as specified in CAN/CSA-S16.

10.18 Composite column with spiral reinforcement

10.18.1
Spiral reinforcement shall be as specified in Clause 10.9.4.

10.18.2

For evaluation of slenderness effects, the radius of gyration of a composite section with spiral reinforcement shall be not greater than the value given by

$$r = \sqrt{\frac{(E_c I_g / 5) + E_s I_t + E_s I_{st}}{(E_c A_g / 5) + E_s A_t + E_s A_{st}}} \tag{10-26}$$

For computing P_c in Equation (10-17), EI of the composite section shall be not greater than

$$EI = \frac{0.2 E_c I_g}{1 + \beta_d} + E_s I_t + E_s I_{st} \tag{10-27}$$

10.19 Composite column with tie reinforcement

10.19.1

Lateral ties shall extend completely around the structural steel core.

10.19.2

At least 10M ties shall be used when the greatest side dimension of a composite column is 500 mm or less.

10.19.3

At least 15M ties shall be used when the greatest side dimension of a composite column is greater than 500 mm.

10.19.4

Vertical spacing of lateral ties shall not exceed the smallest of 16 longitudinal bar diameters, one-half of the least side dimension of the composite member, or 500 mm.

10.19.5

Welded wire fabric with an area of horizontal wires per unit length of the column not less than that determined as specified in Clauses 10.19.2 to 10.19.4 may be used.

10.19.6

A longitudinal bar shall be located at every corner of a rectangular cross-section, with other longitudinal bars spaced not farther apart than one-half of the least side dimension of the composite member.

10.19.7

For evaluation of slenderness effects, the radius of gyration of a composite section with tie reinforcement shall be not greater than the value given by

$$r = \sqrt{\frac{(E_c I_g / 5) + E_s I_t}{(E_c A_g / 5) + E_s A_t}} \tag{10-28}$$

For computing P_c in Equation (10-17), EI of the composite section shall be not greater than

$$EI = \frac{0.2 E_c I_g}{1 + \beta_d} + E_s I_t \tag{10-29}$$

11 Shear and torsion

11.1 General

11.1.1 Flexural regions
Regions of members in which it is reasonable to assume that plane sections remain plane shall be proportioned for shear and torsion using either the method specified in Clause 11.3 or the strut-and-tie model specified in Clause 11.4. In addition, the applicable requirements of Clause 11.2 shall be satisfied.

11.1.2 Regions near discontinuities
Regions of members in which the plane sections assumption of flexural theory is not applicable shall be proportioned for shear and torsion using the strut-and-tie model specified in Clause 11.4. In addition, the applicable requirements of Clause 11.2 shall be satisfied.

11.1.3 Interface regions
Interfaces between elements such as webs and flanges, between dissimilar materials, and between concretes cast at different times, or at existing or potential major cracks along which slip can occur, shall be proportioned for shear transfer as specified in Clause 11.5.

11.1.4 Slabs and footings
Slab-type regions shall be proportioned for punching shear as specified in Clause 13.

11.1.5 Alternative methods
In lieu of the methods specified in Clauses 11.1.1 to 11.1.4, the resistance of members in shear or in shear combined with torsion may be determined by satisfying the applicable conditions of equilibrium and compatibility of strains and by using appropriate stress-strain relationships for reinforcement and for diagonally cracked concrete.

11.2 Design requirements

11.2.1 Tension due to restraint
In the design for shear, the effects of axial tension due to creep, shrinkage, and thermal effects in restrained members shall be considered wherever applicable.

11.2.2 Variable depth members
For variable depth members, the components of flexural compression and tension in the direction of the applied shear shall be taken into account if their effect is unfavourable, and may be taken into account if their effect is favourable.

11.2.3 Openings
In determining shear resistance, the effect of any openings in members shall be considered.
Note: *Regions of members near openings may be designed using the strut-and-tie model (see Clause 11.4).*

11.2.4 Types of shear reinforcement
Transverse reinforcement provided for shear shall consist of the following:
(a) stirrups or ties perpendicular to the axis of the member;
(b) welded wire fabric with wires perpendicular to the axis of the member, provided that these wires can undergo a minimum elongation of 4% measured over a gauge length of at least 100 mm that includes at least one crosswire;

(c) stirrups making an angle of 45° or more with the longitudinal tension reinforcement, inclined to intercept potential diagonal cracks;

(d) for non-prestressed members, shear reinforcement consisting of 35M or smaller longitudinal bars bent to provide an inclined portion having an angle of 30° or more with the longitudinal bars and crossing potential diagonal cracks. Only the centre three-quarters of the inclined portion of these bars shall be considered effective;

(e) headed shear reinforcement that meets the requirements of Clause 7.1.4 or 13.3.8.1; or

(f) spirals.

11.2.5 Anchorage of shear reinforcement

Stirrups and other bars or wires used as shear reinforcement shall be anchored at both ends as specified in Clause 12.13 to develop the design yield strength of the reinforcement.

11.2.6 Types of torsion reinforcement

Torsion reinforcement shall consist of longitudinal reinforcement and one or more of the following types of transverse reinforcement:

(a) closed stirrups perpendicular to the axis of the member;

(b) a closed cage of welded wire fabric, with wires meeting the minimum elongation requirements of Clause 11.2.4(b) located perpendicular to the axis of the member; and

(c) spirals.

11.2.7 Anchorage of torsion reinforcement

Transverse torsion reinforcement shall be anchored

(a) by 135° standard stirrup hooks; or

(b) as specified in Item (a) or (b) of Clause 12.13.2 in regions where the concrete surrounding the anchorage is restrained against spalling.

A longitudinal reinforcing bar or bonded prestressing tendon shall be placed in each corner of closed transverse reinforcement required for torsion. The nominal diameter of the bar or tendon shall be not less than $s/16$.

Longitudinal torsion reinforcement shall be anchored as specified in Clause 12.1.

11.2.8 Minimum shear reinforcement

11.2.8.1

A minimum area of shear reinforcement shall be provided in the following regions:

(a) in regions of flexural members where the factored shear force, V_f, exceeds $V_c + V_p$;

(b) in regions of beams with an overall thickness greater than 750 mm; and

(c) in regions of flexural members where the factored torsion, T_f, exceeds $0.25T_{cr}$.

11.2.8.2

Where shear reinforcement is required by Clause 11.2.8.1 or by calculation, the minimum area of shear reinforcement shall be such that

$$A_v = 0.06\sqrt{f_c'}\,\frac{b_w s}{f_y}$$

(11-1)

11.2.8.3

In calculating the term A_v in Equation (11-1), inclined reinforcement and transverse reinforcement used to resist torsion may be included.

11.2.8.4

The requirement for minimum shear reinforcement specified in Clause 11.2.8.1 may be waived if it can be shown by tests that the required flexural and shear resistances can be developed when shear reinforcement is omitted. Such tests shall simulate the effects of differential settlement, creep, shrinkage, and temperature change based on a realistic assessment of such effects occurring in service.

11.2.9 Consideration of torsion

11.2.9.1

If the magnitude of the torsion, T_f, determined as specified in analysis using stiffnesses based on uncracked sections exceeds $0.25T_{cr}$, torsional effects shall be considered and torsional reinforcement designed as specified in Clause 11.3 shall be provided. Otherwise, torsional effects may be neglected.

In lieu of more detailed calculations, T_{cr} may be taken as

$$T_{cr} = \left(A_c^2 / p_c \right) 0.38\lambda\phi_c \sqrt{f_c'} \sqrt{1 + \frac{\phi_p f_{cp}}{0.38\lambda\phi_c \sqrt{f_c'}}}$$ (11-2)

For a hollow section, A_c in Equation (11-2) shall be replaced by $1.5A_g$ if the wall thickness is less than $0.75A_c / p_c$.

11.2.9.2

In a statically indeterminate structure where reduction of torsional moment in a member can occur because of redistribution of internal forces, the maximum factored torsion, T_f, at the face of the support may be reduced to $0.67T_{cr}$ provided that the corresponding adjustments to torsions, moments, and shears are made in the member and in adjoining members to account for the redistribution. For a spandrel beam where the torsion is caused by a slab, the factored torsion in the spandrel can be assumed to vary linearly from zero at midspan to $0.67T_{cr}$ at the face of the support.

11.2.10 Effective web width

11.2.10.1

Unless otherwise permitted by Clause 11.2.10.3 or 11.2.10.4, the effective web width shall be taken as the minimum concrete web width within depth d.

11.2.10.2

In determining the concrete web width at a particular level, one-half the diameters of ungrouted post-tensioning ducts or one-quarter the diameters of grouted ducts at that level shall be subtracted from the total web width.

11.2.10.3

For circular members, b_w may be taken as the diameter.

11.2.10.4

For members with tapering webs, b_w may be taken as the average web width calculated over a contiguous height that includes the minimum web width location but does not include any regions of the section where the side faces of the section slope outward at more than 20° from the direction of the applied shear.

11.2.11 Reduced prestress in transfer length

In pretensioned members, the reduction in prestress in the transfer length of prestressing tendons shall be considered when computing V_p, f_{po}, and the tensile force that can be resisted by the longitudinal reinforcement. The prestress force may be assumed to vary linearly from zero at the point at which bonding commences to a maximum at a distance from the end of the tendon equal to the transfer length, assumed to be 50 diameters for strand and 100 diameters for single wire.

11.2.12 Hanger reinforcement for beams supporting other beams

11.2.12.1

When a load is applied to a side face of a beam, additional transverse reinforcement shall be provided. In lieu of a strut-and-tie model design in accordance with Clause 11.4, the requirements of Clause 11.2.12.2 may be used, provided that the soffit of the supported beam is not lower than the soffit of the supporting beam.

11.2.12.2

Additional transverse reinforcement capable of transmitting a tensile force of $(1 - h_b/h_1)$ times the factored shear being transferred shall be provided, with h_b being the distance from the soffit of the supporting beam to the soffit of the supported beam and h_1 being the overall depth of the supporting beam. This additional full-depth transverse reinforcement shall be placed in the supporting beam to intercept 45° planes starting on the shear interface at one-quarter of the depth of the supported beam above its bottom face and spreading down into the supporting beam (see Figure 11.1).

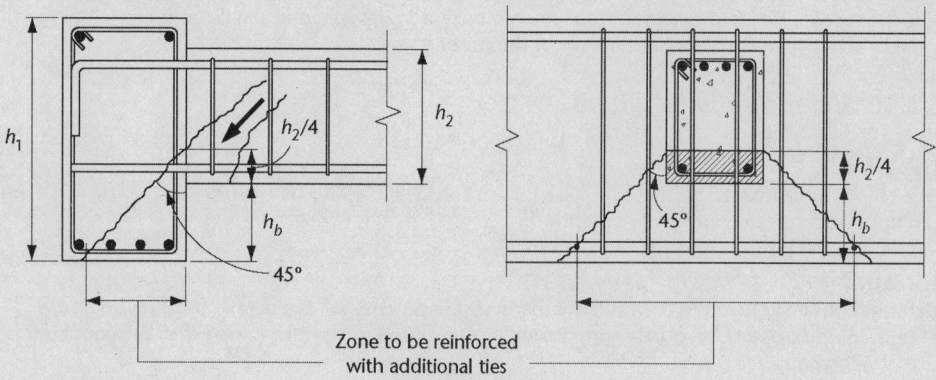

Figure 11.1
Location of additional transverse reinforcement
(See Clauses 2.3 and 11.2.12.2.)

11.2.12.3

The requirements of Clauses 11.2.12.1 and 11.2.12.2 may be waived if
(a) the interface transmitting the load extends to the top of the supporting member; and
(b) the average shear stress on this interface is not greater than $0.23\lambda\phi_c\sqrt{f'_c}$.

11.3 Design for shear and torsion in flexural regions

11.3.1 Required shear resistance

Members subjected to shear shall be proportioned so that

$$V_r \geq V_f \tag{11-3}$$

11.3.2 Sections near supports

Sections located less than a distance d_v from the face of the support may be designed for the same shear, V_f, as that computed at a distance d_v, provided that

(a) the reaction force in the direction of applied shear introduces compression into the member; and

(b) no concentrated load that causes a shear force greater than $0.3\lambda\phi_c\sqrt{f'_c}\,b_w d_v$ is applied within the distance d_v from the face of the support.

11.3.3 Factored shear resistance

The factored shear resistance shall be determined by

$$V_r = V_c + V_s + V_p \tag{11-4}$$

However, V_r shall not exceed

$$V_{r,max} = 0.25\phi_c f'_c\, b_w d_v + V_p \tag{11-5}$$

11.3.4 Determination of V_c

The value of V_c shall be computed from

$$V_c = \phi_c \lambda \beta \sqrt{f'_c}\, b_w d_v \tag{11-6}$$

where β is determined as specified in Clause 11.3.6.

In the determination of V_c, the term $\sqrt{f'_c}$ shall not be taken greater than 8 MPa.

11.3.5 Determination of V_s

11.3.5.1

For members with transverse reinforcement perpendicular to the longitudinal axis, V_s shall be computed from

$$V_s = \frac{\phi_s A_v f_y d_v \cot\theta}{s} \tag{11-7}$$

where θ is determined as specified in Clause 11.3.6.

11.3.5.2

For members with transverse reinforcement inclined at an angle α to the longitudinal axis, V_s shall be computed from

$$V_s = \frac{\phi_s A_v f_y d_v (\cot\theta + \cot\alpha)\sin\alpha}{s} \tag{11-8}$$

where θ is determined as specified in Clause 11.3.6.

11.3.6 Determination of β and θ

11.3.6.1 Members subjected to significant axial tension
For members subjected to significant axial tension, the values of β and θ shall be determined as specified in Clause 11.3.6.4.

11.3.6.2 Values for special member types
Unless otherwise permitted by Clause 11.3.6.3 or Clause 11.3.6.4, the value of β shall be taken as 0.21 and θ shall be taken as 42° for any of the following member types:
(a) slabs or footings with an overall thickness not greater than 350 mm;
(b) footings in which the distance from the point of zero shear to the face of the column, pedestal, or wall is less than three times the effective shear depth of the footing;
(c) beams with an overall thickness not greater than 250 mm;
(d) concrete joist construction defined by Clause 10.4; and
(e) beams cast integrally with slabs where the depth of the beam below the slab is not greater than one-half the width of web or 350 mm.

11.3.6.3 Simplified method
In lieu of more accurate calculations in accordance with Clause 11.3.6.4, and provided that the specified yield strength of the longitudinal steel reinforcement does not exceed 400 MPa and the specified concrete strength does not exceed 60 MPa, θ shall be taken as 35° and β shall be determined as follows:
(a) If the section contains at least the minimum transverse reinforcement as specified by Equation (11-1), β shall be taken as 0.18.
(b) If the section contains no transverse reinforcement and the specified nominal maximum size of coarse aggregate is not less than 20 mm, β shall be taken as

$$\beta = \frac{230}{(1000 + d_v)} \tag{11-9}$$

(c) Alternatively, the value of β for sections containing no transverse reinforcement may be determined for all aggregate sizes by replacing the parameter d_v in Equation (11-9) by the equivalent crack spacing parameter, s_{ze}, where

$$s_{ze} = \frac{35 s_z}{15 + a_g} \tag{11-10}$$

However, s_{ze} shall not be taken as less than $0.85 s_z$. The crack spacing parameter, s_z, shall be taken as d_v or as the maximum distance between layers of distributed longitudinal reinforcement, whichever is less. Each layer of such reinforcement shall have an area at least equal to $0.003 b_w s_z$ (see Figure 11.2).

When the simplified method specified in this Clause is used, all other clauses of Clause 11 shall apply, except Clause 11.3.6.4. Accordingly, this simplified method shall not be used for members subjected to significant tension, and the longitudinal reinforcement for all members shall be proportioned as specified in Clause 11.3.9.

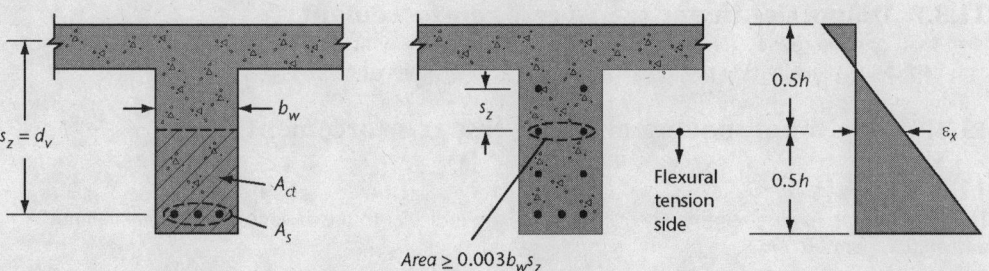

Figure 11.2
Terms in shear design equations
(See Clauses 2.3 and 11.3.6.3.)

11.3.6.4 General method

The value of β shall be determined from the following equation:

$$\beta = \frac{0.40}{(1+1500\varepsilon_x)} \cdot \frac{1300}{(1000 + s_{ze})} \tag{11-11}$$

For sections containing at least the minimum transverse reinforcement required by Equation (11-1), the equivalent crack spacing parameter, s_{ze}, in Equation (11-11) shall be taken as equal to 300 mm. Otherwise, s_{ze} shall be computed using Equation (11-10). If f'_c exceeds 70 MPa, the term a_g shall be taken as zero in Equation (11-10). As f'_c goes from 60 to 70 MPa, a_g shall be linearly reduced to zero.

The angle of inclination, θ, of the diagonal compressive stresses shall be calculated as

$$\theta = 29 + 7000\varepsilon_x \tag{11-12}$$

In lieu of more accurate calculations, the longitudinal strain, ε_x, at mid-depth of the cross-section shall be computed from

$$\varepsilon_x = \frac{M_f/d_v + V_f - V_p + 0.5N_f - A_p f_{po}}{2(E_s A_s + E_p A_p)} \tag{11-13}$$

In evaluating Equation (11-13), the following conditions shall apply:
(a) V_f and M_f shall be taken as positive quantities and M_f shall not be taken as less than $(V_f - V_p)d_v$.
(b) In calculating A_s, the area of bars that are terminated less than their development length from the section under consideration shall be reduced in proportion to their lack of full development.
(c) If the value of ε_x calculated from Equation (11-13) is negative, it shall be taken as zero or the value shall be recalculated with the denominator of Equation (11-13) replaced by $2(E_s A_s + E_p A_p + E_c A_{ct})$. However, ε_x shall not be taken as less than -0.20×10^{-3}.
(d) For sections closer than d_v to the face of the support, the value of ε_x calculated at d_v from the face of the support may be used in evaluating β and θ.
(e) If the axial tension is large enough to crack the flexural compression face of the section, the resulting increase in ε_x shall be taken into account. In lieu of more accurate calculations, the value calculated from Equation (11-13) shall be doubled.
(f) β and θ may be determined from Equations (11-11) and (11-12), respectively, using a value of ε_x that is greater than that calculated from Equation (11-13). However, ε_x shall not be taken greater than 3.0×10^{-3}.

11.3.7 Proportioning of transverse reinforcement

Near locations where the spacing, s, of the transverse reinforcement changes, the quantity A_v/s may be assumed to vary linearly over a length h centred on the location where the spacing changes.

11.3.8 Maximum spacing of transverse reinforcement

11.3.8.1

The spacing of transverse reinforcement, s, placed perpendicular to the axis of the member shall not exceed $0.7d_v$ or 600 mm.

11.3.8.2

Inclined stirrups and bent longitudinal reinforcement shall be spaced so that every line inclined at 35° to the axis of the member and extending toward the reaction from mid-depth of the member to the longitudinal flexural tension reinforcement shall be crossed by at least one line of effective shear reinforcement. See Clause 11.2.4(d).

11.3.8.3

If V_f exceeds $0.125\lambda\phi_c f_c' b_w d_v + V_p$ or if T_f exceeds $0.25T_{cr}$, the maximum spacings specified in Clauses 11.3.8.1 and 11.3.8.2 shall be reduced by one-half.

11.3.9 Proportioning of longitudinal reinforcement

11.3.9.1 Extension of longitudinal reinforcement

At every section, the longitudinal reinforcement shall be designed to resist the additional tension forces caused by shear as specified in Clauses 11.3.9.2 and 11.3.9.3. Alternatively, for members not subjected to significant tension or significant torsion, these requirements may be satisfied by extending the flexural tension reinforcement a distance of $d_v \cot\theta$ beyond the location needed by flexure alone.

11.3.9.2 Flexural tension side

Longitudinal reinforcement on the flexural tension side shall be proportioned so that the factored resistance of the reinforcement at all sections, taking account of the stress that can be developed in this reinforcement, shall be greater than or equal to the force F_{lt}, as follows:

$$F_{lt} = \frac{M_f}{d_v} + 0.5N_f + (V_f - 0.5V_s - V_p)\cot\theta \qquad (11\text{-}14)$$

where M_f and V_f are taken as positive quantities and N_f is positive for axial tension and negative for axial compression. In Equation (11-14), d_v may be taken as the flexural lever arm corresponding to the factored moment resistance.

11.3.9.3 Flexural compression side

At sections where the moment term, M_f/d_v, in Equation (11-14) is less than the sum of the terms accounting for axial load and shear, longitudinal reinforcement on the flexural compression side of the section shall be proportioned so that the factored tensile resistance of this reinforcement, taking account of the stress that can be developed in this reinforcement, shall be greater than or equal to the force F_{lc}, as follows:

$$F_{lc} = 0.5N_f + (V_f - 0.5V_s - V_p)\cot\theta - \frac{M_f}{d_v} \qquad (11\text{-}15)$$

where M_f and V_f are taken as positive quantities and N_f is positive for axial tension and negative for axial compression.

11.3.9.4 Compression fan regions

In regions adjacent to maximum moment locations, the area of longitudinal reinforcement on the flexural tension side of the member need not exceed the area required to resist the maximum moment acting alone. This provision shall apply only if the support or the load at the maximum moment location introduces direct compression into the flexural compression face of the member and the member is not subject to significant torsion.

11.3.9.5 Anchorage of longitudinal reinforcement at end supports

At exterior direct bearing supports, the longitudinal reinforcement on the flexural tension side of the member shall be capable of resisting a tensile force of $(V_f - 0.5V_s - V_p) \cot\theta + 0.5N_f$, where θ is as specified in Clause 11.3.6 and V_s is based on the transverse reinforcement provided within a length of $d_v \cot\theta$ from the face of the support. However, V_s shall not be taken as greater than V_f. The tension force in the reinforcement shall be developed at the point where a line inclined at angle θ to the longitudinal axis and extending from the inside edge of the bearing area intersects the centroid of the reinforcement. See Figure 11.3(b).

11.3.10 Sections subjected to combined shear and torsion

11.3.10.1 Transverse reinforcement for combined shear and torsion

The transverse reinforcement for combined shear and torsion shall be at least equal to the sum of that required for shear and that required for the coexisting torsion.

11.3.10.2 Transverse reinforcement for torsion

The amount of transverse reinforcement required for torsion shall be such that

$$T_r \geq T_f \tag{11-16}$$

11.3.10.3 Factored torsional resistance

The value of T_r shall be computed from

$$T_r = 2A_o \frac{\phi_s A_t f_y}{s} \cot\theta \tag{11-17}$$

where
A_o = $0.85A_{oh}$
and θ is as specified in Clause 11.3.6.

11.3.10.4 Cross-sectional dimensions to avoid crushing

The cross-sectional dimensions to avoid crushing shall be as follows:
(a) for box sections:

$$\frac{V_f - V_p}{b_w d_v} + \frac{T_f p_h}{1.7 A_{oh}^2} \leq 0.25\phi_c f_c' \tag{11-18}$$

If the wall thickness of the box section is less than A_{oh}/p_h, the second term in Equation (11-18) shall be replaced by $T_f/(1.7A_{oh}t)$ where t is the wall thickness at the location where the stresses are being checked.

(b) for other sections:

$$\sqrt{\left(\frac{V_f - V_p}{b_w d_v}\right)^2 + \left(\frac{T_f p_h}{1.7 A_{oh}^2}\right)^2} \leq 0.25\phi_c f_c' \tag{11-19}$$

11.3.10.5 Determination of ε_x for general method

If β and θ are being determined using Clause 11.3.6.4, the value of ε_x for a section subjected to torsion shall be determined by replacing the term $(V_f - V_p)$ in Equation (11-13) and in Clause 11.3.6.4(a) with the expression

$$\sqrt{(V_f - V_p)^2 + \left(\frac{0.9 p_h T_f}{2 A_o}\right)^2} \tag{11-20}$$

11.3.10.6 Proportioning longitudinal reinforcement

The longitudinal reinforcement shall be proportioned to satisfy the requirements of Clause 11.3.9, except that the term $(V_f - 0.5 V_s - V_p)$ shall be replaced by the expression

$$\sqrt{(V_f - 0.5 V_s - V_p)^2 + \left(\frac{0.45 p_h T_f}{2 A_o}\right)^2} \tag{11-21}$$

11.4 Strut-and-tie model

11.4.1 Structural idealization

The strength of reinforced concrete structures, members, or regions may be investigated by idealizing the reinforced concrete as a series of reinforcing steel tensile ties and concrete compressive struts interconnected at nodes to form a truss capable of carrying all of the factored loads to the supports. In determining the geometry of the truss, account shall be taken of the required dimensions of the struts and ties.

11.4.2 Proportioning of strut

11.4.2.1 Strength of strut

The dimensions of a strut shall be large enough to ensure that the calculated compressive force in the strut does not exceed $\phi_c f_{cu} A_{cs}$ where f_{cu} and A_{cs} are determined as specified in Clauses 11.4.2.2 and 11.4.2.3.

11.4.2.2 Effective cross-sectional area of strut

The value of A_{cs} shall be calculated by considering both the available concrete area and the anchorage conditions at the ends of the strut, as shown in Figure 11.3.

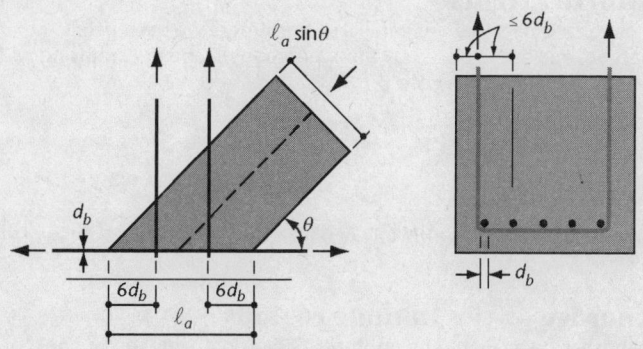

(a) Strut anchored by reinforcement

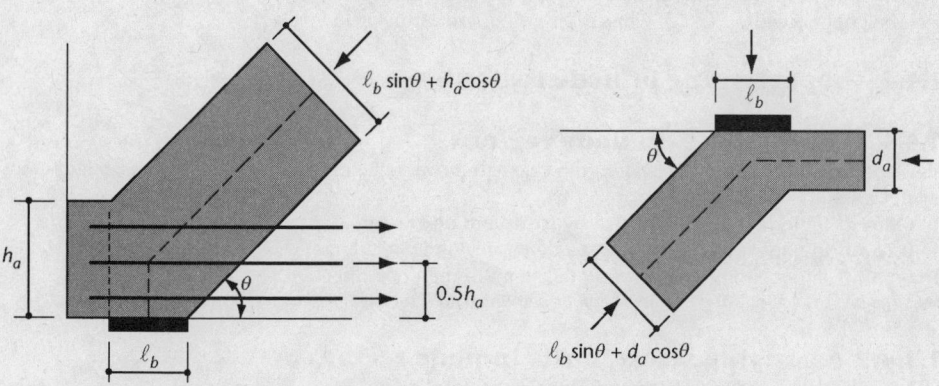

(b) Strut anchored by bearing plate and reinforcement

(c) Strut anchored by bearing plate and strut

Figure 11.3
Influence of anchorage conditions on effective cross-sectional area of strut
(See Clauses 2.3, 11.3.9.5, and 11.4.2.2.)

11.4.2.3 Limiting compressive stress in struts

The value of f_{cu} shall be computed from

$$f_{cu} = \frac{f'_c}{0.8 + 170\varepsilon_1} \leq 0.85 f'_c \tag{11-22}$$

where

$$\varepsilon_1 = \varepsilon_s + (\varepsilon_s + 0.002)\cot^2\theta_s \tag{11-23}$$

and θ_s is the smallest angle between the strut and the adjoining ties and ε_s is the tensile strain in the tie inclined at θ_s to the strut. If the tensile strain in the tie changes as the tie crosses the width of the strut, ε_s may be taken as the strain in the tie at the centreline of the strut.

11.4.2.4 Reinforced struts
If a strut contains reinforcing bars that are parallel to the strut, have been detailed to develop their yield strength in compression, and are enclosed by transverse reinforcement complying with Clause 7.6.5, the calculated force in the strut shall not exceed $\phi_c f_{cu} A_{cs} + \phi_s f_y A_{ss}$.

11.4.3 Proportioning of ties

11.4.3.1 Strength of ties
The area of reinforcement in the tie, A_{st}, shall be large enough to ensure that the calculated tensile force in the tie does not exceed $\phi_s f_y A_{st}$.

11.4.3.2 Anchorage of ties in node regions
The tie reinforcement shall be anchored by appropriate development length, hook, or mechanical anchorage in accordance with Clause 12 so that it is capable of resisting the calculated tension in the reinforcement at the location where the centroid of this reinforcement crosses the edge of the adjoining strut. For straight bars extending a distance x beyond the critical location where $x < \ell_d$, the calculated stress shall not exceed $\phi_s f_y (x/\ell_d)$, where ℓ_d is computed as specified in Clause 12.

11.4.4 Proportioning of node regions

11.4.4.1 Stress limits in node regions
Unless special confinement is provided, the calculated concrete compressive stress in the node regions shall not exceed the following:
(a) $0.85\phi_c f_c'$ in node regions bounded by struts and bearing areas;
(b) $0.75\phi_c f_c'$ in node regions anchoring a tie in only one direction; and
(c) $0.65\phi_c f_c'$ in node regions anchoring ties in more than one direction.
Note: *The beneficial effects of confinement can be accounted for if substantiated by test results.*

11.4.4.2 Satisfying stress limits in node regions
The stress limits in node regions may be considered satisfied if
(a) the bearing stress on the node regions produced by concentrated loads or reactions does not exceed the stress limits specified in Clause 11.4.4.1; and
(b) the tie reinforcement is uniformly distributed over an effective area of concrete at least equal to the tie force divided by the stress limits specified in Clause 11.4.4.1.

11.4.5 Crack control reinforcement
Structures, members, or regions (other than slabs or footings) that have been designed in accordance with Clause 11.4 shall contain an orthogonal grid of reinforcing bars near each face. The ratio of reinforcement area to gross concrete area shall not be less than 0.002 in each direction. The spacing of this reinforcement shall not exceed 300 mm. If located within the tie, the crack control reinforcement may also be considered as tie reinforcement.

11.5 Interface shear transfer

11.5.1 General
A crack shall be assumed to occur along the shear plane and relative displacement shall be considered to be resisted by cohesion and friction maintained by the shear friction reinforcement crossing the crack. The factored shear stress resistance of the plane shall be computed from

$$v_r = \lambda\phi_c(c + \mu\sigma) + \phi_s \rho_v f_y \cos\alpha_f \tag{11-24}$$

where the expression $\lambda\phi_c(c + \mu\sigma)$ shall not exceed $0.25\phi_c f_c'$ and α_f is the angle between the shear friction reinforcement and the shear plane.

11.5.2 Values of c and μ

The following values shall be taken for c and μ:

(a) For concrete placed against hardened concrete with the surface clean but not intentionally roughened:
$c = 0.25$ MPa
$\mu = 0.60$

(b) For concrete placed against hardened concrete with the surface clean and intentionally roughened to a full amplitude of at least 5 mm:
$c = 0.50$ MPa
$\mu = 1.00$

(c) For concrete placed monolithically:
$c = 1.00$ MPa
$\mu = 1.40$

(d) For concrete anchored to as-rolled structural steel by headed studs or by reinforcing bars:
$c = 0.00$ MPa
$\mu = 0.60$

11.5.3 Alternative equation for shear stress resistance

For concrete placed monolithically or placed against hardened concrete with the surface clean and intentionally roughened to a full amplitude of at least 5 mm, the factored shear stress resistance may be computed using the following equation in lieu of Equation (11-24):

$$v_r = \lambda\phi_c k\sqrt{\sigma f_c'} + \phi_s \rho_v f_y \cos\alpha_f \qquad\qquad \text{(11-25)}$$

where
$k =$ 0.5 for concrete placed against hardened concrete
$\ \ =$ 0.6 for concrete placed monolithically
and the expression $\lambda\phi_c k\sqrt{\sigma f_c'}$ shall not exceed $0.25\phi_c f_c'$ and α_f is the angle between the shear friction reinforcement and the shear plane.

11.5.4 Values of σ and ρ_v

The value of σ shall be computed as

$$\sigma = \rho_v f_y \sin\alpha_f + \frac{N}{A_g} \qquad\qquad \text{(11-26)}$$

where

$$\rho_v = \frac{A_{vf}}{A_{cv}} \qquad\qquad \text{(11-27)}$$

and N is the unfactored permanent load perpendicular to the shear plane, positive for compression and negative for tension.

11.5.5 Inclined shear friction reinforcement

In determining the area of inclined shear friction reinforcement to be used in Equation (11-27), only that reinforcement inclined to the shear plane at an angle, α_f, such that the shear force produces tension in the inclined reinforcement, shall be included.

11.5.6 Anchorage of shear friction reinforcement

The shear friction reinforcement shall be anchored on each side of the shear plane so that the specified yield strength can be developed.

11.6 Special provisions for brackets and corbels

11.6.1
Brackets and corbels shall be designed in accordance with Clause 11.4 and Clauses 11.6.2 to 11.6.8.

11.6.2
The depth, d, at the face of a support shall be not less than the distance between the load and the face of the support.

11.6.3
The depth at the outside edge of the bearing area shall be not less than one-half of the depth at the face of the support.

11.6.4
The external tensile force, N_f, acting on the bearing area shall not be taken as less than $0.2V_f$ unless special provisions are made to avoid tensile forces.

11.6.5
In lieu of the crack control reinforcement specified in Clause 11.4.5, closed stirrups or ties parallel to the primary tensile tie reinforcement, A_{st}, and having a total area of not less than 50% of A_{st}, shall be distributed within two-thirds of the effective depth adjacent to A_{st}.

11.6.6
The ratio A_{st}/bd calculated at the face of the support shall be not less than $0.04(f'_c/f_y)$.

11.6.7
At the front face of the bracket or corbel, the primary tensile tie reinforcement, A_{st}, shall be anchored to develop the required force in the tension tie.

11.6.8
The bearing area of the load on the bracket or corbel shall not project beyond the straight portion of the tension tie bars or beyond the interior face of the transverse anchor bar, if one is provided.

11.7 Shear in joints
When gravity load, wind, earthquake, or other lateral forces cause transfer of moment at connections of framing elements to columns, the shear resulting from moment transfer shall be considered in the design of lateral reinforcement in the columns and joints.

12 Development and splices of reinforcement

12.1 Development of reinforcement — General

12.1.1
The calculated tension or compression in reinforcement at each section of reinforced concrete members shall be developed on each side of that section by embedment length, hook, or mechanical device, or by a combination thereof. Hooks may be used in developing bars in tension only.

12.1.2

The maximum permissible value of $\sqrt{f_c'}$ in Clause 12 shall be 8 MPa.

12.2 Development of deformed bars and deformed wire in tension

12.2.1 Minimum development length

The development length, ℓ_d, of deformed bars and deformed wire in tension shall be determined from either Clause 12.2.2 or Clause 12.2.3, but ℓ_d shall be not less than 300 mm.

12.2.2 General development length equation

The development length, ℓ_d, of deformed bars and deformed wire in tension shall be

$$\ell_d = 1.15 \frac{k_1 k_2 k_3 k_4}{(d_{cs} + K_{tr})} \frac{f_y}{\sqrt{f_c'}} A_b \qquad (12\text{-}1)$$

but the term $(d_{cs} + K_{tr})$ shall not be taken greater than $2.5 d_b$ where

$$K_{tr} = \frac{A_{tr} f_{yt}}{10.5 sn}$$

12.2.3 Simplified development length equations

The development length, ℓ_d, of deformed bars and deformed wire in tension may be taken from Table 12.1, provided that the clear cover and clear spacing of the bars or wire being developed are at least d_b and $1.4 d_b$, respectively.

Table 12.1
Development length, ℓ_d, of deformed bars and deformed wire in tension

(See Clause 12.2.3.)

Cases	Minimum development length, ℓ_d
Member containing minimum ties (Clause 7.6.5) or minimum stirrups (Clause 11.2.8.2) within ℓ_d Slabs, walls, shells, or folded plates having clear spacing of not less than $2d_b$ between bars being developed	$0.45 k_1 k_2 k_3 k_4 \dfrac{f_y}{\sqrt{f_c'}} d_b$
Other cases	$0.6 k_1 k_2 k_3 k_4 \dfrac{f_y}{\sqrt{f_c'}} d_b$

Note: *The clear cover and clear spacing requirements specified in Clause 12.2.3 meet the requirements of CSA A23.1 (see Annex A).*

12.2.4 Modification factors

The following modification factors shall be used to calculate the development length in Clauses 12.2.2 and 12.2.3:

(a) bar location factor, k_1:

   k_1 = 1.3 for horizontal reinforcement placed in such a way that more than 300 mm of fresh concrete is cast in the member below the development length or splice

   = 1.0 for other cases

(b)   coating factor, k_2:

k_2 =   1.5 for epoxy-coated reinforcement with clear cover less than $3d_b$, or with clear spacing between bars being developed less than $6d_b$

=   1.2 for all other epoxy-coated reinforcement

=   1.0 for uncoated reinforcement

(c)   concrete density factor, k_3:

k_3 =   1.3 for structural low-density concrete

=   1.2 for structural semi-low-density concrete

=   1.0 for normal-density concrete

(d)   bar size factor, k_4:

k_4 =   0.8 for 20M and smaller bars and deformed wires

=   1.0 for 25M and larger bars

The product $k_1 k_2$ need not be taken greater than 1.7.

12.2.5   Excess reinforcement

The development length, ℓ_d, may be multiplied by the factor (A_s required) / (A_s provided) where reinforcement in a flexural member exceeds that required by analysis, except where anchorage or development for f_y is specifically required or the reinforcement is designed as specified in Clause 21.

12.3   Development of deformed bars in compression

12.3.1   Development length

The development length, ℓ_d, for deformed bars in compression shall be computed as the product of the basic development length, ℓ_{db}, specified in Clause 12.3.2 and the applicable modification factors specified in Clause 12.3.3, but ℓ_d shall be not less than 200 mm.

12.3.2   Basic development length

The basic compression development length, ℓ_{db}, shall be $0.24 d_b f_y / \sqrt{f_c'}$, but not less than $0.044 d_b f_y$.

12.3.3   Modification factors

The basic development length, ℓ_{db}, may be multiplied by the following factors, as applicable:

(a)   for reinforcement exceeding that required by analysis: (A_s required) / (A_s provided); and

(b)   for reinforcement enclosed within spiral reinforcement of not less than 6 mm diameter and not more than 100 mm pitch or within 10M ties in compliance with Clause 7.6.5 and spaced at not more than 100 mm on centre: 0.75.

12.4   Development of bundled bars

The development length of individual bars within a bundle in tension or compression shall be that for the individual bar increased by 10% for a two-bar bundle, 20% for a three-bar bundle, and 33% for a four-bar bundle.

12.5   Development of standard hooks in tension

12.5.1   Tension development length

Except as specified in Clause 12.13, the development length, ℓ_{dh}, for deformed bars in tension terminating in a standard hook as defined in Clause 6.6.2.2 of CSA A23.1 (reprinted in Annex A) shall be computed as the product of the basic development length, ℓ_{hb}, specified in Clause 12.5.2 and the applicable modification factor or factors specified in Clause 12.5.3, but shall be not less than $8d_b$ or 150 mm, whichever is greater.

68

12.5.2 Basic development length
The basic development length, ℓ_{hb}, for a hooked bar with f_y equal to 400 MPa shall be $100d_b/\sqrt{f_c'}$.

12.5.3 Factors modifying hook development length
The basic development length, ℓ_{hb}, shall be multiplied by the following factor(s), as applicable:

(a) For bars with f_y other than 400 MPa	$f_y/400$
(b) For 35M or smaller bars where the side cover (normal to plane of hook) is not less than 60 mm, and for 90° hooks where the cover on the bar extension beyond the hook is not less than 50 mm	0.7
(c) For 35M or smaller bars where the hook is enclosed vertically or horizontally within at least three ties or stirrup ties spaced along a length at least equal to the inside diameter of the hook at a spacing not greater than $3d_b$, where d_b is the nominal diameter of the hooked bar	0.8
(d) Where anchorage or development for f_y is not specifically required for reinforcement exceeding that required by analysis	(A_s required) / (A_s provided)
(e) For structural low-density concrete	1.3
(f) For epoxy-coated reinforcement	1.2

12.5.4 Confinement of hooks
For bars being developed by a standard hook at the ends of members where both the side cover and the top (or bottom) cover over the hook is less than 60 mm, the hook shall be enclosed within at least three ties or stirrup ties spaced along a length at least equal to the inside diameter of the hook at a spacing not greater than $3d_b$, where d_b is the nominal diameter of the hooked bar. For this case, the factor specified in Clause 12.5.3(c) shall not apply.

12.5.5 Development of bars in compression
Hooks shall not be considered effective in developing bars in compression.

12.6 Mechanical anchorage

12.6.1
Any mechanical anchorage, including heads of headed bars or headed studs, demonstrated by test to be capable of developing the strength of reinforcement without damage to the concrete, may be used.

12.6.2
The development of reinforcement may consist of a combination of mechanical anchorage and additional embedment length of reinforcement between the point of maximum bar stress and the mechanical anchorage.

12.7 Development of welded deformed wire fabric in tension

12.7.1
The development length, ℓ_d, of welded deformed wire fabric shall be computed as the product of the development length, ℓ_d, specified in Clause 12.2.2 or 12.2.3 and the applicable wire fabric factor or factors specified in Clause 12.7.2 or 12.7.3, but shall be not less than 200 mm, except in the computation of lap splices by the method specified in Clause 12.18 and in the development of web reinforcement by the method specified in Clause 12.13.

12.7.2
For welded deformed wire fabric with at least one crosswire within the development length and not less than 50 mm from the point of the critical section, the wire fabric factor, k_5, shall be the greater of

$$k_5 = \frac{f_y - 240}{f_y} \tag{12-2}$$

or

$$k_5 = \frac{5d_b}{s_w} \tag{12-3}$$

but need not be taken greater than 1.0.

12.7.3
For welded deformed wire fabric with no crosswires within the development length or with a single crosswire less than 50 mm from the point of the critical section, the wire fabric factor, k_5, shall be taken as 1.0.

12.8 Development of welded smooth wire fabric in tension
The yield strength of welded smooth wire fabric shall be considered to be developed by the embedment of two crosswires, with the closer crosswire not less than 50 mm from the critical section. However, the development length, ℓ_d, measured from the critical section to the outermost crosswire shall be not less than

$$\ell_d = 3.3k_3 \frac{A_w}{s_w} \frac{f_y}{\sqrt{f_c'}} \tag{12-4}$$

If excess reinforcement is present, this length may be reduced in accordance with Clause 12.2.5. ℓ_d shall be not less than 150 mm except in the computation of lap splices by the method specified in Clause 12.19.

12.9 Development of pretensioned strand

12.9.1
Three- or seven-wire pretensioning strand shall be bonded beyond the critical section for a development length, ℓ_d, not less than

$$\ell_d = 0.145\,(f_{pr} - 0.67f_{pe})d_b \tag{12-5}$$

12.9.2
Where bonding of a strand does not extend to the end of a member and the design includes tension at specified loads in the precompressed tensile zone as permitted by Clause 18.3.2 or 18.3.3, the development length specified in Clause 12.9.1 shall be doubled.

12.10 Development of flexural reinforcement — General

12.10.1
Tension reinforcement may be anchored into the compression zone by bending it across the web to be anchored or made continuous with the reinforcement on the opposite face of the member.

12.10.2
Critical sections for development of reinforcement in flexural members are located at points of maximum stress and at points within the span where adjacent reinforcement terminates or is bent. The location of the points of maximum stress and the points at which reinforcement is no longer required to resist flexure shall be derived from the factored bending moment diagram.

12.10.3
Reinforcement shall extend beyond the point at which it is no longer required to resist flexure as specified in Clause 11.3.9.

12.10.4
Continuing reinforcement shall have an embedment length of not less than the development length, ℓ_d, plus the longer of the effective depth of the member or $12d_b$ beyond the point where bent or terminated tension reinforcement is no longer required to resist flexure.

12.10.5
Special attention shall be given to providing adequate anchorage for tension reinforcement in flexural members such as sloped, stepped, or tapered footings; brackets; deep flexural members; or members in which the tension reinforcement is not parallel to the compression face.

12.11 Development of positive moment reinforcement

12.11.1
At least one-third of the positive moment reinforcement in simply supported members and one-quarter of the positive moment reinforcement in continuous members shall extend along the same face of the member into the support. In beams constructed monolithically with the support, such reinforcement shall extend into the support at least 150 mm, but not less than required by Clause 11.3.9.

12.11.2
When a flexural member is part of a primary lateral load resisting system, the positive moment reinforcement required by Clause 12.11.1 to be extended into the support shall be anchored to develop the specified yield strength, f_y, in tension at the face of the support.

12.11.3
At simple supports and at points of inflection, the positive moment tension reinforcement shall be limited to a diameter such that ℓ_d computed for f_y by the method specified in Clause 12.2 shall satisfy the following equation:

$$\ell_d \leq \frac{M_r}{V_f} + \ell_a \tag{12-6}$$

where, at a support, ℓ_a shall be the embedment length beyond the centre of the support, and at a point of inflection, ℓ_a shall be limited to the effective depth of the member or $12d_b$, whichever is greater.

However, Equation (12-6) need not be satisfied for reinforcement terminating beyond the centreline of simple supports by a standard hook or a mechanical anchorage at least equivalent to a standard hook.

The value of M_r / V_f may be increased by 30% when the ends of the reinforcement are confined by a compressive reaction.

12.12 Development of negative moment reinforcement

12.12.1
Negative moment reinforcement in a continuous, restrained, or cantilever member, or in any member of a rigid frame, shall be anchored in or through the supporting member by embedment length, hooks, or mechanical anchorage.

12.12.2
At least one-third of the total tension reinforcement provided for negative moment at a support shall have an embedment length beyond the point of inflection of not less than the effective depth of the member, $12d_b$, or 1/16 of the clear span, whichever is greater.

12.13 Anchorage of shear reinforcement

12.13.1
Web reinforcement shall be carried as close to the compression and tension surfaces of a member as cover requirements and proximity of other reinforcement will permit.

12.13.2
Transverse reinforcement provided for shear shall be anchored by one of the following means:
(a) for 15M and smaller bars, and for MD200 and smaller wire, by a standard stirrup hook (see Clause 7.1.2) around longitudinal reinforcement;
(b) for 20M and 25M stirrups, by a standard hook (see Clause 7.1.2) around longitudinal reinforcement, plus an embedment between mid-depth of the member and the outside end of the hook equal to or greater than $0.33\ell_d$;
(c) for each leg of welded smooth wire fabric forming simple U-stirrups, either
   (i) two longitudinal wires located at a 50 mm spacing along the member at the top of the U; or
   (ii) one longitudinal wire located not more than $d/4$ from the compression face and a second wire closer to the compression face and spaced not less than 50 mm from the first wire. The second wire may be located on the stirrup leg beyond a bend or on a bend with an inside diameter of not less than $8d_b$;
(d) for each end of a single-leg stirrup of welded smooth or deformed wire fabric, two longitudinal wires at a minimum spacing of 50 mm, with the inner wire at least $d/4$ from the mid-depth of the member. The outer longitudinal wire at the tension face shall not be farther from that face than the portion of primary flexural reinforcement closest to the face; or
(e) mechanical anchorage capable of developing the yield strength of the bar.

12.13.3
Between anchored ends, each bend in the continuous portion of a stirrup shall enclose a longitudinal bar.

12.13.4
Longitudinal bars bent to act as shear reinforcement, if extended into a region of tension, shall be continuous with the longitudinal reinforcement and, if extended into a region of compression, shall be anchored beyond the mid-depth, $d/2$, as specified for development length in Clause 12.2 for that part of f_y required to satisfy Clause 11.3.9.

12.13.5
Pairs of U-stirrups or ties placed so as to form a closed unit shall be considered properly spliced when the length of the laps is $1.3\ell_d$. Alternatively, in members at least 450 mm deep, where $A_b f_y$ is not more than 40 kN per leg, the splice shall be considered adequate if the stirrup legs extend the full available depth of the member.

12.14 Splices of reinforcement — General

12.14.1 Limitations on use
Splices of reinforcement shall be made only as required or permitted by design drawings or specifications, or as authorized by the designer.

12.14.2 Lap splices

12.14.2.1
Lap splices shall not be used for bars larger than 35M, except as specified in Clauses 12.16.2 and 15.9.2.4.

12.14.2.2
Lap splices of bundled bars shall be based on the lap splice length required for individual bars within a bundle, increased by 10% for a two-bar bundle, 20% for a three-bar bundle, and 33% for a four-bar bundle. Individual bar splices within a bundle shall not overlap.

12.14.2.3
Bars spliced by lap splices in flexural members shall have a transverse spacing not exceeding the lesser of one-fifth of the required lap splice length or 150 mm.

12.14.3 Welded splices and mechanical connections

12.14.3.1
Welded splices and other mechanical connections may be used.

12.14.3.2
All welding shall comply with to CSA W186.

12.14.3.3
A full welded splice shall have bars welded to develop, in tension, at least 120% of the specified yield strength, f_y, of the bar, but not less than 110% of the actual yield strength of the bar used in the test of the welded splice.

12.14.3.4
A full mechanical connection shall develop, in tension or compression as required, at least 120% of the specified yield strength, f_y, of the bar, but not less than 110% of the actual yield strength of the bar used in the test of the mechanical connection.

12.14.3.5
Welded splices and mechanical connections not meeting the requirements of Clause 12.14.3.3 or 12.14.3.4 may be used as specified in Clause 12.15.4.

12.15 Splices of deformed bars and deformed wire in tension

12.15.1
The minimum length of lap for tension lap splices shall be as required for a Class A or B splice, but not less than 300 mm, where
(a)   the Class A splice length is $1.0\ell_d$; and
(b)   the Class B splice length is $1.3\ell_d$.
In Items (a) and (b), ℓ_d is the tensile development length for the specified yield strength, f_y, as specified in Clause 12.2, but without the modification factor specified in Clause 12.2.5.

12.15.2
Lap splices of deformed bars and deformed wire in tension shall be Class B splices, except that Class A splices shall be permitted when
(a)   the area of reinforcement provided is at least twice that required by analysis at the splice location; and
(b)   less than one-half of the total reinforcement is spliced within the required lap length.

12.15.3
Welded splices or mechanical connections used where the area of reinforcement provided is less than twice that required by analysis shall meet the requirements of Clause 12.14.3.3 or 12.14.3.4.

12.15.4
Welded splices or mechanical connections used where the area of reinforcement provided is at least twice that required by analysis shall meet the following requirements:
(a)   splices shall be staggered by at least 600 mm and in such a manner as to develop, at every section, at least twice the factored tensile force at that section, but not less than 140 MPa for the total area of reinforcement provided; and
(b)   in computing the tensile resistance developed at each section, spliced reinforcement shall be rated at the specified splice strength. Unspliced reinforcement shall be rated at that fraction of f_y defined by the ratio of the shorter actual development length to the development length, ℓ_d, required to develop the specified yield strength, f_y.

12.15.5
Splices in tension tie members shall be made with a full welded splice or a full mechanical connection as specified in Clause 12.14.3.3 or 12.14.3.4. Splices in adjacent bars shall be staggered by at least 800 mm.

12.16 Splices of deformed bars in compression

12.16.1 Minimum lap length
The minimum lap length for compression lap splices shall be $0.073f_y d_b$ for f_y less than or equal to 400 MPa or $(0.133f_y - 24)d_b$ for f_y greater than 400 MPa, but shall not be taken less than 300 mm.

12.16.2 Lap length for bars of different sizes
When bars of different sizes are lap spliced in compression, the splice length shall be the larger of the development length of the larger bar or the splice length of the smaller bar. Bar sizes 45M and 55M may be lap spliced to 35M and smaller bars.

12.16.3 Welded splices or mechanical connections
Welded splices or mechanical connections used in compression shall meet the requirements of Clause 12.14.3.3 or 12.14.3.4.

12.16.4 End-bearing splices

12.16.4.1
In bars required for compression only, the compressive stress may be transmitted by the bearing of square cut ends held in concentric contact by a suitable device.

12.16.4.2
Bar ends shall terminate in flat surfaces within 1-1/2° of a right angle to the axis of the bars and shall be fitted to within 3° of full bearing after assembly.

12.16.4.3
End-bearing splices shall be used only in members containing closed ties, closed stirrups, or spirals.

12.17 Special splice requirements for columns

12.17.1 General
Lap splices, butt-welded splices, mechanical connections, or end-bearing splices shall satisfy the applicable requirements of Clauses 12.17.2 to 12.17.5 for all load combinations for the column.

12.17.2 Reinforcement
Where welded splices, mechanical connections, or end-bearing splices are used, the amount of reinforcement spliced at any location shall not exceed 0.04 times the gross area of the section. Where the gross area of reinforcement exceeds 0.04 times the gross area of the section, connection or splice locations shall be spaced not less than 750 mm apart (see Clause 10.9.2).

12.17.3 Lap splices in columns

12.17.3.1
Where the bar stress due to factored loads is compressive, lap splices shall comply with Clauses 12.16.1 and 12.16.2, and, where applicable, with Clause 12.17.3.4 or 12.17.3.5.

12.17.3.2
Where the bar stress due to factored loads is tensile and does not exceed $0.5f_y$, lap splices shall be Class B if more than one-half of the bars are spliced at any section, or Class A if one-half or fewer of the bars are spliced at any section and alternate lap splices are staggered by ℓ_d.

12.17.3.3
Where the bar stress due to factored loads is greater than $0.5f_y$ in tension, lap splices shall be Class B.

12.17.3.4
In tied reinforced compression members where ties throughout the lap splice length have an effective area of not less than $0.0015hs$, the lap splice length, computed as specified in Clauses 12.16.1 and 12.16.2, may be multiplied by 0.83, but the lap splice length shall be not less than 300 mm. Tie legs perpendicular to dimension h shall be used in determining the effective area.

12.17.3.5
In spirally reinforced compression members, the lap splice length of bars within a spiral, computed as specified in Clauses 12.16.1 and 12.16.2, may be multiplied by 0.75, but the lap splice length shall be not less than 300 mm.

12.17.4 Welded splices or mechanical connections in columns

Welded splices or mechanical connections in columns shall meet the requirements of Clause 12.14.3.3 or 12.14.3.4.

12.17.5 End-bearing splices in columns

End-bearing splices meeting the requirements of Clause 12.16.4 may be used for column bars stressed in compression, provided that the splices are staggered or additional bars are provided at splice locations. The continuing vertical bars in each face of the column shall have an area of at least 0.25 of the area of the vertical reinforcement in that face.

12.18 Splices of welded deformed wire fabric in tension

12.18.1

The minimum length of lap for lap splices of welded deformed wire fabric measured between the ends of each fabric sheet shall be not less than the greater of $1.3\ell_d$ and 200 mm, and the overlap measured between the outermost crosswires of each fabric sheet shall be not less than 50 mm, where ℓ_d shall be the development length, as specified in Clause 12.7, for the specified yield strength, f_y.

12.18.2

The lap splices of welded deformed wire fabric with no crosswires within the lap splice length shall be determined as for deformed wire.

12.19 Splices of welded smooth wire fabric in tension

12.19.1

The minimum length of lap for lap splices of welded smooth wire fabric shall be as specified in Clauses 12.19.2 and 12.19.3.

12.19.2

When the area of reinforcement provided is less than twice that required at the splice location, the length of overlap measured between the outermost crosswires of each fabric sheet shall be not less than the greater of
(a) one spacing of crosswires plus 50 mm;
(b) $1.5\ell_d$; and
(c) 150 mm,
where ℓ_d shall be the development length, as specified in Clause 12.8, for the specified yield strength, f_y.

12.19.3

When the area of reinforcement provided is at least twice that required at the splice location, the length of overlap measured between the outermost crosswires of each fabric sheet shall be not less than the greater of $1.5\ell_d$ and 50 mm, where ℓ_d shall be the development length, as specified in Clause 12.8, for the specified yield strength, f_y.

13 Two-way slab systems

13.1 General

13.1.1
Clause 13 shall apply to the design of slab systems reinforced for flexure in more than one direction, with or without beams between supports.

13.1.2
A slab system may be supported on columns or walls.

13.2 Minimum slab thickness

13.2.1 General
The minimum slab thickness, h_s, shall be based on serviceability requirements but shall be not less than 120 mm.

13.2.2 Two-way slab systems
For regular two-way slab systems (see Clause 2.2), the requirement specified in Clause 9.8.2.6 to show by computation that deflections will not exceed the limits stipulated in Table 9.3 may be waived when the slab thicknesses provided are not less than the minimum thicknesses specified in Clauses 13.2.3 to 13.2.6.
Note: *It is possible that the minimum thickness specified in Clauses 13.2.3 to 13.2.6 will not be adequate for certain sequences of shoring during construction or for large live to dead load ratios.*

Δ 13.2.3 Slabs without drop panels
The minimum thickness, h_s, shall be

$$h_s \geq \frac{\ell_n(0.6 + f_y/1000)}{30} \tag{13-1}$$

where
$\ell_n =$ the longer clear span
At discontinuous edges, an edge beam shall be provided with a stiffness ratio, α, of not less than 0.80, or the thickness required by Equation (13-1) shall be multiplied by 1.1 in the panel with the discontinuous edge or edges.

Δ 13.2.4 Slabs with drop panels
The minimum thickness, h_s, shall be

$$h_s \geq \frac{\ell_n(0.6 + f_y/1000)}{30} - \frac{2x_d}{\ell_n} \, \Delta_h \tag{13-2}$$

where ℓ_n is the longer clear span and Δ_h is the additional thickness of the drop panel below the soffit of the slab and shall not be taken larger than h_s.
In Equation (13-2), $(2x_d/\ell_n)$ is the smaller of the values determined in the two directions and x_d shall not be taken greater than $(\ell_n/4)$.
At discontinuous edges, an edge beam shall be provided with a stiffness ratio, α, of not less than 0.80, or the thickness required by Equation (13-2) shall be multiplied by 1.1 in the panel with the discontinuous edge or edges.

Δ ## 13.2.5 Slabs with beams between all supports

The minimum thickness, h_s, shall be

$$h_s \geq \frac{\ell_n(0.6 + f_y/1000)}{30 + 4\beta\alpha_m} \qquad (13\text{-}3)$$

where ℓ_n is the longer clear span, α_m shall not be taken greater than 2.0, and the value α may be determined by taking I_b equal to

$$I_b = \frac{b_w h^3}{12}\left(2.5\left(1 - \frac{h_s}{h}\right)\right) \qquad (13\text{-}4)$$

13.2.6 Slab bands

The minimum thickness of slab bands shall be that required for beams in Table 9.2.

13.2.7 Computation of slab deflections

A slab thickness less than the minimum thickness required by Clauses 13.2.2 to 13.2.5 may be used if computations show that deflection will not exceed the limits specified in Table 9.3. Deflections shall be computed by taking into account the size and shape of the panel, the conditions of support, and the nature of restraints at the panel edges. For deflection computations, the modulus of elasticity, E_c, for concrete shall be as specified in Clause 8.6.2. The effective moment of inertia shall be that specified by Equation (9-1). The moment, M_a, shall take into consideration loads, such as construction loads, that extend the cracked region. Other values of I_e may be used if the computed deflection is in reasonable agreement with the results of comprehensive tests. The effective modulus of rupture of the concrete shall be taken as one-half of the value specified by Equation (8-3). Additional long-term deflection shall be computed as specified in Clause 9.8.2.5.

13.3 Design procedures for shear for slabs without beams

13.3.1 General

In the vicinity of concentrated loads or reactions, the factored shear stress resistance, v_r, shall be equal to or greater than the maximum factored shear stress, v_f, due to the factored shear force and unbalanced moments. The stress, v_f, shall be determined for full load on all spans as well as any other patterns of loading that might result in larger stresses.

13.3.2 One-way and two-way shear

Slabs in the vicinity of columns shall be designed for two-way shear as specified in Clauses 13.3.3 to 13.3.5. Slabs shall also be designed for one-way shear as specified in Clause 13.3.6.

13.3.3 Critical shear section for two-way action

13.3.3.1

The critical section for two-way action shall be a section perpendicular to the plane of the slab and located so that its perimeter, b_0, is a minimum, but the section need not approach closer than $d/2$ to the perimeter of the concentrated load or reaction area.

13.3.3.2

At changes in slab thickness, a critical section located in the thinner portion at a distance not greater than $d/2$ from the face of the thicker portion and located such that the perimeter, b_0, is a minimum, shall also be investigated.

13.3.3.3

For square or rectangular load or reaction areas, the critical section may be assumed to have four straight sides. For edge supports, the critical section may be assumed to have three straight sides. For corner supports, the critical section may be assumed to have two straight sides. At edge and corner supports where the slab cantilevers beyond the exterior face of the support, the critical section may be assumed to extend into the cantilevered portion of the slab for a distance not exceeding d.

13.3.3.4

When openings in slabs are located at a distance of less than ten times the slab thickness from a concentrated load or reaction area, or when openings in slabs without beams are located within a column strip, that part of the perimeter of the critical section which is enclosed by straight lines projecting from the centre of the load or reaction area and tangent to the boundaries of the openings shall be considered ineffective.

13.3.4 Maximum shear stress resistance without shear reinforcement

13.3.4.1

The factored shear stress resistance, v_r, shall be the smallest of

(a) $v_r = v_c = \left(1 + \dfrac{2}{\beta_c}\right) 0.19 \lambda \phi_c \sqrt{f_c'}$ (13-5)

where
β_c = the ratio of long side to short side of the column, concentrated load, or reaction area

(b) $v_r = v_c = \left(\dfrac{\alpha_s d}{b_o} + 0.19\right) \lambda \phi_c \sqrt{f_c'}$ (13-6)

where
α_s = 4 for interior columns, 3 for edge columns, and 2 for corner columns

(c) $v_r = v_c = 0.38 \lambda \phi_c \sqrt{f_c'}$ (13-7)

13.3.4.2

The value of $\sqrt{f_c'}$ used to calculate v_r in Equations (13-5) to (13-7) shall not exceed 8 MPa.

13.3.4.3

If the effective depth, d, used in two-way shear calculations exceeds 300 mm, the value of v_c obtained from Equations (13-5) to (13-7) shall be multiplied by 1300/(1000+d).

13.3.4.4

The requirements of Clause 13.3.4.3 need not be applied to the design of footings or mat foundations where the distance from the point of zero shear to the face of the column, pedestal, or wall is less than 3d.

13.3.5 Factored shear stress

13.3.5.1

For interior, edge, and corner supports, the shear forces and unbalanced moments to be transferred to the support shall be resolved into a single shear force acting at the centroid of the critical section and moments about the centroidal axes (x and y directions) of the critical section.

13.3.5.2

The shear stress due to the factored shear force acting at the centroid of the section shall be assumed to be uniformly distributed over the critical shear section.

13.3.5.3

The fraction of the unbalanced moment transferred by eccentricity of shear at interior, edge, and corner columns, γ_v, shall be

$$\gamma_v = 1 - \frac{1}{1 + \frac{2}{3}\sqrt{\frac{b_1}{b_2}}} \tag{13-8}$$

13.3.5.4

The shear stress due to moment transfer by eccentricity of shear shall be assumed to vary linearly about the centroid of the critical shear section.

13.3.5.5

The factored shear stress, v_f, shall be computed from the following equation, with the factored shear force and unbalanced moments about the x and y directions obtained from a consistent loading:

$$v_f = \frac{V_f}{b_o d} + \left(\frac{\gamma_v M_f e}{J}\right)_x + \left(\frac{\gamma_v M_f e}{J}\right)_y \tag{13-9}$$

13.3.5.6

The fraction of the unbalanced moment not transferred by eccentricity of shear stress shall be transferred by flexure as specified in Clause 13.10.2.

13.3.6 One-way shear

13.3.6.1 General

One-way shear for a slab with a critical section extending in a plane across the entire width and located at a distance, d, from the face of the concentrated load or reaction area shall be as specified in Clauses 11.1 to 11.3. The one-way shear shall be distributed between the column strip and the middle strip in proportion to the design negative moments in each strip.

13.3.6.2 Corner columns

The factored shear resistance of slabs in the vicinity of corner columns, v_c, shall be taken as

$$v_c = \beta \lambda \phi_c \sqrt{f'_c} \tag{13-10}$$

along a critical shear section located not farther than $d/2$ from the edge of the column or column capital, where β is as specified in Clauses 11.3.6.2 and 11.3.6.3.

Where the slab cantilevers beyond the face of the corner column or the corner column capital, the length of the critical section may be taken as extended into the cantilevered portion for a length not exceeding d.

Corner columns meeting the requirements of this Clause shall be deemed to have satisfied the requirements of Clauses 13.3.4 and 13.3.5.

Note: *For slabs greater than 350 mm deep, or slabs with beams exceeding the limitations specified in Clause 11.3.6.2, application of the one-way shear provisions specified in Clauses 11.3.6.3 and 11.3.6.4 should take into account the reduction of allowable concrete shear stress resulting from the effect of depth in such members.*

13.3.7 Shear reinforcement for slabs without beams

13.3.7.1
Shear reinforcement consisting of headed shear reinforcement, stirrups, or shearheads may be used to increase the shear capacity of slabs and footings. The design of shearheads shall be based on the concepts in ACI 318M-02/ACI 318RM-02.

13.3.7.2
The shear resistance shall be investigated at the section specified in Clause 13.3.3.1 and at successive sections more distant from the support.

13.3.7.3
Within the shear reinforced zone, the factored shear stress resistance, v_r, shall be computed as $(v_c + v_s)$, where v_c and v_s shall be computed as specified in Clauses 13.3.8.3 and 13.3.8.5 for headed shear reinforcement and as specified in Clauses 13.3.9.3 and 13.3.9.4 for stirrups.

13.3.7.4
Shear reinforcement shall be extended to the section where v_f is not greater than $0.19\lambda\phi_c\sqrt{f'_c}$, but at least a distance $2d$ from the face of the column.

13.3.8 Headed shear reinforcement

13.3.8.1
Headed shear reinforcement shall be mechanically anchored at each end by a plate or head bearing against the concrete in such a manner that it is capable of developing the yield strength of the bar. The area of the plate or head shall be at least ten times the cross-sectional area of the bar unless a smaller area can be justified experimentally (see Clause 7.1.4).

13.3.8.2
When headed shear reinforcement is provided, the factored shear stress, v_f, shall be not greater than $0.75\lambda\phi_c\sqrt{f'_c}$.

13.3.8.3
In the zone reinforced by headed shear reinforcement, the factored shear stress resistance of the concrete, v_c, shall be $0.28\lambda\phi_c\sqrt{f'_c}$.

13.3.8.4
Headed shear reinforcement shall be located along concentric lines that parallel the perimeter of the column cross-section.

13.3.8.5
The factored shear stress resistance of headed shear reinforcement, v_s, shall be computed as

$$v_s = \frac{\phi_s A_{vs} f_{yv}}{b_o s}$$ (13-11)

where
A_{vs} = the cross-sectional area of the headed shear reinforcement on a concentric line parallel to the perimeter of the column

13.3.8.6

The distance between the column face and the first line of headed shear reinforcement shall be 0.4d. The upper limits for the spacing, s, between lines of headed shear reinforcement shall be based on the value of v_f at a critical section $d/2$ from the column face, as follows:

(a) $s \leq 0.75d$ when $v_f \leq 0.56\lambda\phi_c\sqrt{f_c'}$ **(13-12)**

(b) $s \leq 0.5d$ when $v_f > 0.56\lambda\phi_c\sqrt{f_c'}$ **(13-13)**

13.3.8.7

Unless the headed shear reinforcement is otherwise protected, the minimum concrete cover over the heads shall be the same as the minimum cover for the flexural reinforcement as specified in Clause 7.9. The concrete cover shall not exceed the minimum cover plus one-half the bar diameter of the flexural reinforcement.

13.3.9 Stirrup reinforcement

13.3.9.1

Stirrups anchored as specified in Clauses 7.1.2 and 12.13 may be used as shear reinforcement provided that the overall thickness of the slab is not less than 300 mm.

13.3.9.2

When stirrups are provided, the factored shear stress, v_f, shall not be greater than $0.55\lambda\phi_c\sqrt{f_c'}$.

13.3.9.3

In the zone reinforced by stirrups, the factored shear stress resistance of the concrete, v_c, shall be $0.19\lambda\phi_c\sqrt{f_c'}$.

13.3.9.4

The factored shear stress resistance, v_s, shall be computed from Equation (13-11), with A_{vs}, the cross-sectional area of the stirrups, on a line parallel to the perimeter of the column.

13.3.9.5

The stirrup spacing, s, shall not exceed $d/2$, with the first stirrup placed at $d/4$ from the column face.

13.4 Shear in slab systems with beams

13.4.1

Beams with $(\alpha_1\ell_{2a}/\ell_1)$ equal to or greater than 1.0 shall be designed to resist shear caused by factored loads on tributary areas bounded by 45° lines drawn from the corners of the panels and the centrelines of the adjacent panels parallel to the long sides.

13.4.2

Beams with $(\alpha_1\ell_{2a}/\ell_1)$ less than 1.0 may be designed to resist shear obtained by linear interpolation, assuming beams carry no load at $\alpha_1 = 0$.

13.4.3

In addition to resisting shears calculated as specified in Clauses 13.4.1 and 13.4.2, beams shall be designed to resist shears caused by factored loads applied directly on the beams.

13.4.4
Slab shears may be computed on the assumption that load is distributed to supporting beams as specified in Clause 13.4.1 or 13.4.2. Resistance to total shear occurring on a panel shall be provided.

13.4.5
The shear resistance of beams shall satisfy the requirements of Clause 11.

13.5 Design procedures for flexure
Note: *See also Clauses 13.6 to 13.12 and Annex B.*

13.5.1
A slab system may be designed using any procedure satisfying conditions of equilibrium and compatibility with the supports, provided that it is shown that the factored resistance at every section is at least equal to the effects of the factored loads and that all serviceability conditions, including specified limits on deflections, are met.

13.5.2
For lateral loads, analysis of unbraced frames shall take into account the effects of cracking and reinforcement on stiffness of frame members.

13.5.3
The results of the gravity load analysis shall be combined with the results of the lateral load analysis.

13.5.4
Openings of any size may be provided in slab systems if it is shown by analysis that the factored resistance is at least equal to the effects of factored loads in accordance with Clauses 8.3, 8.4, and 13.3.3.4, and that all serviceability conditions, including the specified limits on deflections, are met.
Note: *Clause 13.10.10 provides simple rules for regular slabs without beams.*

13.6 Elastic plate theory

13.6.1
Analysis of slab systems may be based on elastic plate theory that uses either classical or numerical techniques.
Note: *The successful application of the results of analysis using elastic plate theory requires proper consideration of factors such as selection of thickness, moment redistribution due to the effects of cracking, creep, shrinkage effects, and construction loading.*

13.6.2
Care shall be taken to ensure realistic modelling of the size and effective stiffness of the supporting elements, including beams, if any.

13.6.3
Appropriate loading patterns shall be considered to ensure determination of maximum values for all stress resultants at each section.

13.6.4

When reinforcement is placed as an orthogonal mat in the x and y directions, the factored design moments shall be adjusted to account for the effects of torsion. In lieu of more detailed calculations, the design moment intensities, $m_{x,des}$ or $m_{y,des}$, in the x and y directions at any point shall be computed as follows:

(a)   positive design moments:

$$m_{x,des} = m_x + |m_{xy}| \tag{13-14}$$

$$m_{y,des} = m_y + |m_{xy}| \tag{13-15}$$

If either $m_{x,des}$ or $m_{y,des}$ is negative, it shall be taken as zero.

(b)   negative design moments:

$$m_{x,des} = m_x - |m_{xy}| \tag{13-16}$$

$$m_{y,des} = m_y - |m_{xy}| \tag{13-17}$$

If either $m_{x,des}$ or $m_{y,des}$ is positive, it shall be taken as zero.

13.6.5

Uniformly spaced reinforcement shall be placed in bands such that

(a)   the total reinforcement provided within a band shall be sufficient to resist the total factored moment computed for that band; and

(b)   the moment resistance per unit width within the band shall be at least two-thirds of the maximum factored moment intensity within the band.

Note: *Additional information on the application of finite element analysis design techniques is provided by the Cement Association of Canada's* Concrete design handbook.

13.7 Theorems of plasticity

13.7.1

Analysis of slab systems for factored loads may be based on either the lower bound or upper bound theorems of plasticity.

Note: *The successful application of the results of plastic analysis requires proper assumptions that will ensure that serviceability requirements, including creep and shrinkage effects, are satisfied.*

13.7.2

The size and effective stiffness of the supporting elements shall be considered in the analysis.

13.7.3

When strength design is based on the upper bound theorem (e.g., yield line method), the factored moments shall be obtained from calculations based on a need for a mechanism to form over the whole or part of the slab at collapse. The mechanism that is the most critical shall be used for the design of the slab.

13.7.4

Factored moments obtained using lower bound theory (e.g., strip method) shall satisfy the requirements of equilibrium and the boundary conditions applicable to the slab.

13.7.5

Reinforcement may be uniformly spaced in bands, with band widths selected to ensure that serviceability requirements are satisfied.

13.8 Slab systems as elastic frames

13.8.1 Definition of frame geometry

13.8.1.1

A regular two-way slab system (see Clause 2.2) may, for purposes of analysis, be considered a series of plane frames acting longitudinally and transversely through the building. Each frame shall be composed of equivalent line members intersecting at member centrelines, shall follow a column line, and shall include the portion of slab bounded laterally by the centreline of the panel on each side.

Note: *A floor system with beams between supports that does not satisfy the limits specified in the definition of a regular two-way slab system in Clause 2.2 may be analyzed as specified in this Clause, but the reinforcing distribution specified in Clause 13.12 will normally not be applicable.*

13.8.1.2

Each floor and roof slab with attached columns may be analyzed separately, with the far ends of the columns considered fixed.

13.8.1.3

Where slab-beams are analyzed separately, it may be assumed in determining moment at a given support that the slab-beam is fixed at any support two panels distant from the slab-beam, provided that the slab continues beyond that point.

13.8.1.4

The change in length of columns and slabs due to direct stress, and deflections due to shear, may be neglected.

13.8.1.5

Member stiffness used in the analysis of the elastic frame shall be selected to simulate the behaviour of the slab system.

13.8.2 Non-prismatic modelling of member stiffness

13.8.2.1

When members are modelled as non-prismatic elements, the member stiffness may be as specified in Clauses 13.8.2.2 to 13.8.2.10.

13.8.2.2

The moment of inertia of column and slab-beam elements at any cross-section outside of joints or column capitals shall be based on the gross area of concrete at that section.

13.8.2.3

The moment of inertia of slab-beams from the centre of the column to the face of the column, bracket, or capital shall be assumed to be equal to the moment of inertia of the slab-beam at the face of the column, bracket, or capital divided by the quantity $(1 - c_2/\ell_{2a})^2$, where c_2 and ℓ_{2a} are measured transverse to the direction of the span for which moments are being determined.

13.8.2.4

The moment of inertia of column elements from top to bottom of the slab-beam at a joint shall be assumed to be infinite.

13.8.2.5

An equivalent column shall be assumed to consist of the actual columns above and below the slab-beam plus an attached torsional member transverse to the direction of the span for which moments are being determined.

13.8.2.6

The flexibility of an equivalent column shall be taken as the sum of the flexibilities of the actual columns above and below the slab-beam and the flexibility of the attached torsional member, as follows:

$$\frac{1}{K_{ec}} = \frac{1}{\Sigma K_c} + \frac{1}{K_t} \tag{13-18}$$

13.8.2.7

Attached torsional members shall be assumed to have a constant cross-section throughout their length consisting of the largest of the following:
(a) a portion of slab having a width equal to that of the column, bracket, or capital in the direction of the span for which moments are being determined;
(b) for monolithic or fully composite construction, the portion of slab specified in Item (a) plus that part of the transverse beam above and below the slab; or
(c) a transverse beam which includes that portion of slab on each side of the beam extending a distance equal to the projection of the beam above or below the slab, whichever is greater, but not greater than four times the slab thickness.

13.8.2.8

The stiffness, K_t, of attached torsional members shall be calculated as follows:

$$K_t = \Sigma \frac{9E_c C}{\ell_t \left(1 - \frac{c_2}{\ell_t}\right)^3} \tag{13-19}$$

13.8.2.9

The section parameter, C, in Equation (13-19) may be evaluated for the cross-section by dividing it into separate rectangular parts and carrying out the following summation:

$$C = \Sigma \left(1 - 0.63\frac{x}{y}\right)\frac{x^3 y}{3} \tag{13-20}$$

13.8.2.10

Where beams frame into columns in the direction of the span for which moments are being determined, the value of K_t shall be multiplied by the ratio of the moment of inertia of the slab with such beam to the moment of inertia of the slab without such beam.

13.8.3 Prismatic modelling of member stiffness

13.8.3.1

When members are modelled as prismatic elements, the member stiffness may be assigned as specified in Clauses 13.8.3.2 and 13.8.3.3.

13.8.3.2

For prismatic modelling of slab-beam elements, the moment of inertia shall be based on the gross area of the concrete outside the joints or column capitals. When the moment of inertia varies outside the joint, e.g., in drop panels, the slab-beam elements may be modelled as a series of prismatic elements with moments of inertia based on the gross concrete dimensions.

86

13.8.3.3

For prismatic modelling of column elements, the effective moment of inertia shall be taken as equal to ψ times the moment of inertia based on the gross area outside the joints, where ψ is given as follows:

(a) for $\ell_2 / \ell_1 \le 1.0$: $\psi = 0.3 + 0.7 \dfrac{\alpha_1 \ell_2}{\ell_1}$ **(13-21)**

(b) for $\ell_2 / \ell_1 > 1.0$: $\psi = 0.6 \left(\dfrac{\ell_2}{\ell_1} - 0.5 \right) + \left(1.3 - 0.6 \dfrac{\ell_2}{\ell_1} \right) \dfrac{\alpha_1 \ell_2}{\ell_1}$ **(13-22)**

In Equations (13-21) and (13-22), ψ shall not be taken less than 0.3 or greater than 1.0, and $\alpha_1 \ell_2 / \ell_1$ shall not be taken greater than 1.0.

13.8.4 Arrangement of live load

13.8.4.1

When the loading pattern is known, the frame shall be analyzed for that load.

13.8.4.2

When the live load is uniformly distributed and does not exceed three-quarters of the specified dead load, or the nature of the live load is such that all panels will be loaded simultaneously, the maximum factored moments may be assumed to occur at all sections with full factored live load on the entire slab system.

13.8.4.3

For loading conditions other than those specified in Clauses 13.8.4.1 and 13.8.4.2, the maximum positive factored moment near midspan of a panel may be assumed to occur with three-quarters of the full factored uniformly distributed live load on the panel and on alternate panels, and the maximum negative factored moment in the slab at a support may be assumed to occur with three-quarters of the full factored uniformly distributed live load on adjacent panels only.

13.8.4.4

Factored moments shall not be taken as less than those occurring with full factored live loads on all panels.

13.8.5 Critical sections

13.8.5.1

Except as required by Clause 13.8.5.2, at interior and exterior supports the critical section for the negative factored moment shall be taken at the face of rectilinear supports, but not at a distance greater than $0.175\ell_1$ from the centre of the column.

13.8.5.2

In addition to the requirements specified in Clause 13.8.5.1, at exterior supports that include brackets or capitals the critical section for the negative factored moment in the span perpendicular to an edge shall be taken at a distance from the face of the supporting element not greater than one-half of the projection of the bracket or capital beyond the face of the supporting element.

13.8.5.3

When the critical section for the negative design moment is being located, circular or regular polygonal supports shall be treated as square supports with the same area.

13.8.5.4
Reinforcement to resist the moments at the critical sections shall be selected in accordance with Clauses 13.10 to 13.12.

13.8.5.5
The flexural capacity shall be checked at any change in the slab depth, e.g., at the edges of drop panels and slab bands.

13.9 Direct design method

13.9.1 Limitations

13.9.1.1
Regular two-way slab systems (see Clause 2.2) that comply with the limitations specified in Clauses 13.9.1.2 to 13.9.1.5 may be designed using the direct design method.
Note: *It is possible that in some circumstances the requirements specified in Clauses 13.9.1.2 to 13.9.1.5 will not address concerns related to slab systems with drop panels and/or beams as rigorously as the requirements specified in Clause 13.8.*

13.9.1.2
There shall be a minimum of three continuous spans in each direction.

13.9.1.3
Successive span lengths centre-to-centre of supports in each direction shall not differ by more than one-third of the longer span.

13.9.1.4
All loads shall be due to gravity only and uniformly distributed over an entire panel. The factored live load shall not exceed twice the factored dead load.

13.9.1.5
Variations from the limitations of Clauses 13.9.1.2 to 13.9.1.4 shall be acceptable if it is demonstrated by analysis that the requirements specified in Clause 13.5.1 are satisfied.

13.9.2 Total factored static moment for a span

13.9.2.1
The total factored static moment for a span shall be determined in a strip bound laterally by the centrelines of the panels on each side of the centreline of supports.

13.9.2.2
For each span of each strip, the sum of the absolute values of the positive and the average negative factored moments, in each direction, shall be not less than

$$M_o = \frac{w_f \ell_{2a} \ell_n^2}{8} \qquad\qquad (13\text{-}23)$$

13.9.2.3
The clear span, ℓ_n, shall extend from face-to-face of columns, capitals, brackets, or walls. The value of ℓ_n used in Equation (13-23) shall be not less than $0.65\ell_1$.

13.9.3 Negative and positive factored moments

13.9.3.1

In an interior span, the total static moment, M_o, shall be distributed as follows:

Negative factored moment at the face of support	0.65
Positive factored moment at midspan	0.35

13.9.3.2

In an end span, the total factored static moment, M_o, shall be distributed as specified in Table 13.1.

Table 13.1
Distribution factors for total factored static moment
(See Clause 13.9.3.2.)

Moment	Exterior edge unrestrained	Slab with beams between all supports	Slab without beams between interior supports	Exterior edge fully restrained
Interior negative factored moment	0.75	0.70	0.70	0.65
Positive factored moment	0.66	0.59	0.52	0.35
Exterior negative factored moment	0	0.16	0.26	0.65

13.9.3.3

Negative and positive factored moments may be modified by 15% provided that the total static moment for a span in the direction considered is not less than that required by Equation (13-23).

13.9.3.4

Negative moment sections shall be designed to resist the larger of the two interior negative factored moments determined for spans framing into a common support; however, the moments may first be modified in accordance with Clause 13.9.3.3.

13.9.4 Unbalanced factored moments in columns and walls

At an interior support, the joint and supporting elements above and below the slab shall resist the factored moment specified in the following equation in direct proportion to their stiffness:

$$M_f = 0.07 \left((w_{df} + 0.5w_{lf}) \ell_{2a} \ell_n^2 - w'_{df} \ell'_{2a} (\ell'_n)^2 \right) \tag{13-24}$$

where w'_{df}, ℓ'_{2a}, and ℓ'_n refer to the shorter span.

13.9.5 Selection of reinforcement

Reinforcement to resist the moments at the critical sections shall be selected in accordance with Clauses 13.10 to 13.12.

13.10 Slab reinforcement

13.10.1 General
Reinforcement in each direction for two-way slab systems shall be determined from moments at critical sections but shall be not less than that required by Clause 7.8.1.

Note: *Where strict crack control is a concern, slabs with drop panels, particularly in a corrosive environment, can require additional reinforcement in the negative middle strip region to limit cracking. This additional reinforcement is not included in the calculation of moment resistance. The reinforcement required to limit cracking is generally more than that required by Clause 7.8.1.*

13.10.2 Shear and moment transfer
When gravity load, wind, earthquake, or other lateral forces cause transfer of moment between slab and column, a fraction of unbalanced moment given by

$$\gamma_f = 1 - \gamma_v \tag{13-25}$$

shall be transferred by flexural reinforcement placed within a width b_b.

Note: *For exterior supports, including corner columns, Clause 13.10.3 satisfies this requirement.*

13.10.3 Exterior columns
Reinforcement for the total factored negative moment transferred to the exterior columns shall be placed within a band width b_b. Temperature and shrinkage reinforcement determined as specified Clause 7.8.1 shall be provided in that section of the slab outside of the band region defined by b_b, or as required by Clause 13.10.9.

13.10.4 Spacing
Except for portions of slab area that are of cellular or ribbed construction, spacing of reinforcement at critical sections shall not exceed the following limits:

Negative reinforcement in the band defined by b_b	$1.5h_s$, but $s \leq 250$ mm
Remaining negative moment reinforcement	$3h_s$, but $s \leq 500$ mm
Positive moment reinforcement	$3h_s$, but $s \leq 500$ mm

In the slab over cellular spaces, reinforcement shall be provided as required by Clause 7.8.

13.10.5 Anchorage

13.10.5.1
Positive moment reinforcement perpendicular to a discontinuous edge shall have embedment, straight or hooked, at least 150 mm into the spandrel beams, columns, or walls.

13.10.5.2
Negative moment reinforcement perpendicular to a discontinuous edge shall be bent, hooked, or otherwise anchored in spandrel beams, columns, or walls, and shall be developed at the face of the support as specified in Clause 12.

13.10.5.3
Where a slab is not supported by a spandrel beam or wall at a discontinuous edge, or where a slab cantilevers beyond the support, both the top and bottom reinforcement shall extend to the edge of the slab.

13.10.6 Structural integrity reinforcement

13.10.6.1

The summation of the area of bottom reinforcement connecting the slab, drop panel, or slab band to the column or column capital on all faces of the periphery of the column or column capital shall be

$$\sum A_{sb} = \frac{2V_{se}}{f_y} \tag{13-26}$$

Integrity reinforcement shall not be required if there are beams containing shear reinforcement in all spans framing into the column.

13.10.6.2

The reinforcement specified in Clause 13.10.6.1 shall consist of at least two bars or two tendons that extend through the column core or column capital region in each span direction.

13.10.6.3

The bottom reinforcement required by Clause 13.10.6.1 shall be provided by one or more of the following:

(a) bottom reinforcement extended such that it is lap spliced over a column or column capital, with the bottom reinforcement in adjacent spans using a Class A tension lap splice;

(b) additional bottom reinforcement passing over a column or column capital such that an overlap of $2\ell_d$ is provided, with the bottom reinforcement in adjacent spans;

(c) at discontinuous edges, bottom reinforcement extended and bent, hooked, or otherwise anchored over the supports such that the yield stress can be developed at the face of the column or column capital as specified in Clause 12; or

(d) continuous tendons draped over column capitals, with a minimum total area of prestressing steel calculated using Equation (13-26), but with f_y replaced by f_{py}.

13.10.7 Effective depth at drop panels

Where a drop panel is used to reduce the amount of negative moment reinforcement over the column, the thickness of the drop panel below the slab shall not be assumed greater than one-quarter of the distance from the edge of the drop panel to the edge of the column or column capital.

13.10.8 Curtailment of reinforcement

13.10.8.1

For regular two-way slabs (see Clause 2.2) that comply with the requirements specified in Clauses 13.9.1.2 to 13.9.1.5, minimum extensions shall be as shown in Figure 13.1.

13.10.8.2

The required extensions for slabs not complying with the requirements specified in Clauses 13.9.1.2 to 13.9.1.5 shall meet the requirements specified in Clauses 12.11 and 12.12, but shall be not less than those shown in Figure 13.1.

13.10.8.3

Where adjacent spans are unequal, the extension of negative reinforcement beyond the face of the support, as shown in Figure 13.1, shall be based on the longer span.

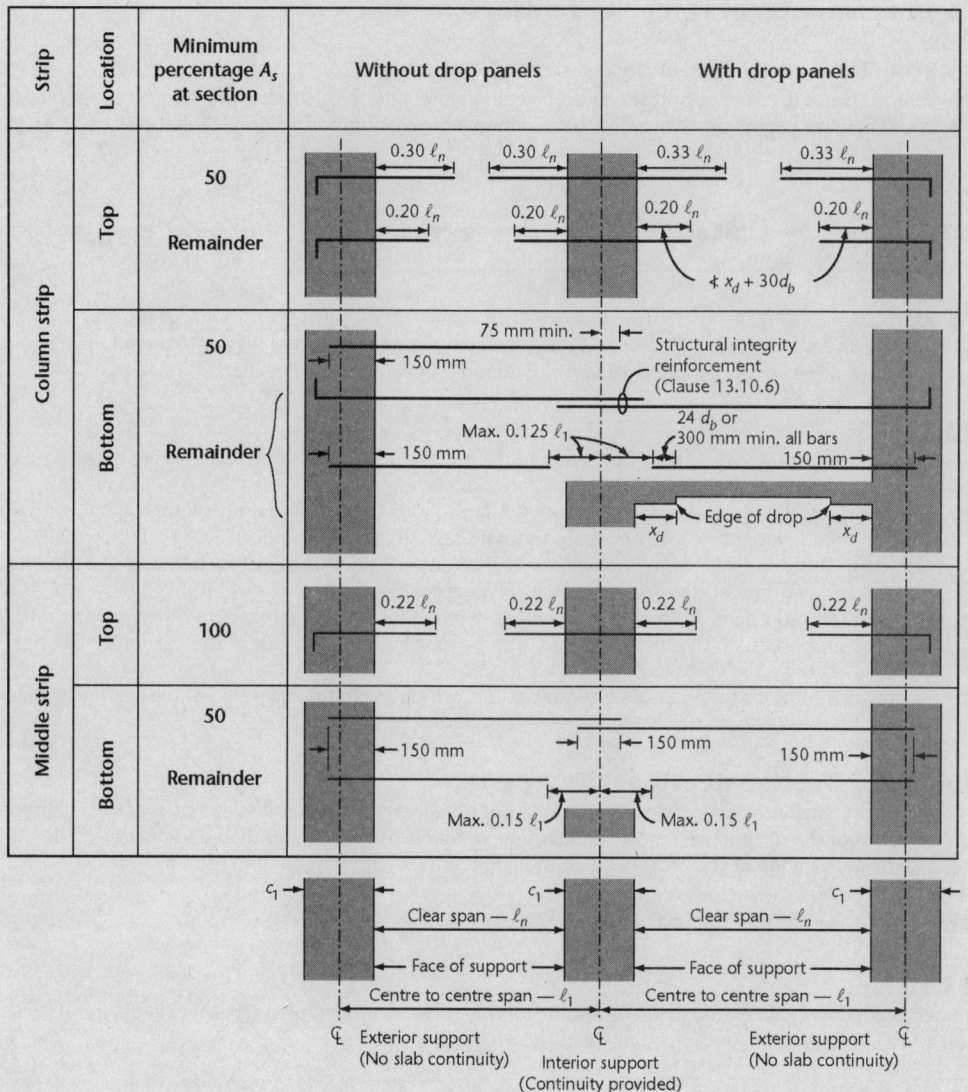

Figure 13.1
Minimum length of reinforcement for slabs without interior beams
(See Clauses 2.3 and 13.10.8.1–13.10.8.3.)

13.10.9 Top reinforcement at slab edges

Slab edges shall be reinforced with top reinforcement perpendicular to the edge to resist the factored moments caused by edge loads, but not less than that required by Clause 7.8.1.

13.10.10 Openings

13.10.10.1

Openings may be placed in regular two-way slabs without beams (see Clause 2.2) without the special analysis required by Clause 13.5.4, provided that the requirements specified in Clauses 13.10.10.2 to 13.10.10.5 are met.

13.10.10.2

Openings of any size may be located in the area common to intersecting middle strips, provided that the total amount of reinforcement required for the panel without the opening is maintained.

13.10.10.3

In the area common to intersecting column strips, not more than one-eighth of the width of the column strip in either span shall be interrupted by openings. An amount of reinforcement equivalent to that interrupted by an opening shall be added adjacent to the sides of the opening.

13.10.10.4

In the area common to one column strip and one middle strip, not more than one-quarter of the reinforcement in either strip shall be interrupted by openings. An amount of reinforcement equivalent to that interrupted by an opening shall be added adjacent to the sides of the opening.

13.10.10.5

The shear requirements specified in Clause 13.3.3.4 shall be satisfied.

13.11 Lateral distribution of moments for slabs without interior beams

13.11.1 General

In addition to the requirements specified in Clause 13.10, slabs without beams designed as specified in Clauses 13.8 and 13.9 shall be reinforced for flexure as specified in Clauses 13.11.2 and 13.11.3.

13.11.2 Factored moments in column strip

13.11.2.1

The column strip shall be designed to resist the total negative or positive factored moments at the critical sections multiplied by an appropriate factor as specified in Clauses 13.11.2.2 to 13.11.2.5.

13.11.2.2

The following multiplication factors shall apply to slabs without drop panels (with or without spandrel beams):

(a) Negative moment at an interior column	0.70 to 0.90
(b) Negative moment at an exterior column	1.00
(c) Positive moment at all spans	0.55 to 0.65

13.11.2.3

The following multiplication factors shall apply to slabs with drop panels (with or without spandrel beams):

(a) Negative moment at an interior column	0.75 to 0.90
(b) Negative moment at an exterior column	1.00
(c) Positive moment at all spans	0.55 to 0.65

13.11.2.4

The following multiplication factors shall apply to slabs with slab bands, in the direction of the slab band:

Negative moment at an interior column	0.80 to 1.00
Negative moment at an exterior column	1.00
Positive moment at all spans	0.80 to 1.00

13.11.2.5

The following multiplication factors shall apply to slabs with slab bands, in the direction perpendicular to the slab band:

Negative moment at an interior column in width b_b	Not less than 0.05 to 0.15, with the remaining negative moment assumed evenly distributed over the entire frame width
Negative moment at an exterior column	1.00
Positive moment at all spans where $(\ell_1/\ell_2) \geq 1.0$	0.50 to 0.60
Positive moment at all spans where $(\ell_1/\ell_2) < 1.0$	$0.5\,(\ell_1/\ell_2)$ to $0.6\,(\ell_1/\ell_2)$

13.11.2.6

For negative moment at an exterior column in slabs with spandrel beams, the requirements specified in Clause 13.11.2.2(b) or 13.11.2.3(b) shall apply.

13.11.2.7

At interior columns, the band width, b_b, shall be designed to resist at least one-third of the total factored negative moment in the entire design strip.

13.11.3 Factored moments in middle strips

13.11.3.1

That portion of negative and positive factored moments not resisted by column strips shall be proportionately assigned to corresponding half middle strips.

13.11.3.2
Each middle strip shall be proportioned to resist the sum of the factored moments assigned to its two half middle strips.

13.11.3.3
A middle strip adjacent to and parallel with an edge supported by a wall shall be proportioned to resist twice the factored moment assigned to the half middle strip corresponding to the first row of interior supports.

13.11.3.4
At slab edges, the requirements specified in Clause 13.10.9 shall be satisfied.

13.12 Reinforcement for slabs with beams between all supports

13.12.1 General
In addition to the requirements specified in Clause 13.10, slabs with beams designed as specified in Clauses 13.8 and 13.9 shall be reinforced for flexure as specified in Clauses 13.12.2 to 13.12.5.

13.12.2 Factored moments in beams

13.12.2.1
Beams shall be reinforced to resist the following fraction of the positive or interior negative factored moments determined by analysis or determined as specified in Clause 13.9.3:

$$\frac{\alpha_1}{0.3+\alpha_1}\left(1-\frac{\ell_2}{3\ell_1}\right)$$

13.12.2.2
Beams shall be proportioned for 100% of the exterior negative moment.

13.12.2.3
In addition to moments calculated for uniform loads applied to the slab as specified in Clauses 13.12.2.1 and 13.12.2.2, beams shall be proportioned to resist moments caused by concentrated or linear loads applied directly to the beams, including the weight of the beam stem.

13.12.3 Slab reinforcement for positive moment
The slab shall be reinforced to resist the factored positive moments not supported by the beams. This reinforcement may be distributed uniformly over the width of the slab.

13.12.4 Slab reinforcement for negative moment

13.12.4.1 Interior supports
The slab shall be reinforced to resist the interior negative moments not resisted by the beams. This reinforcement shall be uniformly distributed over the width of the slab.

13.12.4.2 Exterior supports
The reinforcement for the exterior factored negative moment in the beam shall be placed within a band with a width b_b unless calculations show that reinforcement placed outside this limit can develop its full capacity.

13.12.5 Corner reinforcement

13.12.5.1
In slabs with beams between supports with a value of α greater than 1.0, top and bottom slab reinforcement shall be provided at exterior corners for a distance, in each direction, equal to one-fifth of the shorter span.

13.12.5.2
The reinforcement shall be sufficient to resist a moment per unit width equal to the maximum positive moment per unit width in the slab.

13.12.5.3
The reinforcement at the top of the slab shall be provided to resist moments about axes perpendicular to the diagonal from the corner. The bottom reinforcement shall be provided to resist moments about axes parallel to the diagonal. The reinforcement may be placed in bands parallel to the sides of the slab.

14 Walls
Note: *See Clause 2.2 under "Wall" for wall type definitions.*

14.1 General requirements for all walls

14.1.1 Application
Clauses 14.1.2 to 14.4.6 shall apply to the design of walls, except where the additional requirements specified in Clauses 16 and 21 to 23 apply.

14.1.2 Lateral support of walls
Walls shall be considered laterally supported if
(a) walls or other vertical bracing elements are arranged in two directions so as to provide lateral stability to the structure as a whole; and
(b) connections between the wall and its lateral supports are designed to resist a horizontal force not less than 2% of the total factored vertical load that the wall is designed to carry at the level of the lateral support, but not less than 10 kN per metre length of the wall.

14.1.3 Design length of wall for the distribution of concentrated vertical loads

14.1.3.1
In lieu of a detailed analysis, each concentrated compressive vertical load acting on a wall shall be assumed to be uniformly distributed over a horizontal length ℓ_b of wall. At any position below the level of the concentrated load, the portion of ℓ_b on each side of the centre of the concentrated load shall be one-half of the width of the bearing plus the width enclosed by a line sloping downward at two vertical to one horizontal on each side, limited by intersection with the end of the wall. This stressed width shall not be assumed to exceed nine times the wall thickness on each side of the bearing area. For a wall subjected to more than one concentrated load, the design shall take into account the overlapping of uniformly distributed loads from each of the concentrated loads.

14.1.3.2
Cracking resulting from transverse tensile stresses caused by the spread of the concentrated loads acting on the wall shall be taken into account in the design.

Note: *Strut-and-tie models can be used to compute the amount of reinforcement required to resist the transverse force under bearing loads and to control cracking.*

14.1.4 Columns built integrally with walls
Columns built integrally with walls shall be designed as specified in Clause 10, with outside dimensions that comply with Clause 10.11.2.

14.1.5 Transfer of vertical wall loads through floor
When the specified compressive strength of the concrete in the walls, f'_{cw}, exceeds that specified for the floor, f'_{cs}, the strength of a wall-to-floor joint shall be determined using the lower of the concrete strengths in the wall and the floor. The strength of this joint can be increased by adding dowels or by increasing the strength of the concrete in the floor under and adjacent to the wall. Such concrete shall extend at least 500 mm into the floor from each face of the wall.

14.1.6 Transfer of horizontal wall forces across construction joints
Transfer of horizontal wall forces across construction joints shall be as specified in Clause 11.5. The area of the reinforcement crossing the shear plane shall be the larger of
(a) the reinforcement area provided for flexure and axial loads; and
(b) the reinforcement area required for shear friction.
   In flanged walls, only the vertical reinforcement in those portions of the section assumed to resist horizontal shear shall be included in this calculation.

14.1.7 Minimum thickness of walls

14.1.7.1 Bearing walls and shear walls
The thickness of bearing walls and the webs and flanges of shear walls shall be not less than the smaller of ℓ_w /25 or h_u /25, but not less than 150 mm.

14.1.7.2 Non-bearing walls
The thickness of non-bearing walls shall be not less than 1/30 of the unsupported height or length, whichever is shorter, or less than 100 mm.

14.1.8 Details of wall reinforcement

14.1.8.1 Distributed and concentrated reinforcement
Walls shall have distributed vertical and horizontal reinforcement in layers in accordance with Clauses 14.1.8.2 to 14.1.8.7. Walls shall also have concentrated vertical reinforcement in accordance with Clause 14.1.8.8.

14.1.8.2 Maximum diameter of distributed reinforcement
The diameter of bars used for distributed reinforcement shall not exceed one-tenth of the wall thickness.

14.1.8.3 Number of layers of wall reinforcement
Except for exterior basement walls or retaining walls, bearing or shear walls more than 210 mm thick shall have the reinforcement for each direction placed in two layers. Each layer shall be placed not more than t/3 from the surface of the wall.

14.1.8.4 Spacing of reinforcement
The vertical and horizontal reinforcement in each layer shall not be spaced farther apart than three times the wall thickness or 500 mm, whichever is less.

14.1.8.5 Distributed vertical reinforcement
The minimum area of distributed vertical reinforcement between boundary elements shall be $0.0015A_g$.

14.1.8.6 Distributed horizontal reinforcement
The minimum area of distributed horizontal reinforcement shall be $0.002A_g$. However, where crack control is critical or wall geometry or the length of the wall between joints causes significant restraint of shrinkage or thermal strains, reinforcement additional to that specified in this Clause, or other crack control measures, shall be considered.

14.1.8.7 Ties for distributed vertical compression reinforcement
Distributed vertical reinforcement, if stressed in compression, shall be tied and detailed in accordance with the requirements for column reinforcement specified in Clause 7, except that ties may be omitted if
(a)   the area of vertical steel is less than $0.005A_g$; and
(b)   the bar size is 20M or smaller.

14.1.8.8 Concentrated vertical reinforcement

14.1.8.8.1 Nominal concentrated vertical reinforcement
Concentrated vertical reinforcement consisting of not fewer than two 15M vertical bars shall be provided at each end of all walls.

14.1.8.8.2 Reinforcement for flexure
Concentrated vertical reinforcement shall be provided in boundary elements of shear walls to provide that part of the resistance to strong-axis bending not provided by the reinforcement specified in Clause 14.1.8.5.

14.1.8.8.3 Concentrated vertical reinforcement limits
The reinforcement within any region of concentrated vertical reinforcement shall not exceed the amounts specified in Clause 10.9, substituting A_{gb} for A_g.

14.1.8.8.4 Ties for concentrated vertical reinforcement
Concentrated vertical reinforcement in excess of two 20M bars shall be tied and detailed as specified in Clause 7.

14.1.8.9 Reinforcement at openings
In addition to the reinforcement required by Clauses 14.1.8.5, 14.1.8.6, and 14.1.8.8.1, not less than one 15M bar per layer, or reinforcement having the same area, shall be provided around all window and door or similar openings. Such bars shall extend to develop the bar, but not less than 600 mm beyond each corner of the opening.

14.2 Structural design of bearing walls

14.2.1
Except as permitted by Clause 14.2.2, bearing walls shall be designed as specified in Clauses 7, 10, and 11.

14.2.2

14.2.2.1
Subject to the requirements specified in Clause 14.2.2.2, bearing walls may be designed using the following equation:

$$P_r = \frac{2}{3}\alpha_1\phi_c f'_c A_g \left(1 - \left(\frac{kh_u}{32t}\right)^2\right)$$ (14-1)

14.2.2.2
Clause 14.2.2.1 shall apply only if the following requirements are met:
(a) the wall has a solid rectangular cross-section that is constant over the height of the wall;
(b) the principal moments act about a horizontal axis parallel to the plane of the wall;
(c) the resultant of all factored axial loads, including the effects of the principal moment, is located within the middle third of the overall wall thickness; and
(d) the wall is supported against lateral displacement along at least the top and bottom edges.

14.2.2.3
The effective length factor, k, in Equation (14-1) shall have the following values:

For walls restrained against rotation at one or both ends (top, bottom, or both)	0.8
For walls unrestrained against rotation at both ends	1.0

14.3 Structural design of non-bearing walls
Non-bearing walls, including retaining walls and transversely loaded walls, shall be designed in accordance with the provisions of Clauses 10 and 11.

14.4 Structural design of shear walls

14.4.1 General
In addition to the requirements specified elsewhere in Clause 14, the following shall apply to shear walls:
(a) flexural shear walls shall be designed for factored axial load, factored moment about one or both axes, and factored shear as specified in Clauses 10 and 11; and
(b) squat shear walls may be designed using strut-and-tie models in accordance with Clause 11.4 and the applicable provisions of Clause 14.1.

14.4.2 Assemblies of interconnected shear walls

14.4.2.1 Shear connection
In assemblies of interconnected shear walls designed to act as a unit, reinforcement shall be provided to transmit the shear stresses necessary for the assembly of interconnected walls to act as a unit.

14.4.2.2 Compression flanges of assemblies of interconnected shear walls

If a compression flange of an assembly of interconnected shear walls has a thickness less than $h_c/15$, or less than $w_c/15$ if adjacent shear wall webs are present, the factored axial and moment resistances of the wall assembly shall both be multiplied by

$$\omega = 1.0 - 0.025(\ell_c/t - 15) \qquad \text{(14-2)}$$

where ℓ_c is the lesser of w_c and h_c and ω shall not be less than 0.75 or greater than 1.0.

14.4.2.3 Maximum widths of overhanging flanges

The effective widths of overhanging flanges of walls shall not be assumed to extend farther from the face of the web than the smaller of
(a) half the clear distance to an adjacent shear wall web; or
(b) 25% of the total wall height above the section under consideration.

14.4.3 Horizontal reinforcement in shear walls

Horizontal reinforcement shall extend to the ends of the wall and shall be anchored at each end within the boundary elements or within the regions of concentrated reinforcement required by Clause 14.1.8.8.

14.4.4 Weak axis bending

Weak axis bending of shear walls shall be considered in conjunction with strong axis bending.

14.4.5 Diaphragms

Floor and roof diaphragms shall be designed to transfer lateral forces between walls or other lateral-load-resisting elements and floor and roof diaphragms. Connections between the diaphragms and the frames or other lateral-load-resisting elements shall be designed to resist the forces that are transferred.

14.4.6 Coupling beams

The diameter of flexural reinforcing bars in coupling beams shall be selected to provide a development length not more than one-half of the clear beam span. Alternatively, diagonal reinforcement shall be provided as specified in Clause 21.6.8.7. However, ties satisfying the requirements specified in Clause 7.6 may be provided in lieu of hoops or spirals.

15 Foundations

15.1 General

Clauses 15.2 to 15.12 shall apply to the design of isolated footings and, where applicable, to combined footings, mats, and deep foundations.

15.2 Loads and reactions

15.2.1

Footings, piles, and pile caps shall be proportioned to resist the factored loads and induced reactions.

15.2.2

The base area of the footing or the number and arrangement of piles shall be selected based on the principles of soil mechanics. Where the analysis of footings is based on other than linear distributions of soil pressure, the assumed distributions shall be based on an analysis of the interaction of the soil and the footing in accordance with the stiffness of both elements.

15.2.3

Piles and pile caps in deep foundations shall be designed on the assumption that each axial pile reaction acts at an eccentricity, in any direction, equal to the specified pile location tolerance, but not less than 50 mm.

15.3 Footings and pile caps supporting circular or regular polygonal columns or pedestals

In lieu of detailed analysis, circular or regular polygonal concrete columns or pedestals may be treated as square members, with the same area, for the location of critical sections for moment, shear, and development of reinforcement in the footings or pile caps.

15.4 Flexural design of footings

15.4.1

Design for flexure shall meet the requirements of Clause 10.

Note: *For many types of footings, the strut-and-tie method specified in Clause 11.4 can be used for design.*

15.4.2

The external moment on any section of a footing shall be determined by passing a vertical plane through the footing and computing the moment of the forces acting over the entire area of the footing on one side of that vertical plane.

15.4.3

The maximum factored moment for an isolated footing shall be computed at the critical sections located as follows:

(a) for footings supporting a concrete column, pedestal, or wall: at the face of the column, pedestal, or wall;

(b) for footings supporting a masonry wall: halfway between the middle and the edge of the wall; and

(c) for footings supporting a column with steel base plates: as determined by considering the dimensions and the stiffness of the base plate.

Note: *In many cases, the critical section can be taken halfway between the face of the column and the edge of the base plate.*

15.4.4

15.4.4.1

In two-way rectangular footings, reinforcement shall be distributed as follows:

(a) reinforcement in the long direction shall be distributed uniformly across the entire width of the footing; and

(b) for reinforcement in the short direction, a portion of the total reinforcement specified in Clause 15.4.4.2 shall be distributed uniformly over a band width (centred on the centreline of the column or pedestal) equal to the length of the short side of the footing or equal to the length of the supported wall or column, whichever is greater. The remainder of the reinforcement required in the short direction shall be distributed uniformly outside the centre band width.

15.4.4.2

The portion of the total reinforcement in the short direction distributed over the band width (see Clause 15.4.4.1(b)) is as follows:

$$\frac{\text{Reinforcement in band width}}{\text{Total reinforcement in short direction}} = \frac{2}{(\beta + 1)} \qquad \text{(15-1)}$$

15.5 Shear design of footings and pile caps

15.5.1
Design for shear shall meet the requirements of Clauses 11 and 13.
Note: *For many types of footings, the strut-and-tie method specified in Clause 11.4 can be used for design.*

15.5.2
The location of the critical section for shear, as specified in Clause 13.3, shall be measured from the face of the column, pedestal, or wall for footings supporting a column, pedestal, or wall. For footings supporting a column or pedestal with steel base plates, the critical section shall be measured from the location specified in Clause 15.4.3(c).

15.5.3
Shear on any section through a pile cap shall be computed in accordance with the following:
(a)   the entire reaction from any pile whose centre is located $d_p/2$ or more outside the section shall be considered as producing shear on that section;
(b)   the reaction from any pile whose centre is located $d_p/2$ or more inside the section shall be considered as producing no shear on that section; and
(c)   for intermediate positions of the pile centre, the portion of the pile reaction to be considered as producing shear on the section shall be based on a straight-line interpolation between the full value at $d_p/2$ outside the section and zero value at $d_p/2$ inside the section.

15.6 Development of reinforcement in footings and pile caps

15.6.1
The development of reinforcement in footings and pile caps shall be computed in accordance with Clause 12.

15.6.2
When the strut-and-tie method is used, the development of tension reinforcement shall be as specified in Clause 11.4.3.2.

15.6.3
The critical sections for development of reinforcement shall be assumed to be at the locations specified in Clause 15.4.3 for the maximum factored moment and at all other vertical planes where changes of section or reinforcement occur. (See also Clause 12.10.5.)

15.7 Minimum depth of footings
The depth of footings above the bottom reinforcement shall be not less than 150 mm.

15.8 Piles

15.8.1 Design of piles
The moments and shears in the piles caused by lateral loads shall be calculated using procedures that account for the pile-soil interaction and non-linear soil behaviour.

CSA Standard A23.3-04

15.8.2 Special requirements for piles

15.8.2.1
The stability of portions of piles without lateral restraint from soil shall be assessed as specified in Clause 10.

15.8.2.2
The outer 25 mm concrete layer of uncased drilled piles shall be neglected when the factored resistance of the pile shaft and the end-bearing resistance is determined.

15.8.2.3
For uncased drilled piles, a reduction factor of 0.90 shall be applied to the factored resistance specified in Clauses 10 and 11.

15.8.2.4
Selection of the pile bell diameter and bell side slope shall be based on the concrete shear resistance and the type of the soil (see ACI 336.3R).

15.8.2.5
For the seismic design of piles, the additional requirements specified in Clause 21.11.4 shall be met.

15.8.2.6
Where required by applicable codes, piles shall be interconnected.

15.8.3 Minimum depth of pile caps
The depth of pile caps above the bottom reinforcement and above the top of the pile shall be not less than 300 mm.

15.9 Transfer of force at base of column, pile cap, wall, or pedestal

15.9.1 General

15.9.1.1
The forces and moments at the base of a column, pile cap, wall, or pedestal shall be transferred to the supporting footing or pile.

15.9.1.2
Bearing on concrete at the contact surface between the supported and supporting members shall not exceed the factored bearing resistance of either member specified in Clause 10.8.

15.9.1.3
Reinforcement, dowels, or mechanical connectors between supported and supporting members shall be adequate to transfer
(a) all compressive force that exceeds the concrete bearing strength of either member; and
(b) any computed tensile force across the interface.
   In addition, reinforcement, dowels, or mechanical connectors shall meet the requirements of Clause 12 and of Clause 15.9.2.2 or 15.9.2.3.

15.9.1.4

Lateral forces shall be transferred to the supporting pedestals, caps, piles, and footings in accordance with the interface shear transfer requirements of Clause 11.5 or by other appropriate means.

15.9.2 Cast-in-place construction

15.9.2.1

For columns, pile caps, piles, and pedestals, the area of reinforcement across the interface shall be not less than 0.005 times the gross area of the supported member.

15.9.2.2

For cast-in-place walls, the area of reinforcement across the interface shall be not less than the minimum vertical reinforcement required by Clause 14.1.8.

15.9.2.3

The size of dowels shall not exceed the size of the vertical bars by more than one bar size.

15.9.2.4

At footings, 45M and 55M longitudinal bars (in compression only) may be lap spliced with dowels to provide the reinforcement required to satisfy Clause 15.9.1. Dowels shall not be larger than 35M and shall extend into the supported member for a distance of not less than the development length of 45M or 55M bars, or the splice length of the dowels, whichever is greater, and into the footing for a distance of not less than the development length of the dowels.

15.9.2.5

If a pinned or rocker connection is provided in cast-in-place construction, the connection shall also comply with Clause 15.9.3.

15.9.3 Precast concrete construction

15.9.3.1

In precast concrete construction, the reinforcement required to satisfy Clause 15.9.1 may be provided by anchor bolts or suitable mechanical connectors.

15.9.3.2

Anchor bolts and mechanical connectors shall be designed to reach their factored resistance prior to anchorage failure of the surrounding concrete.
Note: *See Annex D for more information.*

15.10 Sloped or stepped footings

15.10.1

In sloped or stepped footings, the angle of the slope or the depth and location of the steps shall be such that design requirements are satisfied at every section.

15.10.2

Sloped or stepped footings designed as a unit shall be constructed to ensure action as a unit.

15.11 Combined footings and mats

15.11.1
Footings supporting more than one column, pedestal, or wall (combined footings or mats) shall be proportioned, in accordance with the applicable design requirements of this Standard, to resist the factored loads and induced reactions.

15.11.2
The distribution of soil pressure under combined footings and mats shall be consistent with the properties of the soil and the structure and with the established principles of soil mechanics.

15.12 Plain concrete footings and deep foundations
Plain concrete footings and deep foundations shall comply with Clause 22.

16 Precast concrete

16.1 General

16.1.1
All requirements of this Standard not specifically excluded and not in conflict with the requirements of Clauses 16.1.2 to 16.5.3.7 shall apply to structures incorporating precast concrete elements.
Note: *See CSA A23.4 for the suggested division of design responsibilities between the designer and the precast concrete manufacturer.*

16.1.2
Clauses 7.7, 7.8, 10.4, and 13 shall not apply to precast concrete.

16.1.3
For elements produced in manufacturing plants certified in accordance with Clause 16.2, the concrete material resistance factor, ϕ_c, specified in Clause 8.4.2 may be taken as 0.70.

16.2 Prequalification of manufacturer

16.2.1
All precast concrete elements covered by this Standard shall be manufactured and erected in accordance with CSA A23.4.

16.2.2
Exemptions to the requirements specified in Clause 16.2.1 may be made by the designer of the building for the following reinforced concrete elements:
(a) tilt-up walls;
(b) minor structural elements such as stair flights, stair landings, lintels, and sills; and
(c) precast slabs for lift slab construction.
   The designer shall clearly indicate whether such reinforced precast elements are to be manufactured in accordance with CSA A23.4, in which case certification shall be required, or in accordance with CSA A23.1, in which case the certification requirement may be waived by the designer.

16.3 Drawings

In addition to the requirements specified in Clause 5, drawings and related documents shall include the following:

(a) sufficient dimensions to permit preparation of the shop drawings;
(b) sufficient indication of the work supporting, supported by, or attached to the precast concrete to permit preparation of the shop drawings;
(c) the class of surface finish required for structural purposes;
(d) any non-standard tolerances required for the precast concrete elements or the building structure;
(e) any superimposed loads on the precast concrete elements, the location of connections, and the factored forces to be developed at the connections to the elements;
(f) when precast elements are to act as diaphragms, the factored external forces and shears acting on the diaphragms; and
(g) the expected deformations of the structure under specified loads, insofar as they affect the design of the precast concrete elements or associated connections. Deformations due to specified earthquake loads shall be shown separately.

16.4 Design

16.4.1 General

16.4.1.1

The design shall take into account loading and restraint conditions from the initial fabrication to the intended use of the structure, including forces from stripping, storage, transportation, and erection.

16.4.1.2

The effects of initial and long-term deformations shall be considered, including the effects on interconnected elements.

16.4.2 Distribution of forces among elements

16.4.2.1

The distribution of forces that are perpendicular to the plane of the elements shall be established by analysis or test.

16.4.2.2

In-plane forces shall be transferred between the elements of a precast floor or wall system in accordance with the following:

(a) load paths for in-plane forces shall be transferred through both connections and elements;
(b) where tension forces occur, a load path of reinforcement or tendons shall be provided; and
(c) the design of joints, connections, and bearings shall include the effects of all forces to be transmitted, including the effects of specified loads, tolerances, elastic deformation, temperature, creep, and shrinkage.

16.4.3 Reinforcement of precast concrete elements

16.4.3.1

The minimum reinforcement ratio in each direction shall be not less than 0.0016 for reinforcement or 0.0004 for prestressing tendons, except as permitted by Clauses 16.4.3.2 and 16.4.3.3. Additional reinforcement shall be provided at openings and other discontinuities.

16.4.3.2

For one-way floor and roof slabs and for one-way precast, prestressed wall panels, all not exceeding 3660 mm in width, and where elements are not connected to cause restraint in the transverse direction, the minimum transverse reinforcement requirements of Clause 16.4.3.1 may be waived.

16.4.3.3

For non-prestressed walls, the minimum reinforcement ratio shall be not less than 0.001 in each direction. Spacing of reinforcement shall not exceed the smaller of five times the wall thickness or 500 mm.

16.4.4 Joints and connections

16.4.4.1

Forces shall be transferred between elements by grouted joints, shear keys, mechanical connectors, reinforcement, topping, or a combination of these means.

16.4.4.2

Precast segments, when joined and post-tensioned in accordance with CSA A23.1, may be considered homogeneous structural members.

16.4.4.3

The design of each component of a connection shall be based on the most severe combination of load eccentricities, as limited by fabrication and erection tolerances.

16.4.4.4

Special attention shall be given to the design of connections when there is a possibility of corrosion, and in particular to connections in inaccessible locations in the finished structure.

16.4.4.5

Provision for movement of elements due to earthquake shall accommodate $R_d R_o / I_E$ times the elastic deflection of the lateral force resisting system.
Note: *See the* National Building Code of Canada *for more information.*

16.4.4.6

In the design of connections that accommodate movement by deformation of the connection material, consideration shall be given to the magnitude and frequency of the movement and to the fatigue properties and ductility of the connection.

16.4.4.7

In the design of connections that accommodate movement by sliding, the increase of friction due to the tightness of the fastening, the effects of corrosion, and construction tolerances shall be taken into account.
Note: *For connections whose capacity is sensitive to erection tolerances and for connections in inaccessible locations that can be subject to corrosive conditions, connection resistance should be increased.*

16.4.5 Bearing

16.4.5.1

The allowable bearing stress at the contact surface between supported and supporting elements and between any intermediate bearing elements shall not exceed the bearing resistance for either surface as specified in Clause 10.8 or 11.4.4.

16.4.5.2

Unless tests or analysis show that performance will not be impaired, the following minimum requirements shall be met:

(a) Each member and its supporting system shall have design dimensions selected so that, after consideration of tolerances, the distance from the edge of the support to the end of the precast member in the direction of the span is at least 1/180 of the clear span, ℓ_n, but not less than the following:

For solid or hollow-core slabs	50 mm
For beams or stemmed members	75 mm

(b) Bearing pads at unarmoured edges shall be set back a minimum of 12 mm from the face of the support, or the chamfer dimension at chamfered edges, whichever is larger.

16.5 Structural integrity

16.5.1

In buildings where precast concrete elements constitute a portion of the structural system, all structural elements shall be effectively tied together.

16.5.2

16.5.2.1

Except as specified in Clause 16.5.3, precast concrete structures shall meet the structural integrity requirements specified in Clauses 16.5.2.2 to 16.5.2.6.

Note: *Guidance on designing for structural integrity of structural systems incorporating precast elements can be obtained from the following publications:*

(a)   ACI-ASCE Joint Committee 550, "Design recommendations for precast concrete structures";
(b)   Canadian Precast/Prestressed Concrete Institute, Design manual;
(c)   Cement Association of Canada, Concrete design handbook; and
(d)   Precast/Prestressed Concrete Institute, PCI design handbook.

16.5.2.2

Longitudinal and transverse tensile tie reinforcement shall be incorporated so as to provide a load path to the lateral load resisting system, as specified in Clause 16.4.2.2(b).

16.5.2.3

Where precast elements form floor or roof diaphragms, the connections between the diaphragm and those elements being laterally supported shall be designed for all factored loads but shall have a factored tensile resistance of not less than 5 kN/m.

16.5.2.4

Vertical tension tie requirements shall apply to the horizontal joints in all vertical structural elements, except cladding, and shall meet the following requirements:

(a) precast columns shall have a factored tensile resistance of not less than $1.4A_g$ N;
(b) for columns with a larger cross-section than required by analysis, a reduced effective area may be substituted for A_g, but it shall not be less than $A_g/2$; and
(c) precast wall panels shall have a minimum of two ties per panel, with a factored resistance of not less than 30 kN per tie.

16.5.2.5
When factored forces and moments result in compression at the base, the ties required by Clause 16.5.2.4(c) may be anchored to the floor slab on grade.

16.5.2.6
Ties and connections shall be designed in such a manner that the resistance is governed by yielding of the steel component.

16.5.3

16.5.3.1
Structures that are three or more storeys high and are constructed with precast concrete bearing walls shall be tied together as specified in Clauses 16.5.3.2 to 16.5.3.5.

16.5.3.2
Longitudinal and transverse tension ties shall be incorporated in floor and roof systems to provide a factored resistance of not less than 14 kN per metre of width or length. Tie paths shall be provided over interior wall supports and to exterior walls. Ties shall be located in the floor or roof system or within 600 mm of the plane of the floor or roof system.

16.5.3.3
Longitudinal tension ties parallel to the floor or roof spans shall be spaced not more than 3000 mm on centres. Provisions shall be made to transfer forces around openings.

16.5.3.4
Transverse tension ties perpendicular to the span of the floor or roof shall be spaced at a distance not greater than the distance between the bearing walls.

16.5.3.5
Tension ties around the perimeter of each floor and roof, within 1500 mm of the edge, shall provide a factored tensile resistance of not less than 60 kN.

16.5.3.6
Vertical tension ties shall be provided in all walls and shall be continuous over the full height of the building. They shall provide a factored tensile resistance of not less than 40 kN per metre of wall. Not fewer than two tension ties shall be provided for each precast wall panel.

16.5.3.7
During checking for structural integrity, any beneficial effects of friction caused by gravity loads shall not be considered for the transfer of horizontal loads.

17 Composite concrete flexural members
Note: *This Clause uses the terms "transverse shear" and "longitudinal shear". For a composite beam with a horizontal axis, "transverse shear" refers to vertical shear forces and "longitudinal shear" refers to shear on a horizontal plane.*

17.1 General

17.1.1
Clauses 17.1.2 to 17.5.4 shall apply to the design of composite concrete flexural members consisting of concrete elements constructed in separate placements, but interconnected in such a manner that all elements act as a unit.

17.1.2
All of the requirements of this Standard shall apply to composite flexural members, except where modified by Clauses 17.1.3 to 17.5.4.

17.1.3
An entire composite member or portions thereof may be assumed to resist shear and moment.

17.1.4
Individual elements shall be investigated for all critical stages of loading.

17.1.5
If the specified strength, density, or other properties of the elements differ, the properties of the individual elements shall be used for the analysis.
Note: *Differential creep and shrinkage can affect the distributions of strains and deformations in the individual elements.*

17.1.6
In strength computations for composite members, no distinction shall be made between shored and unshored members.

17.1.7
All elements shall be designed to support all loads introduced prior to full development of the design strength of composite members.

17.1.8
Reinforcement shall be provided, as necessary, to control cracking and prevent separation of individual elements of composite members.

17.1.9
Composite members shall meet the requirements for control of deflections specified in Clause 9.8.

17.2 Shoring
When used, shoring shall not be removed until the supported elements have developed the design properties required to support all loads and to limit deflections and cracking at the time of shoring removal.

17.3 Transverse shear resistance

17.3.1
When an entire composite member is assumed to resist transverse shear, the design shall meet the requirements specified in Clause 11 for a monolithically cast member of the same cross-sectional shape.

17.3.2
Shear reinforcement shall be fully anchored into interconnected elements as specified in Clause 12.13.

CSA Standard A23.3-04

17.4 Longitudinal shear resistance

17.4.1
For a composite member, steps shall be taken to ensure full transfer of the longitudinal shear forces at the contact surfaces of the interconnected elements.

17.4.2
Longitudinal shear shall be investigated in accordance with Clause 17.4.3 or 17.4.4.

17.4.3

17.4.3.1
Unless calculated as specified in Clause 17.4.4, the design of cross-sections subject to longitudinal shear shall be based on

$$V_{r\ell} \geq V_f \qquad \qquad \text{(17-1)}$$

17.4.3.2
When contact surfaces are clean, free of laitance, and intentionally roughened, the factored longitudinal shear resistance, $V_{r\ell}$, shall not be taken as greater than $0.7\phi_c b_v d$ unless ties are provided to transfer longitudinal shear.

17.4.3.3
When minimum ties are provided as specified in Clause 17.5 and contact surfaces are clean and free of laitance but not intentionally roughened, the factored longitudinal shear resistance, $V_{r\ell}$, shall not be taken as greater than $0.7\phi_c b_v d$.

17.4.3.4
When the factored shear force, V_f, at the section being considered exceeds $0.7\phi_c b_v d$, the design for longitudinal shear shall be as specified in Clause 11.5.

17.4.4
Longitudinal shear may be investigated by computing the actual compressive or tensile force in any segment and provisions shall be made to transfer that force as longitudinal shear to the supporting element. The factored longitudinal shear force shall not exceed the factored longitudinal shear resistance, $V_{r\ell}$, as specified in Clauses 17.4.3.2 to 17.4.3.4, with the area of contact surface, A_{cv}, substituted for $b_v d$.

17.4.5
When tension exists across any contact surface between interconnected elements, shear transfer by contact may be assumed only when minimum ties are provided as specified in Clause 17.5.

17.5 Ties for longitudinal shear

17.5.1
When ties are provided to transfer longitudinal shear, the tie area shall be not less than that required by Clause 11.2.8, and the tie spacing shall not exceed four times the least dimension of the supported element or 600 mm, whichever is less.

17.5.2
Ties for longitudinal shear shall consist of a single bar or wire, multiple leg stirrups, vertical legs, or welded wire fabric (smooth or deformed).

17.5.3
Ties shall be anchored into the interconnected elements as specified in Clause 12.13.

17.5.4
Reinforcement for transverse shear that is anchored into the interconnected elements as specified in Clause 12.13 may be included as ties for longitudinal shear.

18 Prestressed concrete

18.1 General

18.1.1
Clauses 18.1.2 to 18.13.4 shall apply to members prestressed with wires, strands, or bars that comply with the requirements for prestressing steels specified in Clause 3.1.4 and in CSA A23.1.
Note: *Unbonded tendons are more susceptible to corrosion than bonded tendons. The durability of structures with unbonded prestressing tendons is a function of the environment, occupancy type, and quality of work during construction. Ingress of moisture or chlorides, sulphides, nitrates, carbonates, or other industrial, food processing, or agricultural chemicals can cause corrosion or even failure of the tendons. Water, including rainwater, can enter the sheath during tendon shipping, storage, or construction, and in some cases after occupancy of the structure, if adequate protection is not provided. Materials and quality of work should meet the requirements specified in CSA A23.1.*

18.1.2
All of the requirements of this Standard not specifically excluded and not in conflict with the requirements specified in Clauses 18.1.1 and 18.1.3 to 18.13.4 shall apply to prestressed concrete.

18.1.3
The requirements specified in Clauses 10.3.3, 10.3.4, 10.4, 10.5.1, 10.5.2, 10.6.2, 10.9, 13, 14.1.7.2, and 14.2 shall not apply to prestressed concrete unless otherwise specified.

18.1.4
Prestressed members shall meet the strength requirements specified in this Standard.

18.1.5
The effects of the loads at all loading stages that could be critical during the life of the member from the time the prestress is first applied shall be considered.

18.1.6
The stresses in prestressed members at transfer and under specified loads shall satisfy the requirements of Clause 18.3.

18.1.7
Stress concentrations due to prestressing shall be considered. Adequately anchored transverse reinforcement shall be provided to control splitting.

18.1.8
The deflection of prestressed concrete members shall be determined as specified in Clause 9.8.4.

18.1.9
When adjoining parts of the structure can restrain the elastic and long-term deformations (deflections, changes in length, and rotation) of a member caused by prestressing, applied loading, foundation settlement, temperature, and shrinkage, the restraint shall be estimated and its effects on the member and on the restraining structure shall be considered.

18.1.10
The possibility of buckling in a member between points where concrete and prestressing tendons are in contact and of buckling in thin webs and flanges shall be considered.

18.1.11
In computing section properties, the loss of area due to open ducts or conduits shall be considered.

18.2 Design assumptions for flexure and axial load

18.2.1
The design of prestressed members for flexure and axial loads shall be based on the assumptions specified in Clause 10.1.

18.2.2
For investigation of the stress limits specified in Clauses 18.3 and 18.4, linear elastic material behaviour may be assumed. Concrete may be assumed to resist tension at sections that are uncracked.

18.3 Permissible stresses in concrete flexural members

18.3.1

18.3.1.1
Stresses in concrete immediately after prestress transfer due to prestress, and the specified loads present at transfer, shall not exceed the following:

(a) Extreme fibre stress in compression	$0.6 f'_{ci}$
(b) Extreme fibre stress in tension, except as permitted by Item (c)	$0.25\lambda\sqrt{f'_{ci}}$
(c) Extreme fibre stress in tension at ends of simply supported members	$0.5\lambda\sqrt{f'_{ci}}$

18.3.1.2
The stress specified in Clause 18.3.1.1(a) may be exceeded if tests or analyses demonstrate that performance will not be impaired.

18.3.1.3
Where computed tensile stresses exceed the values specified in Items (b) and (c) of Clause 18.3.1.1, bonded reinforcement with a minimum area of $A_s = N_c/(0.5f_y)$ shall be provided in the tensile zone to resist the total tensile force, N_c, in the concrete computed on the basis of an uncracked section.

18.3.2
Stresses in concrete under specified loads and prestress (after allowance for all prestress losses) shall not exceed the following:

(a) Extreme fibre stress in compression due to sustained loads $0.45f_c'$

(b) Extreme fibre stress in compression due to total load $0.60f_c'$

(c) Extreme fibre stress in tension in precompressed tensile zone, except as specified in Clause 18.3.3 $0.50\lambda\sqrt{f_c'}$

(d) Extreme fibre stress in tension in precompressed tensile zone exposed to a corrosive environment $0.25\lambda\sqrt{f_c'}$

18.3.3

18.3.3.1
Partially prestressed members may exceed the requirements specified in Clause 18.3.2(c) provided that tests or analyses demonstrate adequate fatigue resistance as well as adequate deflection and crack control under specified loads.

18.3.3.2
Partially prestressed members not subjected to fatigue conditions and not exposed to a corrosive environment may be deemed to have adequate deflection and crack control if the requirements of Clauses 9.8.4 and 18.8 are met.

18.4 Permissible stresses in tendons
Tensile stress in tendons shall not exceed the following:

Stress due to tendon jacking force for post-tensioning tendons	$0.85f_{pu}$, but not greater than $0.94f_{py}$
Stress due to tendon jacking force for pretensioning tendons	$0.80f_{pu}$
Stress immediately after prestress transfer	$0.82f_{py}$, but not greater than $0.74f_{pu}$
Stress in post-tensioning tendons at anchorages and couplers immediately after tendon anchorage	$0.70f_{pu}$

However, the stress due to tendon jacking force for post-tensioning and pretensioning tendons shall not exceed the maximum value recommended by the manufacturer of the prestressing tendons or anchorages. If pretensioned tendons are subjected to a temperature drop prior to concreting, the stress at the reduced temperatures shall not exceed $0.80\ f_{pu}$.

Note: *The specified yield strength of prestressing tendons is based on the requirements specified in ASTM A 416/A 416M, ASTM A 421/A 421M, and ASTM A 722/A 722M, which specify the following minimum values for f_{py}:*
(a)   low relaxation strand or wire: $0.90f_{pu}$;
(b)   stress-relieved strand or wire: $0.85f_{pu}$;
(c)   plain prestressing bars: $0.85f_{pu}$; and
(d)   deformed prestressing bars: $0.80f_{pu}$.

CSA Standard A23.3-04

18.5 Loss of prestress

To determine the effective prestress, f_{pe}, allowance for the following sources of loss of prestress shall be considered:
(a) anchorage seating loss;
(b) elastic shortening of concrete;
(c) friction loss due to intended and unintended curvature in post-tensioning tendons;
(d) creep of concrete;
(e) shrinkage of concrete; and
(f) relaxation of tendon stress.

18.6 Flexural resistance

18.6.1

Strain compatibility analyses shall be based on the stress-strain curves of the steels to be used.

18.6.2

In lieu of a more accurate determination of f_{pr} based on strain compatibility, the following approximate values of f_{pr} may be used:
(a) for members with bonded tendons, provided that c/d_p is not greater than 0.5 and f_{pe} is not less than $0.6f_{py}$:

$$f_{pr} = f_{pu}\left(1 - k_p \frac{c}{d_p}\right) \tag{18-1}$$

where
$k_p = 2(1.04 - f_{py}/f_{pu})$
and c shall be determined assuming a stress of f_{pr} in the tendons;
Note: *Further information can be found in the Cement Association of Canada's Concrete design handbook.*
(b) for members with unbonded tendons:

$$f_{pr} = f_{pe} + \frac{8000}{\ell_o} \sum_n (d_p - c_y) \leq f_{py} \tag{18-2}$$

where

$\sum_n (d_p - c_y)$ = sum of the distance $d_p - c_y$ for each of the plastic hinges in the span under consideration
and c_y shall be determined by assuming a stress of f_{py} in the tendons.

18.6.3

Tension and compression reinforcement may be considered to contribute to the flexural resistance with forces of $\phi_s A_s f_y$ and $\phi_s A_s' f_y'$, provided that they are located at least $0.75c$ from the neutral axis. Other reinforcement may be included in resistance computations if a strain compatibility analysis is conducted to determine the stress in such reinforcement.

18.7 Minimum factored flexural resistance

At every section of a flexural member, except two-way slabs, the following shall apply:

$$M_r \geq 1.2 M_{cr} \tag{18-3}$$

where

$$M_{cr} = \frac{I}{y_t}(f_{ce} + f_r)$$

where

$$f_r = 0.6\lambda\sqrt{f_c'}$$

unless the factored flexural resistance at the section is at least one-third greater than M_f.

18.8 Minimum bonded reinforcement

18.8.1
The minimum requirements for bonded reinforcement in beams and slabs shall be as specified in Table 18.1.

18.8.2
The bonded reinforcement required by Table 18.1 shall be uniformly distributed within the precompressed tensile zone as close to the extreme tensile fibre as the cover will permit.

Table 18.1
Minimum area of bonded reinforcement
(See Clauses 18.8.1, 18.8.2, and 18.9.2.)

	Concrete stress (see Clause 18.3.2(c))			
	Tensile stress $\leq 0.5\lambda\sqrt{f_c'}$		Tensile stress $> 0.5\lambda\sqrt{f_c'}$	
	Type of tendon		Type of tendon	
Type of member	Bonded	Unbonded	Bonded	Unbonded
Beams	0	0.004A	0.003A	0.005A
One-way slabs	0	0.003A	0.002A	0.004A
Two-way slabs				
Negative moment regions	0	$0.0006h\ell_n$	$0.00045h\ell_n$	$0.00075h\ell_n$
Positive moment regions, concrete stress $> 0.2\lambda\sqrt{f_c'}$	0	0.004A	0.003A	0.005A
Positive moment regions, concrete tensile stress $\leq 0.2\lambda\sqrt{f_c'}$	0	0	—	—

18.8.3
For partially prestressed beams and one-way slabs, the distribution of the bonded tendons and reinforcement shall be such that the quantity z in Equation (10-6) does not exceed 20 kN/mm for interior exposure and 15 kN/mm for exterior exposure. In lieu of more detailed analysis, the steel stress, f_s, in Equation (10-6) may be calculated as the difference between the stress in the non-prestressed reinforcement due to the specified load moment, M_s, and the stress due to the decompression moment, M_{dc}, specified in the following equation:

$$M_{dc} = f_{ce}\frac{I}{y_t} \qquad\qquad (18\text{-}4)$$

Only the bonded steel shall be considered for the calculation of A. A bonded post-tensioned cable or a bundle of pretensioned tendons may be considered as one bar of equal area or disregarded in the calculation of z.

18.9 Minimum length of bonded reinforcement

18.9.1
Where bonded reinforcement is provided for flexural resistance, the minimum length shall comply with Clause 12.

18.9.2
The minimum length of bonded reinforcement required by Table 18.1 shall be as specified in Clauses 18.9.3 and 18.9.4.

18.9.3
In positive moment areas, the minimum length of bonded reinforcement shall be one-half of the clear span length and shall be centred in the positive moment area.

18.9.4
In negative moment areas, bonded reinforcement shall extend, on each side of the support, one-sixth of the longer clear span beyond the face of the support.

18.10 Frames and continuous construction
Moments for computing the required strength shall be the sum of the moments due to reactions induced by prestressing (with a load factor of 1.0) and the moments due to factored loads specified in Clause 8.3. Where a minimum area of bonded reinforcement is provided as specified in Clause 18.8, negative moments may be redistributed as specified in Clause 9.2.4.

18.11 Compression members — Combined flexure and axial loads

18.11.1 General
The design of prestressed concrete members subject to combined flexure and axial loads shall be based on Clauses 10.9 to 10.16. The effects of prestress, creep, shrinkage, and temperature change shall be included.

18.11.2 Limits for reinforcement of prestressed compression members

18.11.2.1
Members with average prestress, f_{cp}, less than 1.5 MPa shall have the minimum reinforcement specified in Clauses 7.6 and 10.9 for columns or Clause 14.1.8 for walls.

18.11.2.2
Except for walls, members with average prestress, f_{cp}, equal to or greater than 1.5 MPa shall have all of their prestressing tendons enclosed by spirals or lateral ties as follows:
(a) spirals shall comply with Clause 7.6.4; and
(b) ties shall comply with Clause 7.6.5, excluding Clauses 7.6.5.2(a) and 7.6.5.5.

18.12 Two-way slab systems

18.12.1 General
Factored moments and shears in prestressed slab systems reinforced for flexure in two directions shall be determined as specified in Clause 13.8 or by more detailed design procedures.

18.12.2 Stresses under specified loads

18.12.2.1
When Clause 13.8 is used, flexural stresses due to unfactored gravity loads in column strips shall be determined by taking 75% of interior negative moments, 100% of exterior negative moments, and 60% of positive moments unless a more detailed analysis is performed.

18.12.2.2
Concrete stresses due to prestressing may be assumed to be uniformly distributed across the slab unless a more detailed analysis is performed.

18.12.2.3
The minimum average compressive stress, f_{cp}, shall be 0.8 MPa.

18.12.3 Shear resistance

18.12.3.1
In the vicinity of concentrated loads or reactions, the maximum factored shear stress, v_f, calculated as specified in Clauses 13.3.5 and 13.3.6, shall not exceed v_r.

18.12.3.2
The factored shear stress resistance, v_r, in two-way slabs shall be not greater than the factored shear stress resistance provided by the concrete, v_c, computed as specified in Clause 13.3.4 or 18.12.3.3, unless shear reinforcement is provided as specified in Clause 13.3.7, 13.3.8, or 13.3.9.

18.12.3.3
At columns supporting two-way slabs of uniform thickness, the factored shear stress resistance provided by the concrete shall be determined by

$$v_c = \beta_p \lambda \phi_c \sqrt{f'_c} \sqrt{1 + \frac{\phi_p f_{cp}}{0.33\lambda\phi_c\sqrt{f'_c}}} + \frac{V_p}{b_o d} \tag{18-5}$$

where
β_p = the smaller of 0.33 or $(\alpha_s d/b_o + 0.15)$
α_s = 4 for interior columns, 3 for edge columns, and 2 for corner columns
b_o = the perimeter of the critical section specified in Clause 13.3.3
f_{cp} = the average value of f_{cp} for the two directions and shall not be taken greater than 3.5 MPa
V_p = the factored vertical component of all prestress forces crossing the critical section

f'_c shall not be taken greater than 35 MPa and the slab shall extend at least $4h_s$ from all faces of the column. Equation (13-5), (13-6), or (13-7) shall apply to edge and corner columns when the slab extends less than $4h_s$ from a column face.

18.12.4 Shear and moment transfer
The fraction of the unbalanced moment transferred by eccentricity of shear shall comply with Clause 13.3.5.3.

18.12.5 Minimum bonded non-prestressed reinforcement

18.12.5.1
The minimum requirements for bonded reinforcement in two-way slabs shall be as specified in Clauses 18.8, 18.9, and 18.12.5.2.

18.12.5.2
In negative moment areas at column supports, the bonded reinforcement, A_s, shall be distributed within a zone equal to the column width plus 1.5 times the slab thickness beyond each side of the column. At least four bars or wires shall be provided in each direction. The spacing of the bonded reinforcement shall not exceed 300 mm.

18.12.6 Spacing of tendons

18.12.6.1
The spacing of tendons or groups of tendons in one direction shall not exceed eight times the slab thickness or 1500 mm unless adequate additional bonded reinforcement is provided so that the slab has the strength to span between tendons.

18.12.6.2
Tendon spacing shall be given special consideration in slabs supporting concentrated loads.

18.12.6.3
In slabs without beams, a minimum of two tendons or bars shall be provided in each direction over each column. These tendons or bars shall satisfy the requirements specified in Clause 13.10.6.

18.13 Tendon anchorage zones

18.13.1
Post-tensioning anchorage zones shall be designed to resist the specified tensile strength of the tendons.

18.13.2
One of the following methods shall be used for the design of anchorage zones:
(a) equilibrium based on strut-and-tie models (see Clause 11.4);
(b) elastic stress analysis (finite element methods or equivalent); or
(c) methods based on tests.

18.13.3
End blocks shall be provided where necessary for support bearing or distribution of concentrated prestressing forces.

18.13.4
Regions of stress concentrations due to abrupt changes in section or other causes shall be adequately reinforced.

19 Shells and folded plates

19.1 General

19.1.1
Clauses 19.1.2 to 19.5.2 shall apply to thin shell and folded plate concrete structures, including ribs and edge members.

19.1.2
All of the requirements of this Standard not specifically excluded and not in conflict with the requirements of Clauses 19.1 and 19.2 to 19.5.2 shall apply to thin shell structures.

19.2 Analysis and design

19.2.1
Elastic behaviour shall be an acceptable basis for determining internal forces and displacements of thin shells. This behaviour may be established by computations based on an analysis of the uncracked concrete structure in which the material is assumed to be linearly elastic, homogeneous, and isotropic. Poisson's ratio of concrete may be assumed to be equal to zero.
Note: *See Clause 13.7 for further guidance on analysis and design.*

19.2.2
Equilibrium checks of internal resistances and external loads shall be conducted to ensure consistency of results.

19.2.3
Experimental or numerical analysis procedures shall be used only when it can be shown that they provide a safe basis for design.

19.2.4
Approximate methods of analysis not satisfying compatibility of strains either within the shell or between the shell and auxiliary members shall be used only when it can be shown that they provide a safe basis for design.

19.2.5
For prestressed shells, the analysis shall also consider behaviour under loads induced during prestressing, at cracking load, and at factored load. Where prestressing tendons are draped within a shell, the design shall take into account the force components on the shell resulting from the tendon profiles not lying in one plane.

19.2.6
The thickness, h, of a thin shell and its reinforcement shall be proportioned for the required strength and serviceability.

19.2.7
The shell designer shall investigate and preclude the possibility of general or local instability.

19.2.8

Auxiliary members shall be designed in accordance with the applicable requirements of this Standard. A portion of the shell equal to the flange width specified in Clause 10.3 may be assumed to act with the auxiliary member. In such portions of the shell, the reinforcement perpendicular to the auxiliary member shall be at least equal to that required for the flange of a T-beam by Clause 10.5.3.2.

19.3 Specified yield strength of reinforcement

For non-prestressed reinforcement, the yield strength used in calculations shall not exceed 400 MPa.

19.4 Shell reinforcement

19.4.1

Shell reinforcement shall be provided to resist tensile stresses from the internal membrane forces, to resist bending and twisting moments, to control shrinkage and temperature cracking, and as special reinforcement at shell boundaries, load attachments, and shell openings.

19.4.2

Membrane reinforcement shall be provided in two or more directions in all parts of the shell.

19.4.3

The area of shell reinforcement in two orthogonal directions at any section shall be not less than the minimum slab reinforcement required by Clause 7.8, except as specified in Clause 19.4.7.

19.4.4

The reinforcement necessary for resisting shell membrane forces shall be provided so that the factored resistance in any direction shall be at least equal to the component of the principal membrane forces in the same direction due to the factored loads.

19.4.5

The area of shell tension reinforcement shall be limited so that the reinforcement will yield before crushing of concrete in compression can take place.

19.4.6

In regions of high tension, membrane reinforcement shall, if practical, be placed in the general directions of the principal tensile membrane forces. Where this is not practical, membrane reinforcement may be placed in two or more directions.

Note: *If the direction of reinforcement varies more than 15° from the direction of principal tensile membrane force, it is possible that the amount of reinforcement will have to be increased to limit the width of possible cracks under specified loads.*

19.4.7

When the magnitude of the principal tensile membrane stress within the shell varies greatly over the area of the shell surface, reinforcement resisting the total tension may be concentrated in the regions of largest tensile stress if it can be shown that this provides a safe basis for design. However, the ratio of shell reinforcement in any portion of the tensile zone shall be not less than 0.0035 based on the overall thickness of the shell.

19.4.8

Reinforcement required to resist shell bending moments shall be proportioned with due regard for the simultaneous action of membrane axial forces at the same location. When shell reinforcement is required in only one face to resist bending moments, equal amounts shall be placed near both surfaces of the shell, even if calculations do not indicate reversal of bending moments.

19.4.9
When splitting of the shell near its mid-thickness can occur because of transverse tensile stresses, transverse reinforcement shall be provided to prevent the cracks from propagating.

19.4.10
Shell reinforcement in any direction shall not be spaced farther apart than 500 mm or five times the shell thickness. Where the principal membrane tensile stress on the gross concrete area due to factored loads exceeds $0.4\lambda\phi_c\sqrt{f'_c}$, reinforcement shall not be spaced farther apart than three times the shell thickness.

19.4.11
Shell reinforcement at the junction of the shell and supporting members or edge members shall be anchored in or extended through such members in accordance with Clause 12, except that the minimum development length shall be $1.2\ell_d$ but not less than 500 mm.

19.4.12
Splice development lengths of shell reinforcement shall meet the requirements of Clause 12, except that the minimum splice length of tension bars shall be 1.2 times the value specified in Clause 12 but not less than 500 mm. The number of splices in principal tensile reinforcement shall be kept to a practical minimum. Where splices are necessary, they shall be staggered at least ℓ_d, with not more than one-third of the reinforcement spliced at any section.

19.5 Construction

19.5.1
When removal of formwork is based on a specific modulus of elasticity of concrete because of stability or deflection considerations, the value of the modulus of elasticity, E_c, shall be determined from flexural tests of field-cured beam specimens. The number and dimensions of the test beam specimens, and the test procedures, shall be specified by the designer.
Note: *For guidance see CSA A23.2-3C.*

19.5.2
If a thin shell is constructed with deviations from the shape greater than the tolerances specified by the designer, an analysis of the effect of such deviations shall be conducted and all necessary remedial actions shall be taken to ensure the shell's safe behaviour.

20 Strength evaluation procedures
Note:
(1) *This Clause specifies requirements and procedures for evaluating the strength or safe load rating of structures or structural elements where*
    (a) doubt exists about their adequacy because of apparent or suspected deficiencies or defects;
    (b) the strength or load-bearing capacity is unknown;
    (c) a change of function creates loading characteristics different from those provided for in the design of the structure; or
    (d) damage that has possibility reduced the strength or load-bearing capacity has occurred.
(2) *If the structure under investigation does not meet the requirements specified in Clause 20.2.3, 20.3.1.9, or 20.3.2.1, a lower load rating for the structure based on the results of the load test or analysis may be assigned.*

20.1 General
When the safety of a structure or structural member is in doubt and a structural strength investigation is necessary, it shall be carried out by analysis, by means of load tests, or by a combination of these methods.

20.2 Analytical investigation

20.2.1
If the strength evaluation is performed by analytical means, a thorough field investigation of the dimensions and details of the members as actually built, of the properties of the materials, and of other pertinent conditions of the existing structure shall be conducted.

20.2.2
If drawings or other documents are used in the evaluation specified in Clause 20.2.1, their completeness and any modifications of the structure not reflected on the drawings shall be considered in the evaluation.

20.2.3
The analysis based on the investigation specified in Clause 20.2.1 shall satisfy the requirements of this Standard.

20.3 Load tests
Notes:
(1) *Although load tests should be conducted in a manner that will provide for safety of life and structure, safety measures should not interfere with the load test procedures or affect results.*
(2) *Load testing prestressed systems with unbonded tendons where corrosion is suspected is generally not an acceptable method for evaluating such tendons.*

20.3.1 General

20.3.1.1
If the strength evaluation is based on load tests, an engineer experienced in such evaluations shall control the tests.

20.3.1.2
A load test shall generally not be conducted until the portion of the structure subjected to load is at least 28 d old.
Note: *When the owner of the structure, the contractor, and all other involved parties mutually agree, the test may be conducted when the structure is less than 28 d old.*

20.3.1.3
The structure or portion of the structure to be load tested shall be loaded in such a manner as to test adequately the suspected weakness and to allow for the characteristics and pattern of the expected loads.

20.3.1.4
A load to simulate the effect of the portion of the dead loads not already present shall be applied 24 h before application of the test load and shall remain in place until all testing has been completed.

20.3.1.5
The superimposed test load shall be applied in not fewer than four approximately equal increments without shock to the structure and in a manner that avoids arching of the load materials.

20.3.1.6
When an entire structural system in doubt is load tested or an entire questionable portion of a system is load tested, the test load shall be 90% of the factored loads M_f, V_f, and P_f.

20.3.1.7

When only a portion of a structural system in doubt is tested and the results of the tests are taken as representative of the structural adequacy of untested portions of the system, the test load shall be equal to the factored loads M_f, V_f, and P_f.

20.3.1.8

The test load shall be left on the structure for 24 h.

20.3.1.9

If the portion of the structure tested fails or shows visible indications of impending failure, it shall be considered to have failed the test.

20.3.2 Load tests of flexural systems or members for moment resistance

20.3.2.1

Note: *The requirements of this Clause are in addition to the requirements specified in Clause 20.3.1.9.*

When flexural systems or members, including beams and slabs, are load tested for moment resistance, they shall have a deflection recovery, within 24 h of removal of the test load, as follows:

Non-prestressed members	
First test	60%
Retest	75%
Prestressed members	80%

20.3.2.2

Deflections of beams, cantilevers, and one-way slabs shall be measured relative to the ends of the span.

20.3.2.3

In the case of two-way slabs, the central slab deflection shall be measured relative to the deflection at the supporting columns or walls.

20.3.2.4

Immediately before application of the test load, the necessary initial readings shall be made as a datum for the measurements of deflections caused by the application of the test load.

20.3.2.5

After the test load has been in position for 24 h, deflection readings shall be taken.

20.3.2.6

Following the action specified in Clause 20.3.2.5, the test load shall be removed. Deflection readings shall be taken 24 h after removal of the test load.

20.3.2.7

Retests of non-prestressed construction shall not be conducted until 72 h after removal of the first test load.

21 Special provisions for seismic design

21.1 Scope
Clauses 21.2 to 21.12 specify requirements for the design and construction of reinforced concrete members of structures for which the design earthquake forces have been determined on the basis of energy dissipation in the non-linear range of response.

21.2 General

21.2.1 Capacity design
The structures identified in Clause 21.1 shall be the subject of capacity design. In the capacity design of structures, kinematically consistent mechanisms are chosen, and the energy-dissipating elements are designed and detailed as specified in Clauses 21.2 to 21.9. All other structural elements in the seismic force resisting system (SFRS) are then provided with sufficient reserve capacity to ensure that the chosen energy-dissipating mechanisms are maintained in the selected locations without the formation of any additional mechanisms throughout the deformations that can occur.

21.2.2 Seismic force resisting systems
Clauses 21.2 to 21.9 specify requirements covering the design and detailing of six SFRSs identified in the *National Building Code of Canada*. These are ductile moment-resisting frames, moderately ductile moment-resisting frames, ductile shear walls, ductile coupled shear walls, ductile partially coupled shear walls, and moderately ductile shear walls. Additional systems are considered in Clause 21.2.3.

Clauses 21.2 to 21.9 are intended for SFRSs that are substantially regular in strength and stiffness.

Combinations of SFRSs acting in the same direction shall be permitted, provided that each system continues over the full building height. When SFRSs are not continuous over the building height or change type over the building height, when elements from two or more SFRS types are combined to create a hybrid system, or when a significant irregularity exists, an inelastic analysis such as a static pushover analysis shall be performed to
(a) verify the compatibility of the systems;
(b) confirm the assumed energy-dissipating mechanism;
(c) show that the inelastic rotational demands are less than the inelastic rotational capacities; and
(d) account for redistribution of forces.

The inelastic analysis may be waived if the performance of the system has been previously verified by experimental evidence or analysis. Systems requiring inelastic analysis shall be treated as equivalents under Section 2.5 of the *National Building Code of Canada*.

Note: *A discussion of acceptable discontinuous and combined systems can be found in the "Explanatory Notes" to CSA A23.3 in the Cement Association of Canada's* Concrete design handbook.

21.2.3 Other structural systems
A reinforced concrete structural system other than one specified in Clause 21.2.2 shall be permitted if experimental evidence and analysis demonstrate that the proposed system will have strength and toughness equal to or exceeding the strength and toughness provided by a monolithic reinforced concrete structure that meets the requirements of Clauses 21.2 to Clauses 21.12. These systems shall be treated as equivalents under Section 2.5 of the *National Building Code of Canada*.

21.2.4 Applicable clauses
The requirements of Clauses 1 to 16 and 23 shall apply to the design and detailing of structural members unless modified by the requirements of Clause 21.

21.2.5 Analysis and proportioning of structural members

21.2.5.1
The interaction of all structural and non-structural elements that materially affect the linear and non-linear response of the structure to earthquake motions shall be considered in the analysis.

21.2.5.2

21.2.5.2.1
For the purpose of determining forces in and deflections of the structure, reduced section properties shall be used. The effective property to be used as a fraction of the gross section property shall be as specified in Table 21.1.

Table 21.1
Section properties for analysis
(See Clause 21.2.5.2.)

Element type	Effective property
Beam	$I_e = 0.4I_g$
Column	$I_e = \alpha_c I_g$
Coupling beam (Clause 21.6.8.6)	$A_{ve} = 0.15A_g$; $I_e = 0.4I_g$
Coupling beam (Clause 21.6.8.7)	$A_{ve} = 0.45A_g$; $I_e = 0.25I_g$
Slab frame element	$I_e = 0.2I_g$
Wall	$A_{xe} = \alpha_w A_g$; $I_e = \alpha_w I_g$

Note: See Clause 21.2.5.2.2 for the values of α_c and α_w.

21.2.5.2.2
The values of α_c and α_w specified in Table 21.1 shall be determined as follows:

(a) $\alpha_c = 0.5 + 0.6\dfrac{P_s}{f'_c A_g} \leq 1.0$ (21-1)

(b) $\alpha_w = 0.6 + \dfrac{P_s}{f'_c A_g} \leq 1.0$ (21-2)

P_s in Equation (21-2) shall be determined at the base of the wall. For multiple wall segments, an average value of P_s/A_g may be used.

21.2.5.3
Structural members below the base of the structure that are intended to transmit earthquake-induced forces to the foundation shall meet the requirements of Clause 21.

21.2.5.4
In the calculation of the slenderness effects for sway frames in accordance with Clause 10.16, Q shall be calculated with Δ_0 multiplied by R_d/I_E. The value of Q shall not exceed 1/3.

21.2.5.5

All structural and non-structural members assumed not to be part of the SFRS shall comply with Clause 21.12.

21.2.6 Concrete in members resisting earthquake-induced forces

21.2.6.1

Specified concrete compressive strengths used in the SFRS shall not exceed 80 MPa.
Note: *See Clauses 10.12 and 14.1.5 for transmission of column and wall loads through floor systems.*

21.2.6.2

The specified compressive strength of structural low-density concrete used in the SFRS shall not exceed 30 MPa unless experimental evidence demonstrates that structural members made with such concrete provide strength and toughness equal to or exceeding the strength and toughness of comparable members made with normal-density concrete of the same strength.

21.2.6.3

Where the term $\sqrt{f_c'}$ is used in calculations of capacity in Clause 21, its value shall be limited to 8 MPa.

21.2.7 Reinforcement in members resisting earthquake-induced forces

21.2.7.1

Reinforcement for SFRS designed with a force modification factor, R_d, greater than 2.5 shall be weldable grade in compliance with CAN/CSA-G30.18. Reinforcement for SFRS designed with a force modification factor, R_d, of 2.5 or less shall comply with CAN/CSA-G30.18 but need not be weldable grade.

   The design, detailing, and ductility requirements for structures designed using a reinforcement grade greater than 400 shall account for the increased strains.
Note: *The procedures specified in Clause 21, with the exception of those specified in Clause 21.4.4.2, were developed for Grade 400 reinforcement. The additional strains required for higher-yield-strength steel will, in general, reduce ductility.*

21.2.7.2

Clause 12.2.5 (which permits a reduction of lap splice length when the area of reinforcing steel provided exceeds the area required) shall not apply to reinforcement in members resisting earthquake-induced forces.

21.2.8 Mechanical splices

21.2.8.1

Mechanical splices shall be classified as either Type 1 or Type 2, as follows:
(a) Type 1 mechanical splices shall be those that comply with Clause 12.14.3.4.
(b) Type 2 mechanical splices shall be those that develop the specified tensile strength of the spliced bar.

21.2.8.2

Type 1 mechanical splices shall not be used within a distance equal to twice the member depth from the column or beam face, or from sections where yielding of the reinforcement is likely to occur as a result of inelastic lateral displacements. Type 2 mechanical splices may be used in any location.

21.2.9 Welded splices

21.2.9.1
Welded splices in reinforcement resisting earthquake-induced forces shall comply with Clause 12.14.3.3 and shall not be used within a distance equal to twice the member depth from the column or beam face, or from sections where yielding of the reinforcement is likely to occur as a result of inelastic lateral displacements.

21.2.9.2
Welding of stirrups, ties, inserts, or similar elements to longitudinal reinforcement that is required by design shall not be permitted.

21.3 Ductile moment-resisting frame members subjected to predominant flexure ($R_d = 4.0$)

21.3.1 Application

21.3.1.1
The requirements of Clause 21.3 shall apply to ductile frame members that are part of the ductile moment-resisting frame and are proportioned primarily to resist flexure. These frame members shall also satisfy the following conditions:
(a) the axial compressive force in the member due to factored load effects shall not exceed $A_g f_c' /10$;
(b) the clear span of the member shall be not less than four times its effective depth;
(c) the width-to-depth ratio of the cross-section shall be not less than 0.3; and
(d) the width shall be not less than 250 mm and not more than the width of the supporting member (measured on a plane perpendicular to the longitudinal axis of the flexural member) plus distances on each side of the supporting member not exceeding three-quarters of the depth of the flexural member.

21.3.1.2
Ductile frame members not meeting the requirements of Clause 21.3.1.1 shall be designed as specified in Clause 21.12 and shall not be considered part of the SFRS.

21.3.2 Longitudinal reinforcement

21.3.2.1
At any section of a flexural member, the areas of top reinforcement and bottom reinforcement shall each be not less than $1.4 b_w d/f_y$, and the reinforcement ratio, ρ, shall not exceed 0.025. At least two effectively continuous bars shall be provided at both top and bottom.

21.3.2.2
The positive moment resistance at the face of a joint shall be not less than one-half of the negative moment resistance provided at that face of the joint. Neither the negative nor the positive moment resistance at any section along the member length shall be less than one-quarter of the maximum moment resistance provided at the face of either end joint.

21.3.2.3

Lap splices of flexural reinforcement shall be permitted only if hoop reinforcement is provided over the lap length. The maximum spacing of the transverse reinforcement enclosing the lapped bars shall not exceed $d/4$ or 100 mm. Lap splices shall not be used

(a) within the joints;
(b) within a distance of $2d$ from the face of the joint; and
(c) within a distance d from any plastic hinge caused by inelastic lateral displacements.

21.3.3 Transverse reinforcement

21.3.3.1

Hoops shall be provided in the following regions of frame members:

(a) over a length equal to $2d$, measured from the face of the joint; and
(b) over regions where plastic hinges can occur and for a distance d on either side of these hinge regions.

21.3.3.2

The first hoop shall be located not more than 50 mm from the face of a supporting member. The maximum spacing of the hoops shall not exceed

(a) $d/4$;
(b) eight times the diameter of the smallest longitudinal bars;
(c) 24 times the diameter of the hoop bars; or
(d) 300 mm.

21.3.3.3

In regions where hoops are required, longitudinal bars on the perimeter shall have lateral support complying with Clauses 7.6.5.5 and 7.6.5.6.

21.3.3.4

Hoops in flexural members may be replaced by the following two pieces of reinforcement:

(a) a U-stirrup enclosing the longitudinal reinforcement with seismic hooks at the ends; and
(b) a crosstie to make a closed hoop.

If the longitudinal reinforcing bars secured by the crossties are confined by a slab only on one side of the flexural frame member, the 90° hooks of the crossties shall all be placed on that side.

21.3.3.5

Where hoops are not required, stirrups with seismic hooks at each end shall be spaced not more than $d/2$ throughout the length of the member.

21.3.4 Shear strength requirements

21.3.4.1 Design forces

The factored shear resistance of frame members shall be at least equal to the shear determined by assuming that moments equal to the probable moment resistance act at the faces of the joint so as to produce maximum shear in the member, and that the member is then loaded with the tributary transverse load along the span. The moments corresponding to probable strength shall be calculated using the properties of the member at the faces of the joint. The factored shear need not exceed that determined from factored load combinations, with load effects calculated using $R_d R_o$ equal to 1.0.

21.3.4.2 Shear reinforcement

Shear reinforcement shall be designed to the requirements of Clause 11, with the following exceptions:
(a) the values of $\theta = 45°$ and $\beta = 0$ shall be used in the regions specified in Clause 21.3.3.1; and
(b) transverse reinforcement required to resist shear shall be hoops over the lengths of members, as specified in Clause 21.3.3.1.

21.4 Ductile moment-resisting frame members subjected to flexure and significant axial load (R_d = 4.0)

21.4.1 Application

21.4.1.1

The requirements of Clause 21.4.2.1 to 21.4.5.2 shall apply to ductile frame members that are part of the ductile moment-resisting frame, are subject to an axial compressive force due to factored load effects that exceeds $A_g f'_c / 10$, and satisfy the following conditions:
(a) the shortest cross-sectional dimension, measured on a straight line passing through the geometric centroid, shall not be less than 300 mm; and
(b) the ratio of the shortest cross-sectional dimension to the perpendicular dimension shall not be less than 0.4.

21.4.1.2

Ductile frame members not meeting the requirements of Clause 21.4.1.1 shall be designed as specified in Clause 21.12 and shall not be considered part of the SFRS.

21.4.2 Minimum flexural resistance of columns

21.4.2.1

The flexural resistance of any column proportioned to resist a factored axial compressive force exceeding $A_g f'_c / 10$ shall meet the requirements of Clause 21.4.2.2. Columns not meeting the requirements of Clause 21.4.2.2 shall not be considered as contributing to the resistance of the SFRS and shall meet the requirements of Clause 21.12.

21.4.2.2

The flexural resistances of the columns and the beams shall satisfy

$$\Sigma M_{nc} \geq \Sigma M_{pb} \tag{21-3}$$

where

ΣM_{nc} = the sum of moments, at the centre of the joint, corresponding to the nominal resistance of the columns framing into the joint. The nominal resistance of the columns shall be calculated for the factored axial force, consistent with the direction of the lateral forces considered, that results in the lowest flexural resistance

ΣM_{pb} = the sum of moments, at the centre of the joint, corresponding to the probable resistance of the beams and girders framing into that joint. In T-beam construction where the slab is in tension under moments at the face of the joint, slab reinforcement within an effective slab width specified in Clause 10.3 shall be assumed to contribute to flexural strength if the slab reinforcement is developed at the critical section for flexure

Flexural resistances shall be summed such that the column moments oppose the beam moments. Equation (21-3) shall be satisfied for beam moments acting in either direction.

21.4.2.3

Axial design loads in frame columns shall account for beams yielding at levels above the level being considered. The shears from the beams shall be those given by the method specified in Clause 21.3.4.1 and using nominal rather than probable strengths. Allowance may be made for the reduction in accumulated beam shears with increasing numbers of storeys.

21.4.3 Longitudinal reinforcement

21.4.3.1

The area of longitudinal reinforcement shall be not less than 0.01 or more than 0.06 times the gross area, A_g, of the section.

21.4.3.2

Lap splices shall be permitted only within the centre half of the member length, shall be designed as tension lap splices, and shall be enclosed within transverse reinforcement complying with Clauses 21.4.4.2 and 21.4.4.3.

21.4.4 Transverse reinforcement

21.4.4.1

Shear resistance shall meet the requirements of Clause 21.4.5.

21.4.4.2

Transverse reinforcement, specified as follows, shall be provided unless a larger amount is required by Clause 21.4.4.3 or 21.4.5:

(a) the volumetric ratio of circular hoop reinforcement, ρ_s, shall be not less than that given by

$$\rho_s = 0.4k_p \frac{f'_c}{f_{yh}}$$ (21-4)

where
$k_p = P_f / P_o$
and f_{yh} shall not be taken as greater than 500 MPa. However, ρ_s shall not be less than that required by Equation (10-7);

(b) the total effective area in each of the principal directions of the cross-section within spacing s of rectangular hoop reinforcement shall be not less than the larger of the amounts required by the following equations:

$$A_{sh} = 0.2k_n k_p \frac{A_g}{A_{ch}} \frac{f'_c}{f_{yh}} sh_c$$ (21-5)

$$A_{sh} = 0.09 \frac{f'_c}{f_{yh}} sh_c$$ (21-6)

where
$k_n = n_\ell / (n_\ell - 2)$
$k_p = P_f / P_o$
and f_{yh} shall not be taken as greater than 500 MPa;

(c) transverse reinforcement may be provided by single or overlapping hoops. Crossties of the same bar size and spacing as the hoops may be used. Each end of the crosstie shall engage a peripheral longitudinal reinforcing bar; and

(d) if the thickness of the concrete outside the confining transverse reinforcement exceeds 100 mm, additional transverse reinforcement shall be provided within the cover at a spacing not exceeding 300 mm.

21.4.4.3

Transverse reinforcement shall be spaced at distances not exceeding the smallest of the following:
(a) one-quarter of the minimum member dimension;
(b) six times the diameter of the smallest longitudinal bar; or
(c) s_x, as follows:

$$s_x = 100 + \left(\frac{350 - h_x}{3} \right) \qquad \text{(21-7)}$$

21.4.4.4

On each face of a column, the distance h_x shall not exceed the greater of 200 mm or one-third of the core dimension in that direction, and shall not be more than 350 mm.

21.4.4.5

Transverse reinforcement in the amount specified in Clauses 21.4.4.1 to 21.4.4.3 shall be provided over a length, ℓ_o, from the face of each joint and on both sides of any section where flexural yielding can occur as a result of inelastic lateral displacement of the frame. The length, ℓ_o, shall be determined as follows:
(a) where $P_f \leq 0.5\phi_c f'_c A_g$, ℓ_o shall be not less than 1.5 times the largest member cross-section dimension or one-sixth of the clear span of the member; and
(b) where $P_f > 0.5\phi_c f'_c A_g$, ℓ_o shall be not less than twice the largest member cross-section dimension or one-sixth of the clear span of the member.

21.4.4.6

Columns that can develop plastic hinges because of their connection to rigid members such as foundations or discontinued walls or because of their position at the base of the structure shall be provided with transverse reinforcement as specified in Clauses 21.4.4.1 to 21.4.4.3 over their clear height. This transverse reinforcement shall continue into the discontinued member for at least the development length of the largest longitudinal reinforcement in the column. If the column terminates on a footing or mat, this transverse reinforcement shall extend into the footing or mat as required by Clause 21.11.

21.4.4.7

Where transverse reinforcement, as specified in Clauses 21.4.4.2 to 21.4.4.4, is not provided throughout the length of the column, the remainder of the column length shall contain hoop reinforcement with centre-to-centre spacing not exceeding the smaller of six times the diameter of the longitudinal column bars or 150 mm.

21.4.5 Shear strength

21.4.5.1

A column shall have a factored shear resistance that exceeds the greater of
(a) shear forces due to the factored load effects; or
(b) the design shear force determined from consideration of the maximum forces that can be generated at the joints at each end of the member. These joint forces shall be determined using the maximum probable moment strengths of the member associated with the range of factored axial loads on the member. The member shears need not exceed those determined from strengths based on the probable moment strength of the transverse members framing into the joint.

The factored shear resistance of the column need not be greater than the factored load effect calculated using $R_d R_o$ equal to 1.0.

21.4.5.2

Shear reinforcement shall be designed to the requirements of Clause 11, with the following exceptions:

(a)   values of $\beta \le 0.10$ and $\theta \ge 45°$ shall be used in the region specified in Clause 21.4.4.5; and

(b)   the transverse reinforcement required to resist shear shall be hoops.

21.5 Joints of ductile moment-resisting frames ($R_d = 4.0$)

21.5.1 General

21.5.1.1

The requirements of Clauses 21.5.1.2 to 21.5.5.7 shall apply to joints of ductile frames serving as parts of the SFRS.

21.5.1.2

Factored forces in joints shall be determined by assuming that the tensile stress in the longitudinal beam reinforcement at the joint is $1.25f_y$, except that they need not exceed the forces determined from the factored load combinations with factored load effects calculated using R_dR_o equal to 1.0.

21.5.1.3

Longitudinal beam reinforcement terminated in a column shall be extended to the far face of the confined column core and anchored in tension as specified in Clause 21.5.5 and in compression as specified in Clauses 12.3 and 12.5.5.

21.5.2 Transverse reinforcement in joints

21.5.2.1

Transverse hoop reinforcement, as specified in Clause 21.4.4 and calculated using the larger of f_c' for the column or the joint, shall be provided within the joint unless the joint is confined by structural members as specified in Clause 21.5.2.2.

21.5.2.2

Within the depth of the shallowest framing member, transverse reinforcement equal to at least one-half of the amount required by Clause 21.5.2.1 shall be provided where members frame into all four sides of the joint and each member width is at least three-quarters of the column width. At these locations, the spacing, s_x, specified in Clause 21.4.4.3 may be taken as 150 mm.

21.5.2.3

The transverse reinforcement required by Clause 21.4.4 shall be provided through the joint to provide confinement for longitudinal beam reinforcement located outside the column core, if such confinement is not provided by a beam framing into the joint.

21.5.3 Longitudinal column reinforcement

21.5.3.1

Longitudinal column reinforcement in round column cores shall be uniformly distributed around the column core with a centre-to-centre spacing not exceeding the larger of

(a)   200 mm; or

(b)   one-third of the column core diameter.

21.5.3.2

Longitudinal column reinforcement in rectangular column cores shall have the reinforcing in each face uniformly distributed along that face, with a centre-to-centre spacing corresponding to the tie spacing specified in Clause 21.4.4.4.

21.5.4 Shear resistance of joints

21.5.4.1

The factored shear resistance of the joint shall not exceed the following, where f'_c is the strength of the concrete in the joint:

(a) for confined joints: $2.2\lambda\phi_c\sqrt{f'_c}A_j$;
(b) for joints confined on three faces or on two opposite faces: $1.6\lambda\phi_c\sqrt{f'_c}A_j$; and
(c) for other joints: $1.3\lambda\phi_c\sqrt{f'_c}A_j$.

A member that frames into a face shall be considered to provide confinement to the joint if at least three-quarters of the face of the joint is covered by the framing member. A joint shall be considered confined if such confining members frame into all faces of the joint.

21.5.4.2

The shear force, V_{fb}, in the joint determined using the forces specified in Clause 21.5.1.2, and accounting for other forces on the joint, shall not exceed the factored resistance specified in Clause 21.5.4.1.

21.5.5 Development length for tension reinforcement in joints

21.5.5.1

Hooks, if used, shall be standard 90° hooks and shall be located within the confined column core.

21.5.5.2

For normal-density concrete, the development length, ℓ_{dh}, for a bar with a standard 90° hook shall not be less than the greatest of

(a) $8d_b$;
(b) 150 mm; or
(c) for bar sizes of 35M and smaller, the length given by

$$\ell_{dh} = 0.2\frac{f_y}{\sqrt{f'_c}}d_b \qquad\qquad (21\text{-}8)$$

21.5.5.3

For structural low-density concrete, the development length for a bar with a standard hook shall be not less than 1.25 times that required by Clause 21.5.5.2.

21.5.5.4

For bar sizes of 35M and smaller, the development length, ℓ_d, for a straight bar in a joint shall be not less than

(a) 2.5 times the length required by Clause 21.5.5.2 or 21.5.5.3, if the depth of the concrete cast in one lift beneath the bar does not exceed 300 mm; and
(b) 3.5 times the length required by Clause 21.5.5.2 or 21.5.5.3, if the depth of the concrete cast in one lift beneath the bar exceeds 300 mm.

21.5.5.5

Straight bars terminated at a joint shall pass through the confined core of a column. Any portion of the straight embedment length not within the confined core shall be considered 60% effective.

21.5.5.6

The diameter of straight beam and column bars passing through the joint shall satisfy the following equation:

$$d_b \leq \lambda \frac{\ell_j}{24k_2} \qquad\qquad\qquad (21\text{-}9)$$

21.5.5.7

If epoxy-coated reinforcement is used, the development lengths specified in Clauses 21.5.5.2 to 21.5.5.5 shall be multiplied by the applicable factor specified in Clause 12.2.4 or 12.5.3.

21.6 Ductile walls (R_d = 3.5 or 4.0)

21.6.1 Application

21.6.1.1

The requirements specified in Clauses 21.6.1.2 to 21.6.9.7 shall apply to ductile shear walls and ductile coupled or partially coupled shear walls serving as parts of the SFRS. Walls with h_w/ℓ_w of 2.0 or less shall be designed for R_d = 2.0 in accordance with Clause 21.7.4.

21.6.1.2

A ductile wall with openings shall be designed as
(a) a ductile shear wall with a single plastic hinge in accordance with Clauses 21.6.2 to 21.6.7 and Clause 21.6.9; or
(b) a ductile coupled or partially coupled shear wall in accordance with Clauses 21.6.2 to 21.6.9.
   To be classified as a ductile shear wall, a wall with openings shall be proportioned in such a manner that at every vertical section the strength and stiffness of the elements connecting the wall segments shall be sufficient for the wall to resist the total overturning and gravity forces through a single compression stress block at the wall end.
Note: *The intent of this Clause is to restrict ductile shear walls to walls where plane sections remain essentially plane.*

21.6.2 General requirements

21.6.2.1

Each wall shall be detailed for plastic hinges to occur at all locations over its height, except as specified in Clauses 21.6.2.2 and 21.6.2.3.

21.6.2.2

The following shall apply to buildings where the SFRS does not contain structural irregularity types 1, 3, 4, 5, or 6 as defined in Article 4.1.8.6 of the *National Building Code of Canada* over the building height:
(a) the walls shall be detailed for plastic hinges over a height equal to at least 1.5 times the length of the longest wall above the design critical section. In the case of walls designed to the requirements of Clause 21.6.8, the height to be taken shall be at least 1.5 times the length of the longest individual element in the direction under consideration;
(b) the flexural and shear reinforcement required for the critical section shall be maintained over the height specified in Item (a);
(c) for all elevations above the plastic hinge region, the design overturning moments and shears shall be increased by the ratio of the factored moment resistance to the factored moment, both calculated at the top of the plastic hinge region; and
(d) detailing for plastic hinging shall extend below the critical section to the footing unless there is a significant increase in strength and stiffness below the critical section, in which case the detailing shall extend down the distance specified in Item (a) or to the footing, whichever is less.

21.6.2.3

For buildings containing structural irregularity types 1 or 3 over their height, the detailing specified in Clauses 21.6.2.2(a) and 21.6.2.2(b) shall be applied at each irregularity and shall continue for the distance specified in Clause 21.6.2.2(a) above and below each irregularity.

21.6.3 Dimensional limitations

21.6.3.1

The effective flange widths to be used in the design of L-, C-, or T-shaped sections shall not be assumed to extend farther from the face of the web than
(a) one-half of the distance to an adjacent structural wall web; or
(b) 25% of the wall height above the section under consideration.

21.6.3.2

The wall thickness within a plastic hinge shall be not less than $\ell_u/10$, except as permitted by Clauses 21.6.3.3 to 21.6.3.5, but shall not be less than $\ell_u/14$.

21.6.3.3

Clause 21.6.3.2 shall be required to apply only to those parts of a wall that under factored vertical and lateral loads are more than halfway from the neutral axis to the compression face of the wall section.

21.6.3.4

Clause 21.6.3.2 shall not be required to apply to simple rectangular walls where the distance from the neutral axis to the compression face, calculated for factored load effects, is located within a distance of the lesser of $4b_w$ or $0.3\ell_w$ from the compression face of the wall section.

21.6.3.5

Clause 21.6.3.2 shall not be required to apply to any part of a wall that lies within a distance of $3b_w$ from a continuous line of lateral support provided by a flange or cross wall. The width of the flange providing effective lateral support shall be not less than $\ell_u/5$.

21.6.4 Reinforcement

21.6.4.1

Unless otherwise specified, all reinforcement in walls shall be anchored, spliced, or embedded in accordance with the requirements for reinforcement in tension specified in Clause 12 and modified by Clause 21.6.4.2. All lap splices shall have a minimum length of $1.5\ell_d$.

21.6.4.2

Where Type 2 mechanical splices are used, not more than alternate bars in each layer of distributed and concentrated longitudinal reinforcement shall be spliced at any section, and the centre-to-centre distance between splices of adjacent bars shall be not less than $40d_b$, measured along the longitudinal axis of the wall.

21.6.4.3

The reinforcement ratio within any region of concentrated reinforcement, including regions containing lap splices, shall be not more than 0.06.

21.6.4.4

The diameter of the bars used in a wall shall not exceed one-tenth of the thickness of the wall at the bar location.

21.6.5 Distributed reinforcement

21.6.5.1
Both vertical and horizontal distributed reinforcement shall be provided in such a manner that the reinforcement ratio for this distributed reinforcement is not less than 0.0025 in each direction. The reinforcement spacing in each direction shall not exceed 450 mm. Splices shall comply with Clause 21.6.4.1 or 21.6.4.2. Vertical distributed reinforcement shall be tied as specified in Clause 7.6.5. Ties may be omitted if
(a) the area of vertical steel is less than $0.005A_g$; and
(b) the maximum bar size is 20M or smaller.

21.6.5.2
In regions of plastic hinging, the spacing of distributed reinforcement in each direction shall not exceed 300 mm, and if the area of vertical distributed reinforcement is greater than $0.005A_g$ or the maximum bar size is greater than 15M, the vertical distributed reinforcement shall be tied as specified in Clause 21.6.6.9.

21.6.5.3
At least two curtains of reinforcement shall be used if, in regions of plastic hinging, the in-plane factored shear force assigned to the wall exceeds $0.18\lambda\phi_c\sqrt{f'_c}A_{cv}$.

21.6.5.4
Horizontal reinforcement shall extend to the ends of the wall and shall be contained at each end of the wall within a region of concentrated reinforcement as specified in Clause 21.6.6.

21.6.5.5
In regions of plastic hinging, horizontal reinforcement shall be anchored within a region of concentrated reinforcement to develop $1.25f_y$.

21.6.6 Concentrated vertical reinforcement

21.6.6.1
Concentrated vertical reinforcement shall be provided at each end of the wall. Each concentration shall be a minimum of four bars placed in at least two layers.

21.6.6.2
The concentrated reinforcement shall be proportioned to resist that portion of factored load effects, including earthquake, not resisted by distributed vertical reinforcement.

21.6.6.3
The minimum concentrated reinforcement shall be not less than $0.001b_w\ell_w$ at each end of the wall.

21.6.6.4
The minimum area of concentrated reinforcement in regions of plastic hinging shall be at least $0.0015b_w\ell_w$ at each end of the wall.

21.6.6.5
In the case of flanged walls, concentrated reinforcement at the end(s) of the effective flanges may supply up to one-half of the required minimum wall web concentrated reinforcement, with the remainder placed at the end of the wall web.

21.6.6.6
The concentrated reinforcement shall consist of straight bars without cranks.

21.6.6.7
In regions of plastic hinging, not more than 50% of the reinforcement at each end of the walls shall be spliced at the same location. In such walls, a total of at least one-half of the height of each storey shall be completely clear of lap splices in the concentrated reinforcement.

21.6.6.8
The concentrated reinforcement shall be at least tied as a column as specified in Clause 7.6, and the ties shall be detailed as hoops. In regions of plastic hinging, the concentrated reinforcement shall be tied with buckling prevention ties as specified in Clause 21.6.6.9.

21.6.6.9
Buckling prevention ties shall comply with Clause 7.6.5.5 or 7.6.5.6 and be detailed as hoops. The tie spacing shall not exceed the smallest of
(a) six longitudinal bar diameters;
(b) 24 tie diameters;
(c) one-half of the least dimension of the member; or
(d) the tie spacing required by Clause 21.6.7, if applicable.

21.6.7 Ductility of ductile shear walls
Note: *This Clause applies to individual walls that are effectively continuous in cross-section from the base of the structure to the top of the wall and are designed to have a single plastic hinge at the base.*

21.6.7.1
To ensure ductility in the hinge region, the inelastic rotational capacity of the wall, θ_{ic}, shall be greater than the inelastic rotational demand, θ_{id}.

21.6.7.2
The inelastic rotational demand on a wall, θ_{id}, may be taken as

$$\theta_{id} = \frac{\left(\Delta_f R_o R_d - \Delta_f \gamma_w\right)}{\left(h_w - \dfrac{\ell_w}{2}\right)} \geq 0.004 \tag{21-10}$$

where
$\Delta_f R_o R_d =$ the design displacement
$\Delta_f \gamma_w$ = the elastic portion of the displacement
ℓ_w = the length of the longest wall in the direction being considered
The value of 0.004 is a minimum rotational demand.

21.6.7.3
The inelastic rotational capacity of a wall, θ_{ic}, may be taken as

$$\theta_{ic} = \left(\frac{\varepsilon_{cu}\ell_w}{2c} - 0.002\right) \leq 0.025 \tag{21-11}$$

where
ℓ_w = the length of the individual wall

138

ε_{cu} shall be taken as 0.0035 unless the compression region of the wall is confined as a column in accordance with Clause 21.6.7.4. The value of 0.025 is the upper limit on inelastic rotation capacity governed by tension steel strain. The distance to the neutral axis, c, shall be determined by plane section analysis or as follows:

$$c = \frac{P_s + P_n + P_{ns} - \alpha_1 \phi_c f_c' A_f}{\alpha_1 \beta_1 \phi_c f_c' b_w}$$

(21-12)

21.6.7.4
When ε_{cu} is taken greater than 0.0035 but less than or equal to 0.014, the compression region of the wall shall be confined as a column. The transverse reinforcement shall be determined from Equation (21-5), with k_p taken as $(0.1 + 30\varepsilon_{cu})$. This reinforcement shall be provided over a distance of not less than $c(\varepsilon_{cu} - 0.0035)/\varepsilon_{cu}$ from the compression face of the wall. The minimum vertical reinforcement ratio in any part of this confined region shall be 0.005.

21.6.8 Additional requirements for ductile coupled and partially coupled shear walls
Note: *This Clause applies to an assembly of wall segments that are joined together by ductile coupling beams designed to dissipate energy.*

21.6.8.1
To ensure ductility of coupled systems, the inelastic rotational capacity of both the walls and the coupling beams shall be greater than their respective inelastic rotational demands.

21.6.8.2
The inelastic rotational demand on ductile coupled and partially coupled walls shall be taken as

$$\theta_{id} = \frac{\Delta_f R_o R_d}{h_w} \geq 0.004$$

(21-13)

where
$\Delta_f R_o R_d = $ the design displacement

21.6.8.3
The inelastic rotational capacity of the wall segment shall be calculated using the methods specified in Clause 21.6.7.3, except that ℓ_w shall be taken as the lengths of the individual wall segments for partially coupled walls and as the length of the system for coupled walls.

21.6.8.4
The inelastic rotational demand on coupling beams shall be taken as

$$\theta_{id} = \left(\frac{\Delta_f R_o R_d}{h_w} \right) \frac{\ell_{cg}}{\ell_u}$$

(21-14)

The inelastic rotational capacity of coupling beams, θ_{ic}, shall be taken as
(a)   0.04 for coupling beams designed with diagonal reinforcement in accordance with Clause 21.6.8.7; and
(b)   0.02 for coupling beams designed in accordance with Clause 21.6.8.6.

21.6.8.5

Ductile coupled and partially coupled shear walls shall have ductile coupling beams. Ductile coupling beams shall have a depth not greater than twice the clear span of the beam. Diagonally reinforced coupling beams meeting the requirements of Clause 21.6.8.7 shall be provided unless the shear stress resulting from factored load effects is less than $0.1(\ell_u / d)\sqrt{f'_c}$, in which case conventionally reinforced coupling beams meeting the requirements of Clause 21.6.8.6 or diagonally reinforced coupling beams meeting the requirements of Clause 21.6.8.7 shall be provided.

21.6.8.6

Coupling beams without diagonal reinforcement shall meet the requirements of Clause 21.3 and the following requirements:
(a) the clear span, ℓ_u, shall be not less than $2\ell_d$;
(b) the anchorage of the flexural reinforcement into the wall shall meet the requirements of Clause 21.5 or 21.6.8.7;
(c) beams wider than the wall shall have
    (i)   the front interface between the beam and the wall designed for the beam forces within the wall width; and
    (ii) the side interface(s) between the beam and the wall designed to transfer all of the forces in the beam overhang(s) to the wall; and
(d) beams not centred on the wall shall have
    (i)   the beams and the walls designed for the eccentricities; and
    (ii) the beam stiffness reduced to account for the out-of-plane deformations.

21.6.8.7

Coupling beams with diagonal reinforcement shall resist the entire in-plane factored shear and flexure by diagonal reinforcement in both directions. The width of the coupling beam shall be less than or equal to the width of the wall. Where beams are not centred on the width of the wall, the resultant eccentricities shall be considered in the design of the beams and the walls. The diagonal reinforcement in each direction shall be interlocked and enclosed by hoops or spirals whose spacing shall not exceed the smallest of
(a) six diagonal bar diameters;
(b) 24 tie diameters; or
(c) 100 mm.
The centroid of each diagonal group shall be centred in the beam. Reinforcement shall be anchored into the wall with a minimum embedment of $1.5\ell_d$, where the 1.5 factor includes top bar effects but not bundled bar effects. Bars terminating with a standard hook contained within confinement ties shall have a minimum straight embedment into the wall of $1.0\ell_d$.
Note: *When the dimensions of a coupling beam are such that V_f/bh exceeds $1.0\sqrt{f'_c}$, it can be difficult to construct the beam on account of reinforcement congestion, particularly at the intersection of the coupling beam reinforcement with the concentrated wall reinforcement.*

21.6.8.8

Except as permitted by Clause 21.6.8.9, walls at each end of a coupling beam shall be designed so that the factored moment resistance of the wall about its centroid, calculated using axial loads P_s and P_n, exceeds the moment at its centroid resulting from the nominal resistance of the coupling beams framing into the wall and the factored moment in the wall.

21.6.8.9

If the wall at one end of the coupling beam has a factored resistance less than the nominal coupling beam resistance, the following requirements shall apply:
(a) the coupling beam shall meet the shear stress requirement specified in Clause 21.6.8.5 and the requirements specified in Clause 21.6.8.6;
(b) the wall shall be designed to the requirements specified in Clauses 21.4.4.1 to 21.4.4.3, 21.4.4.6, and 21.4.5; and

(c)   the joint between the wall and the coupling beam shall meet the requirements specified in Clause 21.5.

21.6.8.10
Concentrated vertical reinforcement, as specified in Clause 21.6.6, shall be provided in the walls at both ends of coupling beams over the full height of the building and shall be tied as specified in Clause 21.6.6.9.

21.6.8.11
Coupled and partially coupled shear walls shall be designed with that portion of the overturning moment resisted by axial forces in the walls increased at each level by the ratio of the sum of the nominal capacities of coupling beams to the sum of the factored forces in the coupling beams above the level under consideration.

21.6.8.12
Assemblies of coupled and partially coupled shear walls connected together by coupling beams that function as a closed tube or tubes shall be designed with
(a)   that portion of the overturning moment due to lateral loads resisted by axial forces in the walls, increased at each level by the ratio of the sum of the nominal capacities of coupling beams to the sum of the factored forces in the coupling beams required to resist lateral loads above the level under consideration; and
(b)   an additional increase in overturning moment resisted by axial forces in the walls at each level corresponding to the increase in the sum of the nominal capacities of the coupling beams required to resist the accidental torsion above the level under consideration.

21.6.8.13
In lieu of a more detailed assessment, wall segments that act as tension flanges in the flexural mode shall be assumed to have no shear resistance over the height of the plastic hinge. For wall assemblies carrying torsion as a tube, the shear forces in the tension flange shall be redistributed.

21.6.9 Shear strength of ductile walls

21.6.9.1
Walls shall have a factored shear resistance greater than the shear due to the effects of factored loads. The shear due to the effects of factored loads shall account for the magnification of the shear due to the inelastic effects of higher modes. In addition, the factored shear resistance shall not be less than the smaller of
(a)   the shear corresponding to the development of the probable moment capacity of the wall system at its plastic hinge locations; or
(b)   the shear resulting from design load combinations that include earthquake, with load effects calculated using $R_d R_o$ equal to 1.0.

21.6.9.2
The shear design of ductile walls shall meet the requirements specified in Clauses 11 and 21.6.9.3 to 21.6.9.7.

21.6.9.3
The effective shear depth, d_v, of a wall shall be as specified in Clause 2.3, but need not be taken as less than $0.8\ell_w$.

21.6.9.4

All construction joints in walls shall be clean and free of laitance and shall meet the requirements specified in Clause 11.5.

21.6.9.5

The effect of openings in walls shall be accounted for using the procedures specified in Clause 11.4.

21.6.9.6

For regions of plastic hinging, the following additional requirements shall apply:

(a)   The factored shear demand on the wall shall not exceed $0.10\phi_c f_c' b_w d_v$ unless it is shown that the inelastic rotational demand on the wall, θ_{id}, given by Equation (21-10) or (21-13) is less than 0.015. When $\theta_{id} = 0.005$, the factored shear demand shall not exceed $0.15\phi_c f_c' b_w d_v$. For inelastic rotational demands between these limits, linear interpolation may be used.

(b)   The value of β specified in Clause 11.3.4 shall be taken as zero unless it is shown that the inelastic rotational demand on the wall, θ_{id}, given by Equation (21-10) or (21-13) is less than 0.015. When $\theta_{id} \leq 0.005$, the value of β shall not be taken greater than 0.18. For inelastic rotational demands between these limits, linear interpolation may be used.

(c)   The value of θ in Clause 11.3.5 shall be taken as 45° unless the axial compression $(P_s + P_p)$ acting on the wall is greater than $0.1 f_c' A_g$. When $(P_s + P_p) \geq 0.2 f_c' A_g$, the value of θ shall not be taken less than 35°. For axial compressions between these limits, linear interpolation may be used.

21.6.9.7

When the strut-and-tie model of Clause 11.4 is used for shear design, the following exceptions shall apply in regions of plastic hinging:

(a)   The limiting compressive stress in the strut shall be taken as 0.8 times the value determined from Equation (11-22).

(b)   A compression strut that, during the reverse direction of seismic loading, is a tension tie designed to yield, shall contain a minimum of four bars placed in at least two layers. This reinforcement shall be tied as a column in accordance with Clause 7.6, and the ties shall be detailed as hoops. In addition, the spacing of the ties shall not exceed the smallest of six longitudinal bar diameters, 24 tie diameters, or 100 mm.

21.7 Building members designed for moderate ductility (R_d = 2.0 or 2.5)

21.7.1 Application

21.7.1.1

The requirements specified in Clauses 21.7.1.2 to 21.7.4.8 shall apply to SFRSs designed using a force modification factor, R_d, of 2.0 for walls and 2.5 for frames.

21.7.1.2

Tilt-up wall panels shall be designed to the requirements of Clause 23, except that the requirements of Clause 21.7.2 shall apply to wall panels with openings when the maximum inelastic rotational demand on any part of the panel exceeds 0.02 radians. However, the inelastic rotational demand shall not exceed 0.04 radians. The requirements specified in Clause 21.7.4 shall apply to solid wall panels when the maximum in-plane shear stress exceeds $0.1\phi_c \sqrt{f_c'}$.

Note: *Methods for calculating rotational demand on elements of tilt-up panels with openings can be found in the "Explanatory Notes" to CSA A23.3 in the Cement Association of Canada's Concrete design handbook. The seismic performance of tilt-up buildings depends not only on the performance of the concrete wall panels but also on the performance of the roof structure and the connection between the wall panels and the roof. This Standard covers only the design of the concrete wall panels.*

21.7.2 Moderately ductile moment-resisting frames

21.7.2.1 Detailing of beams

21.7.2.1.1
The positive moment resistance at the face of the joint shall be not less than one-third of the negative moment resistance provided at that face of the joint. Neither the negative nor the positive moment resistance at any section along the length of the member shall be less than one-fifth of the maximum moment resistance provided at the face of either joint.

21.7.2.1.2
At both ends of the member, 10M or larger stirrups detailed as hoops shall be provided over lengths equal to twice the member depth measured from the face of the supporting member toward midspan. The first stirrup shall be located not more than 50 mm from the face of the supporting member and the spacing shall not exceed the smallest of
(a) $d/4$;
(b) eight times the diameter of the smallest longitudinal bar enclosed;
(c) 24 times the diameter of the stirrup bar; or
(d) 300 mm.

21.7.2.1.3
Stirrups shall be spaced not more than $d/2$ throughout the length of the member.

21.7.2.2 Detailing of columns

21.7.2.2.1
Transverse reinforcement shall be detailed as hoops and crossties or spirals.

21.7.2.2.2
The sum of the factored flexural resistances of the column sections framing into a joint, accounting for axial loads, shall exceed the sum of the nominal flexural resistances of the beams framing into the same joint. In T-beam construction where the slab is in tension under moments at the face of the joint, slab reinforcement within an effective slab width as specified in Clause 10.3 shall be assumed to contribute to flexural strength if the slab reinforcement is developed at the critical section for flexure.

Flexural resistances shall be summed in such a manner that the column moments oppose the beam moments. This requirement shall be satisfied for beam moments acting in either direction. The design column forces need not exceed those determined from the factored load combinations, with factored load effects calculated using $R_d R_o$ equal to 1.0.

21.7.2.2.3
Transverse reinforcement shall be provided at both ends of the columns over a length equal to the largest of one-sixth of the clear height, the maximum cross-sectional dimension, or 450 mm, with a spacing not exceeding the smallest of
(a) eight longitudinal bar diameters;
(b) 24 tie diameters; or
(c) one-half of the minimum column dimension.

21.7.2.2.4
In the direction perpendicular to the longitudinal axis of the column, crossties or legs of overlapping hoops shall have centre-to-centre spacings not exceeding 350 mm.

21.7.2.2.5

Columns that can develop plastic hinges because of their connection to rigid members such as foundations or discontinued walls, or because of their position at the base of the structure, shall be provided with transverse reinforcement over their clear height, as follows:

(a) the volumetric ratio of circular hoop reinforcement, ρ_s, shall be not less than

$$\rho_s = 0.3 k_p \frac{f'_c}{f_{yh}} \qquad (21\text{-}15)$$

where
$k_p = P_f / P_o$
and f_{yh} shall not be taken as greater than 500 MPa. However, ρ_s shall not be less than that required by Equation (10-7);

(b) the total effective area in each of the principal directions of the cross-section within spacing s of rectangular hoop reinforcement, A_{sh}, shall be not less than the larger of the following:

$$A_{sh} = 0.15 k_n k_p \frac{A_g}{A_{ch}} \frac{f'_c}{f_{yh}} sh_c \qquad (21\text{-}16)$$

$$A_{sh} = 0.09 \frac{f'_c}{f_{yh}} sh_c \qquad (21\text{-}17)$$

where

$$k_n = \frac{n_\ell}{(n_\ell - 2)}$$

$k_p = P_f / P_o$
and f_{yh} shall not be taken as greater than 500 MPa;

(c) transverse reinforcement may be provided by single or overlapping hoops. Crossties of the same bar size and spacing as the hoops shall be permitted. Each end of the crosstie shall engage a peripheral longitudinal reinforcing bar; and

(d) if the thickness of the concrete outside the confining transverse reinforcement exceeds 100 mm, additional transverse reinforcement shall be provided within the cover at a spacing not exceeding 300 mm.

21.7.2.3 Shear in frames

The factored shear resistance of beams and columns resisting earthquake effects shall be not less than the lesser of

(a) the sum of the maximum shear associated with development of nominal moment strengths of the member at each restrained end of the clear span and the shear calculated using earthquake load combinations for gravity loads; or

(b) the maximum shear obtained from factored load combinations, with factored load effects calculated using $R_d R_o$ equal to 1.0.

21.7.2.4 Joints in frames

21.7.2.4.1

The design shear forces acting in a beam column joint shall be those induced by the nominal resistance of the beams or the columns framing into the joint, whichever is less, except that they need not exceed those determined from the factored load combinations, with factored load effects calculated using $R_d R_o$ equal to 1.0. Where beams frame into the joint from two directions, each direction may be considered independently.

144

21.7.2.4.2
The factored shear resistance of the joint shall not exceed the following, where f_c' is the strength of the concrete in the joint:
(a) for confined joints: $2.2\lambda\phi_c\sqrt{f_c'}A_j$;
(b) for joints confined on three faces or on two opposite faces: $1.6\lambda\phi_c\sqrt{f_c'}A_j$; and
(c) for other joints: $1.3\lambda\phi_c\sqrt{f_c'}A_j$.
   A member that frames into a face shall be considered to provide confinement to the joint if at least three-quarters of the face of the joint is covered by the framing member. A joint shall be considered to be confined if such confining members frame into all faces of the joint.

21.7.2.4.3
Horizontal joint reinforcement shall be designed for shear in accordance with Clause 11.

21.7.2.4.4
Transverse hoop reinforcement shall be provided over the depth of the joint and spaced a maximum distance of 150 mm. Longitudinal column reinforcement shall have a centre-to-centre spacing not exceeding 300 mm and shall not be cranked within the joint.

21.7.2.4.5
The diameter of straight beam and column bars passing through the joint, d_b, shall satisfy the following equation:

$$d_b \le \lambda\frac{\ell_j}{20\,k_2} \tag{21-18}$$

21.7.3 Moderately ductile shear walls

21.7.3.1 General
The requirements specified in Clauses 21.7.3.2 to 21.7.3.4 shall apply to walls with h_w/ℓ_w greater than 2.0. The dimensional limitations specified in Clause 21.6.3 shall apply, except that in Clause 21.6.3.2 the limit $\ell_u/10$ shall be taken as $\ell_u/14$ and $\ell_u/14$ shall be taken as $\ell_u/20$.

21.7.3.2 Ductility of walls
Ductility of walls shall be determined in accordance with the methods specified in Clause 21.6.7, except that the minimum rotational demand may be taken as 0.003. The requirements specified in Clause 21.6.7 shall be considered satisfied if
(a) the depth to the neutral axis, c, determined in accordance with Equation (21-12) is less than 0.15 ℓ_w; or
(b) the depth to the neutral axis, c, determined in accordance with Equation (21-12) is less than 0.33 ℓ_w and the displacement, Δ_f, of the wall does not exceed $h_w/350$.

21.7.3.3 Detailing of walls

21.7.3.3.1
The distributed reinforcement ratio for walls shall be not less than 0.0025 in the vertical and horizontal directions and shall be tied in accordance with Clause 14.1.8.7.

21.7.3.3.2
Concentrated longitudinal reinforcement in plastic hinge regions shall meet the requirements of Clauses 21.6.4.1, 21.6.6.6, and 21.6.6.9 and shall be tied as columns in accordance with Clause 7 outside these regions.

21.7.3.3.3

Corners and junctions of intersecting walls shall be adequately tied to ensure unity of action. All horizontal bars shall extend to the far face of the joining wall and be bent around a vertical bar with a standard 90° hook.

21.7.3.4 Shear strength of moderately ductile shear walls

21.7.3.4.1

Shear walls shall have a factored shear resistance greater than the shear due to the effects of factored loads, but not less than the smaller of
(a) the shear corresponding to the development of the nominal moment capacity of the wall system at its plastic hinge locations; or
(b) the shear resulting from design load combinations that include earthquake effect, with loads calculated using $R_d R_o$ equal to 1.0.

21.7.3.4.2

Walls with moderate ductility shall be designed as specified in Clauses 21.6.9.2 to 21.6.9.7. The requirements of these clauses shall be considered satisfied if
(a) the factored shear force in the wall does not exceed $0.1\phi_c f_c' b_w d_v$;
(b) the value of β in Clause 11.3.4 is taken as 0.1; and
(c) the value of θ in Clause 11.3.5 is taken as 45°.

21.7.4 Squat shear walls

21.7.4.1

The requirements specified in Clauses 21.7.4.2 to 21.7.4.8 shall apply to walls with h_w/ℓ_w of 2.0 or less. Squat walls shall be designed using an R_d of 2.0.

21.7.4.2

The foundation and diaphragm components of the SFRS shall have factored resistances that are greater than the nominal wall capacity, which shall be based on one of the following energy-dissipation mechanisms:
(a) a flexural mechanism where the shear corresponding to the development of the nominal moment capacity of the wall is less than the nominal shear resistance; or
(b) a shear mechanism where the shear corresponding to the development of the nominal moment capacity of the wall is greater than the nominal shear resistance. The minimum shear resistance shall be taken as not less than $0.2\sqrt{f_c'} b_w d_v$.
However, the nominal wall capacity need not be taken larger than the load calculated with design load combinations that include earthquake effects calculated using $R_d R_o$ equal to 1.0.
Note: *Squat walls can develop either a flexural or a shear mechanism to absorb seismic energy; however, the factored resistance can be significantly higher than the factored forces as a result of minimum reinforcement requirements and wall geometries. Consequently, the selection of an overstrength to use when applying capacity design principles to other components of the SFRS is very important.*

21.7.4.3

The dimensional limitations specified in Clause 21.6.3.1 shall apply.

21.7.4.4

The reinforcement requirements specified in Clause 21.6.4 shall apply.

21.7.4.5
The distributed reinforcement shall satisfy the following requirements:
(a) Both vertical and horizontal distributed reinforcement shall be provided in such a manner that the reinforcement ratio for this distributed reinforcement is not less than 0.003 in each direction. The reinforcement spacing in each direction shall not exceed 300 mm.
(b) At least two curtains of reinforcement shall be used if the in-plane factored shear force assigned to the wall exceeds $0.18\lambda\phi_c\sqrt{f_c'}b_wd_v$.
(c) Horizontal reinforcement shall extend to the ends of the wall and shall be contained at each end within a region of tied vertical reinforcement as specified in Clause 21.7.4.6.

21.7.4.6
Tied vertical reinforcement shall be provided at each end of the wall and at junctions of intersecting walls. The minimum reinforcement ratio of 0.005 shall be provided over a minimum wall length of 300 mm. The tied vertical reinforcement shall consist of a minimum of four bars and shall be tied as a column in accordance with Clause 7.6. The ties shall be detailed as hoops.

21.7.4.7
The vertical tension force required to resist overturning at the base of the wall shall be provided by concentrated reinforcement and vertical distributed reinforcement in addition to the amount required by Clause 21.7.4.8 to resist the shear corresponding to the applied bending moment. Plane sections analysis may be used for these calculations. All vertical reinforcement required at the base of the wall shall be extended the full height of the wall.

21.7.4.8
The shear design of squat walls shall meet the requirements specified in Clauses 11 and 21.6.9.3 to 21.6.9.5, and the following additional requirements:
(a) The factored shear demand on the wall shall not exceed $0.15\phi_cf_c'b_wd_v$.
(b) The value of β in Clause 11.3.4 shall be taken as zero. The value of θ may be freely chosen between a maximum value of 45° and a minimum value of 30°. The same value of θ shall be used to determine the required amount of distributed horizontal reinforcement in accordance with Clause 11.3.5 and the corresponding amount of distributed vertical reinforcement for shear in accordance with Clause 21.7.4.8(c).
(c) The amount of distributed vertical reinforcement required to resist shear shall be determined from the following equation as a function of the required amount of distributed horizontal reinforcement, ρ_h:

$$\rho_v = \rho_h\cot^2\theta - \frac{P_s}{\phi_sf_yA_g} \tag{21-19}$$

(d) When the strut-and-tie model of Clause 11.4 is applied to short walls, the additional requirements of Clause 21.6.9.7 shall apply.

21.8 Conventional construction (R_d = 1.5)

21.8.1 General
The requirements specified in Clauses 21.8.2 to 21.8.4 shall apply to elements of the SFRS.
   Structures designed with an R_d of 1.5 need only comply with Clauses 21.8.2 to 21.8.4, i.e., not with Clauses 21.1 to 21.7 and 21.9 to 21.12.

CSA Standard A23.3-04

21.8.2 Frames

Frame members shall comply with the requirements of Clauses 7.7, 11.7, and 12.11.2. The columns shall contain ties that comply with Clause 21.6.6.9 unless

(a) the sum of the factored resistances of columns framing into a joint is greater than the factored resistance of the beams framing into the joint;

(b) the factored resistances of the columns are greater than the effects of factored loads calculated using $R_d R_o$ equal to 1.0; or

(c) $I_E F_a S_a (0.2)$ is less than 0.2.

21.8.3 Walls

21.8.3.1

Walls shall be designed to the requirements of Clauses 14 and 21.2.7.2.

21.8.3.2

Walls shall have a factored shear resistance greater than the shear due to the effects of factored loads, but not less than the smaller of

(a) the shear corresponding to the development of the factored moment capacity of the wall system at its critical sections; or

(b) the shear resulting from design load combinations that include earthquake effect, with loads calculated using $R_d R_o$ equal to 1.0.

21.8.4 Two-way slabs without beams

21.8.4.1

The factored slab moment at support related to earthquake effect shall be determined for factored load combinations including earthquake effects. All reinforcement provided to resist M_s, the portion of slab moment balanced by support moment, shall be placed within the column strip (see Clause 2.2).

21.8.4.2

The fraction of the moment, M_s, determined using Equation (13-25) shall be resisted by reinforcement placed within the effective width b_b. The effective slab width for exterior and corner connections shall not extend beyond the column face a distance greater than c_t, measured perpendicular to the slab span.

21.8.4.3

Not less than one-half of the reinforcement in the column strip at a support shall be placed within the effective slab width b_b.

21.8.4.4

Not less than one-quarter of the top reinforcement at the support in the column strip shall be continuous throughout the span.

21.8.4.5

Continuous bottom reinforcement in the column strip shall be not less than one-third of the top reinforcement at the support in the column strip.

21.8.4.6

Not less than one-half of all bottom middle strip reinforcement and all bottom column strip reinforcement shall be continuous and shall develop its yield strength at the face of support as specified in Clause 13.8.5.1.

148

21.8.4.7
At discontinuous edges of the slab, all top and bottom reinforcement at a support shall be developed at the face of support as specified in Clause 13.8.5.1.

21.8.4.8
At the critical section for columns specified in Clause 13.3.3.1, two-way shear caused by factored gravity loads shall not exceed $0.4V_c$, where V_c shall be calculated as specified in Clause 13.3.4 for non-prestressed slabs and in Clause 18.12.3.3 for prestressed slabs. This requirement may be waived if the contribution of the earthquake-induced factored two-way shear stress transferred by eccentricity of shear in accordance with Clauses 13.3.5.3 to 13.3.5.5 at the point of maximum stress does not exceed one-half of the stress, v_c, permitted by Clause 13.3.4.

21.9 Precast concrete

21.9.1 General
The seismic design of ductile moment-resisting frames, ductile flexural walls, and moderately ductile flexural walls constructed using precast concrete shall comply with Clause 21.9.

21.9.2 Ductile moment-resisting frames constructed using precast concrete (R_d = 4.0)

21.9.2.1
Ductile moment-resisting frames with ductile connections constructed using precast concrete shall satisfy the following requirements, as well as all requirements for ductile moment-resisting frames constructed with cast-in-place concrete:
(a) the factored shear resistance for connections computed as specified in Clause 11.5.1 shall be greater than or equal to 150% of the shear calculated as specified in Clause 21.3.4.1 or 21.4.5.1; and
(b) mechanical splices of beam reinforcement shall be located not closer than $h/2$ from the joint face and shall meet the requirements of Clause 21.2.8.

21.9.2.2
Ductile moment-resisting frames with strong connections constructed using precast concrete shall satisfy the following requirements as well as all requirements for ductile moment-resisting frames constructed with cast-in-place concrete:
(a) the requirements of Clause 21.3.1.1(b) shall apply to segments between locations where flexural yielding is intended to occur as a result of design displacements;
(b) the factored resistance of the strong connection, S_r, shall be not less than S_p;
(c) primary longitudinal reinforcement shall be made continuous across connections and shall be developed outside both the strong connection and the plastic hinge region; and
(d) column-to-column connections shall have a factored resistance not less than $1.4S_p$. At column-to-column connections, the factored resistance shall be not less than 0.4 times the maximum probable flexural strength for the column within the storey height, and the factored shear resistance of the connection shall be not less than that determined in accordance with Clause 21.4.5.1.

21.9.2.3
Ductile moment-resisting frames constructed using precast concrete and not meeting the requirements of Clause 21.9.2.1 or 21.9.2.2 shall comply with ACI T1.1/T1.1R and the following requirements:
(a) the details and materials used for the test specimens shall be representative of those used in the structure; and
(b) the design procedure used to proportion the test specimens shall define the mechanism by which the frame resists gravity and earthquake effects and shall establish acceptance values for sustaining that mechanism. Portions of the mechanism that deviate from code requirements shall be contained in the test specimens and shall be tested to determine upper bounds for acceptance values.

21.9.3 Ductile shear walls constructed using precast concrete ($R_d = 3.5$ or 4.0)
Ductile shear walls constructed using precast concrete shall meet all of the requirements of Clause 21.6 for cast-in-place ductile shear walls and shall contain strong connections. The factored resistance of the strong connection, S_r, shall be not less than S_p.

21.9.4 Moderately ductile shear walls constructed using precast concrete ($R_d = 2.0$)

21.9.4.1
Moderately ductile shear walls constructed using precast concrete shall meet all of the requirements of Clause 21.7.3 or 21.7.4 for cast-in-place moderately ductile walls unless they are designed in accordance with Clause 23, in which case the requirements of Clause 21.7.1.2 shall apply.

21.9.4.2
In connections between wall panels, yielding shall be restricted to steel elements or reinforcement. If connections between the wall panels and the foundations are relied on for energy dissipation, the reinforcement shall be adequately anchored to both the wall panel and the foundation to develop the probable strength of reinforcement, in accordance with Clause 12.

21.9.4.3
Elements of the connection that are not designed to yield shall develop at least 150% of the specified yield strength of the yielding element.

21.10 Structural diaphragms ($R_d = 2.0, 2.5, 3.5,$ or 4.0)

21.10.1 General
Floor and roof systems acting as structural diaphragms to transmit and transfer forces induced by earthquake ground motions shall be designed in accordance with Clauses 21.10.2 to 21.10.8.

21.10.2 Design forces
Design forces for diaphragms and their connections shall comply with Article 4.1.8.15 of the *National Building Code of Canada*.

21.10.3 Diaphragm systems

21.10.3.1

A diaphragm shall be idealized as a system consisting of the following components arranged to provide a complete load path for the forces:

(a) chords proportioned to resist diaphragm moments as tensions and compression forces;

(b) collectors arranged to transfer the forces to, from, and between the vertical SFRSs; and

(c) either

    (i) shear panels to transfer forces to, from, and between the chords and collectors; or

    (ii) continuous strut-and-tie in-plane shear trusses.

21.10.3.2

Diaphragm elements shall be made effectively continuous by the provisions for force transfer at all edges and ends. Embedment, tying, and anchorage shall be provided at all edges of shear panels to transfer shears to adjacent chords, collectors, and shear panels. Collectors shall be anchored to the vertical SFRSs.

21.10.4 Reinforcement

21.10.4.1

The minimum reinforcement ratio for structural diaphragms shall comply with Clause 7.8. Reinforcement spacing in each direction in non-post-tensioned floor and roof systems shall not exceed 500 mm. Reinforcement provided for shear strength shall be continuous and shall be distributed uniformly across the shear plane.

21.10.4.2

The diameter of the bars used in diaphragm struts, ties, chords, and collector elements shall not exceed one-sixth of the minimum element dimension at the bar location.

21.10.4.3

All continuous reinforcement in struts, ties, chords, and collector elements shall be anchored or spliced as specified in Clauses 12 and 21.2.8. Anchorage and splice lengths for reinforcement not contained within confinement or buckling prevention ties shall be increased by 50%, or, for splices, laps shall be staggered with at least one lap length from the end of one lap to the start of the next.

21.10.4.4

Splices of tensile reinforcement in the chords and collector elements of diaphragms shall develop the yield strength of the reinforcement. Mechanical and welded splices shall comply with Clauses 21.2.8 and 21.2.9, respectively. Type 2 splices shall be required where mechanical splices are used to transfer forces between collectors and the vertical components of the SFRS.

21.10.4.5

Bonded prestressing tendons used as primary reinforcement in diaphragm chords or collectors shall be proportioned in such a manner that the stress due to design seismic forces does not exceed 400 MPa. Precompression from unbonded tendons shall be permitted to resist diaphragm design forces if a complete load path is provided.

21.10.5 Monolithic concrete systems

21.10.5.1

Slabs serving as shear panels shall be not less than 50 mm thick for joist and waffle systems and 100 mm for all other systems.

21.10.5.2

The factored shear strength of a shear panel shall be taken as

$$V_r = A_{cv}(0.2\phi_c\sqrt{f'_c} + \phi_s\rho_n f_y) \le 0.8\phi_c A_{cv}\sqrt{f'_c} \tag{21-20}$$

21.10.5.3

Chords, collectors, struts, and ties shall be proportioned to have compressive stresses less than $0.2f'_c$ or shall be provided with buckling prevention ties. The dimensions of the section shall provide for a minimum cover of 2-1/2 bar diameters, but not less than 50 mm for all longitudinal reinforcement, and a minimum clear spacing of three diameters, but not less than 40 mm at splices and anchorage zones.

21.10.6 Precast systems

21.10.6.1

Cast-in-place composite and non-composite toppings shall be permitted to serve as shear panels. Composite toppings shall be not less than 50 mm thick and non-composite toppings not less than 65 mm thick. The surface of the previously hardened concrete on which composite topping slabs are placed shall be clean, free of laitance, and intentionally roughened.

21.10.6.2

The factored shear strength of a shear panel shall be taken as

$$V_r = \phi_s A_{cv}\rho_n f_y \le 0.6\phi_c A_{cv}\sqrt{f'_c} \tag{21-21}$$

where A_{cv} is calculated based on the thickness of the topping slab. The required web reinforcement shall be distributed uniformly in both directions. Where welded wire fabric is used as the distributed reinforcement, the wires parallel to the span of the precast elements shall be spaced not less than 250 mm on centre.

21.10.6.3

Chords, collectors, struts, and ties shall comply with Clause 21.10.5.3.

21.10.7 Composite systems

21.10.7.1

Composite concrete toppings on steel decks may be used as shear panels. The composite toppings shall be not less than 60 mm thick above the top of the flutes.

21.10.7.2

The factored shear strength of composite toppings on steel decks may be taken from manufacturer's data, with appropriate modifications of the published data to account for the effects of reverse cyclic loading.

21.10.7.3

For decks bounded by steel beams and girders designed as full composite members with headed stud shear connectors, the shear strength of a reinforced topping slab shall be taken as

$$V_r = \phi_s A_{cv}\rho_n f_y \le 0.6\phi_c A_{cv}\sqrt{f'_c} \tag{21-22}$$

where A_{cv} is calculated based on the topping thickness above the flutes.

21.10.7.4

Chords, collectors, struts, and ties may be structural steel and/or reinforced concrete sections. Structural steel members used for this purpose shall have headed stud shear connectors designed to transfer the shear forces from the topping. Reinforced concrete sections shall comply with Clause 21.10.5.3.

21.10.8 Construction joints

All construction joints in diaphragms shall comply with Clause 6.3. Contact surfaces shall be treated as specified in Clause 11.5.

21.11 Foundations (R_d = 2.0, 2.5, 3.5, or 4.0)

21.11.1 General

21.11.1.1

Foundations resisting earthquake-induced forces or transferring earthquake-induced forces between structure and ground shall comply with Clauses 21.11.1.2 to 21.11.4.6.

21.11.1.2

The factored resistance of the foundation system and the supports of frames or walls shall be sufficient to develop the nominal moment capacity of the frames or walls and the corresponding shears. Where the factored moment resistance of any wall or frame exceeds the required factored moment, the following shall apply:

(a) the factored resistance of unanchored footings supporting those walls or frames need not exceed the maximum factored load effects determined with loads calculated using $R_d R_o$ equal to 2.0; and

(b) where frames or walls are supported by anchored footings or elements other than foundations, the factored resistance of those elements need not exceed the maximum factored load effects determined with loads calculated using $R_d R_o$ equal to 1.0.

21.11.1.3

The requirements of Clause 21.11 for piles, drilled piers, caissons, and slabs on grade shall be in addition to the requirements specified in Clause 15.

21.11.2 Footings, foundation mats, and pile caps

21.11.2.1

Longitudinal reinforcement of columns and structural walls resisting forces induced by earthquake effects shall extend into the footing, mat, or pile cap and shall be fully developed for tension at the interface.

21.11.2.2

Columns designed assuming fixed-end conditions at the foundation shall comply with Clause 21.11.2.1 and, if hooks are required, longitudinal reinforcement resisting flexure shall have 90° hooks near the bottom of the foundation, with the free end of the bars oriented toward the centre of the column.

21.11.2.3

Concentrated wall reinforcement shall extend to the bottom of the footing, mat, or pile cap and terminate with a 90° hook.

21.11.2.4

Columns or areas of concentrated wall reinforcement that have an edge within one-half of the footing depth from an edge of the footing shall have the same transverse reinforcement provided below the top of the footing as provided above the footing. This transverse reinforcement shall extend into the footing a distance not less than the smaller of the depth of the footing, mat, or pile cap or the development length in tension of the longitudinal reinforcement.

21.11.2.5

Where earthquake effects create uplift forces in columns or concentrated reinforcement of flexural walls or columns, flexural reinforcement shall be provided in the top of the footing, mat, or pile cap. Such reinforcement shall be not less than 0.001 times the gross sectional area in each direction or 120% of the required factored capacity calculated using the nominal resistance of the wall or column tension reinforcement, whichever is less.

21.11.3 Grade beams and slabs on grade

21.11.3.1

Grade beams and slabs designed to act as horizontal ties between pile caps or footings shall have continuous longitudinal reinforcement that shall be developed within or beyond the supporting column or anchored within the pile cap or footing at all discontinuities.

21.11.3.2

Grade beams not connected to a slab designed to act as horizontal ties between pile caps or footings shall be proportioned in such a manner that the smallest cross-sectional dimension shall be equal to or greater than the clear spacing between connected columns divided by 20, but need not be greater than 450 mm. Closed ties shall be provided at a spacing not exceeding one-half of the smallest cross-sectional dimension or 300 mm, whichever is smaller.

21.11.3.3

Grade beams and beams that are part of a mat foundation subject to flexure from columns that are part of the SFRS shall comply with Clause 21.3. Joints between these columns and grade beams shall comply with Clause 21.5.

21.11.3.4

Slabs on grade that resist seismic forces from walls or columns that are part of the SFRS shall be designed as structural diaphragms in accordance with Clause 21.10. The design drawings shall clearly state that the slab on grade is a structural diaphragm and part of the SFRS.

21.11.4 Piles and piers

21.11.4.1

The requirements of Clauses 21.11.4.2 to 21.11.4.6 shall apply to concrete piles and piers supporting structures designed for earthquake resistance.

21.11.4.2

Piles or piers resisting tension loads shall have continuous longitudinal reinforcement over the length resisting design tension forces. The longitudinal reinforcement shall be detailed to transfer tension forces within the pile cap to supported structural members.

21.11.4.3

Piles or piers shall have transverse reinforcement as specified in Clause 21.4.4 at the following locations:
(a) at the top of the member for at least five times the largest member's cross-sectional dimension, but not less than 2000 mm below the bottom of the pile cap;
(b) along the entire unsupported length plus the length specified in Clause 21.11.4.3(a) for piles in air, in water, or in soil incapable of providing lateral support; and
(c) within five pile diameters of the interface between soils of different strength or stiffness.

21.11.4.4

For precast concrete driven piles, the length of transverse reinforcement provided shall be sufficient to account for potential variations in the elevation of pile tips.

21.11.4.5

The slenderness effects of piles shall be considered for the portion of the piles in air, in water, or in soil incapable of providing lateral support.

21.11.4.6

Pile caps incorporating batter piles shall be designed to resist the full compressive strength of the batter piles acting as short columns.

Note: *Batter pile systems should be used with extreme caution because subsoil deformations caused by earthquake effects can cause pile loads far in excess of those due to the seismic forces in the superstructure.*

21.12 Frame members not considered part of the seismic force resisting systems (R_d = 2.0, 2.5, 3.5, or 4.0)

Note: *The intent of this Clause is to provide a minimum level of ductility and strength for all structural members subject to seismically induced deformations but not considered part of the SFRSs.*

21.12.1 General

21.12.1.1

Elements not required to resist either gravity or lateral loading shall be considered non-structural elements. These elements need not be detailed to the requirements of Clauses 21.12.1.2 to 21.12.3.3, provided that
(a) the effects of their stiffness and strength on forces and deformations in all structural elements at the design displacement are calculated;
(b) the factored capacity of the structural elements is sufficient to resist these forces and deformations; and
(c) the non-structural elements are anchored to the building in accordance with Article 4.1.8.17 of the *National Building Code of Canada.*

21.12.1.2

Unless it can be shown that factored moments in structural members will not exceed their nominal resistance when the complete structure is deformed laterally to the design displacement, these members shall be designed to accommodate lateral deflection through the formation of a plastic hinge mechanism. When the effects of design displacement are not explicitly checked, the requirements of Clauses 21.12.2.2 and 21.12.3 shall be applied.

21.12.1.3

The resistance of each structural member shall be sufficient to carry all forces due to factored gravity loads as well as the axial and shear forces induced in the member when subject to the design displacement.

21.12.2 Plastic hinges in members

21.12.2.1
Where Clause 21.12.1.2 indicates the formation of plastic hinges under the effects of factored gravity loads and the design displacement, the plastic hinge regions shall be detailed as specified in Clauses 21.12.2.2 to 21.12.2.4 to ensure adequate rotational capacity.

21.12.2.2
Where the member forces induced at 1/2.5 of the design displacement are greater than their nominal resistances, the members shall meet the following requirements:
(a) Flexural members (beams) shall meet the requirements Clauses 21.3.2 and 21.3.4, and stirrups shall be spaced not more than $d/2$ throughout the length of the member.
(b) Flexural members with factored axial loads exceeding $A_f f_c'/10$ but less than $0.35P_0$ shall meet the requirements of Clauses 21.4.4, 21.4.5, and 21.5.2.1.
(c) Flexural members with factored axial loads in excess of $0.35P_0$ shall have a nominal resistance greater than the induced member force or, where member forces are not explicitly calculated, shall not be permitted.

21.12.2.3
Where the member forces induced at 1/1.3 of the design displacement are less than their nominal resistances, the members shall be required to meet the requirements of Clauses 3 to 18 only.

21.12.2.4
Members not meeting the requirements of Clause 21.12.2.2 or 21.12.2.3 shall be detailed to the requirements of Clause 21.7.

21.12.3 Slab column connections

21.12.3.1
Where the maximum gravity load two-way shear stresses, excluding shear stresses from unbalanced moment and determined using seismic load combinations, exceed R_E times the limiting stresses in Clause 13.3.4 or 18.12.3.3, shear reinforcement shall be provided as specified in Clause 21.12.3.2, with R_E calculated as follows:

$$R_E = \left(\frac{0.005}{\delta_i} \right)^{0.85} \leq 1.0 \tag{21-23}$$

where δ_i is ≤ 0.025.

21.12.3.2
When shear reinforcement is required by Clause 21.12.3.1, the following requirements shall be satisfied:
(a) Shear reinforcement shall be provided in such a manner that the maximum gravity load two-way shear stresses, excluding shear stresses from unbalanced moment and determined using seismic load combinations, do not exceed R_E times the limiting shear resistance calculated using 50% of v_c, calculated in accordance with Clause 13.3.8.3, 13.3.9.3, or 18.12.3.3, and acting in combination with v_s, calculated in accordance with Clause 13.3.8.5.
(b) The factored shear stress resistance of the shear reinforcement, calculated in accordance with Clause 13.3.8.5, shall be not less than $0.3\sqrt{f_c'}$.
(c) The factored shear stress resistance of the shear reinforcement shall be not less than that required by Clause 13.3.
(d) Shear reinforcement shall be detailed in accordance with Clause 13.3.
(e) Shear reinforcement shall extend a minimum of $4d$ beyond the face of the column.

21.12.3.3

For post-tensioned slabs, mild steel bottom reinforcement meeting the requirements of Clause 13.10.6 shall be provided in accordance with Item (a), (b), or (c) of Clause 13.10.6.3. The minimum total prestressing steel need not satisfy the requirements of Clause 13.10.6.3(d).

22 Plain concrete

22.1 General

22.1.1

Clause 22 specifies requirements for the design of concrete members containing less reinforcement than the minimum amount specified for reinforced concrete members elsewhere in this Standard. The requirements of Clause 22 shall be limited to pedestals with $\ell_c/h \leq 3$, walls not exceeding 3 m in total height that have continuous vertical support, pad footings, spread footings, drilled piles, and slabs on grade. The requirements of Clause 22 shall be further limited to concretes with compressive strengths not less than 15 MPa.

22.1.2

Plain concrete shall not be used for structural members where ductility is required, such as for earthquake or blast resistance.

22.1.3

Plain concrete shall not be used for pile caps.

22.1.4

Plain concrete shall not be used for members relied on to transmit tension force.

22.2 Control joints

22.2.1

In plain concrete construction, control joints shall be provided to divide a structural member into discontinuous elements. The size of each element shall be limited to control stresses caused by restraint to movements from creep, shrinkage, temperature effects, and differential settlement.

22.2.2

In determining the number and location of control joints, consideration shall be given to the influence of climatic conditions; selection and proportioning of materials; mixing, placing, and curing of concrete; the degree of restraint to movement; and stresses due to load.

22.2.3

The locations and details of control joints shall be indicated on the drawings or in the specifications.

22.2.4

Concrete placement shall be interrupted only at control joints.

22.3 Design

22.3.1
The strength design of plain concrete members for factored flexural and axial loads shall be based on a linear stress-strain relationship in both tension and compression.

22.3.2
The flexural tensile strength of concrete may be considered in the design.

22.3.3
No strength shall be assigned to reinforcement that might be present.

22.3.4
The bearing stress on the concrete at the contact surface between supporting and supported members shall not exceed the permissible bearing stress for each surface as specified in Clause 10.8.

22.3.5
The entire cross-section of a member shall be considered in the design, except for footings cast against soil (see Clause 22.6.3).

22.4 Walls

22.4.1

22.4.1.1
The effective length factor, k, for walls braced at the top and bottom against lateral translation shall be as follows:

If restrained against rotation at one or both ends (top, bottom, or both)	0.8
If unrestrained against rotation at both ends	1.0

22.4.1.2
Except as specified in Clause 22.4.1.3, walls subject to combined flexure and axial load shall be proportioned so that the maximum compressive stress under factored loads is limited to

$$0.75\phi_c f_c' \left[1 - \left(\frac{k\ell_c}{32t} \right)^2 \right]$$

and the maximum tensile stress shall not exceed $0.37\lambda\phi_c\sqrt{f_c'}$. The minimum eccentricity shall be 0.1t.

22.4.1.3
Plain concrete walls of solid rectangular cross-section may be designed in accordance with the following equation if the resultant of all factored loads, including the effects of lateral loads applied to the wall, is located within the middle third of the overall thickness of the wall:

$$P_r = 0.37\phi_c f_c' A_g \left(1 - \left(\frac{k\ell_c}{32t} \right)^2 \right) \qquad \text{(22-1)}$$

22.4.2
The horizontal length of wall to be considered effective for each concentrated load or reaction shall not exceed the centre-to-centre distance between loads or the width of bearing plus four times the wall thickness.

22.4.3
Plain concrete bearing walls shall have a thickness of not less than 1/20 of the unsupported height or length, whichever is shorter.

22.4.4
Foundation walls and exterior basement walls shall be not less than 190 mm thick.

22.4.5
Walls shall be braced against lateral translation and keyed or dowelled to other intersecting members as required for lateral stability.

22.4.6
Not less than two 15M bars shall be provided around all window and door openings. Such bars shall extend at least 600 mm beyond the corners of the openings.

22.5 Pedestals
Pedestals subject to combined flexural and axial load shall be proportioned so that the maximum compression stress under factored loads does not exceed $0.75\phi_c f_c'$ and the maximum tension stress does not exceed $0.37\lambda\phi_c\sqrt{f_c'}$. The minimum eccentricity shall be $0.1h$.

22.6 Footings

22.6.1 Base area of footing
The base area of the footing shall be determined from forces and moments transmitted by the footing to the soil. The soil pressure shall be selected in accordance with the principles of soil mechanics.
Note: *See the* National Building Code of Canada *for information on limit states design of foundations.*

22.6.2 Minimum thickness
The specified thickness of plain concrete footings shall be not less than 200 mm.

22.6.3 Minimum thickness for calculations
For footings cast against soil, the overall thickness, h, used in calculations shall be taken as 50 mm less than the specified thickness.

22.6.4 Critical sections

22.6.4.1
The critical sections for moment and shear shall be as specified in Clause 15.4.3.

22.6.4.2
For the location of critical sections for moment and shear, circular or regular polygonal concrete columns or pedestals may be treated as square members with the same area.

22.6.5 Strength in bending

The factored resistance in bending shall be based on a maximum stress in tension of $0.37\lambda\phi_c\sqrt{f'_c}$ and a maximum stress in compression of $0.75\phi_c f'_c$.

22.6.6 Shear resistance

22.6.6.1 One-way action

22.6.6.1.1

The maximum factored shear, V_f, shall be computed at a distance h from the face of the support. Sections located closer to the support may be designed for the same shear.

22.6.6.1.2

The factored shear resistance for rectangular sections, V_r, shall be

$$V_r = \frac{2}{3}(0.18\lambda\phi_c\sqrt{f'_c}\,bh)$$

(22-2)

22.6.6.2 Two-way shear

22.6.6.2.1

The maximum factored shear, V_f, shall be computed at a critical section perpendicular to the plane of the footing and located so that its perimeter, b_o, is a minimum, but not closer than $h/2$ to the perimeter of the concentrated load or reaction area.

22.6.6.2.2

The factored shear resistance, V_r, shall be

$$V_r = \frac{2}{3}\left(\left(1+\frac{2}{\beta_c}\right)0.18\,\lambda\phi_c\sqrt{f'_c}\,b_o h\right)$$

(22-3)

but

$$V_r \leq \frac{2}{3}(0.37\,\lambda\phi_c\sqrt{f'_c}\,b_o h)$$

(22-4)

22.7 Slabs on grade

Plain concrete slabs shall be designed with due regard to loading and foundation conditions.
Note: *For information on the design of slabs on grade, see ACI 360R.*

22.8 Drilled piles

22.8.1

In addition to meeting the design eccentricity requirement specified in Clause 15.2, the cross-sections of uncased drilled piles shall be designed for a minimum eccentricity of $0.1d_p$.

22.8.2

The outer 25 mm layer of uncased drilled piles shall be neglected when the pile resistance and the stresses in the pile shaft due to factored loads are determined.

22.8.3

For uncased drilled piles, a reduction factor of 0.8 shall be applied to the maximum factored stresses specified in Clause 22.8.5.

22.8.4
The stability of portions of piles without lateral restraint from soil shall be considered.

22.8.5
Drilled piles subjected to combined factored bending moments, shears, and compression loads shall be proportioned so that stresses do not exceed the following limits:
(a) flexure and axial loads:
  (i) extreme fibre stress in compression:

$$0.75\phi_c f'_c \left[1-\left(\frac{k\ell_c}{28d_p}\right)^2\right]$$

  (ii) extreme fibre stress in tension:

$$0.37\lambda\phi_c\sqrt{f'_c}$$

(b) shear:

$$V_r = \frac{3}{4}(0.18\lambda\phi_c\sqrt{f'_c})$$ (22-5)

22.8.6
For proportioning of the pile bell, see Clause 15.8.2.4.

23 Tilt-up wall panels

23.1 General

23.1.1
The requirements of Clauses 23.1.2 to 23.7.2 shall apply to tilt-up wall panels.

23.1.2
The requirements of Clauses 3 to 15 and 21 shall apply to tilt-up wall panels, except as modified by the requirements of Clauses 23.1.1 and 23.1.3 to 23.7.2.

23.1.3
Tilt-up panels are slender vertical flexural slabs that resist lateral wind or seismic loads and are subject to very low axial stresses. Because of their high slenderness ratios, they shall be designed for second-order P-Δ effects to ensure structural stability and satisfactory performance under specified loads.

23.2 Design requirements

23.2.1 Effective panel height
The effective panel height, ℓ, shall be the centre-to-centre distance between lateral supports.

23.2.2 Minimum panel thickness
The minimum panel thickness for a prismatic load-bearing panel without stiffening elements shall be 140 mm.

23.2.3 Maximum height-to-thickness ratio

The maximum effective panel height-to-thickness ratio shall be
(a) 50 for panels with a single mat of reinforcement at mid-depth; or
(b) 65 for panels with a mat of reinforcement near each face.

23.2.4 Minimum reinforcement

Minimum panel reinforcement shall comply with Clauses 10.5, 14.1.8, and 21.7.3.3, as applicable.

23.2.5 Concrete cover and tolerances

23.2.5.1

If quality control procedures are followed so that the designer can be assured that the tilt-up contractor meets the requirements in CSA A23.4 with respect to dimensional control, reinforcement placement, aggregate size, concrete quality, and curing, the cover requirements specified in CSA A23.4 may be used, except as required by Clause 23.2.5.2. Otherwise, the design shall comply with CSA A23.1.

23.2.5.2

The cover and quality of concrete in tilt-up panels that have to withstand the effects of aggressive or corrosive environments shall comply with CSA A23.1.

23.2.5.3

Tilt-up panels requiring a fire resistance rating or forming part of a firewall shall meet the thickness and cover requirements of the applicable building codes.

23.2.6 Thermal effects

The design of tilt-up panels shall take into account the effects of any thermal gradients that could occur through the panel.

23.2.7 Sandwich panels

Sandwich wall panels, in addition to resisting applied loads, shall be designed to resist effects such as composite or non-composite action between wythes, thermal effects between wythes where composite action is assumed, thermal bridging, lifting stresses imposed on one wythe by the other, and vertical and torsional support of one wythe by the other.

23.2.8 Connections

23.2.8.1

The design of connections shall take into account in-plane and out-of-plane forces; the additional effects of shrinkage, creep, temperature, and movement; and the applicable requirements of Clause 21.

23.2.8.2

The resistances of connections between the tilt-up panels and any adjoining elements shall be greater than the effects of factored loads.

23.2.9 Structural integrity

23.2.9.1

Tension ties shall be provided in the transverse and longitudinal directions of the structure and around the perimeter of the structure to effectively tie the elements together.

23.2.9.2
Panels shall have connections top and bottom to resist a minimum factored force of 5 kN/m perpendicular to the panel.

23.2.10 Effective reinforcement
Where vertical reinforcement is placed in two layers, the effect of compression reinforcement shall be ignored.

23.3 Analysis and design

23.3.1 Flexure and axial load interaction and slenderness effects

23.3.1.1
All moment and deflection calculations specified in Clauses 23.3.1.2 to 23.3.2 are based on simple support conditions top and bottom. For other support and fixity conditions, moments and deflections shall be calculated using established principles of structural mechanics.

23.3.1.2
In lieu of a more accurate analysis, the procedures specified in Clauses 23.3.1.3 to 23.3.1.5 shall be used when the stress due to factored vertical loads at the cross-section under consideration meets the following requirement:

$$\frac{P_{wf} + P_{tf}}{A_g} < 0.09\phi_c f'_c \tag{23-1}$$

23.3.1.3
The factored moment, M_f, shall be determined at the mid-height of the panel and shall be equal to

$$M_f = M_b \delta_b \tag{23-2}$$

where

$$M_b = \frac{w_f \ell^2}{8} + P_{tf}\frac{e}{2} + (P_{wf} + P_{tf})\Delta_o$$

$$\delta_b = \frac{1}{1 - \dfrac{P_f}{\phi_m K_{bf}}} \geq 1.0$$

where
$$P_f = P_{wf} + P_{tf}$$

$$K_{bf} = \frac{48 E_c I_{cr}}{5\ell^2}$$

where
$$I_{cr} = \frac{bc^3}{3} + \frac{E_s}{E_c} A_s (d - c)^2$$

and the member resistance factor, ϕ_m, is taken as 0.75.

23.3.1.4

The initial out-of-straightness, Δ_o, at mid-height of the panel shall take into account the effects of non-planar and flexible casting beds, deformations caused by the tilting process, thermal gradients through the panel, and creep, and shall not be taken less than $\ell/400$.

23.3.1.5

The factored resisting moment, M_r, provided by the panel cross-section shall be such that

$$M_r \geq M_f \tag{23-3}$$

The resisting moment may be calculated using an effective area of reinforcement, $A_{s,eff}$, as follows:

$$A_{s,eff} = \frac{\phi_s A_s f_y + P_f}{\phi_s f_y} \tag{23-4}$$

23.3.2 Deflection limitations

Unless serviceability requirements lead to the conclusion that a larger deflection is acceptable, the horizontal mid-height deflection, Δ_s, under specified lateral and vertical loads shall not exceed $\ell/100$, but it shall not be greater than can be tolerated by attached structural or non-structural elements. The horizontal mid-height deflection may be computed as follows:

$$\Delta_s = \frac{5M_s \ell^2}{48 E_c I_e} = \frac{M_s}{K_{bs}} \tag{23-5}$$

where
$$M_s = M_{bs} \delta_{bs}$$

where

$$M_{bs} = \frac{w_s \ell^2}{8} + P_{ts}\frac{e}{2} + (P_{ws} + P_{ts})\Delta_o$$

$$\delta_{bs} = \frac{1}{1 - \dfrac{P_s}{K_{bs}}} \geq 1.0$$

where
$$P_s = P_{ws} + P_{ts}$$

$$K_{bs} = \frac{48 E_c I_e}{5\ell^2}$$

and where I_e is as specified in Clause 9.8.2.3, substituting M_s for M_a.
Note: *Because I_e depends on M_s, iteration is necessary.*

23.4 Effects of openings

23.4.1 Design width

23.4.1.1

A design width on each side of an opening shall support the combined factored axial and lateral loads from its tributary width. This design width shall be used over the full height of the panel.

23.4.1.2

The design width shall be limited to

(a) 12 times the thickness of a solid panel; or

(b) 12 times the thickness of the structural wythe of a sandwich panel.

23.4.2 Tributary width

The tributary width for design shall be the design width plus one-half the width of adjacent openings (see Figure 23.1).

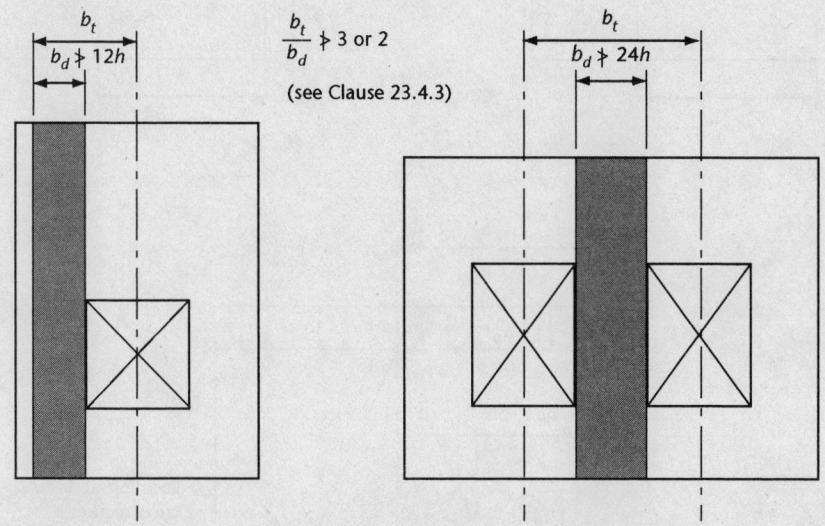

**Figure 23.1
Effect of openings on design width, b_d**
(See Clause 23.4.2.)

23.4.3 Ratio of tributary width to design width

Unless a more detailed analysis, accounting for the internal force effects, indicates otherwise, the ratio of tributary width to design width shall not exceed 3. For panels with a single layer of reinforcement and $\ell/h > 40$, the ratio shall not exceed 2.

23.5 Concentrated loads or reactions

23.5.1 Design width

The design width, b_d, for a panel subjected to concentrated loads or concentrated reactions shall be determined from Figure 23.2.

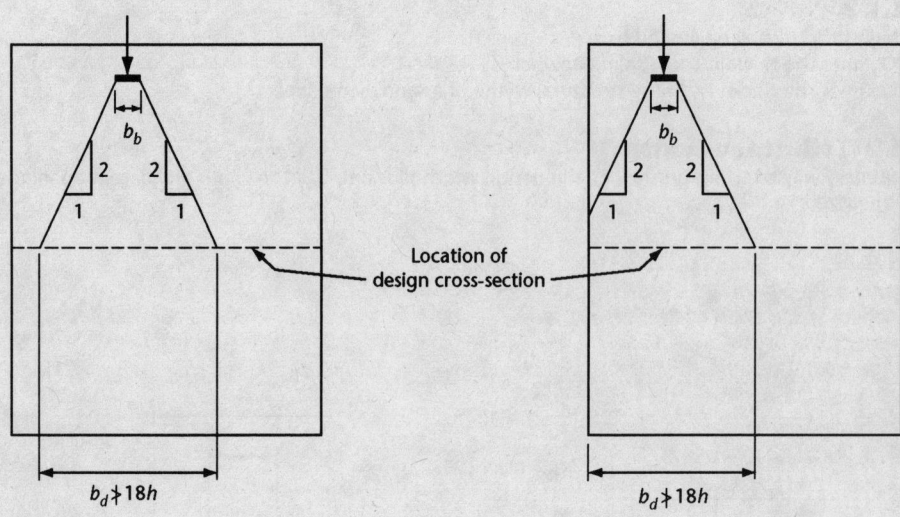

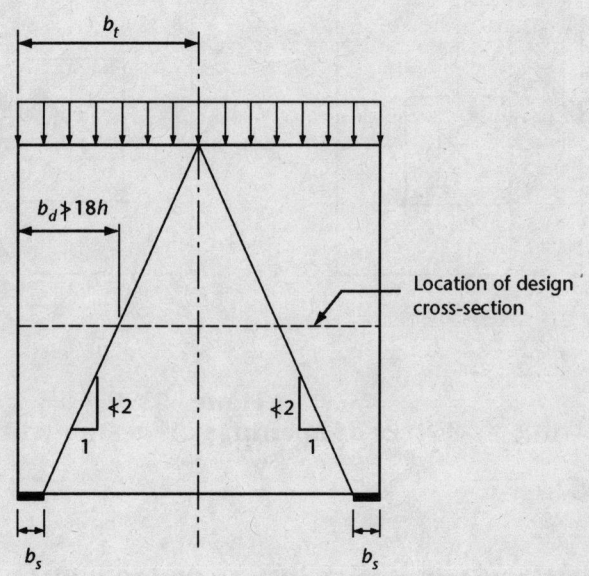

Figure 23.2
Effect of concentrated loads or reactions on design width, b_d
(See Clauses 2.3, 23.5.1, and 23.5.4.)

23.5.2 Bearing

The allowable bearing stress at the contact surface between supported and supporting elements and between any intermediate bearing elements shall not exceed the bearing resistance of either element, as specified in Clause 10.8 or 11.4.4.

23.5.3 Lateral and vertical components

The design of connections to panels for concentrated loads or reactions shall take into account lateral and vertical components in accordance with Clause 11.6.4.

23.5.4 Tributary width for vertical and lateral loads

For panels with concentrated vertical and lateral reactions at the bottom of the panel, the tributary width assumed for vertical and lateral loading shown in Figure 23.2 and the total factored axial load and moment shall be carried only by the design width. For panels with continuous lateral support at the top and bottom of the panel, the factored moment at the design cross-section shall be assumed to be uniformly distributed across the full panel width.

23.5.5 Concentrated loads or reactions

Panels subjected to concentrated loads or reactions shall be designed in accordance with Clause 11.4.

23.6 Shear

23.6.1 In-plane shear

23.6.1.1

Where tilt-up panels are used as shear walls, analysis of the panels shall include the effects of in-plane stresses, local buckling, roof diaphragm connections, and panel stability. The connections between panels shall be designed to provide nominal ductility.

23.6.1.2

The design for factored shear forces in the plane of the panel shall meet the requirements of Clause 11.3.

23.6.2 Out-of-plane shear

The design for shear forces due to loads acting perpendicular to the face of the panel shall meet the requirements of Clause 11.3.

23.7 Lifting stresses

23.7.1 General

The stresses imposed on a panel during lifting shall be limited to ensure that the performance of the erected panel is not impaired.

23.7.2 Elastic — Uncracked analysis

Analysis of tilt-up panels during the lifting operation shall be based on elastic uncracked section properties using specified loads. The effects of suction between the panel and the floor and impact loads from crane equipment shall be considered.

Annex A (informative)
Excerpts from CSA A23.1-04, Concrete materials and methods of concrete construction

Notes:
(1) *This Annex is not a mandatory part of this Standard.*
(2) *A number of clauses from CSA A23.1 that are especially important to design engineers are reprinted in this Annex with their original numbering. It is expected that CSA A23.1 will be revised during the life of this Standard, resulting in minor changes to or renumbering of clauses. If this occurs, users should refer to the revised Standard. Users should also check CSA A23.4 and CAN/CSA-S413 to determine whether the requirements of those two Standards affect the applicability of the clauses reprinted in this Annex.*
(3) *This Annex reprints only those portions of Clause 2 of CSA A23.1 applicable to the other clauses reprinted in this Annex.*

2 Reference publications
This Standard and CSA A23.2 refer to the following publications, and where such reference is made, it shall be to the edition listed below, including all amendments published thereto.

CSA (Canadian Standards Association)
A23.3-94 (R2000)
Design of Concrete Structures

CAN/CSA-S6-00
Canadian Highway Bridge Design Code

CAN/CSA-S413-94 (R2000)
Parking Structures

S478-95 (R2001)
Guideline on Durability in Buildings

S806-02
Design and Construction of Building Components with Fibre-Reinforced Polymers

W59-03
Welded Steel Construction (Metal-Arc Welding)

W186-M1990 (R2002)
Welding of Reinforcing Bars in Reinforced Concrete Construction

ANSI/AWS (American National Standards Institute/American Welding Society)
D1.1:2004
Structural Welding Code — Steel

NRCC (National Research Council Canada)
National Building Code of Canada, 1995

PCA (Portland Cement Association)
IS001.08T, 2001
Effects of Substances on Concrete and Guide to Protective Treatments

4 Materials and concrete properties

4.1 Requirements for concrete and alternative methods for specifying concrete

4.1.1 Durability requirements

4.1.1.1 General

4.1.1.1.1
Concrete that will be subjected in service to weathering, sulphate attack, a corrosive environment, or any other process of deterioration covered by this Standard shall meet the requirements of Clauses 4.1.1.1 to 4.1.1.9 and 7.4, and Tables 1 to 4 and 20 as appropriate.

6.6 Fabrication and placement of reinforcement

6.6.1 General
The sizes and spacing of the reinforcement and its concrete cover shall be as shown on the construction drawings.

6.6.2 Hooks and bends

6.6.2.1 General
Unless otherwise stated on the construction drawings, fabrication and detailing of hooks shall be as specified in Clauses 6.6.2.2 to 6.6.2.5.

6.6.2.2 Standard hooks
The term "standard hook" as used herein shall mean
(a) a semicircular bend plus an extension of at least four bar diameters but not less than 60 mm at the free end of the bar;
(b) a 90° bend plus an extension of at least 12 bar diameters at the free end of the bar; or
(c) for stirrup and tie anchorage only, either a 90° or 135° bend plus an extension of at least six bar diameters but not less than 60 mm at the free end of the bar. Hooks for stirrups or ties shall have a 135° bend, unless the concrete surrounding the hook is restrained from spalling. (See CSA A23.3.)

6.6.2.3 Minimum bend diameter
The diameter of the bend measured on the inside of the bar for standard hooks, except stirrup and tie hooks, shall be not less than the values set out in Table 16.

6.6.2.4 Stirrup and tie hooks

6.6.2.4.1
The inside diameter of bends and 90° hooks for stirrups and ties shall be not less than four bar diameters.

6.6.2.4.2
The inside diameter of 135° hooks shall be not less than 20 mm, four bar diameters, or the diameter of the bar enclosed by the hook, whichever is the greatest.

6.6.2.4.3
The inside diameter of bends in welded wire fabric for stirrups or ties shall be not less than four wire diameters. Bends with an inside diameter less than eight wire diameters shall be not less than four wire diameters from the nearest welded intersection.

6.6.2.5 Bending

6.6.2.5.1
All bars shall be bent at temperatures between 10 °C and 100 °C, unless otherwise permitted by the owner.

6.6.2.5.2
No bars partially embedded in concrete shall be field bent except as shown on the drawings or as permitted by the owner.

6.6.2.5.3
The bending tolerances shall be sufficiently accurate to comply with the placing and protection tolerances stipulated in Clause 6.6.7.

6.6.3 Spirals

6.6.3.1
The size and spacing of spirals shall be as shown on the construction drawings.

6.6.3.5
Anchorage of spiral reinforcement shall be provided by 1-1/2 extra turns of spiral rod or wire at each end of the spiral unit.

6.6.3.6
Splices in spirals shall have a minimum 50 bar diameter lap plus a 90° hook around a longitudinal bar at the free end or shall be welded in accordance with CSA W186.

6.6.3.7
The reinforcing spiral shall extend from the floor level in any storey or from the top of the footing to the level of the lowest horizontal reinforcement in the slab, drop panel, or beam above.

6.6.3.8
Where beams or brackets are not present on all sides of a column, ties shall extend above the termination of the spiral to the bottom of the slab or drop panel.

6.6.3.9
In a column with a capital, the spiral shall extend to a plane at which the diameter or width of the capital is twice that of the column.

6.6.4 Ties

6.6.4.1
The size, spacing, and arrangement of ties shall be as shown on the construction drawings. When welded wire mesh of random length is used as tie reinforcement, the required splice length shall be indicated on the drawings.

6.6.5 Spacing of reinforcement

6.6.5.1
The spacing of bars shall be as shown on the construction drawings.

6.6.5.2
The clear distance between parallel bars or parallel bundles of bars shall be not less than 1.4 times the bar diameter, not less than 1.4 times the nominal maximum size of the coarse aggregate, and not less than 30 mm. This clear distance shall apply to the distance between a contact lap splice and adjacent splices or bars.

6.6.5.3
Where parallel reinforcement is placed in two or more layers, the bars in the upper layer shall be placed directly above those in the bottom layer.

6.6.5.6
Spacing of post-tensioning ducts shall be as specified in Clause 6.8.

6.6.6 Concrete cover

6.6.6.1 General
Concrete cover shall be measured from the concrete surface to the nearest deformation (or surface, for smooth bars or wires) of the reinforcement. Reinforcement includes ties, stirrups, and main reinforcement. For textured architectural surfaces, concrete cover shall be measured from the deepest point of the textured surface.

6.6.6.2 Specified cover for reinforced and prestressed concrete

6.6.6.2.1
The specified cover for reinforcement shall be based on consideration of life expectancy, exposure conditions, protective systems, maintenance, and the consequences of corrosion.
Notes:
(1) *The desired service life should be established early in the design process. See CSA S478.*
(2) *Requirements for corrosion protection can be influenced by the ease of access for inspection and repair and the feasibility and cost of repair or replacement.*
(3) *Service life can be improved by*
    (a) increasing the cover and the duration of moist curing;
    (b) reducing the water-to-cementing materials ratio;
    (c) adding supplementary cementing materials, corrosion inhibitors, or membranes; and
    (d) improving drainage.
(4) *As the positioning of reinforcement is not exact, in some cases it is advisable to increase the specified cover to ensure adequate protection. Service life can be extended by reducing the variability in placement of reinforcement.*

6.6.6.2.2
The specified cover for fibre-reinforced polymer bars, grids, and tendons in prestressed and reinforced concrete shall be in accordance with CSA S806.

6.6.6.2.3
The specified cover for steel reinforcement, tendon sheaths, and ducts in prestressed and reinforced concrete shall be not less than the larger of the values in Table 17.
Note: *See Clause 6.6.8 for tolerances of concrete cover and Clauses 6.8.2.4 and 6.8.2.13 for additional cover requirements for prestressing elements.*

6.6.6.3 Cover for fire resistance

Where a structural concrete member is required to have a fire-resistant rating, the minimum cover for reinforcement shall be specified by the owner.

Note: *Information can be found in the NRCC* National Building Code of Canada, *Annex D.*

6.6.8 Tolerances for location of reinforcement

Unless otherwise specified by the owner, reinforcement, prestressing steel, and post-tensioning ducts shall be placed within the following tolerances:
(a) concrete cover: ±12 mm (but the concrete cover shall in no case be reduced by more than 1/3 of the specified cover);
(b) where the depth of a flexural member, the thickness of a wall, or the smallest dimension of a column is
    (i)   200 mm or less: ±8 mm;
    (ii) larger than 200 mm but less than 600 mm: ±12 mm; and
    (iii) 600 mm or larger: ±20 mm;
(c) lateral spacing of bars: ±30 mm;
(d) longitudinal location of bends and ends of bars: ±50 mm; and
(e) longitudinal location of bends and ends of bars at discontinuous ends of members: ±20 mm.

Note: *Where reinforcement is added to help provide a more rigid reinforcing mat or cage, as for instance in prefabricated reinforcing cages, such additional reinforcement is not subject to the tolerances of this Clause, except for the minimum cover requirements.*

6.6.10 Welding of reinforcement

6.6.10.1

Welding of reinforcement shall conform to the requirements of CSA W186.

6.6.10.2

Tack welding of reinforcing bars shall be performed in accordance with CSA W186.

6.7 Fabrication and placement of hardware and other embedded items

6.7.1 General

Clause 6.7 covers the fabrication and placement of hardware for concrete building structures that have been designed in accordance with CSA A23.3. The details and location of this hardware shall be shown on the construction drawings.

Note: *For reinforced concrete structures other than buildings, the owner should show clearly on the drawings and specifications any departures from the requirements of Clauses 6.7.2 to 6.7.5.*

6.7.3 Tolerances for placing anchor bolts and hardware

6.7.3.1

Unless otherwise specified by the owner, the location of anchor bolts and embedded items shall not vary from the dimensions shown on the erection drawings by more than the following (see also Figure 3):
(a) 3 mm centre-to-centre of any two bolts within an anchor bolt group, where an anchor bolt group is defined as the set of anchor bolts that receives a single fabricated steel or precast concrete member;
(b) 8 mm centre-to-centre of adjacent anchor bolt groups;
(c) a maximum accumulation of 8 mm per 30 m along the established column line of multiple anchor bolt groups, but not to exceed a total of 30 mm. The established column line is the actual field line most representative of the centres of the as-built anchor bolt groups along a line of columns; and
(d) 8 mm from the centre of any anchor bolt group to the established column line through that group.
   The tolerances of Items (b), (c), and (d) apply to offset dimensions, as shown on the construction drawings and measured perpendicular to the nearest column line.

CSA Standard A23.3-04

6.7.3.2
Vertical alignment variations for anchor bolts shall not exceed 3 mm or 1 mm in 40 mm, whichever is larger.

6.7.3.3
Slope variations for hardware serving as bearing plates shall not exceed 1 mm in 40 mm, with a maximum of 3 mm for plates having side dimensions less than 300 mm, and a maximum of 5 mm for plates having side dimensions of 300 mm or larger.

6.7.4 Welding of hardware

6.7.4.1
Welding of steel hardware shall conform to the requirements of CSA W59.
Note: *Welding procedures should be such that no damage to the concrete will result.*

6.7.4.2
Welding of reinforcing bars to hardware shall conform to the requirements of CSA W186.

6.7.4.3
Material and equipment for stud welding of bars and anchors shall be compatible and shall be used in accordance with the recommendations of the manufacturers of the material and equipment.
Note: *See the Supplement to ANSI/AWS D1.1.*

6.8 Post-tensioning

6.8.2 Unbonded tendons

6.8.2.4.1
In corrosive environments, the concrete cover to the sheath shall be not less than 50 mm.

6.8.2.4.2
The concrete cover to the anchorage measured in a direction perpendicular to the tendon shall be not less than 40 mm.

Table 1
Definitions of C, F, N, A, and S classes of exposure
(See Clauses 4.1.1.1.1, 4.1.1.5, 4.4.4.1.1.1, 4.4.4.1.1.2, 6.6.7.5.1, and 8.4.1.2,
and Table 2 [of CSA A23.1].)

C-XL	Structurally reinforced concrete exposed to chlorides or other severe environments with or without freezing and thawing conditions, with higher durability performance expectations than the C-1, A-1, or S-1 classes.
C-1	Structurally reinforced concrete exposed to chlorides with or without freezing and thawing conditions. Examples: bridge decks, parking decks and ramps, portions of marine structures located within the tidal and splash zones, concrete exposed to seawater spray, and salt water pools.
C-2	Non-structurally reinforced (i.e., plain) concrete exposed to chlorides and freezing and thawing. Examples: garage floors, porches, steps, pavements, sidewalks, curbs, and gutters.
C-3	Continuously submerged concrete exposed to chlorides but not to freezing and thawing. Examples: underwater portions of marine structures.
C-4	Non-structurally reinforced concrete exposed to chlorides but not to freezing and thawing. Examples: underground parking slabs on grade.
F-1	Concrete exposed to freezing and thawing in a saturated condition but not to chlorides. Examples: pool decks, patios, tennis courts, freshwater pools, and freshwater control structures.
F-2	Concrete in an unsaturated condition exposed to freezing and thawing but not to chlorides. Examples: exterior walls and columns.
N	Concrete not exposed to chlorides nor to freezing and thawing. Examples: footings and interior slabs, walls, and columns.
A-1	Structurally reinforced concrete exposed to severe manure and/or silage gases, with or without freeze-thaw exposure. Concrete exposed to the vapour above municipal sewage or industrial effluent, where hydrogen sulphide gas may be generated. Examples: reinforced beams, slabs, and columns over manure pits and silos, canals, and pig slats; and access holes, enclosed chambers, and pipes that are partially filled with effluents.
A-2	Structurally reinforced concrete exposed to moderate to severe manure and/or silage gases and liquids, with or without freeze-thaw exposure. Examples: reinforced walls in exterior manure tanks, silos, and feed bunkers, and exterior slabs.
A-3	Structurally reinforced concrete exposed to moderate to severe manure and/or silage gases and liquids, with or without freeze-thaw exposure in a continuously submerged condition. Concrete continuously submerged in municipal or industrial effluents. Examples: interior gutter walls, beams, slabs, and columns; sewage pipes that are continuously full (e.g., forcemains); and submerged portions of sewage treatment structures.
A-4	Non-structurally reinforced concrete exposed to moderate manure and/or silage gases and liquids, without freeze-thaw exposure. Examples: interior slabs on grade.
S-1	Concrete subjected to very severe sulphate exposures (Tables 2 and 3).
S-2	Concrete subjected to severe sulphate exposure (Tables 2 and 3).
S-3	Concrete subjected to moderate sulphate exposure (Tables 2 and 3).

Notes:
(1) *"C" classes pertain to chloride exposure.*
(2) *"F" classes pertain to freezing and thawing exposure without chlorides.*
(3) *"N" class is exposed to neither chlorides nor freezing and thawing.*
(4) *All classes of concrete shall comply with the minimum requirements of "S" class noted in Tables 2 and 3.*

Table 16
Bend diameter for standard hooks
(See Clause 6.6.2.3 [of CSA A23.1].)

Bar size	Minimum bend diameter,* mm		
	Steel grade		
	300 R	400 R or 500 R	400 W or 500 W
10	60	70	60
15	90	100	90
20	—	120	100
25	—	150	150
30	—	250	200
35	—	300	250
45	—	450†	400
55	—	600†	550

*Bend diameters shall not be reduced by more than 10% from those listed unless otherwise permitted by the owner.

†Special fabrication is required for bends exceeding 90° for bars of these sizes and grades.

Table 17
Concrete cover
(See Clauses 4.3.2.2.1 and 6.6.6.2.3 [of CSA A23.1].)

Exposure condition	Exposure class (see Tables 1 and 2)		
	N*	F-1, F-2, S-1, S-2	C-XL, C-1, C-3, A-1, A-2, A-3
Cast against and permanently exposed to earth	—	75 mm	75 mm
Beams, girders, columns, and piles	30 mm	40 mm	60 mm
Slabs, walls, joists, shells, and folded plates	20 mm	40 mm	60 mm
Ratio of cover to nominal bar diameter†	1.0	1.5	2.0
Ratio of cover to nominal maximum aggregate size	1.0‡	1.5	2.0

*This refers only to concrete that will be continually dry within the conditioned space, i.e., members entirely within the vapour barrier of the building envelope.

†The cover for a bundle of bars shall be the same as that for a single bar with an equivalent area.

‡The specified cover from screeded surfaces shall be at least 1.5 times the nominal maximum aggregate size to reduce interference between aggregate and reinforcement where variations in bar placement result in a cover smaller than specified.

Notes:

(1) Greater cover or protective coatings may be required for exposure to industrial chemicals, food processing, and other corrosive materials. See PCA IS001.08T.

(2) For information on the additional protective measures and requirements for parking structures, see CAN/CSA-S413.

(3) For information on the additional protective measures and requirements for bridges, see CAN/CSA-S6.

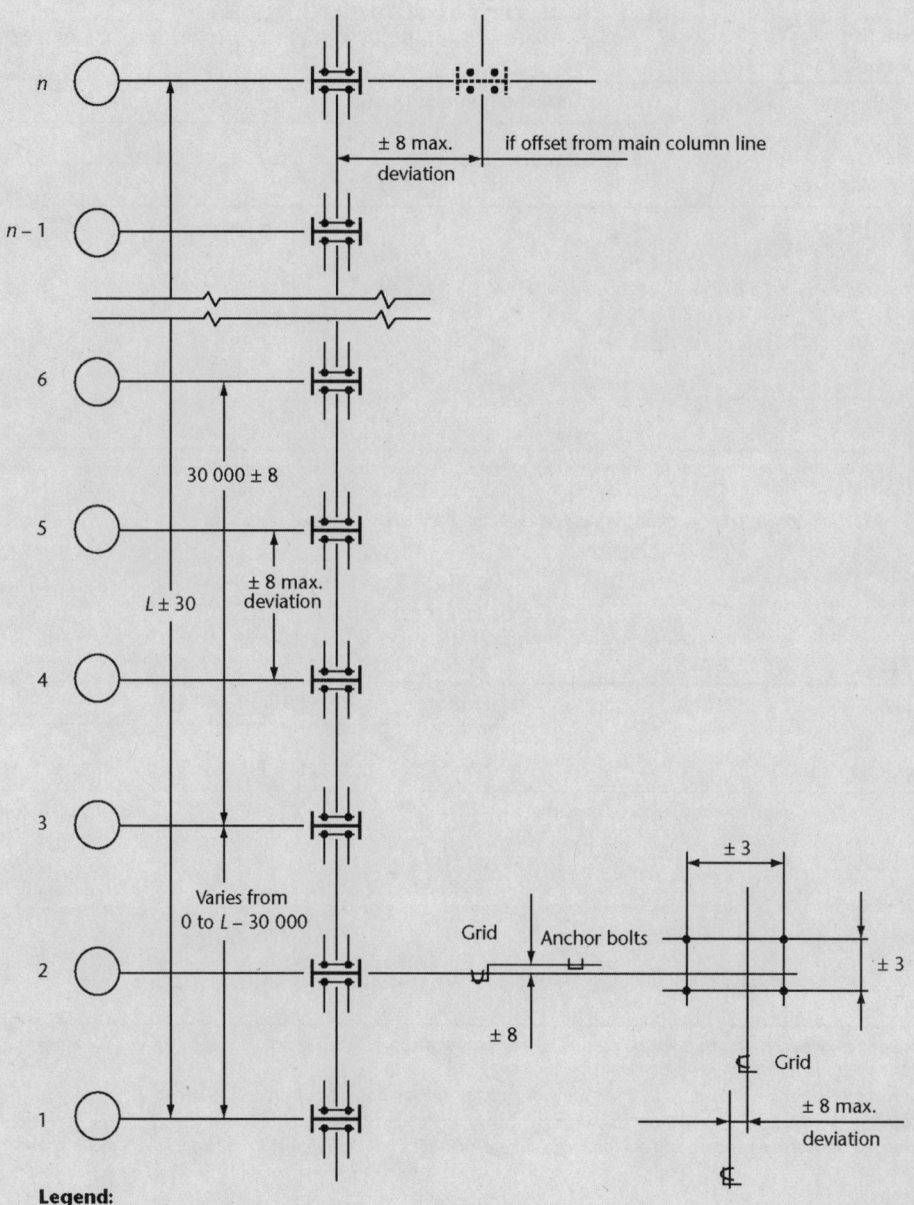

Legend:
n = total number of columns
L = specified length between outermost anchor bolts

Figure 3
Tolerances on anchor bolt placement
(See Clause 6.7.3.1 [of CSA A23.1].)

Annex B (informative)
Rectangular two-way slab systems with stiff supports on four sides

Note: *This Annex is not a mandatory part of this Standard.*

B.1 Introduction

B.1.1

This Annex applies to rectangular two-way systems where the slab is reinforced in two directions and supported on four sides by walls or stiff beams. It may be used to determine slab thicknesses and loads on supporting beams or walls and to determine the moments and shears in slabs.

B.1.2

In this Annex, a stiff supporting beam is one in which $b_w h_b^3 / \ell_n h_s^3$ is not less than 2.0.

B.2 Symbols

The following symbols apply in this Annex:

b_w	=	width of beam web
C_{ad}	=	moment coefficient for positive dead load moment in short span
C_{al}	=	moment coefficient for positive live load moment in short span
$C_a neg$	=	moment coefficient for negative moment in short span
C_{bd}	=	moment coefficient for positive dead load moment in long span
C_{bl}	=	moment coefficient for positive live load moment in long span
$C_b neg$	=	moment coefficient for negative moment in long span
h_b	=	overall depth of supporting beam
h_s	=	overall depth of slab
ℓ_a	=	clear span of a two-way slab in the short direction
ℓ_b	=	clear span of a two-way slab in the long direction
ℓ_n	=	clear span of supporting beam
m	=	ratio of short to long span of a two-way slab, equal to ℓ_a / ℓ_b
$M_{ad}pos$	=	positive dead load moment in short span
$M_{ai}pos$	=	positive live load moment in short span
$M_a neg$	=	negative moment in short span
$M_{bd}pos$	=	positive dead load moment in long span
$M_{bi}pos$	=	positive live load moment in long span
$M_b neg$	=	negative moment in long span
w_{df}	=	factored dead load per unit area
w_f	=	factored load per unit area
w_{lf}	=	factored live load per unit area

B.3 Design method

B.3.1
The minimum slab thickness should be determined in accordance with Clause 13.2, but should not be less than
(a) 100 mm;
(b) the perimeter of the slab divided by 140, in the case of slabs discontinuous on one or more edges; or
(c) the perimeter of the slab divided by 160, in the case of fully continuous slabs.

B.3.2
A two-way slab should be considered as consisting of strips in each direction, as follows:
(a) a middle strip, one-half of a panel in width, symmetrical about the panel centreline and extending through the panel in the direction in which moments are considered; and
(b) a column strip, one-half of a panel in width, occupying the two quarter-panel areas outside the middle strip.

B.3.3
Critical sections for moment should be assumed to be as follows:
(a) for negative moment, along the edges of the panel at the faces of the supports; and
(b) for positive moment, along the centrelines of the panels.

B.3.4
Negative bending moments per unit width for the middle strips should be computed in accordance with the following equations and the coefficients specified in Table B.1:

(a) $M_a neg = C_a neg \, w_f \ell_a^2$ $\qquad\qquad$ **(B-1)**

(b) $M_b neg = C_b neg \, w_f \ell_b^2$ $\qquad\qquad$ **(B-2)**

B.3.5
Positive bending moments per unit width should be computed as the sum of Equations (B-3) and (B-4) for the middle strip in the short direction and Equations (B-5) and (B-6) for the middle strip in the long direction, using the coefficients specified in Table B.2. These equations are as follows:

(a) $M_{al} pos = C_{al} w_{lf} \ell_a^2$ $\qquad\qquad$ **(B-3)**

(b) $M_{ad} pos = C_{ad} w_{df} \ell_a^2$ $\qquad\qquad$ **(B-4)**

(c) $M_{bl} pos = C_{bl} w_{lf} \ell_b^2$ $\qquad\qquad$ **(B-5)**

(d) $M_{bd} pos = C_{bd} w_{df} \ell_b^2$ $\qquad\qquad$ **(B-6)**

B.3.6
The bending moments in the column strips should be two-thirds of the bending moments in the middle strip.

B.3.7
Where the ratio, m, of short to long span is less than 0.5, the slab should be considered a one-way slab in the short direction, but reinforcement for negative moments required for m equal to 0.5 should be provided in the long direction.

B.3.8

At discontinuous edges of two-way slabs, a negative moment of three-quarters of the positive moment should be assumed.

B.3.9

In all cases, special reinforcement should be provided at exterior corners in accordance with Clause 13.12.5.

B.3.10

Where the negative moment on one side of a support is less than 80% of that on the other side, the difference should be distributed between the two slabs in proportion to their relative stiffnesses.

B.3.11

The shear stresses in the slabs should be computed on the assumption that the load, w_f, is distributed to the supports in accordance with Clause B.4.

B.4 Loads on slab supports

B.4.1

The loads on the supporting beams of a two-way rectangular panel may be assumed to be the load within the tributary areas of the panel bounded by the intersection of 45° lines from the corners and the median line of the panel parallel to the long side.

B.4.2

The bending moments in the supporting beams may be determined for design purposes by using an equivalent uniform load per unit length of beam for each panel supported, as follows:

(a) for the short span:

$$\frac{w_f \ell_a}{3} \tag{B-7}$$

(b) for the long span:

$$\frac{w_f \ell_a}{3} \times \frac{(3 - m^2)}{2} \tag{B-8}$$

© Canadian Standards Association

Table B.1
Coefficients for negative moments
(See Clause B.3.4.)

$m = \ell_a/\ell_b$	Coefficient	Case 1	Case 2	Case 3	Case 4	Case 5	Case 6	Case 7	Case 8	Case 9
1.00	$C_a neg$	—	0.045	—	0.050	0.075	0.071	—	0.033	0.061
	$C_b neg$	—	0.045	0.076	0.050	—	—	0.071	0.061	0.033
0.95	$C_a neg$	—	0.050	—	0.055	0.079	0.075	—	0.038	0.065
	$C_b neg$	—	0.041	0.072	0.045	—	—	0.067	0.056	0.029
0.90	$C_a neg$	—	0.055	—	0.060	0.080	0.079	—	0.043	0.068
	$C_b neg$	—	0.036	0.070	0.040	—	—	0.062	0.052	0.025
0.85	$C_a neg$	—	0.060	—	0.066	0.082	0.083	—	0.049	0.072
	$C_b neg$	—	0.031	0.065	0.034	—	—	0.057	0.046	0.021
0.80	$C_a neg$	—	0.065	—	0.071	0.084	0.086	—	0.055	0.075
	$C_b neg$	—	0.026	0.061	0.029	—	—	0.051	0.041	0.017
0.75	$C_a neg$	—	0.069	—	0.076	0.085	0.088	—	0.061	0.078
	$C_b neg$	—	0.022	0.056	0.024	—	—	0.044	0.036	0.014
0.70	$C_a neg$	—	0.074	—	0.081	0.086	0.091	—	0.068	0.081
	$C_b neg$	—	0.017	0.050	0.019	—	—	0.038	0.029	0.011
0.65	$C_a neg$	—	0.077	—	0.085	0.087	0.093	—	0.074	0.083
	$C_b neg$	—	0.014	0.043	0.015	—	—	0.031	0.025	0.008
0.60	$C_a neg$	—	0.081	—	0.089	0.088	0.095	—	0.080	0.085
	$C_b neg$	—	0.010	0.035	0.011	—	—	0.024	0.018	0.006
0.55	$C_a neg$	—	0.084	—	0.092	0.089	0.096	—	0.085	0.086
	$C_b neg$	—	0.007	0.028	0.008	—	—	0.019	0.014	0.005
0.50	$C_a neg$	—	0.086	—	0.094	0.090	0.097	—	0.089	0.088
	$C_b neg$	—	0.006	0.022	0.006	—	—	0.014	0.010	0.003

Notes:
(1) —— means that supports are free to rotate.
(2) ══ means that supports are fixed against rotation.

Table B.2
Coefficients for live and dead load positive moments
(See Clause B.3.5.)

$m = $ ℓ_a/ℓ_b	Coefficient	Case 1	Case 2	Case 3	Case 4	Case 5	Case 6	Case 7	Case 8	Case 9
1.00	C_{al}	0.036	0.027	0.027	0.032	0.032	0.035	0.032	0.028	0.030
	C_{ad}	0.036	0.018	0.018	0.027	0.027	0.033	0.027	0.020	0.023
	C_{bl}	0.036	0.027	0.032	0.032	0.027	0.032	0.035	0.030	0.028
	C_{bd}	0.036	0.018	0.027	0.027	0.018	0.027	0.033	0.023	0.020
0.95	C_{al}	0.040	0.030	0.031	0.035	0.034	0.038	0.036	0.031	0.032
	C_{ad}	0.040	0.020	0.021	0.030	0.028	0.036	0.031	0.022	0.024
	C_{bl}	0.033	0.025	0.029	0.029	0.024	0.029	0.032	0.027	0.025
	C_{bd}	0.033	0.016	0.025	0.024	0.015	0.024	0.031	0.021	0.017
0.90	C_{al}	0.045	0.034	0.035	0.039	0.037	0.042	0.040	0.035	0.036
	C_{ad}	0.045	0.022	0.025	0.033	0.029	0.039	0.035	0.025	0.026
	C_{bl}	0.029	0.022	0.027	0.026	0.021	0.025	0.029	0.024	0.022
	C_{bd}	0.029	0.014	0.024	0.022	0.013	0.021	0.028	0.019	0.015
0.85	C_{al}	0.050	0.037	0.040	0.043	0.041	0.046	0.045	0.040	0.039
	C_{ad}	0.050	0.024	0.029	0.036	0.031	0.042	0.040	0.029	0.028
	C_{bl}	0.026	0.019	0.024	0.023	0.019	0.022	0.026	0.022	0.020
	C_{bd}	0.026	0.012	0.023	0.019	0.011	0.017	0.025	0.017	0.013
0.80	C_{al}	0.055	0.041	0.045	0.048	0.044	0.051	0.051	0.044	0.042
	C_{ad}	0.055	0.026	0.034	0.039	0.032	0.045	0.045	0.032	0.029
	C_{bl}	0.023	0.017	0.022	0.020	0.016	0.019	0.023	0.019	0.017
	C_{bd}	0.023	0.011	0.020	0.016	0.009	0.014	0.022	0.025	0.010
0.75	C_{al}	0.061	0.045	0.051	0.052	0.047	0.055	0.056	0.049	0.046
	C_{ad}	0.061	0.028	0.040	0.043	0.033	0.048	0.051	0.036	0.031
	C_{bl}	0.019	0.014	0.019	0.016	0.013	0.016	0.020	0.016	0.014
	C_{bd}	0.019	0.009	0.018	0.013	0.007	0.012	0.020	0.013	0.007
0.70	C_{al}	0.068	0.049	0.057	0.057	0.051	0.060	0.063	0.054	0.050
	C_{ad}	0.068	0.030	0.046	0.046	0.035	0.051	0.058	0.040	0.033
	C_{bl}	0.016	0.012	0.016	0.014	0.011	0.013	0.017	0.014	0.012
	C_{bd}	0.016	0.007	0.016	0.011	0.005	0.009	0.017	0.011	0.006
0.65	C_{al}	0.074	0.053	0.064	0.062	0.055	0.064	0.070	0.059	0.054
	C_{ad}	0.074	0.032	0.054	0.050	0.036	0.053	0.065	0.044	0.034
	C_{bl}	0.013	0.010	0.014	0.011	0.009	0.010	0.014	0.011	0.009
	C_{bd}	0.013	0.006	0.014	0.009	0.004	0.007	0.014	0.009	0.005
0.60	C_{al}	0.081	0.058	0.072	0.067	0.059	0.068	0.077	0.065	0.059
	C_{ad}	0.081	0.034	0.062	0.053	0.037	0.056	0.073	0.048	0.036
	C_{bl}	0.010	0.007	0.011	0.009	0.007	0.008	0.011	0.009	0.007
	C_{bd}	0.010	0.004	0.011	0.007	0.003	0.006	0.012	0.007	0.004
0.55	C_{al}	0.088	0.062	0.080	0.072	0.063	0.073	0.085	0.070	0.063
	C_{ad}	0.088	0.035	0.071	0.056	0.038	0.058	0.081	0.052	0.037
	C_{bl}	0.008	0.006	0.009	0.007	0.005	0.006	0.009	0.007	0.006
	C_{bd}	0.008	0.003	0.009	0.005	0.002	0.004	0.009	0.005	0.003
0.50	C_{al}	0.095	0.066	0.088	0.077	0.067	0.078	0.092	0.076	0.067
	C_{ad}	0.095	0.037	0.080	0.059	0.039	0.061	0.089	0.056	0.038
	C_{bl}	0.006	0.004	0.007	0.005	0.004	0.005	0.007	0.005	0.004
	C_{bd}	0.006	0.002	0.007	0.004	0.001	0.003	0.007	0.004	0.002

Notes:
(1) —— *means that supports are free to rotate.*
(2) ==== *means that supports are fixed against rotation.*

CSA Standard A23.3-04

Annex C (informative)
Load combinations and load factors in the National Building Code of Canada, 2005

Notes:

(1) This Annex is not a mandatory part of this Standard.

(2) This Annex provides an adapted version of portions of Subsection 4.1.3 from an unpublished draft of the National Building Code of Canada, 2005 (NBC). Those portions deal with load factors and load combinations. This material has been adapted in accordance with CSA editorial requirements and is included for information only.

(3) The load factors and load combinations presented in this Annex are discussed in Part 4 of the NBC User's Guide and should be used in conjunction with the resistance factors specified in Clause 8.4.

(4) The NBC defines the following classes of loads:
(a) permanent loads such as dead loads, D, and effects of prestress, P;
(b) variable loads due to use and occupancy, L, wind loads, W, and snow loads, S;
(c) rare loads such as earthquake loads, E; and
(d) imposed deformations, T (see Clause 8.2.2).

(5) The equations used to compute the loads S, W, and E for snow, wind, and earthquake in the NBC include importance factors I_s, I_w, and I_e, which are a function of the use and occupancy of the building.

(6) The following symbols are used in this Annex:

D = permanent loads due to dead load, or related internal moments and forces

E = earthquake loads, or related internal moments and forces

H = load due to lateral earth pressure, including groundwater, and related internal moments and forces

L = variable load due to intended use and occupancy, including loads due to cranes and pressure of liquids in containers, or related moments or forces

P = effects of prestress, including secondary moments due to prestress

R = nominal resistance of a member, connection, or structure based on the dimensions and on the specified properties of the structural materials

S = variable loads due to ice, rain, and snow (including associated rain)

T = effects of imposed deformations due to moisture changes, shrinkage, creep, temperature, and ground settlement, or combinations thereof

W = variable loads due to wind, or related internal moments and forces

ϕ = resistance factor applied to a specified material property or to the resistance of a member, connection, or structure, which for the limit state under consideration takes into account the variability of dimensions and material properties, quality of work, type of failure, and uncertainty in the prediction of resistance

C.1 Limit states design
Note: See Appendix A of the NBC.

C.1.1 Definitions
The following definitions apply in this Annex:

Companion load — a specified variable load that accompanies the principal load in a given load combination.

Companion-load factor — a factor that, when applied to a companion load in the load combination, gives the probable magnitude of a companion load acting simultaneously with the factored principal load.

Effects — forces, moments, deformations, or vibrations that occur in the structure.

Factored load — the product of a specified load and its principal-load factor or companion-load factor.

Factored resistance — the product of nominal resistance, R, and the applicable resistance factor, ϕ.

CSA Standard A23.3-04

Importance factor — a factor applied in Subsections 4.1.6 to 4.1.8 of the NBC to obtain the specified load, to account for the consequences of failure as related to the limit state and the use and occupancy of the building.

Limit states — those conditions of a building structure in which the building ceases to fulfill the function for which it was designed.
Note: *Those states concerning safety are called ultimate limit states (ULS) and include exceeding the load-carrying capacity, overturning, sliding, and fracture. Those states that restrict the intended use and occupancy of the building are called serviceability limit states (SLS) and include deflection, vibration, permanent deformation, and local structural damage such as cracking. Those limit states that represent failure under repeated loading are called fatigue limit states.*

Principal load — the specified variable load or rare load that dominates in a given load combination.

Principal-load factor — a factor applied to the principal load in the load combination to account for the variability of the load and load pattern and analysis of its effects.

Specified loads (*D, E, H, L, P, S, T,* and *W*) — the loads specified in Note (6) of the preliminary Notes to this Annex.

C.1.2 Strength and stability

C.1.2.1
A building and its structural components shall be designed to have sufficient strength and stability so that the factored resistance, ϕR, is greater than or equal to the effect of factored loads, where the effect of factored loads shall be determined in accordance with Clause C.1.2.2.

C.1.2.2
The effect of factored loads for a building or structural component shall be determined in accordance with the load combinations specified in Table C.1 and the provisions of Clause C.1.2, the applicable combination being that which results in the most critical effect. (See Appendix A of the NBC.)

C.1.2.3
Where the effects due to lateral earth pressure, *H*, restraint effects from prestress, *P*, and imposed deformation, *T*, affect the structural safety, they shall be taken into account in the calculations, i.e., *H* with a load factor of 1.5, *P* with a load factor of 1.0, and *T* with a load factor of 1.25. (See Appendix A of the NBC.)

Table C.1
Load combinations for ultimate limit states
(See Clauses 8.3.2, C.1.2.2, and C.1.2.4 to C.1.2.8.)

| Case | Load combination*† | |
	Principal loads	Companion loads
1	1.4*D*	—
2	(1.25*D*‡ or 0.9*D*§) + 1.5*L***	0.5*S*†† or 0.4*W*
3	(1.25*D*‡ or 0.9*D*§) + 1.5*S*	0.5*L*††,‡‡ or 0.4*W*
4	(1.25*D*‡ or 0.9*D*§) + 1.4*W*	0.5*L*‡‡ or 0.5*S*
5	1.0*D*§ + 1.0*E*§§	0.5*L*††,‡‡ + 0.25*S*††

*See *Clause C.1.2.2.*
†See *Clause C.1.2.3.*
‡See *Clause C.1.2.7.*
§See *Clause C.1.2.4.*
**See *Clause C.1.2.5.*
††See *Article 4.1.5.5 of the NBC.*
‡‡See *Clause C.1.2.6.*
§§See *Clause C.1.2.8.*

Notes:
(1) *This Table corresponds to Table 4.1.3.2 of the NBC.*
(2) *The factored load combinations in this Table each include one or more permanent loads, one principal variable load that dominates a given load combination, and one or more companion variable loads that have a magnitude likely to occur in combination with the given principal variable load when that principal variable load acts on the structure.*

C.1.2.4
Except as provided in Sentence 4.1.8.16.(1) of the NBC, the counteracting factored dead load, 0.9*D* in the load combinations specified in Cases 2 to 4 of Table C.1 and 1.0*D* in the load combination specified in Case 5 of Table C.1, shall be used when dead load acts to resist overturning, uplift, sliding, and failure due to stress reversal, and to determine anchorage requirements and factored member resistances. (See Appendix A of the NBC.)

C.1.2.5
The principal-load factor 1.5 for live load, *L*, in Table C.1 may be reduced to 1.25 for liquids in tanks.

C.1.2.6
The companion-load factor 0.5 for live load, *L*, in Table C.1 shall be increased to 1.0 for storage occupancies, and for equipment areas and service rooms in Table 4.1.5.3 of the NBC.

C.1.2.7
The load factor 1.25 for dead load, *D*, for soil, superimposed earth, plants, and trees in Table C.1 shall be increased to 1.5, except that when the soil depth exceeds 1.2 m, the factor may be reduced to $1 + 0.6/h_s$, but not less than 1.25, where h_s is the depth of soil in metres supported by the structure.

C.1.2.8
Earthquake load, *E*, in the load combination specified in Case 5 of Table C.1 includes horizontal earth pressure due to earthquake determined in accordance with Sentence 4.1.8.16.(4) of the NBC.

C.1.2.9

Provision shall be made to ensure adequate stability of a structure as a whole and adequate lateral, torsional, and local stability of all structural parts.

C.1.2.10

Sway effects produced by vertical loads acting on the structure in its displaced configuration shall be taken into account in the design of buildings and their structural members.

C.1.3 Serviceability

A building and its structural components shall be checked for serviceability limit states as defined in Clause 4.1.3.1.(1)(a) of the NBC under the effect of service loads for serviceability criteria specified or recommended in Articles 4.1.3.5 and 4.1.3.6 of the NBC and in the Standards listed in Section 4.3 of the NBC.

Annex D (informative)
Anchorage

Note: *This informative (non-mandatory) Annex has been written in normative (mandatory) language to facilitate adoption where users of the Standard or regulatory authorities wish to adopt it formally as additional requirements to this Standard.*

D.1 Introduction

D.1.1
This Annex specifies design requirements for anchors in concrete used to transmit forces to concrete elements by tension, shear, or a combination of tension and shear. The specified safety levels are intended for in-service conditions rather than for short-term handling and construction conditions.

D.1.2
This Annex applies to both cast-in anchors and post-installed anchors (see Figure D.1). Specialty inserts, through-bolts, multiple anchors connected to a single steel plate at the embedded end of the anchors, adhesive or grouted anchors, and direct anchors such as powder- or pneumatic-actuated nails or bolts are not covered by this Annex. Reinforcement used as part of the embedment shall be designed in accordance with the applicable clauses of this Standard.

Δ ### D.1.3
Headed studs and headed bolts that have a geometry that has been demonstrated to result in a pullout resistance in uncracked concrete equal to or exceeding 1.4 N_{pr} (where N_{pr} is as specified in Equation (D-16)) are covered by this Annex. Hooked bolts that have a geometry that has been demonstrated to result in a pullout resistance without the benefit of friction in uncracked concrete equal or to exceeding 1.4 N_{pr} (where N_{pr} is as specified in Equation (D-17)) are also covered by this Annex, as are post-installed anchors that meet the assessment requirements of ACI 355.2/355.2R. The suitability of post-installed anchors for use in concrete shall be demonstrated by the ACI 355.2/355.2R prequalification tests.

D.1.4
Load applications that are predominantly high cycle, fatigue, or impact are not covered by this Annex.

D.2 Definitions
The following definitions apply in this Annex:

5% fractile — 90% confidence that there is a 95% probability of the actual strength exceeding the nominal strength.

Anchor — a steel element cast into concrete or post-installed into a hardened concrete member and used to transmit applied forces. Examples include straight bolts, hooked bolts (J- or L-bolts), headed studs, expansion anchors, undercut anchors, and inserts.

Anchor group — a number of anchors of approximately equal effective embedment depth, with each anchor spaced less than three times its embedment depth from one or more adjacent anchors.

Anchor pullout strength — the strength corresponding to the anchoring device or a major component of the device sliding out from the concrete without breaking out a substantial portion of the surrounding concrete (see Figure D.2).

Attachment — the structural assembly, external to the surface of the concrete, that transmits loads to the anchor.

Brittle steel element — an element with a tensile test elongation of less than 14% over a 50 mm gauge length.

Cast-in anchor — a headed bolt or hooked bolt installed before concrete is placed.

Concrete breakout strength — the strength corresponding to a volume of concrete surrounding the anchor or group of anchors separating from the member (see Figures D.2 and D.3).

Concrete pryout strength — the strength corresponding to formation of a concrete spall behind a short, stiff anchor with an embedded base that is displaced in the direction opposite to the applied shear force (see Figures D.2 and D.3).

Distance sleeve — a sleeve that encases the centre part of an undercut anchor, a torque-controlled expansion anchor, or a displacement-controlled expansion anchor but does not expand.

Ductile steel element — an element with a tensile test elongation of at least 14% over a 50 mm gauge length. A steel element meeting the requirements of CSA G40.21 or ASTM A 307 can be considered ductile.

Edge distance — the distance from the edge of the concrete surface to the centre of the nearest anchor.

Effective embedment depth — the overall depth through which the anchor transfers force to the surrounding concrete. The effective embedment depth is normally the depth of the failure surface in tension applications. For cast-in headed anchor bolts and headed studs, the effective embedment depth is measured from the bearing contact surface of the head (see Figure D.1).

Expansion anchor — a post-installed anchor inserted into hardened concrete that transfers loads into the concrete by direct bearing, friction, or both. Expansion anchors can be torque controlled (where the expansion is achieved by a torque acting on the screw or bolt) or displacement controlled (where the expansion is achieved by impact forces acting on a sleeve or plug and the expansion is controlled by the length of travel of the sleeve or plug).

Expansion sleeve — the outer part of an expansion anchor that is forced outward by the centre part by applied torque or impact to bear against the sides of the predrilled hole.

Headed stud — a headed steel anchor that meets the requirements of CSA W59 or AWS D1.1/D1.1M and is affixed to a plate or similar steel attachment by stud arc welding. The underside of the plate or steel attachment is assumed to be cast flush with the concrete surface.

Hooked bolt — a cast-in anchor that is anchored mainly by mechanical interlock from the 90° bend (L-bolt) or 180° bend (J-bolt) at its lower end and has a minimum e_h of $3d_o$.

Post-installed anchor — an anchor installed in hardened concrete. Expansion anchors and undercut anchors are examples of post-installed anchors.

Projected area — the area on the free surface of a concrete member that is used to represent the larger base of the assumed rectilinear failure surface.

Side-face blowout strength — the strength of anchors with deeper embedment but thinner side cover corresponding to concrete spalling on the side face around the embedded head while no major breakout occurs at the top concrete surface (see Figures D.2 and D.3).

Specialty insert — a predesigned and prefabricated cast-in anchor specifically designed for attachment of bolted or slotted connections. Specialty inserts are often used for handling, transportation, and erection, but also for anchoring structural elements. They are not covered by this Annex.

Supplementary reinforcement — reinforcement designed to tie a potential concrete failure prism to a structural member.

Undercut anchor — a post-installed anchor that derives its tensile strength from the mechanical interlock provided by undercutting of the concrete at the embedded end of the anchor. The undercutting is achieved with a special drill before installation of the anchor or by the anchor itself during its installation.

D.3 Symbols
The following symbols apply in this Annex:

A_{bh} = bearing area of the head of stud or anchor bolt

A_N = projected concrete failure area of an anchor or group of anchors, for calculation of resistance in tension, as defined in Clause D.6.2.1. A_N is not taken greater than nA_{No} (see Figure D.6)

A_{No} = projected concrete failure area of one anchor, for calculation of resistance in tension, when not limited by edge distance or spacing, as specified in Clause D.6.2.1 (see Figure D.5)

A_{se} = effective cross-sectional area of anchor

A_V = projected concrete failure area of an anchor or group of anchors, for calculation of resistance in shear, as defined in Clause D.7.2.1. A_V is not taken greater than nA_{Vo} (see Figure D.10)

A_{Vo} = projected concrete failure area of one anchor, for calculation of resistance in shear, when not limited by corner influences, spacing, or member thickness, as specified in Clause D.7.2.1 (see Figure D.9)

c = distance from centre of an anchor shaft to the edge of concrete

c_{ac} = critical edge distance specified in Clause D.9.7

$c_{a,min}$ = minimum edge distance to preclude premature splitting failure of post-installed anchors, as determined from ACI 355.2/355.2R

c_{max} = the largest edge distance

c_{min} = the smallest edge distance

c_1 = distance from the centre of an anchor shaft to the edge of concrete in one direction. Where shear force is applied to anchor, c_1 is in the direction of the shear force (see Figure D.9)

c_2 = distance from centre of an anchor shaft to the edge of concrete in the direction orthogonal to c_1

d_o = outside diameter of anchor or shaft diameter of headed stud, headed anchor bolt, or hooked anchor

d_o' = value substituted for d_o when an oversized anchor is used

e_h = distance from the inner surface of the shaft of a J-bolt or L-bolt to the outer tip of the J- or L-bolt

e_N = actual eccentricity of a normal force on an attachment

e_N' = eccentricity of normal force on a group of anchors. The distance between the resultant tension load on a group of anchors in tension and the centroid of the group of anchors loaded in tension is always positive (see Figure D.8)

e_V = actual eccentricity of a shear force on an attachment

e_V' = eccentricity of shear force on a group of anchors; the distance between the point of shear force application and the centroid of the group of anchors resisting shear in the direction of the applied shear (see Figure D.12)

f_c' = specified compressive strength of concrete

CSA Standard A23.3-04

f_r = modulus of rupture of concrete

f_t = calculated tensile stress in a region of a member

f_{ut} = specified tensile strength of anchor steel

f_y = specified yield strength of anchor steel

F_a = acceleration-based site coefficient, as specified in the *National Building Code of Canada*

h = thickness of member in which an anchor is anchored, measured parallel to anchor axis

h_{ef} = effective anchor embedment depth (see Figure D.1)

I_E = earthquake importance factor of the structure, as specified in the *National Building Code of Canada*

k = coefficient for factored concrete breakout resistance in tension

k_{cp} = coefficient for pryout resistance

ℓ = load-bearing length of anchor for shear, not to exceed $8d_o$

 = h_{ef} for anchors with a constant stiffness over the full length of the embedded section, such as headed studs or post-installed anchors with one tubular shell over the full length of the embedment depth

 = $2d_o$ for torque-controlled expansion anchors with a distance sleeve separated from the expansion sleeve

n = number of anchors in a group

N_{br} = factored concrete breakout resistance in tension of a single anchor in cracked concrete, as defined in Clause D.6.2.2

N_{cbgr} = factored concrete breakout resistance in tension of a group of anchors, as specified in Clause D.6.2.1

N_{cbr} = factored concrete breakout resistance in tension of a single anchor, as specified in Clause D.6.2.1

N_{cpr} = factored pullout resistance in tension of a single anchor, as specified in Clause D.6.3.1

N_f = factored tensile load

N_{pr} = factored pullout resistance in tension of a single anchor in cracked concrete, as specified in Clause D.6.3.4 or D.6.3.5

N_r = factored resistance in tension

N_{sbgr} = factored side-face blowout resistance of a group of anchors

N_{sbr} = factored side-face blowout resistance of a single anchor

N_{sr} = factored resistance of a single anchor or group of anchors in tension as governed by the steel resistance, as specified in Clauses D.6.1.1 and D.6.1.2

R = resistance modification factor

s = anchor centre-to-centre spacing

s_o = centre-to-centre spacing of the outer anchors along the edge in a group

$S_a(0.2)$ = damped spectral response acceleration for a period of 0.2 s, as specified in the *National Building Code of Canada*

t = thickness of washer or plate

V_{br} = factored concrete breakout resistance in shear of a single anchor in cracked concrete, as specified in Clause D.7.2.2 or D.7.2.3

V_{cbgr} = factored concrete breakout resistance in shear of a group of anchors, as specified in Clause D.7.2.1

V_{cbr} = factored concrete breakout resistance in shear of a single anchor, as specified in Clause D.7.2.1

V_{cpgr} = factored concrete pryout resistance of a group of anchors, as specified in Clause D.7.3

V_{cpr} = factored concrete pryout resistance of a single anchor, as specified in Clause D.7.3

V_f = factored shear force

V_r = factored shear resistance

V_{sr} = factored resistance in shear of a single anchor as governed by the steel resistance, as specified in Clauses D.7.1.1 and D.7.1.2

λ = factor to account for low-density concrete

ϕ_c = concrete material resistance factor for concrete

ϕ_s = steel embedment material resistance factor for reinforcement

$\psi_{c,N}$ = modification factor for resistance in tension to account for cracking, as specified in Clause D.6.2.6

$\psi_{cp,N}$ = modification factor for concrete breakout resistance to account for premature splitting failure, as specified in Clause D.6.2.7

$\psi_{c,P}$ = modification factor for pullout resistance to account for cracking, as specified in Clause D.6.3.6

$\psi_{c,V}$ = modification factor for resistance in shear to account for cracking, as specified in Clause D.7.2.7

$\psi_{ec,N}$ = modification factor for resistance in tension to account for anchor groups loaded eccentrically, as specified in Clause D.6.2.4

$\psi_{ec,V}$ = modification factor for resistance in shear to account for anchor groups loaded eccentrically, as specified in Clause D.7.2.5

$\psi_{ed,N}$ = modification factor for resistance in tension to account for edge distances smaller than $1.5h_{ef}$, as specified in Clause D.6.2.5

$\psi_{ed,V}$ = modification factor for resistance in shear to account for edge distances smaller than $1.5c_1$, as specified in Clause D.7.2.6

D.4 General requirements

D.4.1 Analysis
Anchors and anchor groups shall be designed for critical effects of factored loads as determined by elastic analysis. Plastic analysis approaches may be used where factored resistance is controlled by ductile steel elements, provided that deformational compatibility is taken into account.

D.4.2 Load combinations
Anchors shall be designed for all of the factored load combinations specified in Clause 8.

D.4.3 Seismic considerations

D.4.3.1
Where load combinations include earthquake effects, the applicable additional requirements of Clauses D.4.3.2 to D.4.3.6 shall apply.

D.4.3.2
This Annex shall not apply to the design of anchors in plastic hinge zones of concrete structures under seismic loads.

D.4.3.3
In regions where $I_E F_a S_a(0.2) \geq 0.35$ and the load combinations include earthquake effects, the additional requirements of Clauses D.4.3.4 to D.4.3.6 shall apply.

D.4.3.4
Post-installed structural anchors for use as specified in Clause D.1.3 shall pass the simulated seismic tests specified in ACI 355.2/355-2R.

D.4.3.5
The factored design resistance of anchors shall be taken as 75% of the values determined in accordance with Clause D.5.1.1.

D.4.3.6
Anchors shall be designed to be governed by the tensile or shear strength of a ductile steel element unless the attachment connected to the structure by the anchor is designed so that it will undergo ductile yielding at a load level not greater than 75% of the minimum anchor design resistance.

D.4.4 Concrete density
All requirements for anchor axial tension and shear resistance shall apply to normal-density concrete. When low-density aggregate concrete is used, N_r and V_r shall be modified by multiplying all values of $\sqrt{f_c'}$ affecting N_r and V_r by λ. Linear interpolation based on the fraction of natural sand in the mix may be applied.

D.4.5 Concrete strength limit
The values of f_c' used for calculations in this Annex shall not exceed 70 MPa for cast-in anchors and 55 MPa for post-installed anchors. Testing shall be required for post-installed anchors used in concrete with f_c' greater than 55 MPa.

D.5 Resistance of structural anchors

D.5.1

D.5.1.1
The design of structural anchors shall be based on computations that satisfy the requirements of Clause D.5.2 or on test evaluation using the 5% fractile of test results for the following:
(a) steel strength of anchor in tension (Clause D.6.1);
(b) steel strength of anchor in shear (Clause D.7.1);
(c) concrete breakout resistance of anchor in tension (Clause D.6.2);
(d) concrete breakout resistance of anchor in shear (Clause D.7.2);
(e) pullout resistance of anchor in tension (Clause D.6.3);
(f) concrete side-face blowout resistance of anchor in tension (Clause D.6.4); and
(g) concrete pryout resistance of anchor in shear (Clause D.7.3).
In addition, anchors shall have the edge distances, spacings, and thicknesses for precluding splitting failure required by Clause D.9.

D.5.1.2
The following shall apply to the design of anchors, except as required by Clause D.4.3:

$$N_r \geq N_f \qquad\qquad\qquad\qquad\qquad\qquad\qquad\qquad\qquad\qquad \textbf{(D-1)}$$

$$V_r \geq V_f \qquad\qquad\qquad\qquad\qquad\qquad\qquad\qquad\qquad\qquad \textbf{(D-2)}$$

N_r and V_r are the lowest design resistances determined from all applicable failure modes. N_r is the lowest design resistance in tension of an anchor or anchor group, as determined from a consideration of N_{sr}, N_{cpr}, either N_{sbr} or N_{sbgr}, and either N_{cbr} or N_{cbgr}. V_r is the lowest design resistance in shear of an anchor or anchor group, as determined from a consideration of V_{sr}, either V_{cbr} or V_{cbgr}, and either V_{cpr} or V_{cpgr}.

D.5.2

D.5.2.1
The nominal resistance for any anchor or anchor group shall be based on design models that result in predictions of resistance in substantial agreement with results of comprehensive tests. The materials used in the tests shall be compatible with the materials used in the structure. The nominal resistance shall be based on the 5% fractile of the basic individual anchor resistance. For nominal resistances related to concrete strength, modifications for size effects, the number of anchors, the effects of close spacing of anchors, proximity to edges, depth of the concrete member, eccentric loadings of anchor groups, and presence or absence of cracking shall be accounted for. Limits on edge distances and anchor spacing in the design models shall be consistent with the tests that verified the model.

D.5.2.2
The effect of supplementary reinforcement provided to confine or restrain the concrete breakout may be included in the design models specified in Clause D.5.2.1.

D.5.2.3
For anchors with diameters not exceeding 50 mm and tensile embedments not exceeding 625 mm in depth, the concrete breakout resistance requirements specified in Clause D.5.2.1 shall be considered satisfied by the design procedure specified in Clauses D.6.2 and D.7.2.

D.5.3
Resistance to combined tensile and shear loads shall be considered in the design by use of an interaction expression that results in a computation of resistance in substantial agreement with the results of comprehensive tests. This requirement shall be considered satisfied by Clause D.8.

D.5.4
The resistance modification factor, R, specified in Clauses D.6 and D.7 shall be as follows:
(a) for an anchor governed by strength of a ductile steel element:

Tension loads	0.80
Shear loads	0.75

(b) for an anchor governed by strength of a brittle steel element:

Tension loads	0.70
Shear loads	0.65

(c) for an anchor governed by concrete breakout, blowout, pullout, or pryout strength:

	Condition A*	Condition B*
Shear loads	1.15	1.00
Tension loads		
Cast-in headed studs, headed bolts, or hooked bolts	1.15	1.00
Post-installed anchors (category determined in accordance with ACI 355.2/355.2R)		
Category 1 (low sensitivity to installation and high reliability)	1.15	1.00
Category 2 (medium sensitivity to installation and medium reliability)	1.00	0.85
Category 3 (high sensitivity to installation and lower reliability)	0.85	0.70

*Condition A applies where the potential concrete failure surfaces are crossed by supplementary reinforcement proportioned to tie the potential concrete failure prism into the structural member. Condition B applies where such supplementary reinforcement is not provided or where pullout or pryout strength governs.

D.6 Design requirements for tensile loading

D.6.1 Steel resistance of anchor in tension

D.6.1.1
The factored resistance of an anchor in tension as governed by the steel, N_{sr}, shall be evaluated by calculations based on the properties of the anchor material and the physical dimensions of the anchor.

D.6.1.2
The factored resistance of an anchor or anchor group in tension shall not exceed

$$N_{sr} = nA_{se}\phi_s f_{ut} R \qquad\qquad \text{(D-3)}$$

where f_{ut} shall not be taken greater than the smaller of $1.9f_y$ or 860 MPa.
   In this equation the effective area, A_{se}, of a threaded anchor may be assumed to be 70% of the gross area.

D.6.2 Concrete breakout resistance of anchor in tension

D.6.2.1
The factored concrete breakout resistance of an anchor or anchor group in tension shall not exceed
(a) for a single anchor:

$$N_{cbr} = \frac{A_N}{A_{No}}\psi_{ed,N}\psi_{c,N}\psi_{cp,N}N_{br} \qquad\qquad \text{(D-4)}$$

(b) for an anchor group:

$$N_{cbgr} = \frac{A_N}{A_{No}}\psi_{ec,N}\psi_{ed,N}\psi_{c,N}\psi_{cp,N}N_{br} \qquad\qquad \text{(D-5)}$$

In these equations, N_{br} is the factored concrete breakout resistance value for a single anchor in tension in cracked concrete. In these equations, A_N is the projected area of the failure surface for the anchor or anchor group and shall be approximated as the base of the rectilinear geometrical figure that results from projecting the failure surface outward $1.5h_{ef}$ from the centrelines of the anchor, or in the case of an anchor group, from a line through a row of adjacent anchors (see Figure D.4). A_N shall not exceed n times the A_N of the single anchor nearest an edge or corner considered alone, where n is the number of tensioned anchors in the group. A_{No} is the projected area of the failure surface of a single anchor remote from edges, as follows:

$$A_{No} = 9h_{ef}^2 \tag{D-6}$$

D.6.2.2

The factored concrete breakout resistance of a single anchor in tension in cracked concrete shall not exceed

$$N_{br} = k\phi_c\sqrt{f_c'}h_{ef}^{1.5}R \tag{D-7}$$

where
k = 10 for cast-in headed studs, headed bolts, and hooked bolts
= 7.0 for post-installed anchors
The k factor for post-installed anchors may be increased in accordance with ACI 355.2/355.2R product-specific tests, but shall not exceed 10.

Alternatively, for cast-in headed studs and headed bolts with 275 mm $< h_{ef} <$ 625 mm, the factored concrete breakout resistance of a single anchor in tension in cracked concrete shall not exceed

$$N_{br} = 3.9\phi_c\sqrt{f_c'}h_{ef}^{5/3}R \tag{D-8}$$

D.6.2.3

For the special case of anchors in an application with three or four edges with the largest edge distance, c_{max}, less than or equal to $1.5h_{ef}$, the embedment depth h_{ef} used in Equations (D-6) to (D-9), (D-11), and (D-12) shall be limited to $c_{max}/1.5$ but be not less than one-third of the maximum spacing between anchors or anchor groups (see Figure D.7).

D.6.2.4

The modification factor for eccentrically loaded anchor groups shall be

$$\psi_{ec,N} = \cfrac{1}{\left(1 + \cfrac{2e_N'}{3h_{ef}}\right)} \tag{D-9}$$

This equation shall be valid for

$$e_N' \leq \frac{s_o}{2} \tag{D-10}$$

where
s_o = the centre-to-centre spacing of the outer anchors in tension
If the loading on an anchor group is such that only some anchors are in tension, only those anchors that are in tension shall be considered when determining the eccentricity, e_N', for use in Equation (D-9).

In the case where eccentric loading exists about two axes, the modification factor, $\psi_{ec,N}$, shall be computed for each axis individually, and the product of these factors used as $\psi_{ec,N}$ in Equation (D-5).

D.6.2.5

The modification factor for edge effects shall be

$$\psi_{ed,N} = 1 \quad \text{if} \quad c_{min} \geq 1.5h_{ef} \tag{D-11}$$

$$= 0.7 + 0.3\frac{c_{min}}{1.5h_{ef}} \quad \text{if} \quad c_{min} < 1.5h_{ef} \tag{D-12}$$

D.6.2.6

When an anchor is located in a region of a concrete member where analysis indicates no cracking ($f_t < f_r$) at service load levels, the following modification factor may be used:

$\psi_{c,N} = 1.25$ for cast-in headed studs, headed bolts, and hooked bolts
$\phantom{\psi_{c,N}} = 1.4$ for post-installed anchors when $k = 7.0$ is used in Equation (D-7)

Where k used in Equation (D-7) is taken from an ACI 355.2/355.2R product evaluation report for post-installed anchors approved for use in both cracked and uncracked concrete, the value of both k and $\psi_{c,N}$ shall be based on the product evaluation report.

For post-installed anchors approved for use only in uncracked concrete in accordance with ACI 355.2/355.2R, the value of k in the ACI 355.2/355.2R product evaluation report shall be used in Equation (D-7) and $\psi_{c,N}$ shall be 1.0.

Where analysis indicates cracking at service load levels, $\psi_{c,N}$ shall be taken as 1.0 for both cast-in and post-installed anchors.

D.6.2.7

The modification factor for post-installed anchors designed for uncracked concrete in accordance with Clause D.6.2.6 without supplementary reinforcement to control splitting shall be

$$\psi_{cp,N} = 1 \quad \text{if} \quad c_{a,min} \geq c_{ac} \tag{D-13}$$

$$= \frac{c_{a,min}}{c_{ac}} \geq \frac{1.5h_{ef}}{c_{ac}} \quad \text{if} \quad c_{a,min} < c_{ac} \tag{D-14}$$

where the critical distance, c_{ac}, is as specified in Clause D.9.7.

D.6.2.8

When an additional plate or washer is added at the head of the anchor, the projected area of the failure surface may be calculated by projecting the failure surface outward $1.5h_{ef}$ from the effective perimeter of the plate or washer. The effective perimeter shall not exceed the value at a section projected outward a distance t from the outer edge of the head of the anchor, where t is the thickness of the washer or plate.

D.6.3 Pullout resistance of anchor in tension

D.6.3.1

The factored pullout resistance of an anchor in tension shall not exceed

$$N_{cpr} = \psi_{c,p}N_{pr} \tag{D-15}$$

D.6.3.2

For post-installed expansion and undercut anchors, the pullout strength shall not be calculated in tension. Values of N_{pr} shall be based on the 5% fractile of results of tests performed and evaluated in accordance with ACI 355.2/355.2R.

D.6.3.3

For single cast-in headed studs and headed bolts, the pullout resistance in tension may be calculated using Clause D.6.3.4. For single J-bolts or L-bolts, the pullout resistance in tension may be calculated using Clause D.6.3.5. Alternatively, values of N_{pr} based on the 5% fractile of tensile tests performed in the same manner as the ACI 355.2/355.2R procedures but without the benefit of friction may be used.

D.6.3.4

The pullout resistance in tension of a single headed stud or headed bolt, N_{pr}, for use in Equation (D-15) shall not exceed

$$N_{pr} = 8A_{bh}\phi_c f'_c R$$

(D-16)

D.6.3.5

The pullout resistance in tension of a single J-bolt or L-bolt, N_{pr}, for use in Equation (D-15) shall not exceed

$$N_{pr} = 0.9\phi_c f'_c e_h d_o R$$

(D-17)

where $3d_o \le e_h \le 4.5d_o$.

D.6.3.6

For an anchor located in a region of a concrete member where analysis indicates no cracking ($f_t < f_r$) at service load levels, a modification factor of $\psi_{c,P} = 1.4$ may be used. Otherwise, $\psi_{c,P}$ shall be taken as 1.0.

D.6.4 Concrete side-face blowout resistance of a headed anchor in tension

D.6.4.1

For a single headed anchor with deep embedment close to an edge ($c < 0.4h_{ef}$), the factored side-face blowout resistance, N_{sbr}, shall not exceed

$$N_{sbr} = 13.3c\sqrt{A_{bh}}\phi_c\sqrt{f'_c}R$$

(D-18)

If the single anchor is located at a perpendicular distance, c_2, less than $3c$ from an edge, the value of N_{sbr} shall be modified by multiplying it by the factor $(1 + c_2/c)/4$, where $1 \le c_2/c \le 3$.

D.6.4.2

For multiple headed anchors with deep embedment close to an edge ($c < 0.4h_{ef}$) and spacing between anchors less than $6c$, the factored resistance of the anchor group for a side-face blowout failure, N_{sbgr}, shall not exceed

$$N_{sbgr} = \left(1 + \frac{s_o}{6c}\right)N_{sbr}$$

(D-19)

where s_o = distance between the outer anchors along the edge in the group
and N_{sbr} is obtained from Equation (D-18) without modification for a perpendicular edge distance.

CSA Standard A23.3-04

D.7 Design requirements for shear loading

D.7.1 Steel resistance of anchor in shear

D.7.1.1
The factored resistance of an anchor in shear as governed by steel, V_{sr}, shall be evaluated by calculations based on the properties of the anchor material and the physical dimensions of the anchor.

D.7.1.2
The factored resistance of an anchor or anchor group in shear shall not exceed the following:
(a) for cast-in headed stud anchors:

$$V_{sr} = nA_{se}\phi_s f_{ut}R \tag{D-20}$$

where f_{ut} shall not be taken greater than the smaller of $1.9f_y$ or 860 MPa;
(b) for cast-in headed bolts, hooked bolt anchors, and post-installed anchors without sleeves extending through the shear plane:

$$V_{sr} = nA_{se}\phi_s 0.6f_{ut}R \tag{D-21}$$

where f_{ut} shall not be taken greater than the smaller of $1.9f_y$ or 860 MPa; and
Δ (c) for post-installed anchors with sleeves extending through the shear plane, V_{sr} shall be based on the 5% fractile of results of tests performed and evaluated in accordance with ACI 355.2/355.2R. Alternatively, Equation (D-21) may be used if the area of the sleeve is neglected.

D.7.1.3
Where anchors are used with built-up grout pads, the factored resistances specified in Clause D.7.1.2 shall be reduced by 20%.

D.7.2 Concrete breakout resistance of anchor in shear

D.7.2.1
The factored concrete breakout resistance in shear of an anchor or anchor group shall not exceed the following:
(a) For shear force perpendicular to the edge on a single anchor:

$$V_{cbr} = \frac{A_V}{A_{Vo}}\psi_{ed,V}\psi_{c,V}V_{br} \tag{D-22}$$

(b) For shear force perpendicular to the edge on an anchor group:

$$V_{cbgr} = \frac{A_V}{A_{Vo}}\psi_{ec,V}\psi_{ed,V}\psi_{c,V}V_{br} \tag{D-23}$$

(c) For shear force parallel to an edge, V_{cbr} or V_{cbgr} may be twice the value for shear force determined from Equation (D-22) or (D-23), respectively, with the shear force assumed to act perpendicular to the free edge and with $\psi_{ed,V}$ taken to be equal to 1 (see Figure D.11).
(d) For anchors located at a corner, the limiting factored concrete breakout resistance shall be determined for each edge and the minimum value shall be used (see Figure D.11).
In these equations, V_{br} is the factored concrete breakout resistance value for a single anchor. A_V is the projected area of the failure surface on the side of the concrete member at its edge for a single anchor or anchor group. This area may be evaluated as the base of a truncated half-pyramid projected on the side

face of the member where the top of the half-pyramid is given by the axis of the anchor row selected as critical. The value of c_1 shall be taken as the distance from the edge to this axis. A_V shall not exceed nA_{Vo}, where n is the number of anchors in the group. A_{Vo} is the projected area for a single anchor in a deep member and remote from edges in the direction perpendicular to the shear force. This area may be evaluated as the base of a half-pyramid with a side length parallel to the edge of $3c_1$ and a depth of $1.5c_1$, as follows (see Figure D.4):

$$A_{Vo} = 4.5c_1^2 \tag{D-24}$$

Where anchors are located at varying distances from the edge and are welded to the attachment so as to distribute the force to all anchors, the strength may be evaluated based on the distance to the farthest row of anchors from the edge. In this case, the value of c_1 may be based on the distance from the edge to the axis of the farthest anchor row that is selected as critical, and all of the shear shall be assumed to be carried by this critical anchor row alone.

D.7.2.2
The factored concrete breakout resistance in shear of a single anchor in cracked concrete shall not exceed

$$V_{br} = 0.58\left(\frac{\ell}{d_o}\right)^{0.2}\sqrt{d_o}\,\phi_c\sqrt{f'_c}\,c_1^{1.5}R \tag{D-25}$$

D.7.2.3
For cast-in headed studs, headed bolts, or hooked bolts that are rigidly welded to steel attachments having a minimum thickness equal to the greater of 10 mm or half of the anchor diameter, the factored concrete breakout resistance in shear of a single anchor in cracked concrete shall not exceed

$$V_{br} = 0.66\left(\frac{\ell}{d_o}\right)^{0.2}\sqrt{d_o}\,\phi_c\sqrt{f'_c}\,c_1^{1.5}R \tag{D-26}$$

provided that
(a) for an anchor group, the resistance is determined based on the resistance of the row of anchors farthest from the edge;
(b) the centre-to-centre spacing of the anchors is not less than 65 mm; and
(c) supplementary reinforcement is provided at the corners if $c_2 \le 1.5h_{ef}$.

D.7.2.4
For the special case of anchors in a narrow ($c_2 < 1.5c_1$), thin ($h < 1.5c_1$) member, the edge distance, c_1, used in Equations (D-24) to (D-27) and (D-30) shall be limited to

$$\frac{c_2}{1.5} \quad \text{if } c_2 > h$$

$$\frac{h}{1.5} \quad \text{if } c_2 < h$$

D.7.2.5

The modification factor for eccentrically loaded anchor groups shall be

$$\psi_{ec,V} = \frac{1}{1 + \dfrac{2e'_V}{3c_1}}$$ **(D-27)**

This equation shall be valid for

$$e'_V \leq \frac{s_o}{2}$$ **(D-28)**

where
s_o = the centre-to-centre spacing of the outer anchors in shear

D.7.2.6

The modification factor for edge effects shall be

$$\psi_{ed,V} = 1.0 \quad \text{if } c_2 \geq 1.5c_1$$ **(D-29)**

$$= 0.7 + 0.3\frac{c_2}{1.5c_1} \quad \text{if } c_2 < 1.5c_1$$ **(D-30)**

D.7.2.7

For anchors located in a region of a concrete member where an analysis that includes temperature and shrinkage effects indicates no tension ($f_t < f_r$) at service loads, a modification factor of $\psi_{c,V} = 1.4$ may be used.

For anchors located in a region of a concrete member where analysis indicates cracking at service load levels, the following modification factors may be used:

For anchors in cracked concrete with no edge reinforcement or edge reinforcement smaller than a 15M bar	$\psi_{c,V} = 1.0$
For anchors in cracked concrete with edge reinforcement of a 15M bar or greater between the anchor and the edge	$\psi_{c,V} = 1.2$
For anchors in cracked concrete with edge reinforcement of a 15M bar or greater between the anchor and the edge and with the edge reinforcement enclosed within stirrups spaced not more than 100 mm apart	$\psi_{c,V} = 1.4$

D.7.3 Concrete pryout resistance of an anchor in shear

The factored pryout resistance, V_{cpr} or V_{cpgr}, shall not exceed

$$V_{cpr} = k_{cp}N_{cbr}$$ (D-31)

$$V_{cpgr} = k_{cp}N_{cbgr}$$ (D-32)

where
$k_{cp} = 1.0$ for $h_{ef} < 65$ mm

$\quad\;\; = 2.0$ for $h_{ef} \geq 65$ mm

N_{cbr} and N_{cbgr} shall be determined from Equations (D-4) and (D-5), respectively.

D.8 Interaction of tensile and shear forces

D.8.1

Unless determined in accordance with Clause D.5.3, anchors or anchor groups that are subjected to both shear and axial loads shall be designed to satisfy the requirements of Clauses D.8.2 through D.8.4. The value of N_r shall be the smallest of the steel resistance of the anchor in tension, concrete breakout resistance of the anchor in tension, pullout resistance of the anchor in tension, and side-face blowout resistance. The value of V_r shall be the smallest of the steel resistance of the anchor in shear, the concrete breakout resistance of the anchor in shear, and the pryout resistance.

D.8.2

If $V_f \leq 0.2V_r$, full resistance in tension shall be permitted, as follows (see Figure D.13):

$$N_r \geq N_f$$ (D-33)

D.8.3

If $N_f \leq 0.2N_r$, full resistance in shear shall be permitted, as follows (see Figure D.13):

$$V_r \geq V_f$$ (D-34)

D.8.4

If $V_f > 0.2V_r$ and $N_f > 0.2N_r$, the following shall apply (see Figure D.13):

$$\frac{N_f}{N_r} + \frac{V_f}{V_r} \leq 1.2$$ (D-35)

D.9 Required edge distances, spacings, and thicknesses to preclude splitting failure

D.9.1
Minimum spacings and edge distances for anchors and minimum thicknesses of members shall comply with Clauses D.9.2 to D.9.7 unless reinforcement is provided to control splitting. Lesser values from product-specific tests performed in accordance with ACI 355.2/355.2R shall be permitted.

D.9.2
Unless determined in accordance with Clause D.9.5, the minimum centre-to-centre spacing of anchors shall be $4d_o$ for untorqued cast-in anchors and $6d_o$ for torqued cast-in anchors and post-installed anchors.

D.9.3
Unless determined in accordance with Clause D.9.5, minimum edge distances for cast-in headed anchors that will not be torqued shall be based on the minimum cover requirements for reinforcement specified in Clause 7.9. For cast-in headed anchors that will be torqued, the minimum edge distances shall be $6d_o$.

D.9.4
Unless determined in accordance with Clause D.9.5, minimum edge distances for post-installed anchors shall be based on the greater of the minimum cover requirements for reinforcement specified in Clause 7.9 and the minimum edge distance requirements for the products as determined by tests in accordance with ACI 355.2/355.2R, and shall be not less than 2.0 times the nominal maximum aggregate size. In the absence of such product-specific ACI 355.2/355.2R test information, the minimum edge distance shall be taken as not less than the following:

Undercut anchors	$6d_o$
Torque-controlled anchors	$8d_o$
Displacement-controlled anchors	$10d_o$

D.9.5
For anchors where installation does not produce a splitting force and the anchors will remain untorqued, if the edge distance or spacing is less than that specified in Clauses D.9.2 to D.9.4, calculations shall be performed by substituting for d_o a smaller value, d_o', that meets the requirements of Clauses D.9.2 to D.9.4. Calculated forces applied to the anchor shall be limited to the values corresponding to an anchor having that fictitious diameter.

D.9.6
The value of h_{ef} for an expansion or undercut post-installed anchor shall not exceed the greater of two-thirds of the member thickness or the member thickness less 100 mm.

D.9.7
Unless determined from tension tests in accordance with ACI 355.2/355.2R, the critical edge distance, c_{ac}, shall not be taken less than the following:

Undercut anchors	$2.5h_{ef}$
Torque-controlled anchors	$4h_{ef}$
Displacement-controlled anchors	$4h_{ef}$

D.9.8
Project drawings and project specifications shall specify use of anchors with the minimum edge distance assumed in the design.

D.10 Installation of anchors
Anchors shall be installed in accordance with the project drawings and project specifications.

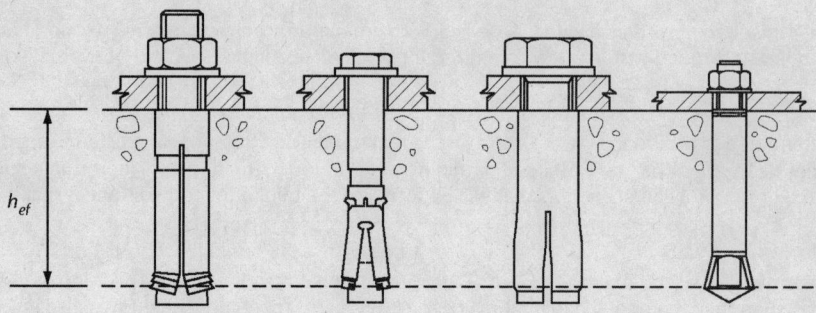

(a) Post-installed anchors

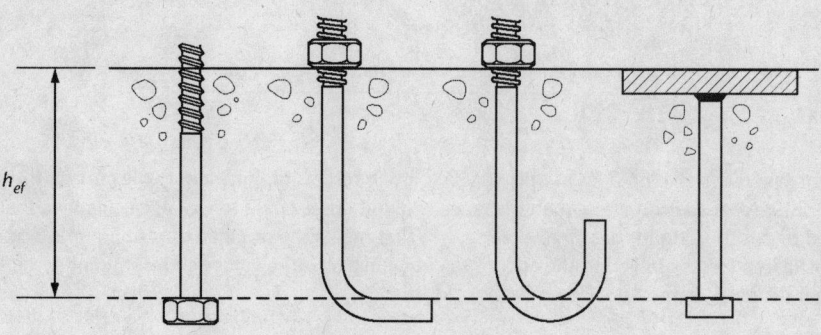

(b) Cast-in anchors

Figure D.1
Types of anchors
(See Clauses D.1.2, D.2, and D.3.)

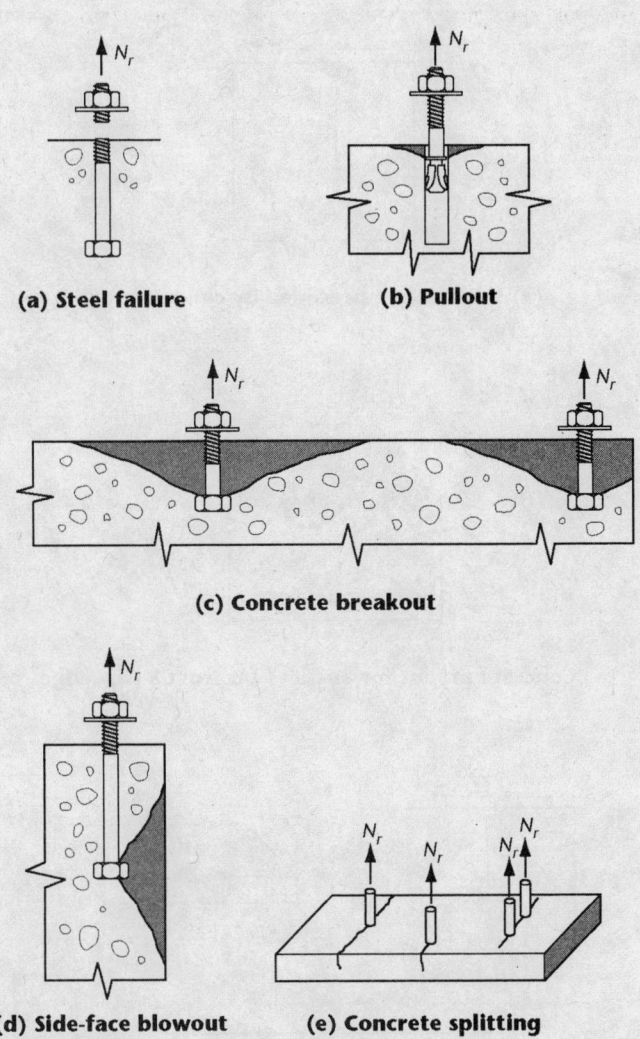

Figure D.2
Failure modes for anchors under tensile loading
(See Clause D.2.)

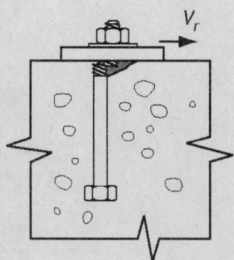

(a) Steel failure preceded by concrete spall

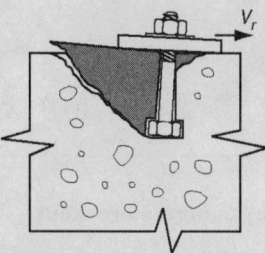

(b) Concrete pryout for anchors far from a free edge

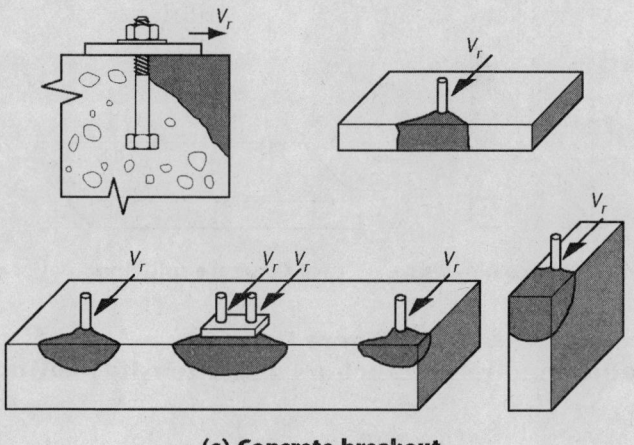

(c) Concrete breakout

Figure D.3
Failure modes for anchors under shear loading
(See Clause D.2.)

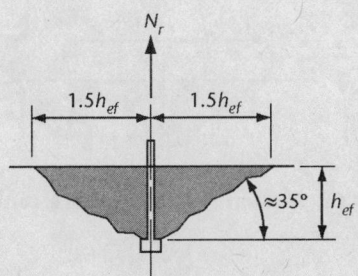

(a) Breakout cone for tension

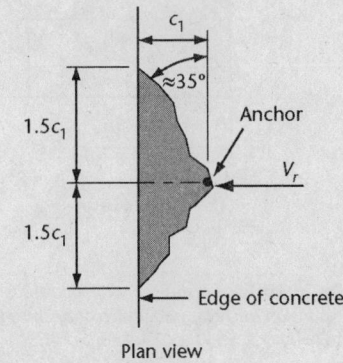

(b) Breakout cone for shear

**Figure D.4
Breakout cones**
(See Clauses D.6.2.1 and D.7.2.1.)

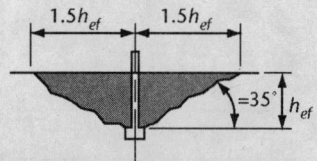

(a) Section through failure cone

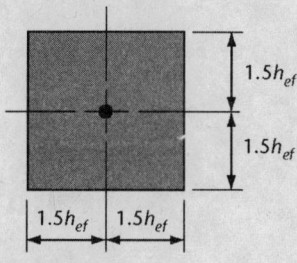

(b) Plan view

Notes:
(1) *The critical edge distance for headed studs, headed bolts, expansion anchors, and undercut anchors is 1.5 h_{ef}.*
(2) $A_{No} = (2 \times 1.5h_{ef}) \times (2 \times 1.5h_{ef})$
$= 3h_{ef} \times 3h_{ef}$
$= 9h_{ef}^2$

Figure D.5
Calculation of A_{No}
(See Clause D.3.)

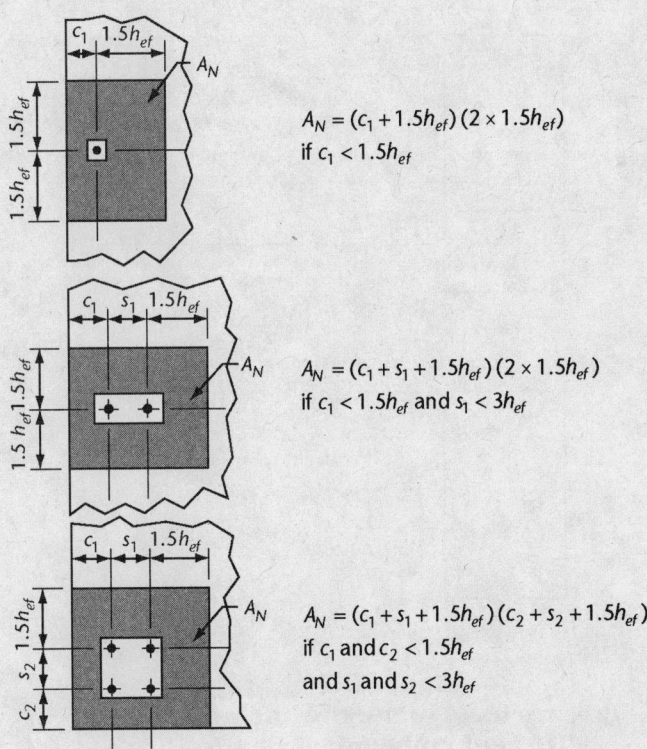

$$A_N = (c_1 + 1.5h_{ef})(2 \times 1.5h_{ef})$$
if $c_1 < 1.5h_{ef}$

$$A_N = (c_1 + s_1 + 1.5h_{ef})(2 \times 1.5h_{ef})$$
if $c_1 < 1.5h_{ef}$ and $s_1 < 3h_{ef}$

$$A_N = (c_1 + s_1 + 1.5h_{ef})(c_2 + s_2 + 1.5h_{ef})$$
if c_1 and $c_2 < 1.5h_{ef}$
and s_1 and $s_2 < 3h_{ef}$

Figure D.6
Projected areas for single anchors and groups of anchors
(See Clause D.3.)

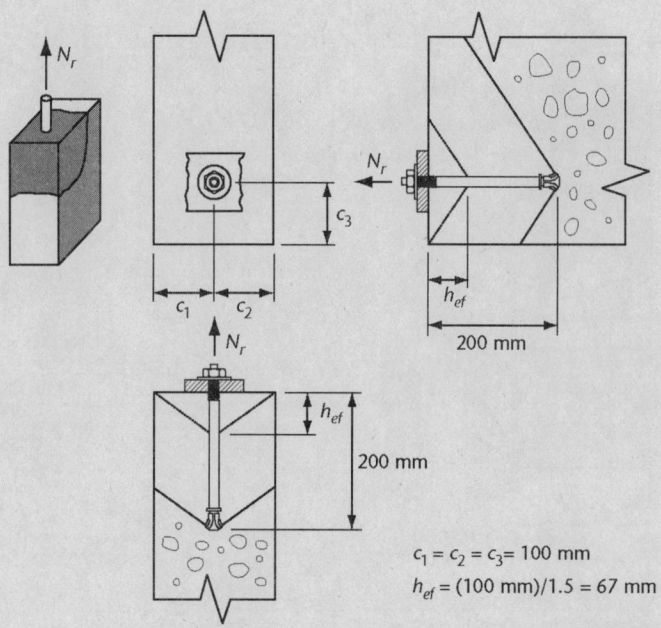

$c_1 = c_2 = c_3 = 100$ mm

$h_{ef} = (100$ mm$)/1.5 = 67$ mm

Figure D.7
Failure surfaces in narrow members for
different embedment depths
(See Clauses D.6.2.3.)

CSA Standard A23.3-04

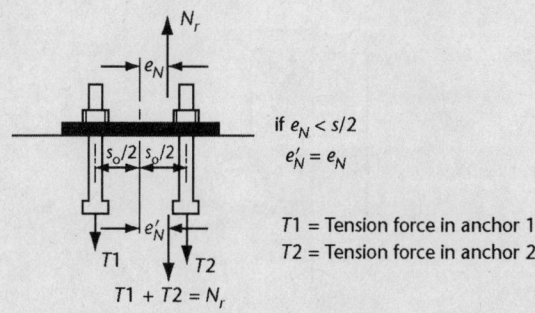

if $e_N < s/2$
$e'_N = e_N$

$T1$ = Tension force in anchor 1
$T2$ = Tension force in anchor 2

$T1 + T2 = N_r$

(a) Determination of e'_N when all anchors in a group are in tension

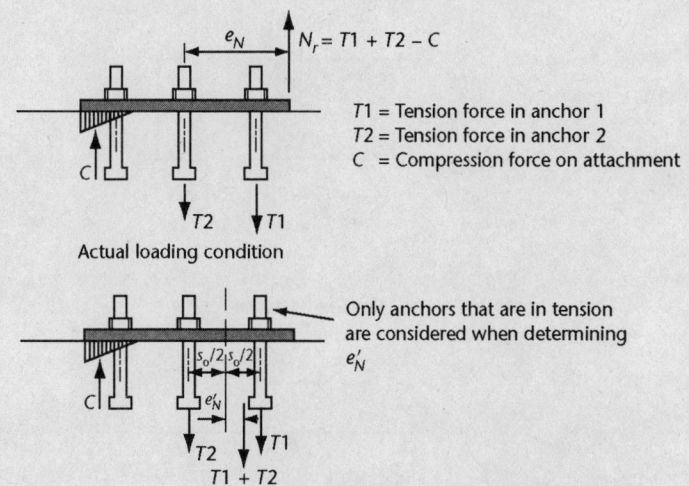

$N_r = T1 + T2 - C$

$T1$ = Tension force in anchor 1
$T2$ = Tension force in anchor 2
C = Compression force on attachment

Actual loading condition

Only anchors that are in tension
are considered when determining
e'_N

$T1 + T2$

(b) Determination of e'_N with only some anchors in tension

Figure D.8
Definition of dimension e'_N
(See Clause D.3.)

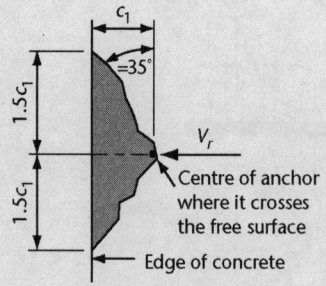

(a) Plan view

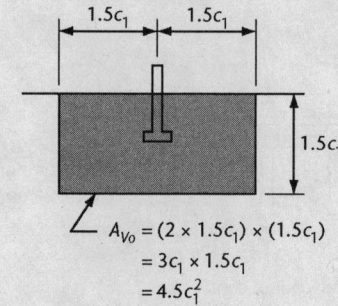

(b) Front view

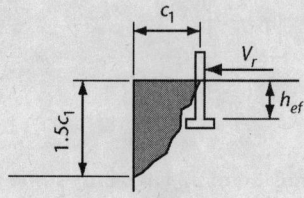

(c) Side section

Note: *The critical edge distance for headed studs, headed bolts, expansion anchors, and undercut anchors is $1.5c_1$.*

Δ

Figure D.9
Calculation of A_{Vo}
(See Clause D.3.)

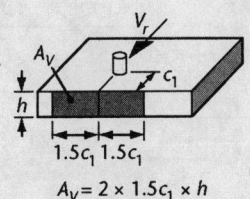

$$A_V = 2 \times 1.5c_1 \times h$$

(a) A single anchor, if $h < 1.5c_1$

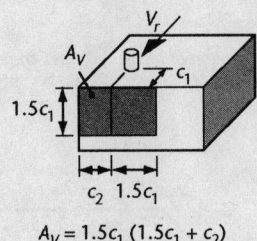

$$A_V = 1.5c_1 (1.5c_1 + c_2)$$

(b) A single anchor, if $c_2 < 1.5c_1$

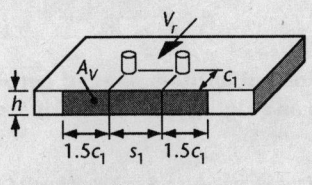

$$A_V = (2 \times 1.5c_1 + s_1) \times h$$

**(c) Two loaded anchors aligned parallel
to edge, if $h < 1.5c_1$ and $s_1 < 3c_1$**

Figure D.10
Projected areas for single anchors and anchor groups
(See Clause D.3.)

(Continued)

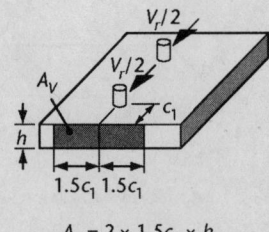

$$A_V = 2 \times 1.5c_1 \times h$$

**(d) Two loaded anchors aligned perpendicular
to edge, if $h < 1.5c_1$***

**One assumption of the distribution of forces indicates that half the shear would be critical
on the front anchor and its projected area.*

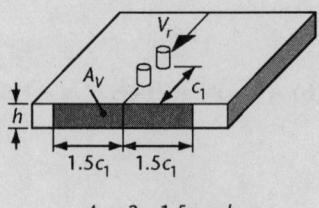

$$A_V = 2 \times 1.5c_1 \times h$$

**(e) Two loaded anchors aligned perpendicular to
edge and rigidly connected, if $h < 1.5c_1$†**

*†Another assumption of the distribution of forces that applies only where anchors are rigidly
connected to the attachment indicates that the total shear would be critical on
the rear anchor and its projected area.*

Figure D.10 (Concluded)

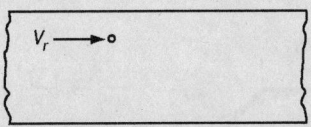

V_r (parallel to edge) $= 2 \times V_r$ (perpendicular to edge)

(a) Shear force parallel to edge

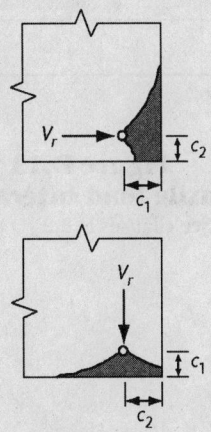

(b) Anchors near a corner

Figure D.11
Shear loading parallel and perpendicular to edge
(See Clause D.7.2.1.)

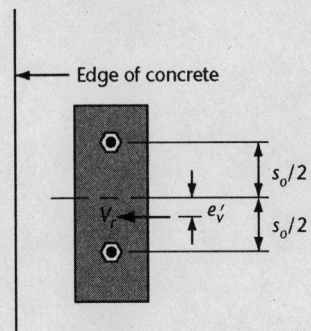

Edge of concrete

Figure D.12
Definition of dimension e'_v
(See Clause D.3.)

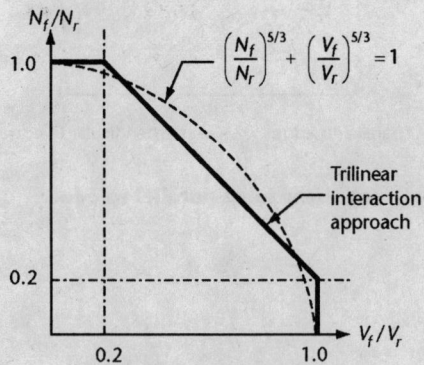

Figure D.13
Shear and tensile load interaction equation
(See Clauses D.8.2–D.8.4.)

Proposition de modification

N'hésitez pas à nous faire part de vos suggestions et de vos commentaires. Au moment de soumettre des propositions de modification aux normes CSA et autres publications CSA prière de fournir les renseignements demandés ci-dessous et de formuler les propositions sur une feuille volante. Il est recommandé d'inclure
- le numéro de la norme/publication
- le numéro de l'article, du tableau ou de la figure visé
- la formulation proposée
- la raison de cette modification.

Proposal for change

CSA welcomes your suggestions and comments. To submit your proposals for changes to CSA Standards and other CSA publications, please supply the information requested below and attach your proposal for change on a separate page(s). Be sure to include the
- Standard/publication number
- relevant Clause, Table, and/or Figure number(s)
- wording of the proposed change
- rationale for the change.

Nom/Name: _____

Affiliation: _____

Adresse/Address: _____

_____

Ville/City: _____

État/Province/State: _____

Pays/Country: _____ **Code postal/Postal/Zip code:** _____

Téléphone/Telephone: _____ **Télécopieur/Fax:** _____

Date: _____

J'accepte que la CSA conserve et utilise les renseignements ci-dessus afin de faciliter la réception de mes suggestions et commentaires.

I consent to CSA collecting and using the above information to facilitate the collection of my suggestions and comments.

Consultez la politique CSA en matière de confidentialité au www.csagroup.org/legal pour savoir comment nous protégeons vos renseignements personnels.

Visit CSA's policy on privacy at www.csagroup.org/legal to find out how we protect your personal information.

PRINTED IN CANADA
IMPRIMÉ AU CANADA

ISBN 1-55397-559-6

Explanatory Notes On
CSA Standard A23.3-04

These Explanatory Notes Were Prepared by:

P. Adebar
S. Alexander
M. Bartlett
M. P. Collins
W. Dilger
W. Kassian

T. Kokai
R.E. Loov
R.J. McGrath
D. Mitchell
J. Mutrie
M. Allen

The explanation and opinions expressed in these notes are those of the authors and are not intended to be considered the opinion of the CSA Committee responsible for the preparation of the A23.3 Standard nor to detract from this Committee's duties insofar as interpretation and revision of the Standard is concerned.

Copyright © Cement Association of Canada - 2006

N1.5 Units

The equations throughout the standard are consistent with the units listed so that units have been deleted from the remainder of the Standard. A designer may use other units but will then need to revise some of the equations which have units imbedded in their constants. An example of this is the equation $l_{db} = 0.044d_bf_y$ in Clause 12.3.2. The constant has units of MPa^{-1} in order to make this equation dimensionally consistent.

N2.4.2 Standard Notation for Reinforcing Bar Diameters

In calculations or spacing limits involving the bar diameter, d_b, it is permissible to take d_b equal to the bar designation number.

N3 Materials

N3.1.1

Geometric properties of standard prestressing tendons are summarized in Table N3-1.

Table N3.1.1
Standard Prestressing Tendons

Tendon Type	Grade f_{pu} MPa	Size Designation	Nominal Dimensions		Nominal Linear Density kg/m
			Diameter mm	Area mm^2	
Seven Wire Strand	1860	9	9.53	55	0.432
	1860	11	11.13	74	0.582
	1860	13	12.70	99	0.775
	1860	15	15.24	140	1.109
	1760	16	15.47	148	1.173
Prestressing Wire	1550	5*	5.00	19.6	0.154
	1720	5	5.00	19.6	0.154
	1620	7	7.00	38.5	0.302
	1760	7	7.00	38.5	0.302
Deformed Prestressing Bars	1080	15	15.0	177	1.44
	1030	26	26.5	551	4.48
	1100	26**	26.5	551	4.48
	1030	32	32.0	804	6.53
	1100	32**	32.0	804	6.53
	1030	36	36.0	1018	8.27

* Available with surface indentation
** Available on special order

N3.1.3

Reinforcing bars conforming to CSA Standard G30.18 with $f_y = 400$ MPa (Grade 400) are the most frequently used type of reinforcement. The weldable grade bars conforming to CSA Standard G30.18 have a more closely controlled chemical composition which results in a more predictable and more ductile stress-strain response. Reinforcement for structures subjected to seismic action may need to be weldable grade (see Clause 21.2.5).

The geometric properties of standard reinforcing bars are summarized in Table N3.1.3

Table N3.1.3
Standard Deformed Reinforcing Bars

Bar Number[*]	Nominal Dimension[**]			Nominal Linear Density kg/m
	Area mm^2	Diameter mm	Perimeter mm	
10M	100	11.3	36	0.785
15M	200	16.0	50	1.570
20M	300	19.5	61	2.355
25M	500	25.2	79	3.925
30M	700	29.9	94	5.495
35M	1000	35.7	112	7.850
45M	1500	43.7	137	11.775
55M	2000	56.4	177	19.625

*   Bar numbers are based on the rounded off nominal diameter of the bars
** Nominal dimensions are equivalent to those of a plain round bar having the same mass per metre as the deformed bar.

N7   Details of Reinforcement

N7.1
The CSA Standard A23.1 Clauses concerning hooks and bends are reproduced in Annex A (see Clause 6.6.2).

N7.3.1
See Clause 6.6.8 in Annex A.

N7.4.1.1
See Clause 6.6.5 in Annex A.

N7.4.2.1
The phrase "bundled in contact" is intended to preclude bundling more than two bars in the same plane. Fig. N7.4.2.1strates acceptable bar arrangements.

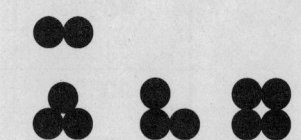

Fig. N7.4.2.1 Bar Arrangements for Bundles

N7.4.4
See Clause 6.6.6.2 in Annex A.

N7.5.1

The details and design of ties near bends in offset bars are illustrated in Fig. N7.5.1.

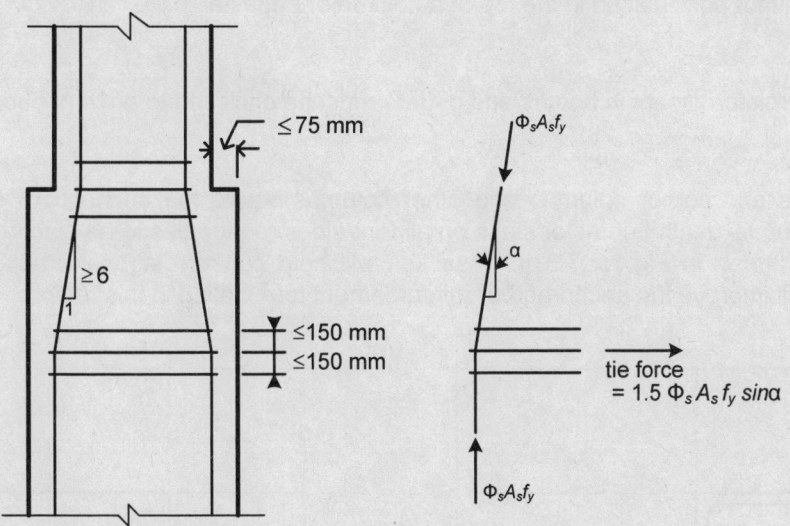

Fig. N7.5.1   Tie Reinforcement Near Offset Bars

N7.6.4.1

See Clause 6.6.3 in Annex A.

N7.6.5.2

The purpose of ties is primarily to restrain the longitudinal bars from outward buckling. The diameter and spacing of the ties are therefore related to the diameter of the longitudinal bars with further restrictions relating tie spacing to tie diameter and the least column dimension. For specified concrete strengths greater than 50 MPa, the tie spacings are reduced by 25% to provide more confinement for higher strength concretes.

N7.6.5.5

Fig. N7.5.5 illustrates tie arrangements which satisfy the requirements for lateral support of column bars.

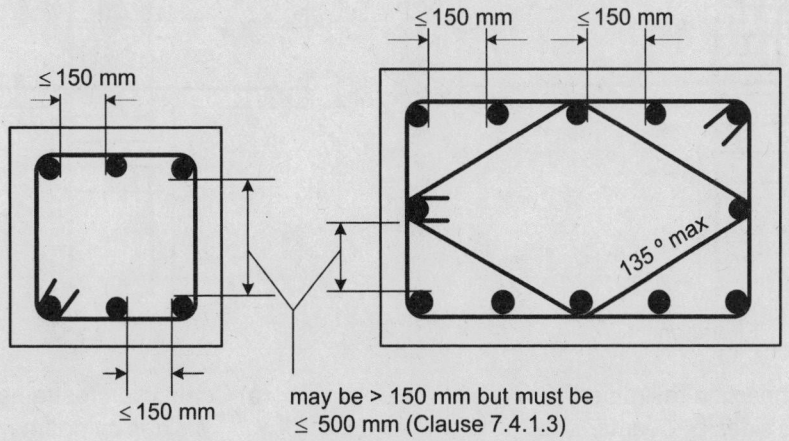

Fig. N7.6.5.5   Requirements for Lateral Support of Column Bars

N7.6.5.8

This new clause introduced in the 2004 Standard requires the designer to provide containment ties around anchor bolts placed in the top of a column or pedestal.

N7.6.6.1

Compression reinforcement in beams and girders must be enclosed to prevent buckling.

N7.7.3

Edge columns and corner columns and other columns where the connection regions are not restrained by equal depth beams or slabs on all four sides require ties to be placed within the joint region as illustrated in Fig. N7.7.3. These ties will help control diagonal cracking in the joint region, and will improve the anchorage of reinforcement terminating in this region.

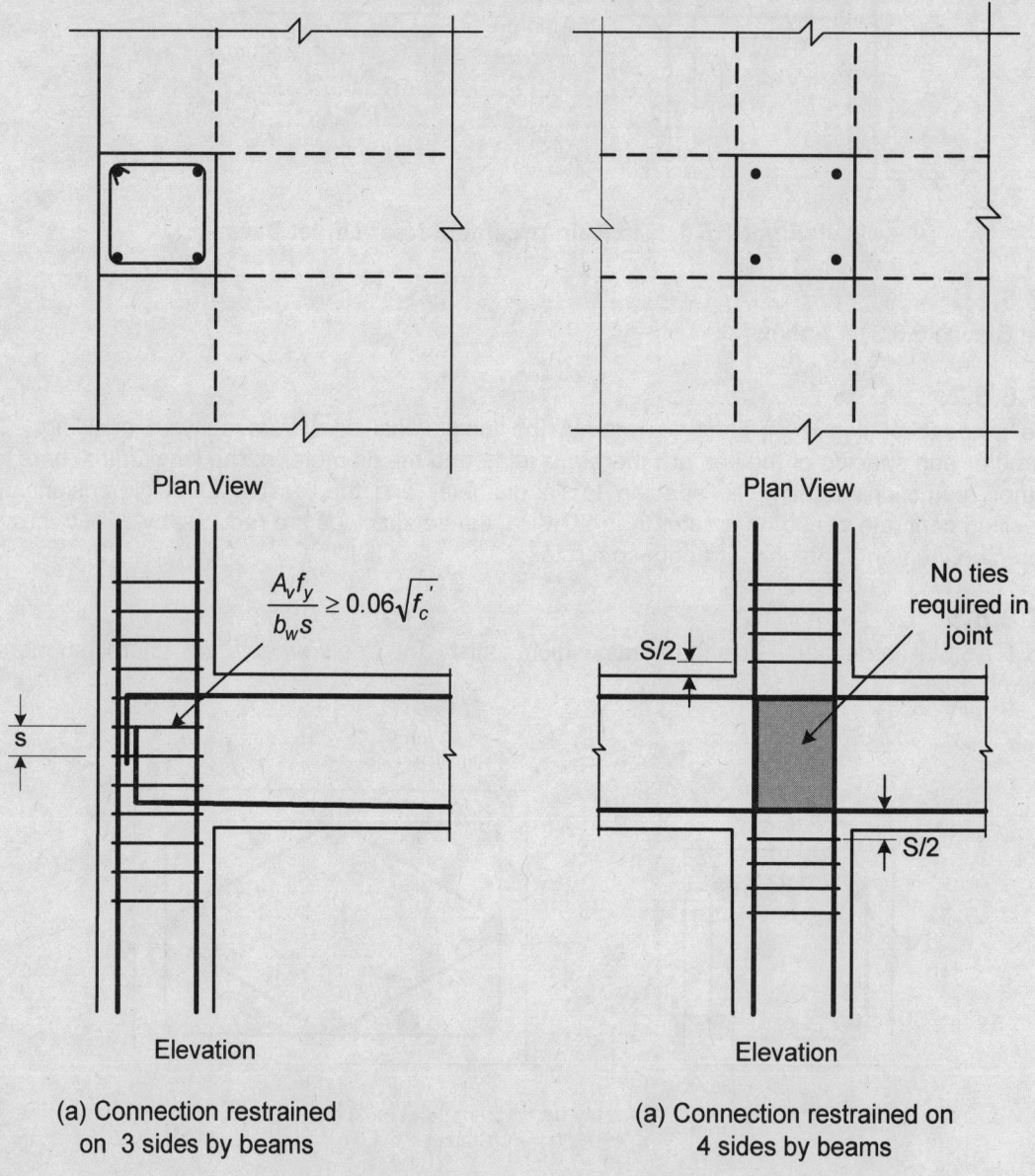

$$\frac{A_v f_y}{b_w s} \geq 0.06\sqrt{f_c'}$$

Plan View   Plan View

No ties required in joint

$S/2$

s

$S/2$

Elevation   Elevation

(a) Connection restrained on 3 sides by beams   (a) Connection restrained on 4 sides by beams

Fig. N7.7.3   Tie Requirements within Connections of Framing Elements

N7.8.1

The purpose of this minimum reinforcement is to provide some control of the cracking caused by shrinkage and temperature effects and to tie the structure together after cracking.

N7.8.2

The amounts of shrinkage and temperature reinforcement given in the standards prior to 1994 were found to be inadequate in preventing wide shrinkage and temperature cracks in slabs. In deciding upon appropriate distribution and amounts of reinforcement needed for better crack control the skin reinforcement concept of Clause 10.6.2 provides useful guidance as illustrated in Fig. N7.5.

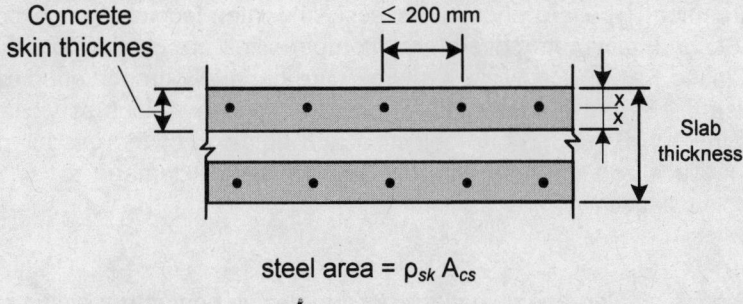

steel area = $\rho_{sk} A_{cs}$

Fig. N7.8.2   Skin Reinforcement for Crack Control

N8 — Design — Limit States, load combinations and material properties

Clause 8 includes general requirements for all concrete structures including limit states, loads, and material properties. The load factors and load combinations are consistent with those in the 2005 National Building Code of Canada (NBCC) as shown in an abridged form in Annex C of this standard.

N8.1   Limit states

The various limit states to be considered in the design of concrete structures are listed in Clauses 8.1.1 to 8.1.5. For specialized structures, such as water tanks, other limit states such as resistance to leakage may also apply.

With the exception of structural integrity, the limit states are listed in the order that they should be considered in the design process. First, the concrete strength, water-cement ratio, air entrainment and cement type are chosen to satisfy the intended use and exposure conditions (Clause 8.1.1). Second, minimum covers and member sizes are chosen to achieve the desired fire resistance (Clause 8.1.2). Concrete structures are generally proportioned to satisfy ultimate limit states (Clause 8.1.3) and are checked for compliance with various serviceability limit states (Clauses 8.1.4.1 through 8.1.4.3). The selection and detailing of the overall structural system should ensure that localized damage will not result in major damage to, or collapse of, the structure as a whole (Clause 8.1.5).

N8.2   Loading

The loads, load factors and load combinations used to design concrete structures in this standard should be obtained from the applicable building code, typically a provincial building code based on the 2005 National Building Code of Canada. If other types of structures are designed, such as bridges or tunnel liners, it may be necessary to use load factors derived specifically for these structures.

N8.2.2   Imposed deformations

Loads caused by the restraint of imposed deformations, including secondary reactions and internal force effects in indeterminate prestressed structures, are no longer included in the general load combinations for ultimate limit states specified in the 2005 National Building Code of Canada. While these loads are self-equilibrated and so do not alter the load that causes a full plastic collapse mechanism to form in a ductile structure, they should generally be considered for concrete structures having limited ductility. Load factors for T and P loads specified in the 2005 NBCC are presented in Section C.1.2.3 of A23.3-04.

N8.3   Load combinations and load factors

The 2005 edition of the National Building Code of Canada includes several significant changes from the 1995 edition. Snow is now a separate load type that is independent of live load due to use and occupancy. Specified snow and wind loads are based on 50-year return periods instead of 30-year return periods. Importance factors are specified for snow, wind and earthquake loads depending on the building classification.

The 2005 NBCC also adopts the "companion action" format for all load combinations. This format is recognized internationally for its simplicity and appropriateness for combining transient loads without explicitly requiring load combination factors ψ. Each load combination specifies the magnitude of a principal transient load plus magnitudes of companion transient loads that are consistent with the time period while the principal load acts at its maximum value.

Load factors are intended to account for variability and uncertainty of the magnitude, position and combination of the loads, inaccuracies introduced by the simplified modelling of the loads (e.g., the use of uniform floor loads) and inaccuracies introduced by assumptions made in the structural analysis.

N8.4   Factored resistance

A material resistance factor for the steel resistance, ϕ_s, is intended to account for variations in resistance that result from the variability of the mechanical properties of the reinforcement, the normal tolerances of bar placement, and inaccuracies resulting from the steel terms in the design equations. A material resistance factor for concrete accounts for a similar set of variations resulting from the variability of the concrete strength, cross section geometry, and model error in the design equations. When computing the factored moment resistance of a beam, M_r, the designer would compute:

$$M_r = \phi_s A_s f_y \left[d - \frac{\phi_s A_s f_y}{2 \phi_c \alpha_1 f_c' b} \right]$$

If the factored resistance of a beam or beam column is being computed using a plane sections analysis, the material resistance factor is applied to the stress at any strain to give factored stress-strain relationships as shown in Fig. N8.4.

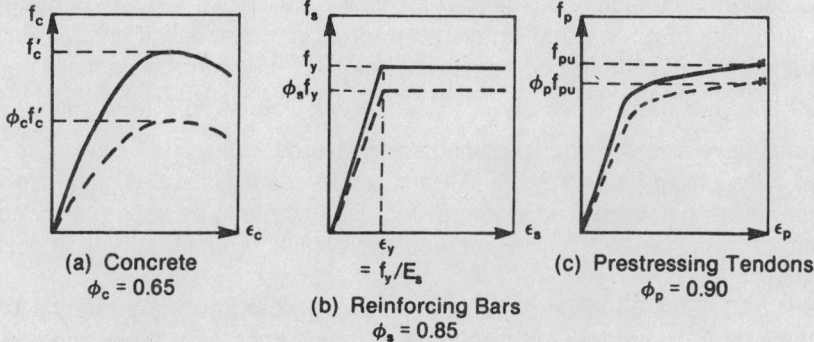

Fig. N8.4 Factored Material Stress-Strain Relationships

Equations defining empirical limits, such as Eq. (10-4) in Clause 10.5.1.2 or the equations in Clause 12, do not include ϕ factors because they are recognized to already include a safety margin.

N8.4.2 Factored concrete strength

The resistance factor for concrete has been increased from 0.60 to 0.65 in this edition of A23.3, primarily to achieve margins of safety for components cast from concretes with compressive strengths between 20 and 35 MPa that are consistent with past editions of the standard.

N8.4.3 Factored reinforcement and tendon force

Clauses 8.4.3 and 8.5.3.1 require that, when determining the factored resistance of bars and tendons, the resistance factor is applied regardless of whether the steel has yielded or not. For example, as shown in Fig. N8.4, the resistance factor ϕ_s is applied to the bar force $\phi_s A_s f_y$ or $\phi_s A_s E_s \varepsilon_s$ to account for deviations of the location of the reinforcement and uncertainty in the prediction of the resistance as well as variability of the yield strength.

N8.5.1 Design strength for reinforcement

CSA Standard G30.18 specifies requirements for steels with yield strengths of 400 and 500 MPa. Crack widths and deflections may be excessive in beams with f_y in excess of 500 MPa.

Explanatory Notes on CSA A23.3-04

N8.5.2 Compression reinforcement

Section 10.1.3 defines the maximum strain at the extreme concrete compression fibre to be 0.0035. Thus the maximum compressive strain that can be developed in the reinforcement before the concrete crushes is 0.0035, and steels supplied in accordance with a specification that defines the yield strength at greater than a strain of 0.0035 may not yield before the concrete crushes. For this reason, Clause 8.5.2 limits the value of f_y that can be used in design calculations to 400 MPa, which can be achieved by a strain of 0.0035, or to the stress corresponding to a strain of 0.0035.

N8.6.1 Design strength of concrete

The strength equations and detailing rules of this standard are applicable for concretes with compressive strengths from 20 to 80 MPa. Clause 12.1.2 limits the value of $\sqrt{f_c'}$ for use in bond and anchorage calculations to 8 MPa. This is not intended to imply an upper limit on f_c' of 64 MPa, but merely reflects the upper limit of extensive bond test data. Similarly, the limitations given in Clause 11.3.6.3 reflect the upper limit of compressive strengths investigated in tests used to establish design equation constants empirically. Clause 21.2.6.1 permits specified compressive strengths of up to 80 MPa for some forms of construction involving normal density concrete, but limits the maximum compressive strength of structural low-density concretes to 30 MPa and limits the maximum value of $\sqrt{f_c'}$ used in calculations to 8 MPa. Some structural low density concretes have displayed brittle compression failures.

Concrete strengths greater than 80 MPa may be used if the designer can establish the structural properties and detailing requirements for the concrete to be used. Major areas requiring documentation are requirements for column ties and confining reinforcement in columns, beams and beam-column joints.

CSA Standard A23.1-04 defines concretes having compressive strengths of 70 MPa or higher as high-strength concretes and gives special requirements for producing and testing such concretes.

N8.6.2 Modulus of elasticity

The modulus of elasticity computed using the either Eq. (8-1) in Clause 8.6.2.2 or Eq. (8-2) in Clause 8.6.2.3 represents a secant modulus as shown in Fig N8.6.2. The modulus of elasticity of Canadian concretes varies markedly depending on the concrete strength, the concrete density and, especially for higher strength concretes, on the type of coarse aggregate.

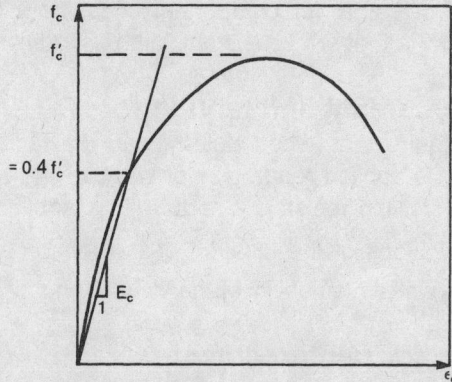

Figure N8.6.2 Modulus of Elasticity of Concrete, E_c

N8.6.5 Modification factors for concrete density

The tensile strength of some low-density concretes is lower than that for normal density concrete. This is accounted for by the factor λ that appears in equations for the tensile strength of concrete and shear carried by concrete in Clauses 11, 13, 18, 21, 22 and Annex D.

N9.1 Methods of analysis

The methods of analysis considered in Clause 9 are elastic frame analysis, approximate frame analysis, analysis by strut-and-tie methods, elastic stress analysis, elastic plate analysis and plastic analysis.

N9.2.1 Stiffness

As stated in Clause 9.2.1.2, the member stiffnesses used in elastic analyses to determine lateral deflections of frames, or in second-order frame analyses should be representative of the degree of cracking and inelastic action at the loading stage that the calculations apply to. Thus, when computing second-order effects in unbraced or lightly braced structures to enable the beams and columns to be designed for strength, the EI assumptions should be representative of the stage just prior to ultimate. In this case, the values specified in Clause 10.14.1 should be used.

At service loads, the member stiffnesses are greater than at ultimate because the extent of cracking and inelastic action is less. For analysis of lateral frame deflections at service loads the EI of the columns should be taken as 1.0 EI_g, where I_g is the gross moment of inertia, or (1.0/0.7 =) 1.4 times the value given in Clause 10.14.1. Similarly, the EI of beams, walls and slabs used in a service-load analysis may be taken as 1.4 times the values given in Clause 10.14.1.

If needed, the torsional stiffness may be taken as 0.15 GJ for an analysis at ultimate loads or 0.20 GJ at service loads.

For the analysis of moments in braced frames, where second-order effects are not significant, it is only necessary that the relative magnitudes of the beam and column stiffnesses be modelled accurately. Again in this case the EI values in Clause 10.14.1 can be used.

Values of E and I to be used for the computation of the deflection of beams subjected to gravity loads are given in Clauses 9.8.2.3 and 9.8.2.4.

N9.2.2 Span length

The span lengths used in the analysis of continuous frames should be taken centre-to-centre of joints. Clause 9.2.2.2 allows the moments at the faces of the joints to be used for the design of members. The computation of the moments at the face of the joints should account for the increase in negative moments due to the higher stiffness within the joint. Thus for uniformly loaded prismatic beams it is customary to compute the moment at the face of the joint, M_F, as:

$$M_F = M_{CL} + Vc/3$$

where M_{CL} is the moment in the beam at the centre of the joint, V is the shear in the beam at the centre of the joint, and c is the width of the column in the direction parallel to the beam. The factor of 3 in this equation empirically accounts for the increase of the fixed end moments at the center of the joint and the resulting reduction of the moments at the face of the columns.

N9.2.2.4

When a structure containing shear walls deflects laterally, the deflections of the walls impose a relative displacement on the ends of the beams as shown in Fig. 9.2.2.4. The effect of the width of the shear wall can be idealized by assigning very high moments of inertia to the extensions of the beams within the shear walls. The localized reduction of the stiffness of the coupling beams due to cracking within the column-wall joints is sometimes modelled by terminating the region of very high beam stiffness about half the beam depth inside the wall from the face of the wall.

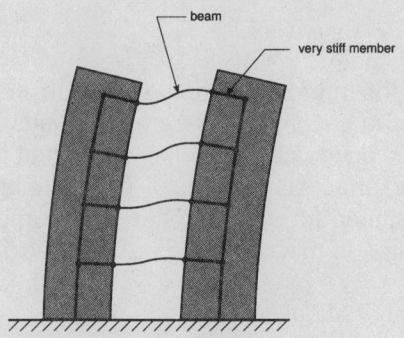

Fig. N9.2.2.4
Idealization of Beams in a Shear-Wall Frame Structure

N9.2.3.1   Continuous beams and one-way slabs

Dead loads due to the self weight of materials depend on density and construction tolerances and so are usually highly correlated from span to span. Thus they are not patterned, but according to Clause 9.2.3.1 (a), (b) and (c) are applied uniformly with a dead load factor of 1.25 in all spans or with a dead load factor of 0.90 in all spans. Superimposed dead loads, such as permanent machinery or earth fill, may in some cases be placed on the structure in a patterned manner and in such circumstances can be patterned with zero superimposed dead load in some spans and with a dead load factor of 1.25 times the superimposed dead load in other spans.

N9.2.4 Redistribution of moments in continuous flexural members

Redistribution of elastic bending moments can occur prior to failure due to inelastic rotations in regions with high moments. Beam sections having low percentages of tension reinforcement or containing compression reinforcement have low c/d values and so can tolerate larger redistributions. Due to redistribution, the computed bending moments at a support may be reduced provided that the bending moments in each adjacent span are increased to satisfy equilibrium for the loading case under consideration. Since the loading that causes the maximum moment at a support is different from the loading case causing maximum moments in the adjacent spans, accounting for moment redistribution can result in a reduction of the required flexural reinforcement at the support and span regions, as shown in Fig. N9.2.4.

Clause 9.2.4 refers to the redistribution of negative moment since this is the normal case in design. Occasionally, as for example, in the case of a continuous inverted T-beam, the amount of redistribution may be limited by the c/d ratio at the point of maximum positive moment.

Explanatory Notes on CSA A23.3-04

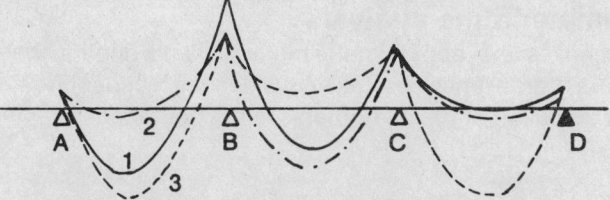

load case 1 — LL on AB and BC + DL on all spans
load case 2 — LL on BC + DL on all spans
load case 3 — LL on AB and CD + DL on all spans
load case 4 — LL on BC and CD + DL on all spans (not shown)

(a) Moment Diagrams for Pattern Loading

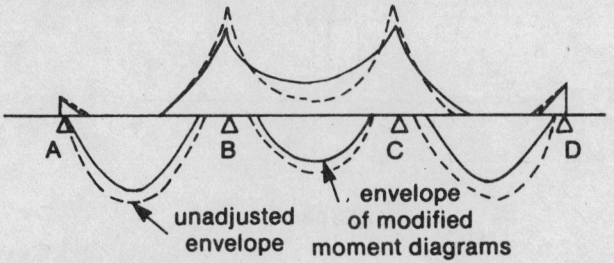

Moment Diagrams Modified as follows:-
 (i) load cases 1 and 4 — support moments decreased with corresponding increases made to positive moments
 (ii) load cases 2 and 3 — support moments increased with corresponding decreases made to positive moments

(b) Moment Envelopes

Fig. N9.2.4
Illustration of Moment Redistribution

N9.3   Approximate frame analysis

Figure N9.3.3 summarizes the approximate moments and shears that may be used in lieu of performing a series of frame analyses that consider the various live load patterns specified in Clause 9.2.3.1. Redistribution of these moments is not permitted.

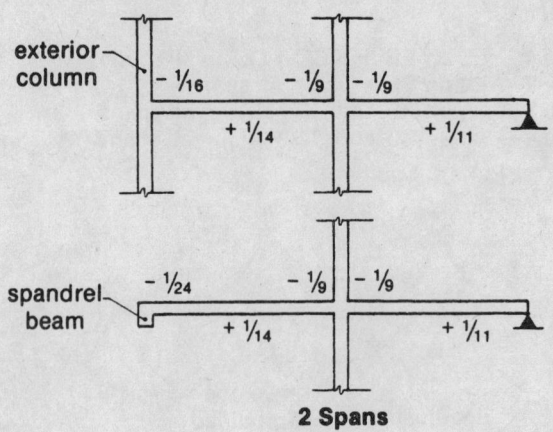

2 Spans

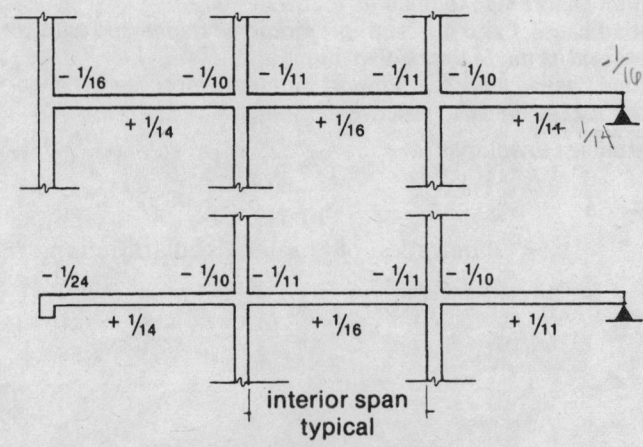

interior span typical

More than 2 Spans

Note: shear force = 1.15 $w_f \ell_n/2$ in end members at face of first interior support and $w_f \ell_n/2$ at face of all other supports

$$\text{moment} = \text{coefficient} \times w_f \, \ell_n^2$$

Fig. N9.3.3
Approximate Moments and Shears for the Design
of Flexural Members Satisfying the Conditions of Clause 9.3.3

N9.4   Analysis by strut-and-tie models

Although strut-and-tie models can be used to proportion all types of concrete structures, they are generally used in regions where the plane sections theory of flexure is not applicable such as deep beams, members with discontinuities such as holes, dapped ends and corbels, beam-column joints and prestress anchorage zones.

Clause 9.4 permits the use of strut-and-tie models. Clause 11.4 and the Notes on that clause present design guidance. The most important single requirement of a strut-and-tie model is that it be a complete force field in equilibrium with the applied loads and reactions.

N9.5   Finite element analysis

Clause 9.5 sets out requirements for the use of finite element analyses in design. A major requirement of Clause 9.5.1 is that differences between the idealized finite element model and the reinforced concrete structure must be implicitly considered. This is particularly true if an elastic analysis that ignores cracking is conducted. Clause 9.5.4 requires an independent check of the analysis.

N9.7   Plastic analysis

Braced frames or slabs may be designed using plastic analysis. The use of plastic analysis in two-way slab design is discussed in Clause 13.7.

N9.8   Control of deflections

This clause addresses deflections of beams due to gravity loads. The selection of two-way slab thicknesses to control deflection and the computation of two-way slab deflections are considered in Clause 13.2. The control of lateral deflections of frames subjected to service loads is not specifically addressed in this standard. Note N9.2.1 suggests EI values to be used for such an analysis.

N9.8.2.3 E and I

As shown in Fig. N9.8.2.3, the flexural stiffness of a beam decreases after cracking and approaches the fully cracked flexural stiffness, $E_c I_{cr}$. Equation (9-1) gives an expression for the effective secant stiffness for this case.

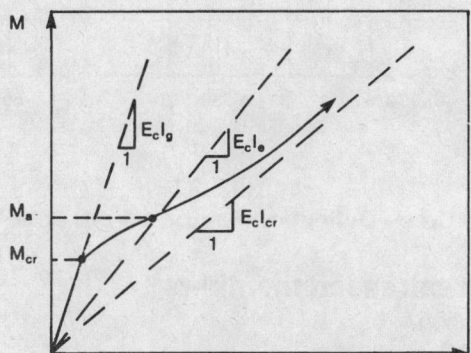

Fig. N9.8.2.3
Effective Flexural Stiffness

N9.8.2.5   Sustained load deflections

The term $S/(1+50\rho')$ accounts for the long-term deflections caused by creep and shrinkage. The total deflection is computed using

$$\Delta_t = (\Delta_d + \Delta_{\ell s})\left(1+\frac{S}{1+50\rho'}\right) + (\Delta_\ell - \Delta_{\ell s})$$

Explanatory Notes on CSA A23.3-04

where:

Δ_t = total immediate and long-term deflection

Δ_d = immediate deflection due to dead loads

Δ_ℓ = immediate deflection due to live loads

$\Delta_{\ell s}$ = immediate deflection due to sustained portion of live loads

The incremental deflection, Δ_i, that occurs after partitions are installed is computed using:

$$\Delta_i = (\Delta_d + \Delta_{\ell s})\left(\frac{S}{1 + 50\rho'}\right) + (\Delta_\ell - \Delta_{\ell s})$$

If the dead load and the sustained live load are applied at different times it may be desirable to use different values of S for the dead and sustained live load.

N9.8.2.6   Deflection limits

In checking the limits stipulated in Table 9.3, it is necessary to compute the long-term deflection that will occur after attachment of non-structural elements. In performing these calculations, Fig. N9.8.2.6, which shows the variation of S with load duration, may be useful.

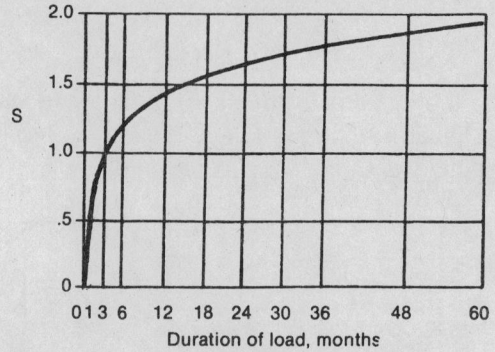

Fig. N9.8.2.6
Variation of Creep Deflection Factor, S with Load Duration>

N9.8.4.3   Partially prestressed members

See N18.3.3 for more information.

N Table 9-3 Maximum permissible computed deflections

Ponding may be a problem for medium- to long-span roofs in regions where snow loads are light. See Commentary H of the "User's Guide - NBC 2005 Structural Commentaries (Part 4 of Division B)" for further guidance. Minor cracking of partitions may occur even if the $\ell/480$ deflection limit is satisfied.

N10   Flexure and Axial Loads

Clause 10.1 presents the basic assumptions for both flexural and axial load resistance. Clauses 10.2 through 10.7 deal with concerns related to flexural members. Items such as T-beam flanges and joist geometry are located here. Clause 10.8 deals with bearing and Clauses 10.9 through 10.19 deal with columns.

N10.1   General Principles

Fig. N10.1 illustrates the plane section method that uses equilibrium conditions, compatibility conditions and stress-strain relationships for concrete and reinforcement.

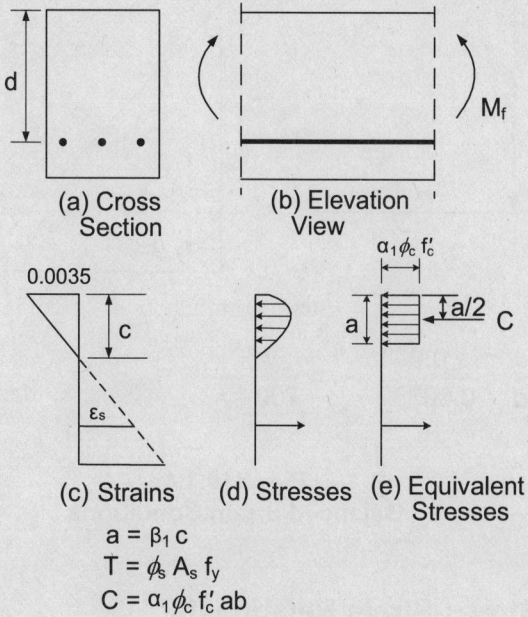

$$a = \beta_1 c$$
$$T = \phi_s A_s f_y$$
$$C = \alpha_1 \phi_c f'_c ab$$

Fig. N10.1
Plane Sections Method

N10.1.3   Maximum Concrete Strain

A strain of 0.0035 is used because this is representative of the strain at peak load for the higher strength concretes now being used. This is the value that has been used in Europe for many years.

N10.1.4   Balanced Strain Conditions

The balanced strain condition is illustrated in Fig. N10.1.4.

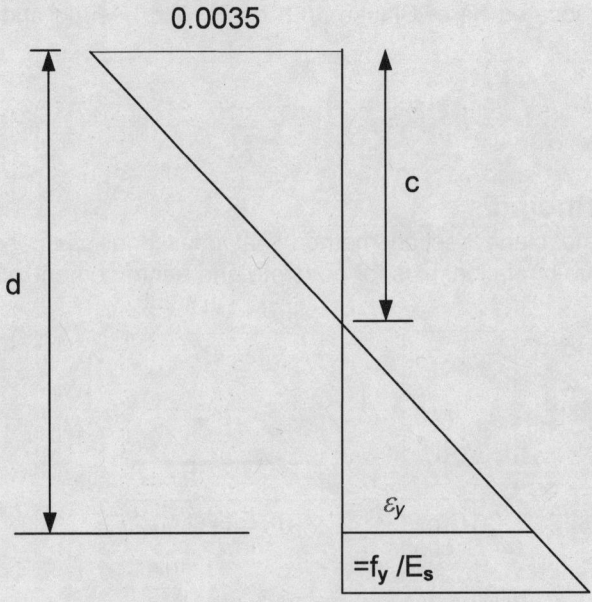

Strain Distribution

$$\frac{c}{d} = \frac{0.0035}{0.0035 + \varepsilon_y} = \frac{700}{700 + f_y}$$

Fig. N10.1.4
Balanced Strain Conditions

N10.1.6   Concrete Stress-Strain Relationship

The concrete in a structure is not expected to be as strong as the control cylinders that are cast from the same batch. This occurs from a variety of causes including bleeding, differences in compaction and differences in loading and restraint.

N10.1.7   Equivalent Rectangular Concrete Stress Distribution

The value of β_1 is larger than that traditionally used and a constant α_1 replaces the traditional constant of 0.85. These coefficients take into account the more nearly triangular stress block of higher strengths of concrete and result in more conservative M_r values for columns. To keep these factors simple, straight-line variations have been assumed that are applicable throughout the range of the current standard (20 MPa to 80 MPa). The minimum values of 0.67 do not apply until $f'_c > 120$ MPa.

N10.2   Flexural Members — Distance between Lateral Supports

Lateral instability is more critical for narrow deep beams and for beams subjected to eccentric or inclined loads.

N10.5.1   Minimum Reinforcement
The provision of a minimum amount of flexural reinforcement is intended to prevent a brittle failure at first cracking by providing adequate post-cracking strength.

N10.5.1.2
Footings of uniform thickness can be designed according to Clause 7.8.
Specific guidance is now provided for determining b_t, the width of the tension zone for the negative moment region of T-beams with a flange on one or both sides of the web.

N10.5.2   Limit of c/d for Yielding of Tension Reinforcement
The strain distribution corresponding to Eq. (10-5) is illustrated in Fig. N10.1.4. The factored concrete strength $\phi_c \alpha_1 f_c'$ and the factored bar force $\phi_s A_s f_s$ are used when calculating the neutral axis depth $c = a / \beta_1$.

Over-reinforced beams that do not meet the c/d limit of Eq. (10-5) are not permitted. Columns, on the other hand, frequently have c/d ratios larger than this value. This is permitted, but the strains in the different layers of reinforcement have to be calculated. The stress of 700 MPa is a consequence of assuming a limiting concrete strain of 0.0035 at failure with an E_s of 20 GPa.

N10.5.3   Reinforcement in T-Beam Flanges
To help the designer, the required reinforcing is explicitly defined. The intent is to ensure sufficient reinforcement in the tension zone of the slab adjacent to the web so that cracks in this region will be adequately controlled.

N10.5.3.2   Transverse Reinforcement
This situation normally occurs when a number of smaller beams supporting a one-way slab are supported by a girder, which therefore is parallel to the one-way slab. The transverse reinforcement in the girder is required to extend beyond the web of the girder, a distance equal to 0.3 of the clear spacing between the smaller beams. The purpose of this Clause is to control the cracks that will tend to occur in the flange above the edge of the web, and to avoid the necessity of complex computations to determine a suitable amount of reinforcement.

N10.6.1   Crack Control Parameter
Equation (10-6) is intended to provide a distribution of flexural reinforcement that will provide reasonable control of flexural cracking at specified loads. It is based on Gergely and Lutz's empirical equation. (Gergely, P. and Lutz, L.A. "Maximum Crack Width in Reinforced Concrete Flexural Members," Causes, Mechanisms and Control of Cracking in Concrete, SP-20, American Concrete Institute, Detroit, 1968, pp. 87-117).

$$w \approx 11 f_s \ \sqrt[3]{d_c A} \ \frac{h_2}{h_1} \ x \ 10^{-6} \ mm$$

where,
    w = crack width at tensile face
    h_1 = distance from centroid of tension steel to neutral axis
    h_2 = distance from extreme tension fibre to neutral axis.

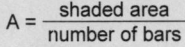

$$A = \frac{\text{shaded area}}{\text{number of bars}}$$

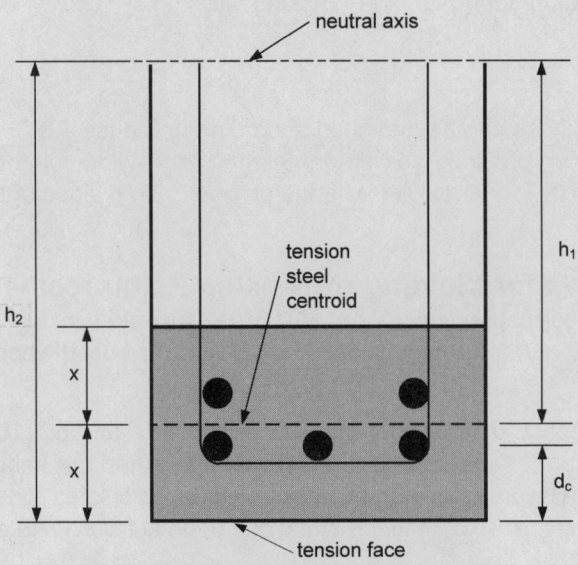

Fig. N10.6.1
Crack Width Parameters

Limiting z to 30 kN/mm and 25 kN/mm corresponds to limiting crack widths to about 0.4 mm and 0.33 mm respectively.

It may be difficult to satisfy Eq. (10-6) if covers greater than 50 mm are required for durability, fire resistance or in such members as footings. For this reason, it is not necessary to take the cover greater than 50 mm when computing A and d_c.

N10.6.2   Skin Reinforcement

While the main tension reinforcement satisfying Eq. (10-6) should provide adequate crack control in the shaded area shown in Fig. N10.6.1, it is possible that wider cracks may form on the side faces of the beam in the zone between the neutral axis and the main tension reinforcement. For this reason skin reinforcement is needed in the area A_{cs} shown shaded in Fig. N10.6.2.

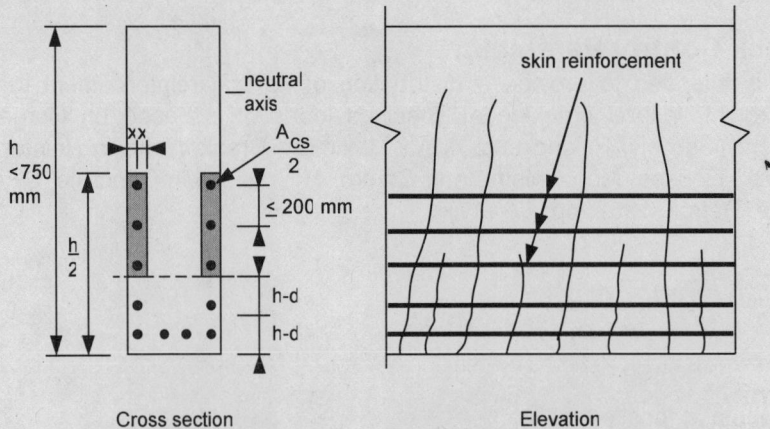

Cross section   Elevation

Fig. N10.6.2
Side-Face Cracks Controlled by Skin Reinforcement

Explanatory Notes on CSA A23.3-04

Clause 10.6.2 is based on tests reported in Franz and Breen, "Design Proposal for Side Face Crack Control Reinforcement for Large Reinforced Concrete Beams" Concrete International Design and Construction, October 1980. The value of ρ_{sk} required by Clause 10.6.2 is somewhat lower than that proposed by Franz and Breen.

N10.7 Deep Flexural Members

The flow of forces in deep flexural members can be investigated with the aid of the strut-and-tie model described in Clause 11.4.

N10.8 Design of Bearing Zones

When the loaded area is surrounded on all sides by unloaded concrete, this unloaded concrete confines and hence increases the bearing capacity of the loaded area. Fig. N10.8 illustrates the determination of A_2 for two different situations of bearing and confinement.

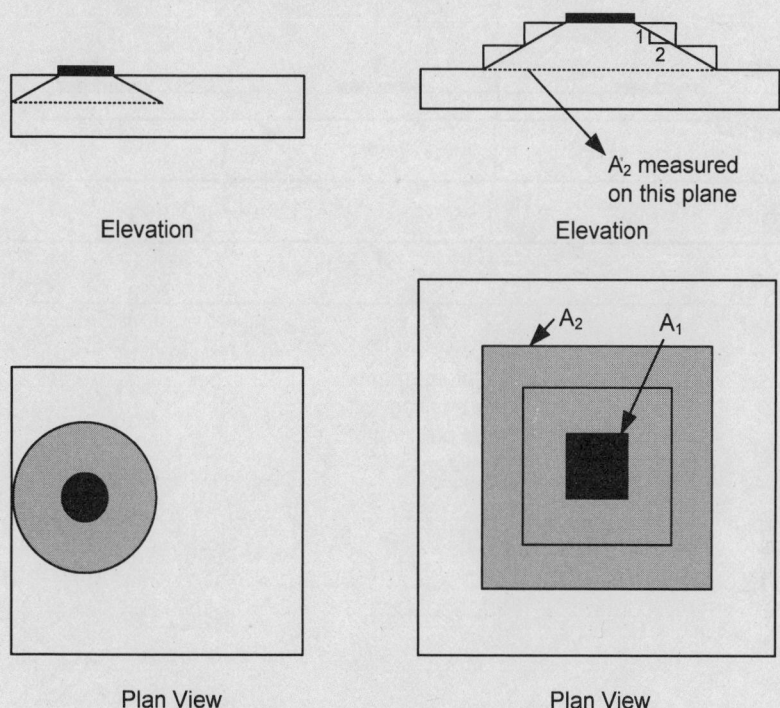

Fig. N10.8 Determination of A_2

See Clause 18.13 for information on bearing stresses associated with tendon anchorage zones.

N10.8.2

In bearing zones the possibility of bursting, splitting or spalling should be considered. If the unconfined concrete cover is directly loaded in bearing it may spall off as shown in Fig. 10.8.2(a). Hence, direct bearing on the concrete cover is undesirable. The dispersion of the bearing stresses under a bearing plate causes transverse tensile stresses, which may lead to splitting, particularly in thin members. (see Fig. N10.8.2(b)).

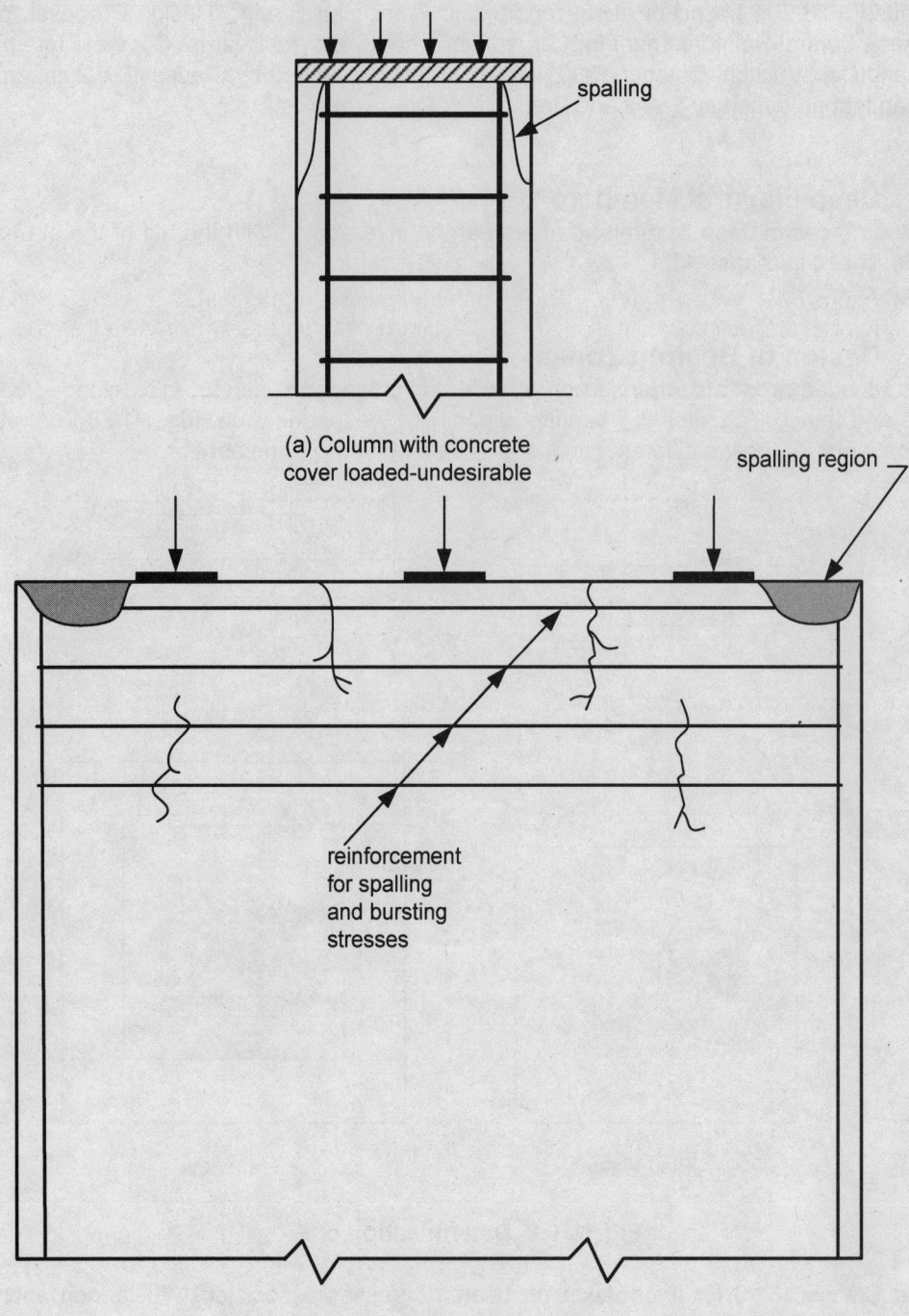

(a) Column with concrete
cover loaded-undesirable

(b) Thin wall subjected to
concentrated loads

Fig. N10.8.2
Examples of Spalling and Splitting

Explanatory Notes on CSA A23.3-04

N10.9.4

The amount of spiral reinforcement provided by Eq. (10-7) is intended to provide sufficient confinement to the core concrete so that the capacity lost when the concrete cover spalls off, can be regained due to the increased capacity of the confined core.

N10.10.1

Due to the non-linear nature of the axial load-moment curvature diagram, it is necessary to check the column for at least two combinations of axial load and moment as shown in Fig. N.10.10.1.

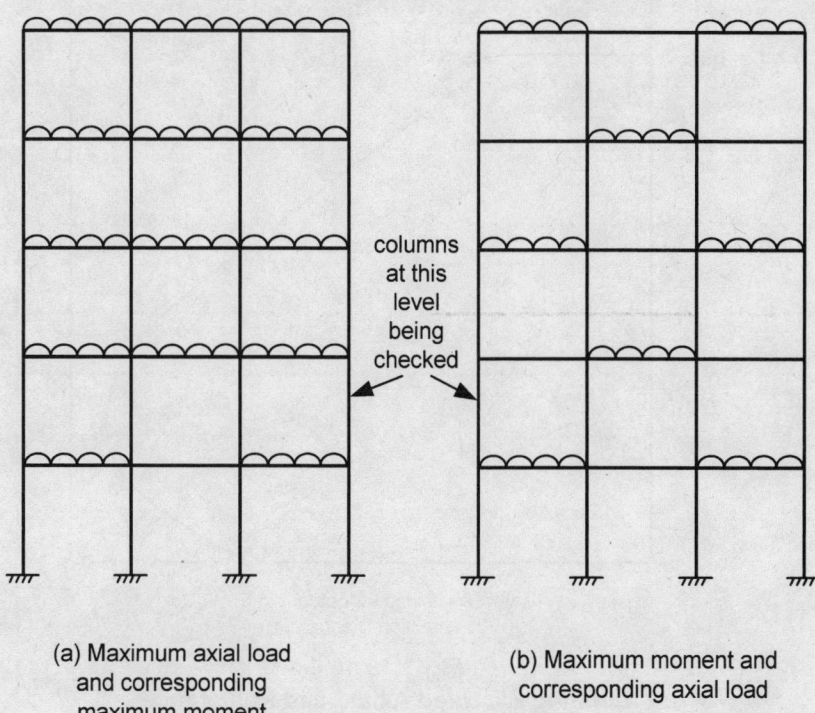

columns at this level being checked

(a) Maximum axial load and corresponding maximum moment

(b) Maximum moment and corresponding axial load

Fig. N10.10.1
Live Load Patterns to be considered for Column Design

N10.10.4   Maximum Axial Load Resistance

Limiting the factored axial load resistance to $P_{r, max}$ is intended to account for eccentricities not considered in the analysis, (see Fig. N10.10.4) and for the possibility that the concrete strength may be reduced by sustained high axial loads.

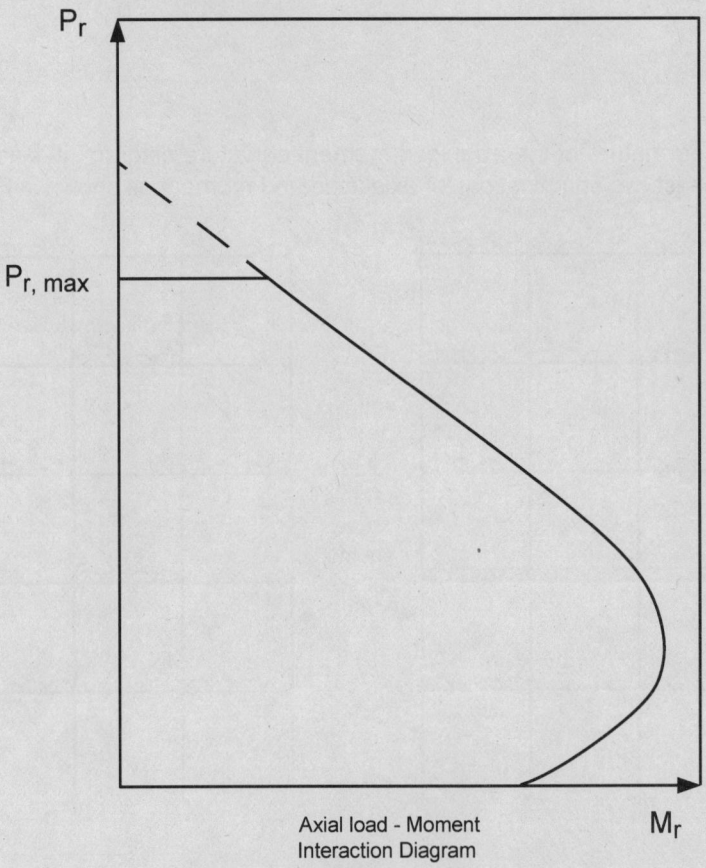

Axial load - Moment
Interaction Diagram

Fig. N10.10.4
Limiting Factored Axial Load Resistance

Equation 10-10 is a general equation applicable to all types of concrete columns. In the normal case of a reinforced column, A_t and A_p are equal to zero. There is no ϕ factor in the final term with A_p in Eq. (10-10) because this term reduces the capacity. The computed axial load resistance is reduced from that traditionally used by using the factor α_1 instead of 0.85. This reflects the observed reduction in the strength of columns made with high strength concrete.

N10.10.5

This clause has been revised so that the load reduction for columns with $0.005 \leq \rho_t < 0.01$ is not as severe as in previous editions of this Standard.

N10.12   Columns — Transmission of Loads Through Floor System

Application of the concrete placement procedure described in Clause 10.12.2 requires the placing of two different concrete mixes in the floor system. The lower strength mix must be placed while the higher strength concrete is still plastic and must be adequately vibrated to ensure the concretes are well integrated. This requires careful co-ordination of the concrete deliveries and possible use of a retarder. It is important that the high strength concrete in the floor in the region of the column be placed before the lower strength concrete in the remainder of the floor to prevent accidental placing of the low strength concrete in the column area. It is the designer's responsibility to indicate on the drawings where the high and low strength concrete are to be placed.

N10.12.3

Test results indicate that under some circumstances the code provisions in the 1984 standard were unsafe. For interior columns the current provisions result in an effective strength of column concrete equal to the specified column concrete for $f'_{cc} \leq 1.4f'_{cs}$. For higher ratios of f'_{cc}/f'_{cs}, the effective strength of the column concrete increases more slowly than predicted by the equation in the 1984 Standard.

The effective strength of the concrete in edge columns also remains equal to that of the specified strength of the column concrete for $f'_{cc} \leq 1.4f'_{cs}$. However, further increases in the specified strength of the column concrete do not further increase the effective strength.

Because of the lack of lateral restraint, the effective strength of the concrete in corner columns may not be taken higher than the specified strength of the slab concrete. See Gamble, W.L., and Klinar, J.D., "Tests of High-Strength Concrete Columns with Intervening Floor Slabs," ASCE Journal of Structural Engineering, Vol. 117, No. 5, May 1991, pp. 1462-1476, and Shu, C-C. and Hawkins, N.M., "Behaviour of Columns Continuous through Concrete Floors," ACI Structural Journal, Vol. 89, No.4, July-August 1992, pp. 405-414.

N10.13   Slenderness Effects — General

A conventional frame analysis (first-order analysis) neglects the influence of the changing geometry caused by deflections. A second-order analysis includes these effects when calculating moments and forces.

The stiffness, EI, used in an elastic analysis for strength design should represent the stiffness of the members immediately prior to failure. This is particularly true for second-order analyses that should predict the lateral deflections at loads approaching ultimate. The EI values should not be based totally on the moment-curvature relationship for the most highly loaded section along the length of the member. Instead, they should correspond to the moment-end rotation relationship for a complete member.

In a second-order analysis the axial loads in all columns that are not part of the lateral load resisting system but depend on these elements for stability must be included.

The term "effect of member curvature" refers to amplification of the column moments to account for moments induced by deflection of the column relative to the chord line joining the ends of the column. This is illustrated in Fig. N10.13(a) for a column in a non-sway frame. To account for the deflection between the ends of the column, the maximum moment is taken as the magnified moment M_c.

The term "effect of lateral drift" refers to the additional moments caused by vertical loads acting on a structure that has been displaced laterally. The first order column moments, M_s due to factored lateral loads acting on a frame are shown in Fig. N10.13(b). These cause lateral deflections as shown, and the interaction of these deflections and the gravity loads, P, causes an increase in the column moment for M_s to $\delta_s M_s$ as shown. Lateral drift effects usually result from loadings involving combinations of vertical and lateral loads but can occur due to vertical loads acting on an unsymmetric structure.

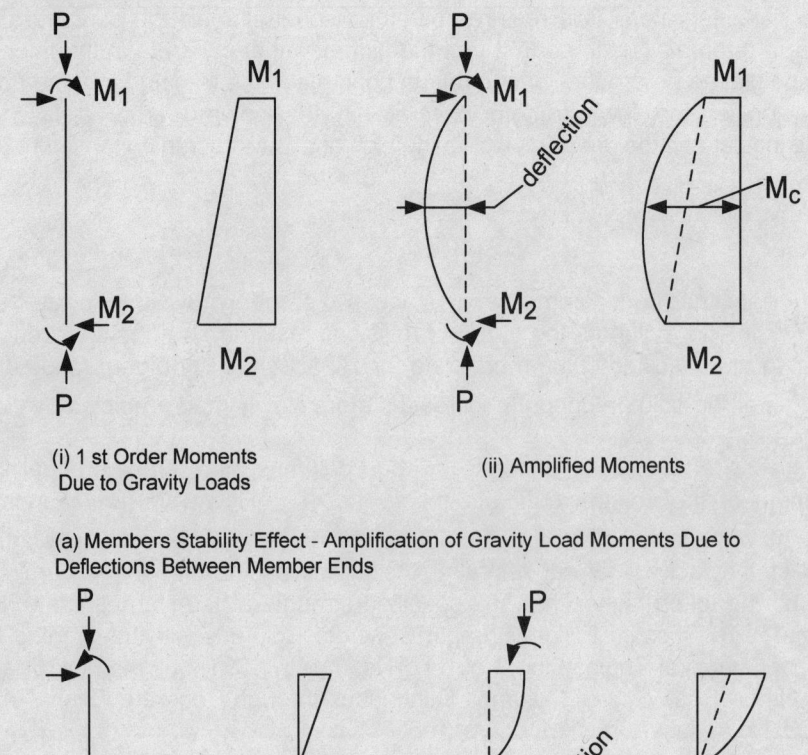

(i) 1 st Order Moments
Due to Gravity Loads

(ii) Amplified Moments

(a) Members Stability Effect - Amplification of Gravity Load Moments Due to
Deflections Between Member Ends

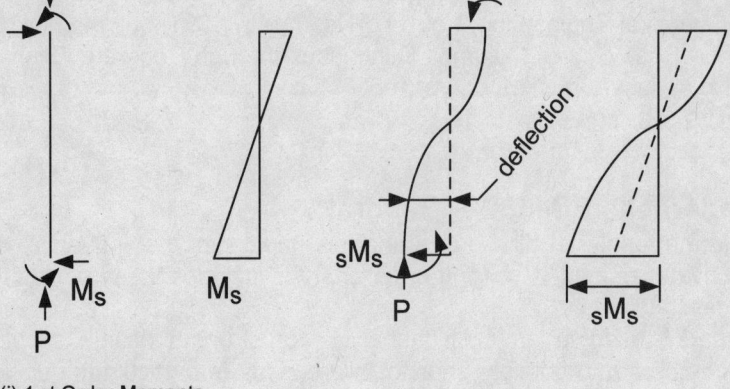

(i) 1 st Order Moments
Due to Gravity Loads

(ii) Amplified Moments

(a) Lateral Drift Effect - Amplification of lateral Load Moments Due to Relative End
Deflections

Fig. N10.13
Slenderness Effects

In lieu of a second order analysis the standard permits an approximate evaluation of the influence of deflection on moments and forces provided the $k\ell_u/r$ ratios for all columns is not greater than 100.

N10.14.1   General

It is generally sufficiently accurate to take I_g of a T-beam as two times the I_g for the web.

If the factored moments from an analysis of a wall based on the moment of inertia taken equal to $0.70\,I_g$ indicate that the wall will crack in flexure, based on the modulus of rupture, the analysis should be repeated with $I_g = 0.35\,I_g$ in those storeys where cracking is predicted at factored loads.

The term β_d is defined differently for non-sway and sway frames. See Cl. 10.14.1.3. Sway deflections due to short-time loads such as wind or earthquake are a function of the short-time stiffness of the columns following a period of sustained gravity load. For this case $\beta_d = 0$. Sustained lateral loads, which result in non-zero values of β_d, might exist, for example, if there were permanent lateral loads resulting from unequal earth pressures on opposite sides of a building. Sustained lateral loads should not be resisted by a column-beam frame because excessive lateral deflections may occur.

N10.14.4   Designation as Non-sway

A frame is "non-sway" if the lateral drift effects are resisted by stiff bracing elements such as shear walls, elevator shafts, stairwells and the like. A frame is a "sway frame" if the lateral drift effects are resisted by the frame itself. Generally it will be obvious from inspection whether a frame is sway or non-sway since the lateral stiffness of the bracing elements generally greatly exceeds that of the frame. Eq. (10-14) provides a means for categorizing structures that are not obviously in one class or the other. In the unlikely event that the frame is subjected to sustained lateral loads, the stiffness EI must be reduced by dividing by $1 + \beta_d$ where β_d is based on definition (b) in Cl. 10.14.1.3.

N10.15.1   Effective Length Factor

The effective length factor, k, is frequently estimated using the Jackson and Moreland Alignment Charts reproduced in Fig. N10.15.1. Because of the assumptions made in deriving these charts, they tend to underestimate the value of k. This is unconservative. For this reason it is desirable to err on the high side when computing ψ for use in these charts. It is considered satisfactory to compute ψ using the member stiffnesses given in Clause 10.14.1.

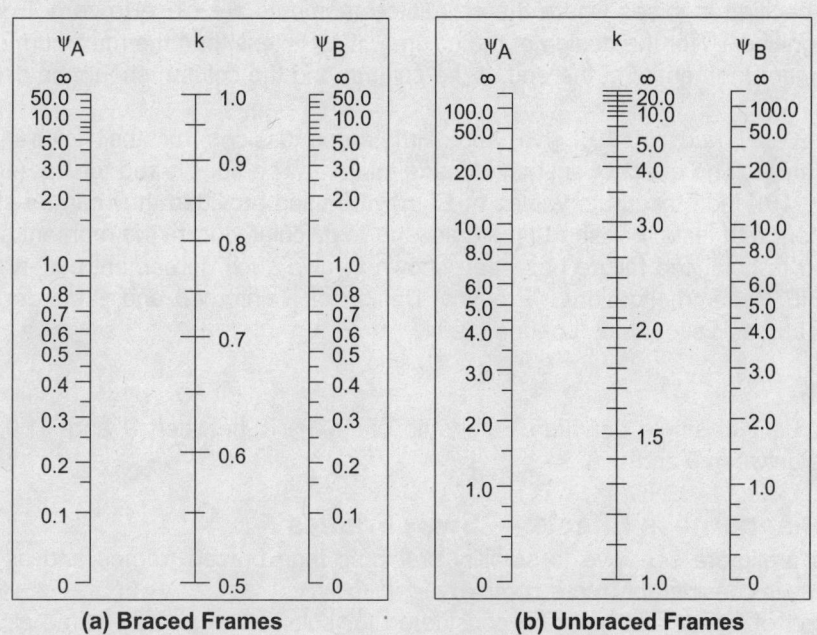

(a) Braced Frames   (b) Unbraced Frames

Fig. N10.15.1
Effective Length Factors

N10.15.2   Non-Sway Frames

In evaluating the slenderness limits in Clause 10.15.2, k can be taken as 1.0 or based on Fig. N10.15.2.

Studies of actual structures indicate that slenderness effects can be neglected for about 90 per cent of the columns in non-sway frames (MacGregor, Breen and Pfrang, "Design of Slender Concrete Columns", Journal American Concrete Institute, Vol. 67, No. 1, Jan. 1970, pp 6-28).

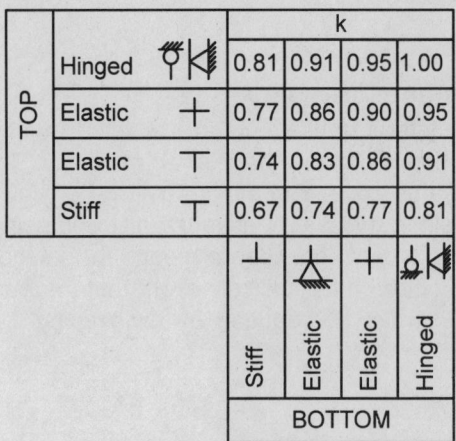

Fig. N10.15.2
Effective Length Factors for Non-sway Frames

N10.15.3   Member Stability Effect

The design of columns in a non-sway frame involves the calculation of magnified moments using Eq. (10-16) with M_2 taken as the moments from a conventional frame analysis. A minimum value of $C_m M_2$ is specified in cases where the calculated moments are close to zero. Equation 10-16 gives the magnified M_c for the design of the column. If M_c is less than the maximum end moment, M_2, the maximum moment is at the end of the column and the column should be designed for P_f and M_2.

Eqns. (10-18) and (10-19) give approximate expressions for the flexural stiffness of individual columns. The effect of sustained loads must now be considered for Eq. (10-19) as well as for Eq. (10-18). More accurate values of EI may be used provided they can be shown to give good agreement with tests. For short-time loads the EI calculated from the moment and curvature corresponding to balanced failure has been shown to give such agreement except for low axial loads. See FIP Recommendations, "Practical Design of Reinforced and Prestressed Concrete Structures," Thomas Telford Ltd., London, 1984.

N10.15.3.2

For columns bent in single curvature, the ratio of M_1/M_2 is between 0 and +1.0. For double curvature it is between 0 and -1.0.

N10.16   Slenderness Effects — Sway Frames

Sway-frames are more sensitive to stability problems than braced frames and as a result the design process is considerably more complex.

The effect of lateral drift must be considered for columns in a sway frame as illustrated in Fig. N10.16 for a symmetrical frame subjected to gravity load moments and lateral load moments. The first-order end moments M_{ns} due to gravity loads are shown in Fig. 10.16(a). The moments M_s and $\delta_s M_s$ due to lateral loads are shown in Fig. N10.16(b). The total moments at each end of the columns are obtained by adding the moments M_{ns} and $\delta_s M_s$ at each end, see Fig N10.16(c).

Explanatory Notes on CSA A23.3-04

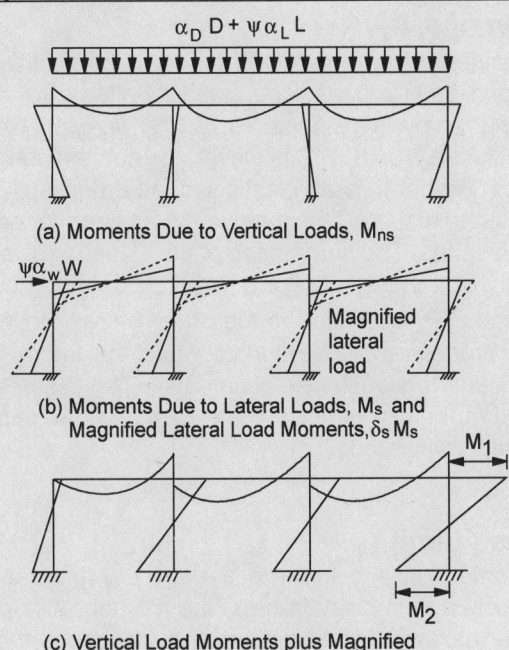

(a) Moments Due to Vertical Loads, M_{ns}

(b) Moments Due to Lateral Loads, M_s and Magnified Lateral Load Moments, $\delta_s M_s$

(c) Vertical Load Moments plus Magnified Lateral Load Moments, $M_{ns} + \delta_s M_s$

Fig. N10.16
End Moments M_1 and M_2 For Column in Sway Frame

NBC 2005 requires a check under three load combinations that don't include lateral loads.
1.4D;
(1.25 or 0.9)D + 1.5L + 0.5S;
(1.25 or 0.9)D + 0.5L + 1.5S

Three combinations that do include lateral loads must then be considered:
Compute factored gravity load moments, M_{ns}, resulting from the following factored loads:
(i) (1.25 or 0.9)D + 1.5(L or S);
(ii) (1.25 or 0.9)D + 0.5(L or S);
(iii) 1.0D + 0.5L + 0.25S.

Combine these three load cases with lateral load moments, M_s, from the corresponding three factored lateral loads:
(i) 0.4W;
(ii) 1.4W;
(iii) 1.0E.

Magnify the lateral load moments according to Clause 10.16.3 to account for the lateral drift effect. This gives $\delta_s M_s$.

Add the gravity load moments, M_{ns}, to the magnified lateral load moments, $\delta_s M_s$, at both ends of each column to get M_1 and M_2 as shown in Fig. N10.16.

If ℓ_u / r for any column exceeds the limit given in Eq. (10-25) check whether the moment between the ends of that column exceeds the end moment M_2. This is done using Clause 10.15.3. If M_c is less than M_2, the maximum moment M_2 occurs at the end of the column. If M_c exceeds M_2 the maximum moment M_c will occur between the ends of the column.

If a frame undergoes appreciable lateral deflections under gravity loads, serious consideration should be given to rearranging the frame to make it more symmetrical because with time, creep will amplify these deflections leading to both serviceability and strength problems.

N10.16.3   Calculation of $\delta_s M_s$

Lateral drift effects are considered for frames that undergo appreciable lateral drift due to lateral loads or combined lateral and gravity loads. The standard allows the designer to compute $\delta_s M_s$ using either a second order analysis (Clause 10.16.3.1) or Eq. (10-23) or Eq. (10-24). The second-order analysis in Clause 10.16.3.1, however, is not the same second-order analysis referred to in Clause 10.13.1. Rather, it is an elastic second-order analysis based on the member stiffnesses prescribed in Clause 10.14.1. The iterative $P\Delta$ analysis for second-order moments can be represented by an infinite series. The summation of this series is given by Eq. (10-24).

In checking the stability of a storey using Eq. (10-23), δ_s is computed as an average value based on the use of ΣP_f and ΣP_c because the top of the storey moves as a unit relative to the bottom of the storey. This procedure is appropriate when the lateral drifts of all columns in a storey are equal. If significant torsional displacements exist, Eqs. (10-23) and (10-24) may underestimate the magnified moments for columns farthest from the centre of twist. In such cases a second-order analysis is recommended.

N10.16.4   Slenderness Limit

Normally the maximum moment in a column in a sway frame is at one end of the column. However, for very slender columns in sway frames, the moment at a point between the ends of the column may exceed the maximum end moment. If ℓ_u/r exceeds the value given by Eq. (10 - 25), this may occur. Clause 10.16.4 specifies how this moment should be determined:
(a) M_1 and M_2 are computed using Clause 10.16.2.
(b)   The maximum moment along the length of the column is computed using these values of M_1 and M_2 in Eqs. (10-20) and (10-16). The EI values used to compute P_c are those given by Eqs. (10-18) or (10-19). β_d corresponds to definition (a) in Clause 10.14.1.3.

N10.16.5

Because the factored gravity loads may be greater in cases not involving lateral loads than they are in cases involving lateral loads, and because the EI for gravity loads is reduced by dividing by $1+\beta_d$ there is a possibility that a sway frame may buckle under gravity loads alone. Clauses 10.16.5(a) and (b) describe two additional loading cases, one of which may have to be checked, depending on how $\delta_s M_s$ or δ_s was calculated.

Clause 10.16.5(a) deals with cases designed using second-order analysis where appreciable lateral deflections occur due to gravity loads acting on a symmetrical or unsymmetrical frame, and the factored lateral load. The frame should be analyzed twice, once using a first-order analysis and once using a second order analysis. If one storey is much more flexible than the others, the deflection ratio should be based on that storey. In unsymmetric frames, which deflect laterally under gravity loads alone, the lateral load should act in the direction for which it will increase the lateral deflections. Since it is the ratio of the lateral deflections that is determined, the precise value of this load is not important. The factored value has been chosen for convenience.

The limit on δ_s in Clause 10.16.5(b) is intended to prevent instability under gravity loads alone. For values of δ_s above the limit, the frame would be very susceptible to variations in EI, foundation rotations and the like. If δ_s exceeds 2.5 the frame must be stiffened to reduce δ_s.

N10.16.6   Moment Magnification for Flexural Members

The lateral drift of a sway frame will cause the moments in both the columns and the beams to be magnified (see Fig. N.10.14.6(b)). The beams must be designed to resist these magnified moments.

Explanatory Notes on CSA A23.3-04

N11 Shear and torsion

N11.1 General

N11.1.1 Flexural regions

Typical beams, columns and walls are designed using engineering beam theory, which assumes that plane sections remain plane and that the shear stresses are distributed in a reasonably uniform manner over the depth of the member. Such members can be designed by the sectional method of Clause 11.3, or the strut-and-tie method of Clause 11.4.

N11.1.2 Regions near discontinuities

Engineering beam theory studies the response of a member section-by-section and is not concerned with the details of how the forces are introduced into the member. Because of this, the theory is not appropriate for regions of members near static or geometric discontinuities, such as abrupt changes in cross-sectional dimensions or cross-sectional forces. See examples in Fig. N11.1.2(a). Such regions should be designed by the strut-and-tie method of Clause 11.4, which is capable of more accurately modelling the actual flow of forces in these regions.

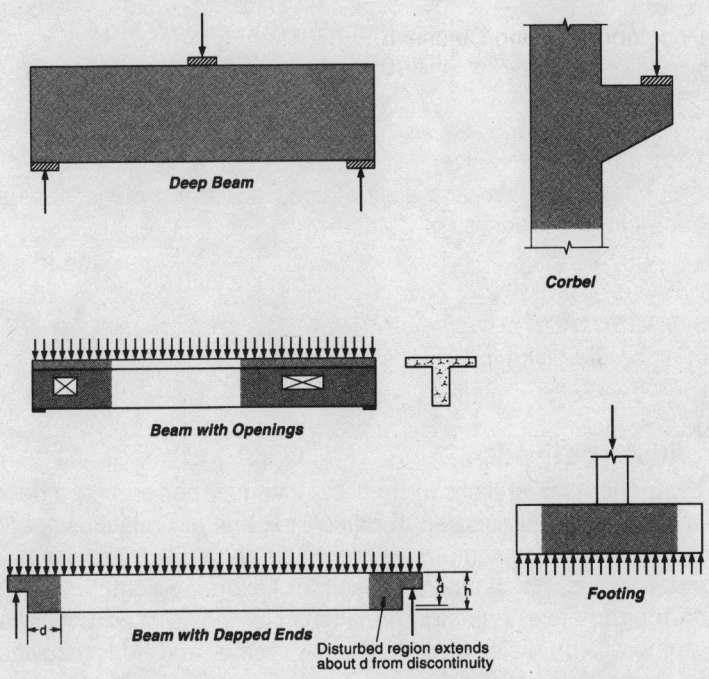

Fig. N11.1.2(a)
Examples of disturbed regions

An example of applying both the strut-and-tie model of Clause 11.4 and the sectional model of Clause 11.3 is illustrated in Fig. N11.1.2(b), which shows how the shear strength of a simply supported reinforced concrete beam loaded with two point loads changes as the "shear span", a, changes. It can be seen that when the load is closer than about 2d to the support, the sectional model is inappropriate. For such "deep beams" the strut-and-tie model provides more accurate results.

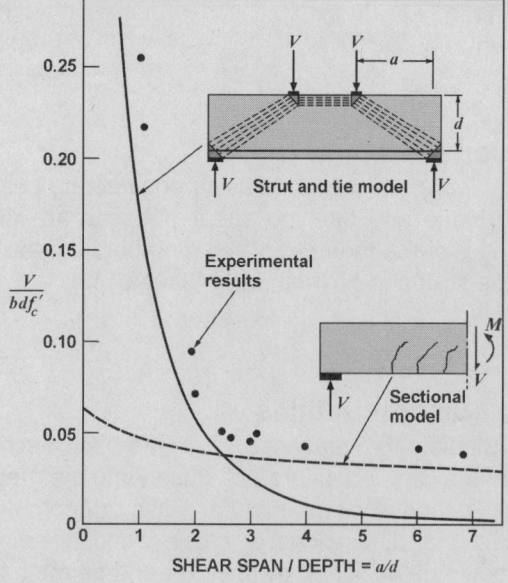

Fig. N11.1.2(b)
Use of Strut-and-Tie Model and Sectional Model
to Predict the Strengths of a Series of Beams

N11.1.3 Interface regions

The possibility of a shear failure involving sliding along a defined plane of weakness should be checked by the shear friction procedures of Clause 11.5.

N11.1.4 Slabs and footings

Shear provisions for slabs are given in Clauses 13.3 and 13.4.

N11.1.5 Alternative methods

The resistance of components in shear can be determined by performing a detailed analysis that considers equilibrium, compatibility, and appropriate stress-strain relationships. Such an analysis could be a non-linear finite element analysis, which could be used for regions near discontinuities, or a detailed sectional analysis, which could be used for flexural regions.

An example of appropriate stress-strain relationships for cracked concrete are those given by the "modified compression field theory" (F.J. Vecchio and M.P. Collins, "The Modified Compression Field Theory for Reinforced Concrete Elements Subjected to Shear," Journal of the American Concrete Institute, Vol. 83, No. 2, March/April 1986, pp. 219-231).

N11.2 Design requirements

N11.2.1 Tension due to restraint

Axial tension reduces the shear capacity of beams, with the reduction being particularly severe for members containing only small amounts of longitudinal reinforcement and not containing stirrups. In continuous frame structures, which have widely spaced expansion joints and stiff vertical elements, the restraint of shrinkage strains and other volume change effects may result in significant axial tension building up in the beams over time. The detrimental effect of such axial tensions on the shear strength should be taken into account.

N11.2.2 Variable depth members

If the member depth increases as the moment increases, the vertical components of the flexural compression and tension forces help to resist the applied shear. These forces can be treated in a similar manner to the vertical component of the prestressing force, V_p.

N11.2.3 Openings

Webs with openings need to be designed in a rational manner to ensure that the forces and moments can be adequately transferred in the vicinity of the openings. The strut-and-tie model of Clause 11.4 can be used for the design of these disturbed regions.

N11.2.4 Types of shear reinforcement

(b) To effectively increase shear capacity, transverse reinforcement must be capable of undergoing substantial strains prior to failure. Welded wire fabric, particularly if fabricated from small wires and not stress-relieved after fabrication, may fail before the required strain is reached. Such failures may occur at or between the cross-wire intersections.

(c) There is concern that stirrups inclined at less than 45° to the longitudinal reinforcement will slip along the longitudinal bars.

(d) In tests, major inclined cracks tend to occur at points where longitudinal reinforcement is bent up. The effective portion of bent-up bars is restricted to 75% of their inclined length due to concern with anchorage conditions at the bends, and because the effectiveness of these bars is sensitive to misplacement.

N11.2.5 Anchorage of shear reinforcement

To be effective, transverse shear reinforcement must tie together the longitudinal tension reinforcement and the flexural compression zone of the member. Further, the reinforcement must be anchored so that it can develop its yield strength without suffering any significant slip. To this end, stirrups require 135° hooks for most situations. See Clause 7.1.2.

N11.2.7 Anchorage of torsion reinforcement

Diagonal compressive stresses in the concrete due to torsion push outwards at the corners of the beam tending to spall the cover concrete. This spalling renders 90° hooks ineffective. The longitudinal corner bars help to support the outward thrusts in the zones between the hoops. Torsion causes tension in the longitudinal reinforcement. Longitudinal torsional reinforcement should be anchored so that it can develop its yield stress in tension at the face of the support.

N11.2.8 Minimum shear reinforcement

N11.2.8.1

Minimum shear reinforcement controls the propagation of diagonal cracks and changes the pattern of cracking prior to shear failure. Regions with such reinforcement, if overloaded in shear, will display a number of wide diagonal cracks, prior to failure. On the other hand, regions without such reinforcement can fail in shear upon the formation of the first diagonal crack. The benefits of minimum shear reinforcement are particularly significant for large beams ($h > 750$ mm) and so it is required in all regions of such members irrespective of the calculated value of V_f.

N11.2.8.2

The amount of shear reinforcement required to control the propagation of diagonal cracks increases as the strength of concrete increases.

N11.2.8.4

The requirements for large beams ($h > 750$) to contain minimum shear reinforcement can be waived if appropriate tests show that the beams behave in a satisfactory manner even when the shear reinforcement is omitted. In determining "the required flexural and shear resistances" to compare with test results, careful attention must be given to the appropriate treatment of the resistance factors ϕ_c, ϕ_p and ϕ_s. The test results can be taken as corresponding to the case where these factors are all one. Before a comparison with the factored moments and shear forces is made, the test values should be reduced by the appropriate resistance factors.

N11.2.9   Consideration of torsion

N11.2.9.1

Torques that do not exceed one-quarter of the pure torsional cracking torque will not cause significant reduction in either flexural or shear strength and hence, can be neglected.

Equation (11-2) is an approximate expression for the torsion causing cracking. The expression has been derived by replacing the actual section with an equivalent thin walled tube with a wall thickness $0.75A_c / p_c$ and an area enclosed by the tube centreline of two-thirds of A_c.

The cracking stress is assumed to be $0.38\lambda\phi_c\sqrt{f_c'}$.

For a hollow section replacing A_c in Equation (11-2) by $1.5A_g$ will lead to a rather conservative estimate of the pure torsional cracking load. This is appropriate as hollow sections display a stronger interaction between cracking shear and cracking torsion than do solid sections.

N11.2.9.2

After cracking, there is a substantial reduction in the torsional stiffness relative to the flexural stiffness. If the torsion in a member is a function of torsional stiffness, the resulting redistribution of internal forces will maintain the maximum torsion in the member at about the cracking torque, even as the loads are increased. This cracking torque will be about two-thirds of the pure torsional cracking load.

N11.2.10   Effective web width

N11.2.10.2

Post-tensioning ducts act as stress-raisers and hence can reduce the crushing strength of the concrete web. To account for this, the effective web width is reduced at locations containing ducts.

N11.2.10.3
For circular sections, the highest shear stresses typically occur near mid-depth where the width of the section is equal to the diameter.

N11.2.10.4
The use of this clause is illustrated in Fig. N11.2.10.4

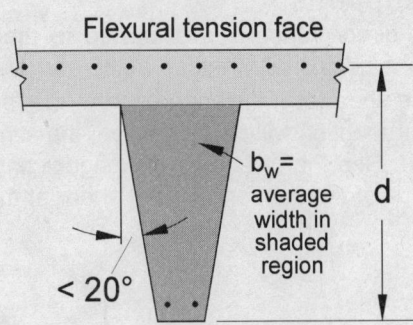

Fig. N11.2.10.4
Determination of b_w for section of continuous joist with tapered web.

N11.2.11   Reduced prestress in transfer length
The reduced prestress in the transfer length reduces V_p and f_{p0} and also reduces the tensile force that can be resisted by the tendons near the ends of members. For a strand, the increase of stress from zero to say 1300 MPa in a length of 50 strand diameters corresponds to an average bond stress of about 5 MPa.

N11.2.12   Hanger reinforcement
The intersection of two beams is a disturbed region and, as such, the flow of forces in this region can be represented by a strut-and-tie model in accordance with Clause 11-4. However if the sectional model of Clause 11-3 is used, additional transverse reinforcement will be needed to ensure that a push-out failure of the supporting beam does not occur. For this additional reinforcement to be effective, it should be placed in a zone close to the loaded interface. This zone is defined in Figure 11-1. If the shear stress is low enough that diagonal cracks are unlikely to form under factored loads, no additional reinforcement is needed.

N11.3   Design for shear and torsion in flexural regions
In the previous edition of this standard, there were two very different sectional shear design procedures called the simplified method and the general method. The simplified method was based on the traditional ACI procedures whereas the general method was based on the more recently developed modified compression field theory. In many practical situations, these two methods gave notably different results. Where the results were different, experimental evidence indicated that the general method was closer to observed behaviour. Because of this, in this edition of the code there is only one sectional design procedure. While this procedure is derived from the modified compression field theory, it is significantly easier to apply than the 1994 general method. Further, a method which is as easy to apply as the 1994 simplified method is included as a special case of the general method.

N11.3.1 Required shear reinforcement

Members need to be proportioned so that at every section, the factored shear resistance is at least equal to the factored shear load.

N11.3.2 Sections near supports

Loads applied in regions near direct supports are carried to the support by strut action, see Fig. N11.1.2(b), and do not cause additional stresses in the stirrups. Hence, the stirrups in these regions may be designed for the shear at a distance d_v from the face of the support. However, if the support is such that direct strut action will be ineffective, the stirrups must be designed for the shear at the face of the support. See Fig. N11.3.2. If a significant concentrated load is applied within a distance dv from the face of the support, the full shear at the face of the support must be used in the shear design.

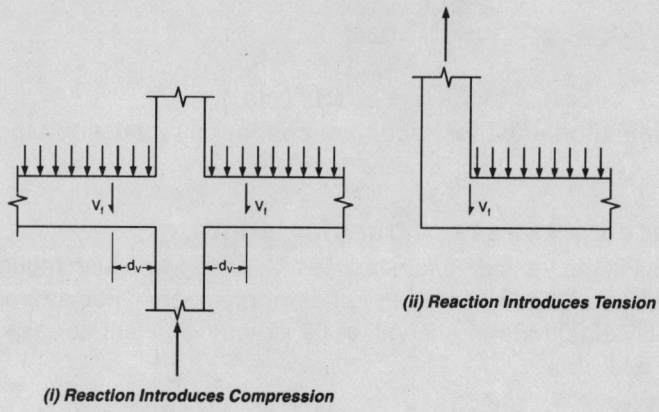

(i) Reaction Introduces Compression

(ii) Reaction Introduces Tension

Fig. N11.3.2
Influence of support conditions on location of critical section for shear

N11.3.3 Factored shear resistance

Shear resistance may be separated into a component, V_c, which relies on tensile stresses transmitted across cracks via aggregate interlock, a component, V_s, which relies on tensile stresses in the transverse reinforcement, and V_p, which relies on the vertical component of the factored effective prestressing force. Note that in this edition of the standard, the definition of V_p has been changed to include the reduction factor ϕ_p.

The intent of Eq. (11-5) is to ensure that the transverse reinforcement will yield prior to the diagonal crushing of the web concrete.

N11.3.4 Determination of V_c

In Eq. (11-6), the factor β accounts for the ability of concrete to transmit shear stresses across cracks by aggregate interlock action. Also note that the effective shear area is $b_w d_v$ rather than $b_w d$ as used in the previous simplified method. The upper limit of 8 MPa for the value of $\sqrt{f_c'}$ has been set because aggregate interlock is less effective for higher strength concretes.

N11.3.5   Determination of V_s

The expressions for V_s are the traditional equations for the shear carried by the tensile stresses in the transverse reinforcement for the case where the diagonal compressive stresses in the cracked concrete are inclined at an angle of θ to the longitudinal axis of the member. See Fig. N11.3.5.

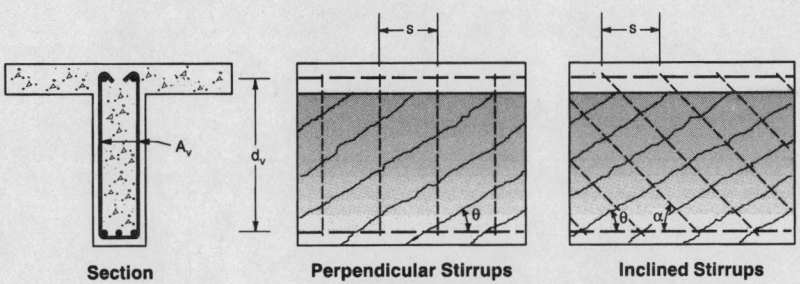

Section   **Perpendicular Stirrups**   **Inclined Stirrups**

Fig. N11.3.5
Illustration of Parameters Involved in Determination of V_s

Stirrups inclined to intersect the diagonal cracks, see Fig. N11.3.5, are more effective in resisting shear. This is reflected in Eq. (11-8).

The expression for the shear at which the web concrete will crush, Eq. (11-5), does not distinguish between members with perpendicular stirrups and members with inclined stirrups. For the same shear force, members with inclined stirrups will have smaller diagonal compressive stresses in the web concrete and hence, can tolerate higher shears prior to web crushing.

N11.3.6   Determination of β and θ

This clause gives three different procedures for determining the factor β and the angle θ. The most direct of these procedures specifies that β can be taken as 0.21 and θ can be taken as 42° for the types of members specified in Clause 11.3.6.2. The most general procedure, which is specified in Clause 11.3.6.4, gives equations for β and θ which account for the influence of axial load, prestressing, crack spacing, amount of longitudinal reinforcement, and moment-to-shear ratio on shear resistance. The third procedure, which can be used in most practical designs, is the simplified method described in Clause 11.3.6.3.

N11.3.6.1   Members subjected to significant axial tension

If the axial tension is large enough to crack the flexural compression face of the member, or large enough to cause a significant stress increase (say, 50 MPa), in the longitudinal reinforcement near the flexural tension face, then its detrimental effect on shear strength needs to be accounted for using the general method.

N11.3.6.2   Values for special member types

If β is taken as 0.21, and θ is taken as 42°, the expressions for V_c and V_s result in designs that are comparable to those given by the traditional ACI expressions for shear strength. The use of 42° rather than the traditional 45° compensates for the use of d_v as the shear depth rather than d.

Recent research has shown that these traditional procedures can be unconservative for large members not containing transverse shear reinforcement and because of this, these procedures are restricted to members with relatively small depths. An exception to this is the case of footings such as that shown in Fig. N11.3.6.2 where the loads and reactions cause significant vertical compressive stresses. These beneficial clamping stresses counteract the detrimental effects of large size.

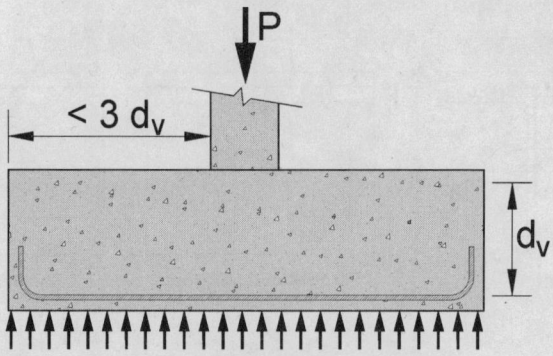

Fig. N11.3.6.2
Footing for which $\beta = 0.21$

N11.3.6.3   Simplified method

The β and θ values given by the simplified method are derived from the general method by assuming that $\varepsilon_x = 0.85 \times 10^{-3}$. This corresponds to a strain in the flexural tension reinforcement somewhat less than the yield strain of 400 MPa reinforcement. For members without transverse reinforcement, aggregate interlock stresses transmit a large portion of the shear across the flexural cracks. Hence the shear resistance of such members depends on the maximum aggregate size. If the concrete strength exceeds about 60 MPa, the cracks cleave through the aggregate particles and, hence, the size of the aggregate no longer influences the shear strength. For these higher strength concretes, the smoother crack surfaces reduce aggregate interlock capacity. Equation 11-10 allows the effect of different aggregate sizes to be accounted for by calculating an effective crack spacing parameter, s_{ze}.

N11.3.6.4   General method

The previous edition of this code gave tabulated values of β and θ which were based on the modified compression field theory. It has now proved possible to derive simple expressions for β and θ which are much easier to use. The derivation of these expressions is described in a paper by Bentz and Collins titled "Development of the 2004 CSA A23.3 Shear Provisions for Reinforced Concrete", in press, Canadian Journal of Civil Engineering. The values of β and θ are based on calculating the stresses that can be transmitted across diagonally cracked concrete. As the cracks get wider, the stress that can be transmitted decreases. Crack widths can be taken as the average tensile strain multiplied by the crack spacing. That is, a strain factor times a spacing factor. The factor β accounts for the ability of concrete to transmit shear stresses across cracks by aggregate interlock action. The equation for β, Eq. (11-11), consists of a strain factor multiplied by a spacing factor. As the strains in the member becomes larger, β becomes smaller which can be called the strain effect in shear. As the crack spacing becomes larger, β again becomes smaller, which is called the size effect in shear.

For members without transverse reinforcement, the angle of inclination, θ, of the principal compressive stresses in the concrete is uniquely determined from the equations of the modified

Explanatory Notes on CSA A23.3-04

compression field theory. This theoretical angle was tabulated in the previous version of this code and can be reasonably approximated as:

$$\theta = (29° + 7000\varepsilon_x)(0.88 + s_{ze} / 2500) \le 75°$$

For members with transverse reinforcement, there is a range of values of θ possible for design. The previous code tabulated the values of θ which would result in approximately the minimum cost of reinforcement needed to resist a given shear load. These values depended both on ε_x and the level of shear stress. In this code, a simple expression for θ, applicable to both members with and without transverse reinforcement, was derived, Eq. (11-12).

To understand the background to Eq. (11-13), it is helpful to appreciate the "more accurate calculations" which could be used to calculate ε_x. The actual cross section is represented by an idealized section consisting of a flexural tension flange, a flexural compression flange, and a web. The area of concrete in the flexural tension flange, A_{ct}, is taken as the area of concrete within $0.5h$ of the flexural tension face, see Fig.11.2. Similarly, the concrete area in the flexural compression flange is taken as the concrete area within $0.5h$ of the flexural compression face. In dividing the total area of reinforcing bars and prestressing tendons between the two flanges, the same simple procedure can be followed. Thus A_p can be taken as the area of tendons within $0.5h$ of the flexural tension face.

The forces resisted by the flexural tension flange and the flexural compression flange of the idealized section are shown in Fig. N11.3.6.4(a). After diagonal cracks have formed in the web, the shear force applied to the web concrete V_f-V_p, will be primarily carried by diagonal compressive stresses in the web concrete. These diagonal compressive stresses will result in a longitudinal compressive force in web concrete of $(V_f-V_p)\cot\theta$. Equilibrium requires that this longitudinal compressive force in the web needs to be balanced by tensile forces in the two flanges, with half of the force, that is, $0.5(V_f-V_p)\cot\theta$, being taken by each flange. To avoid a trial and error process, it is a convenient and conservative simplification to take this flange force due to shear as (V_f-V_p).

The axial strains in the compression flange (ε_c) and the axial strain in the tension flange (ε_t) can be calculated from the axial forces in the flanges using a bilinear relationship such as that shown in Fig. N11.3.6.4(b). The longitudinal strain, ε_x, at mid-depth of the section can then be calculated as $(\varepsilon_t + \varepsilon_c)/2$. Note that ε_c will usually be a small negative quantity. For this case, it is a convenient and conservative assumption to take ε_x as $\varepsilon_t/2$. This is the basis of Eq. 11-13.

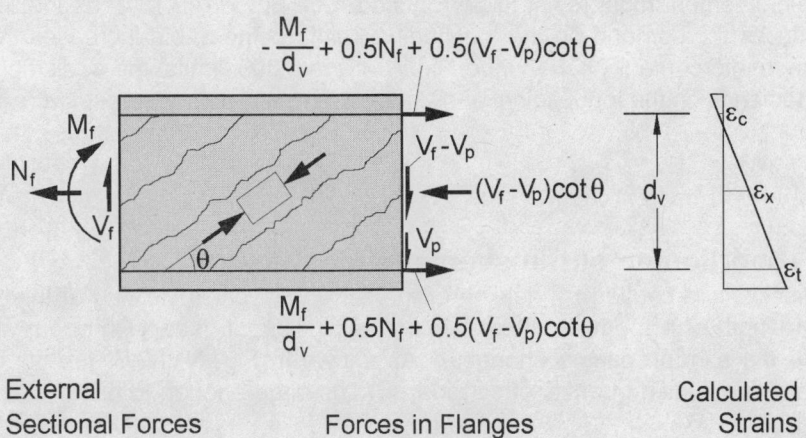

External Sectional Forces   Forces in Flanges   Calculated Strains

Fig. N11.3.6.4(a)
More accurate procedure for determining ε_x.

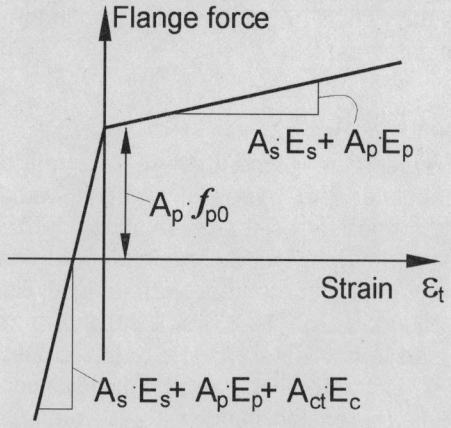

Fig. N11.3.6.4(b)
Determination of ε_t from flexural tension flange force

The following explanations apply to the conditions a) to f) that apply to Eq. 11-13.

a)   If M_f is less than $(V_f - V_p)d_v$, then ε_c may become tensile, which would render unconservative the assumption that ε_x is $\varepsilon_t/2$.

c)   Eq. (11-13) assumes that ε_t is tensile and hence the axial stiffness of the concrete in the tension flange can be neglected. If the tension flange is prestressed or if the section has axial compression applied, ε_t may be compressive and then it is necessary to account for the stiffness of the concrete in compression, see Fig. N11.3.6.4(b).

e)   Under high axial tension ε_c will become tensile and, hence, either ε_x should be calculated as $(\varepsilon_t + \varepsilon_c)/2$ or, for simplicity, as ε_t.

f)   The use of a higher value of ε_x than that calculated with Eq. (11-13) will result in a higher value of θ and a lower value of β. A higher value of θ will cause the calculated force which the longitudinal reinforcement must resist to be reduced, See Eq. (11-14). Thus the use of a higher value of ε_x reduces the demand on the longitudinal reinforcement, but increases the demand on the transverse reinforcement. The upper limit of $\varepsilon_x = 0.003$ limits the redistribution required between the demands on the longitudinal and transverse reinforcements.

N11.3.7   Proportioning of transverse reinforcement

Because a shear failure caused by yielding of the stirrups involves yielding of this reinforcement over a certain length of a member, there will not be an abrupt change in shear strength at the location where the stirrup spacing changes. As shown in Fig. N11.3.7, the stirrup spacing is chosen so that the provided quantity of stirrups, A_v/s, is large enough to ensure that V_r equals or exceeds V_f.

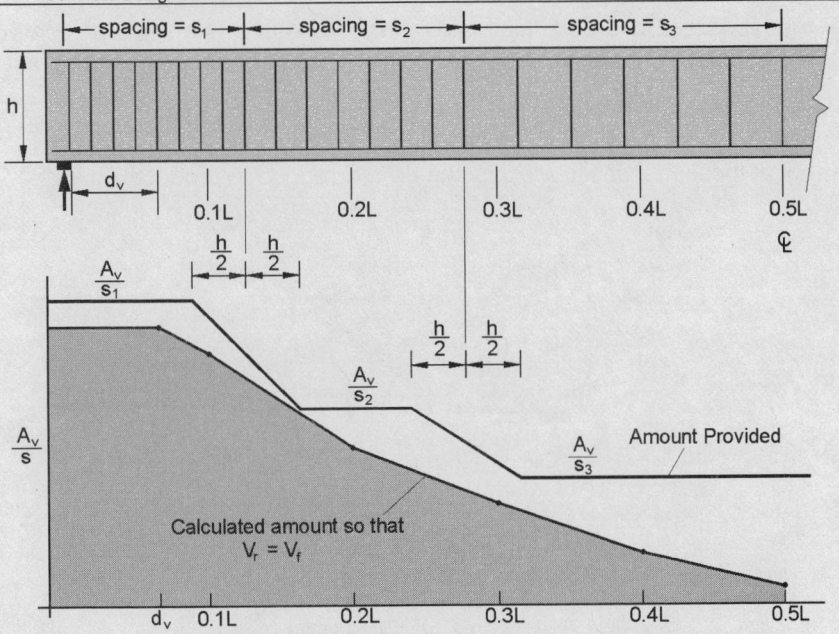

Fig. N11.3.7
Proportioning of transverse reinforcement

Explanatory Notes on CSA A23.3-04

N11.3.8 Maximum spacing of transverse reinforcement

N11.3.8.1
The requirements in Clause 11 of this edition of the standard are expressed in terms of the effective shear depth, d_v, rather than the distance from the extreme compression fibre to the centroid of the longitudinal tension reinforcement, d. Thus the maximum spacing limits for stirrups are expressed in terms of d_v.

N11.3.9 Proportioning of longitudinal reinforcement

N11.3.9.1 Extension of longitudinal reinforcement
In a cracked beam shear causes additional tension in the longitudinal reinforcement. A conservative approach to account for this additional tension is to extend the longitudinal reinforcement a distance of $d_v \cot\theta$ beyond the location dictated by flexure alone. For a member subjected to point loads this is equivalent to assuming that the additional tension in the longitudinal reinforcement on the flexural tension side of the member is equal to $V_f \cot\theta$.

N11.3.9.2 Flexural tension side
The influence of moment, axial load and shear on the tensile force F_{lt} in the longitudinal reinforcement can be seen from the free body diagram in Fig. N11.3.9.2. The figure illustrates a region of the beam with constant shear force, V_f, where F_{lt} is being calculated a distance x from the centre of the support. The diagonal crack at inclination θ to the longitudinal axis of the member intersects a number of stirrups and the resultant force from these stirrups equals V_s. The shear stresses on the crack face v_c contribute to resisting the applied shear V_f but also require

additional tensile stresses in the longitudinal reinforcement. The vertical component of the prestress, V_p, if present, also contributes to resisting V_f. Taking moments about point O gives:

$$V_f\left(x+d_v\cot\theta\right)+N_f 0.5d_v = F_{lt}d_v +V_s 0.5d_v\cot\theta+V_p d_v\cot\theta$$

With the moment at location x called M_f, this can be rearranged to produce Eq. (11-14).

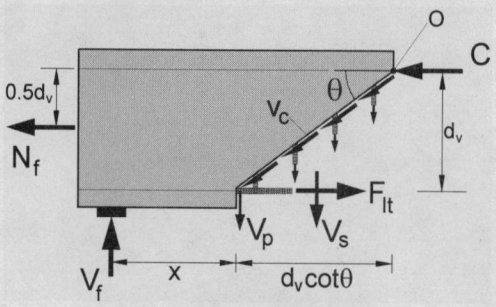

Fig. N11.3.9.2
Free body diagram showing member forces at a crack.

In determining the stress that can be developed in the longitudinal reinforcement at sections near bar cut-off locations, it can be assumed that the tensile capacity of a bar varies linearly from zero at the free end, to a value of $\phi_s A_b f_y$ at a distance of ℓ_d from the free end, where A_b is the bar area and ℓ_d is the development length.

N11.3.9.4 Compression fan regions

At maximum moment locations, the shear force changes sign and hence, the inclination of the diagonal compressive stresses changes. At direct supports and point loads, this change of inclination is associated with a fan-shaped pattern of compressive stresses radiating from the point load or the direct support, as shown in Fig. N11.3.9.4(a). This fanning of the diagonal stresses reduces the tension in the longitudinal reinforcement caused by shear (i.e., angle θ becomes steeper). Due to this effect, the tension in the reinforcement does not exceed that due to the maximum moment alone.

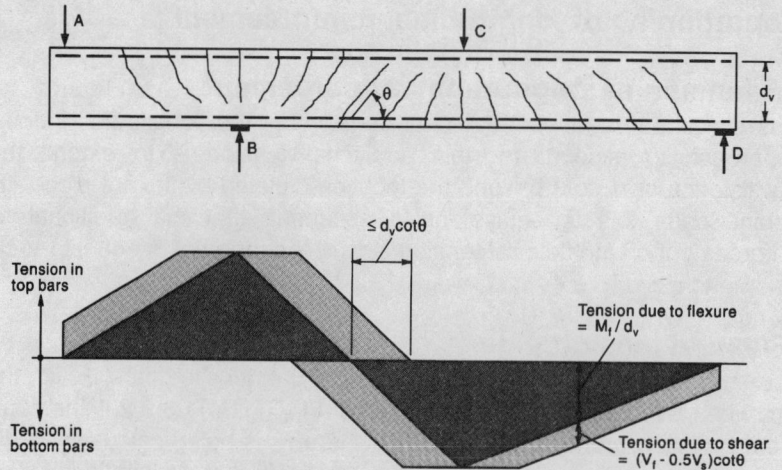

Fig. N11.3.9.4(a)
Influence of shear on required tensile forces in longitudinal reinforcement of beam on direct supports subjected to point loads

If a member is indirectly loaded or supported, then a pattern of parallel diagonal cracks is likely to occur near the maximum moment locations. See Fig. N.11.3.9.4(b). In this case, the maximum tension required in the longitudinal reinforcement will be greater than that required for flexure alone.

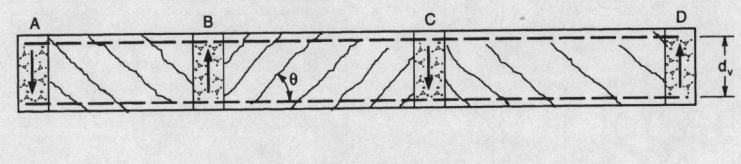

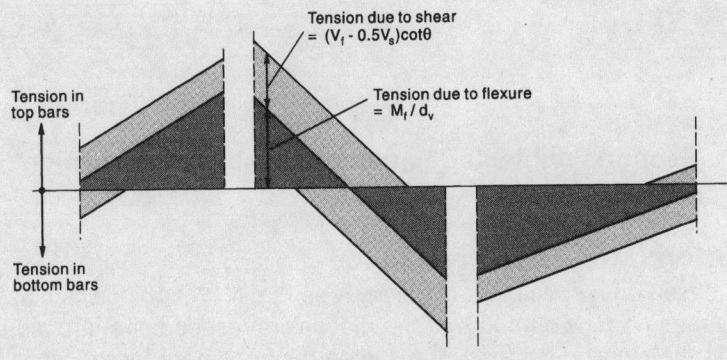

Fig. N11.3.9.4(b)
Influence of shear on required tensile forces in longitudinal reinforcement of beam indirectly loaded and indirectly supported by crossbeams

N11.3.9.5 Anchorage of longitudinal reinforcement at end supports

The expression for the tensile force in the longitudinal reinforcement given in this clause is the same as Eq. (11-14) except that the influence of the small moment at the support is neglected. In evaluating the tensile capacity of the longitudinal reinforcement at end supports, it can be assumed that the linear variation of capacity described in N11.3.9.2 is applicable.

N11.3.10   Sections subjected to combined shear and torsion

N11.3.10.1   Transverse reinforcement for combined shear and torsion

The shear stresses due to torsion and shear will add on one side of the section and counteract on the other side. The transverse reinforcement must be designed for the side where the effects are additive. Usually the loading that causes the highest torsion differs from the loading that causes the highest shear. While it is conservative to design for the highest torsion combined with the highest shear, it is only necessary to design for the highest shear and its associated torsion and the highest torsion and its associated shear.

In calculating the required spacing of transverse reinforcement care must be exercised in combining the A_v/s term required to provide the needed V_s from Eq. (11-7) with the A_t/s term required to provide the needed T_r from Eq. (11-17). Consider the typical rectangular spandrel beam reinforced with closed stirrups shown in Fig. N11.3.10.1. If there were no torsion, A_v would be the area of the two vertical bars, $2A_b$. If there were no shear, A_t would be the area of one bar, A_b. Under combined loading, the spacing, s, of the closed stirrups must be chosen so that:

$$\frac{A_b}{s} \geq 0.5\frac{A_v}{s} + \frac{A_t}{s}$$

Explanatory Notes on CSA A23.3-04

For the hollow box in Fig. N11.3.10.1, the spacing of the "double legged" closed stirrups can be determined from the above inequality with A_b now representing the area of the two legs within each wall.

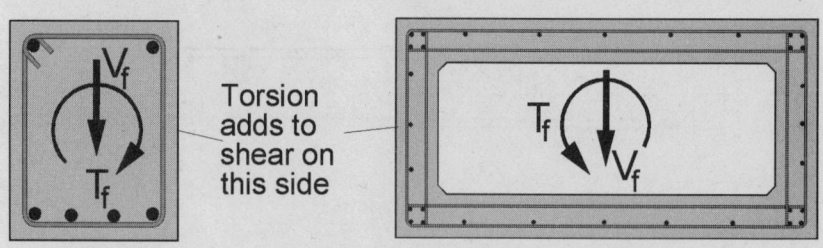

Fig. N11.3.10.1
Sections subjected to combined shear and torsion

N11.3.10.3   Factored torsional resistance

Equation (11-17) is based on a space truss analogy, see Fig. N11.3.10.3, which assumes that the cracked concrete carries no tension and that the diagonal stresses spiral around the member at an inclination of θ to the longitudinal axis. Transverse reinforcement for torsion is required on all sides of the member and should be in the form of closed stirrups.

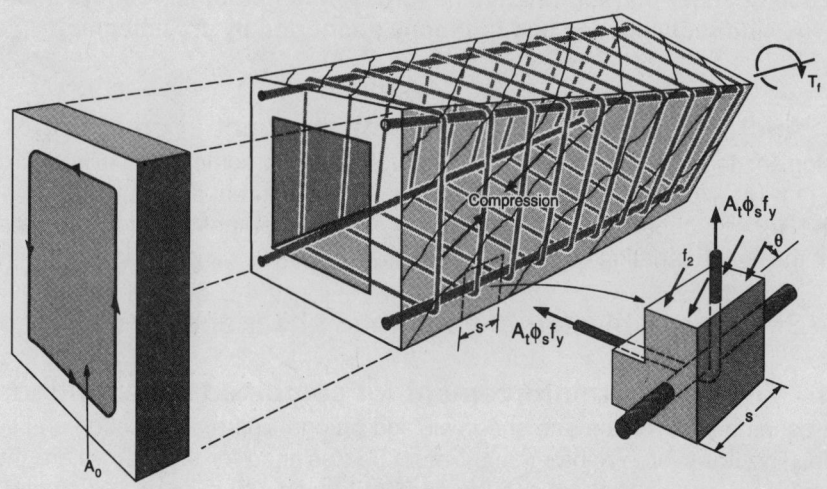

Fig. N11.3.10.3
Design of transverse reinforcement for torsion

N11.3.10.4   Cross-sectional dimensions to avoid crushing

For a box girder, the shear stress due to shear and the shear stress due to torsion will add together on one side of the box girder. Further, the magnitude of these stresses is largely determined by statics. For other cross-sectional shapes such as a solid rectangle, there is the possibility of considerable redistribution of shear stresses. To make some allowance for this favourable redistribution, a "root-mean-square" approach is used in calculating the nominal shear stress under combined torsion and shear for these cross-sections.

Explanatory Notes on CSA A23.3-04

The 1.7 factor in the torsional shear stress expression of Eqns. (11-18) and (11-19) has been introduced in this edition of the standard to better predict the crushing load of heavily reinforced sections loaded in combined torsion and shear. In the original development of the method the term $T_f p_h / A_{oh}^2$ was called the nominal torsional shear stress and taken as the indicator of the intensity of torsional loading on the cross section. The maximum value of this parameter was set to $0.25\phi_c f_c'$ to be consistent with the limit on shear. Later studies showed that this limit was very conservative for sections subjected to high torsional loading. Thus for members subjected to pure torsion, the limiting value of the stress is closer to 1.7 times $0.25\phi_c f_c'$. Rather than changing the value of the limiting shear stress as the loading ratio changes, the expression for the torsional shear stress has been changed to include this factor of 1.7.

The previous edition of this standard did not permit the use of thin walled boxes where the distance from the centreline of the transverse torsion reinforcement to the inside face of the wall was less than $0.5A_{oh}/p_h$. In this edition boxes with actual wall thicknesses less than A_{oh}/p_h can be used provided that the torsional shear stress is calculated from the traditional thin-walled box expression. That is, the torsional shear stress is equal to $T_f/(2A_o t)$. If A_o is taken as $0.85A_{oh}$ as specified in Clause 11.3.10.3, the torsional shear stress becomes $T_f/(1.7A_{oh}t)$.

N11.3.10.5   Determination ε_x for general method

For members subjected to combined flexure, axial load, torsion and shear, the longitudinal strain at mid-depth of the member, ε_x, can be calculated from a space truss model such as that shown in Fig. N11.3.10.5.

The axial load and moments would be resisted by longitudinal forces in the four chords while the torsion and shears would be resisted by shear flows in the four walls. For cracked concrete these shear flows would cause tensions in the adjacent chords as well. The strains in each of the four chords could then be calculated and ε_x taken as the average of the four chord strains.

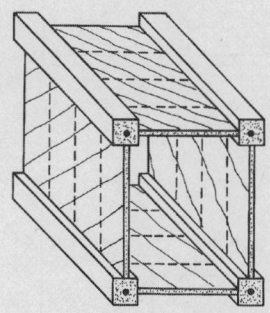

Fig. N11.3.10.5
Space truss model for combined loading

As a simplification of this procedure, Eq. (11-13) can be used except that the shear term is replaced by the root mean squared term given in Eq. (11-20).

N11.3.10.6   Proportioning longitudinal reinforcement

To account for the fact that on one side of the section the torsional and shear stresses will counteract each other, the required equivalent tension is taken as the square root of the sum of the squares of the individually calculated tensions.

N11.4   Strut-and-tie Model

N11.4.1   Structural idealization

Cracked reinforced concrete carries load principally by compressive stresses in the concrete and tensile stresses in the reinforcement. After significant cracking has occurred, the principal compressive stress trajectories in the concrete tend towards straight lines and hence, can be approximated by straight struts. Ties are used to model the principal reinforcement. The regions of the concrete subjected to multi-directional stresses, where the struts and ties meet (the nodes of the truss) are represented by node regions.

A number of typical strut-and-tie models are shown in Fig. N11.4.1. In sketching such models it should be kept in mind that space must be left to accommodate the required dimensions of the struts and the ties. A second important consideration is to ensure that the angles between the struts and the adjoining ties, θ_s, are not too small.

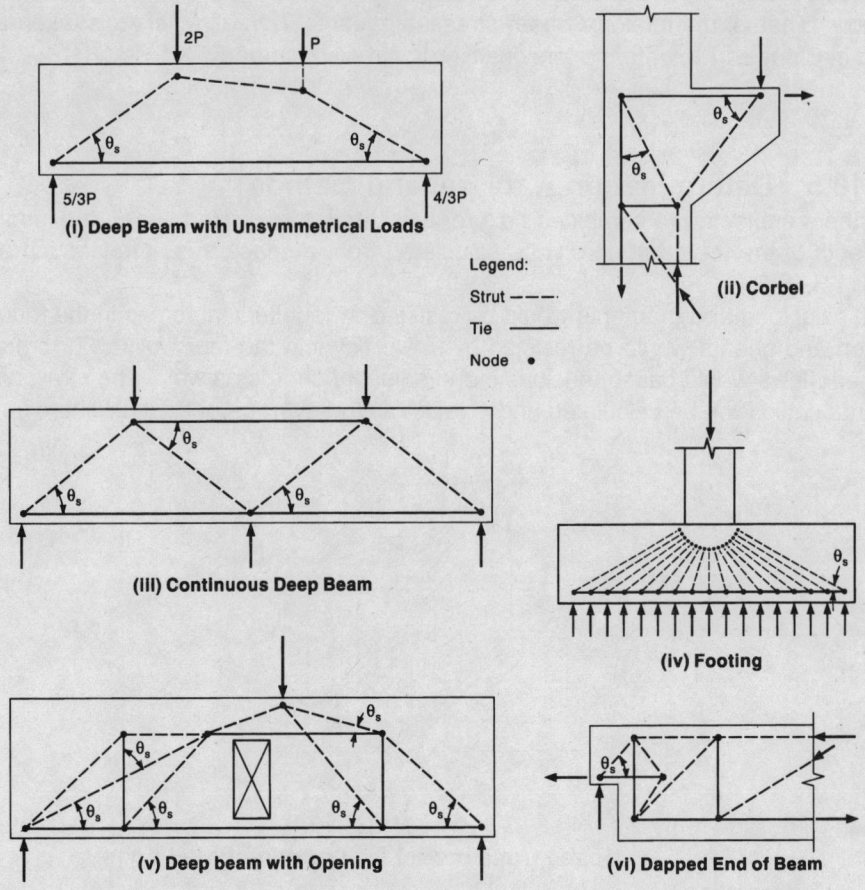

Fig. N11.4.1
Examples of strut-and-tie models

While, for each situation, a number of different strut-and-tie models are feasible, those which involve the most direct path for the loads to travel to the supports will be the most efficient.

In some cases it may be appropriate to choose a strut-and-tie model with multiple load paths, e.g., Fig. N11.4.1(v). For these internally statically indeterminate trusses, the load may be assigned between the alternative load paths based on the yield capacity of the ties.

N11.4.2.2 Effective cross-sectional area of strut

The effective cross-sectional area of a strut is typically controlled by the anchorage conditions at the end of the strut. Figure 11-3 suggests that, for a strut anchored by reinforcement, the effective concrete area will extend to a distance of up to six bar diameters from the anchored bar.

N11.4.2.3 Limiting compressive stress in struts

This clause requires that, in determining the limiting compressive stress in the concrete, some consideration be given to the strains imposed on the cracked concrete.

If the concrete is not subjected to principal tensile strains greater than about 0.002, it can resist a compressive stress of $0.85f'_c$. This will be the limit for regions of the struts that are not crossed by or joined to ties. The reinforcing bars of a tie are bonded to the surrounding concrete. If the reinforcing bars are to yield in tension, there should be significant tensile strains imposed on the concrete. As these tensile strains increase, f_{cu} decreases.

The expression for ε_1 is based on the assumption that the principal compressive strain ε_2 in the direction of the strut equals 0.002 and that the tensile strain in the direction of the tie equals ε_s. As the angle between the strut and tie decreases, ε_1 increases and hence, f_{cu} decreases. In the limit, no compressive stresses would be permitted in a strut that is superimposed on a tie, i.e., $\theta_s = 0$, a situation that violates compatibility. See Fig. N11.4.2.3.

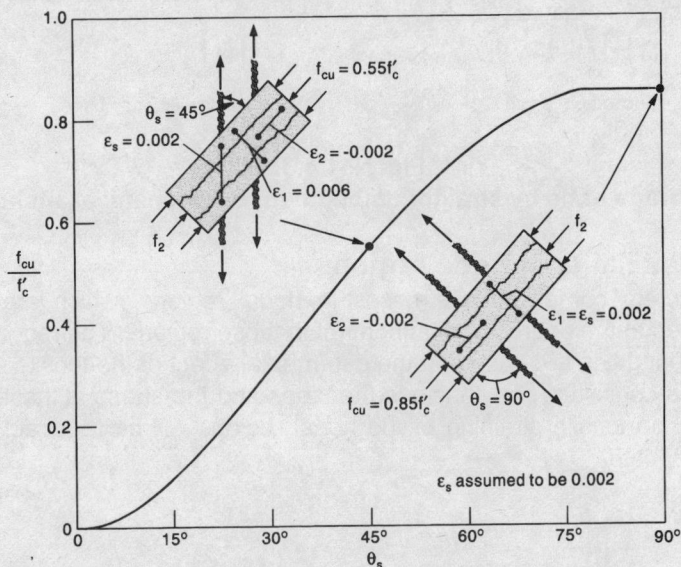

Fig. N11.4.2.3
Crushing Strength of Strut as a Function of Angle between Strut and Adjoining Tie

For a tie consisting of reinforcing bars, ε_s can be taken as the tensile strain due to factored loads in the reinforcing bars, or can be taken conservatively as f_y/E_s. For a tie consisting of prestressing tendons, ε_s can be taken as zero until the tensile stress in the tendon exceeds the decompression stress f_{po}. For higher stresses, ε_s would equal $(f_{pr} - f_{po})/E_p$.

If the strain, ε_s, varies over the width of the strut, it is appropriate to use the value at the centreline of the strut. Thus, for the situation shown in Fig. 11-3(b), where the tie is being developed in the length that crosses the strut, ε_s can be taken as one-half of the tensile strain in the tie at the face of the strut.

Some strut-and-tie models may involve two struts, say "a" and "b", that "share" the same concrete. See example at left support of deep beam in Fig. N11.4.1(v). One approach to check the crushing of the concrete in this situation is to assume that the compressive stresses in the two struts, f_{2a} and f_{2b}, and the limiting compressive stresses for these two struts, f_{cua} and f_{cub}, should satisfy the following limit:

$$\frac{f_{2a}}{f_{cua}} + \frac{f_{2b}}{f_{cub}} \leq 1.0$$

N11.4.2.4   Reinforced struts
To be effective as compression reinforcement, the bars would have to be enclosed in column ties.

N11.4.3.2   Anchorage of ties in node regions
Figure N11.4.3.2 illustrates some aspects of this clause.

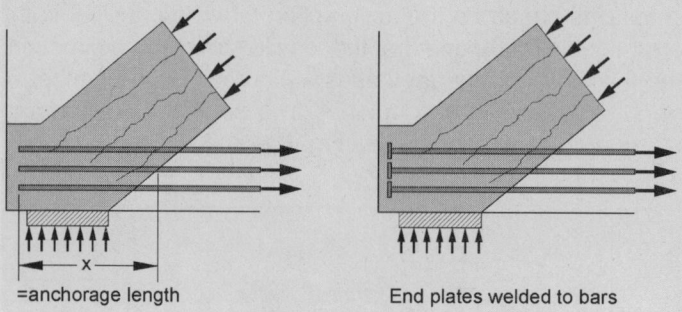

=anchorage length   End plates welded to bars

Fig. N11.4.3.2
Anchorage of tie by straight embedment or mechanical anchorage

N11.4.4.1   Stress limits in node regions
The allowable concrete compressive stresses in nodal regions, which are illustrated in Fig. N11.4.4.1, are related to the degree of confinement in these regions. The reduced stress limits for nodal regions anchoring ties are based on the detrimental effect of the tensile straining caused by these ties. If the ties consist of post-tensioned tendons and the stress in these tendons does not need to exceed f_{po}, no tensile straining of the nodal regions will be required. For this case, the $0.85f'_c$ limit is appropriate.

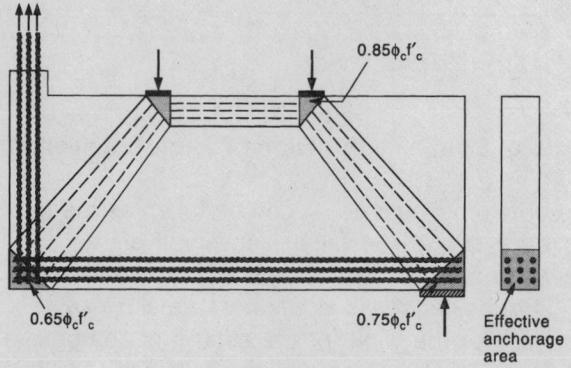

Fig. N11.4.4.1
Stress limits in node regions

N11.4.4.2   Satisfying stress limits in node regions

The stresses in the nodal regions are reduced by increasing the size of the bearing plates, by increasing the dimensions of the struts, and by increasing the effective anchorage area of the ties.

N11.4.5   Crack control reinforcement

This reinforcement is intended to control the width of the cracks and to ensure a minimum ductility for the member so that, if required, significant redistribution of internal stresses is possible. The 0.002 limit was chosen to be similar to the traditional minimum reinforcement limits used for walls and deep beams.

N11.5   Interface shear transfer

N11.5.1   General

Figure N11.5.1(a) illustrates the shear friction concept for the case where the reinforcement is perpendicular to the potential failure plane. Because the interface is rough, shear displacement will cause a widening of the crack. This crack opening will cause tension in the reinforcement balanced by compressive stresses, σ, in the concrete across the crack. The shear resistance of the face is assumed to be equal to the cohesion, c, plus the coefficient of friction, μ, times the compressive stress, σ, across the face. Hence, for this case,

$$v_r = \lambda\phi_c(c + \mu\sigma)$$

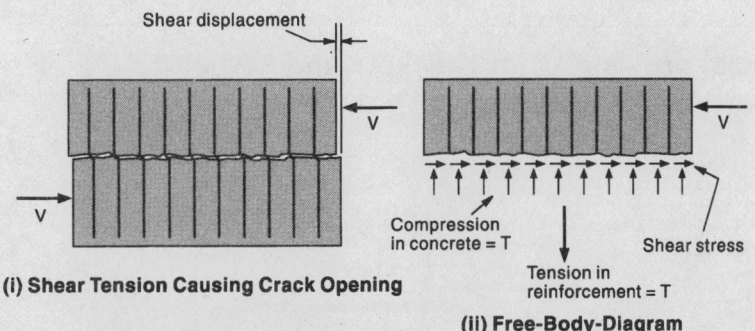

(i) Shear Tension Causing Crack Opening

(ii) Free-Body-Diagram

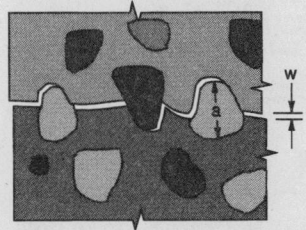

(iii) Aggregate Interlock at Crack Interface

Fig. N11.5.1(a)
Shear friction concept

Explanatory Notes on CSA A23.3-04

If inclined reinforcement is crossing the crack, part of the shear can be directly resisted by the component, parallel to the shear plane, of the tension force in the reinforcement. See Fig. N11.5.1(b)

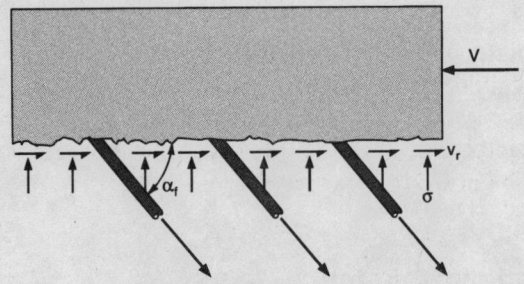

Fig. N11.5.1(b)
Shear-friction reinforcement inclined to crack

The upper limit on the term $\lambda\phi_c(c + \mu\sigma)$ is to avoid concrete crushing failures.

N11.5.3   Alternative Equation for shear stress resistance

The alternative method given in this clause is based on the work of Loov and Patnaik (Loov, R.E. and Patnaik, A.K., "Horizontal Shear Strength of Composite Concrete Beams with a Rough Interface," *PCI Journal*, Vol. 39, no. 1, pp. 48-69). In this method, the shear resistance is a function of both the concrete strength and the amount of reinforcement crossing the failure crack. For small amounts of reinforcement, this method can give values of factored shear resistance that are higher than those from Eq. (11-24).

N11.6   Special provisions for brackets and corbels

Parameters used in this clause are illustrated in Fig. N11.6.

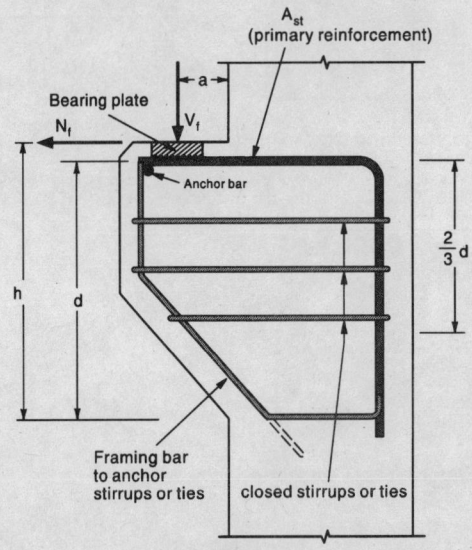

Fig. N11.6
Parameters in design of corbel

N11.6.3

A minimum depth at the outside edge of the bearing area is specified because of concern with failures involving an inclined crack propagating from below the bearing area to the outer sloping face.

N11.6.4

This provision allows for the tension on the corbel caused by the restraint of shrinkage, creep and temperature movements. Connection details shall be such that the tension can be transmitted into the corbel by shear friction or by mechanical anchorage.

N11.6.7

This anchorage may be achieved by welding the tension tie reinforcement to a structural steel plate, bar, or angle, or by bending the tie bars into a horizontal loop. Anchorage by means of a vertical hook should be avoided because the concrete outside the hook will tend to split off. If vertical hooks must be used, the outside edge of the bearing plate under the load should not be closer to the edge of the corbel than the point of tangency at the start of the hook, after allowing for tolerances in bar placement.

N12.   Development and Splices of Reinforcement

N12.2.2

Equation (12-1) is a modified form of the general equation for the development length of deformed bars or wires in tension proposed by ACI Committee 408[12.1] which is based on the research carried out by Orangun et al.[12.2] In the Standard, the term, d_{cs}, is taken as the smaller of the minimum cover measured to the centre of the bar or two-thirds of the centre-to-centre spacing of the bars. The factor, K_{tr}, represents the contribution of transverse reinforcement across potential planes of splitting.

The factor k_1 reflects the adverse effects of top-bar casting position, k_2 is the epoxy-coating factor, k_3 reflects the lower tensile strength of low-density concrete and k_4 is a factor reflecting the more favourable performance of smaller diameter deformed bars and wires (see N12.2.4 for more details).

Equation (12-1) expresses the development length when the bond strength is limited by splitting failures. The term $(d_{cs} + K_{tr})$ is limited to $2.5d_b$ to safeguard against pullout type failures.

N12.2.3

Table 12-1 gives the development length of deformed bars and deformed wires in tension in a simplified format, as a function of the bar diameter, d_b. These simplified expressions have been determined by substituting into Equation (12-1) minimum values of cover and spacing and/or minimum amounts of transverse reinforcement.

For example, consider a case where bars in a slab have a minimum clear cover of $1.0d_b$ and a clear spacing between the bars of $2d_b$. It is assumed that the slab reinforcement perpendicular to the bars being developed serve to control splitting cracks in the cover concrete. Thus the bond strength would be controlled by splitting between the bars in a layer and the value of d_{cs} would be controlled by the bar spacing, giving d_{cs} equal to $2/3 \times 3.0d_b = 2.0d_b$. For this case where K_{tr} equals zero, Equation (12-1) becomes:

$$\ell_d = 1.15 \frac{k_1 k_2 k_3 k_4}{(2 d_b + 0)} \frac{f_y}{\sqrt{f_c'}} \frac{\pi d_b^2}{4} = 0.45 \, k_1 k_2 k_3 k_4 \frac{f_y}{\sqrt{f_c'}} \, d_b$$

This simplified equation is also used for the case where the minimum clear cover is 1.0db, the minimum clear spacing is $1.4d_b$ and confinement in the form of minimum ties or stirrups is provided.

For the situation where a minimum clear cover of $1.0d_b$ and a minimum clear spacing between bars of $1.4d_b$ are provided, without any transverse reinforcement, then d_{cs} becomes the smaller of $1.5 d_b$ or $2/3 \times 2.4d_b = 1.6d_b$. Hence the simplified equation for the case labelled "other cases" in Table 12-1 becomes:

$$\ell_d = 1.15 \frac{k_1 k_2 k_3 k_4}{(1.5 d_b + 0)} \frac{f_y}{\sqrt{f_c'}} \frac{\pi d_b^2}{4} = 0.6 \, k_1 k_2 k_3 k_4 \frac{f_y}{\sqrt{f_c'}} \, d_b$$

The equations in Table 12-1 may be readily evaluated for commonly occurring situations as simple multiples of d_b. For example, for normal density concrete ($k_3 = 1.0$) with f = 35 MPa and using uncoated 20M or larger bottom bars ($k_2 = k_4 = k_1 = 1.0$) with $f_y = 400$ Mpa these expressions, with rounding, reduce to:

$\ell_d = 30d_b$

and $\ell_d = 40d_b$

N12.2.4

The bar location factor, k_1, accounts for the position of the bar in freshly placed concrete. The factor was reduced from 1.4 in the 1984 Standard to 1.3 in 1994 in light of research[12.3,12.4]. This factor remains unchanged at 1.3 in the 2004 edition.

Studies[12.5,12.6,12.7] of the mechanical anchorage of epoxy-coated bars show that bond strength is reduced because the coating significantly reduces both adhesion and friction between the bar and

Explanatory Notes on CSA A23.3-04

the concrete. The factor, k_2, reflects the type of anchorage failure likely to occur. When the cover or spacing is small, a splitting failure can occur and the anchorage or bond strength is substantially reduced. If the cover and spacing between bars is large, a splitting failure is precluded and the effect of the epoxy coating on anchorage strength is not as large. Studies[12.2] have shown that although the cover or spacing may be small, the anchorage strength may be increased by adding transverse steel crossing the plane of splitting, and restraining the splitting crack.

Although no studies on the effect of coated transverse steel have been reported to date, the addition of coated transverse steel should improve the anchorage strength of epoxy-coated bars. Since the bond of epoxy-coated bars is already reduced due to loss of adhesion between the bar and the concrete, an upper limit of 1.7 is established for the product of the top reinforcement and epoxy-coated reinforcement factors.

The low-density concrete factor, k_3, has been rounded to reflect the degree of accuracy associated with this factor.

N12.2.5

The reduction factor based on area is not used in those cases where anchorage development for full f_y is required. For example, the excess reinforcement factor does not apply for development of positive moment reinforcement at supports according to Clause 12.11.2, for development of shrinkage and temperature reinforcement according to Clause 7.8.4, or for development of reinforcement provided according to Clause 13.10.6.3.

N12.3.2

Bars in compression have shorter development lengths because the development length is not crossed by cracks due to tension in the concrete and because the end bearing of the bars on the concrete is usually beneficial.

N12.4

An increased development length is required when two, three or four bars are bundled together. The extra extension is needed because the grouping makes it more difficult to mobilize bond resistance from the "core" between the bars.

The designer should also note Clause 7.4.2.3 relating to the cutoff points of individual bars within a bundle and Clause 12.14.2.2 relating to splices of bundled bars.

N12.5.1

The definition of hook development length is shown in Fig. N12.5.1. This development length is typically controlled by splitting of the concrete in the plane of the hook caused by high local stresses shown.

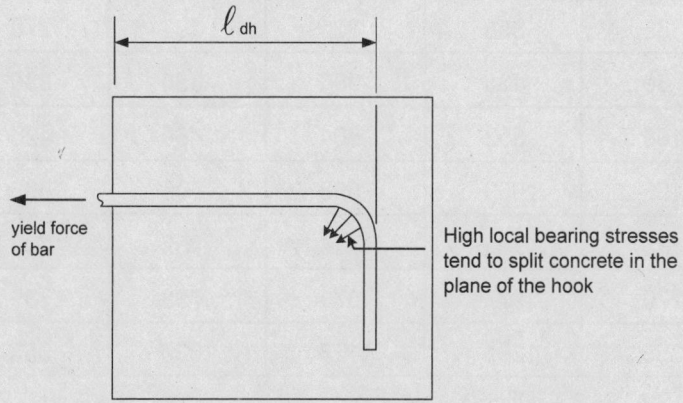

Fig. N12.15.1 Hook Development Length

N12.5.2

Fig. N12.5.2 and Table N12.5.2 gives geometric details for standard hooks and basic hook development length ℓ_{hb} for the case of $f_y = 400$ MPa.

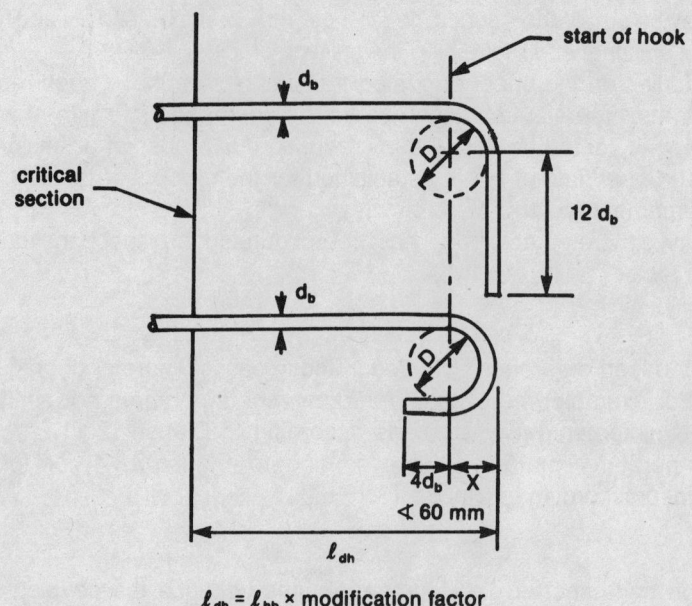

$\ell_{dh} = \ell_{hb} \times$ modification factor

Fig. N12.15.2   Hook Geometry Details

Table N12.5.2
Values of Hook Basic Development Length for Grade 400 Bars

Bar No.	X* (mm)	ℓ_{hb} (mm)				
		f_c' (MPa)				
		20	25	30	35	40
10M	45	253	226	206	191	179
15M	65	358	320	292	270	253
20M	80	436	390	356	330	308
25M	100	563	504	460	426	398
30M	155	669	598	546	505	473
35M	185	798	714	652	603	565
45M	270	977	874	798	739	691
55M	355	1261	1128	1030	953	892

*   X = bend radius + d_b, (values given are for bend radii for Grade 400 R Steel)

N12.5.3

Fig. N12.5.3 illustrates some situations in which the basic hook development length is modified.

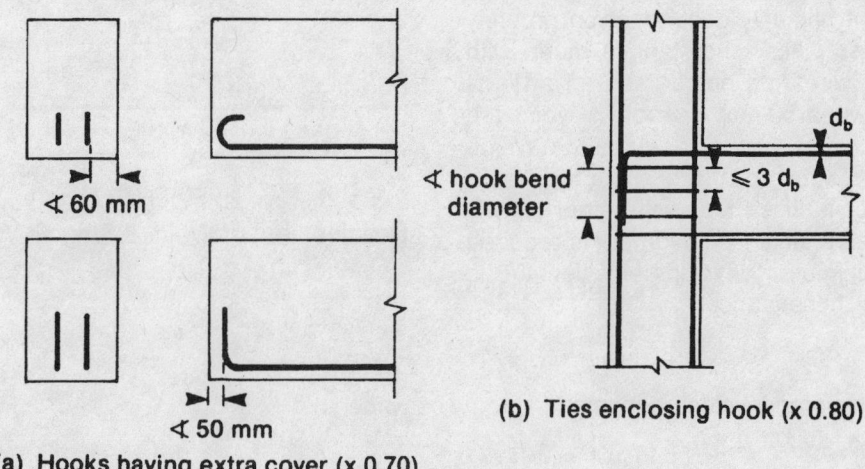

(a) Hooks having extra cover (x 0.70)

(b) Ties enclosing hook (x 0.80)

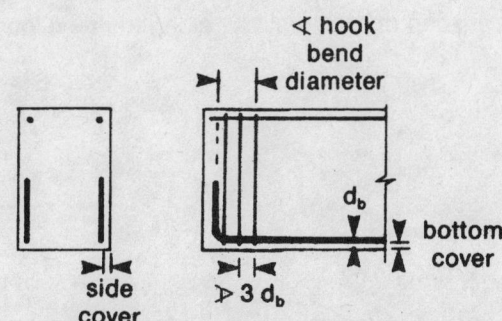

(c) Stirrups required if both side and bottom
cover are less than 60 mm (0.80 factor not applicable)
If side or bottom cover exceeds 60 mm (x 0.80)

Fig. N12.5.3   Factors Modifying Hook Development Length for 35M or Smaller Bars

N12.6.2

Total development of a bar simply consists of the sum of all the parts that contribute to the anchorage. When a mechanical anchorage is not capable of developing the required strength of the reinforcement, additional embedment length of reinforcement must be provided.

N12.7

Fig. N12.7 shows the development requirements for deformed wire fabric with one cross wire within the development length. Some of the development is assigned to the welds and some assigned to the length of deformed wire.

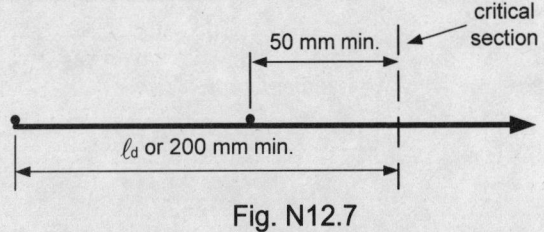

Fig. N12.7
Development of Deformed Wire Fabric

N12.8

Fig. N12.8 shows the development requirements for smooth wire fabric with development primarily dependent on properly located cross wires. For fabrics made with the smaller wires, an embedment of at least two cross wires 50 mm or more beyond the point of critical section is adequate to develop the full yield strength of the anchored wires. However, for fabrics made with larger closely spaced wires a longer embedment is required and a minimum development length is provided for these fabrics.

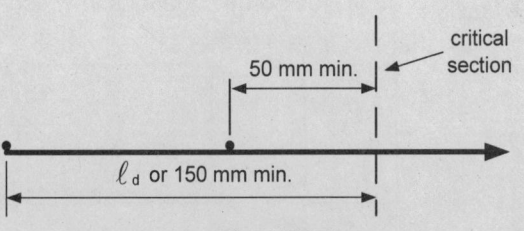

Fig. N12.8
Development of Welded Smooth Wire Fabric

N12.9.1

The expression for development length, ℓ_d, may be written as:

$$\ell_d = 0.048\, f_{se}\, d_b + 0.145\, (f_{ps} - f_{se})\, d_b$$

The first term represents the transfer length of the strand which is the length over which the prestress, f_{se}, develops. The second term represents the additional length required to increase the stress from f_{se} to f_{ps}. The variation of strand stress along the development length is shown in Fig. N12.9.1.

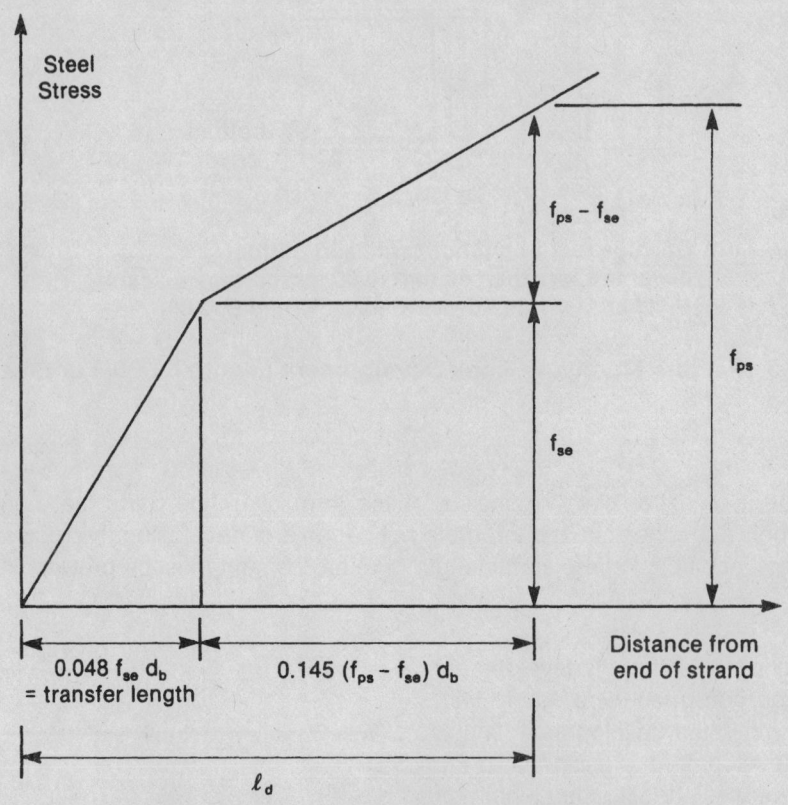

Fig. N12.9.1
Development of Prestressing Strand

Explanatory Notes on CSA A23.3-04

N12.10.3

The inclined cracking which occurs in regions subjected to shearing forces leads to bar forces which are larger than those calculated from the bending moment diagram. The longitudinal reinforcement needs to be designed for the tensions arising from the moment and the shear at every section. In the 2004 edition of A23.3 both the Simplified and General Methods of shear design now require that longitudinal reinforcement be proportioned in accordance with Clause 11.3.9 to account for the above effects. The 1994 requirements of extending reinforcement a distance "d" past the point where it is no longer needed for flexure, no longer applies to Simplified Shear design. Clause 11.3.9.1 provides an alternative solution for members not subjected to significant tension or torsion. In these members it calls for all reinforcement to be extended a distance $d_v \cot \theta$ past the point where it is needed for flexure alone. Clause 12.10.3 has been modified to reflect these changes. Bar cut-offs are determined to ensure that the M_r provided exceeds the equivalent moments at all sections, see Fig N12.10.3.

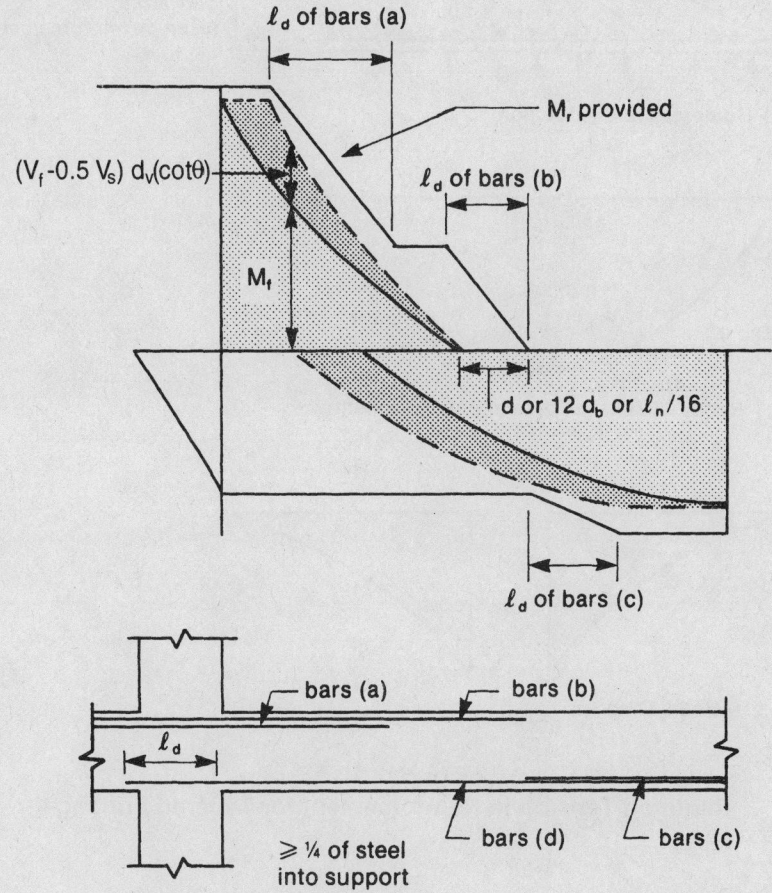

Fig. N12.10.3
Development of Longitudinal Reinforcement in Continuous Beam with Shear Reinforcement as Required by Clause 11.3.9

N12.10.5

In these types of members the required tension in the reinforcement is not directly proportional to the moment. This is illustrated in Fig. N12.10.5 for a tapered footing. In evaluating the variation of this force, the strut and tie model of Clause 11.4 will often be useful.

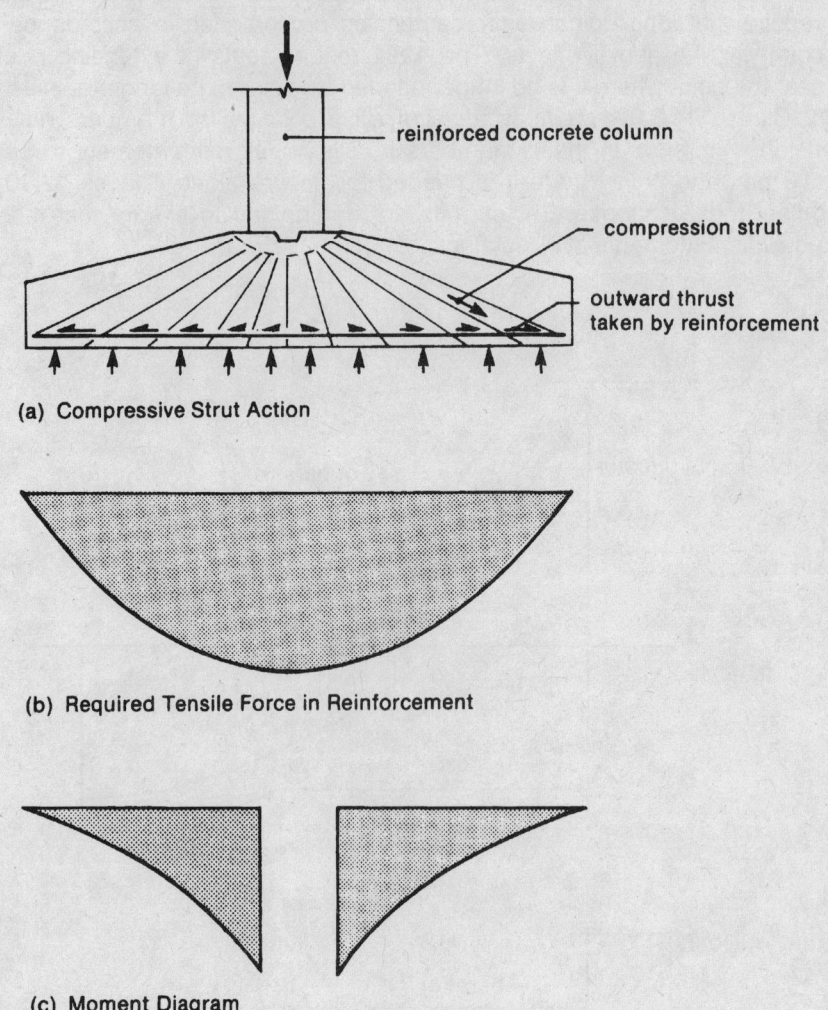

reinforced concrete column

compression strut

outward thrust
taken by reinforcement

(a) Compressive Strut Action

(b) Required Tensile Force in Reinforcement

(c) Moment Diagram

Fig. N12.10.5
Required Tension in Reinforcement for Tapered Footing

N12.11.1

These traditional requirements are intended to give the structure an ability to tolerate some unanticipated actions.

N12.11.2

Unexpected loadings such as blasts or earthquakes may cause load reversals. To provide a minimum level of ductility for these situations it is necessary to anchor the required reinforcement so that it can develop its yield stress.

Explanatory Notes on CSA A23.3-04

N12.11.3

In regions of low moment and high shear the tension force in the reinforcing bars will increase rapidly in the direction of increasing moment. This clause is intended to assure that the bond characteristics of such bars will enable this rapid build up of force to occur. As illustrated in Fig. N12.11.3, the "bond" characteristics are considered adequate if the development length of the bars, ℓ_d, is less than $\ell_a + M_r/V_f$. When this requirement is not satisfied, reduce the bar diameter (ℓ_d reduced).

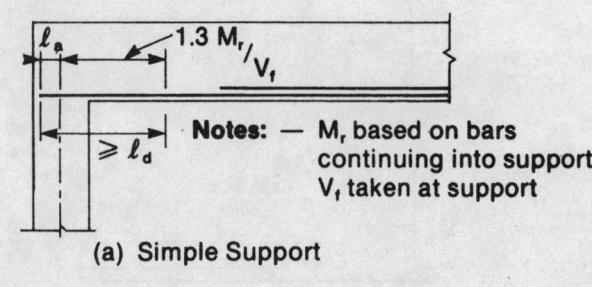

Notes: — M_r based on bars continuing into support
V_f taken at support

(a) Simple Support

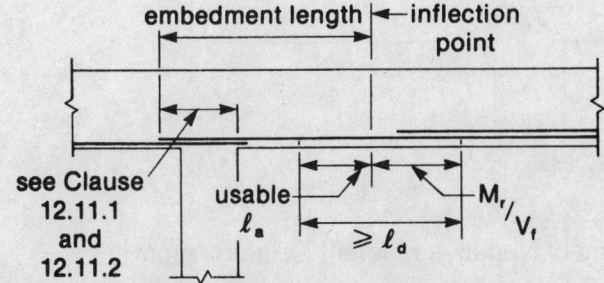

Notes: — usable ℓ_a limited to d or 12 d_b
— M_r based on bars extending past inflection point
— V_f taken at inflection point
— Negative moment steel not shown

(b) Inflection Point

Fig. N12.11.3
Development of Positive Moment Reinforcement at Simple Support and Inflection Point

N12.12

Fig. N12.12 illustrates the development requirements for negative moment reinforcement.

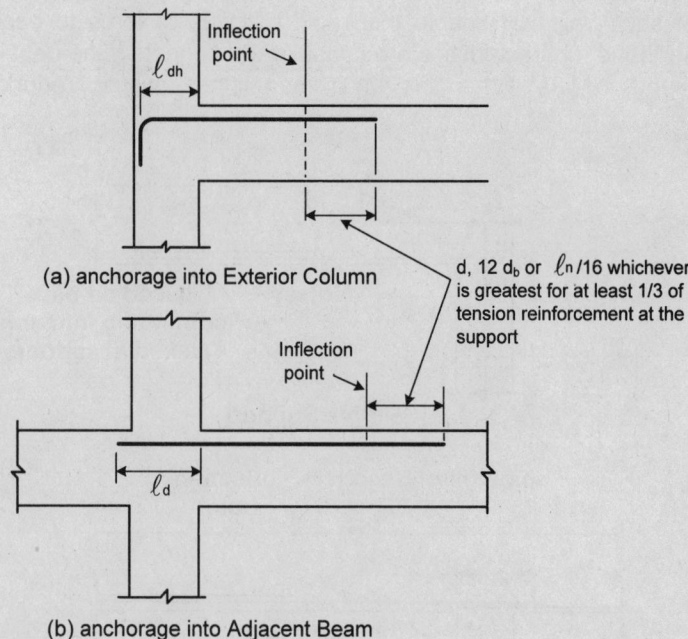

(a) anchorage into Exterior Column

d, 12 d_b or $\ell_n/16$ whichever is greatest for at least 1/3 of tension reinforcement at the support

(b) anchorage into Adjacent Beam

Fig. N12.12
Development of Negative Moment Reinforcement

N12.13.1

To be effective, web reinforcement must be capable of tying the main tension reinforcement to the compression zone of the beam.

N12.13.2

For shear reinforcement made with 15M and smaller bars or with MD200 and smaller wire there is no need to calculate the straight embedment length in addition to the hook. However, Clause 12.13.1 requires "full-depth" web reinforcement and in addition the web reinforcement must be anchored around longitudinal reinforcement.

Fig. N12.13.2 illustrates stirrup anchorage requirements for 20M and 25M stirrups.

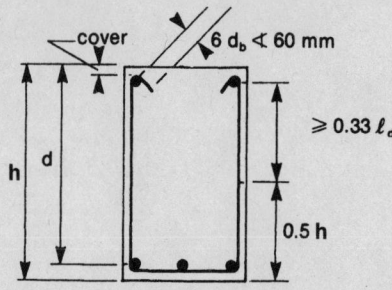

Fig. N12.13.2
Development of 20M and 25M Stirrups

Explanatory Notes on CSA A23.3-04

N12.13.2.c

Fig. N12.13.2(c) illustrates anchorage details for welded wire fabric stirrups.

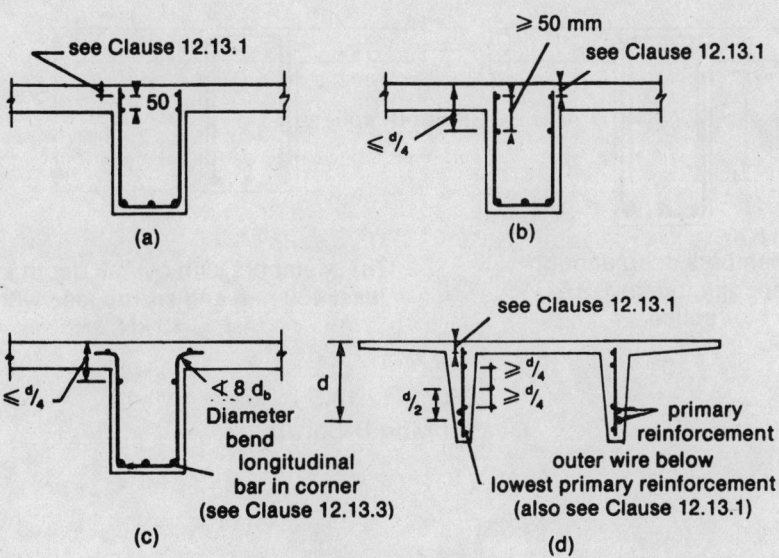

Fig. N12.13.2(c)
Anchorage of Welded Wire Fabric Stirrups

N12.13.4

See Fig. N12.13.4.

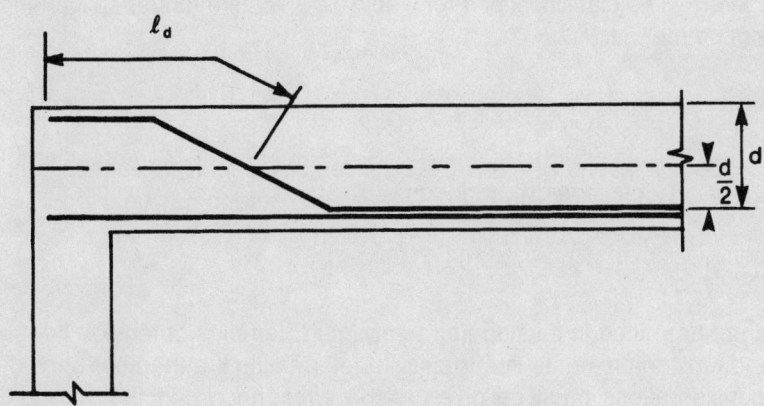

Fig. N12.13.4
Anchorage of Inclined Longitudinal Bars Used as Shear Reinforcement

N12.13.5
See Fig. N12.13.5.

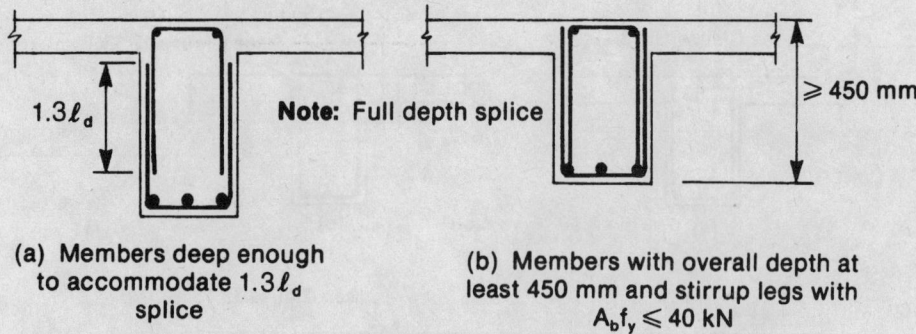

(a) Members deep enough to accommodate $1.3\ell_d$ splice

(b) Members with overall depth at least 450 mm and stirrup legs with $A_b f_y \leqslant 40$ kN

**Fig. N12.13.5
Overlapping U-Stirrups**

N12.14.2.2
In calculating the lap splice length required for individual bars within a bundle the increases in development length of Clause 12.4 should not be included as these would duplicate the increases required by Clause 12.14.2.2 for the effect of bundling.

N12.15.1
In calculating ℓ_d, the modification factor of (A_s required / A_s provided) of Clause 12.2.5 is not to be applied as this factor is already taken into account in the classifications of Table 12-2. Where feasible, splices should be located in regions of low stress in the reinforcement and the splices should be staggered. The classifications for Table 12-2 require longer splice lengths when these conditions cannot be met.

N12.15.4
This clause describes situations where welded splices or mechanical connections of less strength than 1.25 times the specified yield strength of the reinforcement may be used.

N12.15.5
Lap splices are not permitted in tension tie members. Examples of tension tie members are arch ties, hangers and tension elements in a truss. In determining if a member should be classified as a tension tie, considerations must be given to the importance, function, proportions and stress conditions of the member. For example, a circular tank with many bars and with well-staggered, widely spaced splices should not be classified as a tension tie member.

N12.16
Splice strengths in compression depend considerably on end bearing and hence do not increase proportionally in strength for increasing lap splice length. Table N12.16 gives the minimum lap splice lengths for bars in compression having a yield strength of 400 MPa.

Explanatory Notes on CSA A23.3-04

Table N12.16
Minimum Compression Lap Splice Lengths Without Special Confinement, f_y = 400 MPa

Bar Size	10M	15M	20M	25M	30M	35M
Splice length	330	467	569	736	873	1049

Note: *for concrete strength < 20 MPa, increase lap length by 1/3.*

N12.16.4.1
Experience with end-bearing splices has been almost exclusively with vertical bars in columns. If bars are significantly inclined from the vertical, special attention is required to insure that adequate end-bearing contact can be achieved and maintained.

N12.17
In columns subject to flexure and axial loads, tension stresses may occur on one face of the column if moderate or large moments must be transmitted. When such tensions occur, Clause 12.17 requires tension splices to be used or an adequate tensile resistance provided. Furthermore, a minimum tension capacity is required in each face of all columns even where analysis indicates compression only. This is achieved by requiring at least compression splices, which give tension capacities of at least one-quarter f_y.

Note that the column splice must satisfy requirements for all load combinations for the column. A load combination, including wind or seismic loads, may induce tensions greater than $0.5f_y$ in some column bars, in which case the column splice must be Class B.

N12.17.3.4
To qualify for the 0.83 reduction factor a rectangular column must satisfy the 0.0015hs tie area requirement for both directions. As an example, for the column shown in Fig. N12.17.3.4 we would have:

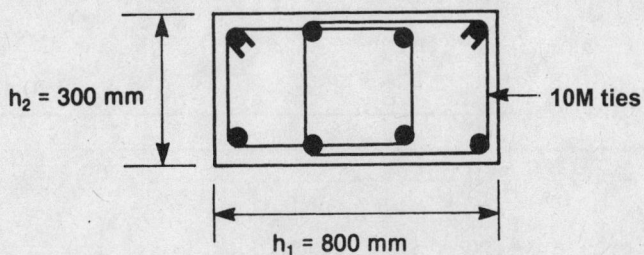

h_2 = 300 mm   ← 10M ties

h_1 = 800 mm

Fig. N12.17.3.4
Rectangular Tied Column for Example Calculation

In the direction perpendicular to h_1 there are 4 legs, hence the required spacing is (4 x 100)/(0.0015 x 800) = 333 mm. In the direction perpendicular to h_2 there are 2 legs, hence the required spacing is (2 x 100)/(0.0015 x 300) = 444 mm. Hence ties must be spaced at no greater than 333 mm and must be place throughout the lap splice length to qualify.

N12.17.3.5
Spirals meeting the requirements of Clauses 7.6.4 and 10.9.4 increase splitting resistance and hence enable compression lap splice lengths to be reduced.

N12.17.4

The intent of this clause is to avoid excessive congestion at splice locations and to give guidance concerning the staggering of splice locations in very heavily reinforced columns.

N12.18.1

Fig. N12.18.1 illustrates the tension lap splice requirements for welded deformed wire fabric. In computing the ℓ_d from Clause 12.7, the 200 mm minimum length of that clause is neglected. As shown in Fig. N12.18.1, a 200 mm minimum is applied to the overall splice length.

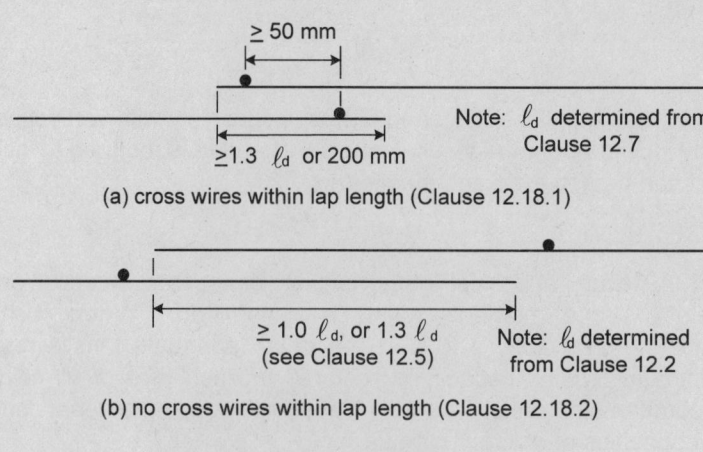

(a) cross wires within lap length (Clause 12.18.1)

(b) no cross wires within lap length (Clause 12.18.2)

Fig. N12.18.1
Lap Splices of Deformed Fabric

N12.19

The strength of lap splices of welded smooth fabric is dependent primarily on the anchorage obtained from the cross wires, rather than on the length of wire in the splice. Hence the lap is specified in terms of overlap of cross wires (see Fig. N12.19).

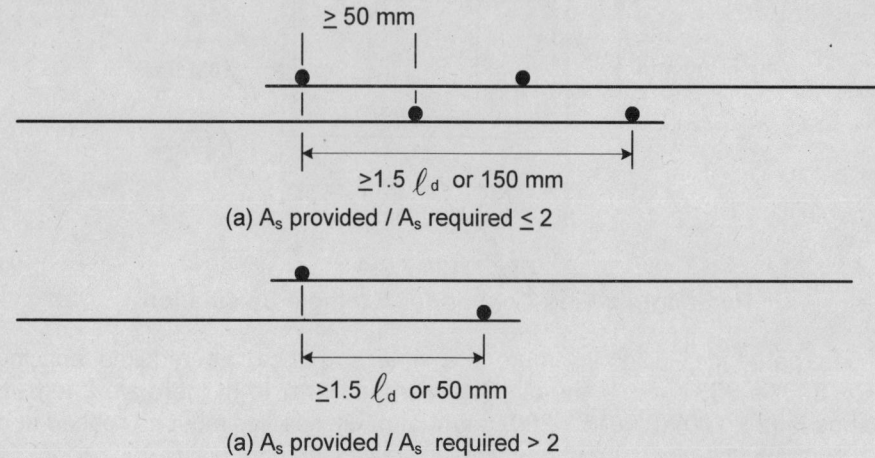

(a) A_s provided / A_s required ≤ 2

(a) A_s provided / A_s required > 2

Fig. N12.19
Lap Splices of Smooth Fabric

References, Chapter 12

12.1   ACI Committee 408, "Suggested Development, Splice, and Standard Hook Provisions for Deformed Bars in Tension", Concrete International, ACI, V.1, N.7, July 1979, pp. 44-46.

12.2   Orangun, C.O., Jirsa, J.O. and Breen, J.E., "A Reevaluation of Test Data on Development Length and Splices", ACI Journal, Proceedings, V.74, Mar. 1977, pp. 114-122.

12.3   Jirsa, J.O. and Breen, J.E., "Influence of Casting Position and Shear on Development and Splice Length-Design Recommendations", Research Report 242-3F, Center for Transportation Research, Bureau of Engineering Research, The University of Texas at Austin, Nov. 1981.

12.4   Jeanty, P.R., Mitchell, D., and Mirza, M.S., "Investigation of 'Top Bar' Effects in Beams", ACI Structural Journal, V.85, N.3, May-June 1988, pp. 251-257.

12.5   Treece, R.A, "Bond Strength of Epoxy-Coated Reinforcing Bars", Master's thesis, Department of Civil Engineering, The University of Texas at Austin, May, 1987.

12.6   Johnston, D.W., "Bond Characteristics of Epoxy-Coated Reinforcing Bars", Department of Civil Engineering, North Carolina State University, Report No. FHWA/NC/82-002, August, 1982.

12.7   Mathey, R.G. and Clifton, J.R.,"Bond of Coated Reinforcing Bars in Concrete", Journal of Structural Division, ASCE, V. 102, N. ST1, Jan., 1976, pp. 215-228.

Explanatory Notes on CSA A23.3-04

N13   Introduction

Clause 13 has been revised to provide different distribution factors for factored moments in column strips. New requirements for slab band construction are also specified. Expressions for determining the minimum thickness of two-way slabs have been simplified to provide a closed form solution as opposed to the 1994 expression that required an iterative approach. Additional requirements for slab edge reinforcement have been included in the 2004 edition. . Provisions for defining design moments based on finite element or finite difference solutions have been clarified. The treatment of shear transfer at a corner column has been simplified.

Regular Two-Way Slab Systems - Two-way slabs are slab systems that can deform and carry load in two orthogonal directions. Many of the provisions for their design are based on studies in which the curvatures in the two directions are equal or nearly equal. As the ratio of long to short clear spans increases, there is a tendency for the curvatures in the central portion of the panel to be more uniform in one direction than the other. For slabs without beams this tendency will be in the long span direction whereas for slabs with stiff beams on all sides this tendency will be in the short span direction. The geometric limitations listed are to ensure that the curvatures in the two directions will be approximately equal resulting in two-way behaviour. When provisions for regular two-way slab systems are used for slabs not meeting these geometric limitations, care must be taken to account for the manner in which the load is carried.

N13.1.2

Fig. N13.1.2(b) illustrates that portion of a capital that qualifies as a support. Fig. N13.1.2(c) illustrates the definitions of column and middle strips.

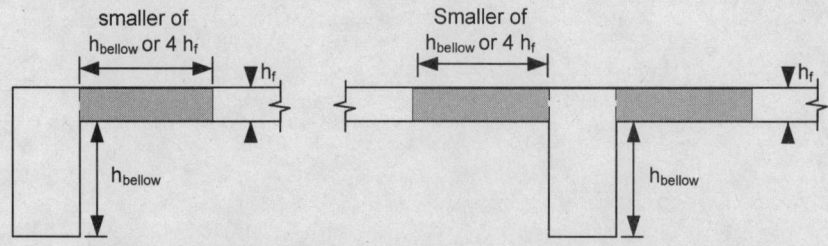

Fig. N13.1.2(a)   Portions of Slab to be included with Beam

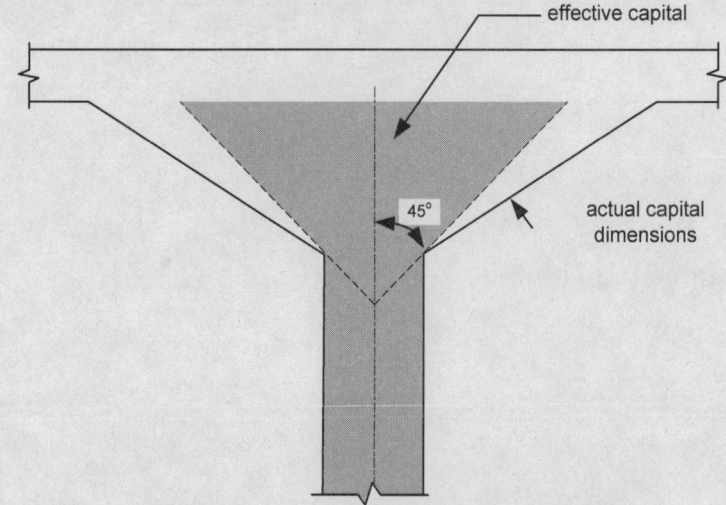

Fig. N13.1.2(b)   Effective Column Capital

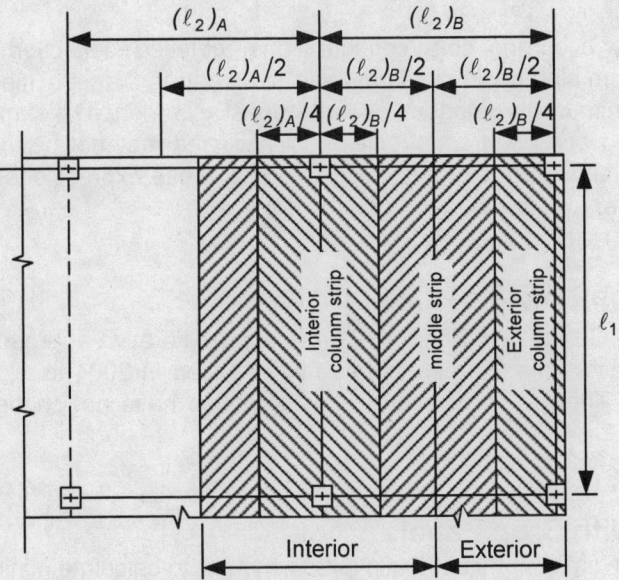

(a) Column strip for $\ell_2 \le \ell_1$

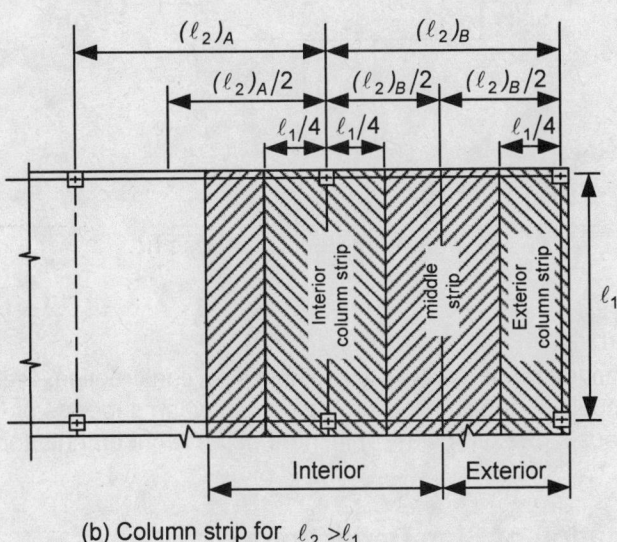

(b) Column strip for $\ell_2 > \ell_1$

Fig. N13.1.2(c)   Definition of Design Strip

N13.2   Minimum Slab Thickness

N13.2.1

This clause requires that all slabs designed using the provisions of Clause 13 shall have a thickness sufficient to ensure that slab deflections and crack widths will be satisfactory for the intended use.

N13.2.2

For many commonly occurring slab configurations, detailed deflection computation are not required if the minimum slab thickness is as least as great as that specified in Clauses 13.3.2 to 13.3.6. These are minimum thicknesses based on past experience of slabs with usual values of uniform gravity loading and good construction practice, and may not be the most economical or suitable thickness for all applications. For f_y = 400 MPa, these expressions result in clear span to overall thickness ratios, l_n/h, in the range of 30 to 46.

N13.2.3   Slabs with Drop Panels

In the 1994 edition of CSA A23.3 Eqn. (13-2) required an iterative approach in the calculation of minimum slab thickness. This expression has been revised in 2004 to provide designers with a closed form solution. The minimum slab thickness values have not changed from the previous edition.

N13.2.4   Slabs with Drop Panels

Fig. 13.2.4 depicts the dimensions used in expression 13-2 to calculate minimum slab thickness.

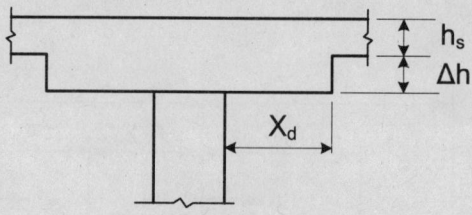

Fig. N13.2.4
Minimum Slab Thickness h$_s$

N13.2.6   Slab Bands

New in the 2004 edition is the inclusion of Slab Band slab construction. Slab bands are defined in Clause 2.2 as a continuous extension of a drop panel between supports or between a support and another slab band. Clause 13.2.6 provides minimum depth requirements for slab bands.

N13.2.7   Computation of Slab Deflections

Clause 13.2.7 gives requirements for the selection of factors to be used in computing deflections of two-way slab systems. It should be noted that in these calculations the modulus of rupture of the concrete, f_r, shall be taken as $0.3\lambda\sqrt{f_c'}$ (one-half the value specified in Equation (8-3)). The computed deflections must be no greater than those permitted by Clause 9.8.5.3.

N13.3   Design Procedures for Shear for Slabs Without Beams

This Clause consolidates the shear provisions for slabs.

Explanatory Notes on CSA A23.3-04

N13.3.3   Critical Section for Two-way Action

Critical sections that must be investigated for shear are illustrated in Fig. N13.3.3. Expressions for the maximum shear stress resistance to be used when evaluating the punching shear capacity are given in Clause 13.4.4. In checking the capacity of the critical section around a large drop panel such as that shown in Fig. N13.3.3, the maximum shear stress resistance approaches that for one-way shear.

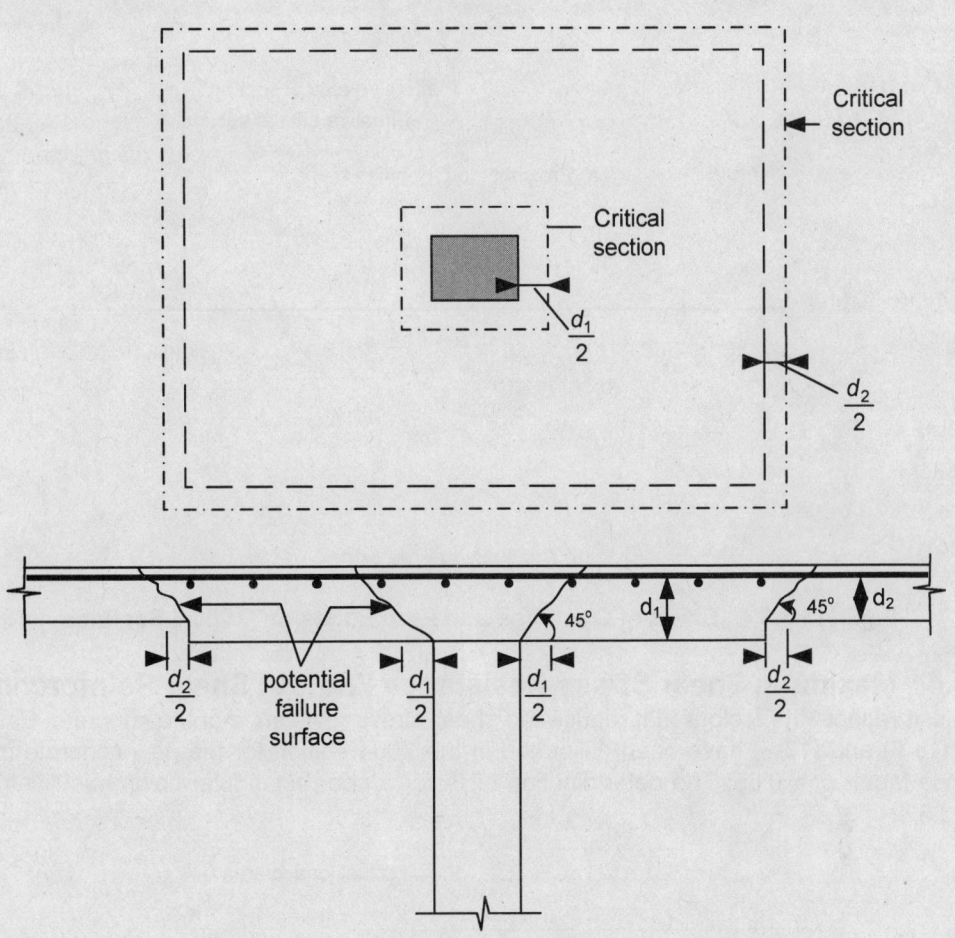

Fig. N13.3.3
Critical Sections for Punching Shear

N13.3.3.4   Openings in Slabs

The reduction in critical shear perimeter to account for the effect of openings located at a distance less than 10 times the slab thickness is shown in Fig N13.3.3.4(a). When the concentrated load or reaction area (column) is located near a free edge, the free edge may be considered as a large opening. Although the Standard is not specific as to the appropriate reduction in the critical section for this case, a procedure suggested by the CEB Code is illustrated in Fig N13.3.3.4(b) and is recommended.

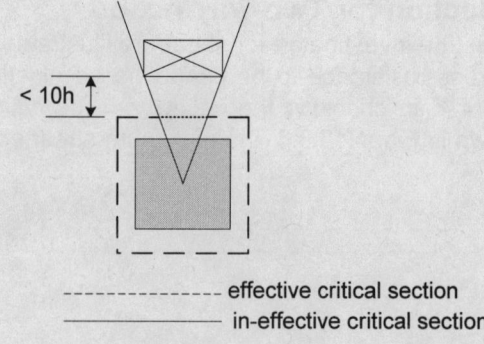

effective critical section
in-effective critical section

(a) Proximity to Openings

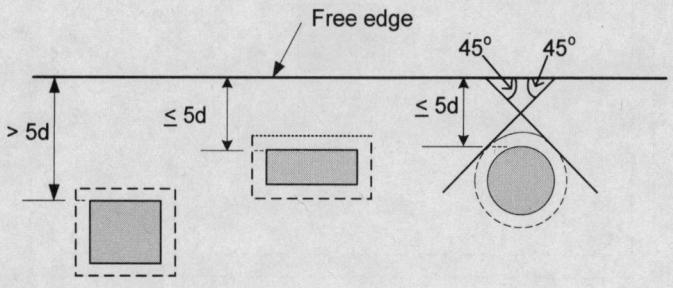

(b) Proximity to Free Edge

Fig. N13.3.3.4   Effect of Openings and Free Edges on Critical Sections

N13.3.4   Maximum Shear Stress Resistance Without Shear Reinforcement

This clause reflects the factors that reduce the shear stress resistance of the concrete. Equations (13-5), (13-6) and (13-7) have been calibrated in the 2004 edition for the new concrete material resistance factor $\phi_c = 0.65$. The determination of β_c for a non-rectangular column is illustrated in Fig. N13.3.4.

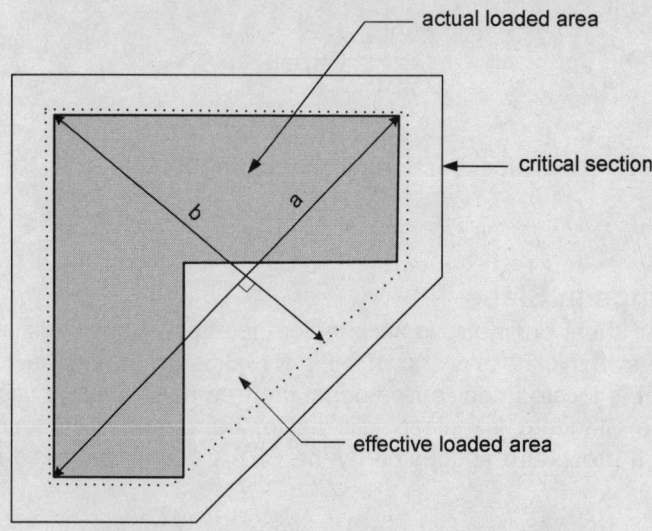

Fig. N13.3.4 β_c for a Non-Rectangular Column

N13.3.4.1

The nominal resistances provided by the expressions for shear in Clause 13 are consistent with those provided by the ACI 318-05 Code. For example, the nominal punching shear stress corresponding to Eq. (13-7) is:

$$v_n = 0.33\lambda\sqrt{f'_c} \ \text{MPa}$$

To ensure this consistent level of nominal shear resistance, the coefficients in Eqs. (13-5) to (13-7) have been increased over those contained in ACI 318. This was necessary to offset the greater reduction in capacity provided by the lower value of ϕ_c in comparison to the ACI 318 ϕ factor for shear. With the increase in ϕ_c from 0.60 to 0.65 in A23.3-04, the shear coefficients have again been adjusted to ensure that the nominal shear capacity remains unchanged.

N13.3.5.1

The critical sections and orientation of the Centroidal axes (x and y) for typical column locations are shown in Fig. N13.3.5.1. An alternate solution for a corner column is given in N13.3.5.5.

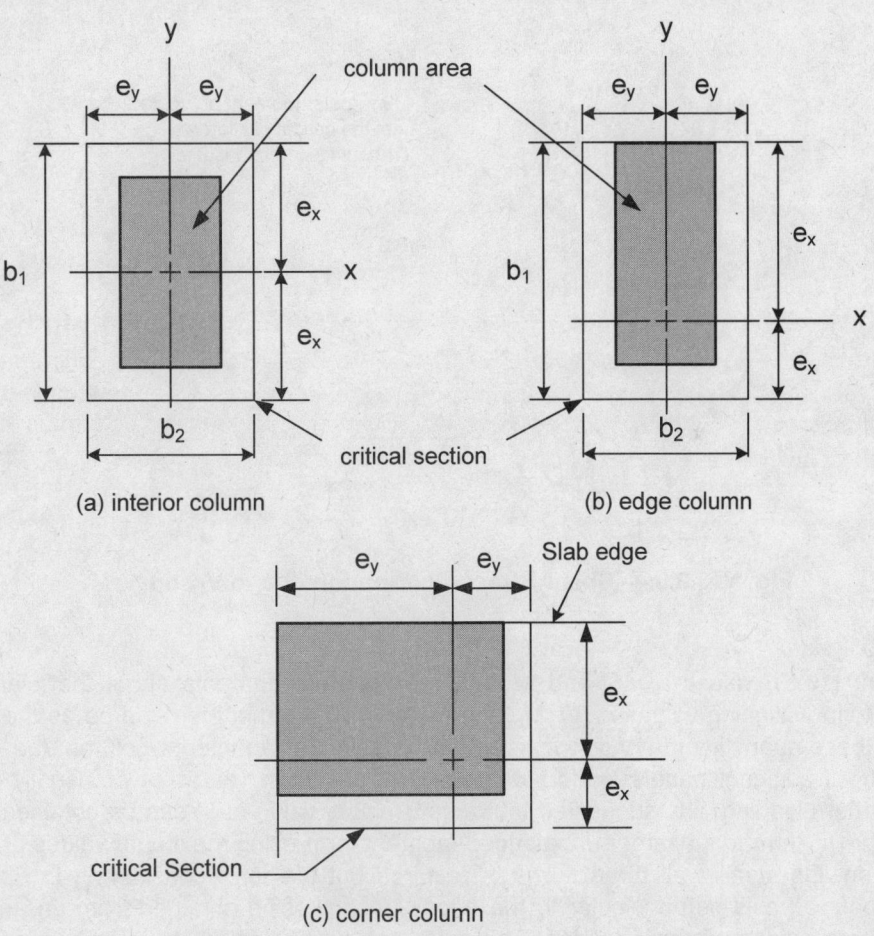

(a) interior column   (b) edge column

(c) corner column

Fig. N13.3.5.1
Critical Sections at Centroidal Axis at Columns

N13.3.5.4

The vertical shear distributions caused by the shear force and the fraction of the unbalanced moment transferred by shear for an interior column are shown in Fig. N13.3.5.4.

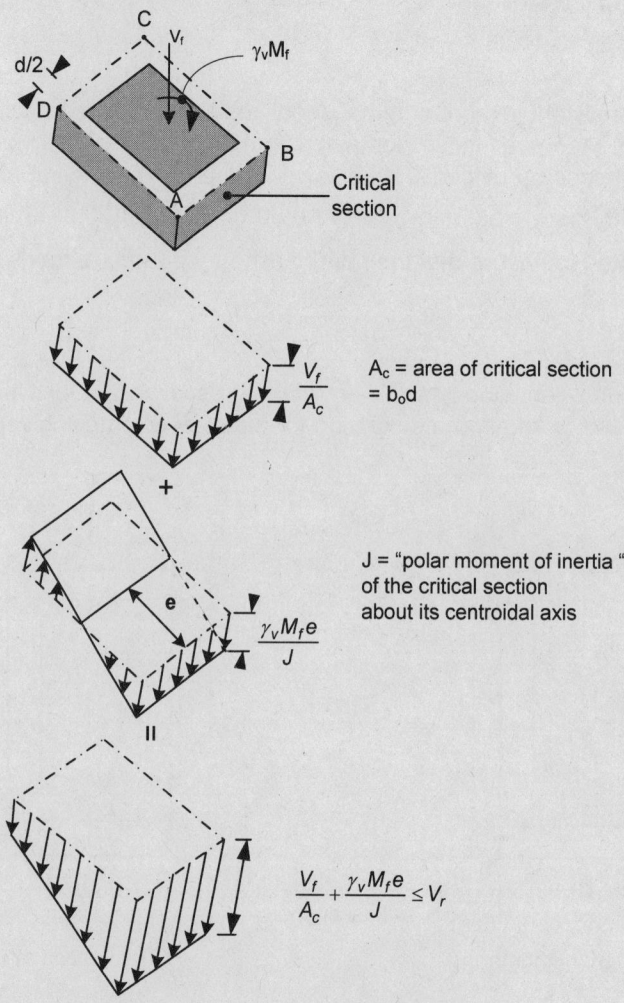

A_c = area of critical section
= $b_o d$

J = "polar moment of inertia " of the critical section about its centroidal axis

$$\frac{V_f}{A_c} + \frac{\gamma_v M_f e}{J} \le V_r$$

Fig. N13.3.5.4   Shear Stress Distribution due to V_f and $\gamma_v M_f$

N13.3.5.5

In Equation. (13-9), values of M_{fx} and M_{fy} are the factored moments about the x and y axes, respectively. In assigning values of V_f, M_{fx} and M_{fy} some judgement is required as the maximum values for these quantities may not occur simultaneously. For an interior column, the value of V_f occurs with all adjacent panels loaded whereas the maximum values of M_f usually occur with selected pattern loading. It is suggested that a satisfactory value of V_f can be obtained by adding the maximum V_f term to the larger unbalanced moment term using maximum values of M_f. For an edge column, the sum of all three terms is required but the term considering the unbalanced moment about an axis perpendicular to the edge, M_{fy}, must be obtained from an analysis that considers both adjacent panels loaded. This term can be neglected when the spans along the edge are equal. For a corner column, the maximum value for all three terms occurs when the corner panel is loaded.

Corner column designs meeting the requirements of Clause 13.3.6.2 are not required to meet the requirements of Clause 13.3.5.5.

N13.3.5.6
See Fig. N13.10.2.

N13.3.6.2   Corner Columns
The critical section for one-way shear at corner columns is illustrated in Fig. N13.3.6.2.

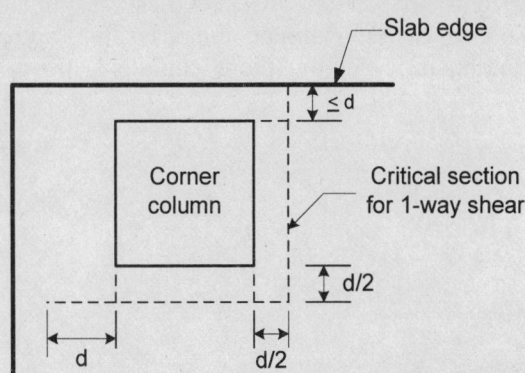

Fig. 13.3.6.2   Critical Section for One-Way Shear at Corner Columns

N13.3.7   Shear Reinforcement in Slabs Without Beams
Shear reinforcement to increase the punching shear capacity of slabs may consist of either stirrups or headed shear reinforcement. Effective anchorage of stirrups may be difficult to achieve by standard hooks, particularly for thin slabs, and special mechanical anchorage may be required (see Clause 13.3.8.1).

N13.4   Shear in Slab Systems with Beams.

N13.4.1
The tributary area used in computing the shear carried by an interior beam is shown in Fig. N13.4.1. For $\alpha_1 \ell_1 / \ell_2 < 1.0$ the beams framing into the column will not account for all of the shear force transferred to the column. The remaining shear force will produce shear stresses in the slab around the column. For these cases the total shear strength of the slab-beam-column connection must be checked.

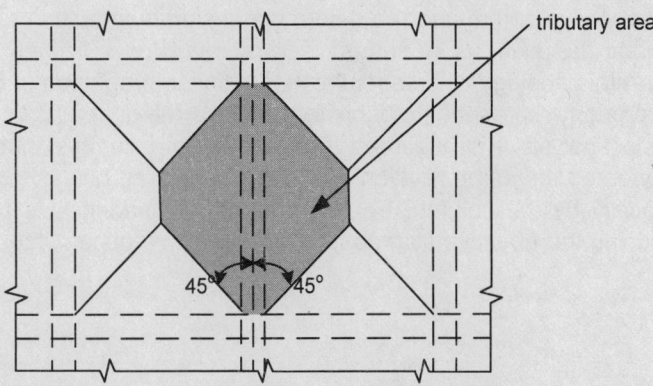

Fig. N13.4.1   Tributary Area for Calculating Shear on Interior Beam

Explanatory Notes on CSA A23.3-04

N13.5   Design Procedures for Flexure

N13.5.1

This section permits a designer to base a design directly on the fundamental principles of structural mechanics provided it is demonstrated that all safety and serviceability criteria are satisfied. Guidance for applying many of the more commonly used procedures are given in Clauses 13.6 to 13.12.

N13.6   Elastic Plate Theory

N13.6.2

When slab systems are analyzed using classical or numerical techniques based on elastic theory, it is necessary that stiffness assigned to the various slab components reflect the effects of cracking, creep and shrinkage of the concrete. Stiffness based on gross concrete dimensions is not satisfactory.

N13.7   Theorems of Plasticity

The analysis of many slabs with irregular geometry is simplified using techniques based on plasticity. The designer must ensure that when selecting reinforcement the ductility demand requirements are met. For slabs, this can generally be considered satisfied by selecting reinforcement with a failure strain greater than or equal to 0.03. Since the theorems of plasticity only ensure strength requirements, serviceability requirements at service load must be evaluated independently.

N13.8   Slab Systems as Elastic Frames

Probably the most frequently used method to determine design moments in regular two-way slab systems is to consider the slab as a series of two-dimensional frames that are analyzed elastically. When using this analogy, it is essential that stiffness properties of the elements of the frame be selected to properly represent the behaviour of the three-dimensional slab system.

In a typical frame analysis it is assumed that at a beam-column connection all members meeting at the joint undergo the same rotation. For slabs supported only by columns the slab will be restrained only locally by the column. For uniform gravity loading this reduced restraint is accounted for by reducing the effective stiffness of the column by either Clause 13.8.2 or Clause 13.8.3.

Explanatory Notes on CSA A23.3-04

N13.8.2 Non-Prismatic Modelling of Member Stiffness

Examples of the variation in moment of inertia along typical slab-beams and columns are given in Fig. N13.8.2.

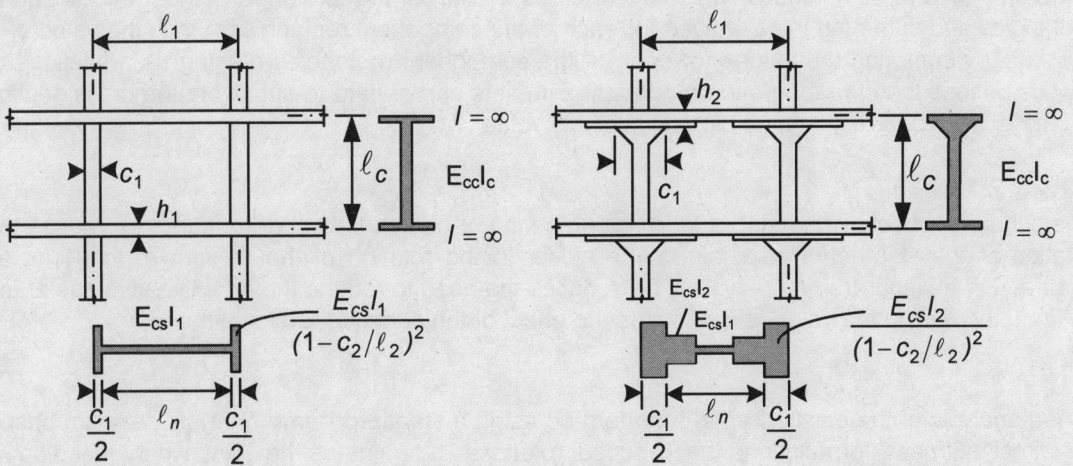

Fig. N13.8.2
Variation of Moment of Inertia for Slab Beams and Columns

N13.8.2.5 and N13.8.2.6

In the non-prismatic modelling procedure, the effective column stiffness is reduced using the attached torsional member concept. The effective column stiffness is a function of the stiffness of the column and the torsional stiffness of the attached members framing into the sides of the column.

N13.8.2.7

Fig. N13.8.2.7 illustrates that portion of the slab that is to be included in computing the stiffness of the attached torsional member.

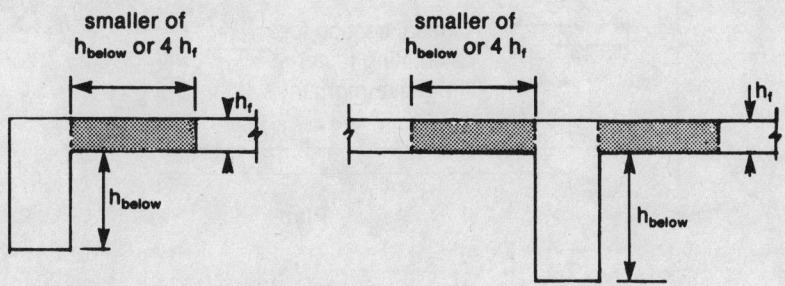

Fig N13.8.2.7
Portions of Slab to be Included with Torsional Members

N13.8.2.8

The stiffness, K_t, is the sum of the stiffnesses of the attached torsional members perpendicular to the direction in which moments are being computed. Thus for an interior column K_t accounts for the stiffness of two torsional members while for an edge column K_t will account for only one torsional member when moments are being calculated in a direction parallel to the face edge.

N13.8.2.9

The term C is a property of the cross section having the same relationship to the torsional rigidity of a non-circular cross section as does the polar moment of inertia for a circular cross section. The value of C is computed by dividing the cross section of the torsional member into separate rectangles and summing the C-values for each of the component rectangles. Since the value of C obtained by summing the values for each of the component rectangles making up a section will always be less than the theoretically correct value, it is appropriate to subdivide the cross section in such a way as to result in the highest possible value of C.

N13.8.2.10

The stiffening effect on the slab due to the presence of beams between the columns causes the rotation of the slab-beam at a joint to be closer to the rotation of the column at that joint as assumed in a planar frame analysis. This reduces the need to reduce the effective stiffness of the column. Increasing the value of K_t reduces the effect of the attached torsional members.

N13.8.3

When analysis of the elastic frame is performed using a standard frame analysis program based on direct stiffness formulation, the reduced rotational restraint at the joint when the slab is supported on columns can be accounted for by reducing the effective moment of inertia of the column by the factor ψ. In equations (13-21) and (13-22) α_1 should be taken as 0.0 when beams are not present in span ℓ_1.

N13.8.5

Generally, the output from an elastic frame analysis will give the moments at the ends of the members. From these the moments at the critical sections are calculated. The location of the critical sections for large rectilinear interior supports and for exterior supports with brackets are shown in Fig. N13.8.5.

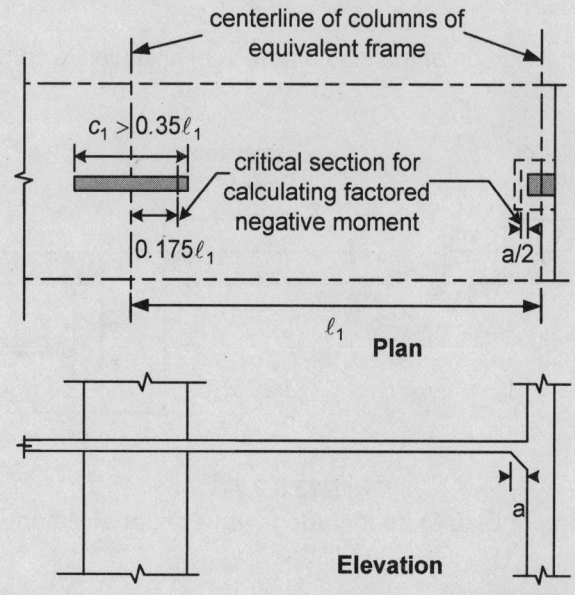

Fig. N13.8.5
Critical Sections for Negative Forced Moment for Cases with Large Rectilinear Interior Supports and Exterior Supports with Brackets

N13.9   Direct Design Method

Although the name has been retained, the Direct Design Method in CSA Standard A23.3-94 has been reduced from a complete design method to a procedure for determining moments at the critical sections and so is essentially a simplified elastic frame analysis. That portion of the design related to the lateral distribution of moments across the critical sections is applicable to all elastic frame solutions and has been incorporated in Clauses 13.11 and 13.12.

N13.9.1.1

When the design strip consists of only two spans the magnitude of the negative moment at the interior support is significantly greater than when there are three or more spans. Distribution coefficients in Table 13-1 are based on three or more spans.

N13.9.1.2

The limitation of this clause is to prevent the possibility of developing negative moments beyond the point where the negative moment reinforcement is terminated according to Fig. 13-1.

N13.9.1.3

The distribution coefficients in Table 13-1 are essentially those from an elastic analysis for a uniformly distributed loading on all spans. In the absence of provisions to adequately handle pattern loadings the factored live load is limited to two times the factored dead load.

N13.9.2.1

See Fig. N13.1.2(c).

N13.9.2.3

When circular or regular polygonal supports are used, it is recommended that the clear span, ℓ_n, be calculated by treating the supports as square sections with the same area as illustrated in Fig. N13.9.2.3.

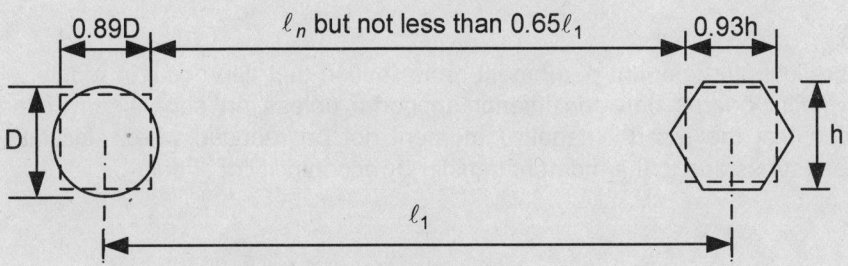

Fig. N13.9.2.3
Examples of Equivalent Square Supports

N13.9.3.1 and N13.9.3.2

The total factored static moment for a span, M_o, is distributed between negative and positive moment regions in a manner that reflects the influence of the stiffness of the supporting members. See Fig. N13.9.3 for some examples. The positive factored moments given in this clause are maximum values and do not necessarily occur at mid span.

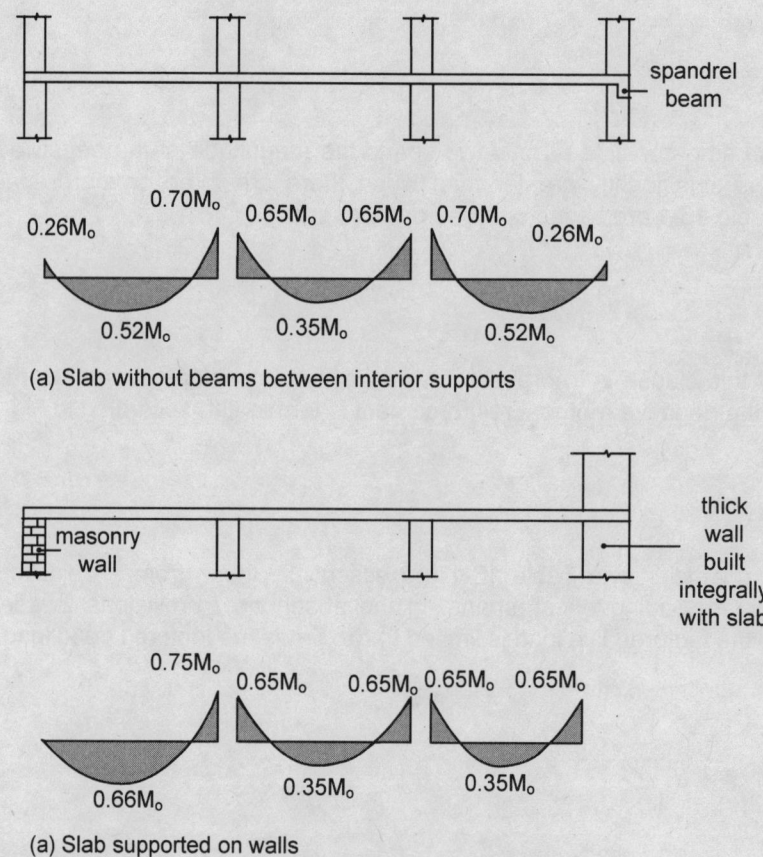

(a) Slab without beams between interior supports

(a) Slab supported on walls

Fig. N13.9.3
Examples of Design Moments for Slabs

N13.9.3.3

This clause reflects the amount of moment redistribution that can occur in regular slab systems. For slabs without beams between interior supports, unless an edge beam is provided, it is recommended that the exterior negative moment not be reduced when calculating maximum factored shear stress due to the moment transfer by eccentricity of shear.

N13.10   Slab Reinforcement

N13.10.1   General

Experience has shown that when stiff drop panels are used there is a greater tendency for the slab to crack in the negative middle strip region. In those applications where crack control is important (i.e. where a brittle topping is used or the slab is located in a corrosive environment) additional reinforcement is required. The Note to Clause 13.10.1 now contains the material dealing with reinforcement for crack control which was previously located in Clause 13.12.4 in the 1994 edition.

N13.10.2   Shear and Moment Transfer

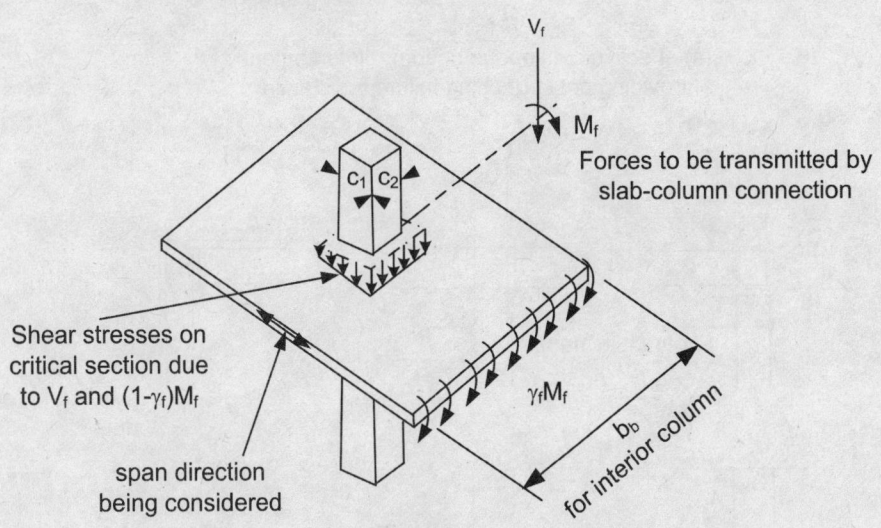

Fig. N13.10.2
Shear and Moment Transfer in Slab-Column Connections

N13.10.3   Exterior Columns

Clause 13.10.3 has been introduced in 2004 to clarify that at exterior supports, in addition to the reinforcement placed in band b_b, minimum temperature and shrinkage reinforcement meeting the requirements of Clause 7.8.1 must still be placed in regions outside the band.

N13.10.4   Spacing

Except in the negative moment regions in the vicinity of the columns, this clause permits a wider spacing of flexural slab reinforcement compared to the previous edition of the Standard.

N13.10.6   Reinforcement for Structural Integrity at Slab-Column Connections

The intent of this clause is to provide a minimum level of structural integrity to the slab system to limit the spread from a local failure that would result in progressive collapse. The provision of properly anchored bottom reinforcing bars or tendons enables the slab to hang from the supports after the initial local failure occurs (see Fig. N13.10.6).

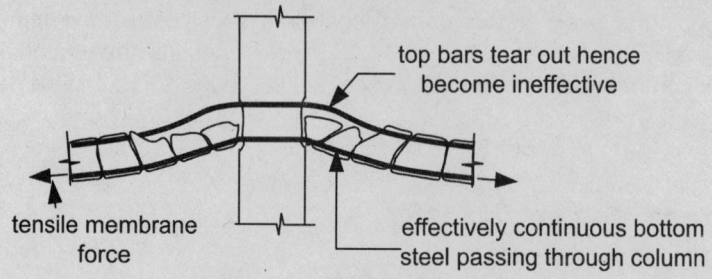

top bars tear out hence become ineffective

tensile membrane force

effectively continuous bottom steel passing through column

(a) effective continuous bottom reinforcement providing post punching failure resistance

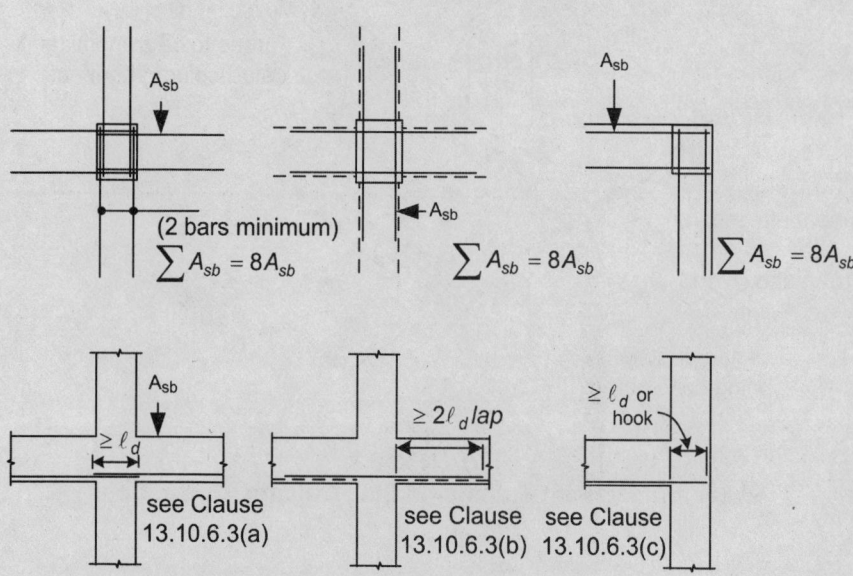

A_{sb}

(2 bars minimum)
$\sum A_{sb} = 8A_{sb}$

A_{sb}

$\sum A_{sb} = 8A_{sb}$

A_{sb}

$\sum A_{sb} = 8A_{sb}$

A_{sb}
$\geq \ell_d$
see Clause 13.10.6.3(a)

$\geq 2\ell_d\,lap$
see Clause 13.10.6.3(b)

$\geq \ell_d$ or hook
see Clause 13.10.6.3(c)

(b) ways of proving effectively continuous bottom reinforcement

Fig. N13.10.6
Structural Integrity Requirements for Slabs

N13.10.7 Effective Depth at Drop Panels
See Fig. N13.10.7.

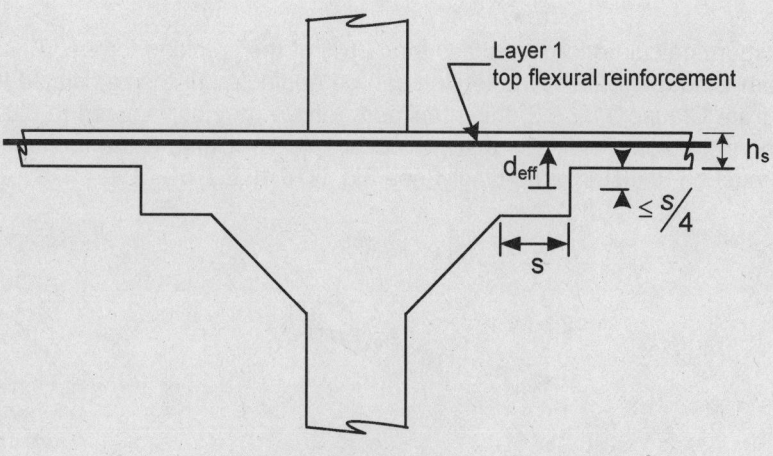

Fig. N13.10.7
Effective Depth at Drop Panel

N13.10.8 Curtailment of Reinforcement
This material has been relocated from Clause 13.12.5 in the previous edition.

N13.10.9 Top Reinforcement at Slab Edge
This new clause highlights the fact that edge reinforcement must be provided to resist edge loads.

N13.11 Lateral Distribution of Moments for Slabs Without Interior Beams
This new clause in the 2004 edition replaces Clause 13.12 in the previous edition of CSA A23.3. It incorporates the new requirements for the lateral distribution of moments in the newly introduced slab band systems as well as regular slabs without beams. The objective is to laterally distribute moment to those sections that will experience the greatest curvature or have the greatest stiffness. These distribution factors were developed from FEA studies and proven historical practice.

N13.11.2 Factored Moments in Column Strips
The range of values for the portion of the factored moment to be assigned to the column strip has been narrowed slightly from the previous edition in the case of Clauses 13.11.2.2(a) and 13.11.2.2(c).

N13.11.2.6

This clause draws the designers attention to the fact that the requirements of Clause 13.11.2.2 and 13.11.2.3 are applicable to slabs with spandrel beams for negative moments at exterior supports.

If the maximum calculate torque is less than 25% of the cracking torque, T_{cr}, of the spandrel beam, then, from Clause 11.2.9.1, the torsion can be neglected. If the calculated torque exceeds $0.67T_{cr}$, then, from Clause 11.2.9.2, this maximum torque may be reduced to $0.67T_{cr}$ to account for the reduction in torsional stiffness that will occur after cracking. If the torsion is reduced, the slab moments must be adjusted accordingly (see Fig. N13.12.2.2(b)).

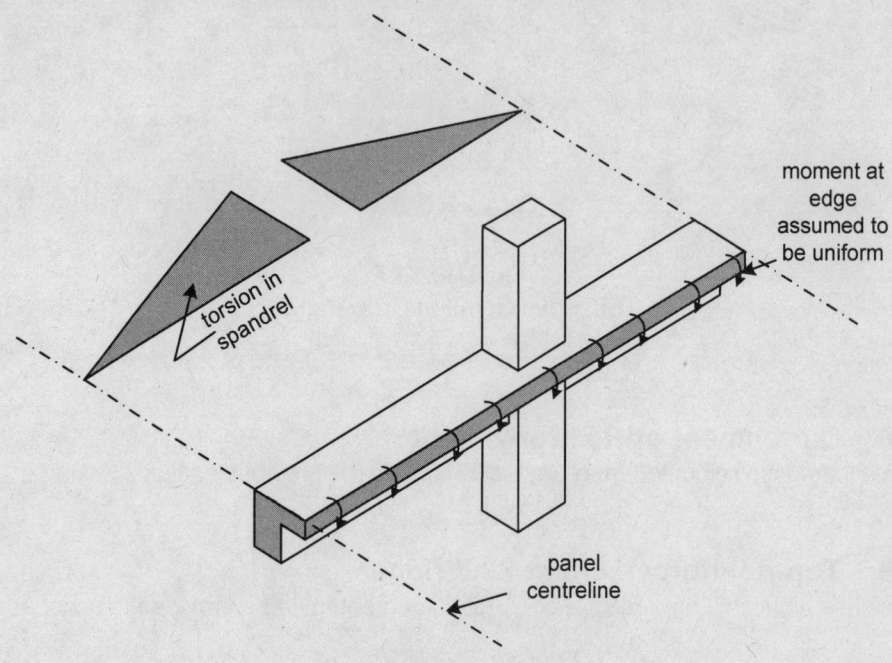

Fig. N13.11.2.6(a)
Calculation of Torsion at Exterior Edge

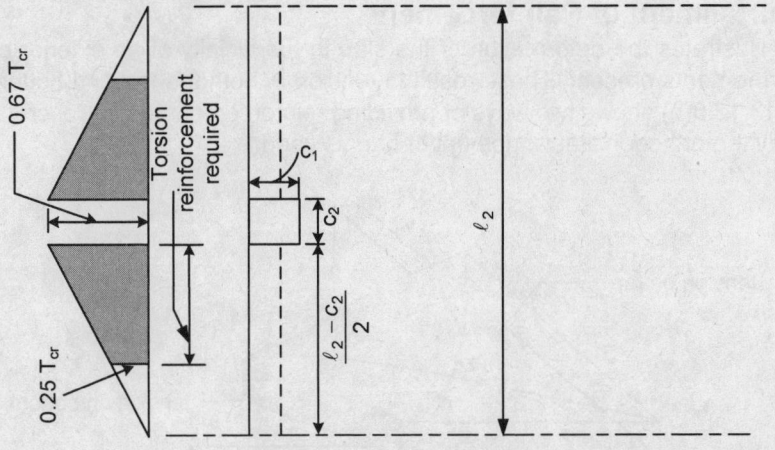

(b) Torsion Diagram if Calculated torsion exceeds $0.67\,T_{cr}$
(see Clause 11.2.9.2)

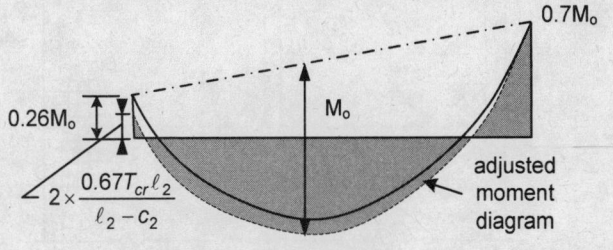

(c) adjusted moment diagram

**Fig. N13.11.2.6(b)
Redistribution of Moments Caused by Reduced Torsional
Stiffness of Spandral Beam After Cracking**

N13.12.5   Curtailment of Reinforcement

Fig. N13.12.5(a) illustrates the deformation of the slab in the vicinity of an exterior corner due to the high twisting moments present. These result in tension in both the top and bottom of the slab as shown. Fig N13.12.5(b) shows two ways of providing reinforcement to control cracking in these regions. Generally the orthogonal arrangement of bars is used.

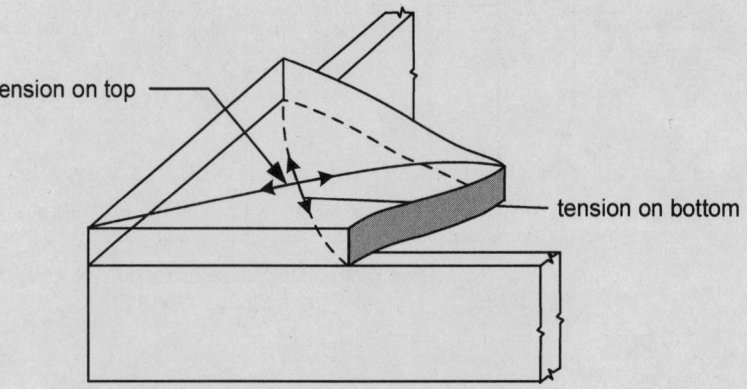

(a) Deformations of exterior corner slab element

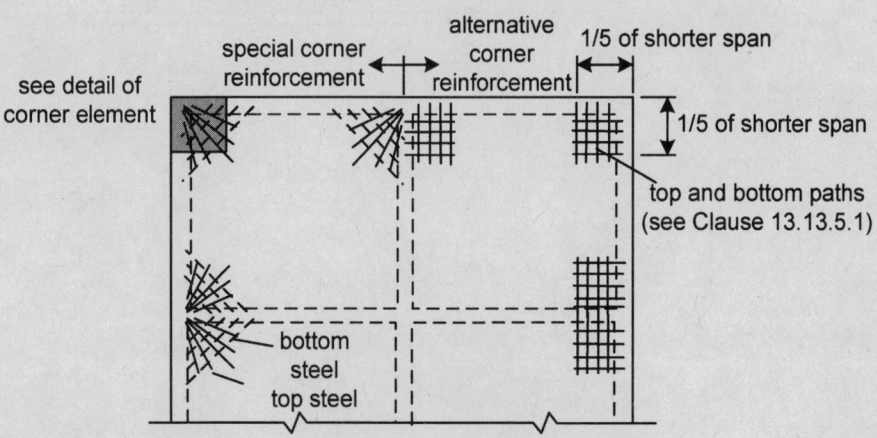

(b) Plan View of slab supported on walls or stiff beams
showing reinforcement

Fig. N13.12.5
Special Slab Reinforcement at Exterior Corners

N14   Walls

The prime difference of clause 14 of this standard compared to the previous A23.3-94 is the consideration of different wall types. Clause 2.2 provides a revised definition of a "wall" to more clearly distinguish between this structural element and a column. Furthermore, 5 different types of walls are defined. Clause 14 has general requirements which apply to all walls but also specific requirements that apply to each of the different wall types. The designer will have to be familiar with these different wall types to be able to correctly interpret the provisions of Clause 14.

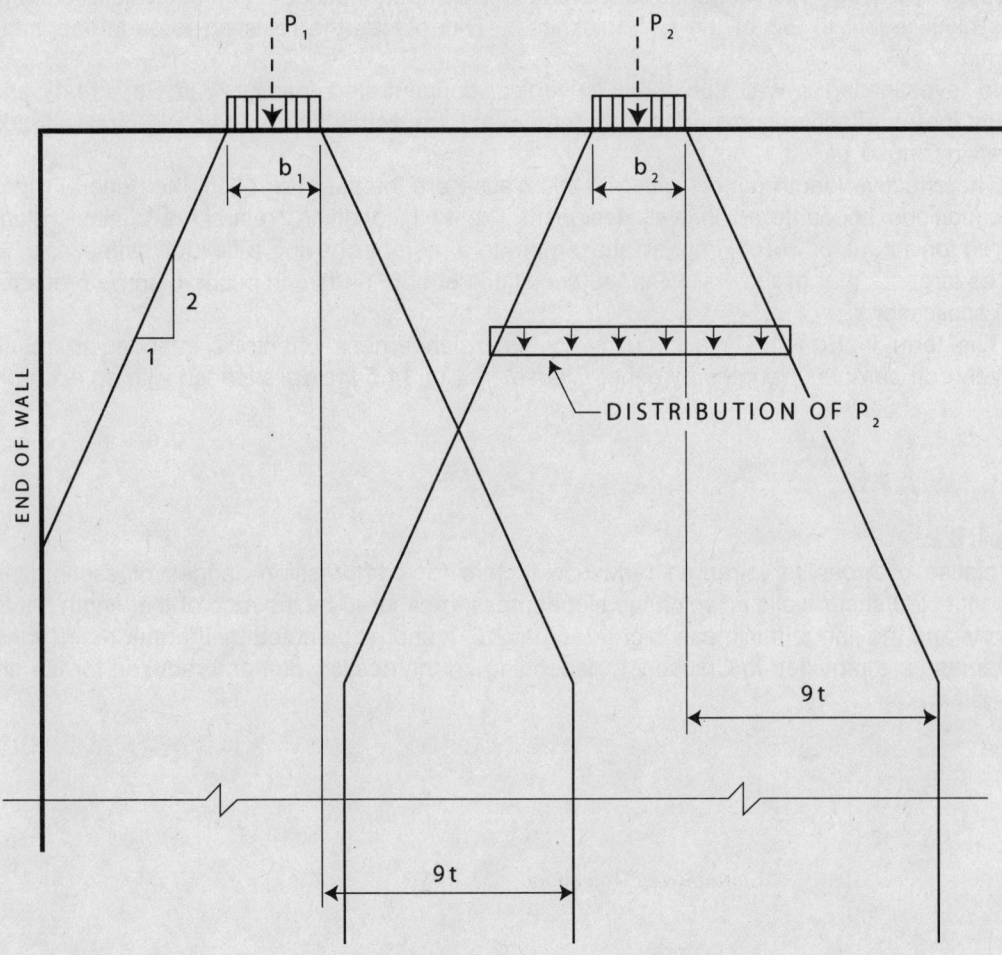

WALL ELEVATION

b₁ and b₂ are bearing widths of concentrated loads P_1 and P_2

Fig. N14.1.3.1   Distribution of concentrated loads on wall of thickness "t"

N14.2.2

The provisions for the design of bearing walls using the simplified expression of equation 14-1 have been revised to clarify the conditions when this equation can be used. The wall must be a bearing wall with principal moments acting about a horizontal axis parallel to the plane of the wall. This equation does not apply to shear walls in which moments act about a horizontal axis perpendicular to the wall.

N14.2.2.1

Eccentric loads and lateral forces are used to determine the total eccentricity of the factored axial load, P_f. Only loads which produce moments about a horizontal axis parallel to the plane of wall may be considered for the use of equation 14-1. When the resultant load for all applicable load combinations falls within the middle third of the wall thickness (eccentricity not greater than $t/6$ at all sections along the length of the wall), the design method of Clause 14.2.2.1 may be used. The design is then carried out considering P_f as a concentric load which must be less than Pr computed by Eq. (14-1). The factored resistance is computed based on an equivalent rectangular stress block equal to 2/3 of the wall thickness. This places the resisting force in line with the assumed load.

In investigating a wall subjected to vertical concentrated loads, A_g in Eq. (14-1) should account for the effective horizontal length for the uniform distribution of the concentrated loads as defined in Clause 14.1.3.1.

The effective length factors given in this clause are intended to reflect the general range of end conditions encountered in wall designs. The end condition "restrained against rotation", required for a k factor of 0.8, implies attachment to a member having a flexural stiffness, EI/ℓ, at least as large as that of the wall. Pinned conditions at both ends can occur in some precast and tilt-up applications.

The term in Eq. (14-1) accounting for wall slenderness effects is intended to result in relatively comparable strengths by either Clause 14.4 or 14.5 for walls loaded with an eccentricity of $t/6$.

N14.4.2.2

This clause provides for strength reduction factors for compression flanges of assemblies of interconnected shear walls in which the slenderness, measured by the ratio of the length between supports and the flange thickness is greater than 15. It should be noted that further restrictions on slenderness are provided in Clause 21, depending on the ductility demand required for the shear wall system.

N15.2.2

Factored loads and factored soil resistance shall be used for calculating the minimum footing area and the cross sectional forces of a footing or a deep foundation. Note that NBCC 2005 does not specify service load combinations.

N15.2.3

Minimum eccentricity of 50 mm, or the construction tolerance, is specified in any direction for design of the pile caps and piles. This new criterion affects the pile cap shear check and the pile design. Piles shall therefore always be checked for an eccentric pile reaction.

N15.4.3

Fig. N15.4.3 illustrates the critical sections where flexural resistance and development of reinforcement must be checked.

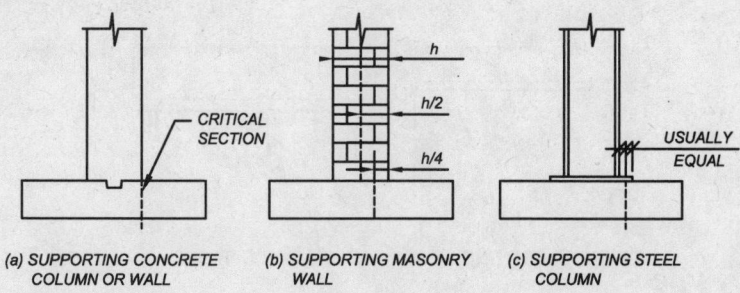

(a) SUPPORTING CONCRETE COLUMN OR WALL

(b) SUPPORTING MASONRY WALL

(c) SUPPORTING STEEL COLUMN

Fig. N15.4.3
Critical sections for moment in footings

N15.4.4

The amount of flexural reinforcement in the short direction is determined by considering the moment acting on the critical section (see Fig. N15.4.4). In recognition of the fact that the moment per unit length will be higher in the vicinity of the column, the flexural reinforcement is concentrated in this region (see Fig. N15.4.4).

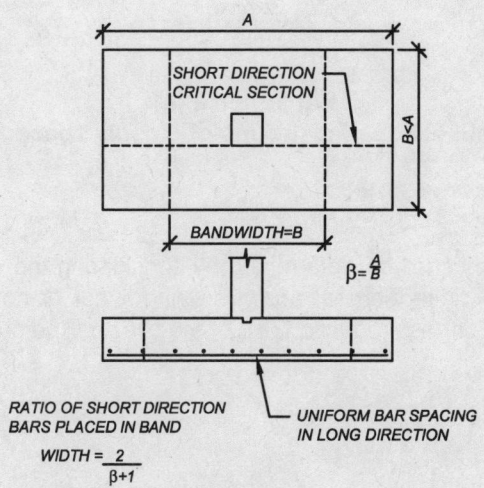

Fig. N15.4.4
Distribution of flexural reinforcement in a rectangular footing

N15.5.2

Fig. N15.5.2(a) illustrates the critical sections (Cl. 13.3.3.1. and Cl. 11.3.2.) for which shear resistance must be investigated in accordance with Clause 11 & 13.

When investigating punching shear for closely spaced piles where the individual critical perimeters overlap, a critical section around the pile group may govern (see Fig. N15.5.2(b)).

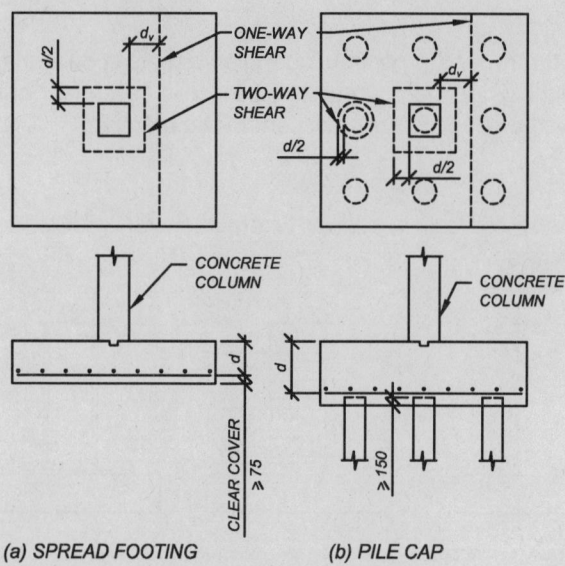

(a) SPREAD FOOTING   (b) PILE CAP

Fig. N15.5.2 (a)
Critical sections for shear

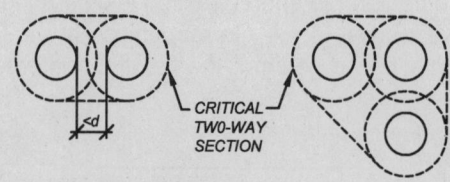

Fig. N15.5.2 (b)
Critical sections for groups of closely spaced piles

N15.8.1

Cross-sectional forces in piles shall be determined by considering the soil-pile interaction and non-linear soil behaviour. Usually finite element analysis using linear or non-linear springs are used to capture pile-soil interaction. Stiffness reduction (EI) of the pile shall be considered.

N15.9

Joints between cast-in-place columns or walls and footings should be designed in accordance with Clauses 15.9.1 and 15.9.2. Joints between precast columns or walls and footings shall satisfy Clauses 15.9.1 and 15.9.3.

N15.9.1.1

Factored soil stresses and pile reactions shall be determined by accounting for column or wall base moments. Additional shear due to unbalanced moments in spread footings supporting columns shall be calculated as defined in Cl. 13.3.5.

N15.9.1.2

Bearing of the contact surfaces shall consider the beneficial effect of the reinforcement. Minimum reinforcement (dowel area) is defined in Cl. 15.9.2.1.

Column bearing: $B_r = 0.85\phi_c f_c' A_{col} + \phi_s f_y A_{dowel}$

Footing bearing: $B_{r,footing} = 0.8\phi_c f_c' A_{col} \sqrt{\dfrac{A_2}{A_{col}}} + \phi_s f_y A_{dowel}$; where A_2 is per Cl.10.8.1.

N15.9.1.3

When net uplift or moments (resulting in tensile stresses in the reinforcement) are transferred to footings or pile caps the reinforcement shall be anchored accordingly.

N16.1.3

The ϕ_c factor for precast concrete has been increased to 0.70 to reflect the better quality control in certified plants.

N16.4.1

While the design of precast concrete follows the same rules presented for cast-in-place concrete, special considerations are necessary for precast concrete. The use of the strength design method based on 28-day strengths may not be appropriate for the design of elements subjected to the effects of stripping and handling at earlier ages. Cracking of the concrete, although acceptable from structural considerations, may result in unacceptable appearance. Some architectural finishes may tend to exaggerate the effects of early cracking. Further guidance on the design of precast concrete elements and connections can be obtained from the CPCI *Design Manual*.

N16.4.1.1

The loads imposed on precast elements during the period from casting to placement may be greater than the actual service loads.

The behaviour of precast concrete structures may differ substantially from that of monolithic cast-in-place structures. Design of joints to transmit forces due to shrinkage, creep, temperature, elastic deformation, wind forces and earthquake forces requires particular care in precast construction. Details of such joints are especially important for adequate performance of precast construction.

N16.4.3.1

The minimum reinforcement ratios of Clause 16.4.3.1 are not sufficient to control the width of full depth cracks caused by the restraint of shrinkage, creep and thermal movements. If it is necessary to limit the width of such cracks, additional reinforcement will be required unless special provisions are made to relieve restraint forces.

N16.4.4

Guidelines summarizing current practice for the design of connections can be found in the CPCI *Design Manual*.

N16.4.5.2

To prevent spalling under heavily loaded bearing areas, bearing pads should not extend to the edge of the support unless the edge is armoured. Edges can be armoured with anchored steel plates or angles. Clause 11.6.8 provides additional requirements for bearing areas on brackets or corbels.

N17.1.6

The stresses in, and the deflections of, a composite member at specified loads will be influenced by whether or not the first element cast was shored during casting and curing of the subsequent element(s). However, tests and analysis show that the strength of such a member is not measurably affected by shoring due to the inelastic stress redistributions that occur prior to failure.

N17.1.8

The extent of cracking permitted is dependent on such factors as environment, aesthetics and type of loading. Irrespective of these considerations, cracks wide enough to impair shear transfer cannot be tolerated.

N17.1.9

Premature loading of precast elements can cause excessive deflections as a result of the high creep of young concrete.

N17.4.3.1

This simplified procedure is based on the assumption that the horizontal shear stress on the interface equals the factored shear force divided by the area, bvd.

N17.4.3.2

Surfaces are intentionally roughened to provide satisfactory interlock. It is noted that in Clauses 11.7 and 17.5.3.4 "intentionally roughened" implies an interface roughened to a full amplitude of approximately 5 mm.

N17.4.4

Fig N17.4.4 illustrates the application of this clause. It is conventional to calculate the average longitudinal shear stress between the maximum moment section and the adjacent zero-moment section.

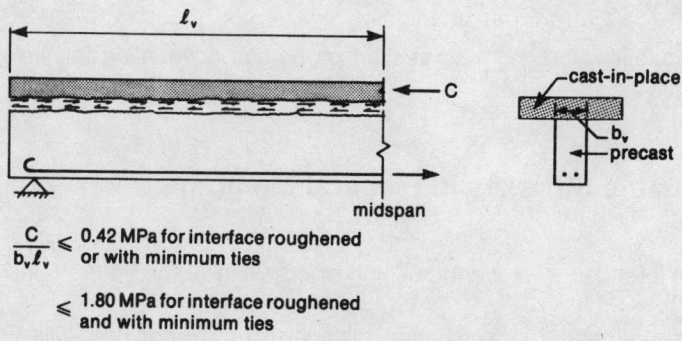

$$\frac{C}{b_v \ell_v} \leqslant 0.42 \text{ MPa for interface roughened or with minimum ties}$$

$$\leqslant 1.80 \text{ MPa for interface roughened and with minimum ties}$$

Fig. N17.4.4
Example of Investigating Longitudinal Shear

N18.1.   Scope and Definitions

N18.1.3

The empirical provisions of Clauses 10.3.3 and 10.3.4 limiting the geometry of T-beams were developed for conventionally reinforced concrete and if applied to prestressed concrete would exclude many standard prestressed products in satisfactory use today (e.g. see standard T-beams in CPCI Design Manual). Note that when applying Clause 10.5.3 to prestressed T-beams with tapered flanges the spacing limit may be based on the average flange thickness.

The empirical limits for concrete joist construction apply for conventionally reinforced concrete but not for prestressed concrete. Hence Clause 10.4 is excluded. Experience and judgement must be used for prestressed concrete joists.

The limitations on reinforcement amounts given in Clauses 10.5.1, 10.9.1 and 10.9.2 are replaced by those in Clauses 18.8, 18.11.2 and 18.12.5.

The skin reinforcement requirements of Clause 10.6.2 were derived for conventionally reinforced concrete members and were not intended to apply to prestressed concrete members.

Many of the design procedures of Clause 13 are not appropriate for prestressed concrete two-way slabs. The prestressed concrete provisions are given in Clause 18.12.

The empirical design method of Clause 14.2 is not applicable to prestressed concrete walls. These elements should be designed by the more general procedures specified in Clauses 10 and 11.

N18.1.5

Loading stages that are typically considered include:
(1)   jacking stage, or transfer of prestress stage - when the prestressing force is high, and the concrete strength is normally low
(2)   specified load stage - after all prestress losses have occurred and the member is subjected to specified loads,
(3)   factored load stage - when the resistance of the member is checked.

Other load stages that may need to be investigated include: handling, transportation, erection and other construction stages.

N18.2   Design Assumptions for Flexure and Axial Load

N18.2.2

In these stress calculations transformed section properties accounting for the beneficial effects of bonded reinforcement may be used.

N18.3   Permissible Stresses in Flexural Members

N18.3.1.1

These stresses are intended to prevent crushing or cracking of the young concrete due to the high prestress force.

Simply supported beams pretensioned with straight strands will initially have high tensile stresses in the top concrete fibres near the ends of the beams. Experience has shown that a small amount of cracking in these zones can be tolerated and hence higher tensile stresses are permitted.

N18.3.1.3

The tensile stress limits can be exceeded if appropriate reinforcement is provided to control the resulting cracking. This crack control reinforcement should consist of a well distributed array of smaller bars. See Fig. N18.3.1.3.

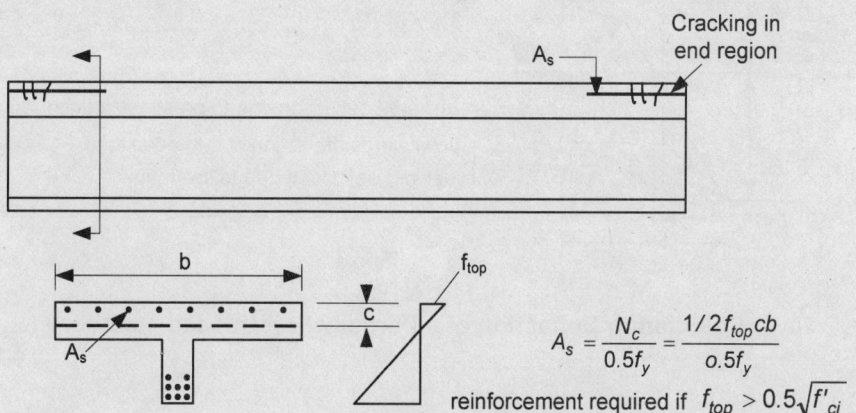

$$A_s = \frac{N_c}{0.5f_y} = \frac{1/2f_{top}cb}{0.5f_y}$$

reinforcement required if $f_{top} > 0.5\sqrt{f'_{ci}}$

Fig. N18.3.1.3
Control of Cracking Occurring at Transfer

Explanatory Notes on CSA A23.3-04

N18.3.2

The tensile stress limits in this clause are intended to control or avoid cracking after all prestress losses have occurred and the full specified loads have been applied. The tensile zones being investigated are those regions of the member where the prestress causes compressive stresses (precompressed) but are in tension under specified loads.

The consequences of cracking for a structure in a corrosive environment (e.g. a parking garage) are much more severe and hence lower tensile stress limits and larger concrete covers should be used.

When low density concrete is used the tensile stress limits should be modified to account for the lower cracking stress of such concretes (e.g. multiply limits by the λ factor of Clause 8.6.5).

N18.3.3. Partial Prestressing

A member is considered to be partially prestressed if the tensile stresses under specified loads exceed the allowable limits of Clause 18.3.2(c). Partially prestressed members are not permitted in corrosive environments.

In checking the deflection of partially prestressed members the reduction in stiffness caused by cracking must be accounted for (see Clause 9.8.4.3). Fig. N18.3.3 illustrates the bi-linear approximation of the load-deflection curve for a simply-supported, partially prestressed, uniformly loaded member. In such calculations the cracking stress may be taken as $0.6\lambda\sqrt{f'_c}$.

The control of crack widths can be investigated by the procedures of Clause 18.8.3. Crack control in situations involving frequently repeated loads requires further investigation.

To investigate fatigue resistance the maximum stress range caused by the repeating loads is calculated and compared to acceptable limits. The allowable stress range is a function of, amongst other things, tendon type and tendon curvature. For strands a limit of 100 MPa will typically be conservative. Anchorages and couplings typically have poor fatigue resistance and hence should not be located in zones subjected to large stress ranges.

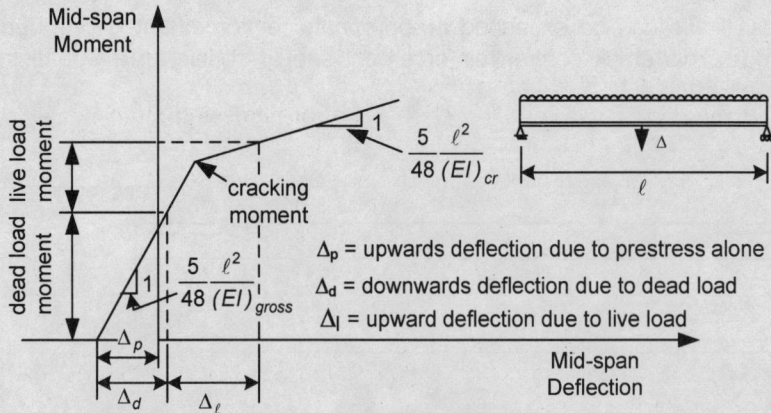

Fig. N18.3.3
Calculating Deflection of a Partially Prestressed Member

N18.4   Permissible Stresses in Tendons

The maximum tensile stress in tendons at jacking and after transfer is limited in order to provide a margin of safety against tendon fracture, to avoid inelastic tendon deformation, and to limit relaxation losses. These stress limits are tabulated below for different types of tendons in terms of the tensile strength f_{pu}.

Tendon Type	f_{py}	At jacking		After Transfer
		Post-tensioned	Pre-tensioned	
Low relaxation strand or wire	0.90	0.85	0.80	0.74*
Normal stress relieved strand or wire	0.85	0.80	0.80	0.70
Plain Prestressing bars	0.85	0.80	0.80	0.70
Deformed Prestressing bars	0.80	0.75	0.80	0.66

• Post-tensioned tendons limited to 0.70 f_{pu} at anchorages and couplers.

Table N18.4
Stress-Limits in Terms of f_{pu}

N18.5   Prestress Losses

Prestress losses may be expected to vary considerably in different situations. Actual losses will have little effect on member strength but will affect serviceability (deflections, stresses and cracking). Either over-estimating or under-estimating prestress losses may cause serviceability problems (e.g. excessive camber or excessive cracking and deflection). Information on

Explanatory Notes on CSA A23.3-04

calculating prestress losses is given in the CAC Concrete Design Handbook and the CPCI Design Manual. Comments on the different losses to be considered are given below:

(a) The anchorage seating loss can be determined from the anchorage set characteristic of the post-tensioning system being used (see Fig. N18.5).

(b) The concrete around the tendons shortens as the prestressing force is applied to it. Those tendons which are already bonded to the concrete shorten with it.

(c) During post-tensioning the variation of force along the length of the tendon can be computed by

$$P_x = P_s e^{-(Kx+\mu\alpha)}$$

where

P_x = tendon force at distance x from jacking end

P_s = jacking force

K = wobble friction coefficient accounting for unintended curvature (per metre of tendon length)

x = distance from jacking end

μ = friction coefficient accounting for intended curvature

α = accumulated angle change of tendon profile over distance x (radians)

The use of this equation is illustrated in Fig. N18.5 Values of the friction coefficients, K and μ to be used for a particular type of tendon and particular types of ducts should be obtained from the manufacturers of the tendons. The range of values given in the table below serve as values that might be expected.

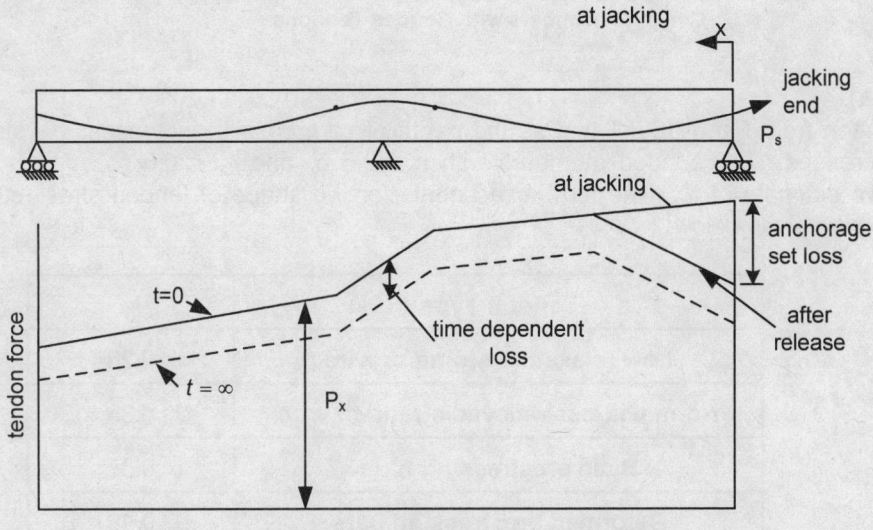

Fig. N18.5
Variation in Tendon Force due to Losses

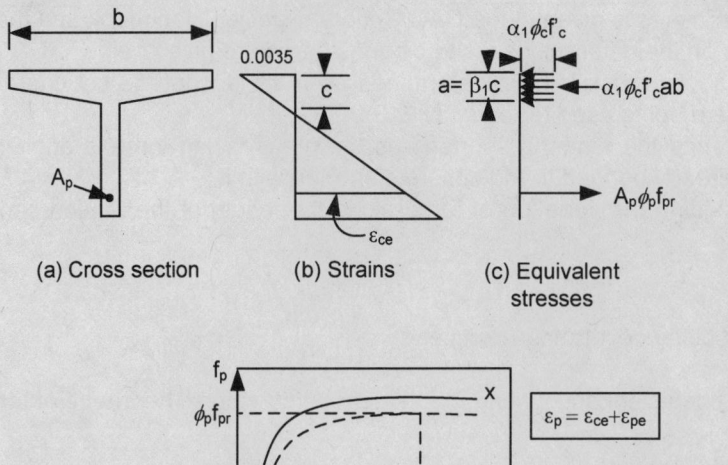

Fig. N18.6.1
Strain Compatibility Analysis for Prestressed
Concrete members with Bonded Tendons

N18.6.2(a)

It can be seen from Fig. N18.6.1 that as the depth of compression increases, the stress in the tendon decreases. For bonded members with $c \leq 0.5\ d_p$ and $f_{pe} \leq 0.6\ f_{py}$ Eq. (18-1) gives a conservative estimate of f_{pr}. The term k_p accounts for the shape of tendon stress-strain curve. Values of k_p are given below:

Tendon Type	k_p
Low relaxation strand or wire	0.28
Normal stress relieved strand or wire	0.38
Plain prestressing bars	0.38
Deformed prestressing bars	0.48

Table N18.6.2
Values of k_p

The value of the neutral axis depth c in Eq. 18-1 can be established by trial and error, or from the equilibrium of internal forces. With $\Sigma T = \Sigma C$ we get for the T-beam of Fig. N18.6.2(a):

$$\phi_p f_{pr} A_p + \phi_s f_y A_s = \alpha_1 \phi_c f'_c b_w \beta_1 c + \alpha_1 \phi_c f'_c (b - b_w) h_f + \phi_s A'_s f_y$$

Substituting $f_{pr} = f_{pu}(1 - k_p c / d_p)$ - Eq.(18-1) - and solving for c/d_p we find

$$\frac{c}{d_p} = \frac{\phi_p f_{pu} A_p + \phi_s f_y A_s - \phi_s f_y' A_s' - \alpha_1 \phi_c f_c' (b - b_w) h_f}{\alpha_1 \phi_c f_c' \beta_1 b_w d_p + k_p \phi_p f_{pu} A_p}$$

This equation is general and applies for $A_s = 0$ and/or $A_s' = 0$ and/or $b = b_w$. If $h_f > \beta_1 c$ the beam should be considered to be a rectangular beam of width b.

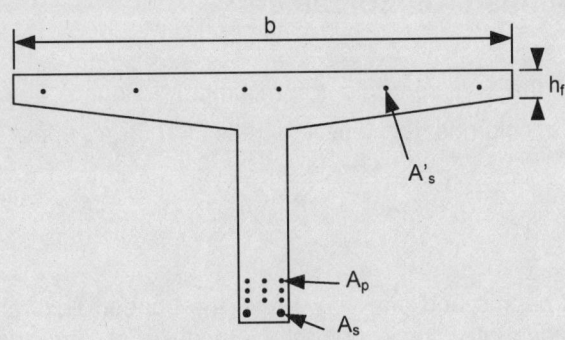

Fig. N18.6.2 (a)
Cross section of Prestressed Concrete Beam

After determining f_{pr} from Eq. (18-1) the rectangular stress block depth, a, at factored resistance can be found. Thus, for the beam in Fig. N18.6.2(a)

$$a = \frac{\phi_p A_p f_{pr} + \phi_s A_s f_s - \phi_s A_s' f_s'}{\alpha_1 \phi_c f_c' b}$$

where f_s and f_s' are the reinforcing bar stresses determined from strain compatibility for a neutral axis depth of $c = a / \beta_1$.

N18.6.2(b)
While bonded tendons exhibit large stress increases in regions of high moment (particularly at crack locations) unbonded tendons must average out their stress increase over the total length between the anchorages (see Fig. N18.6.2(b)).

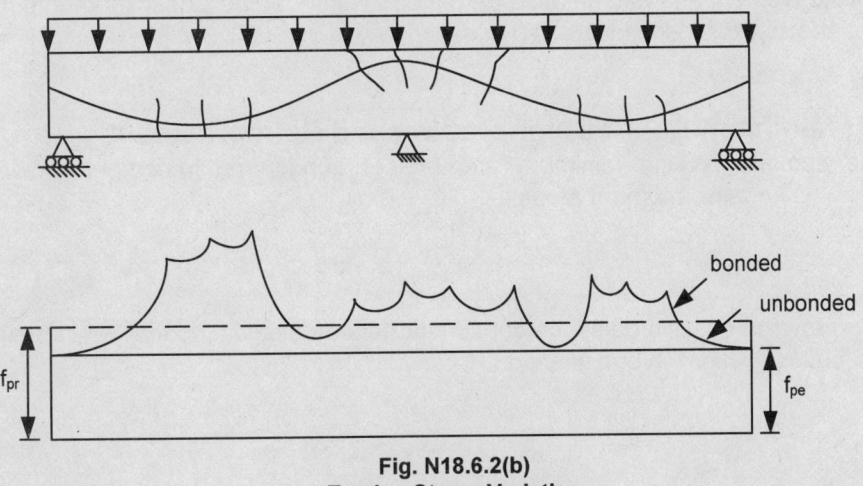

Fig. N18.6.2(b)
Tendon Stress Variation

Eq. (18-2) gives a conservative estimate of the stress in unbonded tendons at the factored resistance. The length ℓ_o is the overall length of the tendon between anchors. The summation sign has been introduced in order to get the sum of the values (d_p-c_y) for each of the plastic hinges in the span under consideration, which is illustrated in Fig. N18.6.2(b).

N18.8   Minimum Bonded Reinforcement

N18.8.1
Table 18-1 summarizes the requirements for minimum amounts of bonded non-prestressed reinforcement. The two columns for tensile stress $> 0.5\lambda\sqrt{f_c'}$ apply to partially prestressed members.

N18.8.3
For partially prestressed beams and one way slabs, the bonded flexural reinforcement must be distributed to provide adequate crack control. Because of the additional uncertainties in computing crack widths for partially prestressed members and because prestressing steel is more susceptible to corrosion, the z limits for these members are smaller than for reinforced concrete members (see Clause 10.6.1).

N18.10   Frames and Continuous Construction
When a statically indeterminate structure is post-tensioned, the deformation of the structure caused by the prestressing is restrained by the supports. The moments produced in the structure by these restraint reactions are usually referred to as "secondary moments". In design, an elastic analysis is first performed to determine the moments due to factored loads and the secondary moments. The standard then permits a certain amount of redistribution of these elastic moments, provided that minimum bonded reinforcement is present at the supports. See comments for Clause 9.2.4.

N18.12   Two-Way Slab Systems
This clause permits the use of the methods of analysis defined in Clause 13.8 to determine the moments and shears in prestressed concrete two-way slab systems. More detailed procedures such as a finite element analysis are also permitted. Note that the elastic moments must include the restraint effects explained in N18.10 (i.e. secondary moments).

N18.12.5   Minimum Bonded Nonprestressed Reinforcement
This clause summarizes the minimum amounts of bonded reinforcement required and its distribution in the negative moment areas.

N18.12.6.1
This Clause provides specific guidance concerning tendon distribution that will permit the use of banded tendon distributions in one direction.

N19.2.1

Linear elastic theory will usually provide an acceptable analytical model for determining internal forces. Cracking, local yielding of reinforcement under factored loads, and time-dependent effects (e.g., creep. shrinkage, thermal loading and load history) may lead to significant redistribution of the internal forces. This redistribution may be accounted for in the analysis. For shells and folded plates of unusual size, shape or complexity, the analysis should consider the full response of the structure from the elastic, uncracked state up to failure.

N19.2.3

The Finite Element Method is the most widely used numerical analysis procedure. Experience is required in selecting appropriate element types and sizes so that internal forces can be determined to the required degree of accuracy. Note that Clause 19.3.2 requires that the results of the analysis must be checked to ensure that the calculated internal forces are in equilibrium with the external loads.

N19.2.4

Analysis methods satisfying equilibrium and compatibility that include both membrane and bending effects are preferred. Approximate methods which satisfy statics but neglect strain compatibility should only be used when documented evidence exists of the reliability of the given method of analysis for the design of the specific type of shell or folded plate under consideration. Such methods include beam type analyses for barrel shells and folded plates having large ratios of span to either width or radius of curvature and membrane analyses for simple shells of revolution.

N19.2.5

Prestressed shell and folded plate structures must be designed to satisfy the requirements of Clause 18.

N19.2.6

The shell's thickness and reinforcement must be proportioned to resist the internal forces obtained from analysis (i.e. factored resistance $\geq$ factored load). In choosing shells thickness, attention should also be given to limiting deflections at specified loads, to providing the required concrete cover over reinforcement and to the practicalities of construction.

N19.2.7

The stability of thin shells is influenced by: (1) overall geometry, (2) geometric imperfections, (3) non-linear material properties, (4) creep and shrinkage of concrete, (5) cracking, (6) location, amount and orientation of reinforcement, and (7) deformation of supporting elements. Practical procedures for investigating the stability of shells is given in "Recommendations for Reinforced Concrete Shells and Folded Plates" (International Association of Shell and Spatial Structures, Madrid, 1979, 66 pp.), "Design and Construction of Circular Prestressed Concrete Structures (1970 report of ACI Committee 344, also in ACI Manual of Concrete Practice, Part 4), and "Concrete Shell Buckling", (SP67, ACI, 1981, 234 pp.).

N19.2.8

As shown in Fig. N19.2.8, reinforcement should be added near both faces to account for the possibility of moment reversals (see Clause 19.4.8).

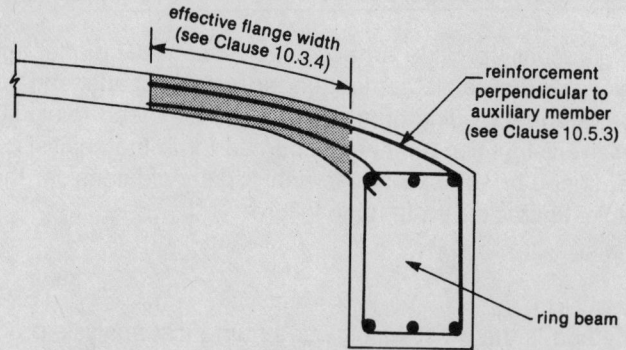

Fig. N19.2.8
Auxiliary Member Consisting of Ring Beam Plus Effective Flange Width

N19.4.1

At any point in a shell two different kinds of internal forces may occur simultaneously: those associated with membrane action, and those associated with bending of the shell (see Fig. N19.4.1). The membrane forces are assumed to act in the tangential plane mid-way between the surfaces of the shell, and are the two axial forces N_x and N_y, and the membrane shears, V_{xy}. Flexural effects include bending moments, M_x and M_y, twisting moment, T_{xy}, and the associated transverse shears, V_{xy} and V_{yz}, as shown in Fig. N19.4.1.

N19.4.2

Membrane reinforcement must be provided in at least two approximately orthogonal directions. In some highly stressed regions, it may be appropriate to utilize reinforcement in three directions.

N19.4.3

Minimum reinforcement corresponding to slab shrinkage and temperature reinforcement must be provided even if the calculated membrane forces are compressive. In regions subjected to significant tensile membrane forces the minimum reinforcement ratio of 0.002 traditionally used for slabs in flexure will be insufficient. Clause 19.4.8 suggests a minimum ratio of 0.0035 for these cases.

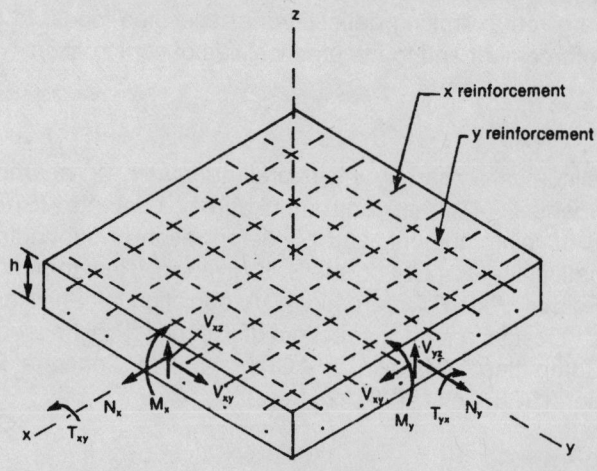

Fig. N19.4.1
Membrane Actions and Bending Actions

Explanatory Notes on CSA A23.3-04

N19.4.4

The reinforcement for an element subjected to membrane forces only can be designed using the principles of the Compression Field Theory described in Clause 11.4. The two sets of reinforcing bars are designed to carry the forces F_x and F_y, where:

$$F_x = N_x + \frac{|V_{xy}|}{\tan\theta}$$

$$F_y = N_y + |V_{xy}|\tan\theta$$

where all of the above actions are expressed in terms of force per unit length.

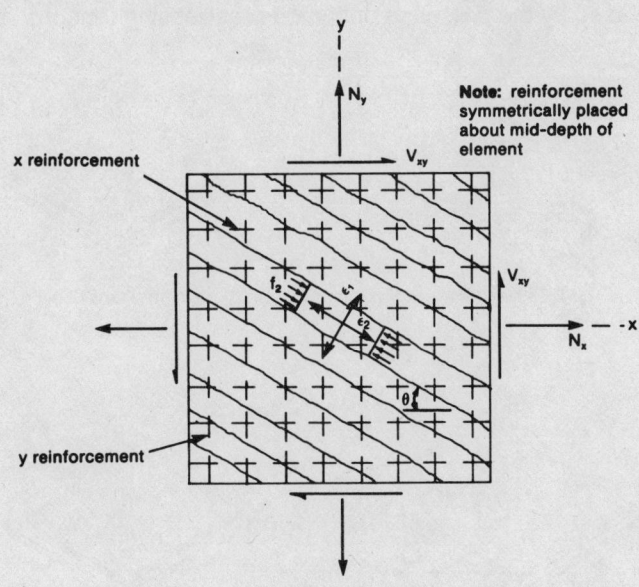

Fig. N19.4.4
Element Subjected to Membrane Forces

N19.4.5

The principal compressive stress in the concrete, f_2, see Fig. N19.4.4, can be computed as:

$$f_2 = (\tan\theta + \frac{1}{\tan\theta})\frac{|V_{xy}|}{h}$$

To avoid crushing $f_2 \leq f_{2max}$ given in Clause 11.4.2.3 where f_{2max} is a function of the principal tensile strain ε_1.

N19.4.7

The practice of concentrating tensile reinforcement in the regions of maximum tensile stress has led to a number of successful designs primarily for long folded plates, long barrel vaulted shells and for domes. The requirement of providing the minimum reinforcement in the remaining tensile zone is intended to control cracking.

N19.4.8

One way of accounting for the interaction between bending effects and membrane effects is to model the shell element as a sandwich consisting of 2 outer reinforced concrete layers joined by an unreinforced middle layer acting as a shear connector. The applied forces and moments may be transformed into statistically equivalent membrane forces on the outer layers as shown in Fig.

N19.4.8. Each layer is then designed for its resulting membrane forces by the procedures described under N19.4.4.

Bending moment diagrams for shells characteristically display a wavelike shape as the moments oscillate between positive and negative values over relatively short lengths of the shell. For this reason, equal amounts of bending reinforcement are to be placed near both outer surfaces of the shell.

N19.4.9

Transverse ties may be required to control splitting of the shell near its centre surface due to high transverse shears and/or transverse tensile stresses (see Fig. N19.4.9). Transverse tensile stresses may be increased by the presence of curved prestressing tendons.

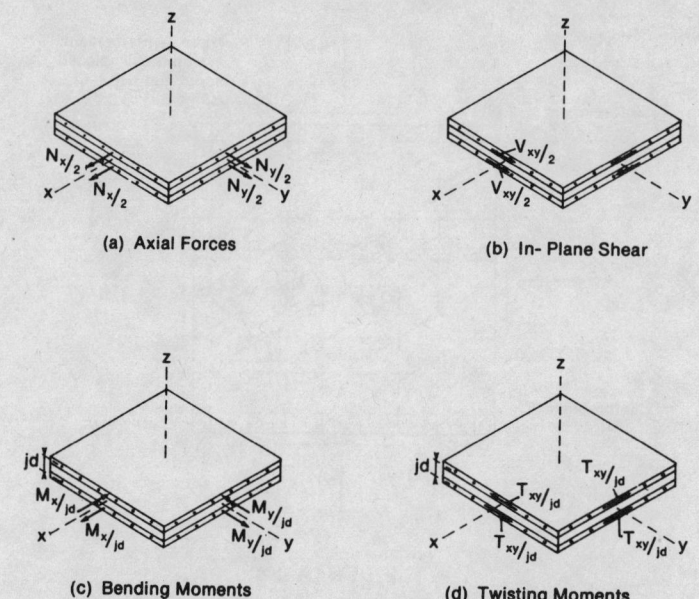

(a) Axial Forces

(b) In- Plane Shear

(c) Bending Moments

(d) Twisting Moments

Fig. N19.4.8
Transforming Sectional Forces into Statically Equivalent Membrane Forces on Outer Reinforced Concrete Layers

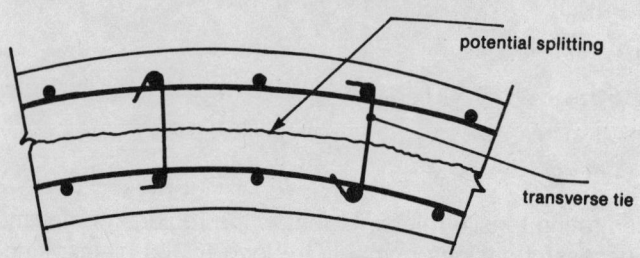

potential splitting

transverse tie

Fig. N19.4.9
Transverse Ties to Control Shell Splitting

N19.4.11 and N19.4.12

On curved shell surfaces it is more difficult to control the alignment of precut reinforcement. These clauses specify extra reinforcement lengths to maintain sufficient splice and development lengths.

N20.1 Strength Evaluation - General

Load testing is not intended as a method of accepting designs known to be deficient. See also N20.2.3. It is generally preferable to carry out a structural evaluation by analysis rather than load testing.

N20.2.1

Guidance on determining in-situ concrete strength can be found in Annex A of CSA Standard A23.2 "Methods of Test for Concrete".

N20.2.3

The analysis must demonstrate that the intent of this Standard and the National Building Code has been satisfied. The intent of this Standard and NBC is to ensure public safety. In general it should be shown that the building will have a strength close to, or in excess of, that envisaged in the original design or as required by this Standard and NBC.

Commentary L of the 2005 National Building Code of Canada discusses the structural evaluation of existing buildings and allows a relaxation in load factors as a function of the completeness of the review process and the risk to human safety if the structure were to fail.

N20.3.1.1

The selection of the portion of the structure to be tested, pre-test preparation, testing, and the interpretation of the results should be done under the direction of a qualified engineer experienced in structural investigations, field tests, and measurements.

N20.3.1.3

Tests to investigate the shear resistance of precast members should simulate the effects of differential settlement, creep, shrinkage and temperature change based on a realistic assessment of such effects occurring in service.

When only a portion of the structural system is tested there is a high likelihood that some of the loads will be resisted by structural elements outside the loaded area. This should be considered in the selection of the area to be tested.

N20.3.1.9

Visible evidence of failure includes spalling, indicative of concrete crushing failure, cracks wide enough to indicate yielding of reinforcement or significant non-linearity in the load-deflection response.

N20.3.2.1

It is desirable to take deflection readings after each increment of load is added. These will help in assessing the resolution of the data and will make it possible to detect non-linear load-deflection response due to cracking or other causes.

N21   Special Provisions for Seismic Design

The Notation and Definitions applicable to Clause 21 have been moved to Clause 2. Where terms such as, for example crosstie, are used in this Clause they refer to the specific seismic definition.

N21.1   Scope

The magnitude of the loads imparted to a structure during a seismic event will depend on the nature of the response of the structure to the event. Structures that are strong enough to remain linear and elastic will attract the largest loads. Structures with lower strength cannot resist the larger loads and will need to dissipate much of the seismic energy through non-linear plastic deformation.

The *National Building Code of Canada (NBCC)* specifies in Subsection 4.1.8, the loads for strength and the corresponding deflection as if the structure remains linear. The earthquake loads are the actual expected loads (for a linear structure). These linear structure loads are reduced to the required factored design load level by dividing them by the product of the force reduction factors R_d and R_o. The product of R_d and R_o is as high as 6.8 for certain concrete structures. The load factors for DL, LL and EQ are generally 1.0 except for some LL cases where it is 0.5. The net result is that, unlike the design for all other types of loads where the design strength must be larger than the maximum load predicted by linear analysis, the design strength for earthquake will be much less than the predicted maximum earthquake loads based on a linear analysis.

Observations of concrete buildings after an earthquake and nonlinear analysis of concrete buildings has shown that buildings without the strength required to resist earthquake forces in the linear range of the structure can withstand the effects of earthquake motion without collapsing as long as the building has adequate ductility. Ductility is the ability to maintain a constant force resistance while deforming in the inelastic range.

Concrete building structures must possess an adequate combination of strength and ductility. Buildings with more ductility can have a lower strength, while buildings with less ductility must have a higher strength. The NBCC defines a variety of concrete building types that have a range of force reduction factors R_d and R_o. Clause 21 provides a range of detailing rules to achieve the corresponding levels of ductility. In a number of places in Clause 21 where it is felt that it may be very difficult to provide the required ductility in a portion of the structure, the designer is given the option to provide additional strength in lieu of ductility.

N21.2.1   Capacity Design

The nonlinear analysis needed to predict the response of typical building structures under earthquake motions is usually too complex for design. Capacity design is a simplified design approach where the designer chooses the inelastic mechanism and then provides the appropriate strengths of the elements of the concrete structure to ensure that the selected mechanism will form when the structure is deformed beyond the linear range. Special detailing for ductility is only required in those elements that have been selected to become inelastic. A simple analogy that has been used to explain capacity design is a chain where all but a few links are made stronger, and when the elastic capacity of the chain is exceeded, only the weak links in the chain will become inelastic. As long as the weak links of the chain have sufficient ductility, the complete chain will have sufficient ductility. The main proponent of using capacity design for the seismic design of concrete structures has been Thomas Paulay, and further reading on this subject can be found in: Paulay, T., and Priestley, M.J.N., "Seismic design of reinforced concrete and masonry buildings," John Wiley & Sons Inc., New York, 1992.

Explanatory Notes on CSA A23.3-04

N21.2.2 Seismic Force Resisting Systems

The design and detailing rules of Clause 21 cover the six standard ductile systems in the 2005 NBCC and two Conventional construction systems as shown in Table N21.2.2 below. These include two types of moment resisting frames (ductile and moderately ductile), two types of shearwalls (ductile and moderately ductile), and two types of ductile coupled walls (partially and fully coupled). The rules were developed for systems that are substantially uniform in strength and stiffness over the building height so that the inelastic mechanisms shown in figure N.21.2.2 below can develop. The black dots in the figure identify the locations of assumed ductile rotational hinges. Clause 21.8 covers Conventional construction.

Table N21.2.2 – Concrete Seismic Force Resisting Systems (SFRS) Designed and Detailed According to CSA A23.3: Ductility Related Force Modification Factors (R_d), Overstrength Related Force Modification Factors (R_o) and General Restrictions (from 2005 NBCC Table 4.1.8.9).

Type of SFRS		R_d	R_o	Restrictions				Cases Where $I_EFvS_a(1.0)$ >0.3
				Cases Where $I_EF_aS_a(0.2)$				
				<0.2	≥0.2 to <0.35	≥0.35 to ≤0.75	>0.75	
Concrete systems designed according to Clause 21								
1	Ductile **moment resisting frames**	4.0	1.7	NL	NL	NL	NL	NL
2	Moderately ductile **moment resisting frames**	2.5	1.4	NL	NL	60	40	40
3	Ductile **coupled walls**	4.0	1.7	NL	NL	NL	NL	NL
4	Ductile partially **coupled walls**	3.5	1.7	NL	NL	NL	NL	NL
5	Ductile **shearwalls**	3.5	1.6	NL	NL	NL	NL	NL
6	Moderately ductile **shearwalls**	2.0	1.4	NL	NL	NL	60	60
Other concrete systems								
▪	Conventional construction • Moment resisting frames • Shearwalls	1.5 1.5	1.3 1.3	NL NL	NL NL	15 40	NP 30	NP 30
▪	Other concrete SFRS(s) not above	1.0	1.0	15	15	NP	NP	NP

NP in table means not permitted.Numbers in table are maximum height limits in metres.
NL in table means system is permitted and not limited in height as an SFRS.
The most stringent requirement governs.

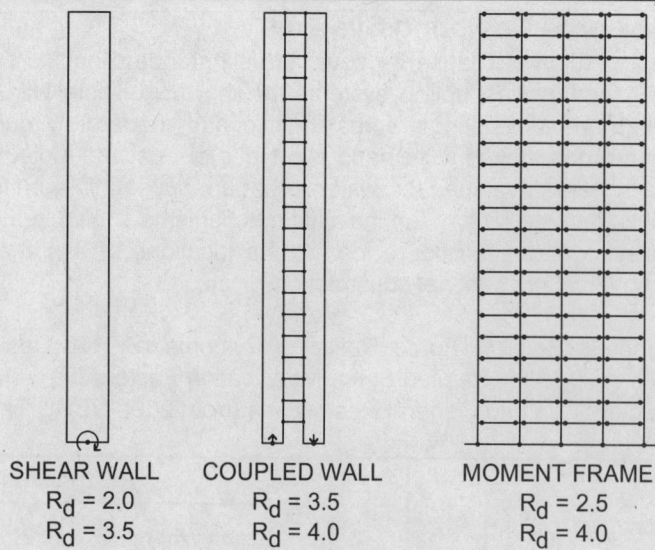

SHEAR WALL   COUPLED WALL   MOMENT FRAME
$R_d = 2.0$ $R_d = 3.5$ $R_d = 2.5$
$R_d = 3.5$ $R_d = 4.0$ $R_d = 4.0$

Fig. N21.2.2

When systems are not substantially uniform over the building height or where combinations of systems are employed or unclassified systems are used, nonlinear analysis is needed. This nonlinear analysis is required to determine if the inelastic rotational demand at any point exceeds the inelastic rotational capacity provided. This does not necessarily mean complex nonlinear analysis by computer, but it does mean consideration of issues beyond what can be determined from a linear analysis. Linear analysis can be used to determine the total displacement demand of the SFRS if the appropriate effective section properties given in 21.2.5.2.1 are used. Linear analysis can also be used to determine a set of design forces that satisfy equilibrium; but consideration needs to be given to how the force distribution will change when the structure is in the inelastic range. Linear analysis cannot be used to determine the concentration of inelastic action in certain portions of the structure, and this is the most important reason for requiring an inelastic analysis.

For many situations, the inelastic analysis that is needed can be done using simple hand calculations. Clause 21.6.7 and 21.6.8 provide explicit procedures for ensuring that inelastic rotational demands in concrete walls will not exceed inelastic rotation capacities. The simple inelastic analysis that is needed to develop the expression for inelastic rotation demand in shearwalls is given in N21.6.7.2. These procedures can be modified to account for different situations. For example, if a concrete wall system is not uniform over the full height of a structure (perhaps larger in section at the bottom), the designer could decide to use a capacity design approach to force yielding to occur at a higher elevation in the building. Equation (21-10) would then need to be modified to account for the actual height of the wall above the centre of the plastic hinge. Note that as the height of hinge formation increases, the inelastic rotation demand increases. The procedures given in Clause 21.6.7.3 for determining the inelastic rotational capacities of walls are general enough to be applied to such situations as well.

Where two recognized systems are employed in parallel, the need for special studies depends on whether they have the same or different inelastic mechanisms. A frame typically deforms beyond its yield capacity in a beam-hinging shear-sway mechanism with hinges developing at multiple levels. A shear wall, on the other hand, deforms with a single flexural wall hinge usually at the base. Two or more wall systems, even if they include coupled walls, have the same final mechanism - a flexural rotational hinge at the plastic hinge level. Two frames also have the same final mechanism - an inelastic beam-hinging shear-sway mechanism. The only

Explanatory Notes on CSA A23.3-04

case of two recognized systems with different inelastic mechanisms is a shear wall and a frame employed in parallel. The typical elastic analysis that is used to determine how they share the load at each floor over the building height is no longer valid once the building enters its inelastic range of deformation. The floor slabs enforce compatible deformations between both systems so the frame must follow the plastic deformations of the wall over the wall's plastic hinge length. This means either the frame must be strong enough to preclude plastic rotations in the wall (not likely), or the frame columns must be able to undergo the same curvature as the wall's inelastic curvature over the height of the wall plastic hinge. When shear walls and frames are used as a combined system, the frame columns need to be investigated by a combined system inelastic analysis to determine if their rotational capacity is greater than the demand. In lieu of the inelastic analysis, frame columns can be detailed in accordance with Clause 21.4.4.6 or Clause 21.7.2.2.5 as applicable over the height of the shear wall plastic hinge.

Discontinuous systems should be avoided if possible as extremely high ductility demands can arise at the discontinuities. Wall systems where walls are not continuous from their top to the foundation are only allowed by NBCC in restricted circumstances and should be avoided. Frames are not subject to the same restrictions in NBCC but frames that are not continuous to the foundations are not uniform systems and therefore are subject to inelastic analysis and design in accordance with Clause 21.2.2. Where walls or frames are not continuous from the foundation to the top of the main roof of a building an alternative to an inelastic analysis would be to treat the continuing elements as if a plastic hinge occurs at the level where the other element(s) terminate. For the continuing elements, walls need to be detailed in accordance with Clause 21.6.2.3 and frames in accordance with either Clause 21.4.4.6 or Clause 21.7.2.2.5 as applicable.

Buildings that have induced lateral or torsional forces in the SFRS due to gravity loading cannot be considered uniform systems. Buildings with lateral or torsional forces in the SFRS due to gravity loading will have magnified inelastic deformations. These systems need inelastic time history analysis to determine if the combined inelastic deformations under simultaneous gravity and seismic loading are within acceptable limits.

N21.2.5   Analysis and Proportioning of Structural Members

N21.2.5.2
A number of design requirements in the current edition of the Standard depend on the predicted displacement of the structure. Thus the section properties to be used to predict displacements have been moved from the commentary to the body of the Standard. The effective section properties provided in this clause are the maximum values permitted when estimating displacements of the structure.

Due to the variation of concrete cracking from one section to another and the variation of cracking as the lateral load is increased, the response of concrete structures will be highly nonlinear. The reduction factors provided in this clause are the single average value to be used for the entire structure in a linear analysis to estimate the displacement demand.

For columns and walls, the effective moment of inertia I_e depends on the level of axial compression applied to the member as given by Eqs. (21-1) and (21-2). Axial compression due to gravity load P_s reduces the amount of flexural cracking and closes flexural cracks when the lateral load levels are reduced during lateral load reversals.

The axial stress ratio used to calculate the effective stiffness is due to gravity loads only. The effect of coupling beam forces on coupled walls is ignored for simplicity since these forces reduce the compression in one wall segment and increase the compression in the adjoining wall segment, and because the reduction in axial compression does not occur in the "tension wall" until significant lateral loading is applied to the system.

For multiple wall segments in a coupled wall system, a single reduction factor based on an average value of axial compression stress may be used to estimate the overall stiffness of the structure.   However, if separate cantilever walls have significantly different stiffnesses and significantly different axial stress ratios, separate reduction factors should be used.

Shear deformations of coupling beams must be included in the analysis of coupled wall systems, and effective shear areas A_{ve} are given for coupling beams in order to account for the influence of diagonal cracking. Coupling beams with diagonal reinforcement (Clause 21.6.8.7) have better diagonal crack control; but less effective flexural crack control compared to coupling beams with conventional reinforcement (21.6.8.6). The combined effect of the shear and flexural reduction factors given in Table 21.1 is similar to the effect of the single reduction factors on flexural rigidities given in the current New Zealand concrete code. To account for strain penetration into the ends of adjoining walls, the length of coupling beams should be taken as 20% longer than the clear span of the beams. This is particularly important for coupled wall systems with lower degrees of coupling as the stiffness of the coupling beams has a significant influence on the system stiffness.

The flexural stiffness of a coupled wall system also depends on the axial stiffness of the walls, and thus the axial stiffnesses of walls need to be reduced to account for cracking using the same reduction factor as the flexural stiffness of cantilever walls.

The effective flexural stiffness of concrete walls varies over a wide range depending on the level of damage in previous load cycles. The reduction factor given by Eq. (21-2) defines the upper-bound of this range, and is appropriate for a wall that is essentially undamaged before being subjected to the load cycle resulting in the maximum displacement demand. The lower-bound reduction factor is given by:

$$\alpha_w = 0.2 + 2.5 \frac{P_s}{f_c' A_g} \le 0.7$$

Note that walls with low axial compression stress ratios have a much larger range between the upper and lower-bound reduction factors, while walls with high axial compression stress have a smaller range. Walls that are designed with a low strength as a ratio of elastic demand (large R/γ_w) are more likely to be damaged during an earthquake, and designers should be aware that their effective stiffness may be closer to the lower-bound. Reference: Ibrahim, A. and Adebar, P., "Effective flexural stiffness for linear seismic analysis of concrete walls," Can. J. Civ. Eng. 31: 597–607 (2004).

N21.2.5.4

This clause requires that the R_d portion of inelastic deformations be included in the stability design of sway frames. See also NBCC Seismic commentary.

N21.2.5.5

It is important that the effects of the inelastic deformation of the SFRS on all building elements be considered as outlined in Clause 21.12.

N21.2.6   Concrete in Members Resisting Earthquake-Induced Forces

N21.2.6.1

The upper limit of 55 MPa on concrete strength contained in previous editions of this Standard has been increased to 80 MPa. Recent research[†] has shown that with the appropriate detailing specified in Clause 21, ductile behaviour can be achieved even with higher strength concrete.

[†] Reference: Paultre, P. and Mitchell, D., "Incorporating High-Strength Concrete in Seismic Provisions of the Canadian Concrete Standard", Proceedings of 13th WCEE, Vancouver, BC, Aug. 2004.

Explanatory Notes on CSA A23.3-04

N21.2.7 Reinforcement in Members Resisting Earthquake-Induced Forces

N21.2.7.1

Reinforcement complying with the weldable grade requirements of CSA G30.18 has a more closely controlled chemical composition which results in a more predictable and ductile stress-strain response. Use of reinforcement with yield strength higher than that assumed in design will lead to higher shear and bond stress at the development of yield moments. This may lead to unexpected brittle failures and hence should be avoided. These more stringent requirements on the properties of the reinforcing steel are not necessary for lateral load resisting systems designed with a modification factor, R_d of 2.5 or less.

N21.2.7.2

Lateral force resisting elements are expected to develop their yield capacity and deform inelastically under the action of seismic forces. Under these circumstances all reinforcement provided is expected to yield and must therefore be spliced for full tension capacity.

N21.2.8 Mechanical Splices

N21.2.8.1

Type 2 mechanical splices are required to develop the specified tensile strength of the reinforcement to enable the bar to yield prior to failure of the splice.

N21.2.9 Welded Splices

N21.2.9.2

Welding or tack welding of crossing reinforcing bars can lead to local embrittlement of the steel. If such welding is needed to facilitate fabrication it must be done only on additional bars added expressly for this purpose. Welding performed to splice bars using a controlled procedure with adequate inspection is permitted.

N21.3 Ductile Moment-Resisting Frame Members Subject to Predominately Flexure

N21.3.1 Application

N21.3.1.1(a)

Frame members (beams) subjected to factored axial compressive forces exceeding $A_g f_c' / 10$ have different behaviour and must be designed and detailed according to Clause 21.4.

N21.3.2 Longitudinal Reinforcement

N21.3.2.1 and N21.3.2.2

These Clauses ensure continuity of reinforcement and some positive and negative moment capacity throughout the beam to allow for unexpected deformations and moment redistributions from severe earthquake loading. The reinforcement limits are intended to ensure that the section displays adequate ductility. The upper limit of 0.025 is to avoid excessive steel congestion and excessive joint shear stresses.

N21.3.2.3

Lap splices are unreliable for inelastic cyclic loading and hence are not permitted within the plastic hinge regions of beams.

N21.3.3 Transverse Reinforcement

N21.3.3.1

These hoops are intended to prevent buckling of the longitudinal bars in the compression zone in plastic hinge regions where both the top and bottom reinforcement can be subjected to yielding in tension and compression due to reversed cyclic flexure. Bars that buckle in compression and are subsequently stressed to yield in tension usually rupture.

N21.3.3.1(b)

When a plastic hinge region is deliberately relocated away form the column then hoop reinforcement must be provided within and adjacent to the plastic hinge region.

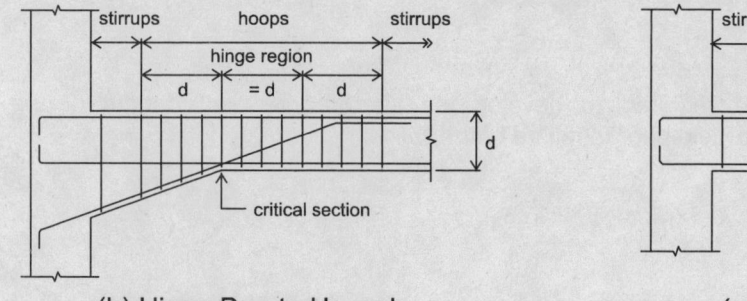
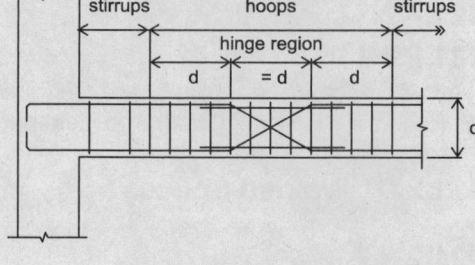

(b) Hinge Due to Haunch

(a) Hinge Due to Special Reinforcement Details

Fig. N21.3.3.1 Plastic Hinges Located Away from Column Faces

N21.3.3.5

The need for hoops in other regions of the beam where only positive moment hinging can occur is a matter of judgement. In these regions the danger of buckling of the top compression bars is far less since these bars will never have yielded in tension in a previous load cycle. Bottom longitudinal bars that are not subjected to compression need not be laterally supported to prevent buckling.

N21.4   Ductile Moment Resisting Frame Members Subjected to Flexural and Axial Load

N21.4.2 Minimum Flexural Resistance of Columns

The energy dissipation necessary for a multi-storey frame to survive a severe earthquake should in general occur by the formation of ductile plastic hinges in beams (see Fig. N21.4.2(b)). Plastic hinges in beams are capable of tolerating larger rotations than hinges in columns. Further, as can be seen from Fig. N21.4.2(b), mechanisms involving beam hinges cause energy to be dissipated at many locations throughout the frame. An additional consideration is that extensive hinging in columns (see Fig. N21.4.2(a)) may critically reduce the gravity load carrying capacity of the structure.

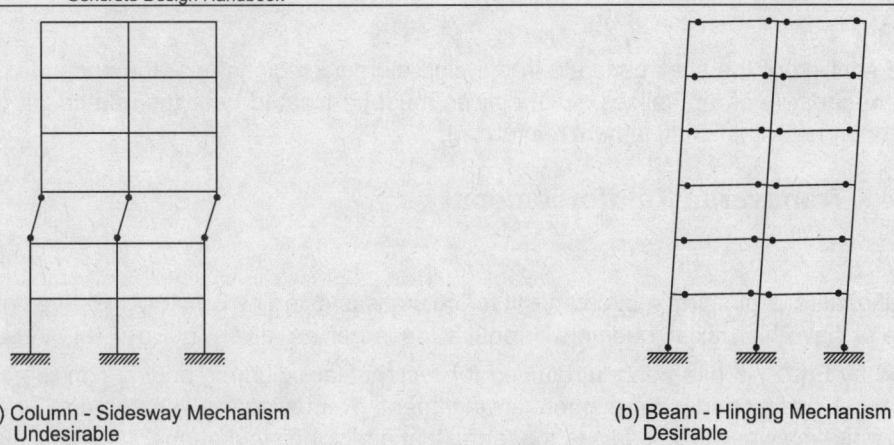

(a) Column - Sidesway Mechanism
    Undesirable

(b) Beam - Hinging Mechanism
    Desirable

Fig. N21.4.2 Types of Mechanisms

N21.4.2.2

To achieve the desired beam hinging mechanism, the Standard specifies a "strong column-weak beam" design approach. Eq. (21-3) requires that the total nominal resistance of the columns must be greater than the total probable resistance, based on $\phi_s = 1.25$, of the beams framing into the joint.

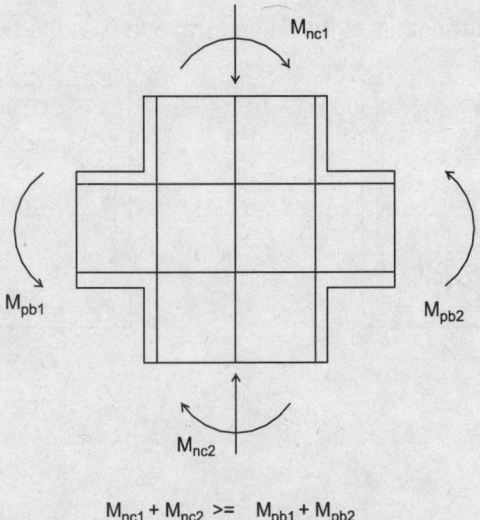

$$M_{nc1} + M_{nc2} \ge M_{pb1} + M_{pb2}$$

Fig. N21.4.2.2 Strong Column – Weak Beam Requirement

N21.4.3   Longitudinal Reinforcement

N21.4.3.1

The lower limit addresses the concern for the effects of time-dependent deformation of columns and the desire to have post-cracking capacity. The upper limit reflects concern for steel congestion.

N21.4.3.2

Because spalling of the shell concrete in the high moment regions near the ends of columns will reduce the capacity of lap splices, such splices must be located near the mid-height of columns and be contained within confinement reinforcing.

N21.4.4   Transverse Reinforcement

N21.4.4.2

The traditional ratio of spiral reinforcement for columns is given by Eq. 10-7. Round columns that are large or have high axial loading will require the larger ρ_s given by Eq. 21-4. A new relation described by Eq. 21-5 has been introduced for rectangular columns, adding consideration of the effect of axial loading and reinforcement arrangement. Removing the "k"s from Eq. 21-5 gives the following equation where you can see the terms that affect the steel quantity.

$$A_{sh} = 0.2 \frac{n_\ell}{(n_\ell - 2)} \frac{P_f}{P_0} \frac{A_g}{A_{ch}} \frac{f'_c}{f_{yh}} sh_c$$

The term 0.2 is a coefficient, $\dfrac{n_\ell}{(n_\ell - 2)}$ is the bar arrangement, $\dfrac{P_f}{P_0}$ is the axial load level, $\dfrac{A_g}{A_{ch}}$ is the ratio of the gross concrete area to the concrete area within the ties, $\dfrac{f'_c}{f_{yh}}$ is the ratio of the concrete strength to tie strength, s is the tie spacing and h_c is the hoop dimension.

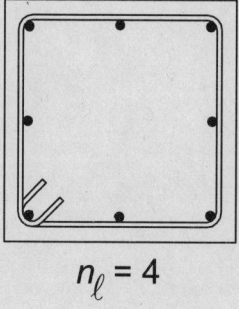

$n_\ell = 4$

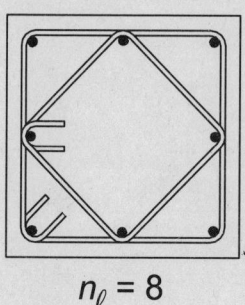

$n_\ell = 8$

N21.4.4.3

The spacing limits are intended to provide a minimum degree of confinement of the core and also to provide lateral support for the longitudinal reinforcing bars.

N21.4.4.4

Fig. N21.4.4.4 illustrates the requirements of this clause.

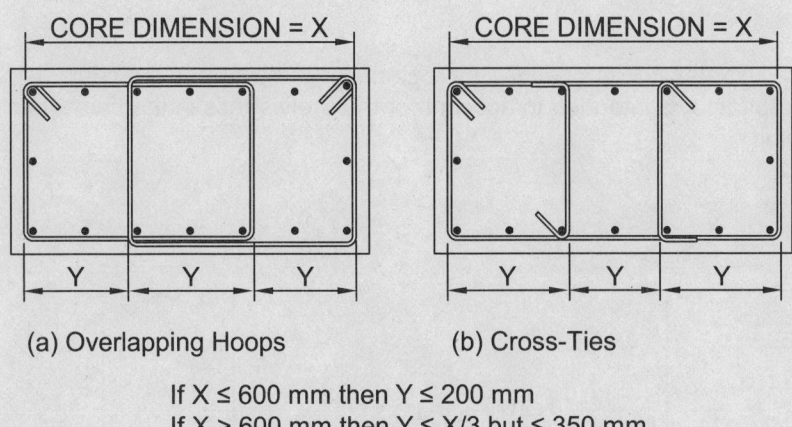

(a) Overlapping Hoops   (b) Cross-Ties

If X ≤ 600 mm then Y ≤ 200 mm
If X > 600 mm then Y ≤ X/3 but ≤ 350 mm

Fig. N21.4.4.4

N21.4.4.5

Fig. N21.4.4.5 illustrates the requirements of this clause.

ℓ_0 *not less than* $\dfrac{L_{clear}}{6}$

and $\ell_0 = 1.5\ Col_{max}$ *when* $P_f \le 0.5\phi_c f_c' A_g$

and $\ell_0 = 2.0\ Col_{max}$ *when* $P_f > 0.5\phi_c f_c' A_g$

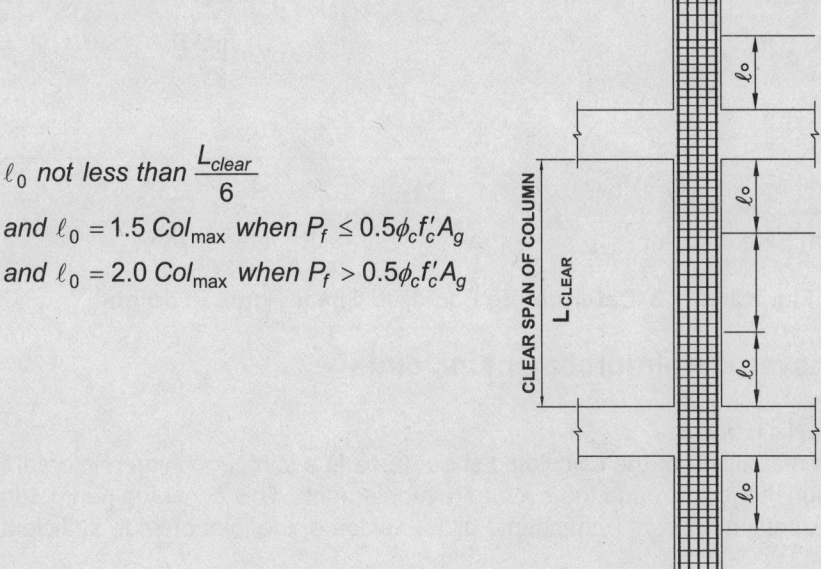

Fig. N21.4.4.5

N21.4.4.6

It is important to appreciate that during a severe earthquake some column hinging (e.g. at the base of the column in Fig 21.4.2(b)) and some yielding of columns will occur even if the "strong column-weak beam" philosophy has been followed. For this reason columns, need to be detailed for ductility in accordance with the requirement of Clause 21.4.4.6.

N21.5   Joints of Ductile Moment Resisting Frames

N21.5.1 General

N21.5.1.2
Fig. N21.5.1.2 illustrates the procedure for determining the factored shear in joints of ductile frames. The 1.25 factor is intended to account for the likely stress in the bars when plastic hinges form in the beams.

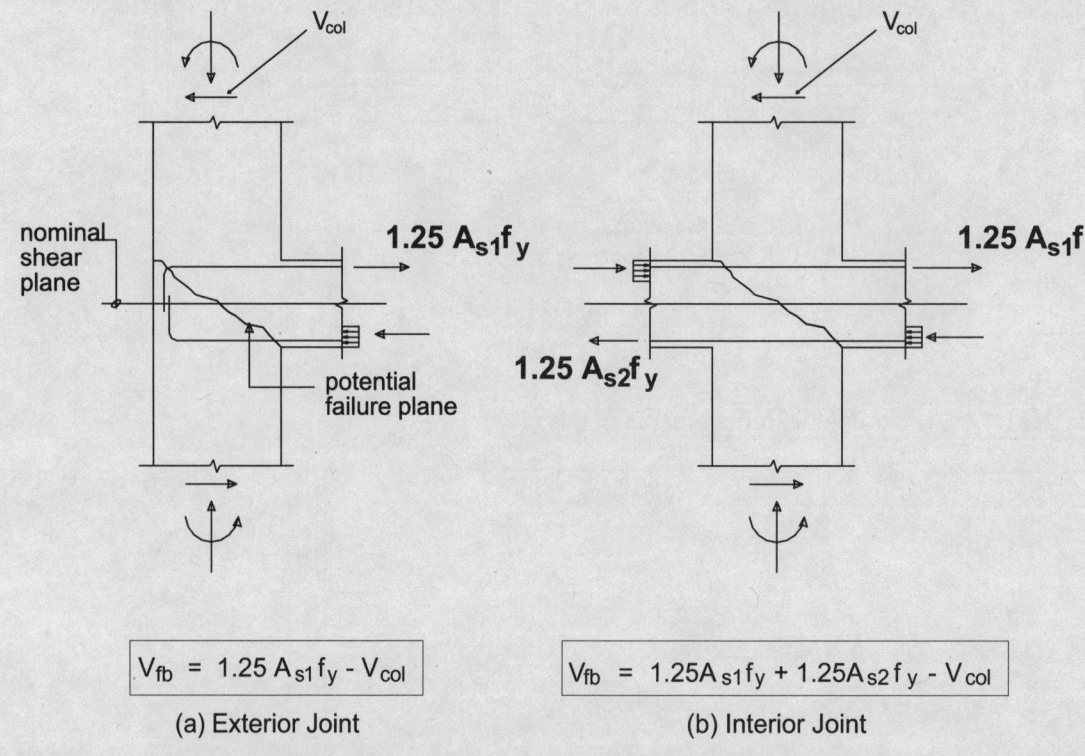

$$V_{fb} = 1.25 A_{s1} f_y - V_{col}$$

(a) Exterior Joint

$$V_{fb} = 1.25 A_{s1} f_y + 1.25 A_{s2} f_y - V_{col}$$

(b) Interior Joint

Fig. N21.5.1.2 Determining Factored Shear Force in Joints

N21.5.2   Transverse Reinforcement in Joints

N21.5.2.1 and N21.5.2.2
Regardless of the magnitude of the calculated shear force in a joint, confining reinforcement must be provided through the joint around the column reinforcement. This confining reinforcement may be reduced if horizontal members framing into all four sides of the joint provide sufficient external confinement.

N21.5.2.3
This Clause may apply in situations where beams are wider than columns.

N21.5.3   Longitudinal Column Reinforcement
Confinement of the joint core is provided by the cage formed from the longitudinal steel and the corresponding hoops and ties. Depending on the size of the column the maximum spacing between adjacent longitudinal bars is between 200 mm (Clause 21.5.3) and 350 mm (Clause 21.4.4.4).

N21.5.4   Shear Resistance of Joints

The shear force is transferred through a joint by diagonal compressive struts in the concrete acting together with tensile forces in the vertical reinforcing bars. Rather than calculating the required amount of joint shear reinforcement, the approach taken is that a joint containing transverse and longitudinal reinforcement satisfying Clauses 21.5.2 and 21.5.3 will have the factored shear resistance given in this clause.

N21.5.5   Development Length for Tension Reinforcement in Joints

N21.5.5.2

35M bars and smaller can be anchored with standard 90 deg. hooks. The development lengths for bars with f_y = 400 MPa are:

Bar Size	X (mm)	ℓ_{dh} (mm) f_c' MPa				
		20	25	30	35	40
10M	44	179	160	150	150	150
15M	64	268	240	219	203	190
20M	80	358	320	292	270	253
25M	100	447	400	365	338	316
30M	150	537	480	438	406	379
35M	216	626	560	511	473	443

These lengths were determined by considering the beneficial effects of confinement which must be present. See Fig. N21.5.5.2 for illustration of the case.

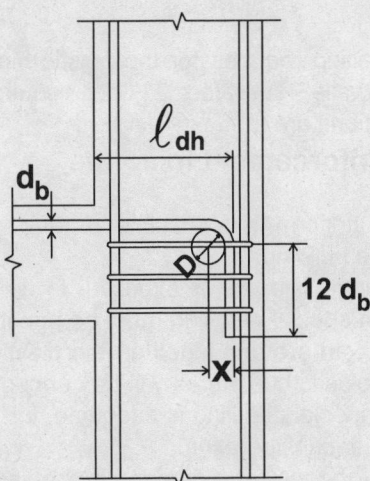

Fig. N21.5.5.2   Values of Development Lengths for Hooked Bars with
f_Y = 400 MPa Anchored in Confined Column Cores

N21.5.5.6

A straight bar passing through a beam-column joint may be subjected to tension on one side of the joint and compression on the other side of the joint (see Fig. N21.5.1.2). Limiting the bar diameter to $\ell/24$ of the joint length provides some control of the bond stresses.

N21.6   Ductile Walls

N21.6.1   Application

N21.6.1.1

Walls with h_w/ℓ_w of 2.0 or less are squat shear walls that are more likely to develop an inelastic shear mechanism rather than an inelastic flexural mechanism. These walls must be designed to the new requirements for squat walls contained in Clause 21.7.4.

N21.6.1.2

The question sometimes arises as to when a wall with openings is a solid shearwall and when it is a coupled wall. The analysis used to determine whether the elements connecting wall segments have sufficient stiffness must account for the reduced section properties given in Clause 21.2.5.2. The effective properties of the elements connecting the vertical wall segments shall be taken as those specified for coupling beams.

The elements connecting the wall segments would have adequate stiffness for the wall to act as a solid shearwall if the vertical strains in all wall segments follow essentially a single linear variation. That is, the horizontal plane section across all wall segments remains plane.

N21.6.2   General Requirements

N21.6.2.1

It is very important that the detailing required for the plastic hinge regions of walls be provided wherever yielding may occur in walls. Therefore 21.6.2.1 requires that this detailing be provided everywhere unless certain conditions are met.

N21.6.2.2

When a building is substantially uniform, it is possible to design a wall so that there is one well-defined plastic hinge region in the building.

The length of the plastic hinge in a wall is expected to be about equal to the length of the wall. Thus the length over which special detailing must be provided is 1.5 times the length of the wall. When walls of different length are tied together, the plastic hinge length will be essentially equal in all the walls, i.e., the inelastic curvatures will be concentrated over a similar height in all walls. To be sure the length of special detailing is adequate, it is controlled by the longest wall or wall segment in the direction under consideration.

Due to diagonal cracking of the wall, the demand in the vertical reinforcement at the critical section will spread over a height approximately equal to the wall length. Thus the vertical reinforcement required at the critical section must be provided over at least this height. Shear failures occur along a diagonal crack that extends over a height approximately equal to the length of the wall. For these two reasons, and to prevent premature yielding above the critical section, both the vertical and horizontal reinforcement calculated for the critical section shall extend over the plastic hinge region.

Once increased strength has been provided over the height of the plastic hinge, the factored bending moment envelope must be modified in order to prevent premature yielding above the plastic hinge region. In the previous commentary it was suggested that a linear variation in factored bending moment be used from the top of the plastic hinge region to the top of the wall. The new Standard permits a shape based on an amplified factored bending moment envelope to be used.

Fig. N21.6.2.2 illustrates a situation for a single wall where hinging will only form at the base of the wall. Note that a portion of the wall bending capacity is derived from the axial compression due to building dead load which reduces approximately linearly over the building height. Thus the bending capacity reduces linearly where the vertical reinforcement is uniform.

Fig. N21.2.2 shows that for coupled systems ductile detailing and consideration of capacity design principles are required over the height of the building. For the uniform coupled wall shown in Fig. N21.2.2 the location of the plastic hinges in the walls is limited to the base, and principles similar to those illustrated in Fig. N21.6.2.2 may be applied but must be supplemented with the additional requirements of Clauses 21.6.8.

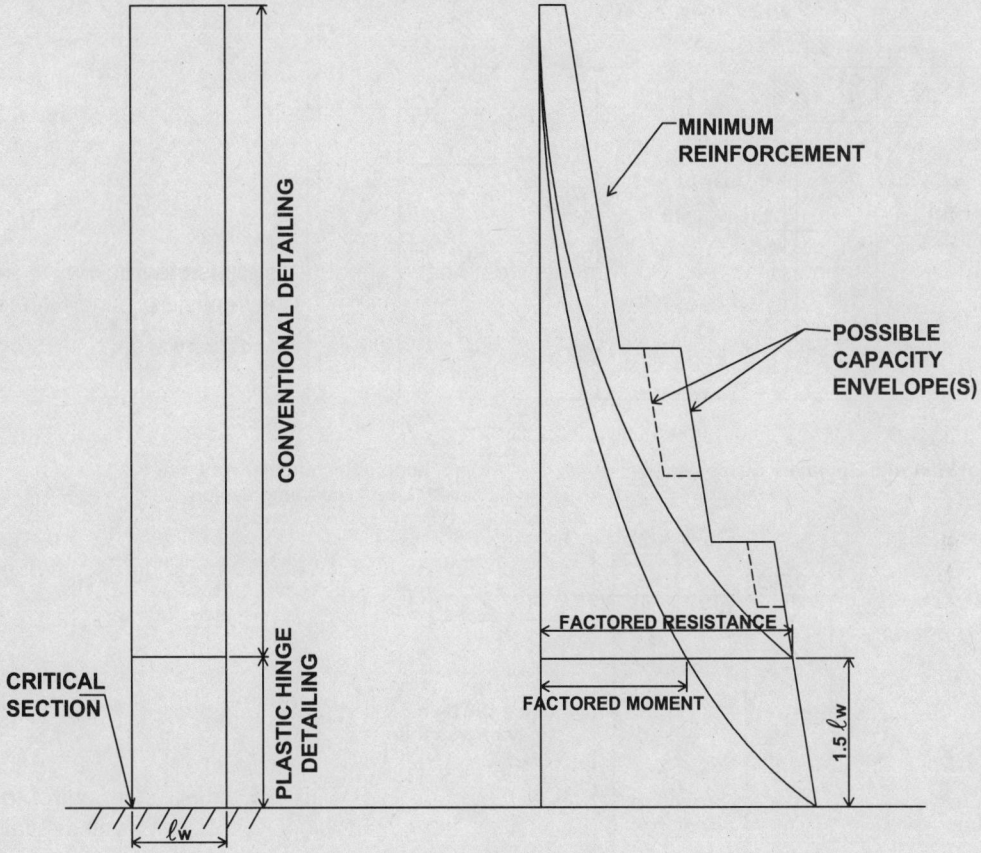

Fig. 21.6.2.2

N21.6.3   Dimensional Limitations

Because wall structures may be relatively thin, care must be taken to prevent possible instability in potential plastic hinge zones.   Regions of the walls, where yielding of the reinforcement and concrete compressive strains in excess of 0.0015 are expected, need to be checked for stability. Fig. N21.6.3 (a) illustrates how thickened boundary elements can be used to provide stability in the highly stressed regions of the walls. For simple rectangular walls with low axial compressions, the required depth of compression may be small enough to enable the remainder of the wall to provide sufficient restraint to the small highly compressed regions (see Fig. N21.6.3 (b)).   Certain parts of walls as shown in Fig. N21.6.3(c) provide continuous lateral support of adjacent components. Therefore any part of a wall which is within a distance of 3b' from a line of support is exempted from the slenderness limitation. The shaded part of the flange in Fig. N21.6.3(c) is considered to be too remote to be effectively restrained by the web portion of the wall and hence it needs to comply with the slenderness requirement.

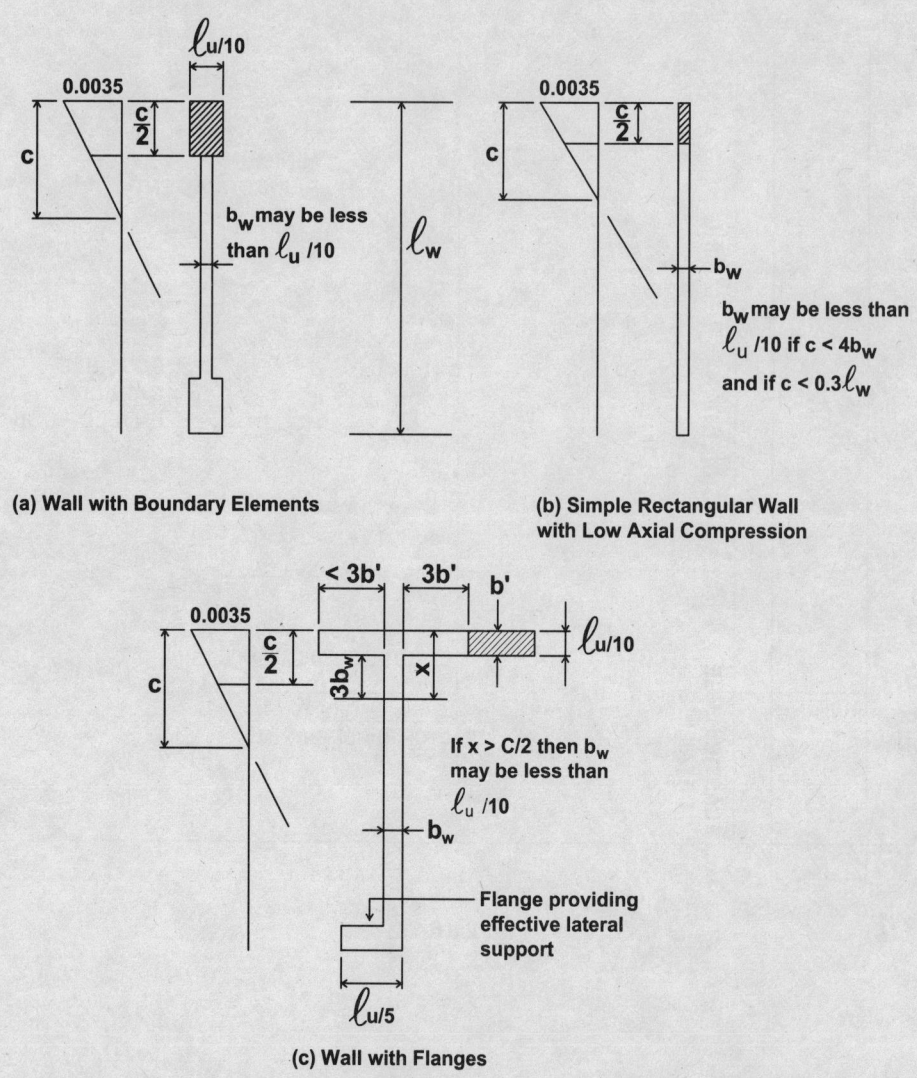

(a) Wall with Boundary Elements

**(b) Simple Rectangular Wall
with Low Axial Compression**

(c) Wall with Flanges

Fig. N21.6.3 Minimum Wall thickness in Plastic Hinge Regions

N21.6.4   Reinforcement

N21.6.4.3

This clause is intended to avoid excessive congestion of reinforcement. The reinforcement ratio is calculated using the area of concrete surrounding the concentrated reinforcement. Several such areas are shown shaded in Fig. N21.6.4.3. Note that this limit applies at lap splice locations.

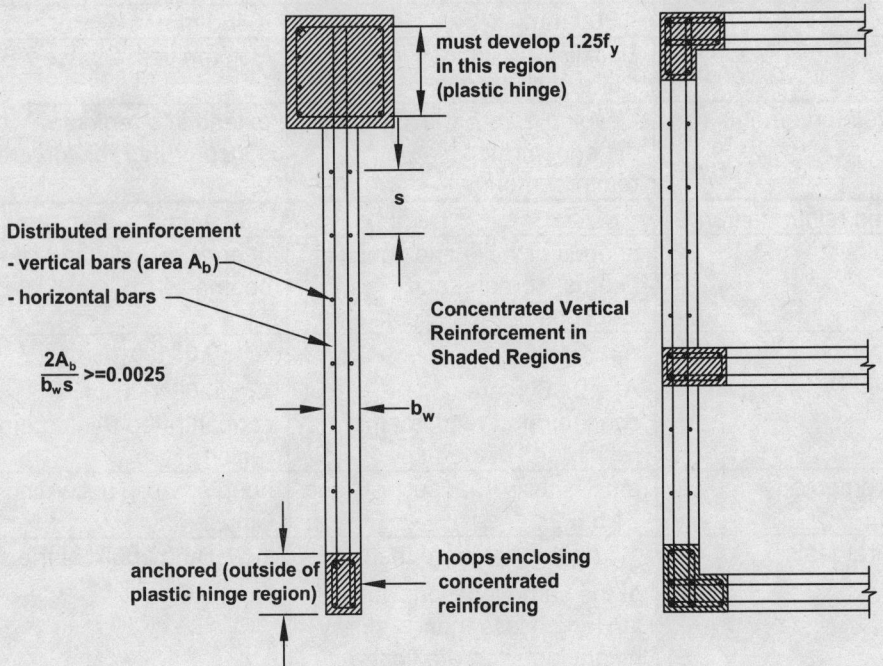

Fig. N21.6.4.3 Distributed Reinforcement and Concentrated Reinforcement

N21.6.5   Distributed Reinforcement

N21.6.5.1

This clause introduces tie requirements for vertical distributed reinforcement similar to those introduced in Clause 14, except that in Clause 21, it applies to all vertical reinforcement.

N21.6.5.2

Buckling prevention ties for vertical distributed reinforcement are required in plastic hinge regions in anticipation of reverse cyclic yielding where 20M and larger bars are used.

Explanatory Notes on CSA A23.3-04

N21.6.6   Concentrated Vertical Reinforcement

The different requirements for distributed and concentrated reinforcement in plastic hinge regions and other regions of ductile flexural walls are summarized below.

	Plastic Hinge	Other Region
Distributed reinforcement		
Amount	$\rho \geq 0.0025$	$\rho \geq 0.0025$
Spacing	≤ 300 mm	≤ 450 mm
Tying	Buckling prevention ties, Clause 21.6.6.9	Column ties, Clause 7.6.5
Horizontal reinforcement anchorage	Develop 1.25 f_y within region of concentrated reinforcement	extend into region of concentrated reinforcement
Concentrated reinforcement		
Where required	at ends of walls and coupling beams, corners, and junctions	at ends of walls and coupling beams
Amount* (at least 4 bars)	$A_s \geq 0.0015\ b_w \ell_w$ $A_s \leq 0.06$ x area of concentrated reinforcement region	$A_s \geq 0.001\ b_w \ell_w$ $A_s \leq 0.06$ x area of concentrated reinforcement region
Hoop requirements	must satisfy Clauses 7.6 and 21.6.6.9	hoop spacing according to Clause 7.6
Splice requirements	1.5 ℓ_d and not more than 50% at the same location. Unless lap length less than ¼ storey height lap alternate floors	1.5 ℓ_d and 100% at the same location.

*Note: *Amount of reinforcement must also satisfy requirements of Clause 21.6.6.2 and 21.6.7.*
Note: *Bar diameters must be less than or equal to 0.1 of the wall thickness.*

N21.6.6.2

The wall moments should be resisted primarily by concentrated reinforcement. Walls designed with only distributed steel often fail by rupture of the edge tension reinforcement prior to developing significant ductility. Nevertheless when calculating the wall resistance the distributed reinforcement is to be taken into account.

N21.6.6.4

This minimum reinforcement requirement is intended to ensure that the wall possesses post-cracking capacity.

N21.6.6.7

The requirement to keep at least half the storey height free of lap splices is intended to provide a section of wall with a capacity no greater than that anticipated in the design.

N21.6.6.8

The closer spacing of ties in the plastic hinge region is intended to prevent buckling of bars under compression.

N21.6.7 Ductility of Ductile Shear Walls

These provisions are completely new from the previous edition of the Standard. The reasons for the changes are given in the reference.[†] Unlike the previous provisions, the expressions are not rearranged and simplified. This has been done in order to preserve the physical meaning of the expressions.

N21.6.7.1

The concept of a "limit state" for inelastic deformations is introduced. The inelastic rotational capacity of a wall plastic hinge must be greater than the inelastic rotational demand.

N21.6.7.2

The inelastic rotation demand given by Eq. (21-10) is simply the inelastic displacement (total displacement minus elastic portion) at the top of the wall divided by the distance from the centre of the plastic hinge in the wall to the top of the wall. The plastic hinge length is assumed to be equal to the length of the wall ℓ_w in Eq. (21-10). The minimum inelastic rotation demand of 0.004 is to ensure a minimum level of ductility in buildings where the predicted inelastic drift is small.

$$\theta_{id} = \frac{\left(\Delta_f R_o R_d - \Delta_f \gamma_w\right)}{\left(h_w - \dfrac{\ell_w}{2}\right)} \geq 0.004$$

Design Displacement $= \Delta_f R_o R_d$

Elastic Displacement $= \Delta_f \gamma_w$

Inelastc Displacement $= \Delta_f R_o R_d - \Delta_f \gamma_w$

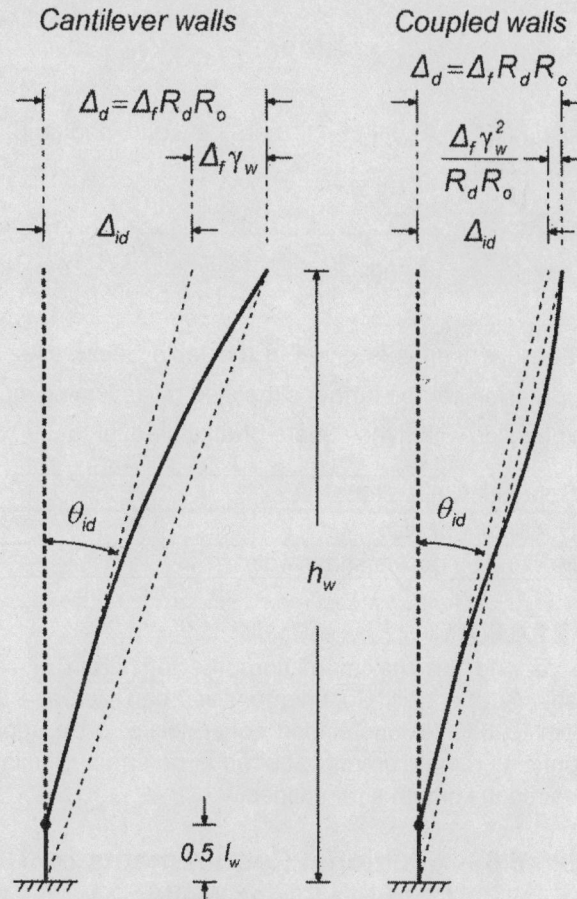

Fig. N21.6.7.2 & N21.6.8.2

[†] Reference: Adebar, P., Mutrie, J., and DeVall, R., "Ductility of concrete walls: the Canadian seismic design provisions 1984 to 2004," *Can. J. Civ. Eng., 32(6), Dec. 2005.*

N21.6.7.3

The inelastic rotation capacity given by Eq. (21-11) is equal to the total curvature capacity of the wall ε_{cu}/c minus the assumed yield curvature of $0.004/\ell_w$ times the assumed plastic hinge length of $\ell_w/2$. As the plastic hinge length varies between ℓ_w and $\ell_w/2$; to be safe the larger value was used to estimate demand and the smaller value was used to estimate inelastic rotation capacity.

$$\theta_{ic} = \left(\frac{\varepsilon_{cu}\ell_w}{2c} - 0.002 \right) \le 0.025$$

Plastic Hinge Length $= \dfrac{\ell_w}{2}$

$$\theta_{ic} = \frac{\ell_w}{2}\left(\frac{\varepsilon_{cu}}{c} - \frac{\varepsilon_{sy} + \varepsilon_{cy}}{\ell_w} \right)$$

$$\theta_{ic\,max} = \frac{\ell_w}{2}\left(\frac{\varepsilon_{smax}}{\ell_w} \right)$$

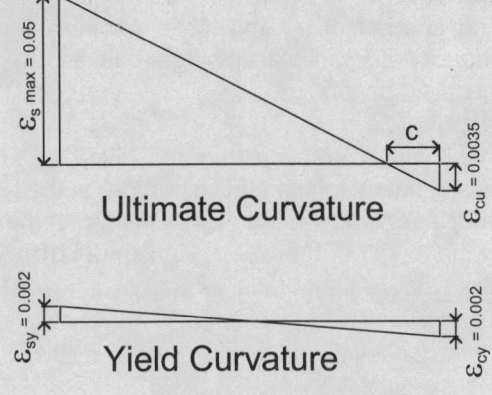

Ultimate Curvature

Yield Curvature

$$\theta_{ic} = \ell_p (\phi_u - \phi_y)$$

Eqs. (21-10) and (21-11) can be combined and rearranged to result in the following single expression:

$$\frac{c}{\ell_w} \le \frac{1}{1 + 500 \left(\dfrac{\Delta_f R_d R_o}{h_w} \right)\left[\dfrac{1 - \gamma_w /(R_d R_o)}{1 - 0.5\ell_w / h_w} \right]} \le A$$

where the limit A is given in the table below. As h_w/ℓ_w does not have a large influence, the expression can be further simplified by assuming $h_w/\ell_w = 5$, which makes the denominator of the expression within the square brackets equal to 0.90.

Concrete wall system	R_d	R_o	$R_d R_o$	A
Ductile shear wall	3.5	1.6	5.6	0.33
Moderately ductile shear wall	2.0	1.4	2.8	0.40

N21.6.7.4

Increasing the maximum compression strain of concrete can increase the inelastic rotational capacity of a wall. Confinement ties can increase the maximum compression strain of concrete from 0.0035 for unconfined concrete up to an upper limit of 0.014. The amount of transverse confining reinforcement required is determined using Equation 21-5 where k_p is a function of the desired maximum strain capacity.

N21.6.8 – Additional Requirements for Ductile Coupled and Partially Coupled Shear Walls

N21.6.8.1

Ductile coupled walls and ductile partially coupled walls dissipate energy by the formation of plastic hinges in all coupling beams and near the base of the walls as shown in Figure N21.2.2.

Explanatory Notes on CSA A23.3-04

N21.6.8.2

The bending moments from coupling beams cause reverse bending at the top of coupled walls. As a result, the elastic portion of the total displacement is generally much smaller in coupled walls than in shear walls without coupling beams. For simplicity, the inelastic rotation (inelastic displacement divided by height above plastic hinge) is assumed to be equal to the global drift (total displacement divided by total height of wall). That is, replacing the height of the wall above the plastic hinge with the total height of the wall compensates for the assumption that the elastic displacement is zero (See Fig N21.6.8.2). While the inelastic displacement is a larger portion of the total displacement in coupled walls, the total displacement demand is greatly reduced by the coupling beams.

N21.6.8.3

Walls with a low degree of coupling will act in a manner similar to that of separate walls. Walls with a very high degree of coupling will act in a manner similar to a single solid wall.

N21.6.8.4

All rotations referred to in this clause are actually total chord rotations, which are equal to the total relative displacement of the beam-ends divided by the total length of the beam.

Coupling beam rotations are proportional to the difference between wall slope and floor slope, where the latter is equal to the relative axial deformation of walls divided by the horizontal distance between wall centroids. The wall slope associated with maximum coupling beam rotation is much greater than the associated floor slope. Thus, the level of maximum coupling beam rotation occurs near the location of maximum wall slope, which is usually in the lower levels of the coupled walls due to inelastic drift being uniform, and elastic drift reducing with height from coupling beams pulling back on the walls. Due to axial displacement of walls, maximum coupling beam rotations do not necessarily result from maximum wall slopes; however a simplified procedure that gives reasonable results is to assume that the critical wall slope is equal to the maximum global drift, and the corresponding floor slope is equal to zero. This approach leads to Eq. (21-14), where ℓ_{cg} is the horizontal distance between centroids of the walls on either side of the coupling beams, and ℓ_u is the clear span of the coupling beam between the walls.

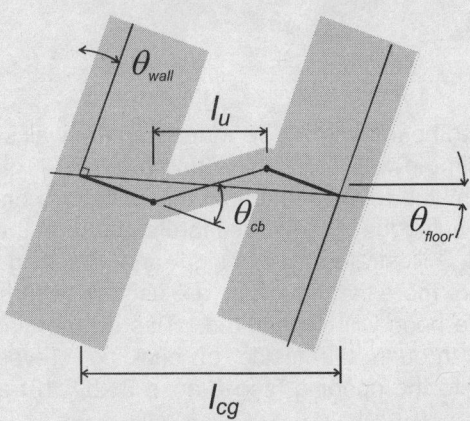

In FEMA 356, the rotational capacity of diagonally reinforced coupling beams is 0.03 and 0.05 for Life Safety and Collapse Prevention performance levels, respectively. For conventionally reinforced coupling beams, the limits are 0.015 and 0.03.

Reference: White, T. and Adebar, P., "Estimating Rotational Demands in High-rise Concrete Wall Buildings," 13th WCEE, Vancouver, BC, Aug. 2004.

N21.6.8.5

Both ductile coupled walls and ductile partially coupled walls require ductile coupling beams. Diagonal reinforcing must be provided in coupling beams to avoid sliding shear failure at the ends of the beams as transverse reinforcement is not effective in preventing such failures. The maximum shear stress that can be applied without causing a sliding shear failure is proportional to the slenderness of the coupling beams. Conventional reinforcement can be used if the shear stress is low and the rotational demands meet the limits in 21.6.8.4.

N21.6.8.6(a)

The longitudinal reinforcement in coupling beams must be capable of yielding in tension at one end and yielding in compression at the other end. Thus the beam must be long enough or the bar diameter small enough to permit the development of $2f_y$ along the length of the beam. The requirement is the same as in Clause 14.4.6.

N21.6.8.6(b)

The Clause 21.5 reference is for cases governed by Clause 21.6.8.9.

N21.6.8.6(c&d)

It is preferred that coupling beams be the same width as the wall and be centered on the wall. When this is not the case, additional design considerations are required. It is important to remember that coupling beams are expected to develop plastic hinges at the wall faces and therefore the design factored resistance of continuing elements of the coupling beams should be based on the probable resistance of the beam at the wall face when considering shear, torsion and out-of-plane bending to provide a hierarchy of capacity.

N21.6.8.7

Diagonally reinforced coupling beams cannot be wider than the wall since the diagonal reinforcing bars must be anchored within the wall. The shear and moment in diagonally reinforced coupling beams are resisted entirely by the reinforcement so the limitations on design capacity are usually dictated by the difficulty of placing the diagonal reinforcing through the wall-zone steel at the ends of the wall. Fig. N21.6.8.7 illustrates the design and detailing requirements for diagonal reinforcing. In the case where more than four bars are used in each diagonal, buckling prevention ties in addition to the outside hoop will be required. Ties on the diagonal reinforcement are not required where they pass through the inside of buckling prevention ties provided for the concentrated steel adjacent to the opening (see Clause 21.6.8.10) and over the last half of the required anchorage.

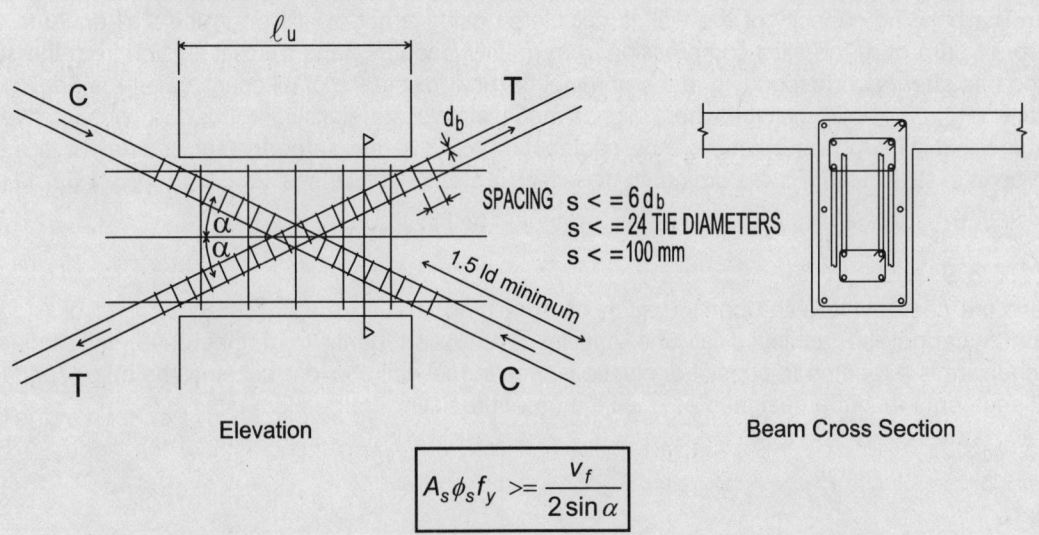

SPACING s < = 6 d$_b$
         s < = 24 TIE DIAMETERS
         s < = 100 mm

$$A_s \phi_s f_y >= \frac{v_f}{2 \sin \alpha}$$

Elevation   Beam Cross Section

Fig. N21.6.8.7 Diagonal Reinforcement in Coupling Beams

Explanatory Notes on CSA A23.3-04

To simplify the design of coupling beams while at the same time avoiding significant over-strength, the shear forces applied to coupling beams may be redistributed from the linear-elastic distribution as illustrated in Fig. N21.6.8.7(b). The shear in any individual beam should not be reduced by more than 20% from the linear-elastic distribution nor should it be reduced below that required for other load cases such as wind. The sum of the resistance over the height of the building must be greater than or equal to the sum of the elastically determined values. For the case where forces are determined using equivalent static loading, the design coupling beam shears should not be reduced to correspond to the overturning moment calculated using the reduction factor J.

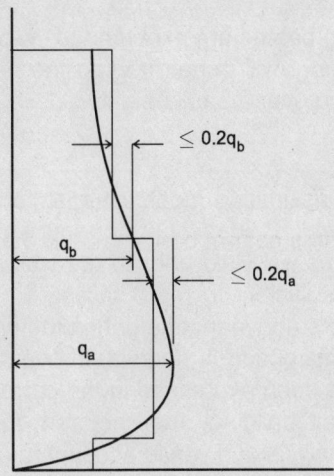

Fig. N21.6.8.7(b) Design of Coupling Beams Using Redistribution

N21.6.8.8
In order to ensure that the plastic hinges form in the coupling beams and not in the walls, the wall at each end of the coupling beam must be stronger than the coupling beams framing into it. This is similar to the requirement for strong columns weak -- beams in section 21.4.2.2 for ductile frames.

The bending capacity of the wall is calculated using a net axial load in the wall equal to the algebraic sum of a) the axial compression from gravity loads (P_s) and b) axial tension from the sum of the end shears corresponding to the nominal flexural resistance of all coupling beams above the section (P_n). For tall buildings where higher mode effects are significant, it is too conservative to assume that all coupling beams will be contributing to P_n at the same instant in time. It is more appropriate to reduce P_n according to the requirements of clauses 21.6.8.11 or 21.6.8.12 as applicable.

N21.6.8.9

There are cases where the configuration of a building is such that the requirements of Clause 21.6.8.8 cannot be achieved at one end of a coupling beam. In that case, the inelastic mechanism is expected to consist of plastic hinges in the wall above and below the beam, and the wall segments must be designed as ductile moment resisting-frame elements.

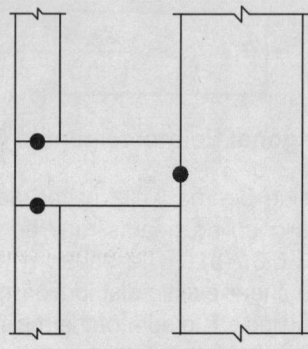

Fig. N21.6.8.9

N21.6.8.10

As shown in Fig. N21.2.2, coupling beams are expected to yield over the full height of the building, and the yielding of the reinforcement will penetrate into the adjacent wall ends. Thus the walls require a minimum level of detailing over the full height.

N21.6.8.11

In order for the assumed energy dissipating mechanism to form in coupled and partially coupled walls, the coupling beams must yield. Clause 21.6.8.8 requires sufficient local bending capacity of the walls to ensure coupling beams will yield prior to the walls. In addition, the axial capacity of the walls at any height must be sufficient to resist the sum of the coupling beam shear forces required to yield the coupling beams above that height. In the previous edition of the Standard, the requirement was expressed in terms of a first-mode push-over mechanism. To account for higher mode effects, the requirement has been expressed in the current provisions as a multiplier on the factored axial forces. For a tall building, the factored axial forces would presumably be determined by a linear dynamic analysis and would account for higher mode effects.

N21.6.8.12

Punched tubes are often used as the SFRS in tall buildings as they tend to be relatively easy to accommodate within building functional plans, provide good drift control and seismic force resistance. Tubes resist torsional loads by shear flow around the tube and through the coupling beams; as a result, there are no net induced overturning moments due to torsion in tubes, as there are in separated walls. It should be noted, however, that there will be local shears, moments and axial forces in the linked sections of tubes to equilibrate the shears and moments applied to them by the coupling beams for all load cases, including those that have a torsional component.

Punched tubes have shears in the coupling beams from two sources, the lateral forces and the accidental torsion. The wall system needs to have sufficient overturning moment capacity to be able to trigger header yield prior to overturning when there is no accidental torsional loading. The required wall design axial load increase needed to provide this overturning moment capacity is divided into two cases, one similar to 21.6.8.11 but only for the lateral loading case plus a second one for the accidental torsional case. For case (a) the ratio is determined from a design with the nominal beam capacities and the factored beam forces determined for lateral load without consideration of accidental torsion. For case (b) the design for lateral and accidental torsion results in an increase in nominal beam capacities above the design for case (a) and this increase is applied as an increase in overturning moment resisted by wall axial forces. The net result of the changes in this edition of the Standard is a reduction in the requirements from the previous edition; but still a retention of some increase in overturning moment capacity to encourage the desirable coupling beam yield mechanism.

N21.6.8.13

Shear cannot be transferred through large cracks such as those that occur in the tension flanges of concrete shearwalls in the plastic hinge zone. The committee felt more research was needed to investigate other possible solutions so the clause was written to allow other approaches if a solution is published in a respected peer reviewed journal over the time period where this Standard is in effect.

Figure N21.6.8.13 illustrates an example of a case this clause is meant to cover. This example is a core shear wall system with ductile coupling beams between the wall segments in the direction of the applied seismic load (It should be noted plastic hinges are expected at the base of the walls in ductile coupled and partially coupled shear wall systems – see Fig. N21.2.2). The tube system on the left is carrying shears due to lateral loading V_L and due to torsion V_T. The torsional shear on the tension flange in the plastic hinge region cannot be carried across the large tension cracks. The portion of the torsion carried by the couple, V_T times the distance between the tension and compression flanges must be redistributed to the perpendicular walls as illustrated in Figure N21.6.8.13(b) over the height of the plastic hinge region. Note: this redistribution changes the shears and moments in the coupling beams as well as the affected wall sections.

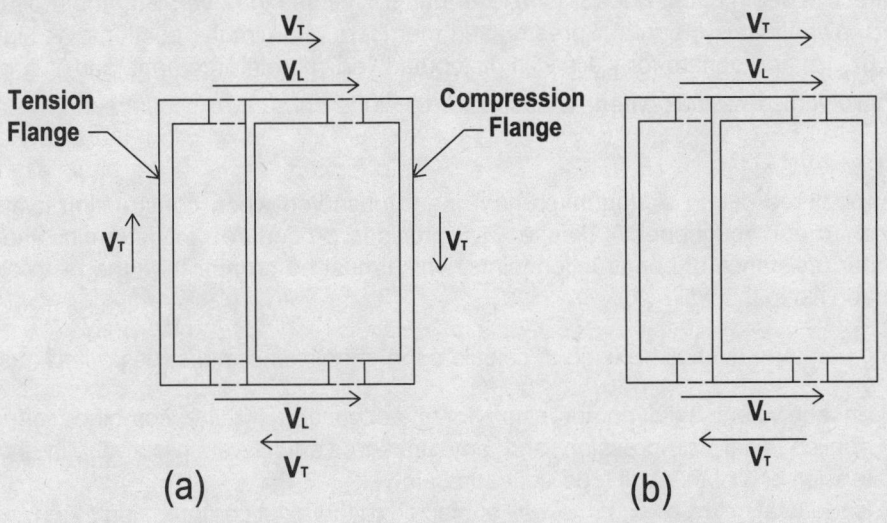

Fig. N21.6.8.13

Explanatory Notes on CSA A23.3-04

N21.6.9   Shear Strength of Ductile Walls

N21.6.9.1

This clause defines the shear force demand (applied shear force), while the remaining clauses are concerned with the shear force capacity (resistance).

A linear analysis is normally used to determine the factored forces on concrete walls. The analysis gives both the maximum bending moment and maximum shear force applied near the base of the wall.

Nonlinear analyses of concrete wall buildings with flexural hinging in the walls has shown that the ratio of maximum bending moment to maximum shear force observed in a linear analysis may not be preserved in a nonlinear analysis. That is, the maximum shear force may not be limited as the moment is by flexural hinging corresponding to the maximum bending moment; particularly in taller buildings where higher modes dominate. Unfortunately, no simplified method is available at this time to account for the magnification of shear due to inelastic effects of higher modes by simply modifying the results of a linear analysis. It is hoped (expected) that such a simplified solution will be available soon.

A capacity design approach is applied to ensure that flexural yielding of the wall will occur prior to a shear failure. For ductile walls, the shear forces determined in a linear analysis are magnified by the ratio of probable moment capacity of the wall to factored moment applied to the wall. In cases where the flexural resistance of the concrete walls exceeds the linear demand, the capacity design approach is not needed since the structure will remain linear. This is the reason for the upper limit given in (b).

N21.6.9.2

All regions of a concrete wall must meet the requirements of Clause 11 and Clauses 21.6.9.3 to 21.6.9.5. In addition, regions of plastic hinging must also meet the requirements of Clauses 21.6.9.6 and 21.6.9.7.

N21.6.9.3

The effective shear depth d_v is the distance between the flexural compression force and flexural tension force, i.e., the internal flexural lever-arm. Clause 2.3 specifies that d_v be calculated as 0.9 times the effective depth d; but need not be less than 0.72 times the overall member dimension h; however this lower limit is meant for prestressed members and circular sections. A higher lower bound of $0.8\ell_w$ is appropriate for walls with distributed vertical reinforcement, and is conservative for walls where vertical reinforcement is concentrated at the ends.

N21.6.9.4

Sliding shear failures during earthquakes have been observed when construction joints are not properly cleaned and roughened. Clause 11.5 provides procedures to determine the factored interface shear resistance of construction joints, which must be greater than the factored seismic shear force applied to the wall.

The following parameters shall be used to calculate the effective normal stress σ in Clause 11.5.4:

N = an equivalent axial compression force accounting for the combined effect of the applied axial compression and any unused vertical reinforcement in the flexural tension end of the wall (see equation below).

A_g = is the total gross area of the wall subjected to the axial compression P_s

A_{vf} = the total area of distributed vertical reinforcement in the shear resisting portion of the wall not considered to be resisting flexural stresses.

$$N = P_s + 2\left(A_s f_y - \frac{M_f}{jd} \right)$$

where: $A_s f_y$ is the strength of the vertical reinforcement resisting flexural tension,

M_f is the applied bending moment

jd is the internal flexural lever-arm.

N21.6.9.5

The procedures in Clause 21.6.9.6 assume that the shear force applied to a wall will be resisted by uniform diagonal compression stresses in concrete and uniformly spaced horizontal reinforcement. When there is an opening in the wall, there will be a concentration of diagonal compression stresses around the opening, which may lead to a brittle concrete shear failure. Additional reinforcement beyond what is calculated assuming a uniform stress field will be required, and special care must be taken to detail this reinforcement so that the diagonal compression forces are able to change direction where needed. The strut-and-tie model in Clause 11.4 is an appropriate design tool to ensure that an opening will not be the weak-link in the shear strength of a concrete wall.

N21.6.9.6

The design for shear in the plastic hinge region of walls shall meet the requirements of Clause 11.3 – Design for shear in flexural region; except as modified by this clause. Clause 11.3 is based on a variable angle truss model with diagonal compression inclined at approximately the same angle as the critical diagonal crack, plus a concrete contribution representing the shear transmitted across diagonal cracks by aggregate interlock.

N21.6.9.6(a)

Clause 11.3.3 limits the maximum shear force in the non-seismic case to $0.25\phi_c f'_c b_w d_v$. Due to the reverse cyclic loading in the plastic hinge region of concrete walls, the flexural compression zone of the wall will become the flexural tension zone during the reverse direction of loading. Thus the flexural compression zone of the wall will be damaged during reverse cyclic loading and less able to resist the concentration of shear that occurs in a "fan region." The inelastic rotation demand is a good indicator of damage in the plastic hinge regions of concrete walls. Inelastic rotation is proportional to inelastic curvature and hence directly related to the vertical tensile strains in the plastic hinge region.

N21.6.9.6(b)

The concrete contribution V_c is given in Clause 11.3.4 as a function of the factor β, which is given in Clause 11.3.6.4 as a function of the axial tension strain at the section mid-depth. The axial tension strain is used as an indicator of the width of diagonal cracks. As the axial strains become larger, the diagonal crack widths become larger and the diagonal cracks are less able to resist interface shear stresses. The inelastic rotation of the plastic hinge region is used as the indicator of diagonal crack widths in the plastic hinge region. The lower bound value of β in Clause 11.3.6.4 for large axial tension strains is 0.18, and this value is to be used for the plastic hinge region when the inelastic rotations are small. When the inelastic rotations are large, β is taken as zero.

N21.6.9.6(c)

The shear resistance provided by transverse shear reinforcement V_s is given in Clause 11.3.5 as a function of θ, which is the angle of inclination of diagonal compression stresses relative to the longitudinal axis of the member. The angle θ varies from about 35 to 29 degrees for non-seismic cases. In the design for seismic shear in the plastic hinge regions of walls, θ is considered to be the critical diagonal crack inclination relative to the vertical axis of the wall. The axial compression applied to the wall is the best indicator of the inclination of the critical diagonal crack. When a wall is subjected to larger axial compression, the critical diagonal crack will be steeper (θ will be smaller), and V_s will be larger for the same amount of horizontal reinforcement in the wall.

Reference: Adebar, P., "Drift Capacity of Walls Accounting for Shear: The 2004 Canadian Code Provisions," ACI SP on Seismic Shear, in press, 2006, 20 pp.

N21.7   Building Members Designed for Moderate Ductility

N21.7.1   Application

N21.7.1.2

Experience from recent California earthquakes has shown that the weak-link in tilt-up buildings is often the out-of-plane connection between the walls and roof. These buildings have predominately timber roofs.

Steel deck diaphragms are normally used in Canada, and CSA S16.1-2001 requires a capacity design check to verify that the strength of steel deck diaphragms is greater than the actual capacity of the vertical bracing system to ensure that inelastic action is avoided in the steel deck. When a significant portion of the building mass is distributed along an elastic flexible diaphragm, the inelastic displacement demands on the vertical system (walls) will be amplified, and this must be accounted for in the seismic design of concrete tilt-up walls.

Tilt-up wall panels with large openings resist in-plane seismic forces in the same way as cast-in-place reinforced concrete frames except that the relationship between system ductility and component ductilities is more severe due to the presence of the elastic flexible diaphragms. The rotational limits given in this clause provide a rational basis to decide when concrete tilt-up walls with large openings must meet the seismic design requirements for moderately ductile cast-in-place frames, and when the inelastic rotation demands on concrete tilt-up walls with openings are too large to be tolerated.

The inelastic rotation limits in FEMA 356 for collapse prevention performance of reinforced concrete columns varies between 0.005 and 0.01 radians for columns with nonconforming ties, and between 0.01 and 0.02 radians for columns with conforming ties. Conforming ties are defined as hoops spaced at $\leq d/3$ and such that the shear resistance is sufficient to resist three-fourths of the design shear. The inelastic rotational limits of 0.02 and 0.04 for tilt-up wall panels with openings were purposely made larger in order to be certain not to err on side of being too restrictive. It is expected that these limits will be reduced to 0.01 and 0.02 in the next edition of the Standard.

The inelastic rotational demand on components of tilt-up wall panels with openings (tilt-up frames) can be determined from a simple rigid-plastic push-over analysis of the frame to the target inelastic displacement demand at the top of the frame. That is, the target displacement is the inelastic portion of the displacement demand, and correspondingly, the frame members are assumed to have infinite rigidity (no elastic displacement). Sufficient hinges must be provided in the frame to form a collapse mechanism, and the relationship between hinge rotation and frame displacement can be determined from the geometry of the mechanism. The hinge rotation is assumed to be concentrated at the centre of the plastic hinge length, which is equal to the member dimension. Fig. N21.7.1.2 shows an example of a column hinge mechanism.

The inelastic displacement demand on concrete tilt-up walls can be estimated from the following expression (Adebar, P., Guan, Z., and Elwood, K., "Displacement-based design of concrete tilt-up frames accounting for flexible diaphragms," 13th WCEE, Vancouver, Aug. 2004):

$$\Delta_{wi} = S(T_a)g\left(\frac{T_a}{2\pi}\right)^2\left(1 - \frac{V_n}{V_e(T_a)}\right)$$

where:

$S(T_a)$ = design spectral response acceleration from NBCC

T_a = fundamental lateral period of vibration of building in direction under consideration accounting for the flexible diaphragm (see below),

g = acceleration due to gravity (9.81 m/s^2),

V_n = nominal strength of walls calculated using a reinforcement over-strength of $1.1f_y$,

$V_e(T_a)$ = lateral earthquake elastic force at base of structure according to 2005 NBCC.

The fundamental period of a building with a flexible diaphragm can be approximated from:

$$T = \sqrt{0.1\Delta_w + 0.078\Delta_d}$$

where Δ_w and Δ_d are in-plane wall and diaphragm displacements in inches, due to a lateral load in the direction under consideration, equal to the weight of the diaphragm (FEMA 356).

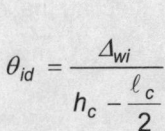

$$\theta_{id} = \frac{\Delta_{wi}}{h_c - \frac{\ell_c}{2}}$$

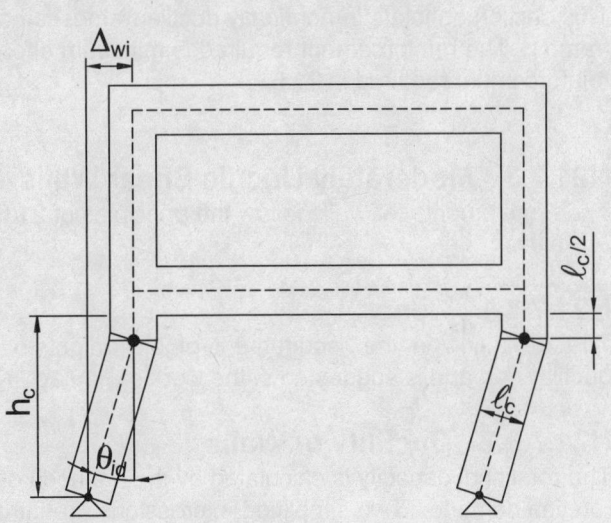

Fig. N21.7.1.2

N21.7.2   Moderately Ductile Moment Resisting Frames

This Clause gives the requirements for lateral force resisting frames designed with an R_d of 2.5.

N21.7.2.1   Detailing of Beams

N21.7.2.1.1

Continuity of reinforcement and some positive and negative moment capacity throughout the beam is required to allow for unexpected deformations and moment distributions from severe earthquake loading.

N21.7.2.1.2

Closely spaced stirrups in regions of potential inelastic action are required to prevent buckling of reinforcement under compression.

N21.7.2.2   Detailing of Columns

N21.7.2.2.2

The requirement for columns to be stronger than beams similar to 21.4.2.2 for $R_d = 4.0$ frames is new in this edition of the Standard.

N21.7.2.2.5

Closely spaced column ties are required in regions of potential inelastic action. Plastic hinges can be expected to develop in ground floor columns or in columns of storeys adjacent to a substantial change in structural stiffness. These ties are similar to those in Clause 21.4.4.2 with the coefficients changed to reflect the lower rotational demand for $R_d = 2.5$ systems.

N21.7.2.3   Shear in Frames

The factored shear resistance for beams and columns shall be based on member capacities not factored load effects so that flexural yielding will occur prior to shear failure. An upper limit is introduced corresponding to an elastic response level.

N21.7.2.4   Joints in Frames

This section on joints in nominally ductile frames is based on the suggestions of ACI 352 for wind frames. The reinforcement required is minimum shear reinforcement as opposed to confinement reinforcement required in 21.5.

N21.7.3   Moderately Ductile Shear Walls

The requirements for walls follow the principles of 21.6 but are not as stringent reflecting the lower R_d values.

N21.7.3.1   General

The relaxation in the requirement of the height to thickness requirements for walls of lower ductility demand is suggested in the work of Paulay.

N21.7.3.2   Ductility of Walls

The rotational capacity is calculated by the methods of Clause 21.6.7 but with a reduced minimum rotation demand. Two simplified expressions are introduced. If either expression is satisfied, full calculations in conformance with Clause 21.6.7 are not required.

N21.7.3.3   Detailing of Walls

N21.7.3.3.2

Concentrated zone steel requires anti-buckling ties in plastic hinge regions, but this requirement can be relaxed elsewhere.

N21.7.3.3.3

The requirements of this clause apply to wall intersections without tied concentrated reinforcement at the intersection. Where tied concentrations exist the horizontal reinforcement shall be anchored within the tied region.

N21.7.3.4   Shear Strength of Moderately Ductile Walls

The requirements for shear design are similar to 21.6.9 for ductile shear walls, but are less onerous reflecting the reduced inelastic demands on moderately ductile walls.

N21.7.3.4.1

A linear analysis is normally used to determine the factored forces on concrete walls. The analysis gives both the maximum bending moment and maximum shear force applied near the base of the wall. A capacity design approach is applied to ensure that flexural yielding of the wall will occur prior to a shear failure. For moderately ductile walls, the shear forces determined in a linear analysis are magnified by the ratio of nominal moment capacity of the wall to the factored moment applied to the wall. In cases where the flexural resistance of the concrete walls exceeds the linear demand, the capacity design approach is not needed since the structure will remain linear. This is the rationale for the upper limit given in 21.7.3.4.1(b).

N21.7.3.4.2
The second sentence of Clause 21.7.3.4.2 in the original release of the A23.3-04 Standard infers that adhering to the requirements of Cl 21.7.3.4.2 a, b, and c, satisfies the requirements of Clauses 21.6.9.2 to 21.6.9.7. This is not correct. The provisions of Cl 21.7.3.4.2 a, b, and c are permitted to be used in lieu of the requirements of Clause 21.6.9.6 only. All the requirements in Clauses 21.6.9.2 to 21.6.9.5 and 21.6.9.7 are also applicable to moderately ductile walls and must be satisfied regardless of whether the conditions given in (a), (b) and (c) have been met.

The procedures given in Clause 21.6.9.6 are general enough that they will account for the reduced inelastic demands on moderately ductile walls. Specifically, the inelastic rotational demand given by Eq. (21-10) will be reduced in moderately ductile walls. To avoid the need to apply Clause 21.6.9.6, three conditions (a), (b) and (c) are given. These conditions represent the most conservative result from Clause 21.6.9.6. Thus more efficient designs will result from using Clause 21.6.9.6 rather than the simplified limits.

N21.7.4 Squat Shear Walls

N21.7.4.1
Walls that have a height-to-length ratio h_w/ℓ_w of 2 or less will have significant shear deformations, and it is very likely that a flexural mechanism will not develop prior to a shear mechanism.

N21.7.4.2
The factored resistance of the foundation, diaphragm and other components of the SFRS shall be greater than the nominal resistance of the wall, which may be limited by either flexure or shear as given in (a) and (b); however the factored resistance of the foundation, diaphragm and other components of the SFRS need not be greater than the factored forces calculated using $R_d R_o = 1.0$.

N21.7.4.3
The maximum effective flange width is important for determining the maximum flexural resistance of a wall. The limits given in Clause 21.6.3.1 are also applicable to squat walls.

N21.7.4.4
The requirements for development and splices of reinforcement, maximum reinforcement ratio of concentrated reinforcement, and maximum diameter of reinforcing bars given in 21.6.4 are also applicable to squat walls.

N21.7.4.5(a)
In a flexural wall the concentrated vertical reinforcement at the tension end and the vertical compression in concrete at the compression end will significantly control diagonal cracking. As these do not exist in squat walls, additional distributed reinforcement is required to control the widths of diagonal cracks.

N21.7.4.5(b)

Poor diagonal crack control may occur if a single layer of reinforcement is offset from the centre of the wall therefore at least two layers of reinforcement is required. When the shear force applied to the wall is higher than the specified limit, significant diagonal cracking is expected.

N21.7.4.5(c)

Extending the horizontal reinforcement into the region of tied vertical reinforcement at the ends of the wall will enhance the anchorage of the horizontal reinforcement thereby permitting yielding of this reinforcement over a longer length.

N21.7.4.6

Concentrated reinforcement at the ends of walls provides an opportunity to enhance the anchorage of horizontal reinforcement (see Clause 21.7.4.5c), and protects the end of the wall. When the factored resistance of a squat wall is sufficient to resist the factored forces calculated using R_d = 1.0, the requirement to provide concentrated vertical reinforcement may be waived. As the squat wall is much longer than needed to resist the applied forces, a significant portion of the wall can be damaged and the remaining portion of the wall will still be sufficient to resist the factored forces calculated using R_d = 2.0.

N21.7.4.7

In a flexural wall, all vertical reinforcement, including the distributed reinforcement, can be included in the calculation of overturning resistance. The diagonal compression that resists the applied shear force flows to the flexural compression zone, and the size of the flexural compression zone is not significantly influenced by the presence of the diagonal compression. The stress field that forms at the base of a wall is referred to as a "fan region." In a squat wall, the diagonal compression that resists the applied shear force is distributed over much of the wall length. Tension stress is needed in the distributed vertical reinforcement to balance the vertical component of the diagonal compression. As the distributed vertical compression stress in concrete due to shear is not included in the calculation of over-turning resistance, the distributed vertical tension in the reinforcement must also not be included.

While plane sections do not remain plane in squat walls, such calculations for the vertical compression stress in concrete and vertical tension stress in reinforcement result in a safe design for the overturning resistance of squat walls.

N21.7.4.8

The requirements of Clauses 21.6.9.3 to 21.6.9.5 deal with the effective shear depth d_v, sliding shear failures of construction joints, and ensuring that an opening in a wall will not be the weak link in the shear strength of a concrete wall. These requirements are also applicable to squat walls.

The factored shear resistance of squat walls can be determined using the procedures in Clauses 11.3.3, 11.3.4, 11.3.5 and the conditions given in (a), (b) and (c).

Clause 11.3.3 limits the maximum shear force in the non-seismic case to $0.25\phi_c f'_c b_w d_v$. Due to damage from reverse cyclic loading in squat walls, the maximum shear force must be reduced to avoid diagonal compression failure of concrete.

The concrete contribution V_c in Clause 11.3 reflects the shear transmitted across diagonal cracks, which reduces the demand on horizontal reinforcement; but increases the demand on the flexural tension reinforcement as given by Eq. (11-14). In squat walls, any shear on the diagonal cracks will transfer the demand from the horizontal reinforcement to the vertical distributed reinforcement. The calculation for the relative demand on the horizontal and vertical reinforcement can be done without a concrete contribution using Eq. (21-19), and this approach is simpler for squat walls. The effect of including a concrete contribution is similar to using a smaller angle θ.

By choosing the angle θ within the allowable limits, a designer can choose the relative amounts of horizontal and distributed vertical reinforcement. When the vertical compression stress in the wall is small (as is often the case in squat walls), choosing θ = 45 deg results in ρ_v = ρ_h, while choosing θ = 30 deg results in 65% as much horizontal reinforcement, and 154% as much vertical reinforcement (i.e., the percentage of vertical reinforcement is 2.4 times the percentage of horizontal reinforcement). When there is significant vertical compression stress in the wall, choosing θ smaller than 45 deg results in less total reinforcement.

The required minimum amount of distributed reinforcement given in Clause 21.7.4.5 provides a factored shear resistance of $\Phi_s f_y \rho_h b_w d_v$ = 1.0 MPa x $b_w d_v$. If the factored shear force applied to the wall is larger, the percentage of distributed reinforcement must be increased, otherwise minimum reinforcement is sufficient.

N21.8   Conventional Construction
The new clause on conventional construction has been introduced to reflect the reduced restrictions on R_d = 1.5 systems in NBCC.

N21.8.2   Frames
This Clause is intended to preclude the development of a column hinging mechanism in frames, which could have disastrous consequences.

N21.8.3   Walls

N21.8.3.2
The requirements of this Clause attempt to preclude shear failure in shear walls.

N21.8.4   Two-way Slabs Without Beams
The 2005 NBCC does not preclude the use of flat plate frames as a SFRS with a R_d of 1.5 though there are some restrictions. Many on the CSA A23.3 committee however are of the opinion that they should not be used. Since they are not precluded by the Code then at least some improved detailing could help. The requirements of 21.8.4 are based on ACI 318-02 21.12.6.

N21.9   Precast Concrete
This is a new clause in this edition. It incorporates the new ACI specifications that provide procedures for the testing of systems thereby allowing these systems as well as those that emulate cast in place construction to be used. The ACI clauses have been modified to fit the NBCC R_d classification system. Further guidance can be found in the ACI 318 commentary.

N21.10   Structural Diaphragms
This is a new clause in this edition of A23.3 and is a much modified version of ACI 318-02 Clause 21.9. It is modified to reflect the new diaphragm requirements contained in the 2005 NBCC and to better separate the system types.

N21.10.3   Diaphragm Systems
Legible load paths are fundamental to the design of diaphragms. Particular attention should be paid to the provision of adequate collector members.

N21.11   Foundations

This is a new clause in this edition of A23.3 with the exception of 21.11.1.2 which was 21.2.2.3 in the previous edition. The clauses give design and detailing guidance for footing, pile caps and piles. The commentary to ACI 318, where this clause originated, provides further guidance on most of the clauses.

N21.11.1.2

The intent of this clause is to provide capacity design of the foundation system. The foundation system shall be taken as all portions of the lateral load resisting system below the lowest design plastic hinge. The upper limit on foundation capacity has been introduced to cover situations where the system capacity approaches that of an elastically responding system. This may be encountered when sizes are set by functional requirements and/or capacity by required minimum reinforcement. The difference between the anchored and un-anchored case has been introduced to recognize that there is some energy absorption in "stamping" or "rocking" footings even though there is not enough information currently available to allow utilization of these systems without special studies. A description of the type of special study required including inelastic analysis of a building is contained in the paper by A. Filiatrault, D. L. Anderson and R. H. DeVall in CSCE Journal, Volume 19, Number 3, June 1992.

N21.11.2.3

This clause was added over concerns that designers may not be providing a complete load path from shear wall zones through the footing into the soil. Fig. N21.11.2.3 illustrates how the strut-and-tie model given in Clause 11.4 may be used to visualize the force flow within a footing. The critical area for anchorage of the vertical wall reinforcement is indicated by a circle. Additional information about anchorage of tension ties is given in Clause 11.4.3.2. It would be possible to develop more refined strut and tie models that account for all the reinforcement in the footing and which, in some cases, could allow the development of the tension force in the vertical reinforcement over the depth of the footing. *It should be noted that the same principles apply to foundations resisting all types of lateral forces not just seismic.*

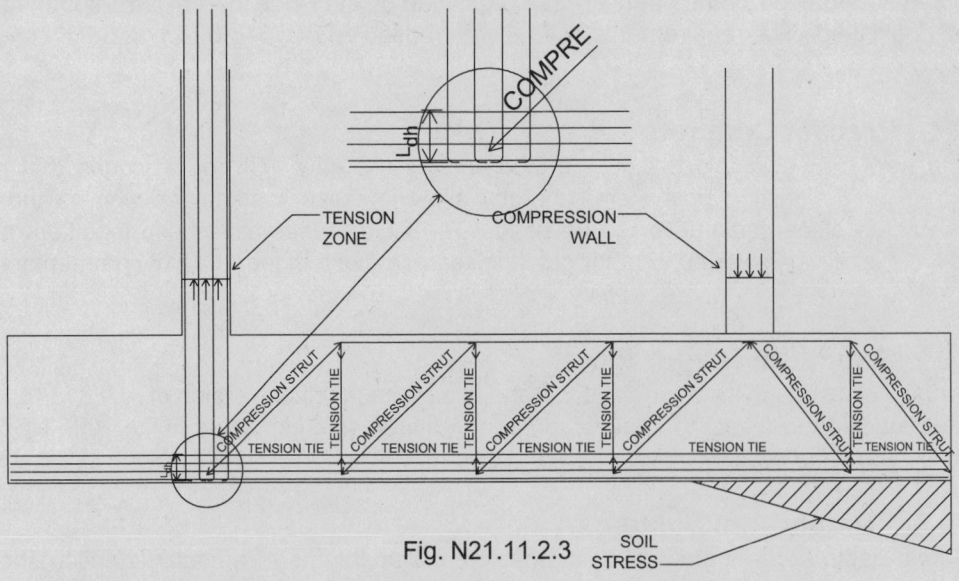

Fig. N21.11.2.3

Fig. N21.11.2.3

N21.12 Frame Members not Considered Part of the Seismic Force Resisting System

This clause is intended to give guidelines to help ensure that the parts of the structural system designed only for gravity loading will continue to function at the lateral displacements of the frame expected during the earthquake.

Examples of members covered by this clause would include members which, by virtue of their flexibility relative to other members, are not included in the primary lateral force resisting system. Other examples are beams not satisfying the dimensional limits of Clause 21.3.1 or columns not satisfying the dimensional limits of Clause 21.4.1. The members need to either be strong enough to tolerate the design displacement in an elastic manner, or the members must be detailed so the plastic hinges can occur without shear or compression failure.

N21.12.1 General

N21.12.1.1

The building envelope failures experienced in the West Coast have encouraged the use of additional concrete elements on buildings as part of the envelope system that are not part of either the gravity or the seismic force resisting systems. These elements have the potential to compromise the gravity and/or the seismic force resisting systems when the building is deformed to the design displacement. This clause provides steps that need to be taken so a solution to one problem does not jeopardize the buildings seismic safety.

N21.12.1.2

This clause outlines the basic principle that provides the basis of the remaining clauses: all components of the structure shall be designed to accommodate plastic hinging unless it can be shown that the maximum forces induced in the members will not exceed the nominal resistances of those members. The influence of the inelastic displacement pattern of the SFRS needs to be accounted for when estimating the forces induced in the gravity frame members

It is anticipated that a mathematical model of the complete building structural system is required which will include the SFRS as well as those portions of the building "going along for the ride". A linear model can only be used when the elastic displacement pattern is very similar to the inelastic pattern. An example is buildings with uniform moment resisting frame SFRS. A linear model of a shear wall system will not provide a reasonable estimate of the forces in the gravity frame over the plastic hinge height but will provide a conservative estimate over the remaining height. The plastic hinge height requires a non-linear analysis or, alternatively, a simplified procedure that accounts for the plastic hinge deformations such as the one outlined below may be used. Consideration should also be given to the effects of possible foundation rotation and/or "rocking" which may have been a significant factor in the failure of some parking garages in the Northridge earthquake.

A simplified analysis can be done for gravity columns in shear wall buildings by assuming the maximum curvature induced in the gravity columns is equal to the maximum curvature demand in the concrete walls controlling the inelastic deformations of the building.[†] Thus the curvature capacity of the gravity columns must be equal to or greater than the curvature demand on the wall. The maximum compression strain depth c of an unconfined concrete column can be determined from the maximum compression strain depth c permitted in a wall according to Eq. 21-11 in Clause 21.6.7.3 so that the inelastic rotational capacity θ_{ic} of the wall is equal to or greater than the inelastic rotational demand θ_{id}. See N21.6.7.3 for a simplified method to calculate the maximum compression strain depth c. For columns with concrete strengths up to 40

[†] *Reference: Adebar, P. "High-rise concrete wall buildings: utilizing unconfined concrete for seismic resistance," CONMAT 05 Conference Proceedings, Vancouver, Aug. 2005.*

MPa, the maximum compression strain depth *c* of a column is equal to the maximum compression strain depth *c* of the wall. When the concrete strength is 80 MPa, the maximum compression strain depth *c* must be reduced to 88% of the value for a wall due to the reduced compression strain capacity of higher strength concrete. Between 40 and 80 MPa, the maximum compression strain depth in a column can be determined by linear interpolation between 100 and 88% of the maximum compression strain depth of a wall.

This clause also provides a default procedure which can be followed to avoid the detailed analysis of the effects on all members at the design displacement.

N21.12.1.3
The intent of this clause is to provide each member with sufficient capacity to prevent a collapse under gravity loads at the design displacement. It is important to check both one way and two-way shear capacity as well as induced compressions since the development of flexural hinges in lightly reinforced horizontal members may be tolerable, but a shear or an axial compression failure is not. Columns with more than light axial compression cannot tolerate significant inelastic rotations and deserve special care.

N21.12.2   Plastic Hinges in Members
The intent here is to separate the members of the structure not part of the lateral force resisting system into three detailing categories depending on the level of ductility demand. See Fig. N21.12.2 for a graphical illustration of these clauses.

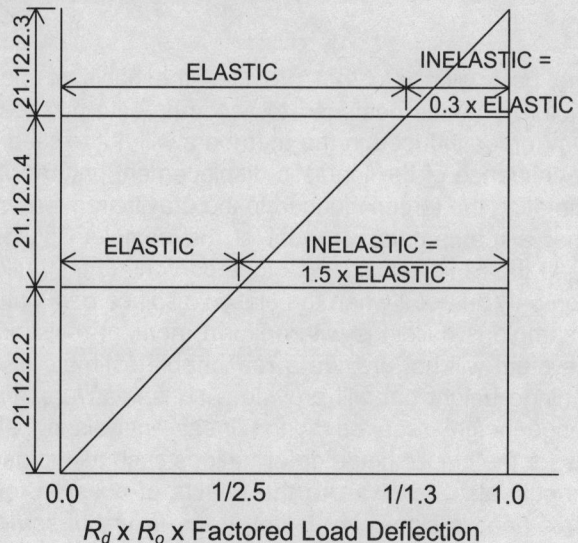

Fig. N21.12.2

N21.12.2.2
If plastic hinges start to form at 40% (1/2.5) of the expected displacement then the element will experience a large ductility demand and must be detailed accordingly.

N21.12.2.3
If plastic hinges have not started at 77% (1/1.3) of the expected displacement then the element ductility demand will be moderate and the standard detailing inherent in the Standard is sufficient.

N21.12.2.4
This section covers the intermediate cases.

N21.12.3   Slab Column Connections

This is a new clause that is meant to prevent punching shear failures of flat slabs around columns in buildings subjected to significant earthquake deformations. Such punching shear failures resulted in un-repairable damage in the Northridge earthquake and could lead to complete collapse of slabs with insufficient integrity reinforcement. The provision considers the interaction between gravity load shear stress in the slab and the interstorey drift demand on the slab column connection as first proposed by Pan, A., and Moehle, J.P., "Lateral Displacement Ductility of Reinforced Concrete Flat Plates, " *ACI Structural Journal*, 86(3), 1989. It is expected that this new provision will increase the use of shear reinforcement in flat slab construction in high seismic areas for tall or flexible buildings.

N21.12.3.1

Equation 21-23 gives the reduction factor R_E to be applied to the concrete contribution for reinforced concrete slabs given in Clause 13.3.4 and the concrete contribution for prestressed concrete slabs given in Clause 18.12.3.3. When the factored shear stress $v_f = V_f/b_o d$ exceeds the reduced concrete contribution, transverse shear reinforcement shall be provided in the slab.

When the interstory drift ratio $\delta_i \leq 0.005$, the reduction factor $R_E = 1.0$, and when the interstorey drift ratio is the maximum value permitted by 2005 NBCC ($\delta_i = 0.025$), the reduction factor $R_E = 0.25$.

Fig. N21.12.3.1 compares Eq. 21-23 with test results from loaded slabs subjected to lateral displacements. All tests were on slabs without shear reinforcement except those by Dilger & Cao (1991), which had shear studs. The slabs with transverse shear reinforcement clearly show a marked increase in drift capacity.

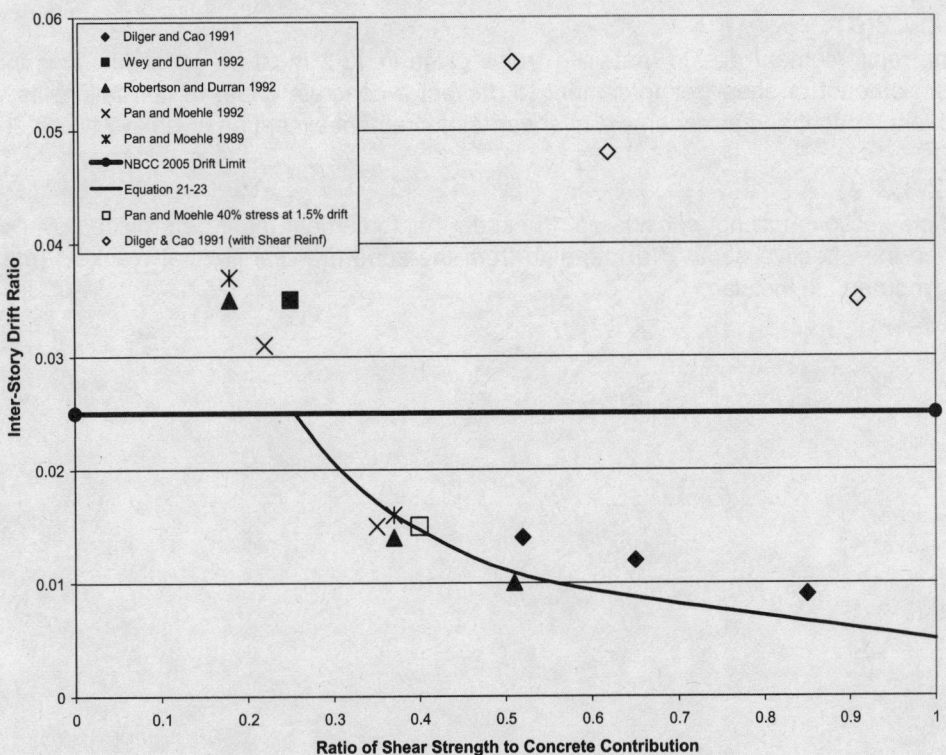

Drift Ratios With and Without Shear Reinforcement

Legend:
- ◆ Dilger and Cao 1991
- ■ Wey and Durran 1992
- ▲ Robertson and Durran 1992
- ✕ Pan and Moehle 1992
- ✱ Pan and Moehle 1989
- ●— NBCC 2005 Drift Limit
- — Equation 21-23
- ☐ Pan and Moehle 40% stress at 1.5% drift
- ◇ Dilger & Cao 1991 (with Shear Reinf)

Y-axis: Inter-Story Drift Ratio
X-axis: Ratio of Shear Strength to Concrete Contribution

Fig. N21.12.3.1

N21.12.3.2

When the concrete contribution to shear strength – reduced to account for damage due to interstorey drift demand on the slab column connection – is not adequate to resist the applied gravity load shear stresses, then either the interstorey drift demand must be reduced by increasing the stiffness of the SFRS, or transverse shear reinforcement must be provided in the slab. This clause specifies the procedure to be used to design shear reinforcement in the slab.

N21.12.3.2(a)

The same reduction factor R_E given by Eq. 21-23 is used to reduce the total shear strength of a slab with shear reinforcement to account for the damage due to interstorey drift demand. In addition, the concrete contribution used to calculate the shear strength of a slab with shear reinforcement is reduced by 50% from the expressions given in Clauses 13 and 18. Sufficient shear reinforcement must be provided so that the reduced shear strength is greater than the factored shear stress $v_f = V_f/b_o d$ due to gravity load only.

As damage due to interstorey drift will be concentrated in the zone of initial flexural cracking (maximum bending moment) in the slab, only one critical section need be considered. That is, a section outside the region defined in 21.12.3.2(e) need not be considered.

N21.12.3.2(b)

This clause specifies the minimum amount of transverse shear reinforcement.

N21.12.3.2(c)

An arrangement of shear reinforcement that satisfies both the seismic requirements of 21.12.3 and the non-seismic requirements of 13.3 must be provided.

N21.12.3.2(d)

All of the reinforcement design (detailing) rules given in 13.3 must be satisfied. This includes: maximum amount of shear reinforcement to prevent a concrete compression failure as well as spacing, anchorage, and arrangement of shear reinforcement except as given in 21.12.3.2(e).

N21.12.3.2(e)

As multiple sections are not considered, the shear reinforcement must be provided over at least four times the effective depth d of the slab from the zone of initial flexural cracking (maximum bending moment) in the slab.

N22.1 Scope

Since the structural integrity of plain concrete members depends solely on the properties of the concrete, their use should be limited to: members that are primarily in a state of compression; members that can tolerate random cracks without detriment to their structural integrity; and members where ductility is not an essential feature of design. The standard does not permit the use of plain concrete columns or plain concrete beams.

The minimum concrete strength for plain concrete is not limited to 20 MPa because there is no concern for bond strength and corrosion protection of reinforcement. See Cl. 8.6.1.3. In many circumstances the minimum concrete strength will be governed by the durability provisions of CSA-A23.1. However, even when concrete durability does not restrict the minimum strength it would be normal to use strengths exceeding 15 MPa in order to achieve reasonably homogeneous concrete with adequate cement so that the concrete can be finished satisfactorily. (ACI 318-05 prescribes a minimum of 17 MPa for plain concrete).

New in the A23.3-04 edition is Clause 22.8 on Drilled Piles.

N22.2 Control Joints

Construction joints are a very important design consideration. Control joints are not required if the random cracking resulting from creep, shrinkage and temperature effects will not affect the structural integrity and is otherwise acceptable (e.g. in a continuous wall footing transverse control joints may not be necessary).

Control joints may be made with sheet metal or sheet plastic inserts, "water-stop" inserts, rubber inserts or formed, sawed, or tooled grooves in the concrete surface to cause cracking at the predetermined location. The thickness of the concrete section at these inserts or grooves should be reduced at least 25 percent to make the control joint effective. It is good practice to form joints only part way through the member so that aggregate interlock in the remaining concrete can hold the elements in line. Adjacent elements may be held in line by the use of appropriately aligned, free-sliding dowels protected against corrosion.

N22.3 Design

Plain concrete members are proportioned for adequate strength by using factored forces and by keeping computed stresses within permissible stress limits for all loading conditions.

N22.4 Walls

Eqs. (22-1) and (22-2) have been revised slightly so that they are consistent with each other. A triangular stress block with a maximum stress of $0.75\ \phi_c f_c'$ and a width equal to the wall thickness will have the resistance given by Eq. (22-2) and a force located within the middle third of the wall. The revised coefficient of 0.75 in A23.3-04 has been used to accommodate the revised ϕ_c factor of 0.65. The maximum tensile stress has been revised in a similar fashion.

N22.6.3

The reduced overall thickness for concrete cast against earth is to allow for unevenness of excavation and for some contamination of the concrete adjacent to the soil.

N22.6.6   Shear Resistance

Shear failure in plain concrete will be a diagonal tension failure occurring when the principal tensile stress near the centroidal axis reaches the tensile strength of the concrete.

Plain concrete members of usual proportions will be controlled by flexural tensile strength rather than shear strength.

For other than rectangular sections the following expression should be used in place of Eq.(22-3).

$$V_r = 0.18 \lambda \phi_c \sqrt{f'_c} \left(\frac{I\,b}{Q} \right)$$

N22.6.6.2.1

The critical sections for shear in plain concrete footings are the same as those shown in Fig. N15.5.2(a) except that d is replaced by h.

N22.6.6.2.2

The coefficients in equations 22-4 and 22-5 have been modified to accommodate the revised $\phi_c = 0.65$ and the coefficient for shear is increased from 2/3 to 3/4 based on the maximum elastic principal tension stress in a circular section, which is 4/3 times the average.

~NOTES~

PART II

Concrete Design Information

with

Design Examples

and

Design Aids

1

By J.G. MacGregor
M. Saatcioglu
S. Cumming
R. J. McGrath

General

General

1.1   Design Method

1.1.1   General

The objective of structural design and construction is to produce safe, serviceable, economic, durable and aesthetic structures. Each of these attributes will be examined more fully here or in other parts of this Handbook.

Safety - Structures must be able to withstand the loads acting on them during a reasonable lifetime. This is accomplished, first and foremost, by a careful selection of the structural system and a clear understanding of how that system will behave under load. This involves identifying and considering possible failure modes during construction and during the life of the structure. Once the structure is chosen, load factors and resistance factors are used in the proportioning of the members to minimize the risk arising from overloads and understrength elements. Care must be taken to avoid gross errors in the design process and in the construction process.

During its life the building should have adequate structural integrity to be able to adapt to unforeseen influences and localized damages without major spread of damage or collapse. This is discussed more fully in Section 1.6 of this Handbook. Similarly, building codes require that structures have specified minimum fire resistances so that they will retain their strength long enough for evacuation of occupants and for fire-fighting operations to be carried out. Design for fire is discussed in Section 1.4 of this Handbook.

Serviceability - In addition to having adequate strength building structures must behave in a satisfactory manner in service. They should not deflect excessively or vibrate excessively and those cracks which occur should not impair the function or the aesthetics of the structure.

Economy - Among other things, a project is judged by its first costs, its lifelong performance and the construction time. In many cases the structure forms a small part of the total cost of a project. Similarly, the cost of concrete and reinforcement form only a fraction of the cost of the structure. For these reasons, optimizing the structure itself may not lead to the most economical project. During the design process it is essential to consider construction costs and maintenance costs.

Durability - Durable structures survive exposure to the environment and corrosive agents and in doing so, maintenance costs are reduced. Inadequate durability has led to rusting reinforcement, spalling concrete and general deterioration of structures. Section 1.5 of this Handbook reviews the factors affecting durability.

Aesthetics - Buildings and bridges should have an attractive appearance and complement their surroundings. Concrete, as a material, allows a wide range of structural and architectural shapes and a wide range of surface treatments which can be used to develop pleasing buildings and bridges.

1.1.2   Load and Resistance Factors

The CSA Standard A23.3-04 "Design of Concrete Structures" has adopted the newly revised load factors and load combinations specified in the 2005 edition of the National Building Code of Canada. The resistance factors contained in CSA A23.3 Standard are applied to material strengths as noted in Section 1.1.4.

1.1.3   Effect of Factored Loads

Definitions and Magnitudes of Loads

The various loads to be considered in design are defined in Section 4.1 of the National Building Code of Canada. They are:

D = dead loads, as provided for in Subsection 4.1.4.

Subsection 4.1.4. Dead Loads

4.1.4.1 Dead Loads

(1)   The specified dead load for a structural member consists of
    a)   the weight of the member itself,
    b)   the weight of all materials of construction incorporated into the building to be supported permanently by the member,
    c)   the weight of partitions,
    d)   the weight of permanent equipment, and
    e)   the vertical load due to earth, plants and trees.

2)   Except as provided in Sentence (5), in areas of a building where partitions other than permanent partitions are shown on the drawings, or where partitions might be added in the future, allowance shall be made for the weight of such partitions.

3)   The partition weight allowance in Sentence (2) shall be determined from the actual or anticipated weight of the partitions placed in any probable position, but shall be not less than 1 kPa over the area of floor being considered.

4)   Partition loads used in design shall be shown on the drawings as provided in Clause 2.2.4.3.(1)(d) of Division C.

5)   In cases where the partition dead load is counteractive, the load allowances as provided in Sentences (2) and (3) shall not be included in the design calculations.

6)   Except for structures where the dead load of soils is part of the load resisting system, where dead load due to soil, superimposed earth, plants and trees is counteractive, it shall not be included in the design calculations. (See Appendix A).

Dead loads are computed from the specified dimensions and the densities of materials. Tables of the unit mass of construction materials are given in Section 1.7 of this Handbook.

Dead loads include an allowance for permanent and movable partitions as described in Clauses 4.1.4.1(2) through (5). Note that 4.1.4.1(5) implies that partition loads are applied in the pattern that gives the largest effect.

Note that NBC Clause 4.1.3.2.3 applies a load factor of 1.0 to prestressing forces and the effects of prestressing. This NBC Clause is reproduced in CSA A23.3-04 Annex "C" under C.1.2.3.

L......live load - a variable load due to intended use and occupancy (including loads due to cranes and pressure of liquids in containers) as specified in Subsection 4.1.5.,

The live loads for use and occupancy specified by the NBC are given in Section 1.7 of this Handbook. These are selected as a high fractile of the loading distributions. Similarly, the specified loads due to snow, ice and rain represent a high fractile of the statistical distributions of these loads, typically 2% chance in 50 that the load will be exceeded in any given year. The National Building Code does not indicate whether the earth pressure should be a high fractile or a mean value. Hydrostatic pressure is normally computed as a mean value for fluids of known density.

W = wind load - a variable load due to wind as specified in Subsection 4.1.7 of the NBC.

E = earthquake load and effects – a rare load due to earthquake as specified in Subsection 4.1.8. of the NBC.

1

T = effects due to contraction, expansion, or deflection caused by temperature changes, shrinkage, moisture changes, creep, temperature, ground settlement, or combination thereof, (see Appendix A on the NBC)

This last category of loading (T) differs from the others in that it results from an imposed deformation. Since it is not caused by an external load, the resulting moments, forces and stresses must be self-equilibrating. Their magnitude is a function of the rigidity of the structure. If the structure becomes less rigid due to cracking, the stressed due to T loads will generally decrease. On one hand, this helps the structural engineer since he may be able to count on cracking or creep to dissipate T stresses. On the other hand however, the cracking which is required for this to occur may be unacceptable.

Load Factors and Load Combinations

A23.3 Clause 8.3.2 refers the designer back to the applicable building code for factored loads and factored load combinations. The 2005 NBCC has adopted a "companion load" approach. Table 4.1.3.2 "Load Combinations for Ultimate Limit States": from the 2005 NBCC is shown below.

Table 4.1.3.2.
Load Combinations for Ultimate Limit States
Forming Part of Sentence 4.1.3.2.(2).

Case	Load Combination[1]	
	Principal Loads	**Companion Loads[2]**
1	$1.4D$	—
2	$(1.25D^{(3)}$ or $0.9D^{(4)}) + 1.5L^{(5)}$	$0.5S^{(6)}$ or $0.4W$
3	$(1.25D^{(3)}$ or $0.9D^{(4)}) + 1.5S$	$0.5L^{(6)(7)}$ or $0.4W$
4	$(1.25D^{(3)}$ or $0.9D^{(4)}) + 1.4W$	$0.5L^{(7)}$ or $0.5S$
5	$1.0D^{(4)} + 1.0E^{(8)}$	$0.5L^{(6)(7)} + 0.25S^{(6)}$

Notes to Table 4.1.3.2.
  (1) See Sentences 4.1.3.2.(2) and (3)
  (2) See Appendix A.
  (3) See Sentence 4.1.3.2.(7)
  (4) See Sentence 4.1.3.2.(4)
  (5) See Sentence 4.1.3.2.(5)
  (6) See Article 4.1.5.5
  (7) See Sentence 4.1.3.2.(6)
  (8) See Sentence 4.1.3.2.(8)

1) A building and its structural components shall be designed to have sufficient strength and stability so that the factored resistance, (R, is greater than or equal to the effect of factored loads, where the effect of factored loads shall be determined in accordance with Sentence 4.1.3.2.(2).

2) The effect of factored loads for a building or structural component shall be determined in accordance with the load combinations listed in Table 4.1.3.2 and the requirements of Article 4.1.3.2., the applicable combination being that which results in the most critical effect. (See Appendix A.)

3)   Where the effects due to lateral earth pressure H, restraint effects from prestress P and imposed deformation T affect the structural safety, they shall be taken into account in the calculations, H with a load factor of 1.5, P with a load factor 1.0 and T with a load factor of 1.25. (See Appendix A.)

4)   Except as provided in Sentence 4.1.8.16.(1), the counteracting factored dead load, 0.9D in load combinations (2), (3) and (4) and 1.0D in load combination (5) shall be used when dead load acts to resist overturning, uplift, sliding, failure due to stress reversal, and to determine anchorage requirements and factored member resistances. (See Appendix A.)

5)   The principal-load factor 1.5 for live load L in Table 4.1.3.2 may be reduced to 1.25 for liquids in tanks.

6)   The companion-load factor 0.5 for live load L in Table 4.1.3.2 shall be increased to 1.0 for storage occupancies, and equipment areas and service rooms in Table 4.1.5.3.

7)   The load factor 1.25 for dead load D for soil, superimposed earth, plants and trees in Table 4.1.3.2 shall be increased to 1.5, except that when the soil depth exceeds 1.2m, the factor may be reduced to $1+0.6/h_s$, but not less than 1.25, where h_s is the depth of soil in metres supported by the structure.

8)   Earthquake load E in load combinations (6) and (7) of Table 4.1.3.2 includes horizontal earth pressure due to earthquake determined in accordance with Sentence 4.1.8.16.(4).

9)   Provision shall be made to ensure adequate stability of a structure as a whole, and adequate lateral, torsional and local stability of all structural parts.

10)   Sway effects produced by vertical loads acting on the structure in its displaced configuration shall be taken into account in the design of buildings and their structural members.

Effect of Factored Loads

Clause 8.3.2 of CSA Standard A23.3-04 uses the term "effect of factored loads" to refer to the moments, axial forces, shears, and torques calculated for the combinations of factored loads specified in the applicable building code.

For problems which do not involve second-order effects (slenderness or PΔ effects in columns or frames), the analysis can either be based on factored loads, giving factored load effects directly, or on unfactored loads, giving unfactored load effects which must then be factored when they are combined. On the other hand, when second-order effects are significant, these effects are affected by the magnitude of the loads and hence the loads must be factored prior to carrying out the analysis.

The symbols M_f, V_f, P_f, T_f, etc. refer to moments, shears, axial forces and torques due to the factored loads. Thus, the subscript "f" signifies a load effect due to factored loads.

1.1.4   Factored Resistance

The 2004 edition of the CSA A23.3 Standard has retained the same method of expressing resistance factors as in the 1994 edition, where the resistance factor is applied to the material strength, $\phi_c f_c'$, or $\phi_s f_y$, rather than to the nominal resistance, ϕM_n, ϕV_n, etc.

Resistance factors account for a number of factors causing variability in strengths. These include:

(a)   Variability in the strengths of concrete and reinforcement,
(b)   Variability in dimensions,

(c)   Approximations in the design equations,

(d)   Mode of failure, brittle or ductile and the resulting warning of failure.

The resistance factor for steel, ϕ_s, accounts for variability of the strength of reinforcement and to a lesser extent the variability in d, etc. resulting from placement tolerances for reinforcement. Similarly, the variability of the strength of concrete and dimensions of concrete are reflected in the resistance factor for concrete, ϕ_c. The brittle nature of failures initiated by failure of the concrete and the higher variability of design equations for failure initiated by failure of the concrete (the shear V_c, for example) were accounted for by using a higher safety index when evaluating the value of ϕ_c than for ϕ_s.

Values of Resistance Factors

A23.3 Clauses 8.4.2 and 8.4.3 give the values of the resistance factors:

8.4.2 - The factored concrete strengths used in checking ultimate limit states shall be taken as $\phi_c f_c'$ and $\phi_c \sqrt{f_c'}$ where $\phi_c = 0.65$. This resistance factor has been increased from 0.60 in the 1994 edition of the A23.3 Standard.

8.4.3 - The factored force in reinforcing bars, tendons, and structural shapes shall be taken as the product of the resistance factor, ϕ, and the respective steel force as specified in other Clauses of this Standard, where

$\phi_s = 0.85$ for reinforcing bars

$\phi_p = 0.85$ for prestressing tendons

$\phi_s = 0.90$ for structural steel

Clause 16.1.3 of CSA Standard A23.3 now permits the use of $\phi_c = 0.70$ for precast elements manufactured and erected in accordance with the requirements of CSA Standard A23.4. This factor has been increased from 0.65 in the 1994 edition of the A23.3 Standard.

Use of Resistance Factors

The resistance factors ϕ_c, ϕ_s, ϕ_p, and ϕ_a are included in the equations for calculating the factored resistances, M_r, V_r, P_r, T_r, etc. The subscripts "r" in these notations refer to "factored resistance".

When concrete is used in compression its strength is taken as $\phi_c f_c'$. In defining the equivalent rectangular stress block Clause 10.1.7 states that a concrete stress of $\alpha_1 \phi_c f_c'$ shall be used. When properties related to the concrete tensile strength are used in calculations, as in the calculation of V_c in Clause 11.3, the tensile strength is taken as a function of $\phi_c \sqrt{f_c'}$

Clause 8.4.3 and 8.5.3.2 require that when determining the factored resistance of bars and tendons, the resistance factor, ϕ_s be applied to the bar force, $\phi_s A_s f_y$ or $\phi_s A_s E_s \varepsilon_s$, regardless of whether the steel has yield or not. The reason for this is that ϕ_s takes into account deviation in the location of the reinforcement and uncertainty in the prediction of resistance as well as variability in yield strength.

In addition to ϕ_c, ϕ_s and ϕ_p a member resistance factor ϕ_m is used in slender column calculations in Clause 10.15 and for certain brittle members in Clause 21.

Resistance factors ϕ_s, ϕ_c and ϕ_p are not included in equations giving empirical limits, such as Eq. 10-26 in Clause 10.18.2 or in the equations in Clause 12. In the latter case it was recognized that the equations in Clause 12 were empirical in nature and implicitly included a safety margin. The expression for the modulus of elasticity of concrete in Clause 8.6.2.2 does not include ϕ_c. When E_c is used in stability calculations in Clause 10.15 and 10.16 the variability of EI and P_c is taken into account using a member resistance factor ϕ_m.

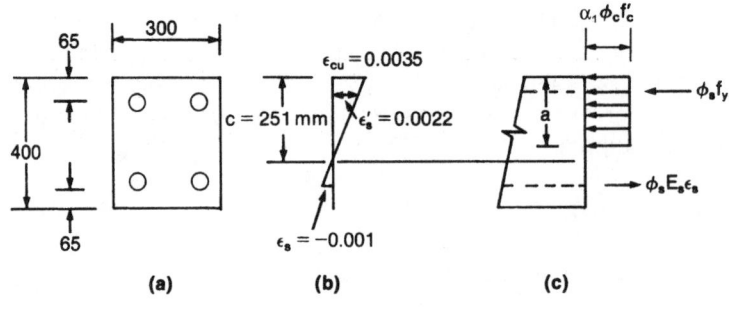

Fig. 1.1

1.2   Structural Concrete

1.2.1   General

Performance of reinforced concrete structures is significantly influenced by the quality of concrete. Structural concrete is affected by the properties of constituent materials and the proportions in which they are mixed. Requirements for proportioning and producing quality concrete as well as acceptance tests for the constituent materials are specified in CSA Standards A23.1 and A23.4 for cast-in-place and precast concrete respectively.

Fig. 1.2 illustrates the range in proportions of materials used in producing concrete. The mass density of concrete is dependent on the aggregates, which constitute 60-80 percent of the total volume. Fine aggregates consisting of natural or manufactured sand, and coarse aggregates consisting of crushed stone, gravel or air-cooled iron blast-furnace slag are used to produce "Normal Density Concrete" with a mass density of about 2400 kg/m^3. Low density aggregates are used to produce "Structural Low Density Concrete" with a mass density not exceeding 1850 kg/m^3. Sometimes normal density fine aggregate is mixed with low density coarse aggregate to produce "Structural Semi Low Density Concrete" having a mass density between 1850 and 2150 kg/ m^3. Occasionally high density aggregates are used to produce "High Density Concrete" for special applications.

Cement	Water	Air	Fine Agg.	Coarse Agg.
7-15%	14-18%	4-8%	24-28%	31-51%

**Fig. 1.2 Proportions of Constituent Materials
by Absolute Volume - Air Entrained Concrete**

In a properly mixed concrete, each particle of aggregate is coated with cement and water paste. Cement, in the presence of water, hydrates and hardens, binding the aggregate particles, to form a solid rocklike mass. The quality of cement paste largely depends on the water-cement ratio. Excess water in the paste reduces concrete quality in terms of strength, watertightness, abrasion resistance and durability.

Five types of Portland cement conforming to CSA Standard A3001 are available for structural use. Type GU, General Use Portland Cement is used in general concrete construction when the special properties or the other types are not required. The cement types and their effects on concrete are summarized in Table 1.1.

1.2.2   Strength and Elastic Modulus

One of the most important properties of structural concrete is its compressive strength. Other properties of concrete, required in structural design, can approximately be expressed in terms of compressive strength f_c'. Therefore, the structural engineer is required to specify f_c' on the drawings or in related specifications. Unless otherwise specified, f_c' is based on the 28-day strength. Generally the concrete strengths used in structural applications vary between 20 MPa and 40 MPa. Higher strength concretes may be used for special applications and in prestressed concrete constructions.

Low density concrete can be used for structural purposes only if the 28 day strength is in excess of 20 MPa. If the structural low density concrete is to be used for earthquake resistant design, the maximum concrete strength is limited to 30 MPa by Clause 21.2.6.2 of CSA Standard A23.3.

Concrete strength is usually determined by testing either 100 X 200 mm cylinders or 150 X 300 mm cylinders under axial compression. Two cylinders are tested at 28 days, and the average of the two results is used as f_c' provided that neither of the cylinders shows a sign of defect. The specimens are prepared in accordance with CSA Test Method A23.2-3C and tested in accordance with CSA Test Method A23.2-9C.

Typical stress-strain relationships obtained from the standard cylinder tests are shown in Fig. 1.3. Test indicate that the ultimate concrete strain recorded at failure varies from 0.003 to as high as 0.008. However, CSA Standard A23.3 limits the maximum usable compressive strain conservatively to 0.0035.

Modulus of elasticity is another important property of concrete that is often used in structural design to compute deformations. Generally the modulus of elasticity is a secant modulus based on the stress and strain at about 50% of f_c'. CSA Standard A23.3 provides an empirical equation for concrete modulus of elasticity based on the secant modulus. Accordingly,

$$E_c = \left(3300 + \sqrt{f_c'} + 6900\right)\left(\frac{(\gamma_c)}{2300}\right)^{1.5} \tag{1.8}$$

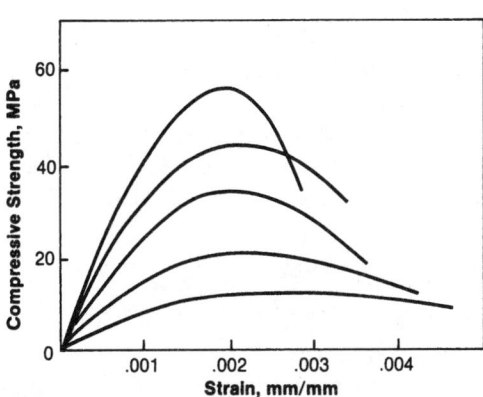

Fig. 1.3 Concrete Stress-Strain Relationships Obtained From Standard Cylinder Tests

where γ is the mass density of concrete in kg/m^3 and f_c' is the compressive strength of concrete in MPa. The above equation is provided for values of γ_c between 1500 and 2500 kg/m^3. For normal density concrete with strengths between 20 and 40 MPa, Ec may be taken as 4500 (where f'_c is in MPa).

1.2.3   Creep and Shrinkage

Creep of concrete is defined as the time dependent increase in strain under sustained loading. Other time dependent deformations are generally attributed to shrinkage and temperature changes in concrete.

Creep is usually expressed in terms of the creep coefficient C_t, defined as the ratio of creep strain ε_{cr} to initial immediate strain ε_i. Creep strain increases with time at a decreasing rate. This is illustrated in Fig. 1.4.

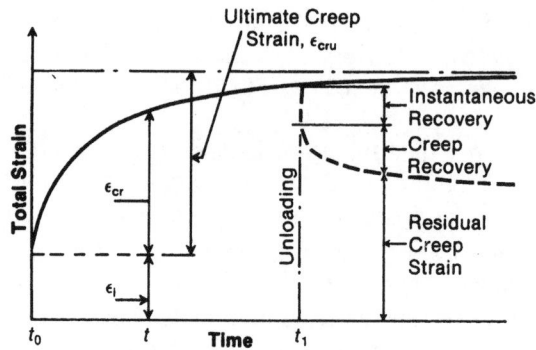

Fig. 1.4 Variation of Creep with Time

A commonly accepted procedure to determine the creep coefficient is to follow the ACI Committee 209 recommendation[*]. The following expression given by ACI Committee 209 is applicable to normal, semi-low and low density concretes.

$$C_t = \frac{t^{0.6}}{10 + t^{0.6}} C_u Q_{cr} \tag{1.9}$$

where t is time in days after loading, and C_u is the ultimate creep coefficient and varies between 1.30 and 4.15. In the absence of specific creep data for local aggregates and conditions, the average value suggested for C_u is 2.35.

The above equation was developed for sustained compressive stress not exceeding 50% of concrete strength. It consists of an expression for creep under standard conditions multiplied by the correction factor Q_{cr} to modify for non-standard conditions. The standard conditions and the correction factor Q_{cr} are specified in Table 1.2.

Shrinkage is the decrease in the volume of hardened concrete with time. Unlike creep, shrinkage is independent of externally applied loads. The decrease in volume is mainly attributed to the moisture loss caused by drying and hydration as well as the chemical changes that result in the carbonation of cement hydration products.

Shrinkage strains start taking place immediately after exposing concrete to drying environment. Fig. 1.5 illustrates the variation of shrinkage with time. According to ACI Committee

---

[*] "Prediction of Creep, Shrinkage, and Temperature Effects in Concrete Structures", Reported by ACI Committee 209, Report No. ACI 209R-92. American Concrete Institute, Special Publication SP-76, 1982, pp. 143-300.

209, the shrinkage strain ε_{sh} is determined using the expression given in Equation 1.10. This expression is applicable to normal, semi-low and low density concretes.

$$\varepsilon_{sh} = \frac{t}{C_s + t}\varepsilon_{shu}P_{sh}$$

(1.10)

where t is time in days starting immediately after the initial wet curing. C_s is equal to 35 if concrete is moist cured for 7 days, and 55 if steam cured for 1-3 days. ε_{shu} is the ultimate shrinkage strain. In the absence of specific shrinkage data for local conditions, the average value of ε_{shu} suggested for use is 0.00078 mm/mm. P_{sh} is a correction factor for conditions that are other than the standard conditions specified in Table 1.2. The values of P_{sh} can be obtained from the same table.

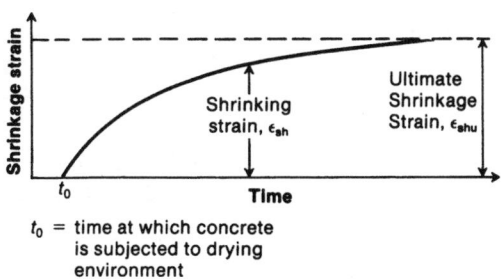

t_0 = time at which concrete is subjected to drying environment

Fig. 1.5: Variation of Shrinkage Strain with Time

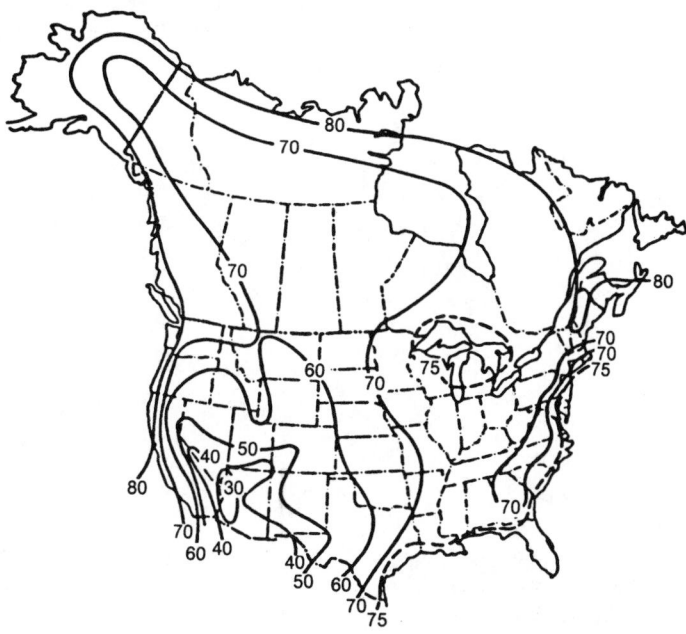

Fig. 1.6: Annual Average A,boemt Relative Humidity (%)
(Reproduced from CPCI Design Manual)

Concrete creep and shrinkage are both sensitive to environmental factors such as relative humidity and temperature. The effect of relative humidity on creep and shrinkage is empirically considered in Eqs. (1.9) and (1.10) through correction factors Q_{cr} and P_{sh}. The effect of temperature is usually considered to be less important than relative humidity. The expressions for creep and shrinkage given in this section are based on concrete temperature of $23 \pm 2°C$. It has been shown that structures exposed to high temperature for an extended period of time experience higher creep strains. At 50°C, creep strain is approximately two to three times the creep strain at 19° to 24°C. Where temperature effects may be a significant design factor, it is recommended an in-depth determination be made to establish more exact values of creep and shrinkage.

The creep coefficient and shrinkage strain given by Eqs. (1-9) and (1-10) are meant for unreinforced, unstrained concrete. In reinforced concrete members, time-dependent deformations are restrained by the reinforcement. While the procedure described in this section provides acceptable results for lightly reinforced members, its application to most reinforced concrete members is questionable. A proper adjustment to these values is recommended to account for the effect of reinforcement. Empirical equations are available for this purpose.

Long term deformations due to creep and shrinkage can be several times the initial deformation. According to CSA Standard A23.3, the total deflection, including long term effects, can be as high as 3.0 times the immediate initial deflection, depending on the percentage of reinforcement and the time for which deflection is computed.

Shrinkage strain alone is in the order of 0.0002 to 0.0008 mm/mm. In reinforced concrete structures with commonly used percentages of reinforcement, the shrinkage strain is in the range of 0.0002 to 0.0003 mm/mm.

Example

A prestressed concrete beam with 8.0 m span and 400 mm by 600 mm rectangular cross-section is pretensioned using 15 Grade 1860 size 11 seven wire strands. The steel stress after transfer is 1300 MPa. If the beam is prestressed immediately after seven days of moist curing, determine the shortening in the beam 60 days after the moist curing, when it is erected for a structure in Calgary. Use the following concrete properties:

Concrete strength at 7 days	: 30 MPa
Air content	: 5%
Slump	: 100 mm
Fine aggregate	: 670 kg/m^3
Coarse aggregate	: 1000 kg/m^3
Type GU cement	: 400 kg/m^3

Solution

i.   Elastic concrete strain (ε_i):

$A_{ps} = (15)\,(74.2) = 1113$ mm^2
$P_o = (1300)\,(1113) = 1447 \times 103$ N
$P_o/A = 1447 \times 103/(400 \times 600) = 6.0$ MPa
$E_c = 5000\,\sqrt{30} = 27400$ MPa
$\varepsilon_i = 6.0\,/\,27400 = 219 \times 10^{-6}$ mm/mm

ii.   Creep and shrinkage modification factors, from Table 1.2:

Age at loading: 7 days, moist cured

$Q_a = 1.00$

Relative humidity: 70% for Calgary from Fig. 1.6

$Q_h = 0.80$
$P_h = 0.70$

Ratio of fine to total aggregate:

$$\frac{670}{670 + 1000} = 0.40mm$$

$Q_f = 0.98$
$P_h = 0.86$

Volume surface ratio: $\dfrac{(400)(600)}{2(400) + 2(600)} = 120mm$

$Q_f = 0.75$
$P_f = 0.69$

Slump: 100 mm

$Q_s = 1.08$
$P_s = 1.05$

Air %: 5

$Q_v = 1.00$
$P_v = 1.00$

Cement content: 400 kg/m^3

$P_c = 0.99$
$Q_{cr} = Q_a\, Q_h\, Q_f\, Q_r\, Q_s\, Q_v$
    $= (1.00)\,(0.80)\,(0.98)\,(0.75)\,(1.08)\,(1.00)$
    $= 0.635$
$P_{sh} = P_c\, P_h\, P_f\, P_r\, P_s\, P_v$
    $= (0.99)\,(0.70)\,(0.86)\,(0.69)\,(1.05)\,(1.00)$
    $= 0.432$

iii. Creep strain (ε_{cr})

$\varepsilon_{cr} = \varepsilon_i C_t$

$$C_t = \frac{t^{0.6}}{10 + t^{0.6}}\, C_u\, Q_{cr} \qquad \text{(from Eq. 1.9)}$$

$C_u = 2.35$ \hfill (average value)

$$C_t = \frac{(60)^{0.6}}{10 + (60)^{0.6}} (2.35)(0.635) = 0.80$$

$$\varepsilon_{cr} = (219 \times 10^{-6})(0.80) = 176 \times 10^{-6} \text{ mm/mm}$$

iv.   Shrinkage strain (ε_{sh}):

$$\varepsilon_{sh} = \frac{t}{C_s + t} \, \varepsilon_{shu} \, P_{sh} \qquad\qquad\text{(from Eq. 1.10)}$$

$$C_s = 35 \qquad\qquad\qquad \text{(moist cured for 7 days)}$$

$$\varepsilon_{shu} = 0.00078 \text{ mm/mm} \qquad\qquad\qquad \text{(average value)}$$

$$\varepsilon_{sh} = \frac{60}{35 + 60}(0.00078)(0.432)$$

$$= 213 \times 10^{-6} \text{ mm/mm}$$

v.   Total shortening due to creep and shrinkage

Total strain$= \varepsilon_{cr} + \varepsilon_{sh}$

$$= 176 \times 10^{-6} \text{ mm/mm}$$

$$= (389 \times 10^{-6})(8000) = 3.1 \text{ mm}$$

1.2.4   Concrete Durability

Durability of concrete is affected by exposure conditions and the presence of chemical constituents and impurities that may react with cement. Severe weather, causing freeze-thaw cycles, may fracture the concrete. Air voids, if present in concrete, relieve the pressure caused by frozen water in concrete. Therefore, air-entrainment producing 5 to 8 percent air is strongly recommended for concretes subjected to severe exposure conditions. De-icing agents are known to accelerate freeze-thaw cycles. CSA Standard A23.1, Clause 4.1.1 provides specific requirements for durability.

Another harmful exposure condition is the soil or ground water that may have high sulphate content. The use of Type MS or Type HS cement, depending on the sulphate concentration, is recommended for protection against sulphate attack. Table 1.1 provides guidelines in selecting the cement type against sulphate action.

Certain chemical constituents and impurities that may be present in mixing water and aggregates are also potential sources of hazard to concrete. In some areas, the chemical composition of aggregate is such that it reacts with alkalies in cement, producing abnormal expansion and cracking. CSA Standard A23.1 should be consulted for the selection of mixing water and aggregates that are free of deleterious substances and organic impurities.

Structural engineers are also concerned with the durability of reinforced concrete and protection of reinforcement in concrete against corrosive environments. Calcium chloride, sometimes used as an accelerating admixture, is a potential corrosion hazard to prestressing tendons. Concrete cover requirements for different exposure conditions and the protection of reinforcement against corrosive environments are discussed in section 1.5.

1.3   Reinforcing and Prestressing Steel

1.3.1   General

The design requirements for non-prestressed reinforcement and prestressing tendons are specified in CSA Standards A23.3 and A23.1. These requirements include a minimum specified yield strength, a minimum ultimate tensile strength, ductility, and a sufficient bendability for hooks.

Non-prestressed reinforcement consists of deformed bars, deformed wire reinforcement and welded wire fabric, fabricated using smooth or deformed wires. Plain reinforcing bars may be used for spirals, and if smaller than 10 mm in diameter, may also be used for stirrups and ties.

Prestressing steel consists of high strength smooth wire, seven-wire strands and high-strength alloy bars.

1.3.2   Strength and Elastic Modulus

Reinforcement is classified on the basis of its minimum specified strength for structural purposes. In the case of non-prestressed reinforcement, minimum specified yield strength, f_y in MPa defines the grade of steel. Hot-rolled deformed and plain billet-steel reinforcing bars conforming to CSA Standard G30.18 are produced in grades 400 and 500. Weldable low alloy steel bars conforming to CSA Standard G30.18 are also produced in grades 400 and 500.

Cold-drawn wires and welded wire fabric are produced with minimum specified yield strengths ranging between 450 and 515 MPa depending on the use, size and whether the wire is deformed or smooth. Mechanical properties of wires and welded wire fabric are discussed in section 1.3.4.

Typical stress-strain relationships for hot-rolled bars and cold-drawn wires are shown in Fig.1.7.

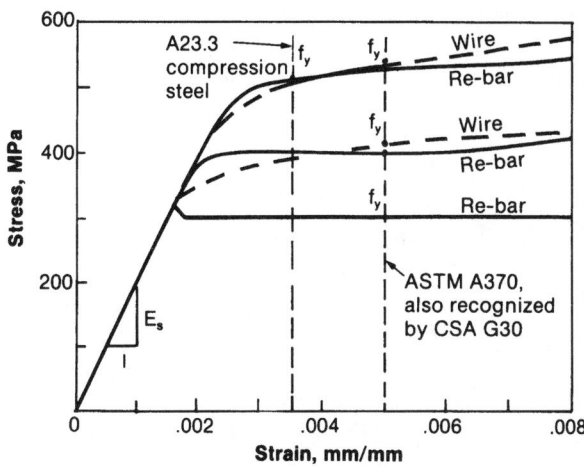

Fig. 1.7: Typical Stress-Strain Curves for Reinforcing Steel

CSA Standard A23.3 provides certain design limitations with respect to reinforcement strength. These limitations are summarized below.

i.   The value of f_y to be used in design calculations is limited to 550 MPa except for prestressing steel. (See Clause 9.4.1.)

ii.   If the compression reinforcement has a yield strength in excess of 400 MPa, the design calculations will be based on either the value of 400 MPa, or the stress corresponding to a strain of 0.0035. (See Clause 9.4.2.)

iii. In earthquake resistant design, when reinforcement conforming to CSA Standard G30.18 is used for members subjected to flexure and axial forces, the reinforcement strength is required to be closely controlled. Accordingly, the actual yield strength determined by mill tests is not permitted to exceed the specified minimum yield strength by more than 125 MPa for grade 400W reinforcement and 150 MPa for grade 500W reinforcement. Furthermore, the ultimate tensile strength of reinforcement is required to be at least 1.15 times the actual yield strength.

Steel grades for tendons depend on the minimum tensile strength, f_{pu} in MPa. Grades and properties of prestressing wires, strands and bars are listed in Tables 1.3 and 1.4.

High strength steels, used in prestressed concrete construction, do not have definite yield points. Typical stress-strain relationships are shown in Fig. 1.8. Yield strengths as specified by ASTM A416/A416M, ASTM A421/A421M, ASTM A722/A722M are indicated in the same figure.

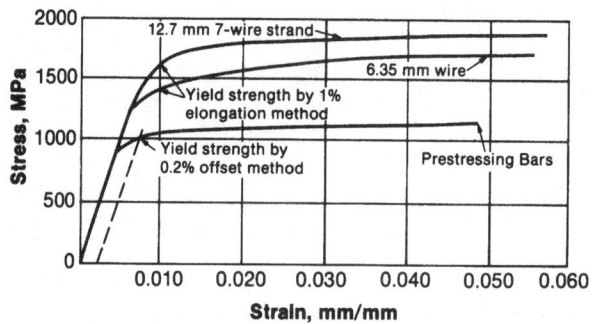

Fig. 1.8: Typical Stress-Strain Curves for Prestressing Tendons

The elastic modulus of steel, E_s, is typically 200,000 MPa. For non-prestressed reinforcement, E_s is specified by CSA Standard A23.3 to be 200,000 MPa. For prestressing tendons, E_s is required to be determined by tests or supplied by the manufacturer. Typical values will range from 190,000 to 200,000 MPa.

1.3.3   Reinforcing Bar Properties

The standard reinforcing bar sizes and their properties are given in Table 1.5. Specifications for deformations on bars, bendability requirements and the related test procedures are given in CSA Standard CSA Standard G30.18 for hot-rolled steel bars and weldable low alloy steel reinforcement. Table 1.6 and 1.7 summarize the tensile and bond test requirements for reinforcing bars. Steel grades and stress-strain characteristics are discussed in Section 1.3.2.

1.3.4   Properties of Wire and Welded Wire Fabric

Specifications for deformed steel wire for concrete reinforcement are given in ASTM A496. At the present time the Metric wire sizes are soft converted from Imperial units. Therefore, wire sizes are expressed in terms of soft converted cross-sectional area in mm^2 prefixed with letters MW or MD for smooth and deformed wires respectively. Tensile and bend test requirements for smooth and deformed steel wire are summarized in Tables 1.8 and 1.9.

Wire reinforcement is generally used in the form of welded wire fabric, consisting of a series of longitudinal and transverse wires welded together to form a mesh. Fabrication requirements, mechanical properties and the test procedures for welded wire fabric are specified in ASTM A185 and ASTM A497/A497M. Table 1.10 gives the sizes that are currently used in Canada.

1.3.5   Properties of Prestressing Steel

The standard tendon sizes and their properties are given in Tables 1.3 and 1.4. Specifications for prestressing wires, strands and bars are outlined in ASTM A416/A416M, ASTM A421/A421M, ASTM A722/A722M. Steel grades and stress-strain characteristics of prestressing tendons are discussed in Section 1.3.2.

1.4   Requirements for Fire Resistance

1.4.1   Introduction

1.4.1.1   General

CSA Standard A23.3 does not cover any aspect of design concerning fire resistance. In fact Clause 1.2 of the Standard reminds designers that all designs must be carried out in accordance with the fire resistance requirements of the applicable building code.

In the design of structures, building code requirements for fire resistance are sometimes overlooked. Such omissions may require costly measures to rectify. For example, slab thicknesses designs which are adequate to satisfy CSA Standard A23.3 provisions may not be sufficient to provide the necessary fire resistance. Similarly, cover to reinforcement may need to be increased for fire design purposes.

The purpose of this section is to make the reader aware of the importance of first examining the fire resistance provisions of the governing building code before proceeding with the structural design.

The field of fire technology is highly involved and complex and it is not the intent here to deal with the chemical or physical characteristics of fire, nor with the behaviour of structures in real fire situations. Rather, the goal is to present some basic information as an aid to designers in establishing those fire protection features of construction which may impact their structural design work.

1.4.1.2   Definitions

- Fire resistance generally refers to the property of a material or assembly to withstand fire or give protection from it; as applied to elements of buildings, it is characterized by the ability to confine a fire or to continue to perform a given structural function, or both.

- Fire resistance rating is defined in NBC, 2005 as the time in hours or fraction thereof that a material or assembly of materials will withstand the passage of flame and transmission of heat when exposed to fire under specified conditions of test and performance criteria, or as determined by extension or interpretation of information derived therefrom as prescribed in this Code.

1.4.1.3   Test Criteria for Fire Resistance

The fire resistance rating of building components is determined in accordance with ULC Standard CAN4-S101-M, Standard Methods of Fire Endurance Tests of Building Construction and Materials. During these tests, a building assembly such as a portion of a floor, wall, roof or column is subjected to increasing temperatures that vary with time as shown in Fig. 1.9. Floor and roof specimens are exposed to the test fire from beneath, beams from the bottom and sides, walls from one side and columns from all sides.

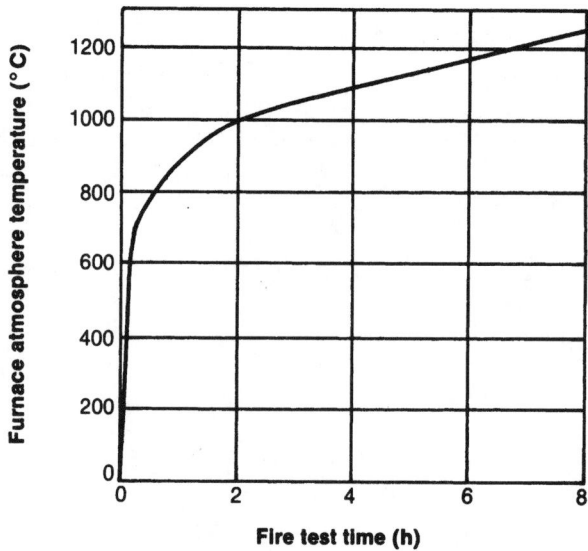

Fig. 1.9: Standard Time-Temperature Curve

The standard time-temperature curve approximates the conditions which would pertain during a fire within a moderate size compartment having a relatively small amount of ventilation and a fire load of about 50 kg of combustibles per square metre, per hour of fire.

The end of the test is reached and the fire endurance of the specimen is established when any one of the following conditions first occurs.

For floor and roof assemblies and for bearing walls and partitions:

(1)   The temperature of the unexposed surface rises an average of 140°C above its initial temperature or 180°C at any location. In addition, walls must sustain a hose stream test.

(2)   Cotton waste placed on the unexposed side of a wall, floor or roof system is ignited through cracks or fissures developed in the specimen.

(3)   The test assembly fails to sustain the full specified load required by CSA Standard A23.3. Additional criteria limiting the reinforcing steel temperature to 593°C also apply in the case of certain restrained and all unrestrained floors, roofs and beams tested restrained.

Though the complete requirements of ULC S101 and the conditions of acceptance are much too detailed for inclusion in this chapter, experience shows that the fire resistance of concrete floor/roof assemblies and walls is usually governed by heat transmission (item 1), and columns and beams by failure to sustain the applied loads (item 3), or beam reinforcement fails to meet the temperature rise criterion (item 3).

1.4.1.4   NBC Requirements

Most NBC requirements for fire resistance are set forth in Part 3 of Division B of the Code, "Use and Occupancy". Part 9, "Housing and Small Buildings", also contains similar requirements.

For design of buildings under Part 9, the fire ratings are prescribed in Appendix "A" of Division "B" in Table A-9.10.3.1.A and A-9.10.3.1.B for the assemblies listed, may be used.

Fire ratings must be provided for major structural assemblies as prescribed in subsection 3.2.2 of the NBC. In addition, such assemblies may be required to possess a fire resistance rating on the basis of the major occupancy separations of Subsection 3.1.3, the spatial separation requirements of Subsection 3.2.3   or other fire separation requirements listed throughout Subsections 3.3 to 3.5 of the NBC. Rules governing the determination of the fire resistance rating of a specific assembly are given in NBC Subsection 3.1.5.

Subsection 3.1.5 requires that fire resistance ratings be determined on the basis of results of tests conducted in conformance with ULC S101. It also provides that assemblies may be assigned a rating according to Appendix "D" of the NBC. It should be noted that the ratings contained in Appendix "D" of the NBC apply strictly to assemblies and structural members of generic materials for which there exist nationally recognized standards. Appendix "D" does not apply to assemblies of materials or structural members whose fire performance depends on proprietary information or where specifications do not meet all Appendix "D" provisions.

In practice, the designer has three options namely:

(a)   Rate an assembly in accordance with Appendix "D" of the NBC.

(b)   Use an existing ULC listing for the specific assembly for which the rating is required.

Note: Relatively few reinforced concrete assemblies are included in ULC listings. While these should be used where applicable, the discussion included in this Section is aimed at the determination of fire resistance ratings, in accordance with Appendix "D", Fire Performance Ratings.

The third option is known as:

(c)   "Rational Design"
Rational design, or analytical procedures for determining fire resistance, refers to an engineering method of calculating the duration that a structural element can be subjected to a standard fire exposure while performing its function, both structurally and as a barrier to heat. As the calculations used in this method are based on ULC S101 test criteria, they may be acceptable to an authority having jurisdiction under the Equivalent provisions of the General Requirements of NBC. It should be emphasized, however, that because no standard for rational design is currently referenced in NBC, specific prior approval must be obtained from the authority having jurisdiction for the use of rational design methods to establish fire ratings. Further detailed discussion of rational design techniques is beyond the scope of this brief Section and the reader is referred to References (1) and (2) for further information.

1.4.2   Factors Which Influence Fire Resistance Ratings

1.4.2.1   General

In order to recognize all of the factors which influence the fire resistance rating which may be assigned to a building construction assembly, on the basis of Appendix "D", a thorough knowledge and understanding of that document is obviously necessary.

For the purposes of this brief Section, the following are the main factors applicable to reinforced concrete assemblies which influence their fire resistance rating.

1.4.2.2   Concrete Type

Concrete is considered to be one of the most highly fire resistive structural materials used in construction. Nonetheless, the properties of concrete and reinforcing steel change significantly in the high temperatures of fire. Strength and the modulus of elasticity are reduced, the coefficient of expansion increases, and creep and stress relaxations are considerably higher.

Two basic types of normal weight concretes are recognized in Appendix "D" of the NBC, namely:

- Type S concrete, in which the coarse aggregate is granite, quartzite, siliceous gravel or other dense materials containing at least 30% quartz, chert or flint; and

- Type N concrete, in which the coarse aggregate is limestone, calcareous gravel, traprock, sandstone, blast furnace slag or similar dense material containing not more than 30% quartz, chert or flint.

Appendix "D" of the NBC recognizes five different types of low density concretes. Structural Low Density concrete, as defined in CSA Standard A23.3, generally corresponds with:

- Type L40S concrete, in which the fine aggregate is sand and the coarse aggregate is low density material and the sand does not exceed 40% of the total volume of all of the aggregate.

The compressive strength of concrete during fire exposure mainly depends upon the aggregate it contains. Generally speaking, for structural concretes, the behaviour of Types N and L40S concrete is superior to that of Type S concrete. As these differences are recognized in the assignment of fire resistance ratings, the designer must clearly specify which aggregate type should be used in critical assemblies.

1.4.2.3   Member Dimensions

Other factors being equal, the fire resistance rating of an assembly is proportional to its thickness or overall cross section. In the case of slab-like members, such as floors, roofs or walls, sufficient thickness must be provided to achieve the desired rating without violation of the temperature limit on the unexposed surface of the assembly. It should be noted that, in the case of hollow core or voided cross sections and ribbed slabs, the "equivalent thickness" of the slab must be used. This is computed in accordance with the rules given in Appendix "D" of the NBC. For beams and columns, dimensionally larger cross sections take longer to heat up, as compared to smaller members. Larger cross sections thus suffer less average concrete strength loss than smaller ones for a given period of fire endurance.

1.4.2.4   Reinforcing Steel

As is the case with concrete, reinforcement loses strength at high temperatures. Hot rolled reinforcing steel used for deformed bars retains its strength longer at elevated temperatures than the cold drawn steel used for prestressing tendons. As the ability of a member to carry load depends largely upon the tensile strength of its reinforcement, its fire resistance rating depends upon the type of reinforcing steel it contains, the temperature the steel reaches and the level of stress required in the steel.

1.4.2.5   Cover to Reinforcement

The rate at which heat reaches the reinforcement of a member and hence the loss of strength of the steel, is inversely proportional to the concrete cover provided. Designers should bear in mind that the covers specified in CSA Standard A23.1 for various members and exposures may not be sufficient to meet the requirements of Appendix "D" of the NBC to provide the necessary fire resistance rating.

1.4.2.6 Restraint and Continuity

The provisions of Appendix "D" of the NBC generally only apply to the rating of simply supported assemblies. In that document it is stated that:

"It is known that both edge restraint of a floor or roof and end restraint of a beam can significantly extend the time before collapse in a standard test",

and also that:

"In a restrained condition the floor, roof or beams would probably have greater fire resistance (than that set forth in this Chapter), but the extent of this increase can be determined only by reference to behaviour in a standard test."

Thus, unless the designer has access to specific test data for restrained or continuous reinforced concrete slabs or beams, or is prepared to undertake rational design computations and have them approved as discussed previously, the benefits of restraint or continuity cannot be utilized. It must, however, be emphasized that in the case of a slab-like member whose fire resistance rating is governed by temperature rise on its unexposed surface and hence the thickness of the slab, no increase in rating can be obtained by rational design, even though the slab may be restrained or continuous.

1.4.2.7 Protected Construction

Appendix "D" of the NBC includes detailed provisions to enable the assessment of the contribution of plaster of gypsum wall board finish to the fire resistance of masonry or concrete. In addition, ULC data covering the use of sprayed fireproofing or special fire retardant mastics is also available. While consideration of protected construction is beyond the scope of this Section, information on the subject is readily available.

1.4.2.8 Column Eccentricities

The A23.3 Standard requires that a minimum eccentricity of $(15 + 0.03h)$ mm be assumed in the design of columns. This equates to a load level equivalent to approximately 90% of the full theoretical factored resistance of the column. As the eccentricity of the applied load increases, the calculated factored resistance of the column decreases in accordance with the load/moment interaction diagram. The ratings for reinforced concrete columns provided in Appendix "A" of the NBC apply to all columns designed in accordance with CSA Standard A23.3-04.

1.4.3 Design Examples

1.4.3.1 General

The following examples illustrate the determination of fire resistance ratings in accordance with Appendix "D" of the NBC 2005. Only those provisions of the code document needed to work the examples have been reproduced here. The numbering used for these is that of the original 2005 document.

Designers should refer to that edition of the NBC which is referenced in the provincial building code governing the building under design for complete information on the assignment of fire resistance ratings to assemblies under consideration.

1.4.4   General Concrete and Masonry Provisions of Appendix "D" of the NBC

D-1.3.   CONCRETE

D-1.3.1   Aggregates in Concrete

Low density aggregate concretes generally exhibit better fire performance than natural stone aggregate concretes. A series of tests on concrete masonry walls, combined with mathematical analysis of the test results, has allowed further distinctions between certain low density aggregates to be made.

D-1.4.   TYPES OF CONCRETE

D-1.4.1   Description

1)   For purposes of this Appendix, concretes are described as Types S, N, L, L_1, L_2, L4OS, $L_1$2OS or $L_2$2OS as described in (2) to (8).

2)   Type S concrete is the type in which the coarse aggregate is granite, quartzite, siliceous gravel or other dense materials containing at least 30% quartz, chert or flint.

3)   Type N concrete is the type in which the coarse aggregate is cinders, broken brick, blast furnace slag, limestone, calcareous gravel, trap rock, sandstone or similar dense material containing not more than 30% of quartz, chert or flint.

4)   Type L concrete is the type in which all the aggregate is expanded slag, expanded clay, expanded shale or pumice.

5)   Type L_1 concrete is the type in which all the aggregate is expanded shale.

6)   Type L_2 concrete is the type in which all the aggregate is expanded slag, expanded clay or pumice.

7)   Type L4OS concrete is the type in which the fine portion of the aggregate is sand and low density aggregate in which the sand does not exceed 40% of the total volume of all aggregates in the concrete.

8)   Type $L_1$2OS and Type $L_2$2OS concretes are the types in which the fine portion of the aggregate is sand and low density aggregate in which the sand does not exceed 20% of the total volume of all aggregates in the concrete.

D-1.4.2.   Determination of Ratings

Where concretes are described as being of Type S, N, L, L_1 or L_2, the rating applies to the concrete containing the aggregate in the group that provides the least fire resistance. If the nature of an aggregate cannot be determined accurately enough to place it in one of the groups, the aggregates shall be considered as being in the group that requires a greater thickness of concrete for the required fire resistance.

D-1.4.3.   Description of Aggregates

1)   The descriptions of the aggregates in Type S and Type N concretes apply to the coarse aggregates only. Coarse aggregate for this purpose means that retained on a 5 mm sieve using the method of grading aggregates described in CSA-A23.1, Concrete Materials and Methods of Concrete Construction.

2)   Increasing the proportions of sand as fine aggregate in low density concretes

requires increased thicknesses of material to produce equivalent fire-resistance ratings. Low density aggregates for Type L and Types L-S concretes used in loadbearing components shall conform to ASTM C330, Lightweight Aggregates for Structural Concrete.

3)   Non-loadbearing low density components of vermiculite and perlite concrete, in the absence of other test evidence, shall be rated on the basis of the values shown for Type L concrete.

D-1.6.   EQUIVALENT THICKNESS

D-1.6.1.   Method of Calculating

1)   The thickness of solid-unit masonry and concrete described in this Appendix shall be the thickness of solid material in the unit or component thickness. For units that contain cores or voids, the Tables refer to the equivalent thickness determined in conformance with (2) to (10).

2)   Where a plaster finish is used, the equivalent thickness of a wall, floor, column or beam protection shall be equal to the sum of the equivalent thicknesses of the concrete or masonry units and the plaster finish measured at the point that will give the least value of equivalent thickness.

3)   Except as provided in (5), the equivalent thickness of a hollow masonry unit shall be calculated as equal to the actual overall thickness of a unit in millimetres multiplied by a factor equal to the net volume of the unit and divided by its gross volume.

4)   Net volume shall be determined using a volume displacement method that is not influenced by the porous nature of the units.

5)   Gross volume of a masonry unit shall be equal to the actual length of the unit multiplied by the actual height of the unit multiplied by the actual thickness of the unit.

6)   Where all the core spaces in a wall of hollow concrete masonry or hollow-core precast concrete units are filled with grout, mortar, or loose fill materials such as expanded slag, burned clay or shale (rotary kiln process), vermiculite or perlite, the equivalent thickness rating of the wall shall be considered to be the same as that of a wall of solid units, or a solid wall of the same concrete type and the same overall thickness.

7)   The equivalent thickness of hollow-core concrete slabs and panels having a uniform thickness and cores of constant cross section throughout their length shall be obtained by dividing the net cross-sectional area of the slab or panel by its width.

8)   The equivalent thickness of concrete panels with tapered cross sections shall be the cross section determined at a distance of 2 t or 150 mm, whichever is less, from the point of minimum thickness, where t is the minimum thickness.

9)   Except as permitted in (10), the equivalent thickness of concrete panels with ribbed or undulating surfaces shall be
a) t_a for s less than or equal to 2 t,
b) $t + (4\ t/s - 1)(t_a$-t) for s less than 4 t and greater than 2 t, and
c) t for s greater than or equal to 4 t
    where
    t = minimum thickness of panel,
    t_a = average thickness of panel (unit cross-sectional area divided by unit width), and
    s = centre to centre spacing of ribs or undulations.

10)   Where the total thickness of a panel described in (9), exceeds 2 t, only that portion of the panel which is less than 2 t from the nonribbed surface shall be considered for the purpose of the calculations in (9).

1.4.5   Masonry and Concrete Walls

1.4.5.1   Applicable Provisions of Appendix "D"

SECTION D.2   FIRE-RESISTANCE RATINGS

D-2.1   MASONRY AND CONCRETE WALLS

D-2.1.1. Minimum Equivalent Thickness for Fire-Resistance Rating

The minimum thicknesses of unit masonry and monolithic concrete walls are shown in Table D-2.1.1. Hollow masonry units and hollow-core concrete panels shall be rated on the basis of equivalent thickness as described in D-1.6.

Table D-2.1.1.
Forming Part of D-2.1.1.

Minimum Equivalent Thicknesses(1) of Unit Masonry and Monolithic Concrete Walls Loadbearing and Non-Loadbearing, mm							
	Fire-Resistance Rating						
Type of Wall	30 min	45 min	1 h	1.5 h	2h	3h	4h
Solid brick units (80% solid and over), actual overall thickness	63	76	90	108	128	152	178
Cored brick units and hollow tile units (less than 80% solid), equivalent thickness	50	60	72	86	102	122	142
Solid and hollow concrete masonry units, equivalent thickness							
Type S or N concrete[2]	44	59	73	95	113	142	167
Type $L_1$20S concrete	42	54	66	87	102	129	152
Type L_1 concrete	42	54	64	82	97	122	143
Type $L_2$20S concrete	42	54	64	81	94	116	134
Type L_2 concrete	42	54	63	79	91	111	127
Monolithic concrete and concrete panels, equivalent thicknesses							
Type S concrete	60	77	90	112	130	158	180
Type N concrete	59	74	87	108	124	150	171
Type L40S or Type L concrete	49	62	72	89	103	124	140

Notes to Table D-2.1.1:
1)   See definition of equivalent thickness in D-1.6.
2)   Hollow concrete masonry units made with Type S or N concrete shall have a minimum compressive strength of 15 MPa base on net area, as defined in CAN3-A165.1, "Concrete Masonry Units"

D-2.1.2. Applicability of Ratings

1) Ratings obtained as described in D-2.1.1. apply to either loadbearing or non-loadbearing walls, except for walls described in (2) to (6).

2) Ratings for walls with a thickness less than the minimum thickness prescribed for load-bearing walls in this Code apply to non-loadbearing walls only.

3) Masonry cavity walls (consisting of 2 wythes of masonry with an air space between) that are loaded to a maximum allowable compressive stress of 380 kPa have a fire resistance at least as great as that of a solid wall of a thickness equal to the sum of the equivalent thicknesses of the 2 wythes.

4) Masonry cavity walls that are loaded to a compressive stress exceeding 380 kPa are not considered to be within the scope of this Appendix.

5) A masonry wall consisting of 2 types of masonry units, either bonded together or in the form of a cavity wall, shall be considered to have a fire-resistance rating equal to that which would apply if the whole of the wall were of the material that gives the lesser rating.

6) A non-loadbearing cavity wall made up of 2 precast concrete panels with an air space or insulation in the cavity between them shall be considered to have a fire-resistance rating as great as that of a solid wall of a thickness equal to the sum of the thicknesses of the 2 panels.

D-2.1.3 Framed Beams and Joists

Beams and joists that are framed into a masonry or concrete fire separation shall not reduce the thickness of the fire separation to less than the equivalent thickness required for the fire separation.

D-2.1.4 Credit for Plaster Thickness

On monolithic walls and walls of unit masonry, the full plaster finish on one or both faces multiplied by the factor shown in Table D-1.7.1. shall be included in the wall thickness in Table D-2.1.1., under the conditions and using the methods described in D-1.7.

D-2.1.5 Walls Exposed to Fire on Both Sides

1) Except as permitted in (2), portions of loadbearing reinforced concrete walls, which do not form a complete fire separation and thus may be exposed to fire on both sides simultaneously, shall have minimum dimensions and minimum cover to steel reinforcement in conformance with D-2.8.2 to D-2.8.5.

2) A concrete wall exposed to fire from both sides as described in (1) has a fire-resistance rating of 2 h if the following conditions are met:

   a) its equivalent thickness is not less than 200 mm,

   b) its aspect ratio (width/thickness) is not less than 4.0,

   c) the minimum thickness of concrete cover over the steel reinforcement specified in (d) is not less than 50 mm,

d) each face of the wall is reinforced with both vertical and horizontal steel reinforcement in conformance with either Clause 10 or Clause 14 of CAN3-A23.3-04, Design of Concrete Structures,

e) the structural design of the wall is governed by the minimum eccentricity requirements of Clause 10.11.6.3. of CAN3-A23.3-04, Design of Concrete Structures, and

f) the effective length of the wall, kl_u, is not more than 3.7 m
where
k = effective length factor obtained from CAN3-A23.3-04, Design of Concrete Structures,
l_u = unsupported length of the wall in metres.

1.4.5.2   Determination of the Fire Resistance Rating of a Ribbed Panel Wall

Given:

The section of wall panel shown. Type L40S concrete.

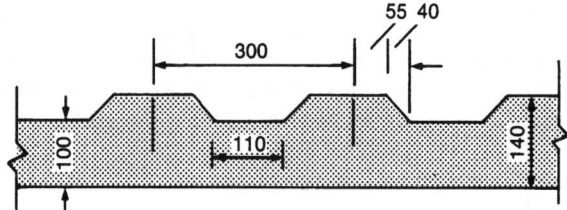

Problem:

Determine the fire resistance rating of the wall.

Solution:

Determine equivalent thickness per D-1.6.6

T = 100 mm

$$t_a = \frac{(100 \times 300) + (150 \times 40)}{300} = 120 \; mm$$

s = 300 mm

As total thickness of panel does not exceed 2t, Sentence (2) does not apply.
As s is less than 4t and greater than 2t, expression (b) of D-1.6.6 applies and:

Equivalent Thickness = $100 + \left(\dfrac{400}{300} - 1 \right)(120 - 100)$

From Table 2.1A, 106.6 mm of L40S concrete qualifies for a 2 hour fire resistance rating.

1.4.6 Reinforced and Prestressed Floor and Roof Slabs

1.4.6.1 Applicable Provisions of Appendix "D"

D-2.2. REINFORCED AND PRESTRESSED CONCRETE FLOOR AND ROOF SLABS

D-2.2.1 Assignment of Rating

1) Floors and roofs in a fire test are assigned a fire-resistance rating which relates to the time that an average temperature rise of 140°C or a maximum temperature rise of 180°C at any location is recorded on the unexposed side, or the time required for collapse to occur, whichever is the lesser. The thickness of concrete shown in Table D-2.2.1.A. shall be required to resist the transfer of heat during the fire resistance period shown.

Table D-2.2.1.A.
Forming Part of D-2.2.1.(1)

Minimum Thickness of Reinforced and Prestressed Concrete Floor or Roof Slabs, mm

Type of Concrete	Fire-Resistance Rating						
	30 min	45 min	1 h	1.5 h	2 h	3 h	4 h
Type S concrete	60	77	90	112	130	158	180
Type N concrete	59	74	87	108	124	150	171
Type L40S or Type L concrete	49	62	72	89	103	124	140

2) The concrete cover over the reinforcement and steel tendons shown in Table D-2.2.1.B. shall be required to maintain the integrity of the structure and prevent collapse during the same period.

Table D-2.2.1.B.
Forming Part of D-2.2.1.(2)

Minimum Concrete Cover over Reinforcement in Concrete Slabs, mm

Type of Concrete	Fire-Resistance Rating						
	30 min	45 min	1 h	1.5h	2 h	3 h	4 h
Type S, N, L40S or L concrete	20	20	20	20	25	32	39
Prestressed concrete slabs Type S, N, L40S or L concrete	20	25	25	32	39	50	64

D-2.2.2. Floors with Hollow Units

The fire resistance of floors containing hollow units may be determined on the basis of equivalent thickness as described in D-1.6.

D-2.2.3. Composite Slabs

1) For composite concrete floor and roof slabs consisting of one layer of Type S or N concrete and another layer of Type L40S or L concrete in which the minimum thickness of both the top and bottom layers is not less than 25 mm, the combined fire-resistance rating may be determined using the following expressions:

   a) when the base layer consists of Type S or N concrete,

   $R = 0.00018\ t^2 - 0.00009\ d\ t + (8.7/t)$

b)   when the base layer consists of Type L40S or L concrete,

$$R = 0.0001\, t^2 - 0.0002\, d\, t - 0.0001\, d^2 + (6.4/t)$$

where

R = fire resistance of slab, h,

t = total thickness of slab, mm, and

d = thickness of base layer, mm.

2)   If the base course described in (1) is covered by a top layer of material other than Type S, N, L40S or L concrete, the top course thickness may be converted to an equivalent concrete thickness by multiplying the actual thickness by the appropriate factor listed in Table D-2.2.3.A. This equivalent concrete thickness may be added to the thickness of the base course and the fire-resistance rating calculated using Table D-2.2.1.A.

Table D-2.2.3.A.
Forming Part of D-2.2.3.A.
Multiplying Factors for Equivalent Thickness

Multiplying Factors for Equivalent Thickness		
Top Course Material	Base Slab Normal Density Concrete (Type S or N)	Base Slab Low Density Concrete (Type L40S or L)
Gypsum wallboard	3	2.25
Cellular concrete (mass density 400 - 560 kg/m³)	2	1.5
Vermiculite and perlite concrete (mass density 560 kg/m3 or less)	1.75	1.5
Portland cement with sand aggregate	1	0.75
Terrazzo	1	0.75

3)   The minimum concrete cover under the main reinforcement for composite floor and roof slabs with base slabs of less than 100 mm thick shall conform to Table D-2.2.3.B. For base slabs 100 mm or more thick, the minimum cover thickness requirements of Table D-2.2.1.B. shall apply.

Table D-2.2.3.B
Forming Part of D-2.2.3.(3)

Minimum Concrete Cover under Bottom Reinforcement in composite Concrete Slabs, mm							
Base Slab Concrete Type	Fire-Resistance Rating						
	30 min	45 min	1h	1.5h	2h	3h	4h
Reinforced Concrete Type S, N, L40S or L	15	15	20	25	30	40	55
Prestressed concrete							
Type S	20	25	30	40	50	65	75
Type N	20	20	25	35	45	60	70
Type L40S or L	20	20	25	30	40	50	60

4)   Where the top layer of a 2-layer slab is less than 25 mm thick, the fire-resistance rating of the slab shall be calculated as though the entire slab were made up of the type of concrete with the lesser fire resistance.

D-2.2.4. Contribution of Plaster Finish

1)   The contribution of plaster finish securely fastened to the underside of concrete may be taken into account in floor or roof slabs under the conditions and using the methods described in D-1.7.

2)   Plaster finish on the underside of concrete floors or roofs may be used in lieu of concrete cover referred to in D-2.2.1.(2) under the conditions and using the methods described in D-1.7.

D-2.2.5   Concrete Cover

1) In prestressed concrete slab construction, the concrete cover over an individual tendon shall be the minimum thickness of concrete between the surface of the tendon and the fire-exposed surface of the slab, except that for ungrouted ducts the assumed cover thickness shall be the minimum thickness of concrete between the surface of the duct and the bottom of the slab. For slabs in which several tendons are used, the cover is assumed to be the average of those of individual tendons, except that the cover for any individual tendon shall be not less than half of the value given in Table D-2.2.1.B. nor less than 20 mm.

2)   Except as provided in (3), in post-tensioned prestressed concrete slabs, the concrete cover to the tendon at the anchor shall be not less than 15 mm greater than the minimum cover required by (1). The minimum concrete cover to the anchorage bearing plate and to the end of the tendon, if it projects beyond the bearing plate, shall be 20 mm.

3)   The requirements of (2) do not apply to those portions of slabs not likely to be exposed to fire, such as the ends and tops.

D-2.2.6.   Minimum Dimensions for Cover

Minimum dimensions and cover to steel tendons of prestressed concrete beams shall conform to D-2.10.

1.4.6.2   Determination of the Fire Resistance Rating of a Hollow Core Slab

Given:

The section of prestressed concrete hollow core slab shown.
Type N concrete slab, Type L40S topping. Cross sectional area of 1200 mm wide slab, from product literature = 134,000 mm^2. 12.7 mm diameter strand.

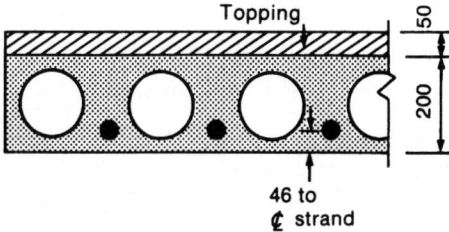

Topping

50

200

46 to
¢ strand

Problem:

Determine the fire resistance rating of the section, both without the topping and topped.

Solution:

(a) Untopped Section

Determine equivalent thickness of slab per D-1.6.4

ET = 134,000 / 1200 = 112 mm

Rating for transfer of heat, per Table 2.2.A, Type N concrete is 1½ hours (+).

Rating for structural integrity, per Table 2. 2B

Concrete cover = 46 - 12.7 over 2 mm to strand

$\qquad\qquad$ = 39.65 mm > 39 mm

∴ Rating for this cover is 2 hours.

However, as transfer of heat governs, rating is 1½ hours.

(b) Topped Section

As the base layer is Type N concrete and the topping Type L40S concrete, 2.2.3.(1)(a) governs, and

$R = 0.0002t^2 - 0.0001\ d\ t + (10/t)$

t = total equivalent thickness of slab =
$\quad$ 112 + 50 = 162 mm

d = equivalent thickness of base slab = 112 mm

Thus $R = 0.0002(162)^2 - 0.0001(112)(162) + \dfrac{10}{162}$

$\qquad\quad$ = 5.25 - 1.81 + .06
$\qquad\quad$ = 3.5 hours

However, by the provisions of 2.2.3(3), the minimum cover thickness of Table 2.2.B governs.

Thus, for 39 mm cover, a rating of 2 hours applies to the topped section.

1.4.7   Reinforced Concrete Columns

1.4.7.1   Applicable Provisions of Appendix "D"

D-2.8.   REINFORCED CONCRETE COLUMNS

D-2.8.1   Minimum Dimensions

Minimum Dimensions for reinforced concrete columns and minimum concrete cover for vertical steel reinforcement are obtained from D-2.8.2. to D-2.8.5., taking into account the type of concrete, the effective length of the column and the area of the vertical reinforcement.

D-2.8.2. Method

1) The minimum dimension, t, in millimetres, of a rectangular reinforced concrete column shall be equal to
  (a) 75 $f(R + 1)$ for all Types L and L40S concrete,
  (b) 80 $f(R + 1)$ for Type S concrete when the design condition of the concrete column is defined in the second and fourth columns of Table D-2.8.2.,
  (c) 80 $f(R + 0.75)$ for Type N concrete when the design condition of the concrete is defined in the second and fourth columns of Table D-2.8.2, and
  (d) 100 $f(R + 1)$ for Types S and N concrete when the design condition of the concrete column is defined in the third column of Table D-2.8.2.

where
  $f =$ the value shown in Table D-2.8.2.,
  $R =$ the required fire-resistance rating in hours,
  $k =$ the effective length factor obtained from CAN3-A23.3-04
  $h =$ the unsupported length of the column in metres, and
  $\rho =$ the area of vertical reinforcement in the column as a percentage of the column area.

Table D-2.8.2.[1]
Forming Part of D-2.8.2.

Values of Factor "*f*"			
	Values of Factor "*f*"		
Overdesign Factor[2]	Where kh is not more than 3.7 m	Where *kh* is more than 3.7 m but not more than 7.3 m	
		t is not more than 300 mm, ρ is not more than 3%[3]	All other cases[4]
1.00	1.0	1.2	1.0
1.25	0.9	1.1	0.9
1.50	0.83	1.0	0.83

Notes to Table D-2.8.2.:
(1) For conditions that do not fall within the limits described in Table D-2.8.2., further information may be obtained from Reference (7) in D-6.1.

(2) Overdesign factor is the ratio of the calculated load carrying capacity of the column to the column strength required to carry the specified loads determined in conformance with CAN3-A23.3-04, Design of Concrete Structures.

(3) Where the factor "*f*" selected from the third column results in a "*t*" greater than 300 mm, the appropriate factor "*f*" selected from the fourth column shall be applicable.

(4) Where "ρ" is equal to or less than 3% and the factor "*f*" selected from the fourth column results in a "*t*" less than 300 mm, the minimum thickness shall be 300 mm.

2) The diameter of a round column shall be not less than 1.2 times the value "*t*" determined in (1) for a rectangular column.

D-2.8.3. Minimum Thickness of Concrete Cover

1) Where the required fire-resistance rating of a concrete column is 3 h or less, the minimum thickness in millimetres of concrete cover over vertical steel reinforcement shall be equal to 25 times the number of hours of fire resistance required or 50 mm, whichever is less.

2)   Where the required fire-resistance rating of a concrete column is greater than 3 h, the minimum thickness in millimetres of concrete cover over vertical steel reinforcement shall be equal to 50 plus 12.5 times the required number of hours of fire resistance in excess of 3 h.

3)   Where the concrete cover over vertical steel required in (2) exceeds 62.5 mm, wire mesh reinforcement with 1.57 mm diameter wire and 100 mm openings shall be incorporated midway in the concrete cover to retain the concrete in position.

D-2.8.4.   Minimum Requirements

The structural design standards may require minimum column dimensions or concrete cover over vertical steel reinforcement differing from those obtained in D-2.8.2(1) and (2). Where a difference occurs, the greater dimension shall govern.

D-2.8.5.   Addition of Plaster

The addition of plaster finish to the concrete column may be taken into account in determining the cover over vertical steel reinforcement by applying the multiplying factors described in D-1.7. The addition of plaster shall not, however, justify any decrease in the minimum column sizes shown.

D-2.8.6.   Built-In Columns

The fire-resistance rating of a reinforced concrete column that is built into a masonry or concrete wall so that not more than one face may be exposed to the possibility of fire at one time may be determined on the basis of cover to vertical reinforcing steel alone. In order to meet this condition, the wall shall conform to D-2.1. for the fire-resistance rating required.

1.4.7.2   Determination of the Fire Resistance of a Reinforced Concrete Column

Given:

300 × 300 mm column, Type S concrete
Column height = 3650 mm
Maximum specified load = 782 kN
Concrete strength f_c' = 35 MPa
Steel strength f_y = 400 MPa
Percentage steel, ρ = 4%
Effective length factor k = 1.0

Problem:

Determine the fire resistance rating of the column.

Solution:

Maximum specified load capacity of column, taking slenderness into account and an eccentricity of

    e/t = 0.1* is 978 kN

*Note that eccentricity is within CSA Standard A23.3 limit for concentric loading.

Over design factor = 978/782 = 1.25

∴ "f" factor from Table 2.8A = 0.9

Since $t = 100\,f\,(R + 1)$

Where R = effective fire resistance in hours,

then $R = (t\,/\,(100\,f)) - 1$

since $t = 300$ mm and $f = 0.9$

$$R = \frac{300}{100x0.9}$$

1.4.8   Reinforced Concrete Beams

1.4.8.1   Applicable Provisions of Appendix "D"

D-2.9.   REINFORCED CONCRETE BEAMS

D-2.9.1.   Minimum Cover Thickness

The minimum thickness of cover over principal steel reinforcement in reinforced concrete beams is shown in Table D-2.9.1 for fire-resistance ratings from 30 min to 4h where the width of the beam or joist is at least 100 mm.

Table D-2.9.1.
Forming Part of D-2.9.1.

Minimum cover to Principal Steel Reinforcement in Reinforced Concrete Beams, mm

Type of Concrete	Fire-Resistance Rating						
	30 min	45 min	1h	1.5h	2h	3h	4h
Type S, N or L	20	20	20	25	25	39	50

D-2.9.2.   Maximum Rating

No rating over 2 h may be assigned on the basis of Table D-2.9.1. to a beam or joist where the average width of the part that projects below the slab is less than 140 mm, and no rating over 3 h may be assigned where the average width of the part that projects below the slab is less than 165 mm.

D-2.9.3.   Beam Integrated in Floor or Roof Slab

For the purposes of these ratings, a beam may be either independent of or integral with a floor or roof slab assembly.

D-2.9.4.   Minimum Thickness

Where the upper extension or top flange of a joist or T-beam in a floor assembly contributes wholly or partly to the thickness of the slab above, the total thickness at any point shall be not less than the minimum thickness described in Table D-2.2.1.A. for the fire-resistance rating required.

D-2.9.5.   Effect of Plaster

The addition of plaster finish to a reinforced concrete beam may be taken into account in determining the cover over principal reinforcing steel by applying the multiplying factors described in D-1.7.

1.4.8.2   Determination of the Fire Resistance of a Reinforced Concrete Beam

Given:

The section of reinforced concrete beam and slab shown:
   Type S concrete

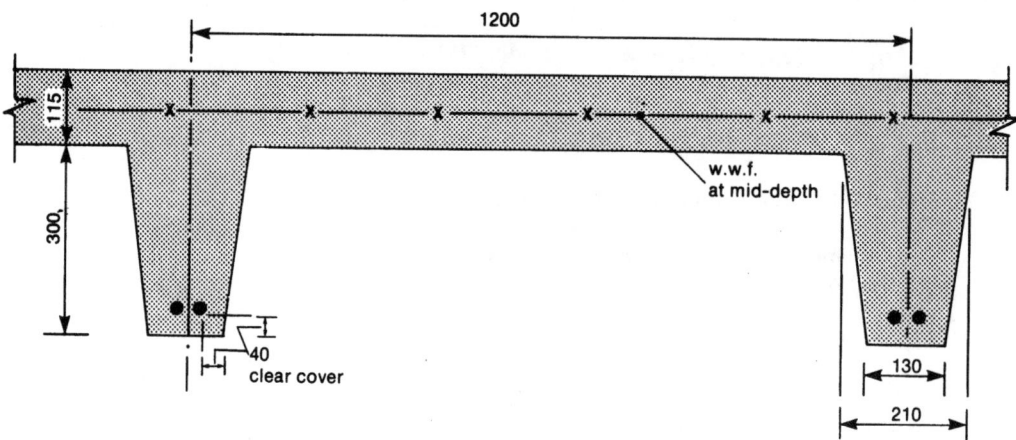

Problem:

Determine the fire resistance of the section.

Solution:

(a)   Determine the fire resistance of the beam section.

   For 40 mm cover, from Table 2.9.A, Type S concrete,

   Maximum rating = 3 hours
   Width of beam, average = 170 mm
   By 2.9.2; 170 mm > 165 mm
   ∴ Rating of 3 hours is justified for the beam

(b)   Determine the fire resistance of the slab.

   From Table 2.2.A, for 115 mm of Type S concrete
   Rating to resist transfer of heat is 1½ hours.

From Table 2.2.B, for a clear cover of 55 mm, a structural rating in excess of 4 hours is achieved.

∴ heat transmission governs

Check to determine whether, by the provisions of 1.6.6, an increased equivalent thickness can be assumed.

t = 115 mm
S = 1200 mm
$4t$ = 460 mm

Because S exceeds $4t$, no increased equivalent thickness can be assumed.
Thus, the total assembly qualifies for a 1½ hour rating.

1.4.9   Prestressed Concrete Beams

1.4.9.1   Applicable Provisions of Appendix "D"

D-2.10.   PRESTRESSED CONCRETE BEAMS

D-2.10.1 Minimum Cross-Sectional Area and Thickness of Cover

The minimum cross-sectional area and thickness of concrete cover over steel tendons in prestressed concrete beams for fire-resistance ratings from 30 min to 4 h are shown in Table D-2.10.1.

Table D-2.10.1.
Forming Part of D-2.10.1

Minimum Thickness of Concrete Cover over Steel Tendons in Prestressed Concrete Beams, mm[1]

Type of Concert	Area of Beam cm^2	Fire-Resistance Rating						
		30 min	45 min	1h	1.5h	2h	3h	4h
Type S or N	260 to 970	25	39	50	64	-	-	-
	over 970 to 1940	25	26	39	45	64	-	-
	Over 1940	25	26	39	39	50	77	102
Type L	Over 970	25	25	25	39	50	77	102

Note to Table D-2.10.1.:
1)   Where the thickness of concrete cover over the tendons exceeds 64 mm, a wire mesh reinforcement with 1.57 mm diameter wire and 100 mm by 100 mm openings shall be incorporated in the beams to retain the concrete in position around the tendons. The mesh reinforcement shall be located midway in the cover.

D-2.10.2. Minimum Cover Thickness

The cover for an individual tendon shall be the minimum thickness of concrete between the surface of the tendon and the fire-exposed surface of the beam, except that for ungrouted ducts the assumed cover thickness shall be the minimum thickness of concrete between the surface of the duct and the surface of the beam. For beams in which several tendons are used, the cover is assumed to be the average of the minimum cover of the individual tendons. The cover for any individual tendon shall be not less than half the value given in Table D-2.10.1. nor less than 25 mm.

D-2.10.3. Applicability of Ratings

The ratings in Table D-2.10.1. apply to a beam that is either independent of or integral with a floor or roof slab assembly. Minimum thickness of slab and minimum cover to steel tendons in prestressed concrete slabs are contained in D-2.2.

D-2.10.4. Effect of Plaster

The addition of plaster finish to a prestressed concrete beam may be taken into account in determining the cover over steel tendons by applying the multiplying factors described in D-1.7.

D-2.10.5 Minimum Cover

1)   Except as provided in (2), in unbonded post-tensioned prestressed concrete beams, the concrete cover to the tendon at the anchor shall be not less than 15 mm greater than the minimum required away from the anchor. The concrete cover to the anchorage bearing plate and to the end of the tendon, if it projects beyond the bearing plate, shall be not less than 25 mm.

2)   The requirements in (1) do not apply to those portions of beams not likely to be exposed to fire (such as the ends and the tops of flanges of beams immediately below slabs).

1.4.9.2   Determination of the Fire Resistance Rating of a Prestressed Concrete Beam

Given:

The section of prestressed concrete T-beam shown, Type S concrete, Eight, 12.7 mm diameter strand. Bottom cover to lowest strand, 40 mm.

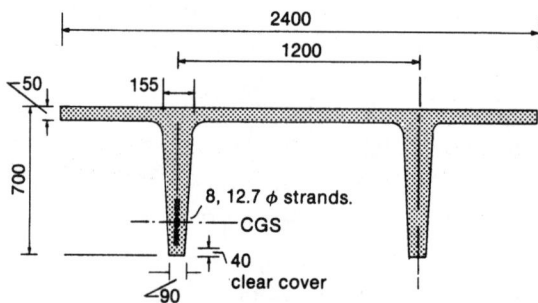

Problem:

Determine the structural fire resistance of the beam section.

Solution:

$$\text{Area of stem} = \frac{90+155}{2}(700-50)\,\text{mm}^2$$

$$= 79625\ \text{mm}^2 = 796\ \text{cm}^2$$

Concrete cover to bottom strand of group = 40 mm

Distance from bottom of stem to CGS
    = 40 + 4 × 12.7 = 90.8 mm

Width of stem at CGS = $\left[\dfrac{155-90}{650}\right]x90.8$

    = 99.1 mm

∴ Clear side cover at CGS = $\dfrac{99.1-90}{2} = 43.2$

Minimum individual strand, bottom cover = 40 mm

Minimum individual strand, side cover

    = 45 - (12.7/2) = 38.65 mm

Fire resistance rating, based on side cover of centroid of strand group (from 2.10.2 and Table 2.10A)

    = ¾ hour (39 mm < 43.2 mm)

Check: Minimum cover to critical bottom tendon is greater
        than (39/2) = 19.5 mm and 25 mm

1.4.9.3   Single T Prestressed Concrete Beam, Tapered Flanges

Given:

The section of flange of prestressed concrete T-beam shown. Type N concrete beam and topping.

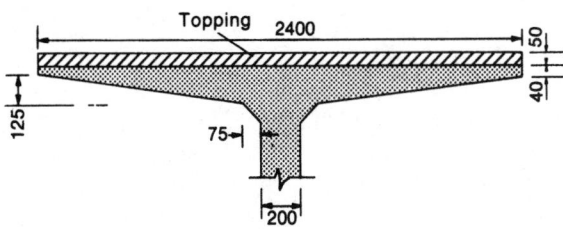

Problem:

Determine the fire resistance rating of the flange for heat transmission.
Solution:

The provisions of Subsection 1.6.5 apply.

Thickness at edge of flange = 50 + 40 = 90 mm = t

    2t = 180 mm > 150 mm

∴ Determine thickness at 150 mm from edge

Slope is 125 mm in 1025 mm

At 150 mm, t = 90 + (125/1025) × 150

   = 90 + 18 = 108 mm

From Table 2.2.A (see 1.4.6.1)

For Type N concrete, rating is 1½ hours.

1.4.10   Reference Publications

(1) Design Manual - Precast and Prestressed Concrete; Canadian Precast / Prestressed Concrete Institute, 85 Albert Street, Ottawa, Ontario K1P 6A4

(2) CRSI - Reinforced Concrete Fire Resistance; Concrete Reinforcing Steel Institute, 933 N. Plum Grove Road, Schaumburg, Illinois, 60195

1.5   Special Requirements for Corrosive Environments

1.5.1   Introduction

In common with other construction materials, unprotected or improperly designed concrete will suffer corrosion if exposed to an environment in which certain chemically aggressive agents are present.

The following provides information on means of minimizing or preventing loss of serviceability* and damage to concrete which may be exposed to commonly occurring corrosive environments.

1.5.2   De-Icer Salt Environment

CSA Standard A23.1 (Clause 4.1.1 and Table 2) requires that concrete subject to applications of de-icing chemicals be designated as Exposure Classes 'C-XL, and C-1 to C-4', which implies a low water:cementing materials ratio, a high content of entrained air and other mix design controls. CSA A23.1 Clause 6 and Table 17 provide requirements for concrete cover to reinforcement where the concrete is exposed to chlorides. It should be borne in mind that specified minimum covers are the minimum anywhere in the member. Reveals, architectural grooving and chamfers at joints, which may reduce the cover to less than acceptable minimum amounts, should not be ignored. Increased cover may also be required for fire resistance. For information on this subject, see Subsection 1.4 of this Handbook.

1.5.3   Sea Water Environment

CSA Standard A23.1, Clause 4 contains requirements for concrete in sea water environments. Deterioration problems due to the presence of salts in the air may occur in

---

* For example, in parking structures, leakage of chloride-laden water onto parked cars constitutes an unserviceable condition.

structures located within a kilometre of the ocean, particularly if covers to reinforcement are small or concrete properties inadequate.

Sea water contains significant amounts of sulphates and chlorides. Although sulphates in sea water are capable of attacking concrete, the presence of chlorides inhibits the expansive reaction that is characteristic of attack by sulphates in groundwaters or soils. Calcium sulphoaluminate, the reaction product of sulphate attack, is more soluble in a chloride solution and can be more readily leached out of the concrete, thus causing less destructive expansion. This is the major factor explaining observations from a number of sources that the performance of concretes in sea water with Portland cements having tricalcium aluminate (C3A) contents as high as 10%, and sometimes greater, have shown satisfactory durability, providing the permeability of the concrete is low.

Maximum permissible water:cement ratios for the submerged portions of a structure should not exceed 0.45 by mass. For portions in the splash zone and above, maximum permissible water:cement ratios should not exceed 0.40 by mass. Water:cement ratios as high as 0.50 by mass may be used for submerged areas provided the C3A content of the Portland cement does not exceed 8%.

Cements meeting the requirements of CSA Standard A3001 and meeting the C3A requirement noted above (that is, not more than 10%) are acceptable. In the case of blended cements, this limitation applies to the Portland cement clinker used in the blended cement.

Calcium chloride should not be used as an admixture in reinforced concrete to be exposed to sea water.

In addition to the proper selection of cement and adherence to the requirements, other requirements for quality concrete such as adequate air entrainment, low slump, low permeability, adequate consolidation, uniformity, adequate clear cover over reinforcement, and sufficient curing to develop the potential properties of the concrete are essential for securing economical and durable concrete exposed to sea water.

References:

- CSA Standard A23.1-04, Concrete Materials and Methods of Concrete Construction

- CSA Standard A3000-05

- ACI Publication SP-65, Performance of Concrete in Marine Environment

1.5.4   Sulphate Soils and Groundwater Exposure

CSA Standard A23.1, Clause 4 contains requirements for concrete which will be exposed to sulphate soils and groundwaters.

Sulphate attack on concrete can occur where soil and groundwater have a high sulphate content and where measures to prevent sulphate attack (such as those contained in CSA Standard A23.1) have not been taken. The attack is confined to concrete that is cool and moist, such as foundations and slabs on ground. It usually causes an expansion of the concrete because of the formation of solids as a result of chemical action. The amount of this expansion in some cases has been higher than 0.1% and the accompanying disruptive effect within the concrete can result in extensive cracking and deterioration.

References:

- CSA Standard A23.1-04, Concrete Materials and Methods of Concrete Construction

- ACI Publication SP-77, Sulphate Resistance of Concrete

1.5.5   Sewage and Waste Water Treatment Exposure

While sanitary engineering structures are considered to be "special structures" within the context of CSA Standard A23.3, the requirements of that Standard are generally valid for their structural design, provided that special consideration is given to control of cracking. ACI 350-01/350R-01, Code Requirements for Environmental Engineering Concrete Structures and Commentary, contains detailed recommendations for loadings to be used for the limitations of concrete and steel stresses at service loads and for the design of joints in such structures.

Specifications for concrete mix design and for construction should be drawn up to provide for dense, impermeable concrete which will be resistant to naturally occurring or commonly used chemicals and have a smooth, well formed surface finish. Recommendations towards obtaining these properties are also set forth in ACI 350R.

Generally speaking, additional protection against corrosion should not be necessary, provided the design and construction meet the requirements outlined above. Certain areas within water treatment plants or domestic sewage plants where chemically aggressive agents may be present, may require the use of protective coatings or linings. Industrial waste treatment plants will probably require the use of chemically resistant surface coatings, depending on the particular wastes being processed. Information on commonly occurring chemicals and advice on types of protective coatings is included in ACI 350R.

Reference:

- ACI 350-01/350R-01Code Requirements for Environmental Engineering Concrete Structures and Commentary

1.5.6   Chemical Attack of Concrete

Parts of some concrete structures, mainly for industrial uses, must be designed for exposure to chemicals, oils, food products and other solid, liquid or gaseous substances which may or may not cause corrosion of concrete.

To determine the effect that most such products or substances will have on exposed concrete surfaces, and for recommendations on protective coatings, the reader is referred to the following publications:

References:

- Effects of Substances on Concrete and Guide to Protective Treatment; Portland Cement Association (IS001.T)
- ACI 515.1R-79 (Revised 1985), A Guide to the Use of Waterproofing, Dampproofing, Protective and Decorative Barrier Systems for Concrete

1.6   Structural Integrity

1.6.1   Definition

A structure is said to have structural integrity if localized damage or failure of a structural member which may be initiated by an abnormal event does not lead to collapse of a disproportionately large part of the structure. Thus, the failure of one element should not lead to a "progressive collapse" or "incremental collapse" of the rest of the structure.

This definition is difficult to quantify. The extent of damage that is expected or acceptable is a function of the magnitude and extent of the overload causing the failure, the tributary area of the member which fails, the structural system and a host of other details. Thus, a multistorey concrete building with 16 to 20 main floor columns should have enough structural integrity to remain standing if one or two of the columns were destroyed in an explosion. However, a building having only two vertical supports would not have structural integrity unless its supports were designed to resist loads and forces of the magnitude created by the explosion.

1.6.2 Types of Incremental Collapse Observed in Reinforced Concrete Buildings

One of the most prominent cases of incremental collapse of a concrete structure occurred when a gas explosion blew two exterior walls out of a corner apartment on the 18th floor of a 22 storey precast building with walls and floors consisting of precast panels (Ronan Point, Canning Town, England). The loss of support of the floors above, caused this floor to collapse. The falling debris then caused all the floors and walls below to collapse progressively.

Progressive collapse failures are rare in continuously reinforced cast-in-place concrete structures. Formerly, a possible exception to this statement involved failure originating due to a punching shear failure at a column to slab connection in a flat plate. The portion of the slab supported by this connection could have then dropped, increasing the shear and moment at adjacent columns, causing them to fail. When this happened, the slab fell onto the slab below, causing it to fail as well. This progressed vertically down the building, causing each lower slab to fail in turn. Such failures could have been initiated by premature form removal, formwork fires, inadequate slab thickness or insufficient slab column reinforcement. The 2004 edition of CSA Standard A23.3 addresses this situation by means of Clause 13.10.6.

Other examples of incremental collapse involve buildings which collapsed when a column or wall was removed by a vehicle collision, a chemical, gas or bomb explosion or similar event. Still others involve collapses which occurred when a floor member failed and, in doing so, displaced its support horizontally so that other floor members were pulled off their supports.

Precast structures or other structures with friction connections between walls and floors are particularly susceptible to such damage. References (1) and (2) review a number of buildings which have developed incremental collapses.

1.6.3 Basic Requirements of NBC and CSA Standard A23.3

Section 4.1.1.3(1) of the 2005 National Building Code of Canada includes structural integrity as a requirement for structural design:

4.1.1.3(1) - Buildings and their structural members including formwork and falsework shall be designed to have sufficient structural capacity and structural integrity to resist safely and effectively all loads and effects of loads and influences that may reasonably be expected, having regard to the expected service life of buildings, and shall in any case satisfy the requirements of this Section.

Further explanation is given in Appendix "D" of the National Building Code.

Clause 8.1.5 of CSA Standard A23.3 restates the NBCC requirement as follows:

8.1.5 - Consideration shall be given to the integrity of the overall structural system to minimize the likelihood of a progressive collapse.

This is followed by a note which states:

Note: Requirements contained in this Standard generally provide a satisfactory level of structural integrity for most concrete structures for buildings. Supplementary provisions for structural integrity may be required for two-way slabs (see Clause 13.11.5), precast concrete structures (see Clause 16.5), tilt-up structures (see Clause 23.3.9), mixed or unusual structural systems and structures exposed to severe loads such as vehicle impact or chemical explosion. For further guidance see Appendix "D" of the National Building Code.

Clause 16.5, entitled Structural Integrity, states:

In buildings where precast concrete elements constitute a portion of the structural system, all structural elements shall be effectively tied together.

A Note to this Clause gives a series of references providing guidance on design for structural integrity in precast buildings.

It should be noted that the governing NBC requirement calls for buildings to be capable of resisting loads and effects of loads and influences that may "reasonably be expected". This clearly implies that only "accidental" abnormal events are to be considered. It must be recognized that well placed explosives or certain "acts of god" can bring down most structures. The Code does not require that buildings usually be designed to have structural integrity to resist collapse due to events like sabotage. Nonetheless, even such abnormal events might reasonably be expected under certain special circumstances and hence, in those specific cases, are worthy of consideration. For example, in countries where civil strife is the norm, sabotage of structures such as police stations is not unusual.

1.6.4   Design for Adequate Structural Integrity

As stated in the Note to Clause 8.1.5 of CSA Standard A23.3, most cast-in-place buildings designed in accordance with the Standard will possess a satisfactory level of structural integrity. This statement assumes that the layout of the structural systems and interaction between structural members will normally ensure a robust and stable design with sufficient redundancy. On this basis, no quantitative evaluation of structural integrity should be necessary insofar as the ordinary design conditions are concerned, which includes the effect of overloads during construction or those occurring in service which may cause localized failures. Thus, normally, only a general review of the structural system of such buildings will be needed to assess its likely failure modes. This review should ensure that no progressive collapse will result from any localized failures.

The Note to Clause 8.1.5 does, however, state that compliance with the requirement may need supplementary provisions to ensure structural integrity in the case of:

(a)   precast concrete structures (as stated in Clause 16.5),

(b)   for mixed or unusual structural systems and

(c)   for structures exposed to severe overloads, such as those due to vehicle impact or chemical explosion.

This subsection will therefore review the basic concepts which may be employed in the design of those buildings whose unusual layout or structural system does not result in a robust and stable design and where sufficient redundancy is absent, or in the design of those other relatively uncommon structures which may reasonably be expected to suffer accidental overloads.

In suggesting these rules of good practice, it must be recognized that definitive guidance for all cases cannot be provided. Just as there are so many ways that a localized failure might be initiated - gas explosions, vehicular collision, flooding, foundation failure, corrosion, fire or just understrength materials - and there are so many different types of structural systems involving different types of potential failures in each of those systems, no one set of rules can be universally applicable.

Four different design strategies are discussed in the structural integrity literature (see for example Ref. (3)):

1. **Control of events causing abnormal loads.** An example would be placing energy absorbing devices adjacent to columns supporting the floor and walls of a building adjacent to a high speed roadway so that the energy from a vehicle colliding with the column is dissipated before it strikes the pier. Other examples would be control of building explosions by avoiding the use of natural gas stoves or heating or the relocation of a high-risk building from an area immediately downstream of a suspect dam. In many cases, however, this type of strategy is impractical and even when it is employed, the structure should be resistant to progressive collapse resulting from other causes.

2. **Design to resist abnormal loads.** An abnormal load is one that is not normally considered in the design of the particular type of structure under consideration such as gas explosion, vehicle impact, etc. If the abnormal load or event can be defined and if loss of a particular member in a structure due to that abnormal event would lead to a progressive collapse, then that member should be able to resist the particular abnormal event or load. In general, this is not a satisfactory design strategy. In some cases, however, such as when the structural integrity of a building depends on, say, less than four columns, it may be the only practical strategy to employ. (See Subsection 1.6.5.)

3. **Design for alternate load paths in the damaged structure.** In this design process, the designer imagines that a column, beam or other member has been removed from the structure and then checks whether the structure can bridge the gap without collapsing. Design is carried out at service load levels to ensure the structure can support the dead load, a third to a half of the live load, the wind load exceeded about once a month, plus any debris resulting from the failure. The structure is permitted to undergo a considerable amount of localized collapse and deformation, provided the damage does not spread progressively. For this to occur, the structure must have a good floor plan with proper layout of walls and columns and be well tied together horizontally and vertically. (See Subsection 1.6.6.)

4. **Design using specified loads and local resistance details.** In this design strategy the designer does not postulate any particular mode of failure. Instead, a minimum structural resistance is provided along with a minimum amount of reinforcement to tie various parts of the structure. In addition, consideration is given to providing strong points in the building to anchor the tie forces. (see Subsection 1.6.7.)

In summary, the first of these scenarios is generally outside the structural engineer's control. The second, third and fourth methods will be discussed further - not to provide hard and fast rules, but rather to form a basis for approaching the problems of progressive collapse.

1.6.5   Design to Resist Abnormal Loads

Adoption of this design strategy is generally less desirable and less economical than either design for alternate load paths or design for specified loads and local resistance details, but for some buildings it cannot be avoided. Where the integrity of the structure depends entirely on one or two structural elements, these elements cannot be assumed to be removed or relied upon to anchor tie forces. Thus if the removal of such an element by an abnormal event that may reasonably be expected would initiate progressive collapse, that element must be designed to remain functional when the abnormal event occurs. The problem with this strategy is that all reasonably foreseeable abnormal events have to be anticipated and their effect assessed.

Assessment of the magnitude of accidental loads is discussed in the reference publications, in particular those adopted in Great Britain, which primarily address gas explosion.

A recent Canadian proposal, which was not adopted for inclusion in the NBC, suggested that:

(a) Vertical load supporting columns and wall columns should be designed to withstand, over a one storey height, a uniformly distributed horizontal load of 44 kN/m and a vertical load consisting of the specified dead load, half the live load and 20% of the specified wind load, and

(b) Exterior bearing walls at corners should be designed for a horizontal load of 135 kN distributed over the storey height for the outer 1.5 m length of wall adjacent to a corner and the vertical load given in (a) above, and

(c) Indispensable structural elements other than columns or corner wall elements should be designed for a lateral force of 33 kN/m^2 and a vertical load as given in (a) above. The lateral force should be assumed to be acting perpendicular to the element over adjacent areas which are capable of transmitting the force to the element in question.

In conclusion, design to resist abnormal loads should normally only be considered as a last resort. In cases when this strategy is employed, the designer should have rationalize, for the building in question, the magnitude of the loads which may reasonably be anticipated. It should be emphasized that the loadings suggested above are only provided to suggest the order of magnitude which these loads and forces may assume.

1.6.6   Design for Alternate Load Paths

The basic method of designing for structural integrity is to design a structure in such a way that it can bridge over the gap left when a structure component is removed.

Two examples are shown in Fig. 1.10 and 1.11. In the first, a wall has failed due to an internal explosion, poor construction, vehicle impact (if on the main floor) or some similar cause. The remaining structure should be able to bridge over the gap. For this to occur, the walls above the lost wall must act as cantilevers to support the loads formerly supported by the missing wall. This requires horizontal tension resistance in the floors, effective vertical ties from floor to floor above the gap and effective ties to transfer the overturning moments generated in the rest of the building. This resistance may involve large deformations in the vicinity of the damaged area, but the extent of damage should be limited.

The floor in the storey below the damaged area should be able to support the weight of any debris which falls onto it. Since this could exceed the conventional capacity of the floor, the floor would be allowed to deflect 100 to 200, or even 300 millimetres under this load, until it carried the load by a catenary action, or carried load in the perpendicular direction, or both. For this to occur, tie forces must be developed in various directions as shown in Fig. 1.11.

It should be emphasized that these actions are accomplished with a load factor greater than 1.0 against total collapse under the loadings expected to occur before the building can be repaired or at least propped up. Typical load combinations to be considered would be

$$R_f \geq D + 0.5L + 0.2W$$

$R_f \geq D - 0.3W$

where R_f is the factored resistance and D, L and W are the specified dead, live and wind loads.

The following are a number of ways in which the necessary load resistance might be developed in a damaged structure:

1. **Good Floor Plan** - The use of a systematic floor plan with a proper layout or walls and columns is probably the most important single step in achieving structural integrity. Such things as number, location and continuity of lateral load resisting elements should be an arrangement of longitudinal spline walls to support and reduce the span of the cross-walls.

2. **Beam Action of Walls** - Walls can be used to span over an opening if sufficient tying steel is provided at the top and bottom of walls to allow them to act as beams with the slabs above and below possibly acting as flanges.

3. **Tensile Action of Floor Slabs** - When an interior support is removed, the floor span will increase. In this case, the sagging of the slab will stretch the reinforcement until the slab carries the load as a membrane. Such a structure can carry very large loads at large deflections provided the tensile forces are adequately anchored in the surrounding structure and provided that shear failures will not occur.

4. **Changing Direction of Span of Floor or Roof Slab** - The membrane action discussed in the preceding paragraph may occur in the original direction of the span or in some other direction if the shrinkage and temperature reinforcement can be counted on to act as membrane reinforcement.

5. **Strong Points** - In some designs certain elements may need to be strengthened to carry the abnormal loads in order to complete an alternate path. Sometimes a return or flange on a wall will allow it to be used as a strong point, especially when tension tie forces must be mobilized at right angles to the wall.

6. **Adequate Diaphragm Action** - Diaphragms should be reinforced with tension tie members around their perimeters and around notches and discontinuities to allow adequate load distribution.

7. **Lines of Weakness** - Occasionally it will be desirable to provide lines of weakness to limit the spread of damage. The effect of such weak areas on other load paths should be carefully examined.

When using this strategy, designers should consider the effect of removal, one at a time, of:

- One span of any floor or roof element,

- One column or hanger in any one storey, except that in a multi-column structure, the loss of resistance of a column need not be considered, providing all columns are designed to resist abnormal loads as discussed in 1.6.5, or

- One length of bearing wall panel for any storey equal to 1½ times the storey height, unless the panels are prefabricated, when this length shall equal the panel length.

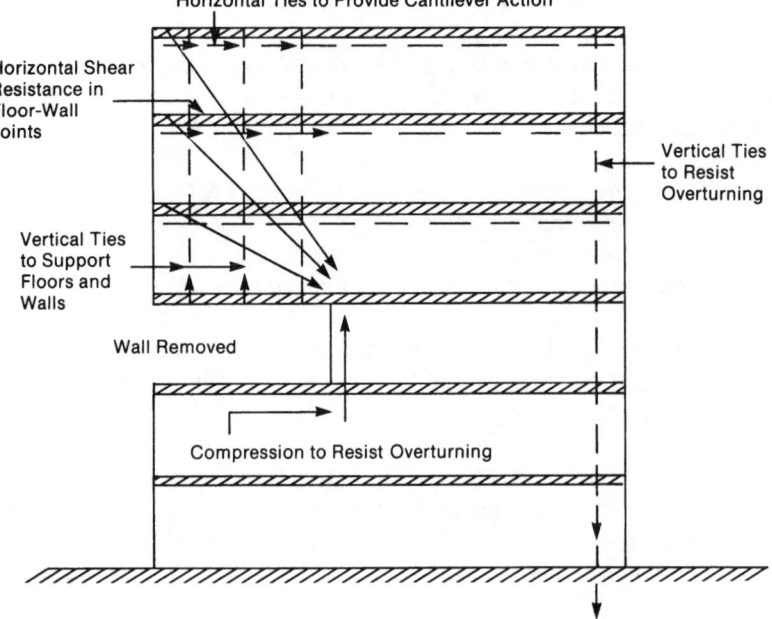

Fig. 1.10 Development of Alternate Load Path

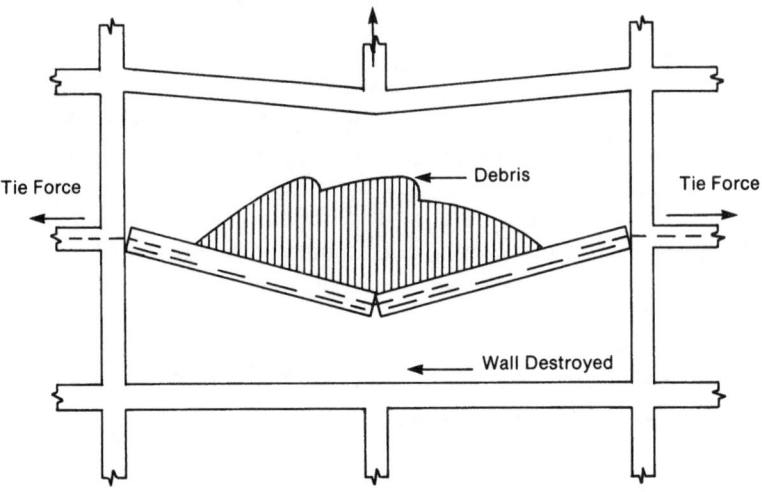

Fig. 1.11 Catenary Action of Floor Slab

1.6.7   Design Using Specified Loads and Local Resistance Details

This design process is an attempt to provide alternate load paths without consideration of specific damage scenarios and specific load paths. This "deemed to satisfy" method is relatively well developed for precast panel buildings, much less so for cast-in-place buildings.

(a) Precast Buildings

Figure 1.12 shows the types of ties required to develop overall structural integrity in a precast structure, the longitudinal ties, often placed in the joints between floor planks, ensure that the floor can develop membrane or catenary action to span over broken wall panels or to support heavy debris loading. The transverse ties, generally placed in the horizontal joints between the walls above and below a floor, serve to tie a series of wall panels together and act as tension flanges if these walls have to cantilever or bridge over a missing support. The peripheral ties act as tension flanges for the diaphragm action of the floors and to provide anchorage of the longitudinal and transverse ties. They also help create an edge member in case a corner loses support. Vertical ties are provided to keep the walls above a damaged support from falling and to serve as a tension tieback to resist overturning moments. Specific recommendations concerning tie forces are contained in References (4), (5), and (6).

It is important the ties be ductile to enable them to survive the movements associated with local damage. The ties must be designed and detailed so that the connections can undergo deformations, resist impact from falling debris, and in some cases undergo load reversals.

(b) **Cast-in-place Buildings**

Cast-in-place concrete buildings have continuity and redundancy that produce an inherent structural integrity. CSA Standard A23.3 recognizes this and, with one exception, does not require any particular details for structural integrity in cast-in-place construction. The exception involves punching shear in column-slab joints in flat-plates. Clause 13.11.5 requires special reinforcement through the column at the bottom of the slab. This reinforcement is not intended to prevent shear failures from occurring. Once such a failure has occurred, however, the slab is prevented from dropping on the floor below.

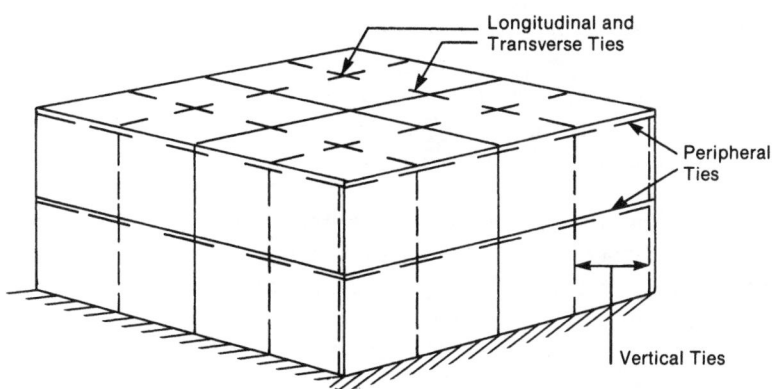

Fig. 1.12 Ties Required In a Precast Building

1.6.8   References

(1) Allen, D.E. and Shriever, W.R., "Progressive Collapse, Abnormal Loads and Building Codes", Structural Failures: Modes, Causes, Responsibilities, American Society of Civil Engineers, 1973, pp 21-47.

(2) Taylor, D.A., "Progressive Collapse", Canadian Journal of Civil Engineering, Vol. 2, No. 4, Dec. 1975, pp 517-529.

(3) Breen, J.E., "Developing Structural Integrity in Bearing Wall Buildings", Journal of the Prestressed Concrete Institute, Vol. 25, No. 1, Jan.-Feb. 1980, pp 42-73; Closure, Vol. 25, No. 4, July-Aug. 1980, pp 146-152.

(4) PCI Committee on Precast Bearing Wall Buildings, "Consideration for the Design of Precast Bearing Wall Buildings to Withstand Abnormal Loads", Journal of the Prestressed Concrete Institute, Vol. 21, No. 2, March/April 1976, pp 18-51.

(5) Fintel, M., Schultz, D.M. and Iqbal, M., "Report 2, Philosophy of Structural Response to Normal and Abnormal Loads", Design and Construction of Large-Panel Concrete Structures, Portland Cement Association, Skokie, Illinois, PCA Publication EB092D, August 1976, 133 pp.

(6) Schultz, D.M., "Report 6, Design Methodology", Design and Construction of Large-Panel Concrete Structures, Portland Cement Association, Skokie, Illinois, PCA Publication EB096D, March 1979, 112 pp.

1.7   Structural Loads

Loads for use in structural design are specified in the National Building Code of Canada. Dead loads include the weight of structural and non-structural members including all construction materials that are supported permanently. Tables 1.11 and 1.12 contain dead loads due to commonly used construction materials. Live loads, based on intended use and occupancy, are tabulated in Table 1.13. For live loads due to snow, rain, wind, earthquake an other effects, users are referred to the National Building Code of Canada.

1.8   Green Building Design

Today developers and owners are asking engineers and architects to design their projects in the most environmentally responsible way possible. Currently LEED Canada V1.0 is the most frequently used building rating system for determining the environmental impact of a building. LEED stands for Leadership in Energy and Environmental Design. LEED Canada V1.0 was adapted from the US Green Building Council's LEED-NC 2.1 rating system and was tailored for the Canadian climate and construction practices. It is designed for new construction and major renovations.

The LEED rating system evaluates project performance from a whole-building, whole-life perspective, encouraging healthy, high-quality performance with reduced environmental impact. This is done by awarding points for certain performance criteria that a project meets. The five principal LEED categories are 1) Sustainable Sites, 2) Water Efficiency, 3) Energy and Atmosphere, 4) Materials and Resources and 5) Indoor Environmental Quality. An additional category called Innovation & Design Process, allows designers to provide solutions not captured in the 5 standard categories. Graduated LEED ratings of Certified, Silver, Gold and Platinum are awarded based on the number of points achieved by the design.

An in depth discussion of Sustainable Development is beyond the scope of the this book, however, the Cement Association of Canada has developed a "Guide to Sustainable Development with Concrete" to assist designers in evaluating the measures necessary to achieve a variety of LEED ratings. Users are encouraged to visit the CAC website at www.cement.ca to obtain a copy of the Guide and more information on green building design and sustainable development with concrete.

1.9   Beam Diagrams

Beam diagrams for single span beams with different support and loading conditions are provided in Table 1.14. The application of these diagram can be extended to cases where more than one loading condition can be superimposed.

Bending moments and support reactions for continuous beams with equal spans are given in Tables 1.15, 1.16 and 1.17. These figures cover either uniformly distributed loads or concentrated loads at centres or at third points. Pattern loading, for design purposes, is also included.

Table 1.18 provides approximate design moments and the expressions specified in CSA Standard A23.3. The use of Table 1.18 is limited to beams with approximately equal spans, where the longer of the two adjacent spans is not greater than the shorter by more than 20 percent.

1.10   Frame Constants

The majority of concrete construction consists of prismatic members between the supporting elements. However, one of the advantages of using concrete as a construction material is that it can be molded into any geometric shape. Sometimes the structural engineer makes use of this advantage and increases the cross section within a member where needed. This results in a change in stiffness and the distribution of moments. Furthermore, concrete members, monolithically cast with the adjoining members, have end regions that are integral parts of the adjoining members. These end regions are generally considered to have very high stiffness and affect the distribution of moments. Tables 1.19 through 1.23 contain frame constants for non-prismatic members and members with one or two infinitely stiff end regions. The stiffness factors included in the tables are used to determine member stiffness K. (K = kEI/L).

1.11   Sectional Properties

Geometric properties of various sections that may be required in a structural design process are given in Table 1.24. For sectional areas and moments of inertia and centroid of 'T' sections see Chapter 6.

Table 1.1:   Cement Types and Their Effect on Concrete

CSA Cement Types		Type GU	Type MS Moderate sulfate resistance	Type MH Moderate heat of hydration	Type HE High early strength	Type LH Low heat of hydration	Type HS High sulfate resistance
Heat of hydration during the first 7 days (% of Type GU)		100	80 to 85	80 to 85	Up to 150%	40 to 60	60 to 75
Relative compressive strength (% of Type GU† at 28 days)	1 day	-	-	-	47	-	-
	3 day	47	38		83	32	40
	7 day	68	60		-	-	60
	28 day	100	100	-	-	94	100
	91 day	-	-	-	-	125	-
Type of cement to be used when % of SO_4 in soil	< 0.10	x	x		x	x	x
	0.10 – 0.20		x			x	x
	> 0.20						x
Type of cement to be used when SO_4 in groundwater (mg/L)	< 150	x	x		x	x	x
	150 – 1000		x			x	x
	> 1000						x

*   Moderate with respect to sulphate-resistance or heat of hydration.

** Temperature *rise* in normal portland cement concrete due to heat of hydration is *approximately* 20°C at 1 day and 30°C at 7 days.

† The values set forth in Table 1.1 reflect the minimum mortar cube strengths required by CSA Standard A5 and are not necessarily representative of concrete strengths. Factors such as variations in water-cement ratios, aggregate type and quantity, concrete admixtures used and curing will have a very significant effect on concrete strength at any age. These variables may also alter the strength relationship in the concrete between types of cement used.

Table 1.2: Creep and Shrinkage Modification Factors for Non-Standard Conditions

$$Q_{cr} = Q_a\,Q_h\,Q_f\,Q_r\,Q_s\,Q_v$$
$$P_{sh} = P_c\,P_h\,P_f\,P_r\,P_s\,P_v$$

Age at Loading days	Q_a	
	moist cured	steam cured
1	1.25	1.00
7	1.00	0.94
20	0.87	0.85
60	0.77	0.76

Relative Humidity %	Q_h	P_h
40	1.00	1.00
60	0.87	0.80
80	0.73	0.60
100	0.60	0.00

Ratio of Fine to Total Aggr.	Q_f	P_f
0.30	0.95	0.72
0.40	0.98	0.86
0.50	1.00	1.00
0.70	1.05	1.04

Volume Surface Ratio, mm	Q_r	P_r
38	1.00	1.00
75	0.82	0.84
150	0.70	0.59
250	0.67	0.37

Slump. mm	Q_s	P_s
50	0.95	0.97
70	1.00	1.00
125	1.15	1.09

Air %	Q_v	P_v
≤ 6	1.00	1.00
8	1.18	1.01
10	1.36	1.03

	Cement Content, kg/m^3		
	225	300	410
P_c	0.89	0.93	1.00

Notes:
— Standard conditions produce modification factors of 1.0.
— Volume – surface ratio of a rectangular member having a X b cross-section is ab/(2a + 2b)
— Ratio of fine aggregate to total aggregate is expressed as the ratio of the weights
— For average ambient relative humidity see Fig. 1.6.

Table 1.3: Properties of Prestressing Wires and Seven-Wire Strands

Tendon Type	Grade F_{pu} Mpa	Size Designation	Nominal Diameter mm	Nominal Area mm^2	Nominal Mass kg/m
Prestressing Wire	1550	8	8.00	50.27	0.394
	1620	7	7.00	38.48	0.302
	1650	6	6.35	31.67	0.248
	1720	6	6.35	31.67	0.248
		7	7.00	38.48	0.302
		8	8.00	50.27	0.394
	1760	7	7.00	38.48	0.302
Seven Wire Strand	1720	6	6.35	23.2	0.182
		8	7.95	37.4	0.294
		9	9.53	51.6	0.405
		11	11.13	69.7	0.548
		13	12.70	92.9	0.730
		15	15.24	138.7	1.094
	1760	16	15.47	148.4	1.173
	1860	9	9.53	54.8	0.432
		11	11.13	74.2	0.582
		13	12.70	98.7	0.775
		15	15.24	140.0	1.109

Table 1.4: Properties of Plain and Deformed Prestressing

Tendon Type	Grade F_{pu} MPa	Nominal Diameter mm	Nominal Area mm^2	Nominal Mass kg/m
Plain Prestressing Bars	1030	19	284	2.23
		22	387	3.04
		25	503	3.97
		28	639	5.03
		32	794	6.21
		36	955	7.52
	1100	19	284	2.23
		22	387	3.04
		25	503	3.97
		28	639	5.03
		32	794	6.21
		36	955	7.52
Deformed Prestressing Bars	1030	26	551	4.48
		32	804	6.54
		36	1018	8.28
	1080	15	177	1.46
		20	314	2.56
	1100	26	551	4.48
		32	804	6.54

Table 1.5: Properties of Deformed Reinforcing Bars

Bar Designation	Nominal Dimensions			Mass per Unit Length kg/m
	Diameter mm	Area mm^2	Perimeter mm	
10	11.3	100	35.5	0.785
15	16.0	200	50.1	1.570
20	19.5	300	61.3	2.355
25	25.2	500	79.2	3.925
30	29.9	700	93.9	5.495
35	35.7	1000	112.2	7.850
45	43.7	1500	137.3	11.775
55	56.4	2500	177.2	19.625

Notes:

1. Bar numbers are based on the rounded off nominal diameter of the bars.
2. Nominal dimensions are equivalent to those of a plain round bar having the same mass per metre as the deformed bar.
3. Both Billet Steel Bars and Weldable Low Alloy Steel Bars are produced in the above standard sizes. However, all sizes may not be available; manufacturers should be consulted to verify availability.

Table 1.6   Tensile and Bend Test Requirements for Billet-Steel Bars Conforming to CSA G30.18-M92

	Grade 400	Grade 500
Tensile Strength, (Min) MPa	1.25 × Actual Yield Strength	1.25 x Actual Yield Strength
Yield Point Strength, Minimum MPA	400	500
Elongation in 200 mm Gauge Length Minimum Percent Bar Designation Number		
10,15,20	9	9
25	8	8
30,35,45,55	7	7
Diameter of Pin for Bend Tests[*] d= Nominal Diameter of Specimen Test Bends 180° Bar Designation Number		
10M,15M	4d	5d
20M	5d	6d
25M	6d	6d
30M, 35M	8d	8d

*   When specified by the purchaser, bar sizes No. 45 and 55 shall stand being bent through 90° around a pin of diameter equal to 10d.

Table 1.7: Tensile and Bend Test Requirements for Weldable Low Alloy Steel Bars Conforming To CSA G30.18-M92

	400W	500W
Tensile strength, min MPa		
Yield Strength*, min. MPa	400	500
Max. MPa	525	650
Elongation in 200 mm, minimum percent; Bar Designation Number		
10M, 15M, 20M and 25M	13	12
30M, 35M, 45M, 55M	12	10
Diameter of Pin for Bend Tests; d = Nominal Diameter of Specimen Test Bends 180°, RBar Designation Number		
10M, 15M	3d	3d
20M, 25M	4d	4d
30M, 35M	6d	6d
45M, 55M	8d	8d

*   Tensile strength be not less than 1.15 times the actual yield strength

Table 1.8: Tensile and Bend Test Requirements for Smooth Wires Conforming to CSA G30.3-M198

Size Number	Minimum Tensile Strength (MPa)	Minimum Yield Strength (MPa)
MW 7.7 and larger	515	450
Smaller than MW 7.7	485	385
	Bend Test (180°)	
MW 45.2 And smaller	Bend around a pin the diameter of which is equal to the diameter of the specimen.	
Larger than MW 45.2	Bend around a pin the diameter of which is equal to twice the diameter of the specimen.	

Table 1.9: Tensile and Bend Test Requirements for Deformed Wires Conforming to CSA G30-14.M1983

Use	Minimum Tensile Strength (MPa)	Minimum Yield Strength (MPa)
Wires *not* to be used for fabrication of welded fabric	585	515
Wires to be used for fabrication of welded fabric	550	485
Size Number	Bend Test (90°)	
MD 38.7 and smaller	Bend around a pin the diameter of which is equal to twice the nominal diameter of the specimen.	
Larger than MD 38.7	Bend around a pin the diameter of which is equal to four times the nominal diameter of the specimen.	

Table 1.10:   Properties of Welded Wire Fabric

Designation*	Wire Diameter mm	Wire Cross-Sectional Area Long. mm²	Wire Cross-Sectional Area Transv. mm²	Mass per Unit Area kg/m²	Cross-Sectional Area Per Metre Width Long. mm²	Cross-Sectional Area Per Metre Width Transv. mm²
152 X 152 MW 9.1 X MW 9.1	3.40	9.1	9.1	1.04	59.8	59.8
152 X 152 MW 11.1 X MW 11.1	3.76	11.1	11.1	1.26	73.0	73.0
152 X 152 MW 13.3 X MW 13.3	4.12	13.3	13.3	1..50	87.5	87.5
152 X 152 MW 18.7 X MW 18.7	4.88	18.7	18.7	2.11	123.0	123.0
152 X 152 MW 25.8 X MW 25.8	5.74	25.8	25.8	2.91	170.0	170.0
152 X 152 MW 34.9 X MW 34.9	6.67	34.9	34.9	3.95	230.0	230.0
152 X 152 MW 47.6 X MW 47.6	7.79	47.6	47.6	5.38	313.0	313.0
102 X 102 MW 9.1 X MW 9.1	3.40	9.1	9.1	1.52	89.2	89.2
102 X 102 MW 11.1 X MW 11.1	3.76	11.1	11.1	1.83	109.0	109.0
102 X 102 MW 13.3 X MW 13.3	4.12	13.3	13.3	2.18	130.0	130.0
102 X 102 MW 18.7 X MW 18.7	4.88	18.7	18.7	3.07	183.0	183.0
102 X 102 MW 25.8 X MW 25.8	5.74	25.8	25.8	4.23	253.0	253.0
51 X 51 MW 3.2 X MW 3.2	2.03	3.2	3.2	1.03	62.8	62.8
51 X 51 MW 5.6 X MW 5.6	2.69	5.6	5.6	1.80	110.0	110.0
51 X 51 MW 9.1 X MW 9.1	3.40	9.1	9.1	2.94	178.0	178.0

*The first two numbers give the spacing in mm, and the second two give the size of wire.

Table 1.11:   Dead Loads for Floors, Ceilings, Roofs and Walls

	Load (kN/m²)
Floorings:	
Normal density concrete topping, per 10mm of thickness	0.24
Semi-low density concrete (1900 kg/m³) topping, per 10mm	0.19
Low density concrete (1500 kg/m³) topping, per 10mm	0.15
22mm hardwood floor on sleepers, clipped to concrete without fill	0.24
40mm terrazzo floor finish directly on slab	0.95
40mm terrazzo floor finish on 25mm mortar bed	1.49
25mm terrazzo floor finish on 50mm concrete bed	1.79
20mm ceramic or quarry tile on 12mm mortar bed	0.80
20mm ceramic or quarry tile on 25mm mortar bed	1.06
8mm linoleum or asphalt tile directly on concrete	0.06
8mm linoleum or asphalt tile on 25mm mortar bed	0.59
20mm mastic floor	0.45
Hardware flooring, 22mm thick	0.19
Subflooring (softwood), 20mm thick	0.13
Asphaltic concrete, 40mm thick	0.90
Ceilings:	
12.7mm gypsum board	0.10
15.9mm gypsum board	0.12
19mm gypsum board directly on concrete	0.24
20mm plaster directly on concrete	0.26
20mm plaster on metal lath furring	0.40
Suspended ceilings, add	0.10
Acoustical tile	0.05
Acoustical tile on wood furring strips	0.15
Mechanical duct allowance	0.19

Table 1.11:   (Continued)

	Load (kN/m^2)
Roofs:	
Five-ply felt and gravel (or slag)	0.31
Three-ply felt and gravel (or slag)	0.27
Five-ply felt composition roof, no gravel	0.20
Three-ply felt composition roof, no ravel	0.15
Asphalt strip shingles	0.15
Slate, 8mm thick	0.57
Gypsum, per 10mm of thickness	0.08
Insulating concrete, per 10mm	0.06

	Load (kN/m^2)		
	Unplastered	One side Plastered	Both sides plastered
Walls (Brick, Concrete Block or Tile)			
100mm brick wall	1.86	2.10	2.33
200mm brick wall	3.77	4.00	4.24
300mm brick wall	5.59	5.83	6.06
100mm hollow normal density concrete block	1.37	1.61	1.84
150mm hollow normal density concrete block	1.67	1.90	2.14
200mm hollow normal density concrete block	2.11	2.34	2.58
250mm hollow normal density concrete block	2.50	2.74	2.97
300mm hollow normal density concrete block	2.94	3.18	3.38
100mm hollow low density block or tile	1.08	1.31	1.55
150mm hollow low density block or tile	1.28	1.51	1.75
200mm hollow low density block or tile	1.62	1.85	2.09
250mm hollow low density block or tile	1.91	2.15	2.38
300mm hollow low density block or tile	2.26	2.49	2.73
100mm brick 100mm hollow normal density block backing ...	3.24	3.47	3.71
100mm brick 200mm hollow normal density block backing ...	3.97	4.21	4.44
100mm brick 300mm hollow normal density block backing ...	4.81	5.04	5.28
100mm brick 100mm hollow low density block backing	2.94	3.18	3.41
100mm brick 200mm hollow low density block backing	3.48	3.72	3.95
100mm brick 300mm hollow low density block backing	4.12	4.36	4.59

	Load (kN/m^2)
Walls (Others):	
Windows, glass, frame and sash	0.38
100mm stone	2.59
Steel or wood studs, lath, 20mm plaster	0.86
Steel or wood studs, lath, 15.9mm gypsum board each side	0.28
Steel or wood studs, 2 layers 12.7mm gypsum board each side	0.44
Exterior stud walls with brick veneer	2.30

Table 1.12   Minimum Design Loads for Materials

Material	Load (kN/m³)	Material	Load (kN/m³)
Bituminous products:		Lead	111.6
Asphaltum	12.7	Lime	
Graphite	21.2	Hydrated, loose	5.0
Paraffin	8.8	Hydrated, compacted	7.1
Petroleum, crude	8.6	Masonry, ashlar:	
Petroleum, refined	7.9	Granite	25.9
Petroleum, benzine	7.2	Limestone, crystalline	25.9
Petroleum, gasoline	6.6	Limestone, oolitic	21.2
Pitch	10.8	Marble	27.2
Tar	11.8	Sandstone	22.6
Brass	82.7	Masonry, brick:	
Bronze	86.7	Hard (low absorption)	20.4
Cast-stone masonry (cement, stone, sand)	22.6	Medium (Medium absorption)	18.1
Cement, portland, loose	14.1	Soft (high absorption)	15.7
Ceramic tile	23.6	Masonry, rubble mortar:	
Charcoal	1.9	Granite	24.0
Cinder fill	9.0	Limestone, crystalline	23.1
Cinders, dry, in bulk	7.1	Limestone, oolitic	21.7
Coal		Marble	24.5
Anthracite, piled	8.2	Sandstone	21.5
Bituminous, piled	7.4	Mortar, hardened:	
Lignite, piled	7.4	Cement	20.4
Peat, dry, piled	3.6	Lime	17.3
Concrete, plain:		Particleboard	7.1
Cinder	17.0	Plywood	5.7
Expanded-slag aggregate	15.7	Riprap (not submerged):	
Haydite (burned-clay aggregate)	14.1	Limestone	13.0
Slag	20.7	Sandstone	14.1
Stone (including gravel)	22.6	Sand	
Vermiculite and perlite aggregate		Clean and dry	14.1
nonload-bearing	4.0–8.0	River, dry	16.7
Other light aggregate, load-bearing	11.0–16.5	Slag	
Concrete, reinforced:		Bank	11.0
Cinder	17.4	Bank screenings	17.0
Slag	21.7	Machine	15.1
Stone (including gravel)	23.6	Sand	8.2
Copper	87.4	Slate	27.0
Cork, compressed	2.3	Steel, cold-drawn	76.8
Earth (not submerged):		Stone, quarried, piled:	
Clay, dry	10.0	Basalt, granite, gneiss	15.1
Clay, damp	17.3	Limestone, marble, quartz	14.9
Clay and gravel, dry	15.7	Sandstone	12.9
Silt, moist, loose	12.3	Shale	14.5
Silt, moist, packed	15.1	Greenstone, hornblende	16.8
Silt, flowing	17.0	Terra cotta, architectural:	
Sand and gravel, dry, loose	15.7	Voids filled	18.9
Sand and gravel, dry, packed	17.3	Voids unfilled	11.3
Sand and gravel, wet	18.9	Tin	72.1
Earth (submerged):		Water	
Clay	12.6	Fresh	9.8
Soil	11.0	Sea	10.1
River mud	14.1	Wood, seasoned:	
Sand or gravel	9.4	Ash, commercial white	6.4
Sand or gravel, and clay	10.2	Cypress, southern	5.3
Gravel, dry	16.3	Fir, Douglas, coast region	5.3
Gypsum, loose	11.0	Hem fir	4.4
Gypsum wallboard	7.9	Oak, commercial reds and whites	7.4
Ice	9.0	Pine, southern yellow	5.8
Iron		Redwood	4.4
Cast	70.7	Spruce, red, white, and Sitka	4.6
Wrought	75.4	Western hemlock	5.0
		Zinc, rolled sheet	70.6

Table 1.13:   Live Loads for Floors or Roofs due to Use and Occupancy (Reproduced from the 2005 NBC)

NBC Table 4.1.5.3.
Specified Uniformly Distributed Live Loads on an Area of Floor/Roof

Use of Area of Floor or Roof	Minimum Specified Load, kPa
Assembly Areas	
a) Except for those areas listed under (b) and (c), assembly areas with or without fixed seats including Arenas, Auditoria, Churches, Dance floors, Dining areas[1] Foyers and entrance halls, Grandstands, reviewing stands and bleachers, Gymnasia, Museums, Promenades, Rinks, Stadia *Theatres* and other areas with similar uses	4.8
b) Assembly areas with fixed seats that have backs over at least 80% of the assembly area for the following uses: Churches, Courtrooms, Lecture Halls *Theatres*	2.4
c) Classrooms with or without fixed seats	2.4
Attics	
Accessible by a stairway in *residential occupancies* only	1.4
Having limited accessibility so that there is no storage of equipment or material[2]	0.5
Balconies	
Exterior	4.8
Interior and *mezzanines* that could be used by an assembly of people as a viewing area[2]	4.8
Interior and *mezzanines* other than above	[3]
Corridors, lobbies and aisles	
Other than those listed below	4.8
Not more than 1200 mm in width and all upper floor corridors of residential areas only of apartments, hotels and motels (that cannot be used by an assembly of people as a viewing area)[2]	[3]
Equipment areas and *service rooms* including Generator rooms Mechanical equipment exclusive of elevators Machine rooms Pump rooms Transformer vaults Ventilating or air-conditioning equipment	3.6[4]
Exits and fire escapes	4.8
Factories	6.0[4]
Footbridges	4.8
Garages for	
Passenger cars	2.4
Light trucks and unloaded buses	6.0
Loaded buses and trucks and all other trucking spaces	12.0
Kitchens (other than residential)	4.8
Libraries	
Stack rooms	7.2
Reading and study rooms	2.9

Use of Area of Floor or Roof	Minimum Specified Load, kPa
Office areas (not including record storage and computer rooms) located in	
Basement and *first storey*	4.8
Floors above *first storey*	2.4
Operating rooms and laboratories	3.6
Patient's bedrooms	1.9
Recreation areas that cannot be used for assembly purposes including	
Billiard rooms, Bowling alleys, Pool rooms	3.6
Residential areas (within the scope of Subsection 2.1.2.)	
Sleeping and living quarters in apartments, hotels, motels, boarding schools and colleges	1.9
Residential areas (within the scope of Subsection 2.1.3.)	
Bedrooms	1.9
Other areas	1.9
Stairs within *dwelling units*	1.9
Retail and wholesale areas	4.8
Roofs	$1.0^{(5)}$
Sidewalks and driveways over areaways and *basements*	12.0
Storage areas	$4.8^{(4)}$
Toilet areas	2.4
Underground slabs with earth cover	$^{(6)}$
Warehouses	$4.8^{(4)}$

NBC Notes to Table 4.1.5.3.:
(1)   See Article 4.1.5.6.
(2)   See Appendix A.
(3)   See Article 4.1.5.4.
(4)   See Article 4.1.5.7.
(5)   See Article 4.1.6.1.
(6)   See Article 4.1.5.5.

Table 1.14:   Beam Diagrams

Simple Beam — uniformly distributed load

$R = V$ .... $= \dfrac{w\ell}{2}$

V_x .... $= w\left(\dfrac{\ell}{2} - x\right)$

M max. (at centre) .... $= \dfrac{w\ell^2}{8}$

M_x .... $= \dfrac{wx}{2}(\ell - x)$

Δ max. (at centre) .... $= \dfrac{5\,w\ell^4}{384\,EI}$

Δ_x .... $= \dfrac{wx}{24\,EI}(\ell^3 - 2\ell x^2 + x^3)$

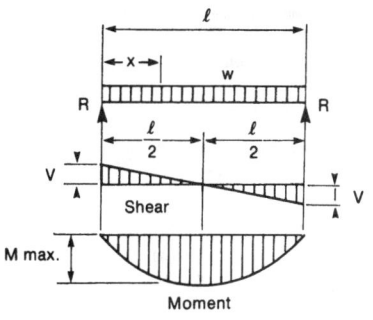

Simple Beam — load increasing uniformly to one end

$R_1 = V_1$ .... $= \dfrac{w\ell}{6}$

$R_2 = V_2$ .... $= \dfrac{w\ell}{3}$

V_x .... $= \dfrac{w\ell}{3} - \dfrac{wx^2}{2\ell}$

M max. $\left(\text{at } x = \sqrt{\dfrac{\ell}{3}} = 0.5774\ell\right)$ .... $= \dfrac{w\ell^2}{9\sqrt{3}} = 0.06415 w\ell^2$

M_x .... $= \dfrac{wx}{6\ell}(\ell^2 - x^2)$

Δ max. $\left(\text{at } x = \ell\sqrt{1 - \sqrt{\dfrac{8}{15}}} = 0.5193\ell\right)$ ...... $0.00652\,\dfrac{w\ell^4}{EI}$

Δ_x .... $= \dfrac{wx}{360\,EI\ell}(3x^4 - 10\ell^2 x^2 + 7\ell^4)$

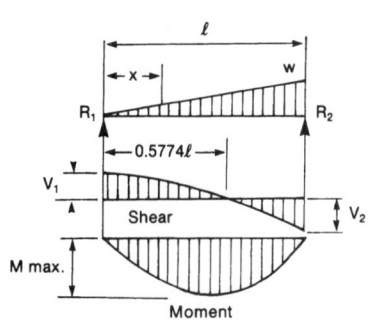

Simple Beam — load increasing uniformly to centre

$R = V$ .... $= \dfrac{w\ell}{4}$

$V_x \left(\text{when } x < \dfrac{\ell}{2}\right)$ .... $= \dfrac{w}{4\ell}(\ell^2 - 4x^2)$

M max. (at centre) .... $= \dfrac{w\ell^2}{12}$

$M_x \left(\text{when } x < \dfrac{\ell}{2}\right)$ .... $= \dfrac{w\ell x}{2}\left(\dfrac{1}{2} - \dfrac{2x^2}{3\ell^2}\right)$

Δ max. (at centre) .... $= \dfrac{w\ell^4}{120\,EI}$

Δ_x .... $= \dfrac{wx}{960\,EI\,\ell}(5\ell^2 - 4x^2)^2$

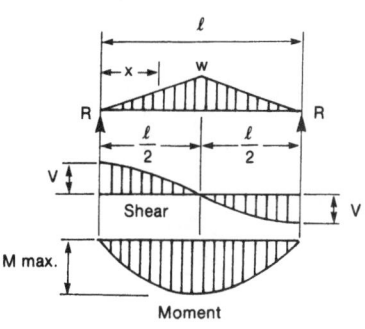

Note:
w: Distributed load per unit length. In the case of triangular distribution, w represents the maximum intensity of load per unit length.
P: Concentrated load.

Table 1.14: (Continued)

Simple Beam — uniform load partially distributed

$R_1 = V_1$ (max. when $a < c$) .... $= \dfrac{wb}{2\ell}(2c + b)$

$R_2 = V_2$ (max. when $a > c$) .... $= \dfrac{wb}{2\ell}(2a + b)$

V_x (when $x > a$ and $< (a + b)$) .... $= R_1 - w(x - a)$

M max. $\left(\text{at } x = a + \dfrac{R_1}{w}\right)$ .... $= R_1\left(a + \dfrac{R_1}{2w}\right)$

M_x (when $x < a$) .... $= R_1 x$

M_x (when $x > a$ and $< (a + b)$) .... $= R_1 x - \dfrac{w}{2}(x - a)^2$

M_x (when $x > (a + b)$) .... $= R_2 (\ell - x)$

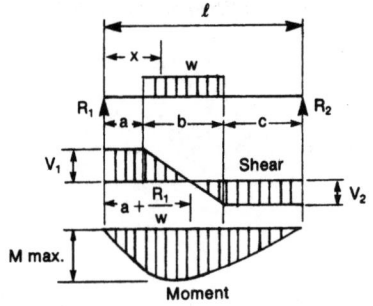

Beam fixed at both ends — symmetrical trapezoidal load

$R = V$ .... $= \dfrac{w\ell}{2}\left(1 - \dfrac{a}{\ell}\right)$

M_1 .... $= -\dfrac{w\ell^2}{12}\left(1 - 2\dfrac{a^2}{\ell^2} + \dfrac{a^3}{\ell^3}\right)$

M_2 .... $= \dfrac{w\ell^2}{24}\left(1 - 2\dfrac{a^3}{\ell^3}\right)$

M_x (when $x < a$) .... $= M_1 + R_1 x - \dfrac{wx^3}{6a}$

M_x (when $a < x < \ell - a$) .... $= M_1 + R_1 x - \dfrac{wa}{2}\left(x - \dfrac{2}{3}a\right)$
$\qquad\qquad\qquad\qquad\qquad\qquad - \dfrac{w}{2}(x - a)^2$

Note: When $a = \ell/2$ loading is triangular

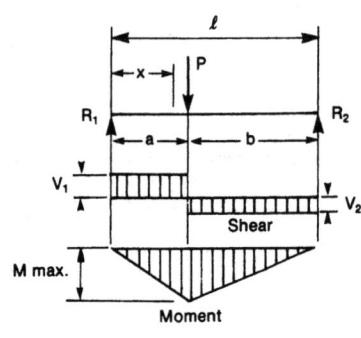

Simple Beam — concentrated load at any point

$R_1 = V_1$ (max. when $a < b$) .... $= \dfrac{Pb}{\ell}$

$R_2 = V_2$ (max. when $a > b$) .... $= \dfrac{Pa}{\ell}$

M max. (at point of load) .... $= \dfrac{Pab}{\ell}$

M_x (when $x < a$) .... $= \dfrac{Pbx}{\ell}$

Δmax. $\left(\text{at } x = \sqrt{\dfrac{a(a + 2b)}{3}} \text{ when } a > b\right)$ $= \dfrac{Pab(a + 2b)\sqrt{3a(a + 2b)}}{27\,EI\ell}$

Δa (at point of load) .... $= \dfrac{Pa^2b^2}{3\,EI\ell}$

Δ_x (when $x < a$) .... $= \dfrac{Pbx}{6\,EI\ell}(\ell^2 - b^2 - x^2)$

Note:
w: Distributed load per unit length. In the case of triangular distribution, w represents the maximum intensity of load per unit length.
P: Concentrated load.

Table 1.14:   (Continued)

Beam fixed at both ends — uniformly distributed loads

$R = V$ .... $= \dfrac{w\ell}{2}$

V_x .... $= w\left(\dfrac{\ell}{2} - x\right)$

M max. (at ends) .... $= -\dfrac{w\ell^2}{12}$

M_1 (at centre) .... $= \dfrac{w\ell^2}{24}$

M_x .... $= \dfrac{w}{12}(6\ell x - \ell^2 - 6x^2)$

Δmax. (at centre) .... $= \dfrac{w\ell^4}{384\ EI}$

Δ_x .... $= \dfrac{wx^2}{24\ EI}(\ell - x)^2$

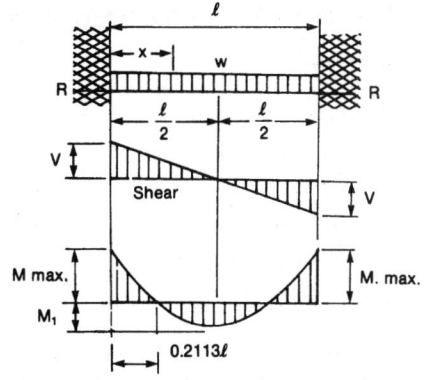

Beam fixed at both ends — concentrated load at any point

$R_1 = V_1$ (max. when $a < b$) .... $= \dfrac{Pb^2}{\ell^3}(3a + b)$

$R_2 = V_2$ (max. when $a > b$) .... $= \dfrac{Pa^2}{\ell^3}(a + 3b)$

M_1 (max. when $a < b$) .... $= -\dfrac{Pab^2}{\ell^2}$

M_2 (max. when $a > b$) .... $= -\dfrac{Pa^2b}{\ell^2}$

M_a (at point of load) .... $= \dfrac{2Pa^2b^2}{\ell^3}$

M_x (when $x < a$) .... $= R_1x - \dfrac{Pab^2}{\ell^2}$

Δmax. $\left(\text{when } a > b \text{ at } x = \dfrac{2a\ell}{3a+b}\right)$ .... $= \dfrac{2Pa^3b^2}{3\ EI\ (3a+b)^2}$

Δ_a (at point of load) .... $= \dfrac{Pa^3b^3}{3\ EI\ell^3}$

Δ_x (when $x < a$) .... $= \dfrac{Pb^2x^2}{6\ EI\ell^3}(3a\ell - 3ax - bx)$

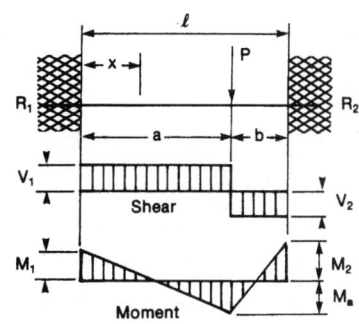

Beam fixed at both ends — uniform load partially distributed

M_1 .... $= \dfrac{w}{12\ell^2}\left[(\ell - a)^3(\ell + 3a) - c^3(4\ell - 3c)\right]$

M_2 .... $= \dfrac{w}{12\ell^2}\left[(\ell - c)^3(\ell + 3c) - a^3(4\ell - 3a)\right]$

$R_1 = V_1$ .... $= \dfrac{1}{\ell}\left[M_1 - M_2 + wc\left(c + \dfrac{b}{2}\right)\right]$

$R_2 = V_2$ .... $= \dfrac{1}{\ell}\left[M_2 - M_1 + wc\left(a + \dfrac{b}{2}\right)\right]$

M_x (when $x < a$) .... $= R_1x - M_1$

M_x (when $a < x < (a + c)$) .... $= R_1x - M_1 - \dfrac{w}{2}(x - a)^2$

M_x (when $x > (a + c)$) .... $= R_2(\ell - x) - M_2$

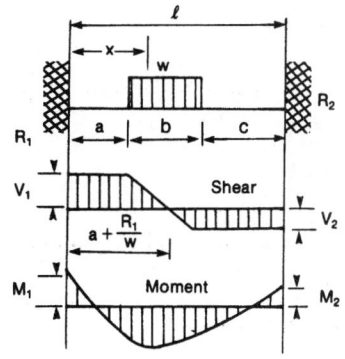

Note:
w: Distributed load per unit length. In the case of triangular distribution, w represents the maximum intensity of load per unit length.
P: Concentrated load.

Table 1.14:   (Continued)

Beam fixed at both ends — load increasing uniformly to one end

$R_1 = V_1$ .... $= \dfrac{3wl}{20}$

$R_2 = V_2$ .... $= \dfrac{7wl}{20}$

V_x .... $= \dfrac{3wl}{20} - \dfrac{wx^2}{2l}$

M_1 .... $= -\dfrac{wl^2}{30}$

M_2 .... $= -\dfrac{wl^2}{20}$

M_x .... $= \dfrac{3wlx}{20} - \dfrac{wl^2}{30} - \dfrac{wx^3}{6l}$

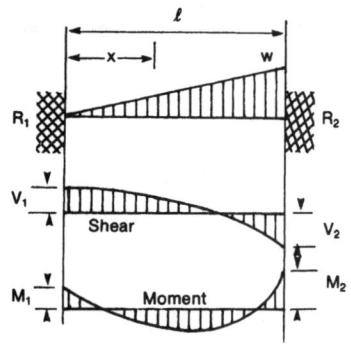

Beam fixed at one end, supported at other — uniformly distributed load

$R_1 = V_1$ .... $= \dfrac{3wl}{8}$

$R_2 = V_2$ max. .... $= \dfrac{5wl}{8}$

V_x .... $= R_1 - wx$

M max. .... $= -\dfrac{wl^2}{8}$

$M_1 \left(\text{at } x = \dfrac{3}{8}l\right)$ .... $= \dfrac{9}{128} wl^2$

M_x .... $= R_1 x - \dfrac{wx^2}{2}$

Δmax. $\left(\text{at } x = \dfrac{l}{16}(1 + \sqrt{33}) = 0.4215l\right)$. $= \dfrac{wl^4}{185\ EI}$

Δ_x .... $= \dfrac{wx}{48\ EI}(l^3 - 3lx^2 + 2x^3)$

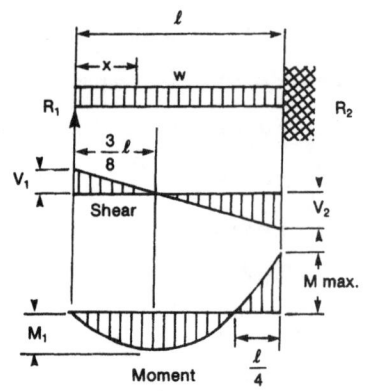

Beam fixed at one end, supported at other — concentrated load at any point

$R_1 = V_1$ .... $= \dfrac{Pb^2}{2l^3}(a + 2l)$

$R_2 = V_2$ .... $= \dfrac{Pa}{2l^3}(3l^2 - a^2)$

M_1 (at point of load) .... $= R_1 a$

M_2 (at fixed end) .... $= -\dfrac{Pab}{2l^2}(a + l)$

M_x (when $x < a$) .... $= R_1 x$

M_x (when $x > a$) .... $= R_1 x - P(x - a)$

Δmax. $\left(\text{when } a < 0.414l \text{ at } x = l\dfrac{l^2 + a^2}{3l^2 - a^2}\right) = \dfrac{Pa}{3\ EI}\dfrac{(l^2 - a^2)^3}{(3l^2 - a^2)^2}$

Δmax. $\left(\text{when } a > 0.414l \text{ at } x = l\sqrt{\dfrac{a}{2l + a}}\right) = \dfrac{Pab^2}{6\ EI}\sqrt{\dfrac{a}{2l + a}}$

Δa (at point of load) .... $= \dfrac{Pa^2b^3}{12\ EIl^3}(3l + a)$

Δx (when $x < a$) .... $= \dfrac{Pb^2x}{12\ EIl^3}(3al^2 - 2lx^2 - ax^2)$

Δx (when $x > a$) .... $= \dfrac{Pa}{12\ EIl^3}(l - x)^2(3l^2x - a^2x - 2a^2l)$

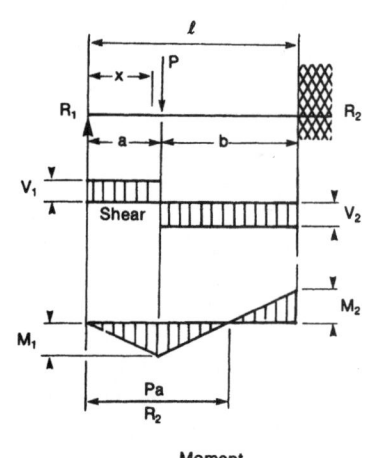

Note:

w: Distributed load per unit length. In the case of triangular distribution, w represents the maximum intensity of load per unit length.

P: Concentrated load.

Moments are positive if they cause compression in the top of the beam.

Table 1.14: (Continued)

Cantilever Beam — uniformly distributed load

$R = V$ .... $= w\ell$

V_x .... $= wx$

M max. (at fixed end) .... $= -\dfrac{w\ell^2}{2}$

M_x .... $= \dfrac{wx^2}{2}$

Δmax. (at free end) .... $= \dfrac{w\ell^4}{8\,EI}$

Δ_x .... $= \dfrac{w}{24\,EI}(x^4 - 4\ell^3 x + 3\ell^4)$

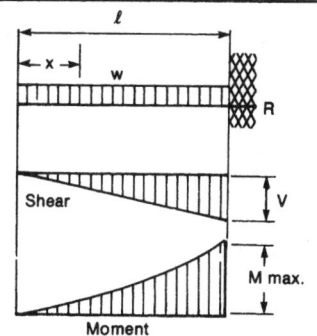

Cantilever Beam — load increasing uniformly to fixed end

$R = V$ .... $= \dfrac{w\ell}{2}$

V_x .... $= \dfrac{wx^2}{2\ell}$

M max. (at fixed end) .... $= -\dfrac{w\ell^2}{6}$

M_x .... $= \dfrac{wx^3}{6\ell}$

Δmax. (at free end) .... $= \dfrac{w\ell^4}{30\,EI}$

Δ_x .... $= \dfrac{w}{120\,EI\ell}(x^5 - 5\ell^4 x + 4\ell^5)$

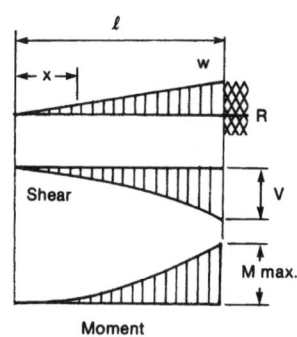

Cantilever Beam — concentrated load at any point

$R = V$ .... $= P$

M max. (at fixed end) .... $= -Pb$

M_x (when $x > a$) .... $= P(x - a)$

Δmax. (at free end) .... $= \dfrac{Pb^2}{6\,EI}(3\ell - b)$

Δa (at point of load) .... $= \dfrac{Pb^3}{3\,EI}$

Δ_x (when $x < a$) .... $= \dfrac{Pb^2}{6\,EI}(3\ell - 3x - b)$

Δ_x (when $x > a$) .... $= \dfrac{P(\ell - x)^2}{6\,EI}(3b - \ell + x)$

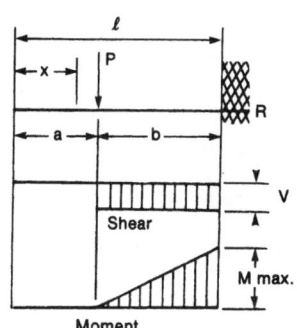

Note:
w: Distributed load per unit length. In the case of triangular distribution, w represents the maximum intensity of load per unit length.
P: Concentrated load.
Moments are positive if they cause compression in the top of the beam.

Table 1.14:   (Continued)

Beam overhanging one support — uniformly distributed load

$R_1 = V_1$ .... $= \dfrac{w}{2\ell}(\ell^2 - a^2)$

$R_2 = V_2 + V_3$ .... $= \dfrac{w}{2\ell}(\ell + a)^2$

V_2 .... $= wa$

V_3 .... $= \dfrac{w}{2\ell}(\ell^2 + a^2)$

V_x (between supports) .... $= R_1 - wx$

V_{x1} (for overhang) .... $= w(a - x_1)$

$M_1 \left(\text{at } x = \dfrac{\ell}{2}\left[1 - \dfrac{a^2}{\ell^2}\right]\right)$ .... $= \dfrac{w}{8\ell^2}(\ell + a)^2(\ell - a)^2$

M_2 (at R_2) .... $= \dfrac{wa^2}{2}$

M_x (between supports) .... $= \dfrac{wx}{2\ell}(\ell^2 - a^2 - x\ell)$

M_{x1} (for overhang) .... $= \dfrac{w}{2}(a - x_1)^2$

Δ_x (between supports) .... $= \dfrac{wx}{24\,EI\ell}(\ell^4 - 2\ell^2x^2 + \ell x^3 - 2a^2\ell^2 + 2a^2x^2)$

Δ_{x1} (for overhang) .... $= \dfrac{wx_1}{24\,EI}(4a^2\ell - \ell^3 + 6a^2x_1 - 4ax_1^2 + x_1^3)$

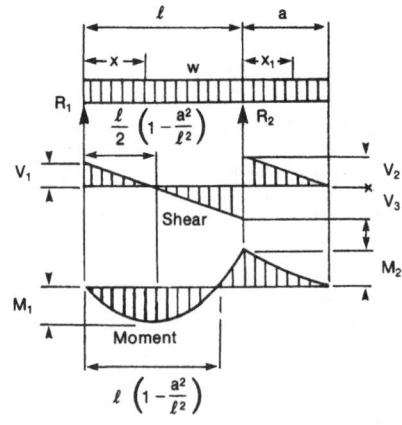

Beam overhanging one support — uniformly distributed load on overhang

$R_1 = V_1$ .... $= \dfrac{wa^2}{2\ell}$

$R_2 = V_1 + V_2$ .... $= \dfrac{wa}{2\ell}(2\ell + a)$

V_2 .... $= wa$

V_{x1} (for overhang) .... $= w(a - x_1)$

M max. (at R_2) .... $= \dfrac{wa^2}{2}$

M_x (between supports) .... $= \dfrac{wa^2x}{2\ell}$

M_{x1} (for overhang) .... $= \dfrac{w}{2}(a - x_1)^2$

Δ max. $\left(\text{between supports at } x = \dfrac{\ell}{\sqrt{3}}\right)$ ... $= \dfrac{wa^2\ell^2}{18\sqrt{3}\,EI} = 0.03208\,\dfrac{wa^2\ell^2}{EI}$

Δ max. (for overhang at $x_1 = a$) .... $= \dfrac{wa^3}{24\,EI}(4\ell + 3a)$

Δ_x (between supports) .... $= \dfrac{wa^2x}{12\,EI\ell}(\ell^2 - x^2)$

Δ_{x1} (for overhang) .... $= \dfrac{wx_1}{24\,EI}(4a^2\ell + 6a^2x_1 - 4ax_1^2 + x_1^3)$

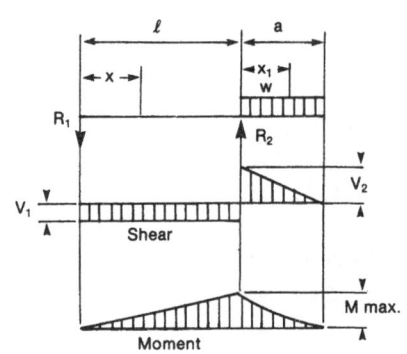

Note:
w: Distributed load per unit length. In the case of triangular distribution, w represents the maximum intensity of load per unit length.
P: Concentrated load.
Moments are positive if they cause compression in the top of the beam.

Table 1.14:   Beam Diagrams

Beam overhanging one support — concentrated load at end of overhang

$R_1 = V_1$ .... $= \dfrac{Pa}{\ell}$

$R_2 = V_1 + V_2$ .... $= \dfrac{P}{\ell}\,(\ell + a)$

V_2 .... $= P$

M max. (at R_2) .... $= Pa$

M_x (between supports) .... $= \dfrac{Pax}{\ell}$

M_{x1} (for overhang) .... $= P\,(a - x_1)$

Δmax. $\left(\text{between supports at } x = \dfrac{\ell}{\sqrt{3}}\right)$ ... $= \dfrac{Pa\ell^2}{9\sqrt{3}\,EI} = 0.06415\,\dfrac{Pa\ell^2}{EI}$

Δmax. (for overhang at $x_1 = a$) .... $= \dfrac{Pa^2}{3\,EI}\,(\ell + a)$

Δ_x (between supports) .... $= \dfrac{Pax}{6\,EI\ell}\,(\ell^2 - x^2)$

Δ_{x1} (for overhang) .... $= \dfrac{Px_1}{6\,EI}\,(2a\ell + 3ax_1 - x_1{}^2)$

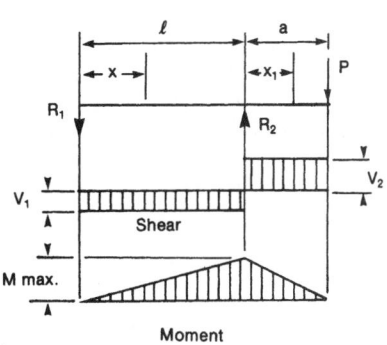

Note:
w: Distributed load per unit length. In the case of triangular distribution, w represents the maximum intensity of load per unit length.
P: Concentrated load.
Moments are positive if they cause compression in the top of the beam.

Table 1.15:   Moments and Reactions in Continuous Beams Uniformly Distributed Loads

Moment :	Coefficient × wℓ²		w:	Uniform load per unit length
Reaction:	Coefficient × wℓ		ℓ :	Length of one span

Two Equal Spans

-0.125
0.375   w   w   0.070
1.250   0.375

-0.063
0.438   w   0.096
0.625   0.063

Three Equal Spans

-0.100   -0.100
0.400   w   0.080   w   0.025   w   0.080   0.400
1.100   1.100

-0.050   -0.050
0.450   w   0.101   w   0.101   0.450
0.550   0.550

-0.050   -0.050
0.050   w   0.075
0.550   0.550   0.050

-0.117   0.033
0.383   w   0.073   w   0.054   0.450   0.033
1.200

-0.067   +0.017
0.433   w   0.094   0.650   0.100   0.017

Four Equal Spans

-0.107   -0.071   -0.107
0.393   w   0.077   w   0.036   w   0.036   w   0.077   0.393
1.143   0.929   1.143

-0.054   -0.036   -0.054
0.446   w   0.098   0.572   0.464   w   0.081   0.572   0.054

-0.121   -0.018   -0.058
0.380   w   0.072   w   0.061   0.357   0.598   w   0.098   0.442
1.223

-0.036   -0.107   -0.036
0.036   0.464   w   0.056   w   0.056   0.464   0.036
1.143

-0.067   +0.018   -0.005
0.433   w   0.094   0.652   0.107   0.027   0.005

-0.049   -0.054   +0.013
0.049   0.545   w   0.074   0.571   0.080   0.013

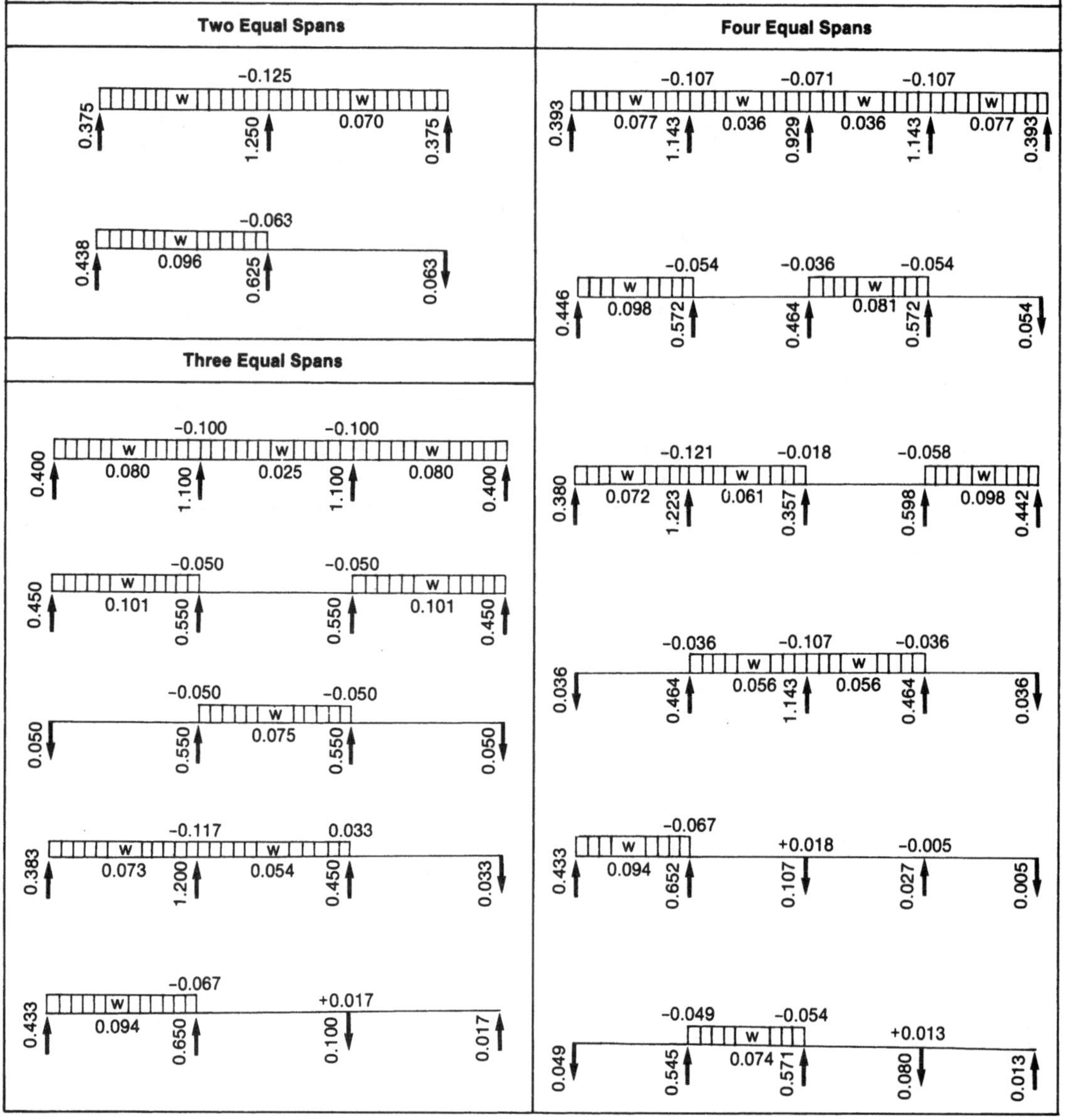

Table 1.16:   Moments and Reactions in Continuous Beams Central Point Loads

Moment :	Coefficient × Pℓ	P:	Concentrated load
Reaction:	Coefficient × P	ℓ :	Length of one span

Two Equal Spans

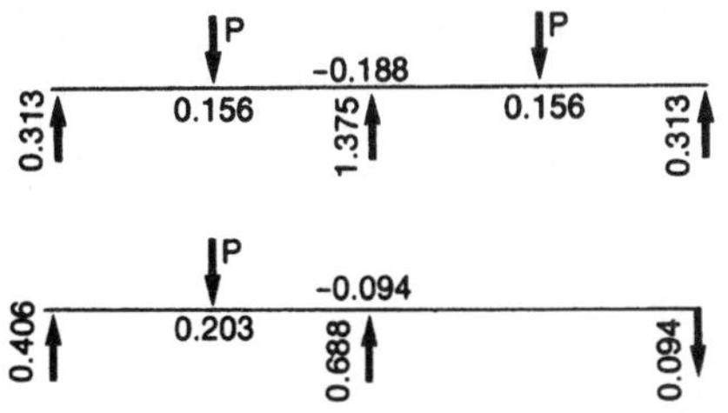

P, P
−0.188
0.313   0.156   1.375   0.156   0.313

P
−0.094
0.406   0.203   0.688   0.094

Three Equal Spans

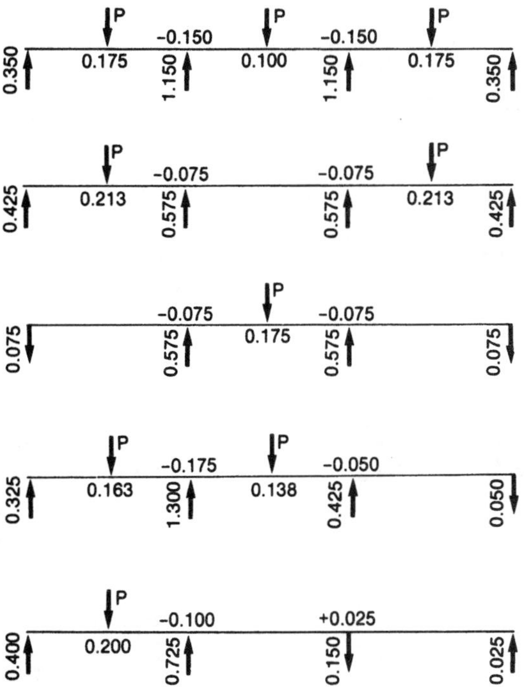

P, P, P
−0.150   −0.150
0.350   0.175   1.150   0.100   1.150   0.175   0.350

P, P
−0.075   −0.075
0.425   0.213   0.575   0.575   0.213   0.425

P
−0.075   −0.075
0.075   0.575   0.175   0.575   0.075

P, P
−0.175   −0.050
0.325   0.163   1.300   0.138   0.425   0.050

P
−0.100   +0.025
0.400   0.200   0.725   0.150   0.025

Four Equal Spans

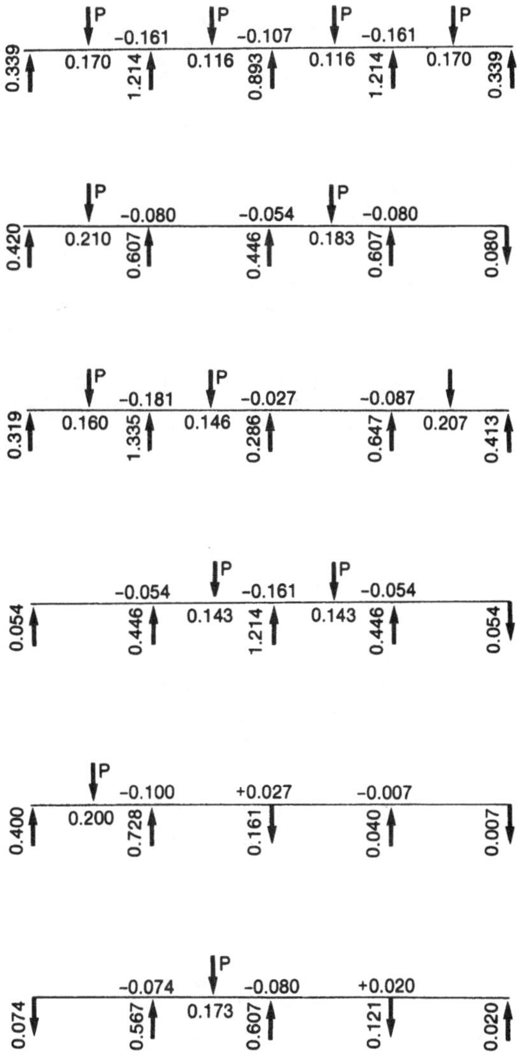

P, P, P, P
−0.161   −0.107   −0.161
0.339   0.170   1.214   0.116   0.893   0.116   1.214   0.170   0.339

P, P
−0.080   −0.054   −0.080
0.420   0.210   0.607   0.446   0.183   0.607   0.080

P, P, P
−0.181   −0.027   −0.087
0.319   0.160   1.335   0.146   0.286   0.647   0.207   0.413

P, P
−0.054   −0.161   −0.054
0.446   0.143   1.214   0.143   0.446   0.054

P
−0.100   +0.027   −0.007
0.400   0.200   0.728   0.161   0.040   0.007

P
−0.074   −0.080   +0.020
0.074   0.567   0.173   0.607   0.121   0.020

Table 1.17:   Moments and Reactions in Continuous Beams Point Loads at Third Points of Span

Moment : Coefficient × Pℓ	P: Total concentrated load on one span
Reaction: Coefficient × P	ℓ : Length of one span

Two Equal Spans

Diagram 1: reactions 0.333, 0.111, −0.167, 1.333, 0.111, 0.333

Diagram 2: reactions 0.417, 0.139, −0.083, 0.667, 0.083

Three Equal Spans

Diagram 1: 0.367, 0.122, −0.133, 1.133, 0.033, 1.133, 0.122, 0.367

Diagram 2: 0.433, 0.145, −0.067, 0.567, −0.067, 0.567, 0.145, 0.433

Diagram 3: 0.067, −0.067, 0.567, 0.100, 0.567, −0.067, 0.067

Diagram 4: 0.345, 0.115, −0.156, 1.267, 0.085, 0.433, −0.045, 0.045

Diagram 5: 0.411, 0.137, −0.089, 0.700, +0.022, 0.133, 0.022

Four Equal Spans

Diagram 1: 0.357, 0.119, −0.143, 1.190, 0.056, 0.905, −0.096, 0.056, −0.143, 1.190, 0.119, 0.357

Diagram 2: 0.428, 0.143, −0.072, 0.596, −0.048, 0.452, 0.111, −0.072, 0.596, 0.072

Diagram 3: 0.340, 0.113, −0.161, 1.298, 0.097, 0.309, −0.024, 0.631, −0.078, 0.141, 0.423

Diagram 4: 0.048, 0.453, −0.048, 0.087, 1.190, −0.143, 0.087, 0.453, −0.048, 0.048

Diagram 5: 0.411, 0.137, −0.089, 0.702, +0.024, 0.143, −0.006, 0.036, 0.006

Diagram 6: 0.066, 0.560, −0.066, 0.099, 0.595, −0.071, 0.107, +0.018, 0.018

Table 1.18:   Approximate Moments and Shears for Continuous Beams and One-Way Slabs

w: **Factored load per unit length**
ℓ_n: **Clear span length**
ℓ_a: **Average length of adjacent clear spans**

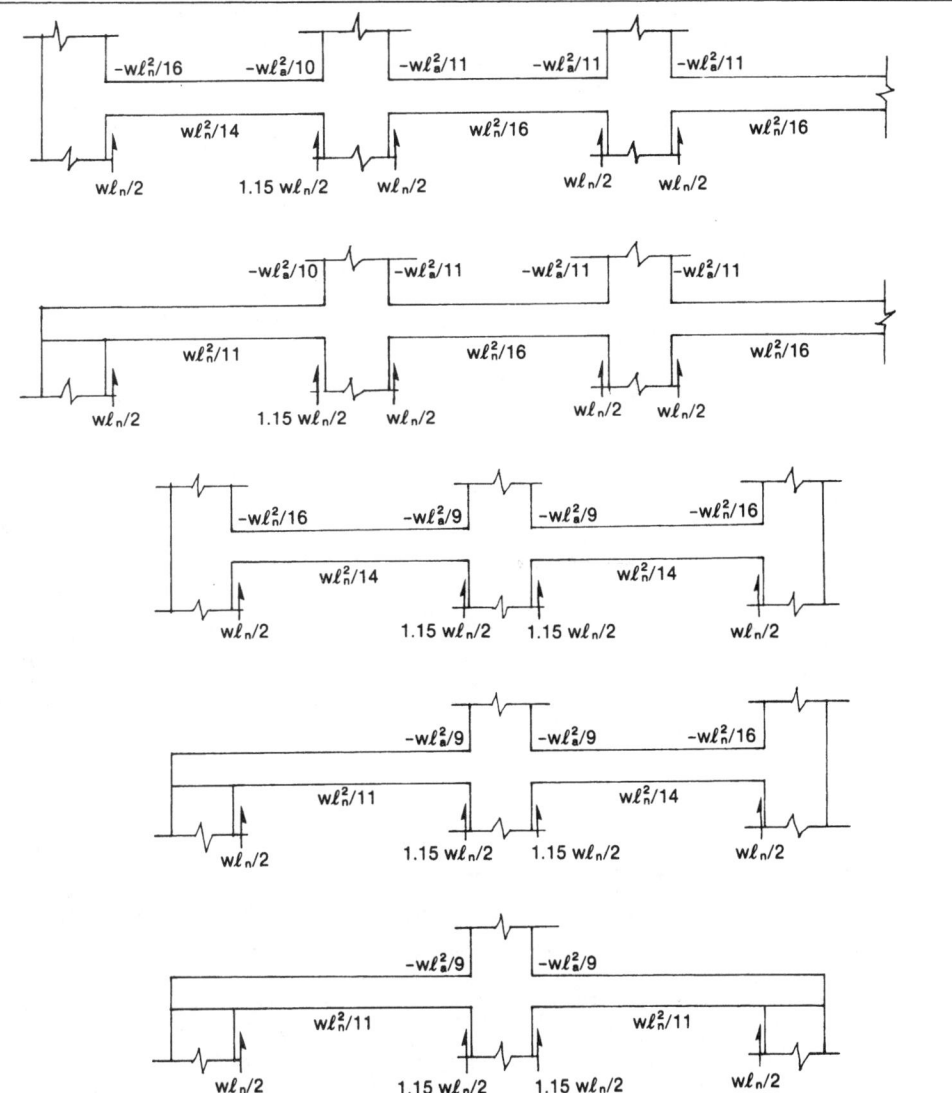

Notes:
1. This figure is applicable to prismatic members loaded with uniformly distributed load where the ratio of factored live load to factored dead load is not greater than 3.0, and the span lengths approximately equal, with the longer of the two adjacent spans not greater than the shorter by more than 20 per cent.
2. If the exterior support is a spandrel or girder, the negative moment at the interior face of exterior support is $w\ell_n^2/24$.
3. For slabs with spans not exceeding 3 m or beams with the ratio of the sum of the column stiffnesses to the beam stiffness exceeds eight at each end, the negative moment at all supports can be taken equal to $w\ell_n^2/12$.

Table 1.19: Beams with Prismatic Haunch at One End

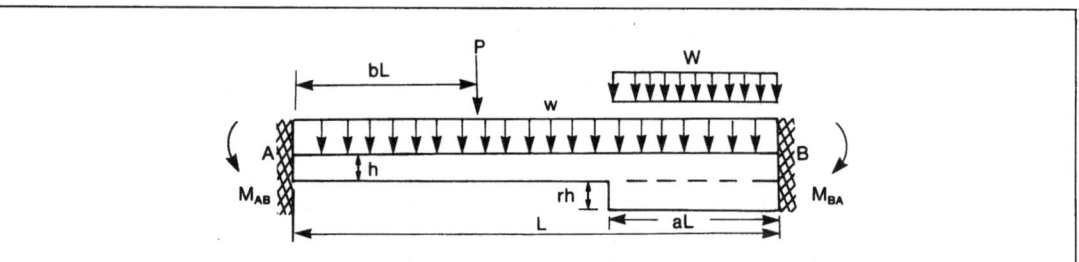

Right haunch		Carry-over factors		Stiffness factors		Unif. load F.E.M. coef. × wL²		Concentrated load F.E.M. — coef. × PL b										Haunch load F.E.M. coef. × WL²	
								0.1		0.3		0.5		0.7		0.9			
a	r	C_{AB}	C_{BA}	k_{AB}	k_{BA}	M_{AB}	M_{BA}	M_{AB}	M_{BA}	M_{AB}	M_{BA}	M_{AB}	M_{BA}	M_{AB}	M_{BA}	M_{AB}	M_{BA}	M_{AB}	M_{BA}
0.1	0.4	0.593	0.491	4.24	5.12	0.0749	0.1016	0.0799	0.0113	0.1397	0.0788	0.1110	0.1553	0.0478	0.1798	0.0042	0.0911	0.0001	0.0047
	0.6	0.615	0.490	4.30	5.40	0.0727	0.1062	0.0797	0.0119	0.1378	0.0828	0.1074	0.1630	0.0439	0.1881	0.0029	0.0937	0.0001	0.0048
	1.0	0.639	0.488	4.37	5.72	0.0703	0.1114	0.0794	0.0125	0.1358	0.0873	0.1035	0.1716	0.0396	0.1974	0.0016	0.0966	0.0001	0.0049
	1.5	0.652	0.487	4.40	5.89	0.0690	0.1143	0.0792	0.0129	0.1346	0.0898	0.1012	0.1764	0.0373	0.2026	0.0008	0.0982	0.0000	0.0049
	2.0	0.658	0.487	4.42	5.97	0.0684	0.1156	0.0791	0.0131	0.1341	0.0910	0.1002	0.1786	0.0361	0.2050	0.0005	0.0990	0.0000	0.0050
0.2	0.4	0.677	0.469	4.42	6.37	0.0706	0.1126	0.0791	0.0134	0.1345	0.0925	0.1020	0.1788	0.0409	0.1975	0.0050	0.0890	0.0013	0.0171
	0.6	0.730	0.463	4.56	7.18	0.0664	0.1225	0.0785	0.0149	0.1302	0.1025	0.0942	0.1972	0.0335	0.2148	0.0037	0.0917	0.0010	0.0178
	1.0	0.793	0.458	4.74	8.22	0.0610	0.1353	0.0777	0.0168	0.1248	0.1154	0.0843	0.2207	0.0242	0.2368	0.0022	0.0951	0.0006	0.0187
	1.5	0.831	0.455	4.86	8.88	0.0576	0.1434	0.0772	0.0180	0.1214	0.1235	0.0781	0.2355	0.0182	0.2507	0.0012	0.0973	0.0003	0.0193
	2.0	0.849	0.453	4.91	9.20	0.0559	0.1473	0.0769	0.0186	0.1197	0.1276	0.0750	0.2429	0.0153	0.2576	0.0007	0.0984	0.0002	0.0196
0.3	0.4	0.741	0.439	4.52	7.63	0.0698	0.1155	0.0787	0.0149	0.1319	0.1013	0.0987	0.1899	0.0420	0.1929	0.0056	0.0868	0.0045	0.0338
	0.6	0.831	0.427	4.75	9.24	0.0642	0.1296	0.0777	0.0175	0.1255	0.1182	0.0877	0.2185	0.0338	0.2130	0.0045	0.0893	0.0036	0.0359
	1.0	0.954	0.415	5.09	11.69	0.0559	0.1511	0.0762	0.0215	0.1158	0.1440	0.0711	0.2621	0.0217	0.2436	0.0028	0.0930	0.0023	0.0391
	1.5	1.036	0.409	5.34	13.53	0.0497	0.1673	0.0751	0.0245	0.1085	0.1633	0.0587	0.2948	0.0128	0.2665	0.0017	0.0959	0.0014	0.0415
	2.0	1.078	0.407	5.48	14.54	0.0464	0.1762	0.0745	0.0262	0.1045	0.1740	0.0520	0.3129	0.0080	0.2792	0.0010	0.0974	0.0008	0.0448
0.4	0.4	0.774	0.405	4.55	8.70	0.0703	0.1117	0.0786	0.0156	0.1315	0.1035	0.0992	0.1855	0.0445	0.1773	0.0059	0.0849	0.0106	0.0509
	0.6	0.901	0.86	4.83	11.28	0.0646	0.1269	0.0774	0.0192	0.1240	0.1254	0.0875	0.2182	0.0377	0.1932	0.0049	0.0869	0.0089	0.0547
	1.0	1.102	0.367	5.33	16.03	0.0549	0.1548	0.0752	0.0257	0.1105	0.1658	0.0671	0.2780	0.0267	0.2222	0.0034	0.0904	0.0063	0.0616
	1.5	1.260	0.357	5.79	20.46	0.0462	0.1807	0.0732	0.0319	0.0982	0.2035	0.0485	0.3339	0.0173	0.2491	0.0022	0.0938	0.0037	0.0679
	2.0	1.349	0.352	6.09	23.32	0.0407	0.1975	0.0719	0.0358	0.0903	0.2278	0.0367	0.3699	0.0113	0.2664	0.0014	0.0959	0.0027	0.0720
0.5	0.4	0.768	0.371	4.56	9.45	0.0700	0.1048	0.0786	0.0154	0.1312	0.0993	0.0983	0.1679	0.0442	0.1663	0.0059	0.0836	0.0189	0.0656
	0.6	0.919	0.343	4.84	12.94	0.0651	0.1176	0.0774	0.0193	0.1240	0.1218	0.0884	0.1935	0.0386	0.1769	0.0051	0.0849	0.0167	0.0702
	1.0	1.200	0.316	5.42	20.61	0.0561	0.1451	0.0749	0.0280	0.1096	0.1709	0.0706	0.2486	0.0299	0.1993	0.0038	0.0877	0.0131	0.0802
	1.5	1.470	0.301	6.10	29.74	0.0466	0.1777	0.0720	0.0384	0.0934	0.2290	0.0516	0.3137	0.0215	0.2255	0.0027	0.0909	0.0094	0.0918
	2.0	1.647	0.295	6.63	37.04	0.0393	0.2036	0.0698	0.0466	0.0807	0.2755	0.0370	0.3655	0.0153	0.2463	0.0019	0.0934	0.0067	0.1011
0.6	0.4	0.726	0.341	4.62	9.84	0.0675	0.0986	0.0782	0.0146	0.1280	0.0916	0.0923	0.1519	0.0419	0.1603	0.0056	0.0829	0.0283	0.0769
	0.6	0.872	0.305	4.88	13.97	0.0630	0.1072	0.0771	0.0183	0.1214	0.1096	0.0835	0.1664	0.0368	0.1666	0.0048	0.0837	0.0254	0.0813
	1.0	1.196	0.267	5.43	24.35	0.0560	0.1277	0.0748	0.0274	0.1092	0.1537	0.0705	0.1999	0.0299	0.1804	0.0038	0.0854	0.0212	0.0913
	1.5	1.588	0.247	6.18	39.79	0.0482	0.1572	0.0718	0.0408	0.0939	0.2183	0.0572	0.2478	0.0237	0.1997	0.0030	0.0878	0.0171	0.1055
	2.0	1.905	0.237	6.92	55.51	0.0412	0.1870	0.0688	0.0544	0.0792	0.2839	0.0455	0.2960	0.0186	0.2189	0.0023	0.0901	0.0136	0.1197
0.7	0.4	0.657	0.321	4.86	9.96	0.0631	0.0954	0.0770	0.0138	0.1175	0.0846	0.0844	0.1461	0.0392	0.1582	0.0053	0.0827	0.0372	0.0854
	0.6	0.770	0.275	5.14	14.39	0.0580	0.1006	0.0758	0.0167	0.1097	0.1097	0.0745	0.1543	0.0335	0.1621	0.0045	0.0832	0.0330	0.0890
	1.0	1.056	0.224	5.62	26.45	0.0516	0.1122	0.0738	0.0243	0.0992	0.1213	0.0626	0.1710	0.0269	0.1694	0.0035	0.0841	0.0280	0.0965
	1.5	1.491	0.196	6.24	47.48	0.0463	0.1304	0.0714	0.0371	0.0890	0.1633	0.0537	0.1959	0.0223	0.1796	0.0028	0.0854	0.0241	0.1076
	2.0	1.944	0.183	6.95	73.85	0.0417	0.1523	0.0687	0.0530	0.0793	0.2149	0.0468	0.2255	0.0191	0.1915	0.0024	0.0869	0.0210	0.1210
0.8	0.4	0.583	0.319	5.46	9.97	0.0585	0.0951	0.0741	0.0137	0.1040	0.0837	0.0793	0.1456	0.0380	0.1580	0.0053	0.0826	0.0452	0.0917
	0.6	0.645	0.263	5.89	14.44	0.0516	0.0990	0.0721	0.0160	0.0921	0.0907	0.0667	0.1520	0.0311	0.1614	0.0043	0.0831	0.0388	0.0951
	1.0	0.818	0.196	6.47	27.06	0.0435	0.1053	0.0696	0.0211	0.0781	0.1025	0.0521	0.1615	0.0232	0.1660	0.0031	0.0838	0.0314	0.1004
	1.5	1.128	0.155	6.98	50.85	0.0385	0.1130	0.0676	0.0296	0.0692	0.1175	0.0432	0.1715	0.0184	0.1705	0.0024	0.0844	0.0268	0.1064
	2.0	1.533	0.135	7.47	84.60	0.0355	0.1222	0.0658	0.0412	0.0638	0.1357	0.0384	0.1824	0.0159	0.1750	0.0020	0.0849	0.0242	0.1133
0.9	0.4	0.524	0.356	6.87	10.10	0.0604	0.0948	0.0674	0.0157	0.1031	0.0835	0.0844	0.1439	0.0418	0.1568	0.0059	0.0824	0.0550	0.0942
	0.6	0.542	0.295	7.95	14.58	0.0497	0.0991	0.0623	0.0184	0.0866	0.0913	0.0691	0.1510	0.0339	0.1605	0.0048	0.0830	0.0460	0.0985
	1.0	0.594	0.206	9.44	27.16	0.0372	0.1052	0.0553	0.0226	0.0642	0.1023	0.0484	0.1609	0.0231	0.1656	0.0032	0.0837	0.0337	0.1044
	1.5	0.695	0.142	10.48	51.25	0.0289	0.1098	0.0506	0.0266	0.0492	0.1105	0.0346	0.1680	0.0159	0.1692	0.0021	0.0842	0.0255	0.1089
	2.0	0.842	0.107	11.07	86.80	0.0245	0.1147	0.0481	0.0306	0.0414	0.1159	0.0274	0.1723	0.0121	0.1714	0.0016	0.0845	0.0213	0.1117

Table 1.20: Beams with Prismatic Haunch at Both Ends

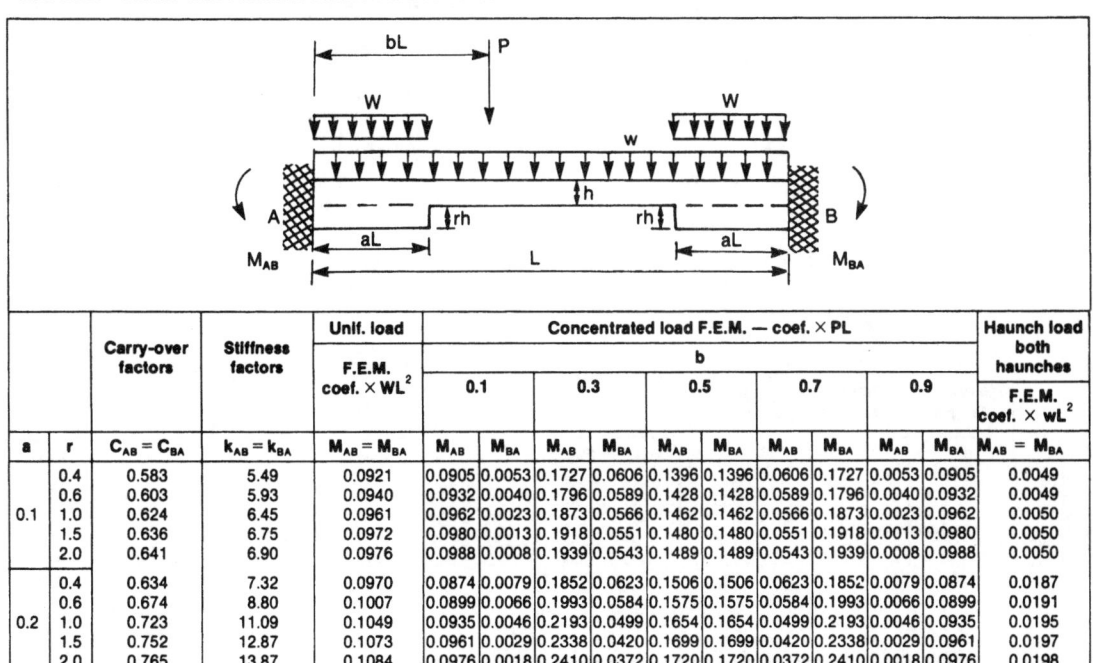

a	r	Carry-over factors $C_{AB} = C_{BA}$	Stiffness factors $k_{AB} = k_{BA}$	Unif. load F.E.M. coef. $\times WL^2$ $M_{AB} = M_{BA}$	Concentrated load F.E.M. — coef. $\times PL$ b=0.1 M_{AB}	M_{BA}	0.3 M_{AB}	M_{BA}	0.5 M_{AB}	M_{BA}	0.7 M_{AB}	M_{BA}	0.9 M_{AB}	M_{BA}	Haunch load both haunches F.E.M. coef. $\times wL^2$ $M_{AB} = M_{BA}$
0.1	0.4	0.583	5.49	0.0921	0.0905	0.0053	0.1727	0.0606	0.1396	0.1396	0.0606	0.1727	0.0053	0.0905	0.0049
	0.6	0.603	5.93	0.0940	0.0932	0.0040	0.1796	0.0589	0.1428	0.1428	0.0589	0.1796	0.0040	0.0932	0.0049
	1.0	0.624	6.45	0.0961	0.0962	0.0023	0.1873	0.0566	0.1462	0.1462	0.0566	0.1873	0.0023	0.0962	0.0050
	1.5	0.636	6.75	0.0972	0.0980	0.0013	0.1918	0.0551	0.1480	0.1480	0.0551	0.1918	0.0013	0.0980	0.0050
	2.0	0.641	6.90	0.0976	0.0988	0.0008	0.1939	0.0543	0.1489	0.1489	0.0543	0.1939	0.0008	0.0988	0.0050
0.2	0.4	0.634	7.32	0.0970	0.0874	0.0079	0.1852	0.0623	0.1506	0.1506	0.0623	0.1852	0.0079	0.0874	0.0187
	0.6	0.674	8.80	0.1007	0.0899	0.0066	0.1993	0.0584	0.1575	0.1575	0.0584	0.1993	0.0066	0.0899	0.0191
	1.0	0.723	11.09	0.1049	0.0935	0.0046	0.2193	0.0499	0.1654	0.1654	0.0499	0.2193	0.0046	0.0935	0.0195
	1.5	0.752	12.87	0.1073	0.0961	0.0029	0.2338	0.0420	0.1699	0.1699	0.0420	0.2338	0.0029	0.0961	0.0197
	2.0	0.765	13.87	0.1084	0.0976	0.0018	0.2410	0.0372	0.1720	0.1720	0.0372	0.2410	0.0018	0.0976	0.0198
0.3	0.4	0.642	9.02	0.0977	0.0845	0.0097	0.1763	0.0707	0.1558	0.1558	0.0707	0.1763	0.0097	0.0845	0.0397
	0.6	0.697	12.09	0.1027	0.0861	0.0095	0.1898	0.0700	0.1665	0.1665	0.0700	0.1898	0.0095	0.0861	0.0410
	1.0	0.775	18.68	0.1091	0.0890	0.0084	0.2136	0.0627	0.1803	0.1803	0.0627	0.2136	0.0084	0.0890	0.0426
	1.5	0.828	26.49	0.1132	0.0920	0.0065	0.2376	0.0492	0.1891	0.1891	0.0492	0.2376	0.0065	0.0920	0.0437
	2.0	0.855	32.77	0.1153	0.0943	0.0048	0.2555	0.0366	0.1934	0.1934	0.0366	0.2555	0.0048	0.0943	0.0442
0.4	0.4	0.599	10.15	0.0937	0.0825	0.0101	0.1601	0.0732	0.1509	0.1509	0.0732	0.1601	0.0101	0.0825	0.0642
	0.6	0.652	14.52	0.0966	0.0833	0.0106	0.1668	0.0776	0.1632	0.1632	0.0776	0.1668	0.0106	0.0833	0.0668
	1.0	0.744	26.06	0.1067	0.0847	0.0112	0.1790	0.0835	0.1833	0.1833	0.0835	0.1790	0.0112	0.0847	0.0711
	1.5	0.827	45.95	0.1131	0.0862	0.0113	0.1919	0.0852	0.1995	0.1995	0.0852	0.1919	0.0113	0.0862	0.0746
	2.0	0.878	71.41	0.1169	0.0876	0.0108	0.2033	0.0822	0.2089	0.2089	0.0822	0.2033	0.0108	0.0876	0.0766
0.5	0.0	0.500	4.00	0.0833	0.0810	0.0090	0.1470	0.0630	0.1250	0.1250	0.0630	0.1470	0.0090	0.0810	0.0833

Table 1.21:   Prismatic Member with Equal Infinitely Stiff End Regions

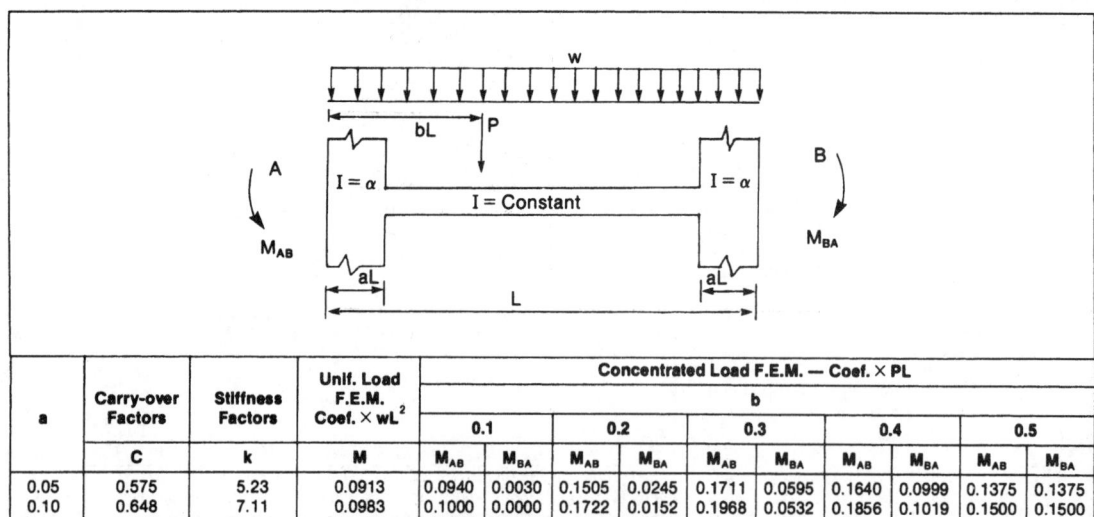

a	Carry-over Factors	Stiffness Factors	Unif. Load F.E.M. Coef. × wL²	Concentrated Load F.E.M. — Coef. × PL									
				b									
				0.1		0.2		0.3		0.4		0.5	
	C	k	M	M_{AB}	M_{BA}	M_{AB}	M_{BA}	M_{AB}	M_{BA}	M_{AB}	M_{BA}	M_{AB}	M_{BA}
0.05	0.575	5.23	0.0913	0.0940	0.0030	0.1505	0.0245	0.1711	0.0595	0.1640	0.0999	0.1375	0.1375
0.10	0.648	7.11	0.0983	0.1000	0.0000	0.1722	0.0152	0.1968	0.0532	0.1856	0.1019	0.1500	0.1500
0.15	0.719	10.17	0.1046	0.1000	0.0000	0.1909	0.0056	0.2247	0.0431	0.2095	0.1013	0.1625	0.1625
0.20	0.786	15.56	0.1100	0.1000	0.0000	0.2000	0.0000	0.2546	0.0286	0.2369	0.0964	0.1750	0.1750
0.25	0.846	26.00	0.1146	0.1000	0.0000	0.2000	0.0000	0.2830	0.0118	0.2699	0.0851	0.1875	0.1875

Table 1.22:   Prismatic Member with Infinitely Stiff Region at One End

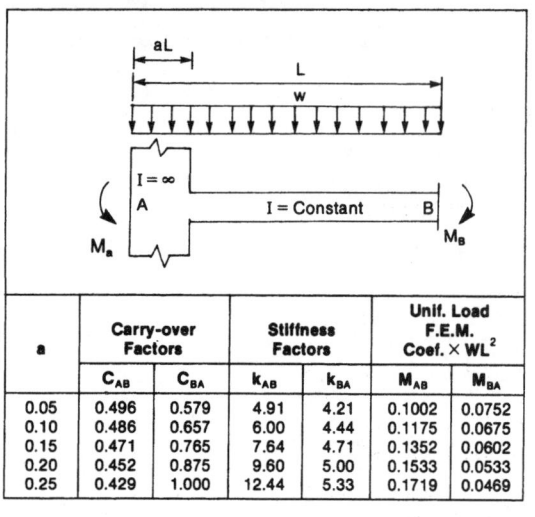

a	Carry-over Factors		Stiffness Factors		Unif. Load F.E.M. Coef. × WL²	
	C_{AB}	C_{BA}	k_{AB}	k_{BA}	M_{AB}	M_{BA}
0.05	0.496	0.579	4.91	4.21	0.1002	0.0752
0.10	0.486	0.657	6.00	4.44	0.1175	0.0675
0.15	0.471	0.765	7.64	4.71	0.1352	0.0602
0.20	0.452	0.875	9.60	5.00	0.1533	0.0533
0.25	0.429	1.000	12.44	5.33	0.1719	0.0469

Table 1.23:   Prismatic Member with Unequal Infinitely Stiff End Regions

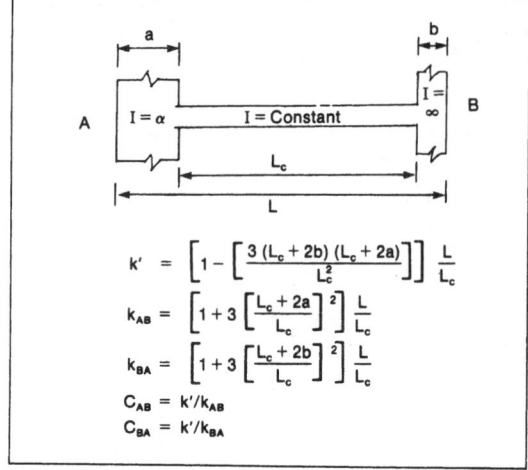

$$k' = \left[1 - \left[\frac{3\,(L_c + 2b)\,(L_c + 2a)}{L_c^2}\right]\right]\frac{L}{L_c}$$

$$k_{AB} = \left[1 + 3\left[\frac{L_c + 2a}{L_c}\right]^2\right]\frac{L}{L_c}$$

$$k_{BA} = \left[1 + 3\left[\frac{L_c + 2b}{L_c}\right]^2\right]\frac{L}{L_c}$$

$$C_{AB} = k'/k_{AB}$$

$$C_{BA} = k'/k_{BA}$$

Table 1.24:   Sectional Properties

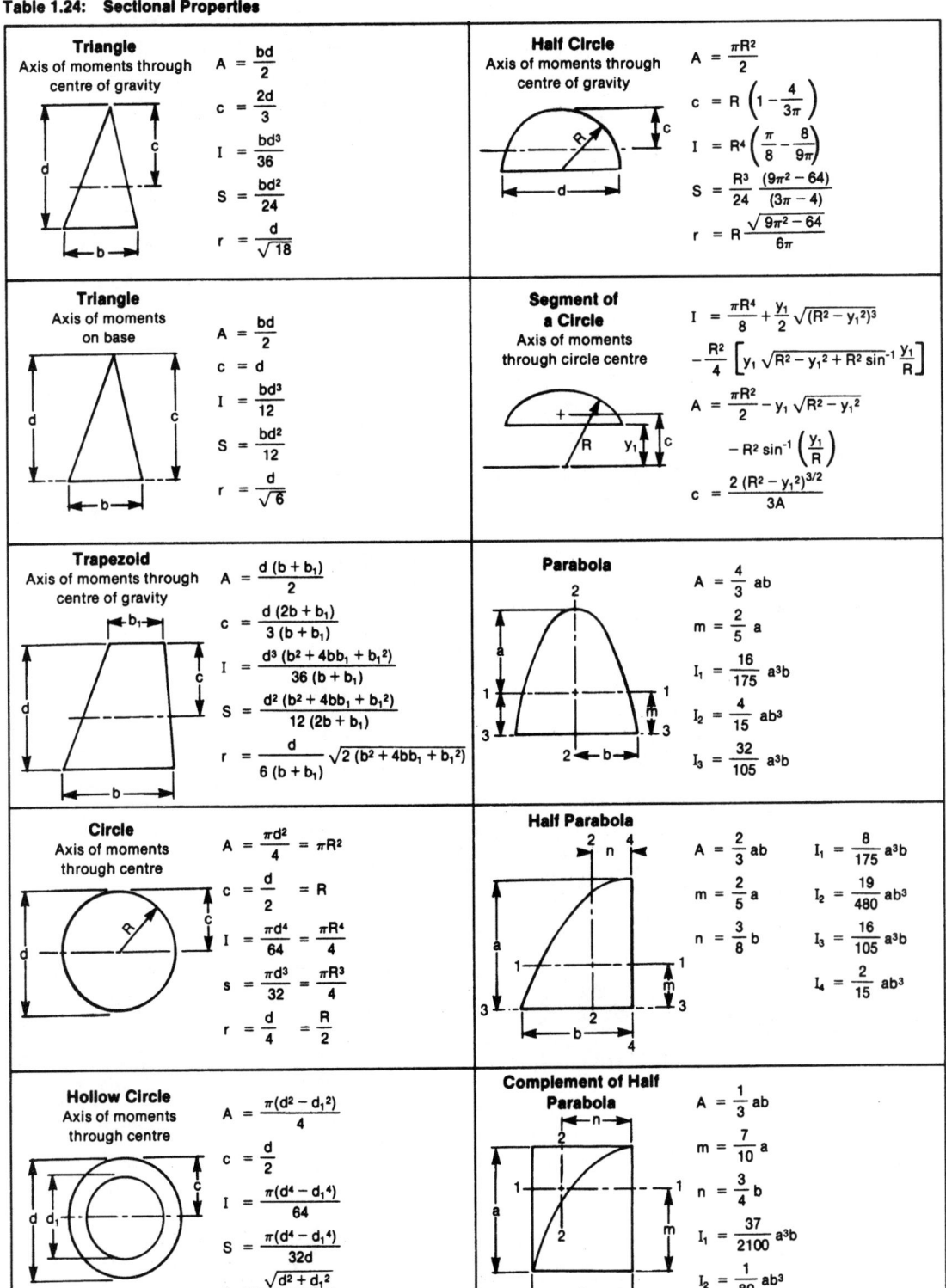

Triangle
Axis of moments through centre of gravity

$$A = \frac{bd}{2}$$

$$c = \frac{2d}{3}$$

$$I = \frac{bd^3}{36}$$

$$S = \frac{bd^2}{24}$$

$$r = \frac{d}{\sqrt{18}}$$

Half Circle
Axis of moments through centre of gravity

$$A = \frac{\pi R^2}{2}$$

$$c = R\left(1 - \frac{4}{3\pi}\right)$$

$$I = R^4\left(\frac{\pi}{8} - \frac{8}{9\pi}\right)$$

$$S = \frac{R^3}{24}\frac{(9\pi^2 - 64)}{(3\pi - 4)}$$

$$r = R\frac{\sqrt{9\pi^2 - 64}}{6\pi}$$

Triangle
Axis of moments on base

$$A = \frac{bd}{2}$$

$$c = d$$

$$I = \frac{bd^3}{12}$$

$$S = \frac{bd^2}{12}$$

$$r = \frac{d}{\sqrt{6}}$$

Segment of a Circle
Axis of moments through circle centre

$$I = \frac{\pi R^4}{8} + \frac{y_1}{2}\sqrt{(R^2 - y_1{}^2)^3}$$
$$- \frac{R^2}{4}\left[y_1\sqrt{R^2 - y_1{}^2} + R^2\sin^{-1}\frac{y_1}{R}\right]$$

$$A = \frac{\pi R^2}{2} - y_1\sqrt{R^2 - y_1{}^2}$$
$$- R^2\sin^{-1}\left(\frac{y_1}{R}\right)$$

$$c = \frac{2(R^2 - y_1{}^2)^{3/2}}{3A}$$

Trapezoid
Axis of moments through centre of gravity

$$A = \frac{d(b + b_1)}{2}$$

$$c = \frac{d(2b + b_1)}{3(b + b_1)}$$

$$I = \frac{d^3(b^2 + 4bb_1 + b_1{}^2)}{36(b + b_1)}$$

$$S = \frac{d^2(b^2 + 4bb_1 + b_1{}^2)}{12(2b + b_1)}$$

$$r = \frac{d}{6(b + b_1)}\sqrt{2(b^2 + 4bb_1 + b_1{}^2)}$$

Parabola

$$A = \frac{4}{3}ab$$

$$m = \frac{2}{5}a$$

$$I_1 = \frac{16}{175}a^3b$$

$$I_2 = \frac{4}{15}ab^3$$

$$I_3 = \frac{32}{105}a^3b$$

Circle
Axis of moments through centre

$$A = \frac{\pi d^2}{4} = \pi R^2$$

$$c = \frac{d}{2} = R$$

$$I = \frac{\pi d^4}{64} = \frac{\pi R^4}{4}$$

$$s = \frac{\pi d^3}{32} = \frac{\pi R^3}{4}$$

$$r = \frac{d}{4} = \frac{R}{2}$$

Half Parabola

$$A = \frac{2}{3}ab \qquad I_1 = \frac{8}{175}a^3b$$

$$m = \frac{2}{5}a \qquad I_2 = \frac{19}{480}ab^3$$

$$n = \frac{3}{8}b \qquad I_3 = \frac{16}{105}a^3b$$

$$\qquad I_4 = \frac{2}{15}ab^3$$

Hollow Circle
Axis of moments through centre

$$A = \frac{\pi(d^2 - d_1{}^2)}{4}$$

$$c = \frac{d}{2}$$

$$I = \frac{\pi(d^4 - d_1{}^4)}{64}$$

$$S = \frac{\pi(d^4 - d_1{}^4)}{32d}$$

$$r = \frac{\sqrt{d^2 + d_1{}^2}}{4}$$

Complement of Half Parabola

$$A = \frac{1}{3}ab$$

$$m = \frac{7}{10}a$$

$$n = \frac{3}{4}b$$

$$I_1 = \frac{37}{2100}a^3b$$

$$I_2 = \frac{1}{80}ab^3$$

Reproduced from the 'Metric Design Manual' with the permission of CPCI.

Table 1.24: (Continued)

Square
Axis of moments through centre

$A = d^2$

$c = \dfrac{d}{2}$

$I = \dfrac{d^4}{12}$

$S = \dfrac{d^3}{6}$

$r = \dfrac{d}{\sqrt{12}} = 0.288675\ d$

Rectangle
Axis of moments on diagonal

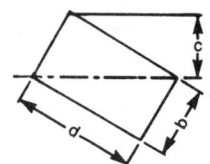

$A = bd$

$c = \dfrac{bd}{\sqrt{b^2 + d^2}}$

$I = \dfrac{b^3d^3}{6\,(b^2 + d^2)}$

$S = \dfrac{b^2d^2}{6\,\sqrt{b^2 + d^2}}$

$r = \dfrac{bd}{\sqrt{6\,(b^2 + d^2)}}$

Square
Axis of moments on base

$A = d^2$

$c = d$

$I = \dfrac{d^4}{3}$

$S = \dfrac{d^3}{3}$

$r = \dfrac{d}{\sqrt{3}} = 0.577350\ d$

Rectangle
Axis of moments any line through centre of gravity

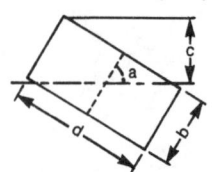

$A = bd$

$c = \dfrac{b \sin a + d \cos a}{2}$

$I = \dfrac{bd\,(b^2 \sin^2 a + d^2 \cos^2 a)}{12}$

$S = \dfrac{bd\,(b^2 \sin^2 a + d^2 \cos^2 a)}{6\,(b \sin a + d \cos a)}$

$r = \sqrt{\dfrac{b^2 \sin^2 a + d^2 \cos^2 a}{12}}$

Square
Axis of moments on diagonal

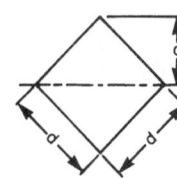

$A = d^2$

$c = \dfrac{d}{\sqrt{2}} = 0.707107\ d$

$I = \dfrac{d^4}{12}$

$S = \dfrac{d^3}{6\,\sqrt{2}} = 0.117851\ d^3$

$r = \dfrac{d}{\sqrt{12}} = 0.288675\ d$

Hollow Rectangle
Axis of moments through centre

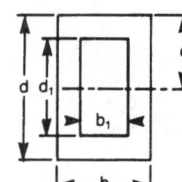

$A = bd - b_1 d_1$

$c = \dfrac{d}{2}$

$I = \dfrac{bd^3 - b_1 d_1^3}{12}$

$S = \dfrac{bd^3 - b_1 d_1^3}{6d}$

$r = \sqrt{\dfrac{bd^3 - b_1 d_1^3}{12\ A}}$

Rectangle
Axis of moments through centre

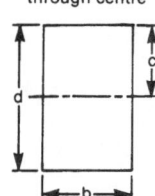

$A = bd$

$c = \dfrac{d}{2}$

$I = \dfrac{bd^3}{12}$

$S = \dfrac{bd^2}{6}$

$r = \dfrac{d}{\sqrt{12}} = 0.288675\ d$

Equal Rectangles
Axis of moments through centre of gravity

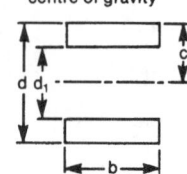

$A = b\,(d - d_1)$

$c = \dfrac{d}{2}$

$I = \dfrac{b\,(d^3 - d_1^3)}{12}$

$S = \dfrac{b\,(d^3 - d_1^3)}{6d}$

$r = \sqrt{\dfrac{d^3 - d_1^3}{12\,(d - d_1)}}$

Rectangle
Axis of moments on base

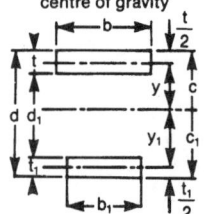

$A = bd$

$c = d$

$I = \dfrac{bd^3}{3}$

$S = \dfrac{bd^2}{3}$

$r = \dfrac{d}{\sqrt{3}} = 0.577350\ d$

Unequal Rectangles
Axis of moments through centre of gravity

$A = bt + b_1 t_1$

$c = \dfrac{\frac{1}{2}\,bt^2 + b_1\,t_1\,(d - \frac{1}{2}\,t_1)}{A}$

$I = \dfrac{bt^3}{12} + bty^2 + \dfrac{b_1 t_1^3}{12} + b_1\,t_1\,y_1^2$

$S = \dfrac{1}{c} \qquad S_1 = \dfrac{1}{c_1}$

$r = \sqrt{\dfrac{1}{A}}$

Table 1.24: (Continued)

Parabolic Fillet in Right Angle

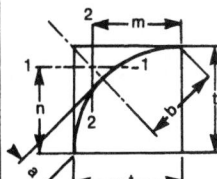

$$a = \frac{t}{2\sqrt{2}}$$

$$b = \frac{t}{\sqrt{2}}$$

$$A = \frac{1}{6}t^2$$

$$m = n = \frac{4}{5}t$$

$$I_1 = I_2 = \frac{11}{2100}t^4$$

*Half Ellipse

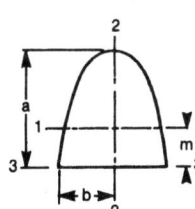

$$A = \frac{1}{2}\pi ab$$

$$m = \frac{4a}{3\pi}$$

$$I_1 = a^3 b\left(\frac{\pi}{8} - \frac{8}{9\pi}\right)$$

$$I_2 = \frac{1}{8}\pi ab^3$$

$$I_3 = \frac{1}{8}\pi a^3 b$$

*Quarter Ellipse

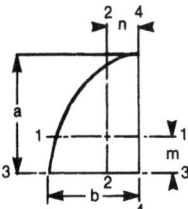

$$A = \frac{1}{4}\pi ab$$

$$m = \frac{4a}{3\pi}$$

$$n = \frac{4b}{3\pi}$$

$$I_1 = a^3 b\left(\frac{\pi}{16} - \frac{4}{9\pi}\right)$$

$$I_2 = ab^3\left(\frac{\pi}{16} - \frac{4}{9\pi}\right)$$

$$I_3 = \frac{1}{16}\pi a^3 b$$

$$I_4 = \frac{1}{16}\pi ab^3$$

*To obtain properties of half circles, quarter circle and circular complement, substitute a = b = R.

*Elliptic Complement

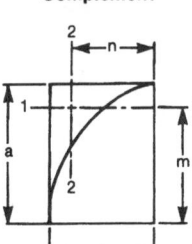

$$A = ab\left(1 - \frac{\pi}{4}\right)$$

$$m = \frac{a}{6\left(1 - \frac{\pi}{4}\right)}$$

$$n = \frac{b}{6\left(1 - \frac{\pi}{4}\right)}$$

$$I_1 = a^3 b\left[\frac{1}{3} - \frac{\pi}{16} - \frac{1}{36\left(1 - \frac{\pi}{4}\right)}\right]$$

$$I_2 = ab^3\left[\frac{1}{3} - \frac{\pi}{16} - \frac{1}{36\left(1 - \frac{\pi}{4}\right)}\right]$$

Regular Polygon
Axis of moments through centre

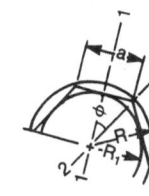

$$n = \text{Number of sides}$$

$$\phi = \frac{180°}{n}$$

$$a = 2\sqrt{R^2 - R_1^2}$$

$$R = \frac{a}{2\sin\phi}$$

$$R_1 = \frac{a}{2\tan\phi}$$

$$A = \frac{1}{4}na^2\cot\phi = \frac{1}{2}nR^2\sin 2\phi = nR_1^2\tan\phi$$

$$I_1 = I_2 = \frac{A(6R^2 - a^2)}{24} = \frac{A(12R_1^2 + a^2)}{48}$$

$$r_1 = r_2 = \sqrt{\frac{6R^2 - a^2}{24}} = \sqrt{\frac{12R_1 + a^2}{48}}$$

Beams and Channels
Transverse force oblique through centre of gravity

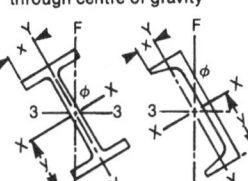

$$I_3 = I_x \sin^2\phi + I_y \cos^2\phi$$

$$I_4 = I_x \cos^2\phi + I_y \sin^2\phi$$

$$f_b = M\left[\frac{y}{I_x}\sin\phi + \frac{x}{I_y}\cos\phi\right]$$

where M is bending moment due to force F.

Angle
Axis of moments through centre of gravity

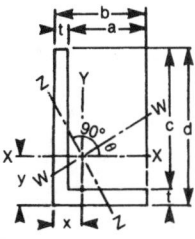

Z-Z is axis of minimum I

$$\tan 2\theta = \frac{2K}{I_y - I_x}$$

$$A = t(b+c) \quad x = \frac{b^2 + ct}{2(b+c)} \quad y = \frac{d^2 + at}{2(b+c)}$$

K = Product of Inertia about X-X & Y-Y

$$= \pm\frac{abcdt}{4(b+c)}$$

$$I_x = \frac{1}{3}\left[t(d-y)^3 + by^3 - a(y-t)^3\right]$$

$$I_y = \frac{1}{3}\left[t(b-x)^3 + dx^3 - c(x-t)^3\right]$$

$$I_z = I_x \sin^2\theta + I_y \cos^2\theta + K\sin 2\theta$$

$$I_w = I_x \cos^2\theta + I_y \sin^2\theta - K\sin 2\theta$$

K is negative when heel of angle, with respect to c.g., is in 1st or 3rd quadrant, positive when in 2nd or 4th quadrant.

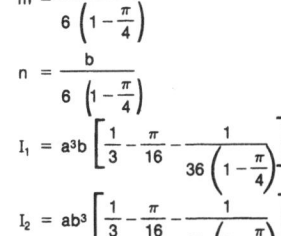

by Murat Saatcioglu

Design for Flexure

2.1   Introduction

The majority of structural members used in practice are subjected to flexural stresses caused by bending moments. Flexural stresses often occur in combination with other types of stresses caused by axial force, shear, and torsion. Typical examples of flexure dominant members include beams and slabs, although the concepts and design aids presented in this chapter also apply to other members that are subjected flexure, including structural walls, retaining walls and footings.

Flexural design is performed in two stages. The first stage involves sectional design, including sections that are subjected to highest negative and positive bending moments. The second stage involves member design, including determination of bar lengths. Length of reinforcement and locations of cut-off points are affected by provisions specified for development length and splice length requirements, as discussed in Chapter 3.

Flexural design of a reinforced concrete section should conform to the Limit States Design provisions of CSA A23.3-04. Accordingly, the ultimate limit state expressed below should be satisfied to meet the required strength.

Moment Resistance ≥ Factored Moment

$Mr \geq Mf$

Factored moments are obtained by structural analysis under factored loads. Load factors and load combinations are discussed in Chapter 1.

2.2   Moment Resistance (M_r)

Moment resistance M_r is obtained by computing the flexural strength of a section, with resistance factors ϕ_c and ϕ_s applied to concrete cylinder strength f'_c and steel yield strength f_y, respectively. The material resistance factor for concrete, ϕ_c is 0.65 as per Clause 8.4.2 of CSA A23.3-04, and may be taken as 0.70 for precast elements produced in certified manufacturing plants. In this chapter, all design aids and examples are produced for the general case of $\phi_c = 0.65$. The material resistance factor for reinforcing steel, ϕ_s is 0.85, as specified in Clause 8.4.3 of CSA A23.3-04.

The flexural strength is computed from internal forces that can be established by a plane section analysis. Accordingly, plane sections of a reinforced concrete member before bending are assumed to remain plane after bending. Furthermore, perfect bond is assumed between the concrete and reinforcing steel. These assumptions lead to a linear distribution of strains across the section depth, with strains in steel and concrete proportional to their distances from the neutral axis. The corresponding stress distribution is obtained from material stress-strain relationships. This leads to a parabolic stress distribution for concrete in compression. Concrete in tension is ignored without affecting the flexural resistance significantly. Internal forces in concrete and steel are then computed from the stress distribution, with due considerations given to the area of concrete and reinforcement. An iterative approach may have to be employed until the neutral axis location that satisfies force equilibrium is established. This procedure is referred to as strain compatibility analysis. The moment resistance is computed for a specific strain distribution that corresponds to a given load stage. Complete response of a section can be established if the analysis is carried out for different load stages and corresponding strain conditions. This is usually done in the form of a moment-curvature relationship (M-ϕ), as illustrated in Fig. 2.1.

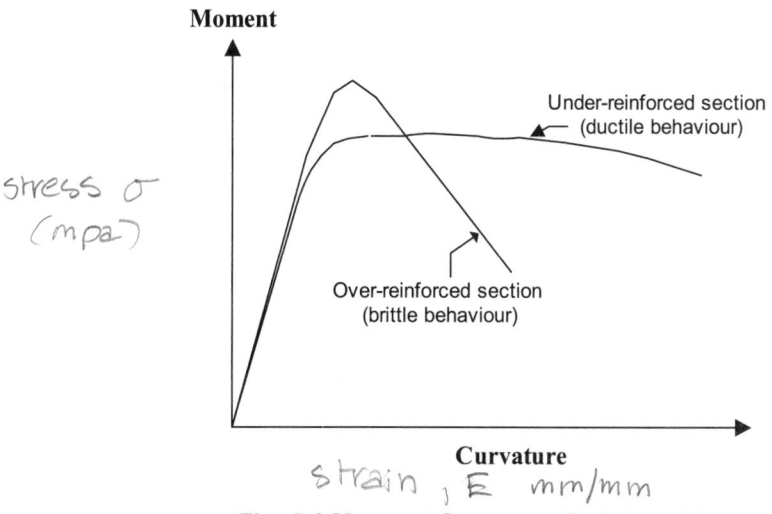

stress σ
(mpa)

strain , Ɛ mm/mm

Fig. 2.1 Moment Curvature Relationship

While the plane section analysis is a powerful tool for establishing the characteristics of sectional response, only one point on the M-ϕ relationship, i.e. the maximum moment resistance, is of interest for design purposes. CSA A23.3-04 defines the strain condition corresponding to the maximum moment resistance in Clause 10.1.3. This condition is illustrated in Fig. 2.2. Accordingly, the maximum strain at the extreme compression fibre is assumed to be 0.0035 when the factored moment resistance is attained. CSA A23.3-04 also defines an equivalent rectangular stress block to represent the parabolic distribution of compression in concrete, simplifying the design process significantly.

The rectangular stress block, with the parameters given in the standard, is applicable to the limiting strain condition, which is used to compute the maximum resistance of a section. The following expressions define the parameters of the rectangular stress distribution, which spreads over a depth of $a = \beta_1 c$ from the extreme compression fibre, with a constant intensity of $\alpha_1 \phi_c f'_c$.

$$\alpha_1 = 0.85 - 0.0015 f'_c \geq 0.67 \tag{2.1}$$

$$\beta_1 \, \alpha_1 = 0.97 - 0.0025 f'_c \geq 0.67 \tag{2.2}$$

Reinforced concrete sections in flexure exhibit different modes of failure depending on the percentage of steel in the section. Sections with small percentage of steel develop yielding of reinforcement in tension, prior to crushing of concrete in compression. These sections are referred to as "under-reinforced" sections. Members designed to have under-reinforced sections deflect excessively prior to concrete crushing, exhibiting ductile behaviour with prior warning of an imminent failure. Sections with excessive tension steel may not develop yielding of reinforcement prior to concrete crushing. These members deflect very little until failure, and the failure is usually brittle, explosive and unexpected. These sections are referred to as "over-reinforced" sections.

The amount of tension steel that causes simultaneous crushing of concrete and yielding of tension steel is referred to as "balanced reinforcement" and the section is referred to as "balanced section." Fig. 2.2 shows the strain condition for each type of behaviour. Ductile behaviour of an under-reinforced section and brittle behaviour of an over-reinforced section are illustrated in Fig. 2.1. It is preferable to design under-reinforced sections. Tension reinforcement, approximately equal to 50% of balanced reinforcement is usually believed to be economically optimum steel content, also producing ductile behaviour.

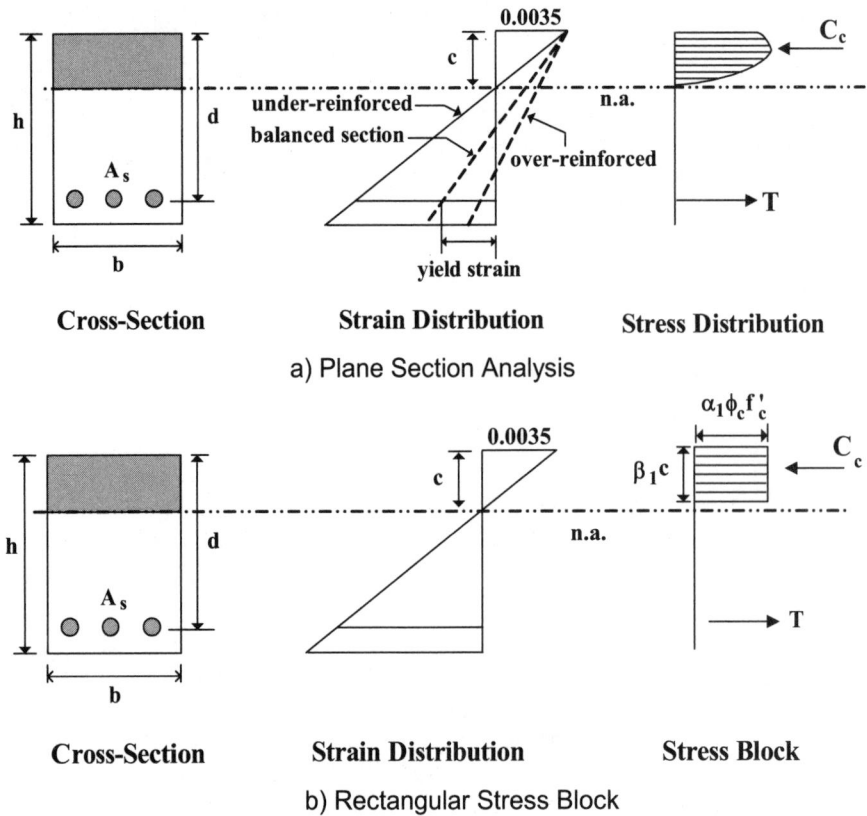

Cross-Section   **Strain Distribution**   **Stress Distribution**

a) Plane Section Analysis

Cross-Section   **Strain Distribution**   **Stress Block**

b) Rectangular Stress Block

Fig. 2.2 Flexural Analysis of Reinforced Concrete Sections

2.2.1   Limit of c/d for Yielding of Tension Reinforcement

Computation of factored moment resistance M_r may require strain compatibility analysis as described above. If the section is under-reinforced, however, the tension steel yields prior to the attainment of the strain condition defined in A23.3 for the computation of factored moment resistance. Hence, the internal tensile force in reinforcement becomes known, and the iterative procedure that is usually required for strain compatibility analysis is not needed. This simplifies the computation of M_r. The limiting strain condition for yielding of tension reinforcement is the same as the strain condition for balanced section. This limiting condition is expressed in Clause 10.5.2 of CSA A23.3-04 in terms of c/d ratio for balanced section. Accordingly, flexural members without axial load shall be design such that Eq. 2.3 is satisfied. This condition ensures the yielding of tension reinforcement prior to the crushing of concrete, which is desirable for ductile behaviour.

$$\frac{c}{d} \leq \frac{0.0035}{0.0035 + \varepsilon_y} = \frac{700}{700 + f_y} \tag{2.3}$$

2.2.2   Minimum Reinforcement

Reinforcement in concrete is not effective until after cracking. The flexural capacity of an uncracked concrete section is primarily provided by concrete alone. Plain concrete members, on the other hand, fail rapidly as soon as the cracking moment M_{cr} is reached. Reinforced sections with very little reinforcement may behave similar to plain concrete sections, and may not be able to sustain M_{cr} upon cracking. Hence, a minimum amount of tension reinforcement may be necessary to provide adequate post-cracking strength as indicated in Eq. 2.4. This requirement may be waved when the factored moment resistance M_r is at least one-third grater than the factored moment M_f.

$$M_r \geq 1.2 M_{cr} \tag{2.4}$$

where;

$$M_{cr} = \frac{f_r I}{y_t} \tag{2.5}$$

and;

$$f_r = 0.6 \lambda \sqrt{f'_c} \tag{2.6}$$

"I" is the moment of inertia of section about centroidal axis, and y_t is the distance between the section centroid and extreme tension fibre. In lieu of the computation of cracking moment, the following expression may be used [Clause 10.5.1.2] to ensure that the section has the minimum required area of tension reinforcement.

$$A_{s,min} = \frac{0.2 \sqrt{f'_c}}{f_y} b_t h \tag{2.7}$$

where, b_t is the width of the tension zone of the section. For T-beams with the flange in tension, b_t need not exceed 2.5 b_w for beams with a flange on both sides of the web, and 1.5 b_w for beams with a flange on one side of the web (L-beams).

The minimum reinforcement for slabs is intended to provide control of cracking due to shrinkage and temperature. It also provides minimum reinforcement to keep the cracked concrete together. A minimum area of $0.002 A_g$, in each direction, is found to be adequate for this purpose [Clause 7.8]. However, this minimum area may have to be increased for exposure conditions that necessitate further crack control. The maximum spacing of minimum reinforcement in slabs is limited to the smaller of 500 mm or five times the slab thickness, with sufficient length to develop yield strength as per Clause 12.

2.2.3   Rectangular Sections with Tension Reinforcement

Factored moment resistance M_r for rectangular sections with tension reinforcement is computed from the internal force couple illustrated in Fig. 2.2. The depth of rectangular concrete stress block is determined from equilibrium of internal forces, especially for under-reinforced sections where the tension force in steel is readily available. This helps define the internal lever arm and the moment resistance.

$$C_c = T \tag{2.8}$$

$$\alpha_1 \phi_c f'_c \, ab = A_s \phi_s f_y \tag{2.9}$$

$$a = \frac{\phi_s A_s f_y}{\alpha_1 \phi_c f'_c \, b} \tag{2.10}$$

$$M_r = A_s \phi_s f_y (d - \frac{a}{2})$$

(2.11)

Substituting "a" from Eq. 2.10, and expressing the area of steel in terms of reinforcement ratio, $\rho = A_s / bd$;

$$M_r = bd^2 \left[1 - \frac{\phi_s \rho f_y}{2\alpha_1 f'_c \phi_c} \right] \rho \phi_s f_y$$

(2.12)

$$M_r = K_r bd^2 \, 10^{-6} \text{ kN.m}$$

(2.13)

where, M_r is expressed in kN.m, and b and d are expressed in mm. The resistance factor K_r, given in Eq. 2.14, is dependent on material properties and related coefficients, and reinforcement ratio ρ.

$$K_r = \left[1 - \frac{\phi_s \rho f_y}{2\alpha_1 f'_c \phi_c} \right] \rho \phi_s f_y \quad \text{MPa}$$

(2.14)

The required ρ can be computed for different material properties and values of K_r, and can be tabulated as a design aid. Table 2.1 was generated in this manner, and it can be used to compute the factored resistance of a rectangular section with tension reinforcement. It can also be used for design. In this case the factored resistance M_r should at least be equal to factored moment, M_f. Therefore, K_r is solved from Eq. 2.13 after substituting M_f in place of M_r. Table 2.1 can then be entered with K_r to read the required reinforcement ratio ρ.

2.2.4   Rectangular Sections with Compression Reinforcement

Flexural members are usually designed for tension reinforcement. Any requirement for an increase in capacity can be accommodated by an increase in tension reinforcement and/or section size. However, sometimes the cross-sectional dimensions may be limited by architectural and/or other functional requirements. The additional moment resistance required in such sections may be provided by placing extra reinforcement in compression and tension regions of the beam. The extra steel provided results in an internal force couple, increasing the flexural capacity. Fig. 2.3 illustrates the components of moment resistance provided in a rectangular section with compression reinforcement.

The compression reinforcement becomes effective in sections where they are needed. A lightly reinforced section requires little concrete in the compression zone to maintain equilibrium. The neutral axis of such a section approaches the extreme compression fibre. Hence, any reinforcement in the compression zone becomes ineffective. In most under-reinforced sections the extension of positive tension reinforcement into the negative compression zone usually does not contribute significantly to the negative moment resistance. Designers usually ignore the presence of bar extension into the compression zone or detailing reinforcement that may be present in the compression zone. A heavily reinforced section, on the other hand, requires a larger compression zone to maintain equilibrium, with neutral axis moving away from the extreme compression fibre. The reinforcement placed near the extreme compression fibre becomes fully effective when the section attains its capacity at 0.0035 fibre strain. When the required moment resistance can not be provided with heavy use of tension reinforcement, the designer may make use of the extension of tension reinforcement from nearby sections into the compression zone, provided that the development and lap length requirements of CSA A23.3-04 are met.

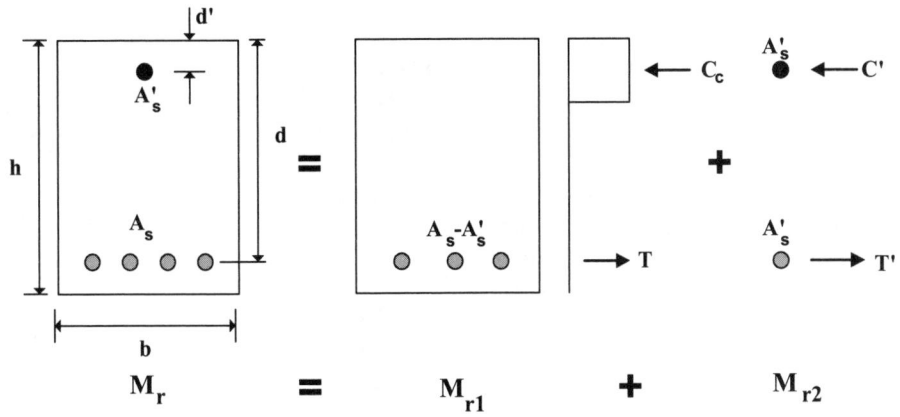

Fig. 2.3 Rectangular Section with Compression Reinforcement

It is clear from the foregoing discussion that compression reinforcement is most effective when the neutral axis approaches the section centroid. The compression reinforcement placed in such a section usually yields when the section reaches its capacity (ε_c = 0.0035). If the compression reinforcement does not yield, it is usually very close to yielding. Hence, it is reasonable to assume, for design purposes, that the compression steel does yield at the limiting strain condition. This simplifies the design process considerably.

The moment resistance of a rectangular section with compression reinforcement can be obtained from the following expressions.

$$M_r = M_{r1} + M_{r2} \tag{2.15}$$

$$M_{r1} = K_r bd^2 \tag{2.16}$$

$$M_{r2} = A'_s \phi_s f_y (d - d') \tag{2.17}$$

$$M_{r2} = K'_r bd^2 \tag{2.18}$$

where;

$$K'_r = \rho' \phi_s f_y \left[1 - \frac{d'}{d} \right] \tag{2.19}$$

$$\rho' = \frac{A'_s}{bd} \tag{2.20}$$

Substituting Eqs. 2.16 and 2.18 into 2.15 yields;

$$M_r = (K_r + K'_r)bd^2 \, 10^{-6} \tag{2.21}$$

where M_r is expressed in kN.m, K_r and K_r' are expressed in MPa, and b and d are expressed in mm. K_r is given in Eq. 2.14, and is based on the reinforcement ratio $\rho = (A_s\text{-}A_s')/bd$. It can also be obtained from Table 2.1. The resistance factor K_r' can be obtained from Table 2.2 in terms of the compression reinforcement ratio ρ', and d'/d ratio.

2.2.5   T-Sections

Most concrete structures are built monolithically with slabs and beams cast together. Fig. 2.4 illustrates a typical reinforced concrete slab system where the floor slab and the supporting beams together provide flexural resistance to applied loading. The resulting structural system includes T-beams, each consisting of a rectangular beam section forming the web, and the slab near the web forming the flange. The slab width near the web, considered to be effective in contributing to load resistance, is referred to as the "effective flange width". The effective flange width, b_f, is defined in CSA A23.3-04 as illustrated in Table 2.4, and should be used in computing the sectional resistance.

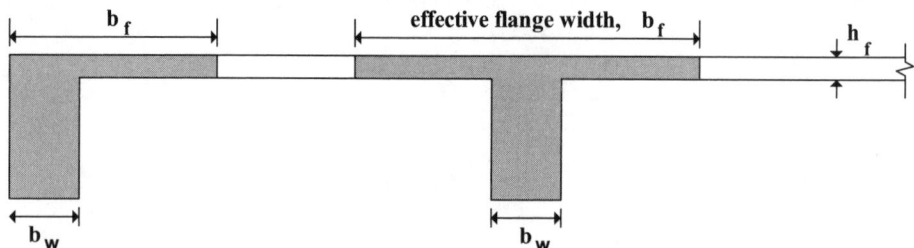

Fig. 2.4 T and L Beams

Although the T-beam example given above is a direct consequence of monolithic construction, T shaped concrete cross-sections are sometimes produced intentionally because of their superior performance in positive bending. These sections provide increased area of compression concrete in the flange, with reduced dead load associated with reduced area of tension concrete in the web. Single T's and double T's are commonly used in the precast industry.

The flange width in most T-sections is significantly wider than the web width. Therefore, the amount of tension reinforcement placed in the web can easily be equilibrated by part of the flange concrete compressed near the extreme compression fibre. This implies that the neutral axis falls within the flange. In fact, in most practical applications it is difficult to create a situation where the neutral axis falls below the flange, since this may require excessive tension force and associated reinforcement that could not be placed in the web without creating construction problems. Therefore, most T-sections behave as rectangular sections with flange width equal to the equivalent width of a rectangular section. T-sections in negative bending also behave as rectangular beams with web width equal to the equivalent width of a rectangular section, while the flange concrete is subjected to tension. However, sections with relatively narrow and thin flanges, subjected to positive bending, may require part of the web concrete below the flange to be compressed to equilibrate heavy tension steel that may be present in the web. In such cases the neutral axis lies within the web, forming concrete compression zone that has a T-shape. These sections are said to behave as T-sections.

The limiting condition for T-section behaviour occurs when the flange concrete is fully compressed. This condition can either be expressed in terms of the limiting area of tension reinforcement, or the limiting thickness of flange. The following inequalities define conditions for T-section behaviour.

$$A_s \phi_s f_y > \alpha_1 \phi_c f'_c \, h_f b_f \tag{2.22}$$

$$A_s > \frac{\alpha_1 \phi_c f'_c \, h_f b_f}{\phi_s f_y} \tag{2.23}$$

$$h_f < \frac{A_s \phi_c f_y}{\alpha_1 \phi_c f'_c \, b_f} \tag{2.24}$$

Fig. 2.5 illustrates the T-beam behaviour. The moment resistance of this section is provided by two internal force couples; one formed by the compression concrete in the overhangs and the corresponding tension steel (M_{rf}, A_{sf}), and the other by the compression in web concrete and the corresponding tension steel (M_{rw}, A_{sw}). Each moment component represents moment resistance of a rectangular section with tension reinforcement. Hence, the design aids prepared for rectangular sections can be used to find moment resistance of a section exhibiting T-beam behaviour. Consequently, Table 2.1 can be used with $\rho_f = A_{sf}/(b_f-b_w)d$ to determine M_{rf}, and with $\rho_w = A_{sw}/b_wd$ to find M_{rw}.

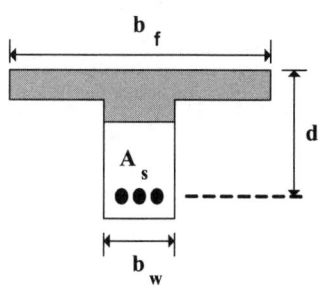

T-Section Behaviour

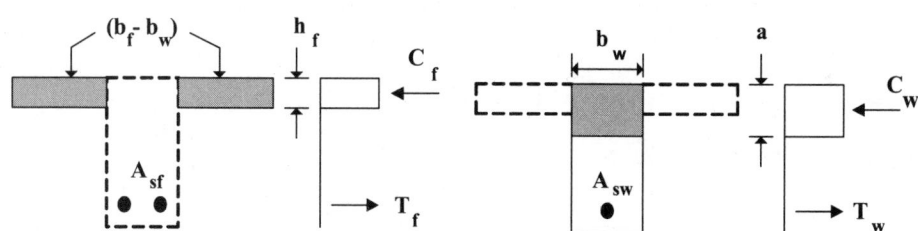

Contribution of Overhangs   **Web Contribution**

Fig. 2.5 T-Section Behaviour

$$M_r = M_{rf} + M_{rw} \tag{2.25}$$

where;

$$M_{rf} = K_{rf}(b_f - b_w)d^2 \tag{2.26}$$

with; $\rho_f = \dfrac{A_{sf}}{(b_f - b_w)d}$

$$M_{rw} = K_{rw}bd^2 \tag{2.27}$$

with; $\rho_w = \dfrac{A_{sw}}{b_wd}$

$$A_{sf} = \dfrac{\alpha_1\phi_cf'_c\,(b_f - b_w)h_f}{\phi_sf_y} \tag{2.28}$$

$$\rho_f = \dfrac{\alpha_1\phi_cf'_c\,h_f}{\phi_cf_yd} \tag{2.29}$$

$$A_{sw} = A_s - A_{sf} \qquad (2.30)$$

$$\rho_w = \frac{A_{sw}}{b_w d} \qquad (2.31)$$

Table 2.3 contains the values of ρ_f for different material strengths and h_f/d ratios.

2.2.6   Joist Construction

Concrete floor joist is another example of a flexural member with a "T" cross-section. Regularly spaced joists, in one or two directions, result in increased redundancy in the structural system, allowing redistribution of loads. Therefore, a monolithically cast joist system is considered to have significant ductility. Certain provisions of CSA A23.3-04 specifically apply to joist construction. Joist construction, not meeting the geometric limitations specified in Table 2.5 [Clause 10.4.1] shall be designed as slabs and beams.

2.3   Placement of Reinforcement

Flexural reinforcement is placed with due considerations given to the spacing of reinforcement and crack control. The crack control is achieved by using well distributed reinforcement. It is usually preferable to use sufficient number of small size bars, as opposed to fewer bars of larger size, while also respecting the spacing requirements. These requirements are discussed in the following sections.

2.3.1   Spacing of Longitudinal Reinforcement

Longitudinal reinforcement should be placed such that the spacing between the bars allow proper placement of concrete. The minimum spacing requirement for beam reinforcement is shown in Table 2.6. The maximum bar spacing in walls and one-way slabs, other than the joist construction illustrated in Table 2.5, is 3 times the member thickness or 500 mm, whichever is smaller [Clause 7.4.1.2].

2.3.2   Crack Control

Beams reinforced with few large size bars may experience cracking between the bars, even if the required area of tension reinforcement is provided and the sectional capacity is achieved. Crack widths in these members may exceed what is usually regarded as acceptable limits of cracking for various exposure conditions. The crack width limitation is specified in CSA A23.3-04 in terms of the quantity "z" given below:

$$z = f_s (d_c A)^{1/3} \qquad (2.32)$$

where; z 30,000 N/mm for interior exposure and 25,000 N/mm for exterior exposure. The crack control is checked under service loads. Hence, the tensile stress in reinforcement f_s can be determined from the strain compatibility analysis presented earlier in Sec. 2.2. Because the strain condition is different than that at maximum factored resistance, the rectangular stress block defined in Sec. 2.2 can not be used. This may require the use of a parabolic stress distribution for concrete, and an iterative strain compatibility analysis to establish the stress in reinforcement. Alternatively, CSA A23.3-04 permits the use 60% of the yield strength f_y as an estimate of stress in steel under service loads. The other terms used in Eq. 2.32 are defined in Table 2.7. In calculating d_c and A, the effective clear concrete cover need not be taken greater than 50 mm. For epoxy coated bars, the "z" valued computed by Eq. 2.32 should be multiplied by 1.2. The crack control requirement described in this section may not be sufficient for structures subjected to very aggressive exposure conditions or for structures designed to be watertight.

2.3.3   Skin Reinforcement

In deep flexural members, the crack control provided by the above procedure may not be sufficient to control cracking near the mid-depth of the section, between the neutral axis and the tension concrete controlled by main flexural reinforcement. For members with a depth $h > 750$ mm, skin reinforcement with a total area of A_{sk} should be provided along the sides.

$$A_{sk} = \rho_{sk} A_{cs} \tag{2.33}$$

where; ρ_{sk} = 0.008 for interior exposure and 0.010 for exterior exposure. The area of concrete, A_{cs}, to be controlled by skin reinforcement is defined in Table 2.8. The maximum spacing of skin reinforcement is limited to 200 mm, [Clause 10.6.2]. The contribution of skin reinforcement to flexural resistance may be included in design if the stress in steel is computed from a strain compatibility analysis.

2.3.4   Tension Reinforcement in T-Beam Flanges

The flexural resistance of T-shaped sections is discussed in Sec. 2.2.5. These sections behave as rectangular beams when subjected to negative bending. While the required reinforcement ratio may be computed using the web width "b_w", the placement of reinforcement should not be limited to the same width. Hence, CSA A23.3-04 calls for some distribution of tension reinforcement within the flange. Accordingly, part of the reinforcement is to be placed over a width of each overhang equal to 1/20 of the beam span, or the width defined in Table 2.9, whichever is smaller. The area of this reinforcement should not be less than 0.4% of the gross area of overhanging flange.

2.4   Design Examples

Example 2.1   Analysis of a Rectangular Beam with Tension Reinforcement

Compute moment resistance M_r for the rectangular section shown in the figure. f'_c = 30 MPa; f_y = 400 MPa.

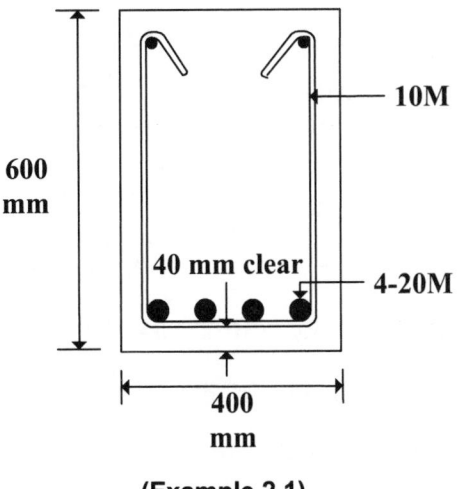

(Example 2.1)

1.   Calculate effective depth d:

$d = 600 - 40 - 11.3 - (19.5/2) = 539$ mm

2.   Calculate reinforcement ratio ρ :

$\rho = A_s / bd = (4 \times 300) / (400 \times 539) = 0.0056 = 0.56\%$

3.   Determine K_r corresponding to $\rho = 0.56\%$ from Table 2.1:

$K_r = 1.8$ MPa

4.   Calculate resisting moment M_r:

$M_r = K_r bd^2 \times 10^{-6} = 1.8 (400) (539)^2 \times 10^{-6} = 209$ kN.m

Example 2.2   Design of a Rectangular Beam with Tension Reinforcement

Design the rectangular beam shown in the figure for a factored moment of $M_f = 415$ kN.m. Use normal density concrete with $f'_c = 40$ MPa, $f_y = 400$ MPa, and maximum aggregate size of 25 mm. The beam is to be built in a non-corrosive environment, having interior exposure.

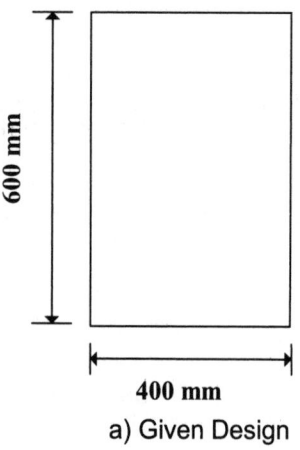

a) Given Design

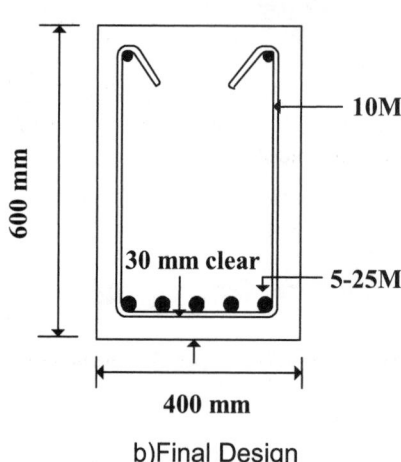

b)Final Design

(Example 2.2)

1.   Estimate effective depth d, assuming 25M bars for flexural reinforcement and 10M stirrups for transverse reinforcement. Select a clear cover of 30 mm from Table 2.6 (for non-corrosive environment, interior exposure).

d = 600 - 30 - 11.3 - (25.2/2) = 546 mm

2.   Calculate resistance factor K_r : For design; M_r, $M_f = 415$ kN.m

$K_r = M_r \times 10^6 / bd^2 = 415 \times 10^6 / (400) (546)^2 = 3.48$ MPa $kr = \dfrac{Mr \times 10^6}{bd^2}$

3.   Determine reinforcement ratio ρ from Table 2.1: $\rho = 1.13\%$

4.   Determine required tension reinforcement:

$A_s = \rho\, bd = 0.0113 \times 400 \times 546 = 2468$ mm^2
No. of 25M bars required; 2468/500 = 4.94
Select 5 25M bars

5.   Check minimum steel requirement:

M_r. 1.2 M_{cr}
M_r = 415 kN.m for 5-25M bars
M_{cr} = 0.6 λ f'_c I/c_t (Eq. 2-5 and 2-6) $Hr = kr(bd^2) \times 10^6 (kN \cdot m)$
I = $bh^3/12$ = $(400)(600)^3 / 12$ = 7.2 x 10^9 mm^4
c_t = 600 / 2 = 300 mm; λ = 1.0 (normal density concrete)
M_{cr} = 0.6 (1.0) . 40 (7.2 x 10^9) / (300) = 91 x 10^6 N.mm $a = \frac{\phi_s A_s f_y}{\phi_c \alpha_1 f'_c b}$
M_r = 415 kN.m > 1.2 (91) = 109 kN.m O.K.
Note: Eq. 2-7 may be used in lieu of Eq. 2-5. $C = \frac{a}{\beta}$
A_{smin} = 0.2 f'_c b_t h / f_y (Eq. 2-7)
A_{smin} = 0.2 (40)(400)(600) / (400) = 759 mm^2 $\frac{c}{d} < \frac{700}{700 f'_c}$
A_s = 5 (500) = 2500 > 759 mm^2 O.K.

6.   Check minimum bar spacing:

s = [400 - 2(30) - 2(11.3) - 5(25.2)] / 4 = 48 mm $S = base - 2(cover) - 2(stir) - \frac{no}{B}(Bar\ Dia)$
From Table 2.6; $s \geq 1.4\ d_b$ = 1.4 (25.2) = 35 mm O.K. $\frac{}{Bar - 1}$
As min $S \geq 1.4\ a_{max}$ = 1.4 (25) = 35 mm O.K.
$\left(\frac{0.2\sqrt{f'c}}{f_y}\right) b_t h$ $s \geq 30$ mm O.K.

7.   Check maximum bar spacing as governed by crack control:

Compute quantity "z" from Eq. 2-32 or Table 2.7: $z = f_s(d_c A)^{1/3}$
Note: For calculation of A and d_c clear cover need not be taken greater than 50 mm.
From Table 2.7; y = h - d = 600 - 546 = 54 mm;
A = $2yb/5$ = 2 (54) (400) / 5 = 8640 mm^2
f_s = 0.6 f_y = 0.6 (400) = 240 MPa; d_c = 600 - 546 = 54 mm
z = 240 (54 x 8640)$^{1/3}$ = 18,614 N/mm
z = 18,614 N/mm < 30,000 N/mm (interior exposure) O.K.

8.   Check if skin reinforcement is needed:

$h \leq 750$ mm no skin reinforcement is needed.

9.   Final design: Use 5-25M bars as longitudinal tension reinforcement with 10M stirrups and 30 mm clear cover for the stirrup steel.

Example 2.3   Analysis of a Rectangular Beam with Tension and Compression Reinforcement

Calculate the flexural resistance of the beam shown in the figure.

f'_c = 30 MPa; f_y = 400 MPa.

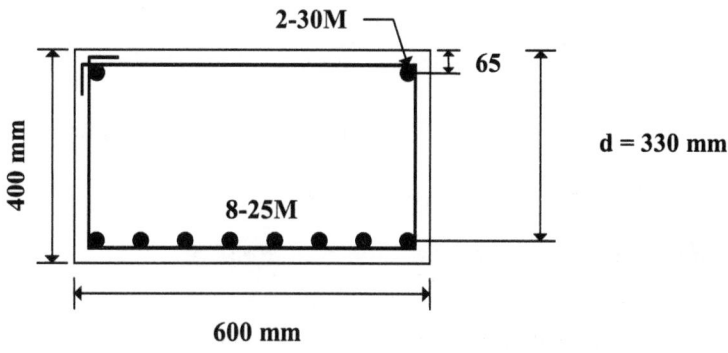

(Example 2.3)

1.   Compute moment resistance provided by steel couple M'_r from Table 2.2 :

Note : Total moment resistance = $M_r + M'_r$
$\rho' = A'_s / bd = (2 \times 700) / (600 \times 330) = 0.0071$; $d'/d = 65 / 330 = 0.20$
From Table 2.2; $M'_r = K'_r bd^2 \times 10^{-6}$ kN.m, and for $\rho' = 0.71$ %,
$K'_r = 1.93$ MPa; $M'_r = 1.93 (600) (330)^2 \times 10^{-6} = 126$ kN.m
Note: $M'_r = 126$ kN.m is found assuming that the compression steel is yielding.

2.   Compute moment resistance provided by tension reinforcement $(A_s - A'_s)$ from Table 2.1:

$\rho = (A_s - A'_s) / bd = (8 \times 500 - 2 \times 700) / (600) (330) = 0.0131$
From Table 2.1; $M_r = K_r bd^2 \times 10^{-6}$ kN.m, and for $\rho = 1.31$ %,
$K_r = 3.83$ MPa; $M_r = 3.83 (600) (330)^2 \times 10^{-6} = 250$ kN.m

3.   Total moment resistance of section:

$M_r + M'_r = 250 + 126 = 376$ kN.m

Example 2.4   Design of a Rectangular Beam with Tension and Compression Reinforcement

Design the rectangular beam section shown in the figure for a factored moment of M_f = 700 kN.m. The beam is to be built as part of a parking structure located in Ottawa, with a limited cross-sectional size due to functional requirements.

$f'_c = 30$ MPa; $f_y = 400$ MPa; maximum aggregate size = 25 mm.

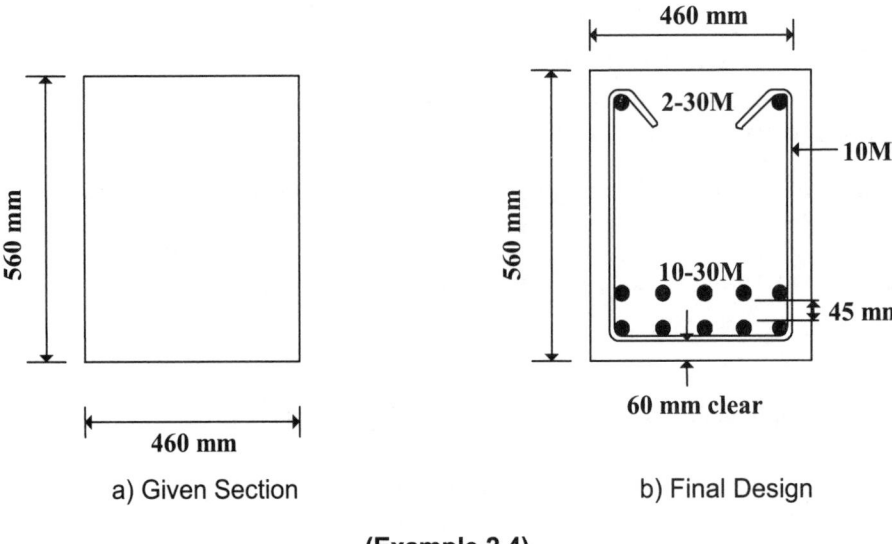

a) Given Section   b) Final Design

(Example 2.4)

1.   Determine concrete cover for corrosive environment from Table 2.6:

Select 60 mm clear cover to stirrups.

2.   Estimate effective depth *d* assuming 30M bars for longitudinal reinforcement and 10M stirrups.

d = 560 - 60 - 11.3 - (29.9/2) = 474 mm

3.   Determine the required tension reinforcement from Table 2.1 :

For design; $M_r \geq M_f$ = 700 kN.m.
For M_r = 700 kN.m; $K_r = M_r \times 10^6/(bd^2)$ = 700x10^6 / [(460)(474)^2] = 6.77 MPa
There is no ρ value given in Table 2.1 for K_r = 6.77 MPa indicating that the section can not be designed to behave in a ductile manner (under-reinforced) unless compression reinforcement is used. Try using compression reinforcement.

4.   Determine required compression reinforcement from Table 2.2:

Provide maximum tension reinforcement given in Table 2.1.
For f'_c = 30 MPa; select ρ = 2.63 %, and read corresponding K_r = 6.4 MPa
Moment resistance provided by this reinforcement; $M_r = K_r\, bd^2 \times 10^{-6}$
M_r = 6.4 (460)(474)$^2 \times 10^{-6}$ = 661 kN.m
Remaining moment resistance to be provided by compression reinforcement;
$M'_r = M_f - M_r$ = 700 - 661 = 39 kN.m
$K'_r = M'_r \times 10^6 / bd^2$ = 39 x 10^6 / (460)(474)^2 = 0.38 MPa
Compute d' based on assumed compression bar size of 15M;
d' = 60 + 11.3 + (16/2) = 79 mm
d' / d = 79 / 474 = 0.17; from Table 2.2; ρ' = 0.14 %
$A'_s = \rho'\, bd$ = 0.0014(460)(474) = 305 mm^2
Use 2-15M with A'_s = 400 mm^2 and d' = 79 mm.

5.   Determine required tension reinforcement:

$\rho + \rho'$ = 2.63 + 0.14 = 2.77; A_s = 0.0277 (460)(474) = 6040 mm^2
Use 9-30M bars with A_s = 6300 mm^2.
Note: 9-30M bars can not be placed within b = 460 mm in a single row without violating the cover and/or minimum spacing limitations specified in Table 2.6. Therefore, use double layers of reinforcement and revise the design.

6.   Revise d:

Revise "d" based on double layers of 30M bars and 45 mm clear spacing between the two layers:
d = 560 - 60 - 11.3 - 29.9 - 45/2 = 436 mm
Note: More reinforcement will be needed since "d" is reduced.

7.   Determine required compression reinforcement from Table 2.2:

Provide maximum tension reinforcement given in Table 2.1.
For f'_c = 30 MPa; select ρ = 2.63 %, and read corresponding K_r = 6.4 MPa
Moment resistance provided by this reinforcement; $M_r = K_r\, bd^2 \times 10^{-6}$
M_r = 6.4 (460)(436)$^2 \times 10^{-6}$ = 560 kN.m
Remaining moment resistance to be provided by compression reinforcement;
$M'_r = M_f - M_r$ = 700 - 560 = 140 kN.m
$K'_r = M'_r \times 10^6 / bd^2$ = 140 x 10^6 / (460)(436)^2 = 1.60 MPa
d' / d = 79 / 436 = 0.18; from Table 2.2 read ρ' = 0.57 %
$A'_s = \rho'\, bd$ = 0.0057(460)(436) = 1143 mm^2 (required)
Use 2-30M with A'_s = 1400 mm^2 (provided)

Note: The effect of the change in *d'* from 79 mm to 86 mm, because of the use of 30M top reinforcement instead of 15M initially assumed, is negligible and is compensated by the extra steel area provided.

8.   Determine required tension reinforcement:

$\rho + \rho' = 2.63 + 0.57 = 3.20$; $A_s = 0.0320 \,(460)(436) = 6418 \text{ mm}^2$
Use 10-30M bars in two layers (5-30M in each layer), with $A_s = 7000 \text{ mm}^2$

9.   Check spacing of tension reinforcement from Table 2.6:

$s = [460 - 2(60) - 2(11.3) - 5(29.9)] / 4 = 42 \text{ mm}$
$42 \text{ mm} = 1.4 \, b_d = 1.4(29.9) = 42 \text{ mm}$
$\qquad\qquad > 1.4 \, a_{max} = 1.4(25) = 35 \text{ mm}$
$\qquad\qquad > 30 \text{ mm}$

Note: This section is heavily reinforced in the tension region and hence is not likely to violate minimum steel and crack control requirements.
Final design is illustrated in the figure.

Example 2.5   Analysis of a T-Section in Positive Bending Behaving as a Rectangular Section

Compute positive bending resistance of the T-beams shown below. The beams are continuous with a span length of 9.0 m. $f'_c = 40$ MPa; $f_y = 400$ MPa.

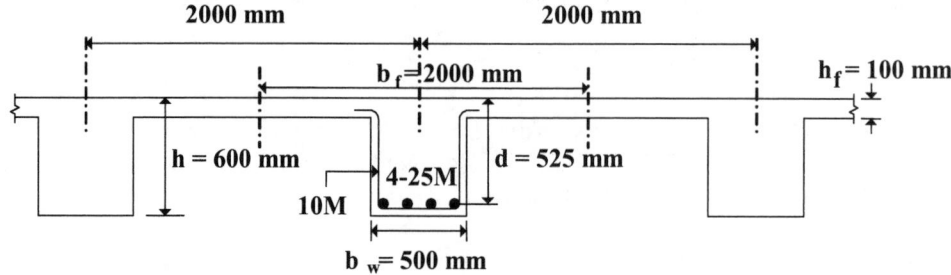

(Example 2.5)

1.   Determine effective flange width b_{eff} from Table 2.4:

Overhanging flange width $b'_T \le 12 \, h_f = 12 \,(100) = 1200 \text{ mm}$
$\qquad\qquad\qquad\qquad\qquad \le \ell / 10 = 9000 / 10 = 900 \text{ mm}$
$\qquad\qquad\qquad\qquad\qquad \le x \text{ or } y = 750 \text{ mm}$
$b'_T = 750 \text{ mm governs.}$ $b_{eff} = 2 \,(750) + (500) = 2000 \text{ mm}$

2.   Determine if the section behaves as a T-section:

Condition for T-section behaviour: Use either Eq. 2-23 or Eq. 2-24.
For T-section behaviour Eq 2-23 gives; $A_s > (\alpha_1 \phi_c \, f'_c \, h_f \, b_f) / (\phi_s \, f_y)$
α_1 can be obtained from Table 2.1
$A_s = 4 \,(500) = 2000 \text{ mm}^2 < [(0.79) \,(0.65) \,(40) \,(100) \,(2000)] / [(0.85) \,(400)] = 12082 \text{mm}^2$
Therefore, the section behaves as a rectangular section, $b = b_f$

Alternatively, for T-section behaviour from Eq. 2-24; $h_f < (A_s \phi_s f_y)/(\alpha_1 \phi_c f'_c b_f)$
$h_f = 100 >$ [(2000) (0.85) (400)] / [(0.79) (0.65) (40) (2000)] $= 17$ mm
Hence, rectangular section behaviour.

3. Compute moment resistance M_r from Table 2.1:

    $\rho = A_s / bd = 2000 / (2000 \times 525) = 0.0019$
    From Table 2.1 for $\rho = 0.19$; $K_r = 0.63$ MPa

    $M_r = K_r bd^2 \times 10^{-6} = 0.63 (2000) (525)^2 \times 10^{-6} = 347$ kN.m

Example 2.6   Analysis of an L-Section in Positive Bending Behaving as a T-Section

Compute factored moment resistance M_r of the L-section shown in the figure.

$f'_c = 30$ MPa; $f_y = 400$ MPa

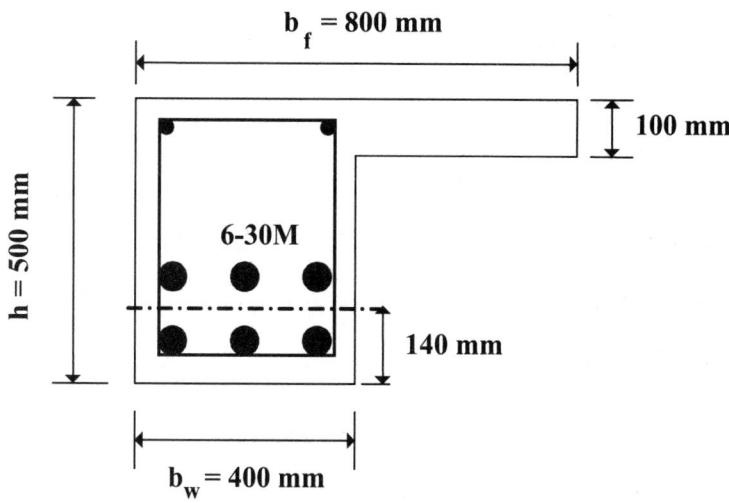

(Example 2.6)

1. Determine if the section behaves as a T-section:

    Condition for T-section behaviour from Eq. 2-24; $h_f < (A_s \phi_s f_y)/(\alpha_1 \phi_c f'_c b_f)$
    $h_f = 100$ mm $< (6 \times 700 \times 0.85 \times 400) / (0.81 \times 0.65 \times 30 \times 800) = 113$ mm
    Therefore, the section behaves as a T-section, and the moment resistance consists of two
    components; M_{rf} and M_{rw}.

2. Compute moment resistance provided by the overhanging flange, M_{rf} :

    Determine ρ_f from Table 2.3: For $d/h_f = 360 / 100 = 3.6$ read $\rho_f = 1.31$ %
    Determine K_{rf} from Table 2.1 using $\rho = \rho_f = 1.31$ %; $K_{rf} = 3.83$ MPa
    $M_{rf} = K_{rf} (b_f - b_w) d^2 \times 10^{-6} = (3.83) (800-400) (360)^2 \times 10^{-6} = 199$ kN.m

3. Compute moment resistance provided by the web, M_{rw} :

    $A_{sf} = \rho_f (b_f - b_w)d = 0.0131 (800 - 400) (360) = 1886$ mm^2

$A_{sw} = A_s - A_{sf} = 6 \times 700 - 1886 = 2314 \text{ mm}^2$
$\rho_w = A_{sw}/b_wd = 2314 / (400 \times 360) = 0.0161 = 1.61 \%$
Determine K_{rw} from Table 2.1 using $\rho = \rho_w = 1.61 \%$; $K_{rw} = 4.52$ MPa
$M_{rw} = K_{rw}b_wd^2 \times 10^{-6} = (4.52)(400)(360)^2 \times 10^{-6} = 234$ kN.m

4.   Total moment resistance, M_r :

$M_r = M_{rf} + M_{rw} = 199 + 234 = 433$ kN.m

Example 2.7   Design of a T-Section in Positive Bending

Design the T-section shown in the figure for a factored positive moment of $M_f = 1500$ kN.m. $f'_c = 30$ MPa; $f_y = 400$ MPa;   clear cover to stirrups = 40 mm; interior exposure condition; maximum aggregate size $a_{max} = 25$ mm.

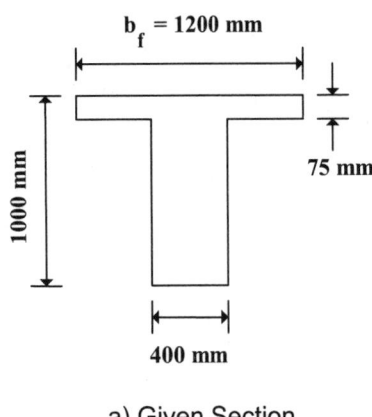

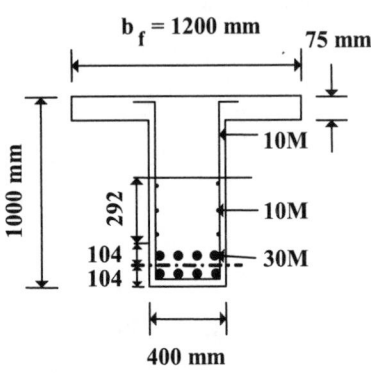

a) Given Section   b) Final Design

(Example 2.7)

1.   Estimate effective depth d, assuming two layers of 30M bars with 45 mm spacing between the layers, and 10M stirrups.

$d = 1000 - 40 - 11.3 - 29.9 - 45/2 = 896$ mm

2.   Determine reinforcement ratio ρ from Table 2.1 assuming rectangular section behaviour :

$M_r \geq M_f;\ K_r = M_r \times 10^6 / b\, d^2 = (1500 \times 10^6) / (1200)(896)^2 = 1.56$ MPa
From Table 2.1 $\rho = 0.48 \%$

3.   Verify if the beam behaves as a rectangular section using Eq 2-23 :

$(\alpha_1\phi_cf'_ch_fb_f)/(\phi_sf_y) = (0.81 \times 0.65 \times 30 \times 75 \times 1200) / (0.85 \times 400) = 4181 \text{ mm}^2$
$A_s = \rho bd = 0.0048 (1200)(896) = 5161 \text{ mm}^2 > 4181 \text{ mm}^2$
Therefore, the section behaves as a T-section, and hence must be designed as a T-section.

4.   Compute the area of tension steel A_{sf} associated with moment resistance of the overhangs from Table 2.3:

for $d/h_f = 896 / 75 = 11.9$; read $\rho_f = 0.39 \%$
$A_{sf} = \rho_f(b_f - b_w)d = 0.0039(1200 - 400)(896) = 2796 \text{ mm}^2$

Moment resistance provided by ρ_f = 0.0039 from Table 2.1;
K_{rf} = 1.27 MPa; $M_{rf} = K_{rf} (b_f - b_w)d^2 \times 10^{-6}$ = 1.27(1200 - 400)(896)$^2 \times 10^{-6}$ = 816 kN.m

5.   Compute area of tension steel A_{sw} associated with web resistance from Table 2.1 :

Moment resistance to be provided by web steel; $M_{rw} = M_f - M_f$ = 1500 - 816 = 684 kN.m
$K_{rw} = M_{rw} \times 10^6 / b_w d^2$ = (684 x 10^6) /[(400)(896)^2] = 2.13 MPa
From Table 2.1; ρ_w = 0.68 % = 0.0068; $A_{sw} = \rho_w b_w d$ = 0.0068 (400)(896) = 2437 mm^2

6.   Total tension steel:

$A_s = A_{sf} + A_{sw}$ = 2796 + 2437 = 5233 mm^2
Use 8-30M bars in two rows, with A_s = 8 x 700 = 5600 mm^2

7.   Check minimum spacing of reinforcement using Table 2.6:

s = [400 - 2(40) - 2(11.3) - 4(29.9)] / 3 = 59 mm
From Table 2.6; $s \geq 1.4 d_b$ = 1.4 (29.9) = 42 mm O.K.
                           $s \geq 1.4 a_{max}$ = 1.4 (25) = 35 mm O.K.
                           $s \geq$ 30 mm O.K.

8.   Check minimum reinforcement ratio:

Use Eq. 2-7; $A_{smin} = 0.2 \sqrt{f'_c} \, b_t \, h / f_y$ = 0.2 $\sqrt{30}$ (400)(1000)/(400) =1095mm^2
A_s = 5600 > 1095 mm^2 O.K.

9.   Check maximum bar spacing as governed by crack control:

Compute quantity "z" from Eq. 2-32 or Table 2.7: $z = f_s (d_c A)^{1/3}$
Note: For calculation of A and d_c clear cover need not be taken greater than 50 mm. From
Table 2.7; $y = h - d$ = 1000 - 896 = 104 mm;
$A = 2yb/8$ = 2 (104) (400) / 8 = 10400 mm^2; $f_s = 0.6 f_y$ = 0.6(400)=240 MPa;
d_c = 40 + 11.3 + 29.9/2 = 66 mm
z = 240 (66 x 10400)$^{1/3}$ = 21,171 N/mm
z = 21,171 N/mm < 30,000 N/mm (interior exposure) O.K.

10. Check if skin reinforcement is needed:

h > 750 mm. Therefore, skin reinforcement, as illustrated in Table 2.8 is needed. Area of skin
reinforcement on each side;
$A_{sk}/2 = 0.008 A_{cs}/2 = 0.008 (2x)[(h/2)-2(h-d)]$
Assuming 10M bars will be used, x = 40 + 11.3 + 11.3/2 = 57 mm
$A_{sk}/2$ = (0.008)(2)(57)[(500-2(1000-896)] = 266 mm^2
Provide 3-10M bars along each side face, uniformly placed within distance [(h/2)-2(h-d)] =
500-2(1000-896) = 292 mm. Note that the spacing of bars does not exceed the maximum
value of 200 mm.
Total A_{sk} = 6 (100) = 600 mm^2 (for two side faces).
Note: The contribution of skin reinforcement to flexural resistance is ignored. Final design is
illustrated in the figure.

2

Design for Flexure

Table 2.1   **Reinforcement ratio ρ (%) for rectangular sections with tension reinforcement f_y = 400 MPa**

$\phi_S = 0.85$
$\phi_c = 0.6$

$$M_r = K_r bd^2 \times 10^{-6} \text{ kN.m}; \qquad K_r = \left[1 - \frac{\rho \phi_c f_y}{2\alpha_1 \phi_c f'_c}\right]\rho \phi_s f_y; \qquad \rho = \frac{A_s}{bd}$$

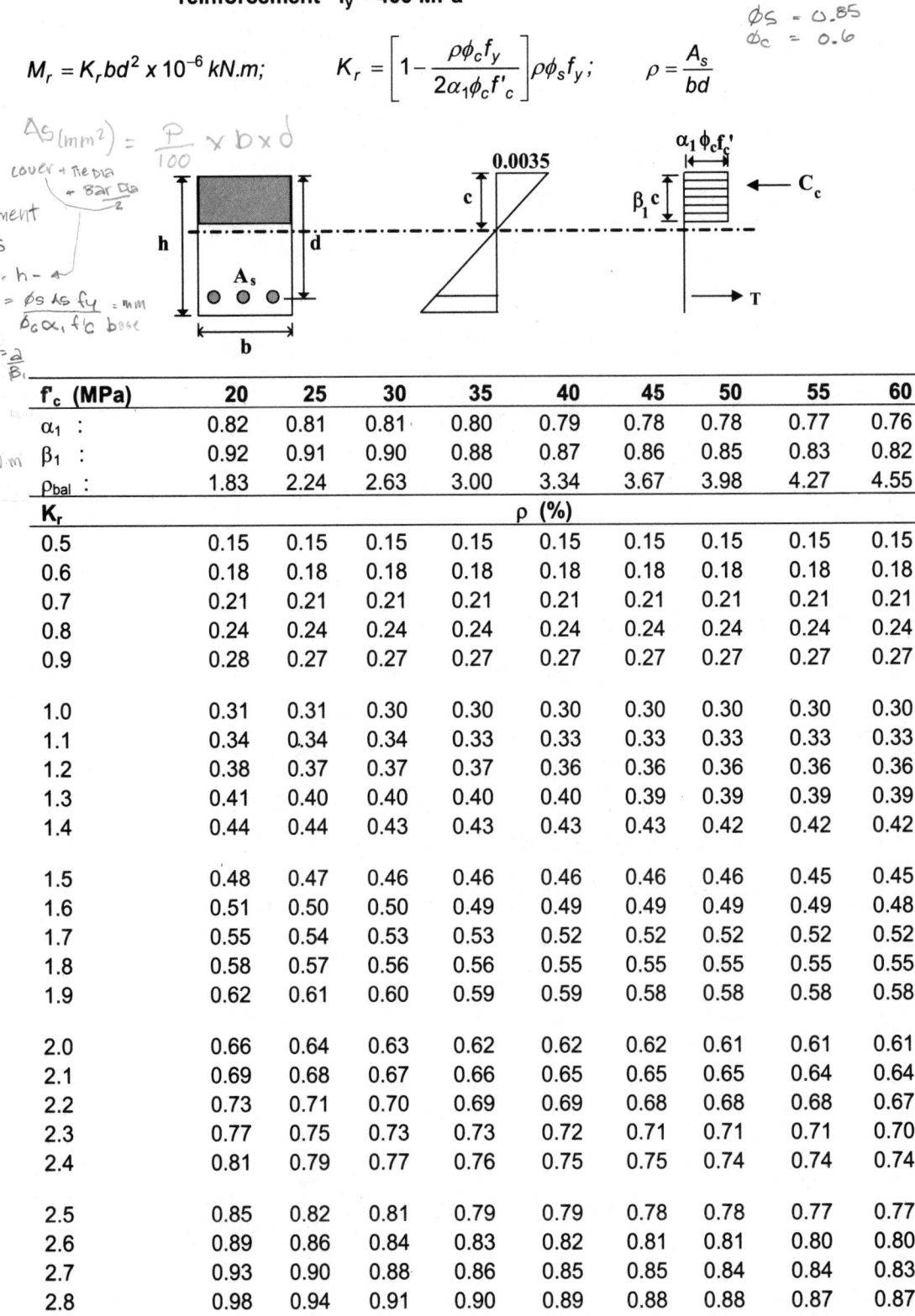

$A_{s(mm^2)} = \dfrac{P}{100} \times b \times d$

cover + Tie Dia
  + $\dfrac{\text{Bar Dia}}{2}$

Moment
AS
$d = h - \triangle$
$a = \dfrac{\phi_s A_s f_y}{b_c \alpha_1 f'_c \, base} = mm$

$c = \dfrac{a}{\beta_1}$

$\dfrac{c}{d}$

$\dfrac{c}{\beta_1}$

kN.m

f'_c (MPa)	20	25	30	35	40	45	50	55	60
α_1 :	0.82	0.81	0.81	0.80	0.79	0.78	0.78	0.77	0.76
β_1 :	0.92	0.91	0.90	0.88	0.87	0.86	0.85	0.83	0.82
ρ_{bal} :	1.83	2.24	2.63	3.00	3.34	3.67	3.98	4.27	4.55
K_r					ρ (%)				
0.5	0.15	0.15	0.15	0.15	0.15	0.15	0.15	0.15	0.15
0.6	0.18	0.18	0.18	0.18	0.18	0.18	0.18	0.18	0.18
0.7	0.21	0.21	0.21	0.21	0.21	0.21	0.21	0.21	0.21
0.8	0.24	0.24	0.24	0.24	0.24	0.24	0.24	0.24	0.24
0.9	0.28	0.27	0.27	0.27	0.27	0.27	0.27	0.27	0.27
1.0	0.31	0.31	0.30	0.30	0.30	0.30	0.30	0.30	0.30
1.1	0.34	0.34	0.34	0.33	0.33	0.33	0.33	0.33	0.33
1.2	0.38	0.37	0.37	0.37	0.36	0.36	0.36	0.36	0.36
1.3	0.41	0.40	0.40	0.40	0.40	0.39	0.39	0.39	0.39
1.4	0.44	0.44	0.43	0.43	0.43	0.43	0.42	0.42	0.42
1.5	0.48	0.47	0.46	0.46	0.46	0.46	0.46	0.45	0.45
1.6	0.51	0.50	0.50	0.49	0.49	0.49	0.49	0.49	0.48
1.7	0.55	0.54	0.53	0.53	0.52	0.52	0.52	0.52	0.52
1.8	0.58	0.57	0.56	0.56	0.55	0.55	0.55	0.55	0.55
1.9	0.62	0.61	0.60	0.59	0.59	0.58	0.58	0.58	0.58
2.0	0.66	0.64	0.63	0.62	0.62	0.62	0.61	0.61	0.61
2.1	0.69	0.68	0.67	0.66	0.65	0.65	0.65	0.64	0.64
2.2	0.73	0.71	0.70	0.69	0.69	0.68	0.68	0.68	0.67
2.3	0.77	0.75	0.73	0.73	0.72	0.71	0.71	0.71	0.70
2.4	0.81	0.79	0.77	0.76	0.75	0.75	0.74	0.74	0.74
2.5	0.85	0.82	0.81	0.79	0.79	0.78	0.78	0.77	0.77
2.6	0.89	0.86	0.84	0.83	0.82	0.81	0.81	0.80	0.80
2.7	0.93	0.90	0.88	0.86	0.85	0.85	0.84	0.84	0.83
2.8	0.98	0.94	0.91	0.90	0.89	0.88	0.88	0.87	0.87
2.9	1.02	0.98	0.95	0.93	0.92	0.92	0.91	0.90	0.90

Table 2.1 (Cont'd)

f'$_{c(}$ (MPa)	200	25	30	35	40	45	50	55	60
K$_r$					ρ (%)				
3.0	1.06	1.02	0.99	0.97	0.96	0.95	0.94	0.94	0.93
3.1	1.11	1.06	1.03	1.01	0.99	0.98	0.98	0.97	0.97
3.2	1.15	1.10	1.06	1.04	1.03	1.02	1.01	1.00	1.00
3.3	1.20	1.14	1.10	1.08	1.06	1.05	1.04	1.04	1.03
3.4	1.25	1.18	1.14	1.12	1.10	1.09	1.08	1.07	1.07
3.5	1.30	1.22	1.18	1.15	1.14	1.12	1.11	1.11	1.10
3.6	1.35	1.26	1.22	1.19	1.17	1.16	1.15	1.14	1.13
3.7	1.40	1.31	1.26	1.23	1.21	1.19	1.18	1.17	1.17
3.8	1.46	1.35	1.30	1.27	1.25	1.23	1.22	1.21	1.20
3.9	1.51	1.40	1.34	1.31	1.28	1.27	1.25	1.24	1.23
4.0	1.57	1.45	1.38	1.35	1.32	1.30	1.29	1.28	1.27
4.1	1.63	1.49	1.43	1.39	1.36	1.34	1.32	1.31	1.30
4.2	1.69	1.54	1.47	1.43	1.40	1.38	1.36	1.35	1.34
4.3	1.76	1.59	1.51	·1.47	1.44	1.41	1.40	1.38	1.37
4.4	1.83	1.64	1.56	1.51	1.47	1.45	1.43	1.42	1.41
4.5		1.69	1.60	1.55	1.51	1.49	1.47	1.45	1.44
4.6		1.75	1.65	1.59	1.55	1.53	1.51	1.49	1.48
4.7		1.80	1.69	1.63	1.59	1.56	1.54	1.53	1.51
4.8		1.85	1.74	1.67	1.63	1.60	1.58	1.56	1.55
4.9		1.91	1.79	.1.72	1.67	1.64	1.62	1.60	1.59
5.0		1.97	1.84	1.76	1.71	1.68	1.66	1.64	1.62
5.1		2.03	1.88	1.81	1.75	1.72	1.69	1.67	1.66
5.2		2.09	1.93	1.85	1.80	1.76	1.73	1.71	1.69
5.3		2.16	1.99	1.90	1.84	1.80	1.77	1.75	1.73
5.4		2.23	2.04	1.94	1.88	1.84	1.81	1.79	1.77
5.5			2.09	1.99	1.92	1.88	1.85	1.82	1.80
5.6			2.15	2.04	1.97	1.92	1.89	1.86	1.84
5.7			2.20	2.08	2.01	1.96	1.93	1.90	1.88
5.8			2.26	2.13	2.06	2.00	1.97	1.94	1.92
5.9			2.32	2.18	2.10	2.05	2.01	1.98	1.95
6.0			2.38	2.23	2.15	2.09	2.05	2.02	1.99
6.1			2.44	2.28	2.19	2.13	2.09	2.06	2.03
6.2			2.50	2.33	2.24	2.17	2.13	2.10	2.07
6.3			2.57	2.39	2.29	2.22	2.17	2.14	2.11
6.4			2.63	2.44	2.33	2.26	2.21	2.18	2.15

(hand-written notes)

c/L
ℓn
COEF
Mr = COEF x wf x ℓn²
(kN·m)
kr req. = Mr x10⁶ / bd²
ρ (%)
As

Table 2.1 (Cont'd)

f'$_c$ (MPa)	20	25	30	35	40	45	50	55	60
K$_r$					ρ (%)				
6.5				2.50	2.38	2.31	2.25	2.22	2.19
6.6				2.55	2.43	2.35	2.30	2.26	2.23
6.7				2.61	2.48	2.40	2.34	2.30	2.26
6.8				2.67	2.53	2.44	2.38	2.34	2.30
6.9				2.73	2.58	2.49	2.43	2.38	2.34
7.0				2.79	2.63	2.54	2.47	2.42	2.39
7.1				2.85	2.68	2.58	2.52	2.46	2.43
7.2				2.91	2.74	2.63	2.56	2.51	2.47
7.3				2.98	2.79	2.68	2.61	2.55	2.51
7.4					2.85	2.73	2.65	2.59	2.55
7.5					2.90	2.78	2.70	2.64	2.59
7.6					2.96	2.83	2.74	2.68	2.63
7.7					3.02	2.88	2.79	2.72	2.68
7.8					3.08	2.93	2.84	2.77	2.72
7.9					3.14	2.99	2.89	2.81	2.76
8.0					3.20	3.04	2.93	2.86	2.80
8.1					3.26	3.09	2.98	2.91	2.85
8.2					3.33	3.15	3.03	2.95	2.89
8.3						3.20	3.08	3.00	2.94
8.4						3.26	3.13	3.05	2.98
8.5						3.32	3.18	3.09	3.02
8.6						3.38	3.24	3.14	3.07
8.7						3.44	3.29	3.19	3.12
8.8						3.50	3.34	3.24	3.16
8.9						3.56	3.40	3.29	3.21
9.0						3.62	3.45	3.34	3.25
9.1							3.51	3.39	3.30
9.2							3.56	3.44	3.35
9.3							3.62	3.49	3.40
9.4							3.68	3.54	3.45
9.5							3.74	3.59	3.49
9.6							3.80	3.65	3.54
9.7							3.86	3.70	3.59
9.8							3.92	3.76	3.64
9.9							3.98	3.81	3.69
10.0								3.87	3.75
10.5								4.16	4.01
11.0									4.29

Table 2.2 Compression reinforcement ratio ρ' (%); f_y = 400 MPa

$$M'_r = K'_r \, bd^2 \times 10^{-6} \; kN.m \quad K'_r = \left[1 - \frac{d'}{d}\right]\rho' \, \phi_s f'_y \quad \rho' = \frac{A'_s}{bd}$$

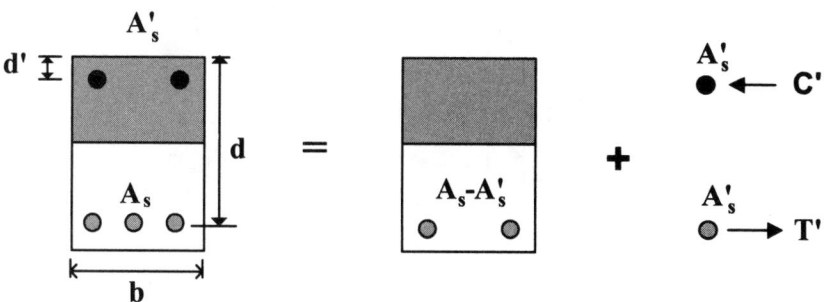

d'/d:	0.05	0.10	0.15	0.20	0.25
K'_r			ρ' (%)		
0.20	0.06	0.07	0.07	0.07	0.08
0.40	0.12	0.13	0.14	0.15	0.16
0.60	0.19	0.20	0.21	0.22	0.24
0.80	0.25	0.26	0.28	0.29	0.31
1.00	0.31	0.33	0.35	0.37	0.39
1.20	0.37	0.39	0.42	0.44	0.47
1.40	0.43	0.46	0.48	0.51	0.55
1.60	0.50	0.52	0.55	0.59	0.63
1.80	0.56	0.59	0.62	0.66	0.71
2.00	0.62	0.65	0.69	0.74	0.78
2.20	0.68	0.72	0.76	0.81	0.86
2.40	0.74	0.78	0.83	0.88	0.94
2.60	0.80	0.85	0.90	0.96	1.02
2.80	0.87	0.92	0.97	1.03	1.10
3.00	0.93	0.98	1.04	1.10	1.18
3.20	0.99	1.05	1.11	1.18	1.25
3.40	1.05	1.11	1.18	1.25	1.33
3.60	1.11	1.18	1.25	1.32	1.41
3.80	1.18	1.24	1.31	1.40	1.49
4.00	1.24	1.31	1.38	1.47	1.57

Table 2.3 Reinforcement ratio, ρ_f (%) that balances concrete in overhang(s) of T or L beams. $f_y = 400$ MPa

$$\rho_f = \frac{\alpha_1 \phi_c f'_c \, h_f}{\phi_s f_y d} \qquad\qquad M_{rf} = \rho_f (b_f - b_w)d\phi_s f_y \left(d - \frac{h_f}{2}\right) \text{ or;}$$

$$M_{rf} = K_{rf}(b_f - b_w)d^2 \times 10^{-6} \ kN.m \ \ (K_{rf} \text{ to be obtained from Table 2.1})$$

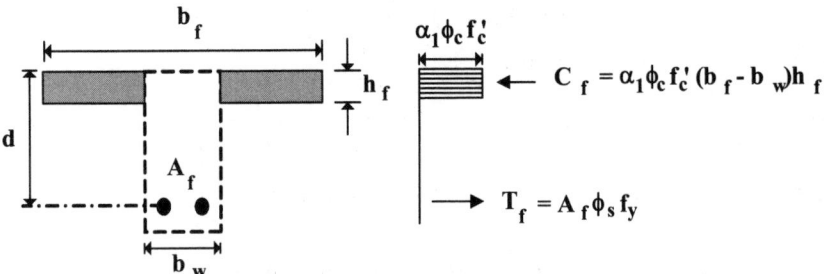

f'_c (MPa)	20	25	30	35	40	45	50	55	60
d/h_f					ρ_f (%)				
3.00	1.05	1.29	1.54	1.78	2.01	2.24	2.47	2.69	2.91
4.00	0.78	0.97	1.15	1.33	1.51	1.68	1.85	2.02	2.18
5.00	0.63	0.78	0.92	1.07	1.21	1.35	1.48	1.61	1.74
6.00	0.52	0.65	0.77	0.89	1.01	1.12	1.23	1.35	1.45
7.00	0.45	0.55	0.66	0.76	0.86	0.96	1.06	1.15	1.25
8.00	0.39	0.49	0.58	0.67	0.76	0.84	0.93	1.01	1.09
9.00	0.35	0.43	0.51	0.59	0.67	0.75	0.82	0.90	0.97
10.00	0.31	0.39	0.46	0.53	0.60	0.67	0.74	0.81	0.87
11.00	0.29	0.35	0.42	0.49	0.55	0.61	0.67	0.73	0.79
12.00	0.26	0.32	0.38	0.44	0.50	0.56	0.62	0.67	0.73
13.00	0.24	0.30	0.36	0.41	0.46	0.52	0.57	0.62	0.67
14.00	0.22	0.28	0.33	0.38	0.43	0.48	0.53	0.58	0.62
15.00	0.21	0.26	0.31	0.36	0.40	0.45	0.49	0.54	0.58

Table 2.4 Effective flange width in T and L-sections

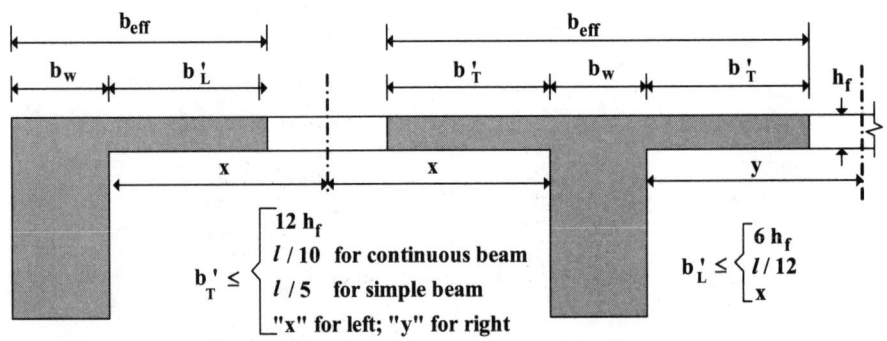

$$b'_T \le \begin{cases} 12\,h_f \\ l/10 \ \text{ for continuous beam} \\ l/5 \ \text{ for simple beam} \\ \text{"x" for left; "y" for right} \end{cases}$$

$$b'_L \le \begin{cases} 6\,h_f \\ l/12 \\ x \end{cases}$$

where, l is the beam span length

Table 2.5 Concrete joist construction

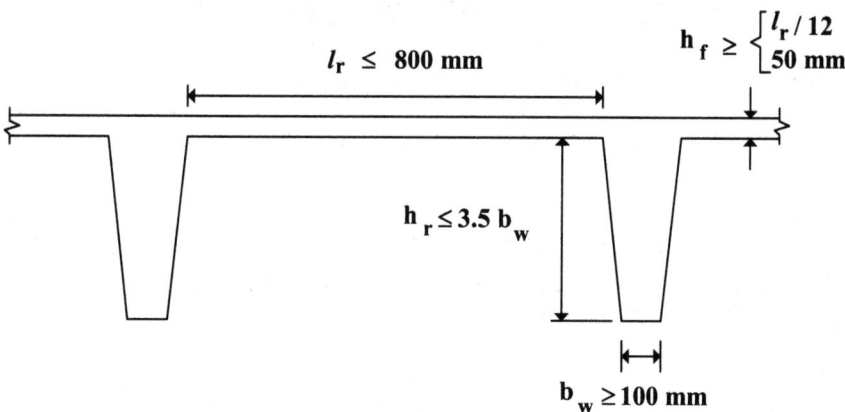

Table 2.6 Spacing and cover requirements for beam reinforcement

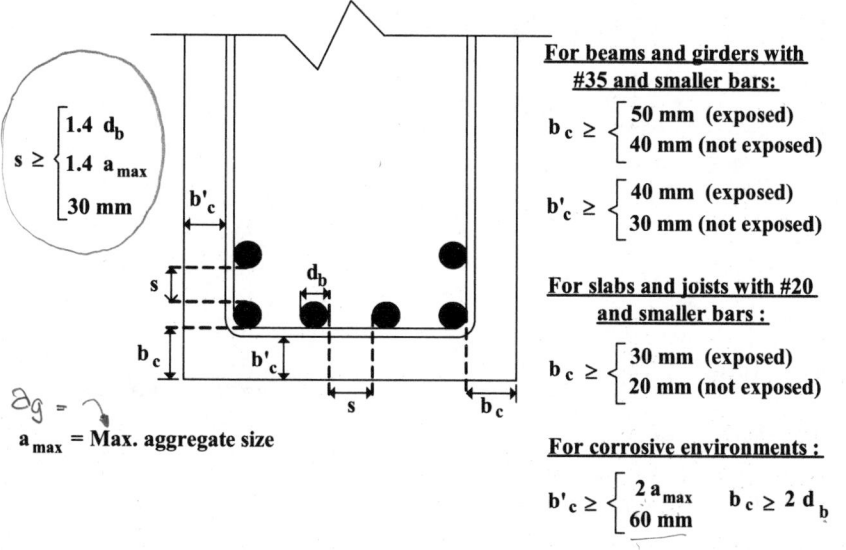

$$s \geq \begin{cases} 1.4\, d_b \\ 1.4\, a_{max} \\ 30 \text{ mm} \end{cases}$$

a_{max} = Max. aggregate size

For beams and girders with #35 and smaller bars:

$$b_c \geq \begin{cases} 50 \text{ mm (exposed)} \\ 40 \text{ mm (not exposed)} \end{cases}$$

$$b'_c \geq \begin{cases} 40 \text{ mm (exposed)} \\ 30 \text{ mm (not exposed)} \end{cases}$$

For slabs and joists with #20 and smaller bars :

$$b_c \geq \begin{cases} 30 \text{ mm (exposed)} \\ 20 \text{ mm (not exposed)} \end{cases}$$

For corrosive environments :

$$b'_c \geq \begin{cases} 2\, a_{max} \\ 60 \text{ mm} \end{cases} \quad b_c \geq 2\, d_b$$

Table 2.7 Crack control requirement

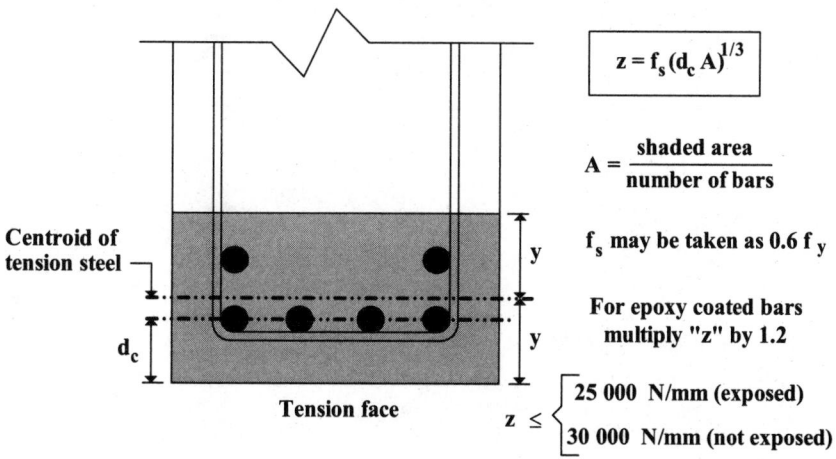

$$z = f_s \left(d_c\, A \right)^{1/3}$$

$$A = \frac{\text{shaded area}}{\text{number of bars}}$$

f_s may be taken as $0.6\, f_y$

For epoxy coated bars multiply "z" by 1.2

$$z \leq \begin{cases} 25\ 000 \text{ N/mm (exposed)} \\ 30\ 000 \text{ N/mm (not exposed)} \end{cases}$$

Table 2.8 Skin reinforcement

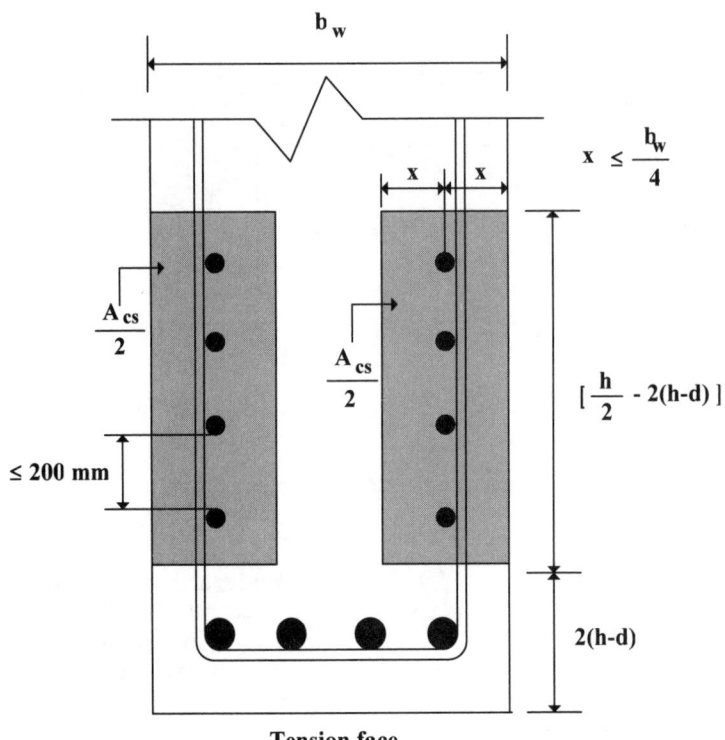

Tension face

$$\text{Area of skin reinforcement in each strip} \atop \text{when } h > 750 \text{ mm} = \begin{cases} 0.008 \; \dfrac{A_{cs}}{2} & \text{for interior exposure} \\[2ex] 0.010 \; \dfrac{A_{cs}}{2} & \text{for exterior exposure} \end{cases}$$

A_{cs}: Total shaded area

Table 2.9 Tension reinforcement in overhangs

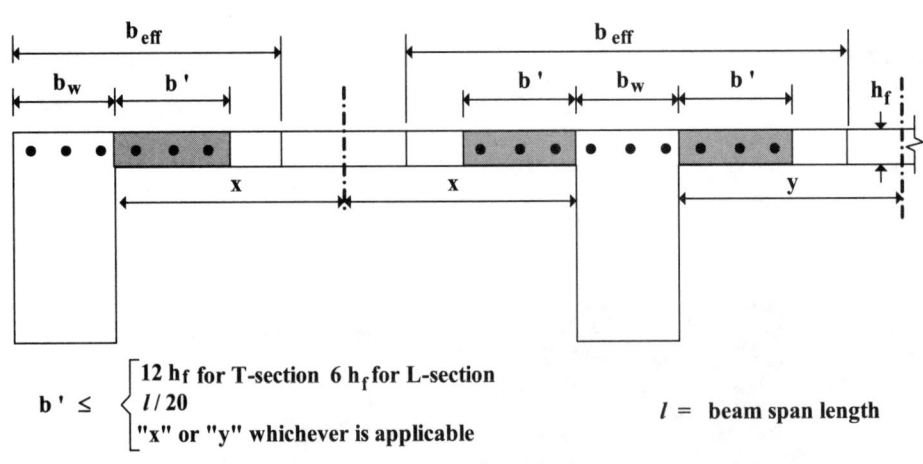

$$b' \le \begin{cases} 12 \, h_f \text{ for T-section } 6 \, h_f \text{ for L-section} \\ l/20 \\ \text{"x" or "y" whichever is applicable} \end{cases} \qquad l = \text{ beam span length}$$

Area of flange steel within width b' $\ge$ 0.004 b' h$_f$

3

By R.E. Loov
T. Rezansoff

3

Development and Splices

Development and Splices of Reinforcement

3.1   Introduction

A strength related failure should not occur at an anchorage or a splice, just as connections in steel construction, and joint details or shear and torsion resistance in concrete construction should not be the weak link when ensuring adequate strength and ductility. Development and splice lengths are intended to have sufficient over-strength to decrease the probability of a bond related failure before failure occurs in a more ductile flexure mode.

For small concrete covers and deformed reinforcement, failures in development or lap splices occur when the concrete confining the reinforcement splits away. This is due to the radial bursting component of the bearing force between reinforcement deformations and the surrounding concrete in straight bar anchorages, and additional lateral bursting forces imposed on the concrete with hooked anchorages or the cross wires in welded wire reinforcement. In flexure, prying of the reinforcement on the confining concrete also occurs because of beam curvature, and dowel action at transverse crack locations.

A bond splitting failure can be prevented by providing sufficient confinement to the reinforcement along its anchorage length using a combination of concrete confinement and confinement provided by stirrups, ties and spirals that intercept bond splitting cracks. Features that improve confinement, such as the restraint provided to bars from adjoining members framing into a common joint, or to stirrup hooks from a slab placed integrally with a beam, require careful attention to detail and construction to ensure realization of the expected strength. Care is also needed to ensure that the hooks used in transverse reinforcement provide positive confinement to the longitudinal bars.

As in previous CSA A23.3 Standards, design for development uses empirical equations with full (unfactored) specified material strengths. The coefficients used in the equations are chosen to provide the required factor of safety without the use of the material factors ϕ_c and ϕ_s.

The requirements for development and splicing of reinforcement are unchanged from A23.3-94.

3.2   Development Tension

3.2.1   General

(a) Detailed approach
Equation (12-1)[1] in Clause 12.2.2 accounts for factors that affect the tension development length of deformed bars or wire or deformed welded wire reinforcement. The benefit of concrete confinement provided by cover and bar spacing, and transverse tie and stirrup reinforcement placed to intercept potential bond splitting cracks, is explicitly included. There is a limit to the total confinement that is effective. Bond failure changes from splitting of the confining concrete, to a pullout failure with crushing of the concrete in front of the reinforcement deformations in a heavily confined anchorage. The total confinement provided by concrete and transverse reinforcement up to an equivalent 2.5 bar diameters of concrete cover, is considered to be effective in preventing splitting bond failures. Additional confinement does not increase pullout strength.

Epoxy coating, used as corrosion protection for reinforcement, has a detrimental influence on bond development. A coating modification factor k_2, is required by Clause 12.2.4 to increase anchorage length when bars are epoxy coated. The reduction in bond resistance is particularly severe when smaller concrete cover and bar spacing is used.

---

[1] References to Equations and Clauses refer to CSA-A23.3-04 "Design of Concrete Structures", from here on referred to as A23.3.

The applicability of the empirical equations used for anchorage of reinforcement in high performance concretes has not been adequately investigated. The maximum concrete compressive strength that is permitted for calculating bond strength is therefore limited to $f_c' = 64$ MPa ($\sqrt{f_c'} \leq 8$ MPa in Clause 12.1.2).

For development of deformed welded wire reinforcement in tension, the ℓ_d calculated for deformed wires by Clause 12.2 is modified by factors from Clause 12.7.2 that recognize the anchorage provided by the cross wires.

If heavier confinement is available, the use of Equation (12-1) may be justified to reduce anchorage lengths. Using design aids, only a little extra design effort is needed to apply this detailed approach

(b) Simple approach
As an alternate to the direct calculation and inclusion of the confinement available to an anchorage carrying tension, Table 12-1 permits a simpler approach for obtaining ℓ_d when the minimum concrete cover of d_b and principal reinforcement clear spacing of $1.4d_b$ are provided. These are the minimum values specified in CSA Standard A23.1-04 (see Annex A of A23.3).

Two coefficients are provided in Table 12-1, depending on the confinement available.

3.2.2 Design Aids

Design aids, in the form of tables and figures, are provided at the end of Chapter 3.

(a) Simple approach – Table 12-1
Table 3.1 provides development lengths for 400 MPa standard deformed reinforcing bars while Table 3.11 provides development lengths for Grade 515 deformed wire when heavier confinement exists. The factor k_4 for bar size is included in both tables. The development length must be multiplied by the appropriate values of k_1, k_2, and k_3. For lighter confinement, satisfying "Other cases" in Table 12-1, lengths in Tables 3.1 and 3.11 are multiplied by 1.33. After applicable factors are applied, the development length must not be less than 300 mm, except when used to calculate tension lap splice lengths.

(b) Detailed approach – Equation (12-1)
Table 3.2 provides development lengths for deformed reinforcing bars made of Grade 400 steel based on a confinement index "C.I." which is the sum of the non-dimensionalized confinements provided by the concrete, d_{cs}/d_b as obtained from Tables 3.3(a), (b) & (c), and by the transverse reinforcement K_{tr}/d_b obtained from Table 3.5.

(c) Welded wire reinforcement
Development lengths for common sizes of deformed and smooth welded wire reinforcement (WWR are given in Tables 3.12 and 3.13 respectively.)

(The designation "welded wire reinforcement" **(WWR)** supersedes previous nomenclature such as "welded wire fabric" or "welded wire mesh")

3.2.3 Design Examples

A simple example using deformed welded wire reinforcement is given in Example 3.5

3

Development and Splices

3.3   Standard Hooks in Tension

3.3.1   General

The development length of a standard hook is the total length of the hook plus the straight lead-in distance required up to the critical section to develop the full specified yield strength of the reinforcing bar.   The basic hook development length ℓ_{hb} before multiplying by applicable modification factors is given by the equation in Clause 12.5.2 for Grade 400 reinforcement. Epoxy coated standard hooks in tension have a single penalty factor of 1.2. (Clause 12.5.3(f))

Minimum bend diameters for standard hooks (Clause 6.6.2 and Table 16 of Annex A), recognize the better ductility available with weldable grade reinforcing bars.

3.3.2   Design Aids

Basic hook development lengths ℓ_{hb} for standard deformed bars are shown in Table 3.6 for $f_y = 400$ MPa.   The dimensions of the hook to satisfy CSA Standard A23.1-04, as excerpted in Annex A of CSA A23.3, are illustrated in Table 3.7.

Heavy confinement is necessary for hook development since large bursting and splitting forces are imposed by the hook into the concrete over a relatively short distance. For standard hooks at the ends of members, either the side cover, or the top or bottom cover over the hook must be used to enclose the hook as specified in Clause 12.5.4. Illustrations explaining the hook confinement required by Clause 12.5.4 are shown in Figure 3.1. The use of extra reinforcement, larger covers, and larger covers coupled with enclosure within ties or stirrups permit the use of modifiers which reduce the required hook development length. Factors that may be applied when good confinement is provided are shown in Figure 3.1.

The development length ℓ_{dh} is obtained by multiplying the basic hook development length ℓ_{hb} by modifying factors for structural low-density concrete, for epoxy-coated reinforcement and for $f_y > 400$ MPa. The 1.3 factor required for straight "top" horizontal reinforcement is not required as a modifier for hook development lengths.

3.4   Tension Lap Splices

3.4.1   General

Tension lap splice lengths governed by Clause 12.15, are calculated by multiplying the development length by a splice "Class" factor which considers the excess bar area provided at the location of the splice, and the percentage of the bars spliced at the same location. The largest required lap is a Class B splice with a factor of 1.3 when more than 50% of the bars are spliced at the same location or the reinforcing area provided at the splice location is less than twice the required area (Clause 12.15.2 and 12.17.3.2.)

3.4.2   Design Aids

Splice lengths, which are multiplied by the Class factor to give the lap length for deformed bars and wire in tension, are obtained in the same fashion as outlined in Sections 3.2.2 (a) & (b). The only difference is that for the "Detailed Approach" using Equation (12-1); Tables 3.4, rather than Tables 3.3, are used to obtain the confinement index provided by the concrete, where the extra beam width needed by the contacting spliced bars along the lap is accounted for. The reduction in development length based on excess reinforcement (Clause 12.2.5) is not used for calculating splice lengths, nor is the minimum development length of 300 mm specified in Clause

12.2.1. However, after application of the Class factor, Clause 12.15.1 requires a lap length of at least 300 mm.

Tensile lap splice lengths for welded wire reinforcement are obtained by using Tables 3.12 and 3.13, based on Clauses 12.18 & 12.19, as defined in Figures N12.18.1 and N12.19.

3.5   Development of Shear Reinforcement and Ties

The ends of deformed bar and wire stirrup legs must be anchored around longitudinal reinforcement using 135 ° hooks as specified in Clauses 12.13 & 7.1.2, unless a pair of stirrups, meeting the requirements of Clause 12.13.5 for lap splicing of straight legs (no hooks) is placed to form a single closed unit. A 90° hook is permitted if the concrete cover over the hook is restrained against spalling (Clause 7.1.2). Stirrups and ties made of 15M and smaller diameter deformed bars and wire are considered to be fully anchored by a standard stirrup or tie hook around longitudinal reinforcement, with no requirement for a straight lead-in length. In stirrups and ties made with smaller bars and wire, requirements are specified separately for 90° and 135° hooks (Annex A, Clause 6.6.2.4 of A23.3).

Stirrups and ties made with 20M and 25M bars require a minimum lead-in distance of $0.33\,\ell_d$ measured from mid depth of the member as specified in Clause 12.13.2 (b) and illustrated in Figure N12.13.12. Minimum bends in stirrups and ties made with 20M and 25M bars are the same as standard hooks (Clauses 7.1.2 & 12.13.2(b)).

Hooked ends are not required on stirrups made with smooth welded wire reinforcement if the cross-wires of the reinforcement, running in the longitudinal direction of the member, meet the spacing and location requirements of Clauses 12.13.2 (c) & (d) as illustrated in Figure N12.13.2(c). The provision for single leg stirrups Clause 12.13.2 (c) also applies to deformed welded wire reinforcement.

Between anchored ends, each bend in the continuous portion of a stirrup must enclose a longitudinal bar (Clause 12.13.3).

Ties in columns may use a 90° hook if $f'_c \le 50$ MPa. (Clause 7.1.2) The required spacing of ties in concrete with compressive strength exceeding 50 MPa is 0.75 of the values specified for lower strength concrete (Clause 7.6.5.2).

For cross ties (Clause 7.1.3), at least one end must have a bend of at least 135°, while the other end can have a 90° hook to facilitate placing. The position of the 90° hook between successive cross ties must alternate to provide an average confinement to each longitudinal bar on the basis of alternating 135° hooks and the less effective 90° hooks.

3.5.1   Design Aids

The overall depth h that is required to provide the necessary straight embedment, in addition to the hook anchorage at the ends of 20M and 25M stirrup legs (Clause 12.13.2(b)) is given in Table 3.8. Illustrations showing the anchorages necessary for web reinforcement are given in Figures N12.13.2, N12.13.2 (c), and N12.13.5.

3.6   Development in Compression

Development of deformed bars in compression is assisted by the end bearing of the bar on the concrete. The development length is also reduced because the bond is not weakened by the transverse flexural tensile cracking that occurs in tensile development zones. Compression reinforcement must be confined inside spirals or ties in compression members (Clauses 7.6.4 & 7.6.5); and inside stirrups or ties for beams and girders (Clause 7.6.6). Modifiers for excess reinforcement area and for enclosure within a spiral or within closely spaced ties can be used to reduce the required development length (Clause 12.3.3).

The modified development length cannot be less than 200 mm (Clause 12.3.1) and hooks cannot be used for compression development (Clause 12.5.5).

3.6.1   Design Aids

Compression development lengths for standard deformed reinforcing bars are provided in Table 3.9.

3.7   Compression Lap Splices

Compression lap splicing of 45M and 55M bars is prohibited, unless these bars are lapped with 35M or smaller bars (Clauses 12.14.2.1, 12.16.2, & 15.9.2.4). Modification factors for reducing the usual lap length apply for the improved confinement provided by special ties and spirals (Clauses 12.17.3.4 & 5, and Fig N12.17.3.4).

3.7.1   Splices in Columns

All columns are designed as beam-columns because some loading conditions may produce tension in column reinforcement, so the reinforcement in each face of a column is required to develop a minimum tensile resistance. It may be possible to achieve sufficient tensile resistance at splice locations by staggering compression butt (end bearing) splices so that some reinforcement is continuous to develop tension. Alternately, compression lap splices may be sufficient to develop the required tensile resistance. Otherwise, tensile splicing is necessary. The tensile resistance requirements for column reinforcement are defined in Clause 12.17 and are illustrated in Figure 3.2.

3.8   Bundled Bars

Bundled bars may be used in columns and beams so that reinforcement can be fit into limited space. The details of bundled bar requirements are covered in Clause 7.4.2. Clause 12.4 covers development and Clause 12.14.2.2 deals with lap splicing. Bars may be bundled in groups of 2, 3 or 4 bars, with no more than two bars in any one plane. For spacing and cover (including crack control requirements), the unit of bundled bars is treated as a single bar with a diameter that provides the same area as all the bars in the bundle.

3.8.1   Bundled Bars in Beams

Only bars 35M and smaller may be bundled in beams and girders (Clause 7.4.2.2). A typical flexural design utilizing bundled bars, where individual bars in the bundle are terminated with reducing moment, is illustrated in Figure 3.3. Clause 7.4.2.3 requires the cutoff locations of individual bars to be staggered. Clause 12.4 requires a 33% increase in development length for an individual bar in a 4-bar bundle, a 20% increase in a 3-bar bundle, and a 10% increase for a 2-bar bundle. Therefore, to achieve the design yield strength, bar 1 requires a tensile development length of $1.33\ell_d$, where ℓ_d is the single bar development length from Table 3.1 or Table 3.2. Similarly, bar 2 requires a development length of $1.2\,\ell_d$.

Clause 12.4 of A23.3 addresses only the development of an individual bar in a bundle, and does not specify requirements for the simultaneous development of more than one bar in a bundle. The two bars of each bundle that extend into the support in Figure 3.3 require a development length based on the size of an equivalent bar with the same area as the two actual bars, if the recommendations of ACI Committee 408, 1979 report (References, Chapter 12, Citation 12.1) are followed. Clause 11.3.9.5 requires that the terminating tensile reinforcement be capable of developing a substantial tensile resistance at the inside face of the support bearing area.

3.8.2   Splicing of Bundled Bars

For tension and compression lap splicing of individual bars in a bundle, Clause12.14.2.2 requires that there be no overlap of the individual bar splices. This requires the cutoff points of the individual bars to be staggered if the full strength is to be developed. The intent of Clause 12.14.2.2 is illustrated in Figure 3.4(a) where the full strength splicing of a two bar bundle is achieved through the introduction of a separate "splice bar," to produce a 3 bar bundle along the total staggered splice length. In any splice length region (A to B, B to C or C to D), load transfer occurs between only two bars, thereby meeting the requirement that "individual bar splices within a bundle shall not overlap."

Bundled bar arrangements in columns, and the tensile resistances that can be developed with full strength compressive butt splices (end bearing or compression mechanical device), are summarized in Figure 3.4(b). In many columns, the required tensile resistance is only a fraction of the compressive strength of the reinforcement (Clause 12.17) as illustrated in Figure 3.2. Full mechanical connection for tension or welding can be used if a larger tensile resistance is necessary with unstaggered splices.

3.9   Development of Cut Off and Continuing Reinforcement

Clause 11.3.9.5 is intended to ensure that sufficient tensile force can be developed in tensile reinforcement that extends into a simple support, an exterior support of a continuous span, or near the free end of a cantilever supporting a concentrated load, where termination of the member does not permit reinforcement to be extended into a "continuing" span. Diagonal flexural-shear cracking increases the tensile force in the longitudinal reinforcement above that predicted on the basis of bending alone, and the horizontal component of the compressive strut force that must be picked up by the longitudinal bars must be capable of being developed through sufficient anchorage beyond the inside face of the bearing area.

Figure N12.11.3 illustrates the embedment requirements necessary to limit flexural bond stresses in positive moment tension reinforcement at locations where moment is rapidly increasing (high shears), as required by Clause 12.11.3. This requirement applies to points of zero moment, i.e.; the supports of simply supported beams and the points of inflection in continuous construction. The flexural bond provision, however, is waived by Clause 12.11.3 if the positive moment reinforcement terminates in a standard hook or equivalent mechanical anchorage that provides full development beyond the centerline of the simple support.

It may be economical to reduce the total flexural reinforcing steel provided in slabs, beams and girders by using different lengths of bars so that the flexural resistance, M_r, provided follows the factored moments, M_f, applied. For beams and girders, Figures N12.10.3, N12.12 & N12.13.4 provide an overview of the embedment requirements to be satisfied for cutoff and continuing reinforcement to ensure development of the bars required at critical sections.

For flat plates and slabs, Clause 13.10.8 and Figure 13.1 provide a guide for choosing bar lengths and cutoff locations. To ensure integrity against progressive collapse, a minimum area of bottom flexural reinforcement must be effectively continuous through the column or support as specified in Clause 13.10.6.

Whether web reinforcement is designed by the "Simple Method" of Clause 11.3.6.3 or the "General Method" of Clause 11.3.6.4, the build-up of force in the flexural reinforcement must include the affect of shear as specified in Clause 11.3.9 and illustrated in Figure N12.10.3.

3.9.1   Design Examples

Examples 3.3 and 3.4 illustrate the design for cut off and continuing reinforcement to ensure adequate development of the reinforcement when web reinforcement is designed by the "Simplified Method" of Clause 11.3.6.3.

3.10   Design Examples and Design Aids

Design Examples 3.1 through 3.5 presented on the following pages utilize several of the design aids (Tables 3.1 through 3.13 located at the end of Chapter 3).

Example 3.1:   Hooked Anchorage
Design negative moment reinforcement for the 150 mm slab and check anchorage into the 200 mm wall for:

A. $M_f(neg)$ = 25 kN·m per m of slab width using normal density concrete.

B. $M_f(neg)$ = 20 kN·m per m of slab width using structural low-density concrete.

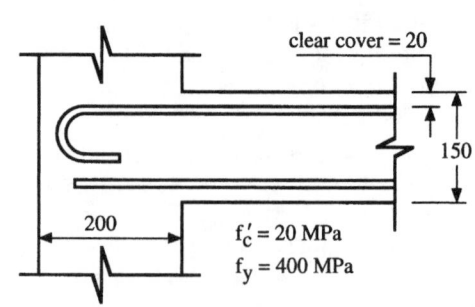

clear cover = 20

150

200

f'_c = 20 MPa
f_y = 400 MPa

Figure Ex. 3.1 Hooked Anchorages

Solution and comments:

A.   **M_f (neg) = 25 kN·m/m normal density concrete**
Assume 10M bars   d = 150 – 20 – 10/2 = 125 mm

$$K_r = \frac{M_f}{bd^2} = 25 \times 10^6/(1000(125^2)) = 1.60 \text{ MPa}$$

ρ = 0.51%   Table 2.1

$s \leq A_b/(\rho d)$ = 100/(0.0051(125)) = 157 mm   use s = 150 mm

Anchorage:
ℓ_{hb}(10M) = 220 mm for f_y = 400 MPa and f'_c = 20 MPa   Table 3.6

Modifiers: Large cover (because hook is embedded in wall), 0.7

$\ell_{dh} = \ell_{hb}(0.7)$ = 220(0.7) = 154 mm

Minimum hook length, Clause 12.5.1
$\ell_{dh} \geq 0.8d_b$ = 8(10) = 80 mm
$\ell_{dh} \geq$ 150 mm

Embedment available = 200 – 20 = 180 mm if the cover to the face of the wall is also 20 mm.
180 mm > 154 mm   therefore O.K.

B.   **M_f(neg) =20 kN·m/m using structural low-density concrete.**

$$K_r = \frac{M_f}{bd^2} = 20 \times 10^6/(1000(125^2)) = 1.28 \text{ MPa}$$

ρ = 0.38 + 0.8(0.41 – 0.38) = 0.004 = 0.40%   Interpolate in Table 2.1

$s = A_b/(\rho d)$ = 100/(0.004(125)) = 200 mm   try s = 200 mm

Anchorage:
ℓ_{hb}(10M) = 220 mm for f_y = 400 MPa and f'_c = 20 MPa   Table 3.6

Modifiers: Large cover (because hook is embedded in wall)   0.7
Structural low-density concrete   1.3
$\ell_{dh} = \ell_{hb}(0.7)(1.3) = 220(0.7)(1.3) = 200$ mm
200 mm > 180 mm   Therefore N.G.

The anchorage for the hook would be satisfactory if the area of steel provided were greater
than the area required.   Clause 12.5.3(d)

Reduce spacing   s = $200(180/200) = 180$ mm   <u>Use s = 180 mm</u>

Example 3.2:   Tensile Lap Splices

The beam section illustrated has $b \times h = 350 \times 600$ mm, is made
of normal density concrete with $f_c' = 25$ MPa, and uses
uncoated, grade 400 deformed reinforcement. The effective
depth, d, is 545 mm. All three 30M bars are lap spliced in the
same high stress region. 10M stirrups spaced at 200 mm confine
the lap length. Compare the required lap length for the simple
approach using Table 12-1 with the detailed approach using
Clause 12.2.2.

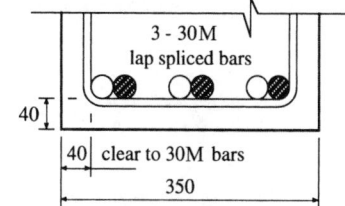

Figure Ex. 3.2
Tensile Lap Splices

A. **Simple approach**   Table 12-1 and Table 3.1
    Check bar spacing and cover
    For clear cover = 40 mm to 30M bars, and $b_w = 350$ mm, a maximum of 3 pairs of contact
    spliced 30M bars can be placed with clear spacing $\geq 1.4d_b$ and 30 mm   Table 3.4(a)

    To use 0.45 coefficient, check for minimum stirrups by Equation 11-1 in Clause 11.2.8.2

$$s \leq \frac{A_v f_y}{0.06\sqrt{f_c'}\, b_w} = \frac{2(100)(400)}{0.06\sqrt{25}(350)} = 762 \text{ mm}$$ Equation 11-1

200 mm < 762 mm   O.K.
$\therefore$ Use the 0.45 coefficient in the equation for ℓ_d

$\ell_d = 1080$ mm   Table 3.1
All bars spliced at same location therefore use a class B splice.   Clause 12.15
$\ell_s = 1.3\,\ell_d = 1.3(1080) = 1404$ mm   <u>use 1410 mm</u>

B. **Detailed approach**

Total confinement index $C.I. = \dfrac{d_{cs}}{d_b} + \dfrac{K_{tr}}{d_b} = 1.67 + 0.85\left(\dfrac{100}{200}\right) = 2.10$ Tables 3.4(a) and 3.5

$\ell_d = 1190 + \dfrac{2.1-1.8}{2.2-1.8}(980-1190) = 1033$ mm   Interpolate in Table 3.2

For a class B splice $\ell_s = 1.3(1033) = 1342$ mm   <u>Use 1350 mm</u>

In this example, the detailed approach results in a splice length that is approximately
4% shorter.

Example 3.3:   Development of Flexural Reinforcement in a Cantilever beam

A cantilever beam, illustrated in Figure Ex. 3.3 with $b \times h = 400 \times 500$ mm and a length of *3500* mm, supports a total factored uniformly distributed load $w_f = 36.5$ kN/m. Material properties are $f'_c = 25$ MPa (Structural low-density concrete) and $f_y = 400$ MPa. Using a clear cover of 60 mm on the 10M vertical stirrups results in a design requiring four 25M bars with a flexural resistance $M_r = 240$ kN·m for the maximum factored negative moment of $M_f = 224$ kN·m at the face of the support. The 10M stirrups are spaced at 200 mm.

A.   Calculate the cutoff location for the two centre 25M bars labelled "B"
with $M_r = 130$ kN·m for the two remaining 25M bars.
$Y = L - X + EXT$; provided $L - X \geq \ell_d$ for bars "B".

$$X = \sqrt{\frac{2M_{r2}}{w_f}} = \sqrt{\frac{2(130)}{36.5}} = 2.67 \text{ m}$$

$EXT = d_v \cot\theta$ Clause 11.3.9.1
$d = 500 - 60 - 10 - 25/2 = 417$ mm
$d_v = 0.9d = 0.9(417) = 375$ mm
Assume Simplified shear design $\therefore \theta = 35°$ Clause 11.3.6.3
$EXT = 375 \cot 35 = 536$ mm
$Y = 3500 - 2670 + 536 = 1366$ mm   (provided bars "B" can be developed)

B.   Check Development and Cutoff Location

(a)   Short bars "B"
Clear cover to 25M bars $= 60 + 10 = 70$ mm
Check for minimum stirrups
$$s \leq \frac{A_v f_y}{0.06\sqrt{f'_c}\, b_w} = \frac{2(100)(400)}{0.06\sqrt{25}(400)} = 667 \text{ mm}$$ Equation (11-1)

200 mm < *667 mm*   O.K. to use 0.45 coefficient
ℓ_d prior to introduction of modification factors is 900 mm   Table 3.1
Modification factors:
Top bars $d > 300$ mm $k_1 = 1.3$
Structural low density concrete $k_3 = 1.3$
$\ell_d = 1.3(1.3)(900) = 1521$ mm
$Y = \ell_d + EXT = 1521 + 536 = 2057$ mm

A more detailed calculation based on the C.I. provides a shorter length. For calculation of K_{tr} consider that only 2 of the 4 bars are being developed at this location.

$$C.I. = \frac{d_{cs}}{d_b} + \frac{K_{tr}}{d_b} = 2.50 + 1.52\left(\frac{100}{200}\right) = 3.26$$ Tables 3.3(c) and 3.5

C.I. is limited to 2.5 ℓ_d without modification factors = 740 mm   Table 3.2

$\ell_d = 1.3(1.3)(740) = 1251$ mm
Increase Y
$Y' = \ell_d + EXT = 1251 + 536 = 1787$ mm   <u>Use $Y' = 1790$ mm</u>

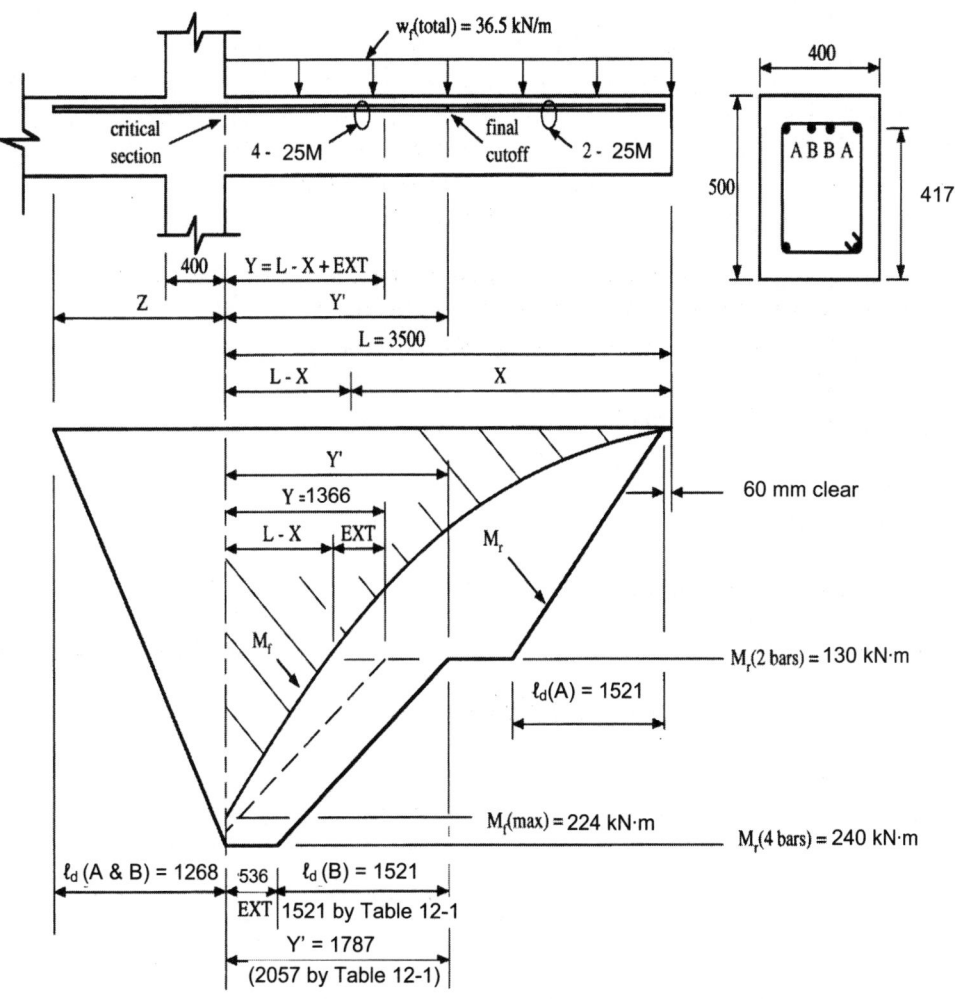

Figure Ex. 3.3 Development of Reinforcing in a Cantilever Beam

(b)   Long bars
      As above $\ell_d = 1.3(1.3)(900) = 1521$ mm   O.K.

A shorter development length can be calculated using Table 3.2 with C.I. from Tables 3.3(c) and 3.5 but there is no need to do so. The moment is changing slowly in this region so the longer length causes no problems.

C.   Anchorage of all four bars to left of column

Assume there is no load on beam to left of column so that anchorage is needed from the right face of the column.

An $\ell_d = 1521$ mm as computed above could be used. However, a more detailed calculation based on the C.I. could be used if a shorter length might be worthwhile.

$$C.I. = \frac{d_{cs}}{d_b} + \frac{K_{tr}}{d_b} = 2.09 + 0.76\left(\frac{100}{200}\right) = 2.47 \le 2.50 \qquad \text{Tables 3.3(c) and 3.5}$$

$$\ell_d = 1.3(1.3)\left(840 + \frac{2.47 - 2.2}{2.5 - 2.2}(740 - 840)\right) = 1268 \text{ mm} \qquad \text{Interpolate in Table 3.2}$$

D.   Check development of the stirrups
No check is necessary for 10M or 15M stirrups. A 135°hook around corner bars is adequate.
Clause 12.13.2(a)

Example 3.4:   Development and Cutoffs in a simply supported beam

A simply supported beam in Figure Ex. 3.4 rests on 800 mm wide masonry pilasters over a clear span of 10 m. Although anchored, the beam is not integral with its supports. The uniformly distributed loading on the beam is 22 kN/m dead (including self-weight) and 25 kN/m live. Using $f_c' = 30$ MPa normal density concrete with $f_y = 400$ MPa, select the flexural reinforcement and choose cutoff locations. Assume a cover of 40 mm to 10M stirrups.

A.   Design the flexural reinforcement:
Determine span length
$$\ell = \ell_n + h = 10000 + 750 \le \ell_n + W = 10000 + 800 \qquad \ell = 10750 \text{ mm} \qquad \text{Clause 9.2.2.3}$$
$$w_f = 1.25(22) + 1.5(25) = 65 \text{ kN/m}$$

$$M_f = 65.0\frac{10.75^2}{8} = 939 \text{ kN·m}$$

Assuming 10M stirrups and 35M bars   d = 750 – 40 – 10 – 35/2 = 682 mm

Required $K_r = \dfrac{M_f}{bd^2} = \dfrac{0.939}{0.50(0.682)^2} = 4.04$ MPa·

$\rho \approx 1.40\%$
Table 2.1

$A_s = 0.014(500)(682) = 4774 \text{ mm}^2$

Number of 35M bars required = 4774/1000 = 4.8
<u>Use 5 – 35M bars</u>

$\rho = 5(1000)/(500(682)) = 0.0147 \qquad K_r = 4.2$
Table 2.1

$$M_{r5} = K_r bd^2 = 4.2(0.5)(0.682^2) = 0.977 \text{ MN·m}$$

Check bar spacing from Table 3.3(a)
For $b_w = 500$ mm   5 – 35M bars O.K. in one layer

B.   Determination of bar cutoff locations
Consider possible location for terminating the two bars labelled "B"

With 2 bars cut off, ρ for the remaining bars is $3(1000)/(500(682)) = 0.0088 = 0.88\%$
$K_r = 2.7$
Table 2.1
M_r for the remaining 3 bars is therefore;

$$M_{r3} = 2.7(0.5)(0.682^2) = 0.628 \text{ MN·m}$$

Locate point where 3 bars are adequate a distance X from the centreline

$$X = \frac{\ell}{2}\sqrt{\frac{M_f - M_{r3}}{M_f}} = \frac{10750}{2}\sqrt{\frac{939 - 628}{939}} = 3093 \text{ mm}$$

The required extension is EXT = d_v cot θ   Clause 11.3.9.1

$d_v = 0.9d = 0.9(682) = 614$ mm

Assume Simplified shear design ∴ θ = 35°   Clause 11.3.6.3

$EXT = 614$ cot $35 = 877$ mm

Total length of bars "B" $\ell_B = 2(3093 + 877) = 2(3970) = 7940$ mm   Use $\ell_B = \underline{7940}$ mm

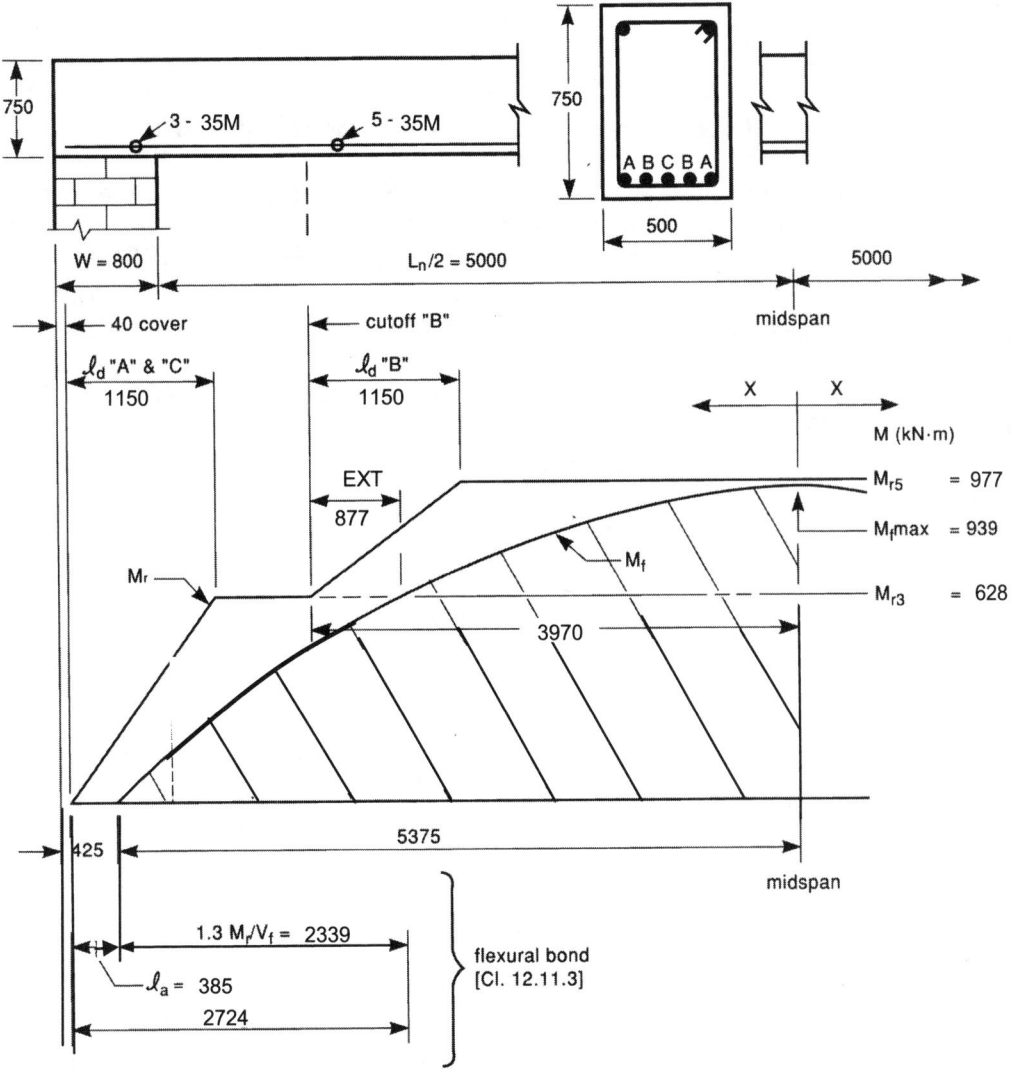

Fig. Ex. 3.4: Development of Reinforcement in a Simply Supported Beam

C.   Check for adequate anchorage of 3 bars at support

Because these bars are close to full length, it doesn't seem worthwhile to terminate bar "C".
Bars "A" and "C" should be full length. Assume 40 mm cover to end of bars.

$\ell_A = 10\ 000 + 2(800 - 40) = 11\ 520$ mm

D.   Check flexural bond at support   Clause 12.11.3

$V_f = 65(10.75/2) = 349$ kN

$$\ell_d \le \frac{1.3M_{r3}}{V_f} + \ell_a \qquad \text{where } \ell_a = 800 - 40 - 750\,/\,2 = 385 \text{ mm}$$

$$\ell_d \le \frac{1.3(628)}{0.349} + 385 = 2724 \text{ mm}$$

$\ell_d = 1150$ mm   Table 3.1

$\ell_d = 1150$ mm < 2724 mm $\therefore$ O.K.

Example 3.5:   Development of Deformed Welded Wire Reinforcement (WWR)

Find the development length for MD47.6 × MD47.6 WWR with a 152 × 152 mm grid and $f_y = 485$ MPa to be used as temperature and shrinkage reinforcement in structural low-density concrete with $f'_c = 20$ MPa. More than 300 mm of concrete is placed below the WWR.

Solution: Table 3.12

For "top" wire and low density concrete $k_1 = 1.3$, and $k_3 = 1.3$

From upper left corner of Table 3.12 the development length for MD47.6 WWR in *20* MPa concrete with both k_1 and $k_3 = 1.3$ is *260* mm.

Table 3.1 **Tension Development length, ℓ_d (mm) for heavier confined deformed reinforcing bars with $f_y = 400$ MPa, for normal density concrete.**

$$\ell_d = 0.45 k_1 k_2 k_3 k_4 \frac{f_y}{\sqrt{f'_c}} d_b$$

f'_c MPa	Bar Size							
	10M	15M	20M	25M	30M	35M	45M	55M
20	320	480	640	1010	1210	1410	1810	2210
25	290	430	580	900	1080	1260	1620	1980
30	260	390	530	820	990	1150	1480	1810
35	240	370	490	760	910	1060	1370	1670
40	230	340	460	710	850	1000	1280	1570
45	210	320	430	670	800	940	1210	1480
50	200	310	410	640	760	890	1150	1400
55	190	290	390	610	730	850	1090	1330
60	190	280	370	580	700	810	1050	1280
≥ 64	180	270	360	560	680	790	1010	1240

Clear cover and clear spacing of bars must be at least $1.0d_b$ and $1.4d_b$, respectively. Clause 12.2.3

Member must contain at least minimum stirrups or ties within length ℓ_d

or Clause 7.6.5, 11.2.8.2
for slabs, walls, shells or folded plates have clear spacing between bars being developed not less than $2d_b$.   Table 12.1

Table gives development lengths for $k_1 = k_2 = k_3 = 1.0$.

Multiply development lengths in this table by k_1, k_2, and k_3 when these differ from 1.0.
(The product $k_1 k_2$ need not be taken greater than 1.7)   Clause 12.2.4

k_1 = 1.3 for horizontal reinforcement placed in such a way that more than 300 mm of fresh concrete is cast in the member below the development length or splice.

k_2 = 1.5 for epoxy-coated reinforcement with clear cover less than $3d_b$, or
with clear spacing between bars being developed less than $6d_b$.
= 1.2 for all other epoxy-coated reinforcement

k_3 = 1.3 for structural low-density concrete
= 1.2 for structural semi-low-density concrete

For $f_y \neq 400$ MPa, multiply development length by $f_y /400$.

For "Other cases" with lighter confinement, multiply the above lengths by 1.33.   Table 12.1

After application of all modification factors, the development length must not be less than 300 mm.   Clause 12.2.1

Table 3.2   Development lengths ℓ_d (mm) for deformed reinforcing bars with $f_y = 400$ MPa before factors k_1 to k_3 are applied, for different confinement indices (C.I.)

Application	C.I.	f_c'	10M	15M	20M	25M	30M	35M	45M	55M
	1.5	20	550	730	820	1370	1600	1960	2290	3120
		25	490	650	740	1230	1430	1750	2040	2790
If no stirrups considered along development length then the following cover and spacing are required for this C.I.:		30	450	600	670	1120	1310	1600	1870	2540
		35	410	550	620	1040	1210	1480	1730	2360
		40	390	520	580	970	1130	1390	1620	2200
		45	370	490	550	910	1070	1310	1520	2080
Minimum clear cover = $1.0d_b$		50	350	460	520	870	1010	1240	1450	1970
Minimum bar spacing = $2.25d_b$		55	330	440	500	830	960	1180	1380	1880
		60	320	420	480	790	920	1130	1320	1800
	1.5	≥ 64	310	410	460	770	890	1100	1280	1740
	1.8	20	460	610	690	1140	1330	1630	1900	2600
		25	410	550	610	1020	1190	1460	1700	2320
If no stirrups considered along development length then the following cover and spacing are required for this C.I.:		30	370	500	560	930	1090	1330	1560	2120
		35	350	460	520	860	1010	1230	1440	1960
		40	320	430	480	810	940	1150	1350	1840
		45	300	410	460	760	890	1090	1270	1730
Minimum clear cover = $1.3d_b$		50	290	390	430	720	840	1030	1200	1640
Minimum bar spacing = $2.7d_b$		55	280	370	410	690	800	980	1150	1570
		60	260	350	400	660	770	940	1100	1500
	1.8	≥ 64	260	340	380	640	750	910	1060	1450
	2.2	20	370	500	560	940	1090	1340	1560	2130
		25	330	450	500	840	980	1190	1390	1900
If no stirrups considered along development length then the following cover and spacing are required for this C.I.:		30	310	410	460	760	890	1090	1270	1740
		35	280	380	420	710	820	1010	1180	1610
		40	260	350	400	660	770	940	1100	1500
		45	250	330	370	620	730	890	1040	1420
Minimum clear cover = $1.7d_b$		50	240	320	350	590	690	840	990	1340
Minimum bar spacing = $3.3d_b$		55	230	300	340	560	660	810	940	1280
		60	220	290	320	540	630	770	900	1230
	2.2	≥ 64	210	280	310	520	610	750	870	1190
	2.5	20	330	440	490	820	960	1180	1370	1870
		25	290	390	440	740	860	1050	1230	1670
If no stirrups considered along development length then the following cover and spacing are required for this C.I.:		30	270	360	400	670	780	960	1120	1530
		35	250	330	370	620	730	890	1040	1410
		40	230	310	350	580	680	830	970	1320
		45	220	290	330	550	640	780	910	1250
Minimum clear cover = $2.0d_b$		50	210	280	310	520	610	740	870	1180
Minimum bar spacing = $3.75d_b$		55	200	260	300	500	580	710	830	1130
		60	190	250	290	480	550	680	790	1080
	2.5	≥ 64	180	250	280	460	540	660	770	1050

The table gives development lengths for $k_1 = k_2 = k_3 = 1.0$.

Multiply development lengths by k_1, k_2, and k_3 when these differ from 1.0.   Table 3.1

The confinement Index, $C.I. = d_{cs}/d_b$ from Table 3.3 or 3.4, plus K_{tr}/d_b from Table 3.5

For $f_y \neq 400$ MPa, multiply development length by $f_y/400$

After application of all modification factors, development length must not be less than 300 mm.

Table 3.3(a) Concrete confinement index d_{cs}/d_b for n deformed bars with a clear cover of 40 mm spaced uniformly across a stem width b_w (mm).

3

Development and Splices

b_w	n	15M	20M	25M	30M	35M	b_w	n	15M	20M	25M	30M	35M
200	2	2.50	2.50	2.10	1.83	1.62	700	≤7	2.50	2.50	2.10	1.83	1.64
	3	2.33	1.67					8	2.50	2.50	2.10	1.83	
250	2	2.50	2.50	2.10	1.83	1.64		9	2.50	2.50	1.98	1.64	
	3	2.50	2.50	1.93				10	2.50	2.22	1.76		
	4	2.30	1.67					11	2.50	2.00			
300	≤3	2.50	2.50	2.10	1.83	1.64		12	2.44	1.82			
	4	2.50	2.22	1.73				13	2.24	1.67			
	5	2.28	1.67					14	2.07				
350	≤3	2.50	2.50	2.10	1.83	1.64	750	≤8	2.50	2.50	2.10	1.83	1.64
	4	2.50	2.50	2.10	1.78			9	2.50	2.50	2.10	1.78	
	5	2.50	2.08	1.63				10	2.50	2.41	1.91		
	6	2.27	1.67					11	2.50	2.17	1.72		
400	≤4	2.50	2.50	2.10	1.83	1.64		12	2.50	1.97			
	5	2.50	2.50	1.97	1.61			13	2.43	1.81			
	6	2.50	2.00					14	2.24	1.67			
	7	2.26	1.67					15	2.08				
450	≤4	2.50	2.50	2.10	1.83	1.64	800	≤8	2.50	2.50	2.10	1.83	1.64
	5	2.50	2.50	2.10	1.83			9	2.50	2.50	2.10	1.83	1.63
	6	2.50	2.33	1.84				10	2.50	2.50	2.06	1.70	
	7	2.50	1.94					11	2.50	2.33	1.85		
	8	2.25	1.67					12	2.50	2.12	1.68		
500	≤5	2.50	2.50	2.10	1.83	1.64		13	2.50	1.94			
	6	2.50	2.50	2.10	1.73			14	2.41	1.79			
	7	2.50	2.22	1.76				15	2.24	1.67			
	8	2.50	1.90					16	2.09				
	9	2.25	1.67				850	≤9	2.50	2.50	2.10	1.83	1.64
	10	2.00						10	2.50	2.50	2.10	1.83	
550	≤6	2.50	2.50	2.10	1.83	1.64		11	2.50	2.50	1.99	1.64	
	7	2.50	2.50	1.98	1.63			12	2.50	2.27	1.81		
	8	2.50	2.14	1.70				13	2.50	2.08	1.66		
	9	2.50	1.88					14	2.50	1.92			
	10	2.25	1.67					15	2.40	1.79			
	11	2.02						16	2.24	1.67			
600	≤6	2.50	2.50	2.10	1.83	1.64		17	2.10				
	7	2.50	2.50	2.10	1.81		900	≤10	2.50	2.50	2.10	1.83	1.64
	8	2.50	2.38	1.89				11	2.50	2.50	2.10	1.76	
	9	2.50	2.08	1.65				12	2.50	2.42	1.93		
	10	2.49	1.85					13	2.50	2.22	1.77		
	11	2.24	1.67					14	2.50	2.05	1.63		
	12	2.04						15	2.50	1.90			
650	≤7	2.50	2.50	2.10	1.83	1.64		16	2.39	1.78			
	8	2.50	2.50	2.08	1.71			17	2.24	1.67			
	9	2.50	2.29	1.82				18	2.10				
	10	2.50	2.04	1.61									
	11	2.47	1.83										
	12	2.24	1.67										
	13	2.06											

Values are provided only if a clear spacing of $1.4d_b$ and 30 mm is available between bars.

Table 3.3(b) Concrete confinement index d_{cs}/d_b for n deformed bars with a clear cover of 50 mm spaced uniformly across a stem width b_w

b_w	n	15M	20M	25M	30M	35M
200	2	2.50	2.50	2.00		
250	2	2.50	2.50	2.50	2.17	1.93
	3	2.50	2.17	1.67		
	4	2.00				
300	2	2.50	2.50	2.50	2.17	1.93
	3	2.50	2.50	2.33	1.89	
	4	2.50	2.00			
	5	2.06				
350	≤ 3	2.50	2.50	2.50	2.17	1.93
	4	2.50	2.50	2.00	1.63	
	5	2.50	1.92			
	6	2.09				
400	≤ 3	2.50	2.50	2.50	2.17	1.93
	4	2.50	2.50	2.44	2.00	1.68
	5	2.50	2.33	1.83		
	6	2.50	1.87			
	7	2.11				
450	≤ 4	2.50	2.50	2.50	2.17	1.93
	5	2.50	2.50	2.17	1.78	
	6	2.50	2.20	1.73		
	7	2.48	1.83			
	8	2.13				
500	≤ 4	2.50	2.50	2.50	2.17	1.93
	5	2.50	2.50	2.50	2.06	1.74
	6	2.50	2.50	2.00	1.64	
	7	2.50	2.11	1.67		
	8	2.44	1.81			
	9	2.14				
550	≤ 5	2.50	2.50	2.50	2.17	1.93
	6	2.50	2.50	2.27	1.87	
	7	2.50	2.39	1.89		
	8	2.50	2.05	1.62		
	9	2.42	1.79			
	10	2.15				
600	≤ 5	2.50	2.50	2.50	2.17	1.93
	6	2.50	2.50	2.50	2.09	1.77
	7	2.50	2.50	2.11	1.74	
	8	2.50	2.29	1.81		
	9	2.50	2.00			
	10	2.40	1.78			
	11	2.16				
650	≤ 6	2.50	2.50	2.50	2.17	1.93
	7	2.50	2.50	2.33	1.93	1.63
	8	2.50	2.50	2.00	1.65	
	9	2.50	2.21	1.75		
	10	2.50	1.96			
	11	2.38	1.77			
	12	2.16				

b_w	n	15M	20M	25M	30M	35M
700	≤ 6	2.50	2.50	2.50	2.17	1.93
	7	2.50	2.50	2.50	2.11	1.79
	8	2.50	2.50	2.19	1.81	
	9	2.50	2.42	1.92		
	10	2.50	2.15	1.70		
	11	2.50	1.93			
	12	2.36	1.76			
	13	2.17				
	14	2.00				
750	≤ 7	2.50	2.50	2.50	2.17	1.93
	8	2.50	2.50	2.38	1.97	1.67
	9	2.50	2.50	2.08	1.72	
	10	2.50	2.33	1.85		
	11	2.50	2.10	1.67		
	12	2.50	1.91			
	13	2.35	1.75			
	14	2.17				
	15	2.02				
800	≤ 7	2.50	2.50	2.50	2.17	1.93
	8	2.50	2.50	2.50	2.13	1.81
	9	2.50	2.50	2.25	1.86	
	10	2.50	2.50	2.00	1.65	
	11	2.50	2.27	1.80		
	12	2.50	2.06	1.64		
	13	2.50	1.89			
	14	2.34	1.74			
	15	2.17				
	16	2.03				
850	≤ 8	2.50	2.50	2.50	2.17	1.93
	9	2.50	2.50	2.42	2.00	1.70
	10	2.50	2.50	2.15	1.78	
	11	2.50	2.43	1.93	1.60	
	12	2.50	2.21	1.76		
	13	2.50	2.03	1.61		
	14	2.50	1.87			
	15	2.33	1.74			
	16	2.18				
	17	2.04				
900	≤ 9	2.50	2.50	2.50	2.14	1.82
	10	2.50	2.50	2.30	1.90	1.62
	11	2.50	2.50	2.07	1.71	
	12	2.50	2.36	1.88		
	13	2.50	2.17	1.72		
	14	2.50	2.00			
	15	2.49	1.86			
	16	2.33	1.73			
	17	2.18				
	18	2.05				

Values are provided only if a clear spacing of $1.4d_b$ and 30 mm is available between bars.

Table 3.3(c) Concrete confinement index d_{cs}/d_b for n deformed bars with a clear cover of 70 mm spaced uniformly across a stem width b_w

b_w	n	15M	20M	25M	30M	35M	b_w	n	15M	20M	25M	30M	35M
200	2	2.00					700	≤5	2.50	2.50	2.50	2.50	2.50
250	2	2.50	2.50	2.27	1.78			6	2.50	2.50	2.50	2.36	2.00
	3	2.11						7	2.50	2.50	2.38	1.96	1.67
300	2	2.50	2.50	2.50	2.50	2.38		8	2.50	2.50	2.04	1.68	
	3	2.50	2.33	1.80				9	2.50	2.25	1.78		
	4	2.15						10	2.50	2.00			
350	2	2.50	2.50	2.50	2.50	2.50		11	2.42	1.80			
	3	2.50	2.50	2.47	2.00	1.67		12	2.20				
	4	2.50	2.11	1.64				13	2.02				
	5	2.17					750	≤6	2.50	2.50	2.50	2.50	2.19
400	2	2.50	2.50	2.50	2.50	2.50		7	2.50	2.50	2.50	2.15	1.83
	3	2.50	2.50	2.50	2.50	2.14		8	2.50	2.50	2.23	1.84	
	4	2.50	2.50	2.09	1.70			9	2.50	2.46	1.95	1.61	
	5	2.50	2.00					10	2.50	2.19	1.73		
	6	2.18						11	2.50	1.97			
450	≤3	2.50	2.50	2.50	2.50	2.50		12	2.40	1.79			
	4	2.50	2.50	2.50	2.07	1.75		13	2.20				
	5	2.50	2.42	1.90				14	2.03				
	6	2.50	1.93				800	≤6	2.50	2.50	2.50	2.50	2.38
	7	2.19						7	2.50	2.50	2.50	2.33	1.98
500	≤3	2.50	2.50	2.50	2.50	2.50		8	2.50	2.50	2.42	2.00	1.70
	4	2.50	2.50	2.50	2.44	2.06		9	2.50	2.50	2.12	1.75	
	5	2.50	2.50	2.23	1.83			10	2.50	2.37	1.88		
	6	2.50	2.27	1.79				11	2.50	2.13	1.69		
	7	2.50	1.89					12	2.50	1.94			
	8	2.19						13	2.39	1.78			
550	≤4	2.50	2.50	2.50	2.50	2.38		14	2.21				
	5	2.50	2.50	2.50	2.11	1.79		15	2.05				
	6	2.50	2.50	2.05	1.69		850	≤7	2.50	2.50	2.50	2.50	2.14
	7	2.50	2.17	1.71				8	2.50	2.50	2.50	2.16	1.84
	8	2.50	1.86					9	2.50	2.50	2.28	1.89	1.61
	9	2.19						10	2.50	2.50	2.03	1.68	
600	≤4	2.50	2.50	2.50	2.50	2.50		11	2.50	2.30	1.83		
	5	2.50	2.50	2.50	2.39	2.02		12	2.50	2.09	1.66		
	6	2.50	2.50	2.32	1.91	1.62		13	2.50	1.92			
	7	2.50	2.44	1.93				14	2.38	1.77			
	8	2.50	2.10	1.66				15	2.21				
	9	2.47	1.83					16	2.06				
	10	2.20					900	≤8	2.50	2.50	2.50	2.32	1.97
650	≤5	2.50	2.50	2.50	2.50	2.26		9	2.50	2.50	2.45	2.03	1.73
	6	2.50	2.50	2.50	2.13	1.81		10	2.50	2.50	2.18	1.80	
	7	2.50	2.50	2.16	1.78			11	2.50	2.47	1.96	1.62	
	8	2.50	2.33	1.85				12	2.50	2.24	1.78		
	9	2.50	2.04	1.62				13	2.50	2.06	1.63		
	10	2.44	1.81					14	2.50	1.90			
	11	2.20						15	2.37	1.76			
	12	2.00						16	2.21				
								17	2.07				

Values are provided only if a clear spacing of $1.4d_b$ and 30 mm is available between bars.

Table 3.4(a) Concrete confinement index d_{cs}/d_b for n pairs of contacting deformed bars lap spliced in tension with a clear cover of 40 mm, spaced uniformly across a stem width b_w (mm)

b_w	n	15M	20M	25M	30M	35M
200	2	2.50	2.00			
250	2	2.50	2.50	2.10	1.78	
	3	2.44				
300	2	2.50	2.50	2.10	1.83	1.64
	3	2.50	2.33	1.60		
	4	2.15				
350	2	2.50	2.50	2.10	1.83	1.64
	3	2.50	2.50	2.10	1.67	
	4	2.50	1.89			
	5	2.00				
400	≤ 3	2.50	2.50	2.10	1.83	1.64
	4	2.50	2.44	1.73		
	5	2.50	1.67			
450	≤ 3	2.50	2.50	2.10	1.83	1.64
	4	2.50	2.50	2.10	1.63	
	5	2.50	2.08			
	6	2.36				
500	≤ 3	2.50	2.50	2.10	1.83	1.64
	4	2.50	2.50	2.10	1.83	
	5	2.50	2.50	1.80		
	6	2.50	1.87			
	7	2.22				
550	≤ 4	2.50	2.50	2.10	1.83	1.64
	5	2.50	2.50	2.10	1.61	
	6	2.50	2.20			
	7	2.50	1.72			
	8	2.13				
600	≤ 4	2.50	2.50	2.10	1.83	1.64
	5	2.50	2.50	2.10	1.83	
	6	2.50	2.50	1.84		
	7	2.50	2.00			
	8	2.44				
	9	2.06				
650	≤ 5	2.50	2.50	2.10	1.83	1.64
	6	2.50	2.50	2.10	1.60	
	7	2.50	2.28	1.64		
	8	2.50	1.86			
	9	2.33				
	10	2.00				
700	≤ 5	2.50	2.50	2.10	1.83	1.64
	6	2.50	2.50	2.10	1.82	
	7	2.50	2.50	1.87		
	8	2.50	2.10			
	9	2.50	1.75			
	10	2.25				

b_w	n	15M	20M	25M	30M	35M
750	≤ 5	2.50	2.50	2.10	1.83	1.64
	6	2.50	2.50	2.10	1.83	1.62
	7	2.50	2.50	2.09		
	8	2.50	2.33	1.70		
	9	2.50	1.96			
	10	2.49	1.67			
	11	2.18				
800	≤ 6	2.50	2.50	2.10	1.83	1.64
	7	2.50	2.50	2.10	1.78	
	8	2.50	2.50	1.89		
	9	2.50	2.17			
	10	2.50	1.85			
	11	2.40				
	12	2.12				
850	≤ 6	2.50	2.50	2.10	1.83	1.64
	7	2.50	2.50	2.10	1.83	
	8	2.50	2.50	2.08		
	9	2.50	2.38	1.73		
	10	2.50	2.04			
	11	2.50	1.77			
	12	2.32				
	13	2.07				
900	≤ 7	2.50	2.50	2.10	1.83	1.64
	8	2.50	2.50	2.10	1.75	
	9	2.50	2.50	1.90		
	10	2.50	2.22	1.61		
	11	2.50	1.93			
	12	2.50	1.70			
	13	2.26				
	14	2.03				
950	≤ 7	2.50	2.50	2.10	1.83	1.64
	8	2.50	2.50	2.10	1.83	
	9	2.50	2.50	2.07		
	10	2.50	2.41	1.76		
	11	2.50	2.10			
	12	2.50	1.85			
	13	2.44				
	14	2.21				
1000	≤ 8	2.50	2.50	2.10	1.83	1.64
	9	2.50	2.50	2.10	1.72	
	10	2.50	2.50	1.91		
	11	2.50	2.27	1.65		
	12	2.50	2.00			
	13	2.50	1.78			
	14	2.38				
	15	2.16				

Values are provided only if a clear spacing of $1.4d_b$ and 30 mm is available between bars.

Table 3.4(b) Concrete confinement index d_{cs}/d_b for n pairs of contacting deformed bars lap spliced in tension with a clear cover of 50 mm, spaced uniformly across a stem width b_w (mm)

b_w	n	15M	20M	25M	30M	35M
200	2	2.44				
250	2	2.50	2.50	2.00		
	3	2.00				
300	2	2.50	2.50	2.50	2.17	1.81
	3	2.50	2.00			
350	2	2.50	2.50	2.50	2.17	1.93
	3	2.50	2.50	2.00		
	4	2.50	1.67			
400	2	2.50	2.50	2.50	2.17	1.93
	3	2.50	2.50	2.50	2.00	
	4	2.50	2.22			
	5	2.33				
450	≤3	2.50	2.50	2.50	2.17	1.93
	4	2.50	2.50	2.00		
	5	2.50	1.92			
	6	2.18				
500	≤3	2.50	2.50	2.50	2.17	1.93
	4	2.50	2.50	2.44	1.85	
	5	2.50	2.33	1.67		
	6	2.50	1.73			
	7	2.07				
550	≤3	2.50	2.50	2.50	2.17	1.93
	4	2.50	2.50	2.50	2.17	1.75
	5	2.50	2.50	2.00		
	6	2.50	2.07			
	7	2.44				
	8	2.00				
600	≤4	2.50	2.50	2.50	2.17	1.93
	5	2.50	2.50	2.33	1.78	
	6	2.50	2.40	1.73		
	7	2.50	1.89			
	8	2.32				
650	≤4	2.50	2.50	2.50	2.17	1.93
	5	2.50	2.50	2.50	2.06	1.62
	6	2.50	2.50	2.00		
	7	2.50	2.17			
	8	2.50	1.76			
	9	2.22				
700	≤4	2.50	2.50	2.50	2.17	1.93
	5	2.50	2.50	2.50	2.17	1.86
	6	2.50	2.50	2.27	1.73	
	7	2.50	2.44	1.78		
	8	2.50	2.00			
	9	2.50	1.67			
	10	2.15				
750	≤5	2.50	2.50	2.50	2.17	1.93
	6	2.50	2.50	2.50	1.96	
	7	2.50	2.50	2.00		
	8	2.50	2.24	1.62		
	9	2.50	1.88			
	10	2.40				
	11	2.09				
800	≤5	2.50	2.50	2.50	2.17	1.93
	6	2.50	2.50	2.50	2.17	1.73
	7	2.50	2.50	2.22	1.70	
	8	2.50	2.48	1.81		
	9	2.50	2.08			
	10	2.50	1.78			
	11	2.31				
	12	2.04				
850	≤6	2.50	2.50	2.50	2.17	1.92
	7	2.50	2.50	2.44	1.89	
	8	2.50	2.50	2.00		
	9	2.50	2.29	1.67		
	10	2.50	1.96			
	11	2.50	1.70			
	12	2.24				
	13	2.00				
900	≤6	2.50	2.50	2.50	2.17	1.93
	7	2.50	2.50	2.50	2.07	1.65
	8	2.50	2.50	2.19	1.68	
	9	2.50	2.50	1.83		
	10	2.50	2.15			
	11	2.50	1.87			
	12	2.44				
	13	2.19				
950	≤6	2.50	2.50	2.50	2.17	1.93
	7	2.50	2.50	2.50	2.17	1.81
	8	2.50	2.50	2.38	1.84	
	9	2.50	2.50	2.00		
	10	2.50	2.33	1.70		
	11	2.50	2.03			
	12	2.50	1.79			
	13	2.37				
	14	2.14				
1000	≤7	2.50	2.50	2.50	2.17	1.93
	8	2.50	2.50	2.50	2.00	
	9	2.50	2.50	2.17	1.67	
	10	2.50	2.50	1.85		
	11	2.50	2.20	1.60		
	12	2.50	1.94			
	13	2.50	1.72			
	14	2.31				
	15	2.10				

Values are provided only if a clear spacing of $1.4d_b$ and 30 mm is available between bars.

Table 3.4(c) Concrete confinement index d_{cs}/d_b for n pairs of contacting deformed bars lap spliced in tension with a clear cover of 70 mm, spaced uniformly across a stem width b_w (mm)

b_w	n	15M	20M	25M	30M	35M	b_w	n	15M	20M	25M	30M	35M
250	2	2.50	1.67				750	≤ 4	2.50	2.50	2.50	2.50	2.50
300	2	2.50	2.50	2.27				5	2.50	2.50	2.50	2.39	1.90
	3	2.22						6	2.50	2.50	2.32	1.78	
350	2	2.50	2.50	2.50	2.50	2.00		7	2.50	2.50	1.82		
	3	2.50	2.17					8	2.50	2.05			
	4	2.00						9	2.50	1.71			
400	2	2.50	2.50	2.50	2.50	2.50		10	2.20				
	3	2.50	2.50	2.13				11					
	4	2.50	1.78				800	≤ 4	2.50	2.50	2.50	2.50	2.50
450	2	2.50	2.50	2.50	2.50	2.50		5	2.50	2.50	2.50	2.50	2.14
	3	2.50	2.50	2.50	2.11	1.62		6	2.50	2.50	2.50	2.00	
	4	2.50	2.33	1.64				7	2.50	2.50	2.04		
	5	2.44						8	2.50	2.29	1.66		
500	2	2.50	2.50	2.50	2.50	2.50		9	2.50	1.92			
	3	2.50	2.50	2.50	2.50	2.10		10	2.44				
	4	2.50	2.50	2.09				11	2.13				
	5	2.50	2.00				850	≤ 4	2.50	2.50	2.50	2.50	2.50
	6	2.27						5	2.50	2.50	2.50	2.50	2.38
550	≤ 3	2.50	2.50	2.50	2.50	2.50		6	2.50	2.50	2.50	2.22	1.77
	4	2.50	2.50	2.50	1.93			7	2.50	2.50	2.27	1.74	
	5	2.50	2.42	1.73				8	2.50	2.50	1.85		
	6	2.50	1.80					9	2.50	2.13			
	7	2.15						10	2.50	1.81			
600	≤ 3	2.50	2.50	2.50	2.50	2.50		11	2.36				
	4	2.50	2.50	2.50	2.30	1.81		12	2.08				
	5	2.50	2.50	2.07			900	≤ 5	2.50	2.50	2.50	2.50	2.50
	6	2.50	2.13					6	2.50	2.50	2.50	2.44	1.96
	7	2.50	1.67					7	2.50	2.50	2.49	1.93	
	8	2.06						8	2.50	2.50	2.04		
650	≤ 3	2.50	2.50	2.50	2.50	2.50		9	2.50	2.33	1.70		
	4	2.50	2.50	2.50	2.50	2.13		10	2.50	2.00			
	5	2.50	2.50	2.40	1.83			11	2.50	1.73			
	6	2.50	2.47	1.79				12	2.28				
	7	2.50	1.94					13	2.04				
	8	2.38					950	≤ 5	2.50	2.50	2.50	2.50	2.50
	9	2.00						6	2.50	2.50	2.50	2.50	2.15
700	≤ 3	2.50	2.50	2.50	2.50	2.50		7	2.50	2.50	2.50	2.11	1.68
	4	2.50	2.50	2.50	2.50	2.44		8	2.50	2.50	2.23	1.71	
	5	2.50	2.50	2.50	2.11	1.67		9	2.50	2.50	1.87		
	6	2.50	2.50	2.05				10	2.50	2.19			
	7	2.50	2.22	1.60				11	2.50	1.90			
	8	2.50	1.81					12	2.48	1.67			
	9	2.28						13	2.22				
								14	2.00				

Values are provided only if a clear spacing of $1.4d_b$ and 30 mm is available between bars.

Table 3.5   **Transverse reinforcing confinement index K_{tr}/d_b for 2 legged 10M vertical stirrups with $f_{yt} = 400$ MPa placed at a spacing $s = 100$ mm, and providing confinement to n equally spaced main reinforcing bars or pairs of lap-spliced bars, across the member width.**

s (mm)	n	15M	20M	25M	30M	35M	45M	55M
100	2	2.54	1.90	1.52	1.27	1.09	0.85	0.69
	3	1.69	1.27	1.02	0.85	0.73	0.56	0.46
	4	1.27	0.95	0.76	0.63	0.54	0.42	0.35
	5	1.02	0.76	0.61	0.51	0.44	0.34	0.28
	6	0.85	0.63	0.51	0.42	0.36	0.28	0.23
	7	0.73	0.54	0.44	0.36	0.31	0.24	0.20
	8	0.63	0.48	0.38	0.32	0.27	0.21	0.17
	9	0.56	0.42	0.34	0.28	0.24	0.19	0.15
	10	0.51	0.38	0.30	0.25	0.22	0.17	0.14
	11	0.46	0.35	0.28	0.23	0.20	0.15	0.13
	12	0.42	0.32	0.25	0.21	0.18	0.14	0.12
	13	0.39	0.29	0.23	0.20	0.17	0.13	0.11
	14	0.36	0.27	0.22	0.18	0.16	0.12	0.10
	15	0.34	0.25	0.20	0.17	0.15	0.11	0.09
100	16	0.32	0.24	0.19	0.16	0.14	0.11	0.09

Transverse reinforcing confinement index: $\dfrac{K_{tr}}{d_b} = \dfrac{A_{tr} f_{yt}}{10.5 \, n \, s \, d_b}$ Clause 12.2.2

Modifiers for stirrup area, A_{tr}:
   Modifier for stirrup size: Multiply by 2 for 15M, 3 for 20M and 5 for 25M
   Modifier for number of legs: Multiply by number of legs and divide by 2
                                                            (Where $n \geq$ number of legs)

Modifier for yield strength $f_{yt} \neq 400$ MPa: Multiply by $f_{yt}/400$

Modifier for spacing, s: Multiply by $100/s$

Table 3.6   **Tension development lengths, ℓ_{hb}, (mm) using standard hooks for deformed bars with $f_y = 400$ MPa, for normal density concrete.**

f'_c MPa	Bar Size							
	10M	**15M**	**20M**	**25M**	**30M**	**35M**	**45M**	**55M**
20	220	340	450	560	670	780	1010	1230
25	200	300	400	500	600	700	900	1100
30	180	270	370	460	550	640	820	1000
35	170	250	340	420	510	590	760	930
40	160	240	320	400	470	550	710	870
45	150	220	300	370	450	520	670	820
50	140	210	280	350	420	490	640	780
55	130	200	270	340	400	470	610	740
60	130	190	260	320	390	450	580	710
≥ 64	130	190	250	310	380	440	560	690

The development length is the out to out dimension including the hook and the straight length to the critical section.

Hooks must satisfy the dimensions for standard hooks.   Table 3.7

Special fabrication is required for bends greater than 90° for 45M and 55M bars with steel grades of 400R and 500R.   Annex A, Table 16

The basic hook development length shall be multiplied by the following factors to obtain the development length ℓ_{dh},:   Cl. 12.5.3

(a)   For bars with $f_y \neq 400$ MPa   *f_y /400*

(b)   For 35M or smaller bars where the side cover (normal to the plane of the hook) is at least 60 mm, and for 90° hooks where the cover on the bar extension beyond the hook is at least 50 mm. [Fig. 3.1(a)]   *0.7*

(c)   For 35M or smaller bars where the hook is enclosed vertically or horizontally within at least three ties or stirrup ties spaced along a length at least equal to the inside diameter of the hook at a spacing not greater than $3d_b$, where d_b is the nominal diameter of the hooked bar. [Fig. 3.1(b)]   *0.8*

(d)   Where anchorage or development for f_y is not specifically required for reinforcing exceeding that required by analysis. $A_{s, required}$ /$A_{s, provided}$

(e)   For structural low-density concrete   *1.3*

(f)   For epoxy-coated reinforcement   *1.2*

The minimum development length, ℓ_{dh}, shall be not less than $8d_b$ or *150* mm, whichever is greater.
                                       Clause 12.5.1

     If both covers "A" and "B" are less than 60 mm then ties or stirrups defined by Fig 3.1(b) must be provided, but the 0.8 modifier does not apply.

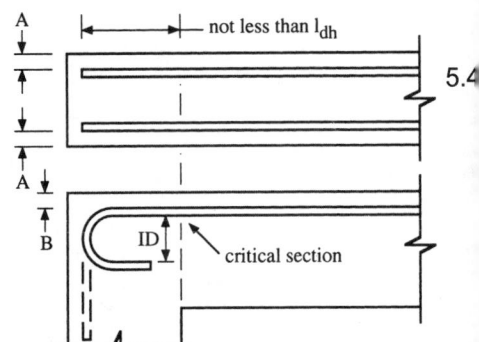

5.4

Table 3.7   Detailing and estimating dimensions (mm) for standard hooks for deformed reinforcing bars.

Bar Size	Steel Grade											
	300 R				400 R or 500 R				400 W or 500 W			
	180 ° Hook			90 ° Hook	180 ° Hook			90 ° Hook	180 ° Hook			90 ° Hook
	ID	J	G*	A or G	ID	J	G*	A or G	ID	J	G*	A or G
10M	60	83	130	150	70	93	140	150	60	83	130	150
15M	90	122	170	210	100	132	180	220	90	122	170	210
20M					120	159	220	260	100	139	200	260
25M					150	200	280	340	150	200	280	340
30M					250	310	400	420	200	260	350	410
35M					300	371	480	510	250	321	430	490
45M					450	537	680	640	400	487	630	630
55M					600	713	900	840	550	663	850	820

Standard hooks are defined in Clause 6.6.2 and Table 16 of CSA A23.1 (See A23.3 Annex A)

The dimensions provided use the minimum diameters (ID) permitted and the nominal bar diameters rather than the bar numbers.

Add the additional hook dimension G to the detailing dimension to estimate the total bar length.

For 180° hooks: $G = (4d_b \geq 60\ mm) + \pi(ID + d_b)/2 - ID/2 - d_b$

For 90° hooks: $G = A = 12d_b + \pi(ID + d_b)/4 - ID/2 - d_b$

Special fabrication is required for bends exceeding 90° for 45M and 55M bars.

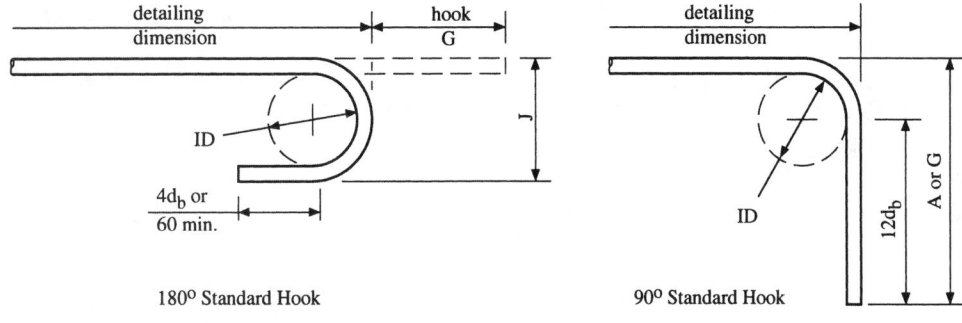

180° Standard Hook   90° Standard Hook

Table 3.8   Minimum depth, *h*, (mm) to provide anchorage for 20M and 25M deformed bar stirrups for shear, with hooks and bends placed around longitudinal reinforcement for vertical or bottom placed, uncoated stirrups in normal density concrete.

Cover to stirrups		30				40				60			
Bar Size		20M		25M		20M		25M		20M		25M	
f'_c	f_{yt}	400	500	400	500	400	500	400	500	400	500	400	500
MPa	s	≥ 60	≥ 60	≥ 65	≥ 65	≥ 75	≥ 75	≥ 80	≥ 80	≥ 75	≥ 75	≥ 100	≥ 100
20		470	570	860	1060	410	490	730	890	450	530	660	800
25		420	520	770	950	370	440	660	800	410	480	610	730
30		390	480	710	880	350	410	610	740	390	450	560	670
35		370	440	660	810	330	390	570	690	370	430	530	630
40		350	420	620	770	310	370	540	650	350	410	500	600
45		330	400	590	730	300	350	510	620	340	390	480	570
50		320	380	570	690	290	340	490	590	330	380	460	550
55		310	370	540	660	280	330	470	570	320	370	450	530
60		300	350	520	640	270	320	450	550	310	360	430	510
≥ 64		290	340	510	620	260	310	440	530	300	350	420	500

A centre-to-centre spacing smaller than listed does not provide the necessary confinement assumed in calculating minimum h.

Hooks must satisfy the dimensions for standard hooks.   Table 3.7

The table gives beam depths for $k_1 = k_2 = k_3 = 1.0$.
For a conservative approximation, multiply beam depths in this table by k_1, k_2, and k_3 when these differ from 1.0.   Clause 12.2.4
k_2 = 1.5 for epoxy-coated stirrups with clear cover less than $3d_b$, or with clear spacing between stirrups less than $6d_b$.
   = 1.2 for all other epoxy-coated stirrups

k_3 = 1.3 for structural low-density concrete
   = 1.2 for structural semi-low-density concrete

For $f_y \neq 400$ MPa, multiply depths by f_y /400.
For "Other cases" with lighter confinement, multiply depths by 1.33.   Table 12.1

Table 3.9 **Compression development lengths, ℓ_{db}, for deformed reinforcing bars with $f_y = 400$ MPa, for normal density concrete.**

$$\ell_{db} \geq 0.24d_bf_y / \sqrt{f_c'} \text{ and } \ell_{db} \geq 0.044d_bf_y$$

f_c'	Bar Size							
MPa	10M	15M	20M	25M	30M	35M	45M	55M
20	210	320	430	540	640	750	970	1180
25	190	290	380	480	580	670	860	1060
≥ 30	180	260	350	440	530	620	790	970

The development length ℓ_d is the product of ℓ_{db} from the above table and the following factors:

Clause 12.3.1

(a)   Reinforcement in excess of that required by analysis $A_{s,required} / A_{s,provided}$

(b)   Enclosure within spiral reinforcement of not less than 6 mm diameter and a pitch no more than 100 mm or within 10M ties in conformance with Clause 7.6.5 and spaced at not more than 100 mm   0.75

The product of (a) and (b) shall not be less than: 0.6

Also $\ell_d \nless 200$ mm

Table 3.10 **Compression lap splice lengths, ℓ_s, (mm) for deformed reinforcing bars with $f_y = 400$ MPa, for normal density concrete**   **[Cl. 12.16.1]**

$$\ell_s = 0.073(400)d_b$$

Confinement	Bar Size					
	10M	15M	20M	25M	30M	35M
Usual	300	440	580	730	880	1020
Columns with special ties	240	360	480	610	730	850
Spiral column	220	330	440	550	660	770

Modification factors:
Columns with special ties: Clause 12.17.3.4
When ties are provided so that the effective tie area (A_{te}) along the splice in each direction (the legs perpendicular to dimension h) satisfies $A_{te} \geq 0.0015hs$, as illustrated in Fig N12.17.3.4 and Clause N12.17.3.4)   0.83

Spiral column: Clause 12.17.3.5
When the lap splice is confined within a spirally reinforced compression member   0.75

45M and 55M bars may be lap spliced with 35M or smaller bars in a compression splice. When bars of different sizes are lap spliced in compression, the splice length shall be the larger of the development length of the larger bar from Table 3.9 or the splice length of the smaller bar from Table 3.10.   Clause 12.14.2.1, 12.16.2 and 15.9.2.5

The minimum lap length is 300 mm.

Table 3.11   Tension development lengths, ℓ_d (mm) for confined deformed wire with $f_y = 515$ MPa for normal density concrete.

$$\ell_d = 0.45k_1k_2k_3k_4\frac{f_y}{\sqrt{f_c'}}d_b$$

f_c' MPa	Wire Size, (Area, mm^2)						
	MD25.8	MD32.3	MD38.7	MD45.2	MD51.6	MD58.1	MD64.5
20	240	270	290	320	340	360	380
25	210	240	260	280	300	320	340
30	190	220	240	260	270	290	310
35	180	200	220	240	250	270	280
40	170	190	210	220	240	250	270
45	160	180	190	210	220	240	250
50	150	170	180	200	210	230	240
55	140	160	180	190	200	210	230
60	140	150	170	180	190	210	220
≥ 64	130	150	160	180	190	200	210

Clear cover and clear spacing of bars must be at least $1.0d_b$ and $1.4d_b$, respectively.

Member must contain at least minimum stirrups or ties within length ℓ_d or,

for slabs, walls, shells, or folded plates have a clear spacing not less than $2d_b$ between bars being developed.

The table gives development lengths for $k_1 = k_2 = k_3 = 1.0$ and $k_4 = 0.8$.
Multiply development lengths in this table by k_1, k_2, and k_3 when these differ from 1.0.

Clause 12.2.4

(The product k_1k_2 need not be taken greater than 1.7)

k_1 = 1.3 for horizontal reinforcement placed in such a way that more than 300 mm of fresh concrete is cast in the member below the development length or splice.

k_2 = 1.5 for epoxy-coated reinforcement with clear cover less than $3d_b$, or with clear spacing between bars being developed less than $6d_b$.
    = 1.2 for all other epoxy-coated reinforcement

k_3 = 1.3 for structural low-density concrete
    = 1.2 for structural semi-low-density concrete

For $f_y \neq 515$ MPa, multiply development length by $f_y/515$

The minimum permissible size of deformed wire is MD25   Clause 3.1.3(d)

For "Other cases" of Table 12.1 multiply the above lengths by 1.33

After application of all modification factors, the development length must not be less than 300 mm

Table 3.12   Tension development lengths, ℓ_d and lap splice lengths, ℓ_s for deformed welded wire reinforcement (WWR) with $f_y = 485$ MPa

$$\ell_d = 0.45 k_1 k_2 k_3 k_4 k_5 \frac{f_y}{\sqrt{f'_c}} d_b \geq 200 \qquad \ell_s = 1.3\ell_d \geq 200$$

Development Length, ℓ_d					Splice Length, ℓ_s									
	f'_c					d_b	f'_c							
Wire Size	20	25	30	≥35	Wire Size	mm	20	25	30	35	40	45	50	≥55
Top bars and low-density concrete k_1 and $k_3 = 1.3$														
MD47.6	260	230	210	200	MD47.6	7.79	340	300	280	260	240	220	210	200
MD34.9	220	200	200		MD34.9	6.67	290	260	240	220	200	200	200	
≤ MD25.7	200				MD25.7	5.74	250	220	200	200				
					MD18.7	4.88	210	200						
					≤ MD13.3	4.12	200							
Top bars and semi-low-density concrete $k_1 = 1.3$, $k_3 = 1.2$														
	20	25	≥30				20	25	30	35	40	45	≥50	
MD47.6	240	210	200		MD47.6	7.79	310	280	250	240	220	210	200	
MD34.9	210	200			MD34.9	6.67	270	240	220	200	200	200		
≤ MD25.7	200				MD25.7	5.74	230	210	200					
					≤ MD18.7	4.88	200	200						
Top bars or low-density concrete $k_1 \, k_3 = 1.3$														
	≥20						20	25	30	≥35				
≤ MD47.6	200				MD47.6	7.79	260	230	210	200				
					MD34.9	6.67	220	200	200					
					≤ MD25.7	5.74	200							
Bottom bars in semi-low-density concrete $k_1 = 1.0$, $k_3 = 1.2$														
	≥20						20	25	≥30					
≤ MD47.6	200				MD47.6	7.79	240	210	200					
					MD34.9	6.67	210	200						
					≤ MD25.7	5.74	200							
Bottom bars in normal density concrete $k_1 = k_3 = 1.0$														
	≥20						≥20							
≤ MD47.6	200				≤ MD47.6	7.79	200							

The number in the wire size is the cross-sectional area of each of the longitudinal wires.

The tabulated values are based on uncoated wires with $k_2 = 1.0$, $k_4 = 0.8$ and $k_5 = (485 - 240)/485 = 0.505$.   (Clause 12.7.2)

(Eq. 12-3 for wire fabric factor, k_5, does not govern for standard mesh sizes.)

The development length, ℓ_d, for welded deformed welded wire reinforcement is measured from the end of the wire. At least one cross wire must be within the development length and not less than 50 mm from the critical section.   (Clause 12.7.2)

The lap length, ℓ_s, for welded deformed wire reinforcement is measured between the ends of the wires of each sheet. The overlap of the end cross wires must be ≥ 50 mm.   (Clause 12.18.1)

Table 3.13   Tension development lengths, ℓ_d and lap splice lengths, ℓ_s for smooth welded wire reinforcement (WWR) with $f_y = 450$ MPa

Designation	≤ MW11.1	≤ MW35.5	≤ MW71.0	≤ MW116
Diameter (mm)	≤ 3.80	≤ 6.73	≤ 9.50	≤ 12.17
s_w (mm)	51 X 51	102 X 102	152 X 152	203 X 203
ℓ_d (mm)	150	150	200	250
ℓ_s (mm)	150	230	300	380

The number in the designation is the cross-sectional area of the longitudinal wires.

As welded wire reinforcement has small diameters, the minimum development lengths, ℓ_d, and minimum splice lengths, ℓ_s, based on cross wire spacing, control for the sizes tabulated for all k_3 and $f'_c \geq 20$ MPa.   Clause 12.8 and 12.19

For larger wires the equation $\ell_d = 3.3k_3 \dfrac{A_w}{s_w} \dfrac{f_y}{\sqrt{f'_c}}$ will govern.

The development length, ℓ_d, for smooth welded wire reinforcement is measured starting from the outer cross wire. At least two cross wires must be within the development length with the closer wire not less than 50 mm from the critical section.
The minimum development length is 150 mm.   Clause 12.8

The splice length, ℓ_s, for smooth welded wire reinforcement is measured between the outermost cross wires of each sheet.   Clause 12.19.2

The splice length may be less than the values tabulated above when the ratio $A_{s,provided}/A_{s,required}$ is greater than 2.0 as illustrated in Figure N12.19, with a minimum of 50 mm.   Clause 12.19.3

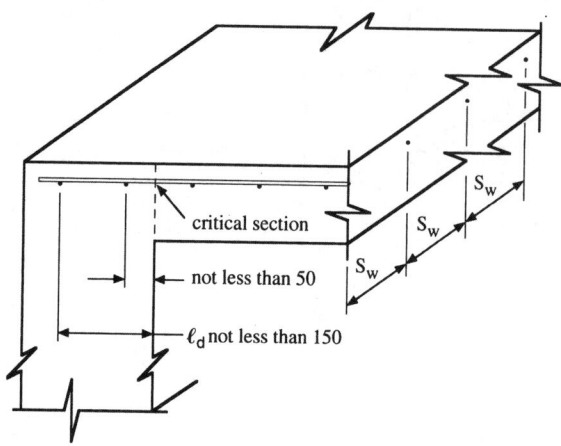

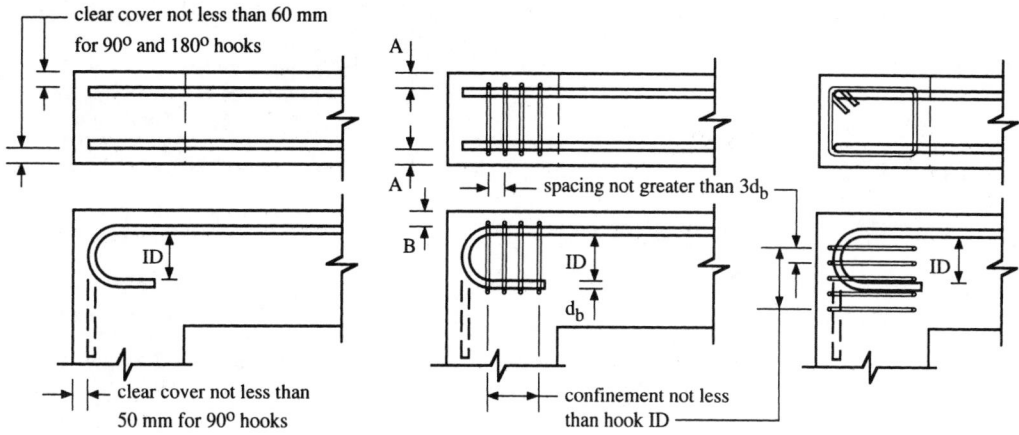

For 35M or smaller bars
Modification factor = 0.7

For 35M bars or smaller where either clear cover "A" or clear cover "B" is at least 60 mm, and at least 3 ties or stirrups with $s \not> 3d_b$ enclose the hook over a distance not less than ID. As shown, the ties may be placed vertically or horizontally.

(a) Large concrete cover is provided
(Clause 12.5.3(b))

(b) Enclosure within ties or stirrups
(Clause 12.5.3(c))

Fig. 3.1 Modification Factors for Improved Confinement to Standard Hooks

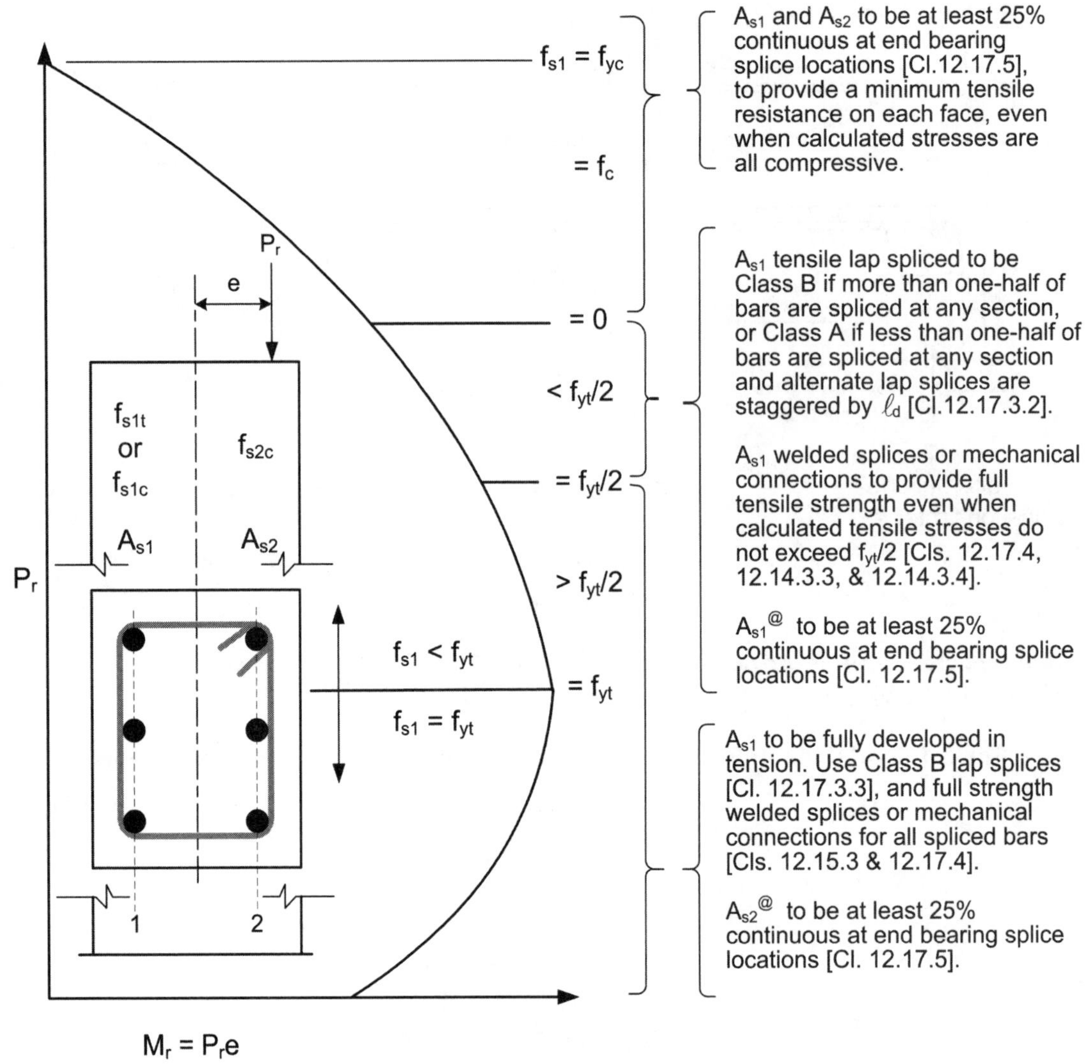

$f_{s1} = f_{yc}$

$= f_c$

A_{s1} and A_{s2} to be at least 25% continuous at end bearing splice locations [Cl.12.17.5], to provide a minimum tensile resistance on each face, even when calculated stresses are all compressive.

P_r

e

f_{s1t} or f_{s1c}

f_{s2c}

A_{s1} A_{s2}

P_r

$f_{s1} < f_{yt}$

$f_{s1} = f_{yt}$

1   2

$= 0$

$< f_{yt}/2$

$= f_{yt}/2$

$> f_{yt}/2$

$= f_{yt}$

A_{s1} tensile lap spliced to be Class B if more than one-half of bars are spliced at any section, or Class A if less than one-half of bars are spliced at any section and alternate lap splices are staggered by ℓ_d [Cl.12.17.3.2].

A_{s1} welded splices or mechanical connections to provide full tensile strength even when calculated tensile stresses do not exceed $f_{yt}/2$ [Cls. 12.17.4, 12.14.3.3, & 12.14.3.4].

A_{s1} @ to be at least 25% continuous at end bearing splice locations [Cl. 12.17.5].

A_{s1} to be fully developed in tension. Use Class B lap splices [Cl. 12.17.3.3], and full strength welded splices or mechanical connections for all spliced bars [Cls. 12.15.3 & 12.17.4].

A_{s2} @ to be at least 25% continuous at end bearing splice locations [Cl. 12.17.5].

$M_r = P_r e$

@ Different loading conditions may produce moment reversal to switch the roles of A_{s1} and A_{s2}

Typical Notation

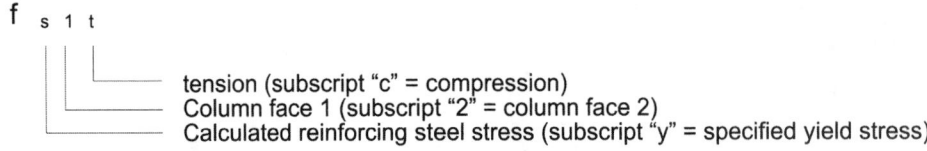

f s 1 t

tension (subscript "c" = compression)
Column face 1 (subscript "2" = column face 2)
Calculated reinforcing steel stress (subscript "y" = specified yield stress)

A_{s1} = reinforcing steel area in column face 1 (subscript "2" = face 2)

Fig. 3.2 Special Splice Requirements for Columns (Clause 12.17)

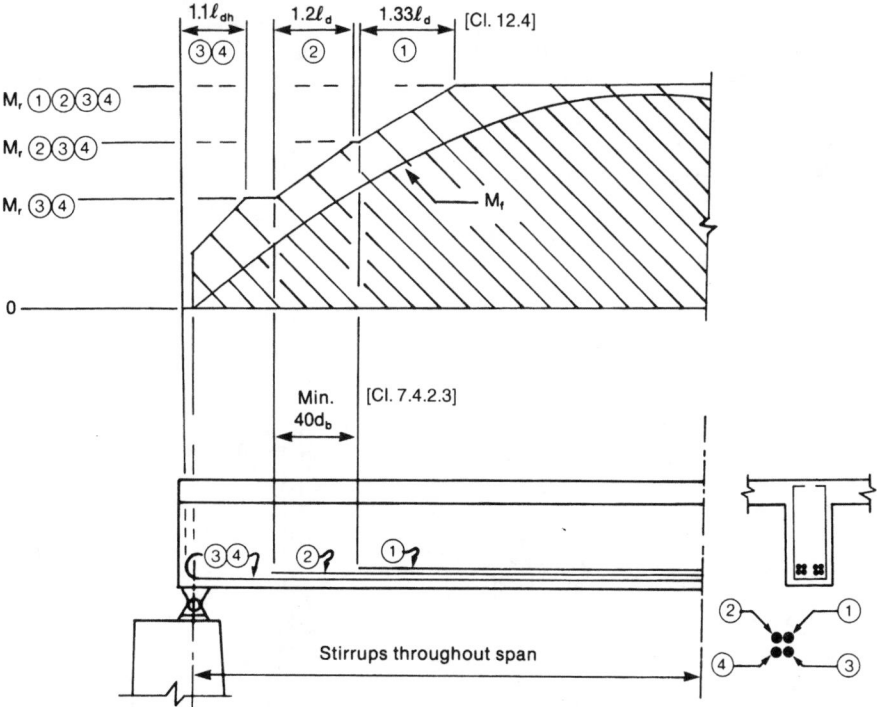

Fig. 3.3 Bundled Bars in Flexural Members

A two bar bundle is spliced in compression or tension to maintain the full strength of $2A_bf_y$, by providing staggered splices and a separate splice bar. With the splice bar, the arrangement becomes a 3 bar bundle, requiring a 20% increase in the individual bar splice length to $1.2\ell_s$ [Cl. 12.14.2.2]. Force transfer between spliced bars is assumed to occur linearly along the required splice length of $1.2\ell_s$.

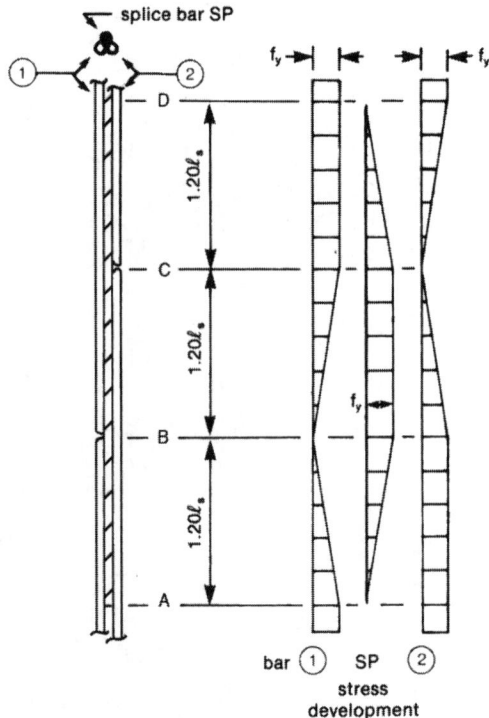

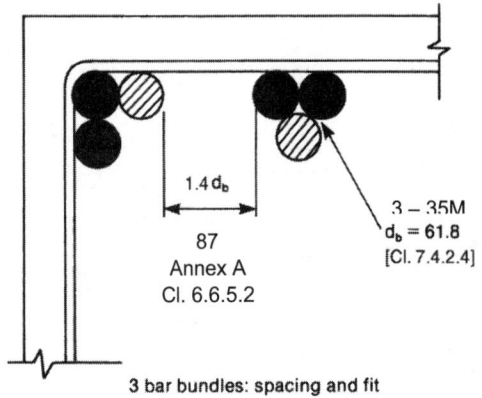

3 bar bundles: spacing and fit

(a) Bundled bar splices for full strength in tension or compression.

		Splice Bar			
	bundle configuration	⊞	⊞	⊞	⊞
	continuing bars in bundle	4	3	3	2
A	length of splice bar	*	$2(1.33\ell_s)$	$2(1.33\ell_s)$	$2(1.20\ell_s)$
A	tensile resistance (%)~	0	33	33	50
B	length of splice bar	*	$4(1.33\ell_s)$	$4(1.33\ell_s)$	$3(1.20\ell_s)$
B	tensile resistance (%)~	75	100	100	100

A All bars butt spliced at same location (no tensile strength).
B Butt splice locations staggered.
 * Splice bar not permitted — Makes a 5 bar bundle.
~ % of area of continuing bars.

(b) Bundled bar lap splices for tensile resistance in columns.

Fig. 3.4   Bundled Bar Splices [Cl. 12.14.2.2]

4

By Michael P. Collins
Evan C. Bentz
and Denis Mitchell

Shear and Torsion

Shear and Torsion

4.1   Introduction

Members subjected to shear and/or torsion may develop diagonal cracks. Unless these members contain appropriate amounts of properly detailed transverse and longitudinal reinforcement, these cracks can result in the premature and perhaps sudden failure of the members. Avoiding such failures is the objective of shear and torsion design.

The shear and torsion chapter of the CSA standard A23.3-04 specifies two different methods of designing for shear: the sectional method appropriate for typical flexural regions and the strut-and-tie method appropriate for regions near discontinuities. Detailed comments on the individual code clauses of these two methods have been given in the "Explanatory Notes" section of this handbook. This chapter will give an overview of the two methods, background information helpful in understanding the methods, together with detailed design examples illustrating the application of both methods.

4.2   Sectional Design Method

The sectional design method is based on the "modified compression field theory" (MCFT) (Refs. 4.1 and 4.2). This theory captures the essential features of the behaviour of cracked reinforced concrete without considering all of the details. It uses the requirements of equilibrium and compatibility combined with experimentally determined stress-strain relationships for cracked concrete to predict the load-deformation behaviour of reinforced concrete elements.

The cracked web of a reinforced concrete beam transmits shear stress in a relatively complex manner. As the load is increased, new cracks open and some pre-existing cracks close. The cracks have rough surfaces capable of transmitting considerable shear stresses. The local stresses in both the concrete and the reinforcement vary from point to point, with high reinforcement stresses but low concrete tensile stresses occurring at crack locations. The MCFT considers the stresses and strains averaged over distances larger than the crack spacing in addition to the local stresses which occur at crack locations. These local stresses often govern the maximum shear capacity of the element.

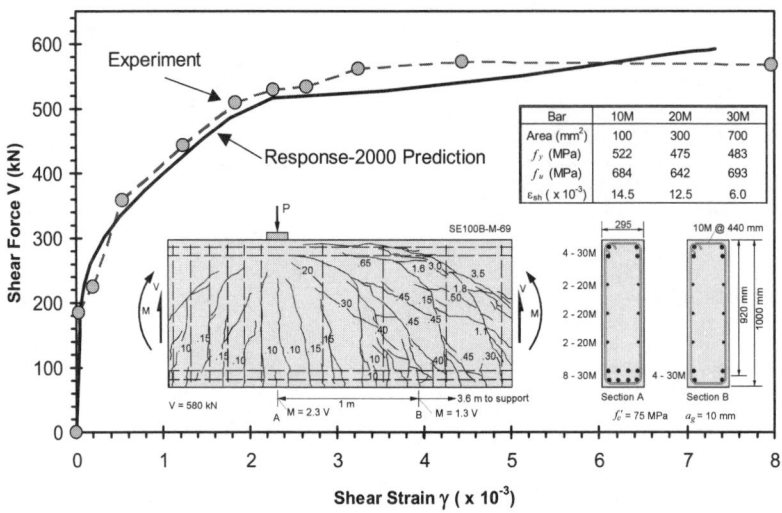

Fig. 4.1 Observed and predicted load-deformation response of large beam at section B

To conveniently solve the equilibrium, compatibility and stress-strain relationships of the MCFT, a computer program is required. Response-2000 is such a program and enables the strains and stresses caused when shear, moment and axial load are applied to a reinforced concrete section to be determined. This program is available in Ref. 4.3. As an example of the capabilities of this program, Fig. 4.1 compares the predicted and observed load-deformation response of a large, high-strength concrete beam tested in shear. It can be seen that the overall load-deformation response is predicted very accurately.

While the MCFT is capable of accurately predicting the complete load-deformation response of a section loaded in moment and shear, for shear design it is typically only the maximum shear capacity of a section that is required. It has proved possible to develop relatively simple equations from the MCFT which are capable of predicting this capacity (Ref. 4.4). These equations form the basis of the sectional design method specified in Clause 11.3.

The factored shear strength, V_r, of a non-prestressed section with a web width of b_w and an effective shear depth of d_v ($d_v = 0.9d$) is expressed as:

$$V_r = V_c + V_s \quad \le 0.25\phi_c f_c' b_w d_v$$
$$V_r = \phi_c \lambda \beta \sqrt{f_c'} \cdot b_w d_v + \phi_s \frac{A_v}{s} f_y d_v \cot\theta \tag{4-1}$$

Where β represents the ability of cracked concrete to transmit shear by aggregate interlock stresses and θ is the angle of inclination of the diagonal compressive stresses. Both of these parameters are functions of the longitudinal strain, ε_x, at the mid-depth of the section and are given as:

$$\beta = \frac{0.40}{(1+1500\varepsilon_x)} \cdot \frac{1300}{(1000 + s_{ze})} \tag{4-2}$$

$$\theta = 29° + 7000\varepsilon_x \tag{4-3}$$

and $\quad \varepsilon_x = \dfrac{M_f/d_v + V_f}{2E_s A_s} \tag{4-4}$

where A_s is the area of longitudinal reinforcement on the flexural tension side of the member and s_{ze} is the effective crack spacing. If the member contains at least minimum stirrups, the value of s_{ze} is taken as 300 mm. For members without stirrups, s_{ze} is related to the crack spacing parameter s_z and the aggregate size a_g, as $s_{ze}=35s_z/(15+a_g)$, but $s_{ze} \ge 0.85s_z$. The crack spacing parameter s_z is the longitudinal crack spacing at mid-depth of the member between transverse

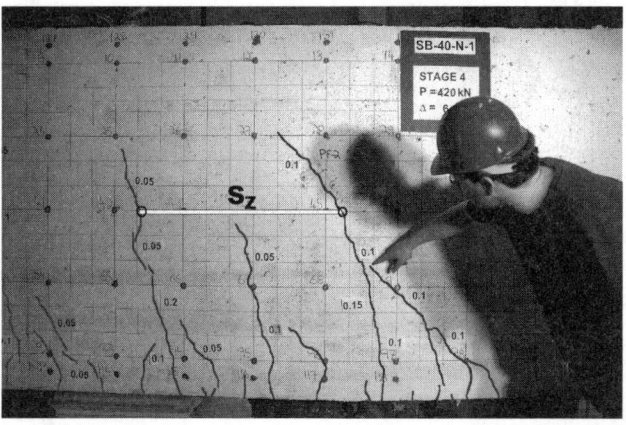

Fig. 4.2 Observed crack pattern in 1.5 metre deep slab not containing transverse reinforcement.

cracks. As can be seen in Fig. 4-2, the spacing of the transverse cracks is much greater at mid-depth than it is at the flexural tension face. For members without intermediate layers of crack control reinforcement, s_z is taken as d_v.

Note that the equation for β consists of the product of a strain effect, governed by ε_x, and a size effect governed by s_{ze}. Thus the shear strength of a member decreases as the longitudinal strain increases and, for members without stirrups, as the member depth increases. For members with stirrups an increase in ε_x also causes an increase in θ which decreases $\cot\theta$ and, hence, decreases shear capacity.

If Eq. 4-4 indicates a reasonably high value of ε_x, it is possible that the capacity of the member may be dictated by yielding of the longitudinal reinforcement on the flexural tension side. This yielding can be checked from Eq. 11-14 of the code. Thus:

$$A_s f_y \geq \frac{M_f}{d_v} + (V_f - 0.5V_s)\cot\theta \qquad (4\text{-}5)$$

As an example of the use of these equations, the strength of the member described in Fig. 4-1 will be calculated. As it is desired to estimate the actual member strength, the capacity reduction factors ϕ_c and ϕ_s will be taken as unity. The calculations will be performed by estimating the value of ε_x at failure, calculating the shear strength from this, and then using Eq. 4-4 to check the estimated value of ε_x. Assuming a value of ε_x equal to 0.001 (which corresponds to a stress in the flexural tension steel of about 400 MPa), β is calculated as 0.160 and θ is 36°. Substituting these into Eq. 4-1 produces an initial estimate of shear strength of 583 kN taking into consideration Clause 11.3.4 that limits the value of $\sqrt{f_c'}$ to 8 MPa. At this shear, the corresponding moment at Section B will be 583 x 1.3 = 758 kN·m. The reinforcing bars in the half-depth of the member on the flexural tension side consist of 4-30M bars and 3-20M bars giving an A_s of 3700 mm^2. Substituting these values into Eq. 4-4 produces a calculated value of ε_x equal to 0.00101 which is close enough to the assumed value to be acceptable. Checking Eq. 4-5 indicates that:

$$4 \cdot 700 \cdot 483 + 3 \cdot 30 \cdot 475 \geq 758/0.828 + (583 - 0.5 \cdot 270)\cot 36°$$

$$1780\,\text{kN} \geq 1532\,\text{kN}$$

Hence, yield of the longitudinal steel does not control strength. Thus the predicted shear capacity of this member is 583 kN. This happens to exactly equal the experimentally observed shear strength.

In the design of new members, no iteration is required to determine ε_x. If the longitudinal reinforcement has been chosen and M_f, and V_f are known, ε_x can be directly calculated from Eq 4-4. With ε_x known, β and θ are calculated from Eqns. 4-2 and 4-3 and then the required quantity of stirrups, A_v/s can be found from Eq. 4-1.

Alternatively, for the design of members where f_c' does not exceed 60 MPa and f_y does not exceed 400 MPa and where the axial tension is insignificant, the value of ε_x may be taken as 0.85×10^{-3}. In this case, Eq. 4-1 becomes

$$V_r = 0.18 \cdot \phi_c \lambda \sqrt{f_c'} \cdot b_w d_v + 1.43 \phi_s \frac{A_v}{s} f_y d_v \quad \leq 0.25 \phi_c f_c' b_w d_v \qquad (4\text{-}6)$$

while for the design of members without stirrups, constructed using concrete with at least 20 mm aggregate, Eq. 4-1 becomes:

$$V_r = \frac{230}{1000 + d_v} \cdot \phi_c \lambda \sqrt{f_c'} \cdot b_w d_v \qquad (4\text{-}7)$$

Equations 4-5, 4-6 and 4-7 are the main equations of the 2004 simplified method.

The sectional design method is illustrated with the shear design of a thick one-way slab (Example 4.1), a heavily loaded coupling beam (Example 4.2), a large beam (Example 4.3), a column (Example 4.4), a spandrel beam subjected to shear, torsion and moment (Example 4.5), and a spandrel beam supporting a two way slab (Example 4.6).

4.3   Design Of Disturbed Regions

The manner in which the resisting compressive stresses flow in a beam determines the different regions that need to be considered in design. These different regions are illustrated in Fig. 4.3 and are described below.

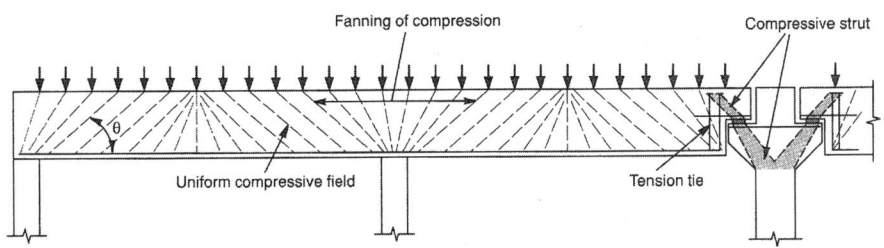

Fig. 4.3 Regions of Uniform Compressive Fields and Disturbed Regions

(a)   Regions of uniform compressive fields. In these regions the principal compressive stress trajectories can be approximated by a series of parallel lines at an angle of θ from the longitudinal axis of the beam, and the shear stress may be assumed to be uniformly distributed over the effective shear depth, d_v. These regions can be designed using the sectional design method.

(b)   Regions of fanning of compressive stresses. These disturbed regions are characterized by radiating compressive stresses near supports and in regions where the shear changes sign. These regions can also be designed using the sectional design approach.

(c)   Regions of compressive struts and tension ties. The flow of the forces in these disturbed regions can be visualized as struts of unidirectional compressive stresses together with ties provided by reinforcing bars. It is appropriate to design these regions using the strut-and-tie method.

The strut-and-tie model described in Clause 11.4 utilizes concepts from plasticity and truss models (Refs. 4.5, 4.6 and 4.7) developed in Europe, together with compatibility concepts from the MCFT to determine the crushing strength of the struts (Ref. 4.1 and 4.8).

The geometry of the truss, which consists of concrete compressive struts and reinforcing tension ties, is determined by following the flow of the forces from the loading points to the support reactions. The intersection of the struts with the ties or the support reactions delineate the nodal regions of multi directionally compressed concrete. Once the geometry of the truss is known the forces in the struts and ties can usually be determined by statics. The items to be checked in the design procedure with reference to the deep beam shown in Fig. 4.4 are listed below.

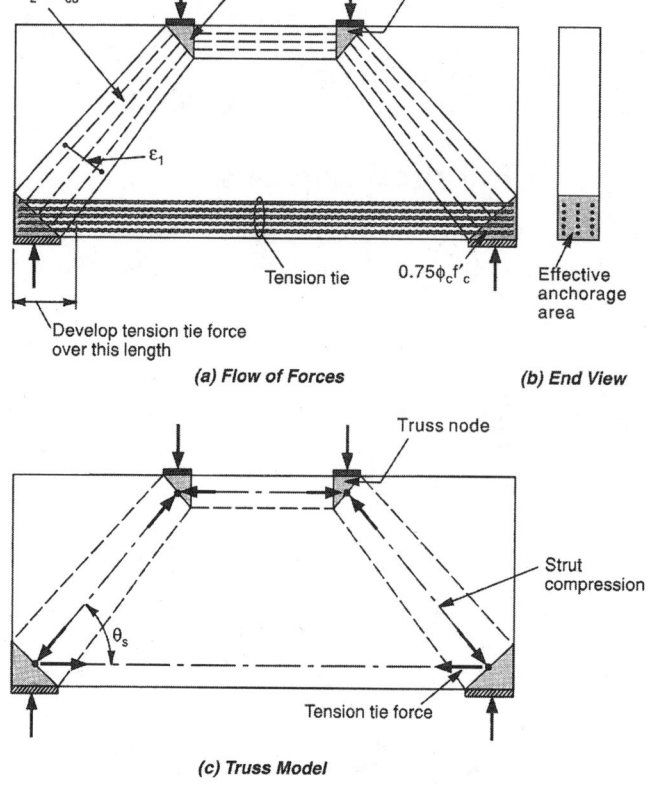

(a) Flow of Forces

(b) End View

(c) Truss Model

Fig. 4.4: Strut-and-Tie Truss Model for a Deep Beam

(i)   Choose bearing areas at the loading points and the support reactions such that the nodal region stresses are not exceeded.

(ii)   Determine the geometry of the truss by first locating the nodes of the truss at the points of intersection of the forces meeting at the nodal regions (see Fig. 4.4c). Solve for the forces in the members of the truss.

(iii) Choose the tie reinforcement such that the factored resistance equals or exceeds the tie force required.

(iv)   Distribute the tie reinforcement such that the stress calculated by dividing the tie force by the effective area of concrete surrounding the tie reinforcement is less than the stress limit for the nodal region anchoring the tie. The effective area of concrete has the same centroid as the tie reinforcement (see Fig. 4.4b).

(v)   Check that the tie can develop the required tensile force at the location where the centroid of the tie crosses the edge of the strut (see Fig 4-4a). If the embedment length is not sufficient then hooks or mechanical anchorages should be provided in accordance with the requirements of Clause 12.

(vi)   Check that the compressive stress, f_2, in the strut is less than the crushing limit, f_{cu}. The compressive stress, f_2, is determined by dividing the strut force by the width and the thickness of the strut. Since the compressive strut is crossed by a tie near the support nodal region (see Fig. 4.4a) then f_{cu} must be reduced to account for the presence of the principal tensile strain, ε_1. Figure N11.4.2.3 describes the variation of the crushing strength of the strut as a function of θ_s.

(vii) Provide uniformly distributed well anchored reinforcing bars in the vertical and horizontal directions to control diagonal cracking and to improve the ductility of the deep beam (Clause 11.4.5).

The application of the strut-and-tie model is demonstrated in the design of a deep beam subjected to uniform loading (Example 4.7), a deep beam subjected to concentrated loads (Example 4.8), a corbel (Example 4.9) and a beam with dapped ends (Example 4.10).

4.4   References

4.1 Vecchio, F.J., and Collins, M.P., "The Modified Compression Field Theory for Reinforced Concrete Elements Subjected to Shear," ACI Journal, Vol. 83, No. 2, Mar. Apr. 1986, pp. 219-231.

4.2 Collins, M.P., Mitchell, D., Adebar, P.E., Vecchio, F.J., "A General Shear Design Method," ACI Structural Journal, Vol. 93, No. 1, Jan.-Feb. 1996, pp. 36-45.

4.3 http://www.ecf.utoronto.ca/~bentz/r2k.htm last accessed Nov. 2005.

4.4 Bentz, E.C., Collins, M.P., "Development of the 2004 CSA A23.3 Shear Provisions for Reinforced Concrete," Canadian Journal of Civil Engineering, in press February 2006.

4.5 Marti, P., "Basic Tools of Reinforced Concrete Beam Design," ACI Journal, Vol. 82, No. 1, Jan. Feb. 1985, pp. 46-56.

4.6 Schlaich, J., Schäfer, K., and Jennewein, M., "Towards a Consistent Design of Reinforced Concrete Structures, " PCI Journal, Vol. 32, No. 3, May June 1987, pp. 74-150.

4.7 Nielsen, M.P., Limit Analysis and Concrete Plasticity, Prentice Hall Inc., Englewood Cliffs, N.J., 1984, 420 pp.

4.8 Collins, M.P., and Mitchell, D., "A Rational Approach to Shear Design – The 1984 Canadian Code Provisions" Journal of the American Concrete Institute, Vol. 83, No. 6, Nov.-Dec. 1986, pp. 925-933.

Example 4.1   Design Of Thick One-Way Slab

It is desired to construct a one-way slab without stirrups to span 16 m between two 400 mm thick bearing walls and carry a superimposed specified live of 20 kN/m^2 due to soil overburden. Design the slab. Use $f_c' = 30$ MPa, $a_g = 20$ mm and $f_y = 400$ MPa.

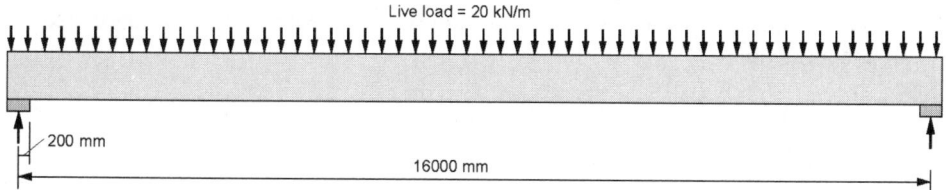

Live load = 20 kN/m

200 mm

16000 mm

1.   *Estimate required slab thickness*

From Table 9-2 deflections need not be calculated if the slab thickness exceeds $\ell_n/20$ = (16000 - 400)/20 = 780 mm. Try a total thickness of 800 mm.

2.   *Calculate the factored loads*

Taking a 1 m wide strip of slab and using a thickness of 800 gives:

$w_f = 1.25\,D + 1.5\,L = 1.25 \cdot 0.8 \cdot 24 + 1.5 \cdot 20$

$\quad = 24 + 30 = 54$ kN/m

3. *Design longitudinal reinforcement at midspan*

The factored moment at midspan is

$M_f = w_f \, \ell^2 / 8 = (54 \cdot 16^2) / 8 = 1728 \text{ kNm}$

In order to choose a trial area of reinforcement we will assume a flexural lever arm equal to 0.9d. Assuming a cover to the bottom bars of 40 mm and assuming that 30M bars are used for the principal reinforcement, the effective depth d is 800 - 40 - 30/2 = 745 mm. Hence, the required area of reinforcement is about

$A_s = 1728 \cdot 10^6 / (0.9 \cdot 745 \cdot 0.85 \cdot 400) = 7574 \text{ mm}^2$

The minimum amount of flexural reinforcement required for this slab (Clause 7.8.1) is

$A_s = 0.002 \cdot 800 \cdot 1000 = 1600 \text{ mm}^2$

Try 30M at a spacing of 90 mm, giving A_s = 7778 mm². The stress block depth, a is

$a = \dfrac{\phi_s A_s f_y}{\phi_c \alpha_1 f'_c b} = \dfrac{0.85 \cdot 7778 \cdot 400}{0.65 \cdot 0.805 \cdot 30 \cdot 1000} = 168 \text{ mm}$

Hence, the factored moment resistance is

$M_r = \phi_s A_s f_y (d - a/2) = 0.85 \cdot 7778 \cdot 400 \cdot (745 - 168/2) = 1747 \text{ kNm}$

Since $M_r > M_f$ the flexural capacity is sufficient.
Check the c/d limit (Clause 10.5.2). The c/d ratio must be less than or equal to 700/(700 + f_y) = 0.636. The flexural stress block factor β_1 = 0.97 - 0.0025 f'_c = 0.895. For this slab c = a/β_1 = 168/0.895 = 188 mm and c/d = 188/745 = 0.252 < 0.636.
Provide minimum reinforcement in the slab in the direction perpendicular to the span. Provide 25M bars at a spacing of 300 mm, giving A_s = (1000/300)·500 = 1667 mm²/m.

4. *Check the shear strength by the simplified method*

For this simply supported, uniformly loaded slab we will first check the shear strength at a location a distance d_v from the face of the support. The value of d_v is taken as 0.9d = 671 mm. At this location

$V_f = (8 - 0.2 - 0.671) \cdot 54 = 385 \text{ kN}$

$M_f = (0.671 + 0.2) \cdot 54 \cdot 8 - 54 \cdot (0.671 + 0.2)^2 / 2 = 356 \text{ kNm}$

In the Simplified Method of shear design (Clause 11.3.6.3), the predicted shear capacity is not affected by the magnitude of the moment or the amount of longitudinal reinforcement and hence V_c for nonprestressed members is predicted to remain constant along the length of the member. Because of this the critical section for shear will occur near the end of the beam where the factored shear force has its maximum value. Checking the shear capacity at this location:

$V_r = V_c = \dfrac{230}{1000 + d_v} \phi_c \lambda \sqrt{f'_c} \cdot b_w d_v = \dfrac{230}{1000 + 671} 0.65 \cdot 1.0\sqrt{30} \cdot 1000 \cdot 671 = 329 \text{ kN}$

As $V_r < V_f$, the shear capacity as calculated by the simplified method is inadequate. Therefore if the design is to be continued using the simplified method, it will be necessary to increase the depth of the slab. The simplified method assumes that ε_x =0.85 x 10^{-3} which is appropriate for sections where the stress in the longitudinal reinforcement is close to the yield stress. Near the supports of this simple span beam, however, the moment is low and, hence, the simplified method will be rather conservative. Because of this, it is worthwhile to investigate the shear capacity using the general method before deciding whether a thicker slab is required.

5. *Check the shear strength by the general method*

The shear strength determined by the general method depends on ε_x, which, in turn, is a function of the amount of longitudinal reinforcement and the magnitude of the applied moment. When using the general method to investigate the shear strength of uniformly loaded simple span beam, it is found that the critical section will occur d_v from the face of the support or at a location somewhat further into the span. For this slab, the value of ε_x calculated at d_v from the face of the support is:

$$\varepsilon_x = \frac{M_f / d_v + V_f}{2E_s A_s} = \frac{356 \times 10^6 / 671 + 385 \times 10^3}{2 \cdot 200000 \cdot 7778} = 0.294 \times 10^{-3}$$

For this slab with only one layer of longitudinal reinforcement made from concrete with 20 mm aggregate, the crack spacing parameter, s_{ze} is equal to d_v = 671 mm. Thus:

$$\beta = \frac{0.4}{(1 + 1500\varepsilon_x)} \cdot \frac{1300}{(1000 + s_{ze})} = \frac{0.4}{(1 + 1.5 \cdot 0.294)} \cdot \frac{1300}{(1000 + 671)} = 0.216$$

Hence:

$$V_r = V_c = \phi_c \lambda \beta \sqrt{f_c'} b_w d_v = 0.65 \cdot 1.0 \cdot 0.216 \cdot \sqrt{30} \cdot 1000 \cdot 671 = 516 \text{ kN}$$

As V_c exceeds V_f the shear strength is adequate at this location. Note that V_r is 34% higher than V_f at this location.

To investigate whether the shear strength might be more critical at a higher moment location, the above calculations will be repeated for a section which is 10% of the span length from the centre of the support. At this location, M_f = 622 kN·m, and V_f = 346 kN. The strain ε_x is calculated as 0.41 x 10^{-3} and V_r = 461 kN. Thus at this location the shear strength is 33% higher than the factored shear which is slightly more critical than for the section at d_v from the face of the support. Because of these large margins, it not necessary to check other locations along the span.

6. *Check tensile capacity of longitudinal reinforcement at end support*

From Clause 11.3.9.5 the reinforcement must be capable of resisting a tensile force of $V_f \cot\theta$. As noted in 11.3.6.4 (d), the value of ε_x used to calculate θ may be that calculated at d_v from the face of the support, i.e. ε_x = 0.294 x 10^{-3}. Thus by Eq. 11-12, θ = 29° + 7000·0.294 x 10^{-3} = 31.1°. Thus the tensile force that must be resisted by the longitudinal reinforcement is equal to 385 cot 31.1° = 639 kN. For 30M bars with a clear spacing of 60 mm between bars the development length from Table 12-1 is

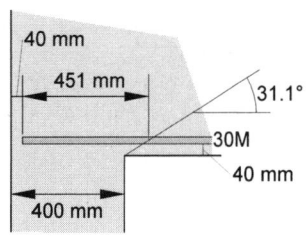

$$\ell_d = 0.45 k_1 k_2 k_3 k_4 \frac{f_y}{\sqrt{f'_c}} d_b = 0.45 \cdot 1.0 \cdot 1.0 \cdot 1.0 \cdot 1.0 \cdot \frac{400}{\sqrt{30}} 30 = 986 \, mm$$

The length available for developing the tension in the longitudinal bars is illustrated in the figure and is equal to 451 mm. Hence, if all of the bars are continued into the support, the tensile capacity at the location specified in Clause 11.3.9.5 and shown in the figure is (451 / 986) · 0.85 · 400 · 7778 = 1210 kN. As 1210 kN considerably exceeds the required force of 639 kN, consider reducing the number of bars going into the support.

7   *Choose bar cut-offs*

If every third bar is to be terminated before reaching the supports, this will reduce both the moment and shear capacities in the regions near the ends of the slab. Using a spreadsheet and the equations for ε_x, θ, and F_{lt}, the impact of this reduction in capacities may be readily determined. The figure compares the force which must be resisted by the longitudinal reinforcement with the capacity of this reinforcement accounting for bar cutoffs and development length. Based on this diagram, it was determined that one third of the longitudinal bars could be cutoff at a distance of 2.4 metres from the centreline of the support.

The influence of the reduction in area of longitudinal reinforcement near the support on the factored shear resistance of the slab is shown in the figure. It can be seen that at the bar cutoff location, the shear resistance of the slab has been reduced by about 18%. However, the shear capacity of the slab is still satisfactory at all locations along the span.

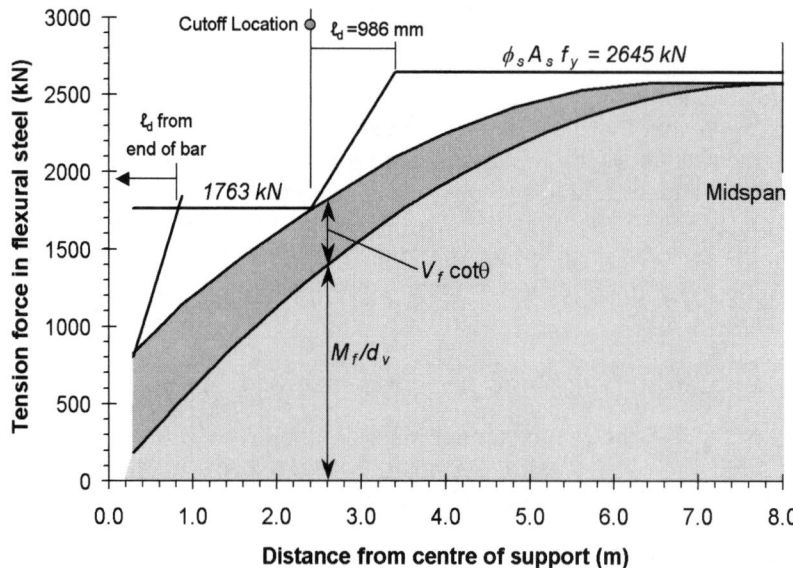

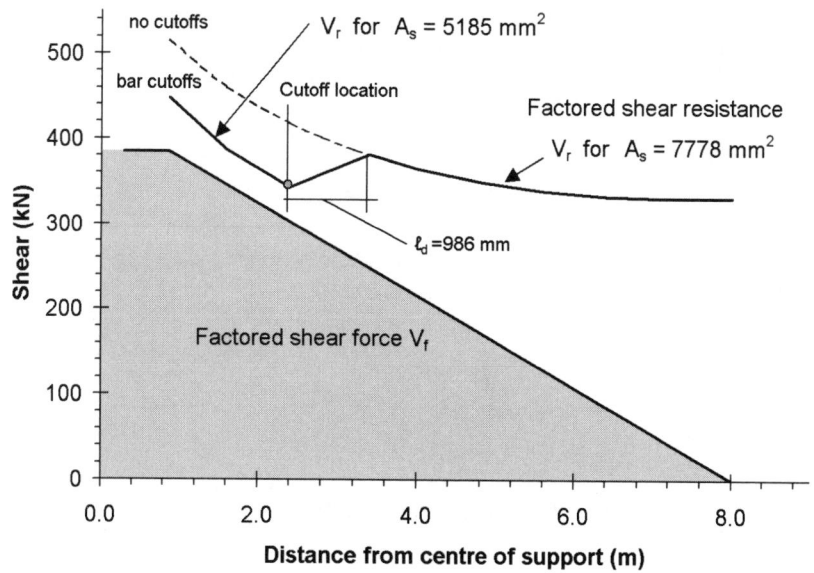

Example 4.2   Design Of Coupling Beam

The lintel beams in coupled shear walls will be subjected to significant shear forces when the building is resisting wind. Further, it is often desired to keep these lintel beams shallow so that the floor-to-floor height of the building can be minimized. Because of this, the specified upper limit on shear capacity will often govern the size of lintel beams. Previous editions of this code used rather conservative values for the maximum allowable shear force if the simplified method was used. The current edition is less restrictive for both the general and the simplified method.

The overall structural analysis on a building with 1250 mm long coupling beams has predicted a factored shear force in a particular coupling beam of V_f =1250 kN with corresponding end moments of M_f = ±800 kN·m. The cross section of the beam is 500 mm by 500 mm, f'_c = 50 MPa, a_g = 20 mm and f_y = 400 MPa. Design the required reinforcement.

1   *Design flexural reinforcement*

As the required cover is 30 mm and assuming that 15M bars will be used for the stirrups, a strain compatibility analysis indicates that with 7 – 35M bars top and bottom, the factored moment capacity will be M_r = 867 kN·m. As shown in the figure, the depth of compression at maximum capacity will be 122 mm and the effective flexural depth d = 413 mm.

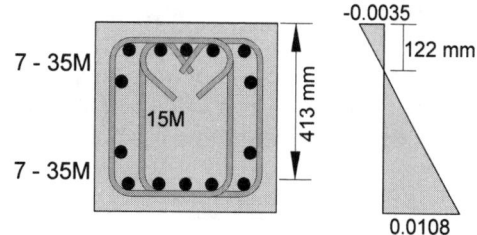

2   *Check maximum shear capacity*

The effective shear depth, d_v, of this section will be 0.9d = 372 mm. In accordance with Clause 11.3.3,

$$V_{r,max} = 0.25\phi_c f'_c b_w d_v + V_p$$
$$= 0.25 \cdot 0.65 \cdot 50 \cdot 500 \cdot 372 + 0 = 1511 \, kN$$

As $V_{r,max} > V_f$, the section size is sufficient to resist the applied shear. Note that with the simplified method from the 1994 standard the maximum shear force would have been limited to 876 kN. Also note that as V_f exceeds 0.5·1511 = 756 kN (Clause 11.3.8.3), the spacing may not exceed $0.35d_v$ or 300 mm. So, for this case, $s \leq 130$ mm.

3   *Design stirrups*

When using the simplified method of Clause 11.3.6.3, to design the required stirrups, the basic shear strength equation can be expressed as shown in Eq. 4-5 of the introduction to this chapter as:

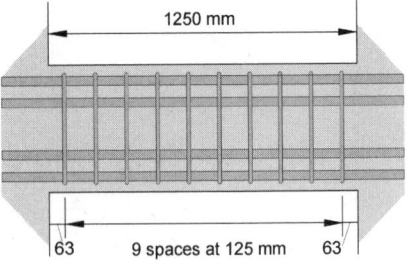

1250 mm

63   9 spaces at 125 mm   63

$$V_r = 0.18 \cdot \phi_c \lambda \sqrt{f_c'} \cdot b_w d_v + 1.43 \phi_s \frac{A_v}{s} f_y d_v$$

Because $V_r \geq V_f = 1250$ kN:

$$1250 \times 10^3 \leq 0.18 \cdot 0.65 \cdot 1\sqrt{50} \cdot 500 \cdot 372 + 1.43 \cdot 0.85 \frac{A_v}{s} 400 \cdot 372$$

$$\frac{A_v}{s} \geq 6.06 \text{ mm}^2/\text{mm}$$

If the stirrups have legs of 15M, $A_v = 4 \cdot 200 = 800$ mm^2 then, $s \leq 132$ mm. A spacing of 125 mm is selected. The resulting stirrup layout is shown in the figure.

4   *Check capacity of longitudinal reinforcement*

As the walls at the ends of the lintel beam will introduce direct compression into the flexural compression face of the beam, Clause 11.3.9.4 states that "the area of longitudinal reinforcement on the flexural tension side of the member need not exceed the area required to resist the maximum moment acting alone." Because the moments will reverse direction when the direction of the wind forces change and due to the short length of the lintel beam, both the top and bottom longitudinal reinforcement will be continuous along the length of the beam and will be anchored into the walls at each end to be fully developed at the face of the wall.

Example 4.3   Design Of Large Beam For Shear And Moment

The beam shown below is subjected to a specified live load of 50 kN/m and a dead load of 40 kN/m (including the weight of the beam). Design the required transverse and longitudinal reinforcement for shear and moment.

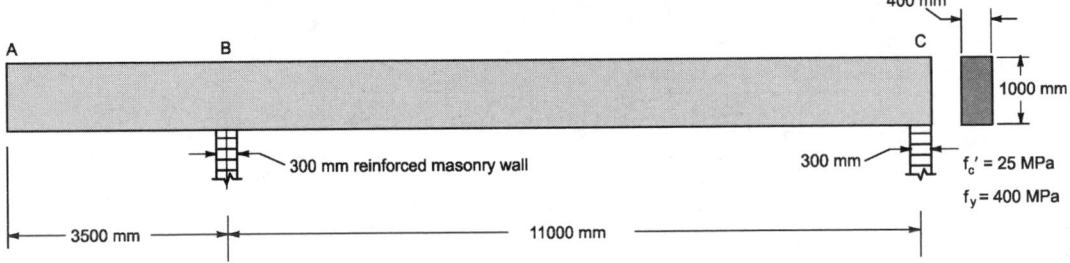

400 mm

A   B   C

1000 mm

300 mm reinforced masonry wall   300 mm $f_c' = 25$ MPa

$f_y = 400$ MPa

3500 mm   11000 mm

1. *Determine shear and moment envelope*

For calculations of shear and moments assume that the reinforced masonry walls apply a uniform bearing stress across the width of each support. Three load cases will be considered: i) live load on full length A-C ii) live load on main span B-C only, iii) live load on cantilever span, A-B only.

Calculate factored applied load:

$$w_f = 1.25 w_D + 1.50 w_L = 1.25 \cdot 40 + 1.5 \cdot 50 = 125.0 \text{ kN/m}$$

The factored shear and factored moment envelopes are illustrated in the figures below.

2. *Determine flexural reinforcement required at locations of maximum moments*

The chosen reinfor-cement is shown in the figure below. Note that because the overall depth exceeds 750 mm, skin reinforcement must be provided. The factored moment resistances were calculated using a strain compatibility analysis and are shown in the figure. The listed values of the effective depth d were taken to the centroid of the reinforcement on the "flexural tension side" of the member which is defined in Figure 11.2 of the code as the reinforcement within the zone $0.5h$ from the extreme flexural tension face

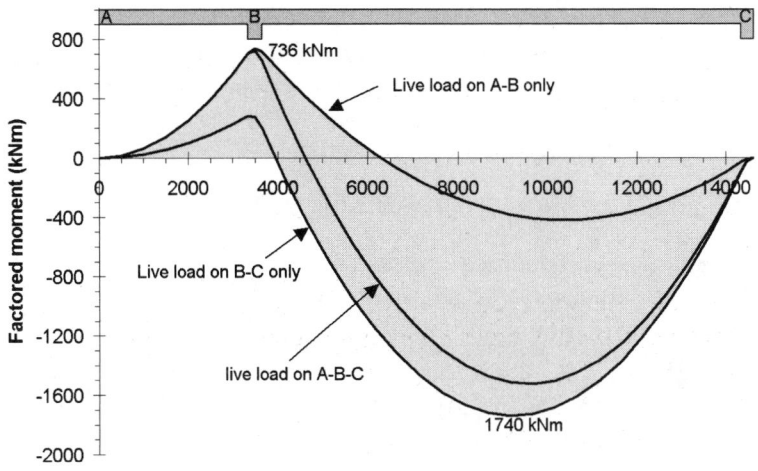

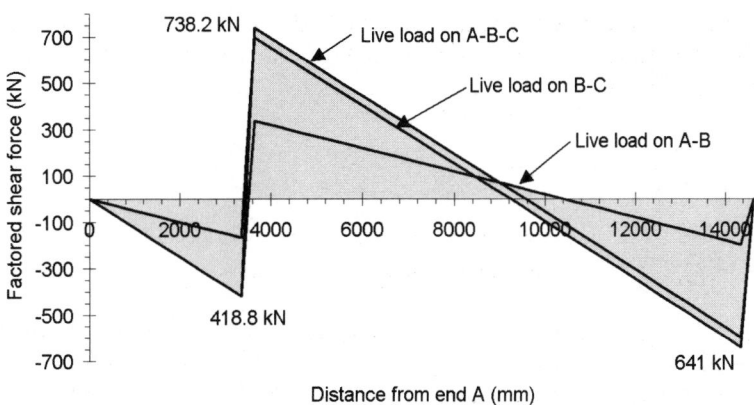

3.   *Design stirrups*

As the overall thickness of this beam is greater than 750 mm, Clause 11.2.8.1(b) requires that at least minimum shear reinforcement is required at all sections throughout the total length of the beam.

Although the stirrups can be designed section-by-section, the stirrups are usually placed in bands, in which the spacing is uniform. It is therefore only necessary to design the stirrups for a relatively small number of sections.   The spacing of the stirrups will be chosen using the procedure described in the Explanatory Notes to the code in N11.3.7.   This requires calculating the quantity A_v/s for a small number of sections along the span. As the location with maximum shear usually controls, this will be done first.

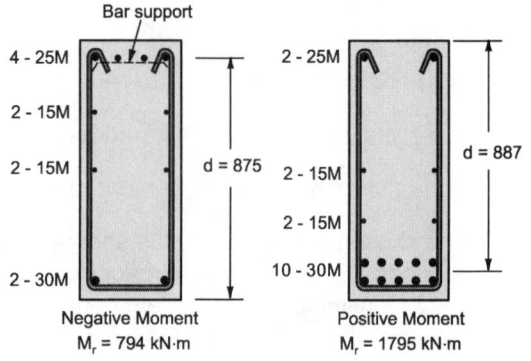

a)   Section in main span which is d_v from face of support B.

As the moment at the support is negative, d_v will be calculated using the value of d for negative moments, thus $d_v = 0.9 \cdot 875 = 788$ mm. At the critical shear location, which is 788 mm from the support face, $V_f = 738 - 0.788 \cdot 125 = 640$ kN. The maximum shear force that can be resisted by this member is:

$$V_{r,max} = 0.25\phi_c f'_c\, b_w d_v = 0.25 \cdot 0.65 \cdot 25 \cdot 400 \cdot 788 = 1281 \text{ kN}$$

Hence the section size is adequate and the shear is just low enough that the maximum permitted stirrup spacing (Clause 11.3.8.3) will be smaller of $0.7d_v = 552$ mm, or 600 mm.

At the critical shear location the moment and shear are both high and for such cases, the simplified method will usually produce similar results to the general method and as it is easier to apply, this is the method that will be used for this example. As noted in Eq. 4-5 of the introduction to this chapter for the simplified method:

$$V_r = 0.18 \cdot \phi_c \lambda \sqrt{f'_c} \cdot b_w d_v + 1.43\phi_s \frac{A_v}{s} f_y d_v$$

Because $V_r \geq V_f = 640$ kN:

$$640 \cdot 10^3 \leq 0.18 \cdot 0.65 \cdot 1\sqrt{25} \cdot 400 \cdot 788 + 1.43 \cdot 0.85 \frac{A_v}{s} 400 \cdot 788 \qquad \text{Hence:}$$

$$\frac{A_v}{s} \geq 1.189 \text{ mm}^2/\text{mm}$$

b)   Section 0.2L from centre of support B in main span.

This point is 2.2 metres from the centre of support A, or 2.05 metres from the face. At this location, the maximum shear will be $738 - 2.05 \cdot 125 = 482$ kN. At this location, the significant flexural moments will cause tension on the bottom face and hence $d_v = 0.9 \cdot 887 = 798$ mm. The quantity of stirrups required at this location is given by:

$$482\text{x}10^3 \le 0.18 \cdot 0.65 \cdot 1\sqrt{25} \cdot 400 \cdot 798 + 1.43 \cdot 0.85 \frac{A_v}{s} 400 \cdot 798 \qquad \text{Hence}$$

$$\frac{A_v}{s} \ge 0.761\,\text{mm}^2/\text{mm}$$

The results for other locations are summarized in the table below.

Span	Location	d_v	Distance from A (mm)	Envelope Shear Force (kN)	V_c (kN)	A_v/s required (mm²/mm)
Cantilever	d_v from B	788	2562	320	184	0.355
Main span	d_v from B	788	4438	640	184	1.188
"	0.2 L	798	5700	482	187	0.760
"	0.3 L	798	6800	344	187	0.406
"	0.8 L	798	12300	385	187	0.510
"	d_v from C	798	13552	541	187	0.914

The required amount of stirrups, A_v/s, for the locations calculated are plotted in figure below. Also plotted is the A_v/s value required to provide the minimum amount of stirrups and the amount provided by 10M stirrups at the maximum allowable spacing. A stirrup layout that satisfies the required amount of A_v/s is also shown. Note that in plotting the line representing the provided A_v/s, use is made of Clause 11.3.7 which allows the value of A_v/s to vary linearly over a length h at locations where the stirrup spacing changes.

4   *Check tensile capacity of longitudinal reinforcement at end support*

From Clause 11.3.9.5, the longitudinal reinforcement on the flexural tension side of the member at end support C must be capable of resisting a tensile force, F_{lt}, given by

$$F_{lt} = (V_f - 0.5V_s)\cot\theta$$

$$= \left(541 \cdot 10^3 - 0.5 \cdot 0.85 \cdot \frac{200 \cdot 400}{200} \cdot 798 \cdot \cot 35° \right)\cot 35° = 496\,\text{kN}$$

for 30M bars in regions with stirrups, the development length from Table 12-1 is

$$\ell_d = 0.45 k_1 k_2 k_3 k_4 \frac{f_y}{\sqrt{f'_c}} d_b = 0.45 \cdot 1 \cdot 1 \cdot 1 \cdot 1 \frac{400}{\sqrt{25}} 30 = 1080\,\text{mm}$$

Assume that 6 of the 30M bottom bars will continue into support C with the pattern shown in the figure below. On the flexural tension side of the member, the area of longitudinal reinforcement A_s will be $6 \cdot 700 + 3 \cdot 200 = 4800$ mm² and the centroid of this reinforcement will be 115 mm from the bottom face. Allowing for 40 mm of cover at the end of the beam, the length available for developing tension is 424 mm. Thus the maximum factored tensile force which can be resisted at this location is

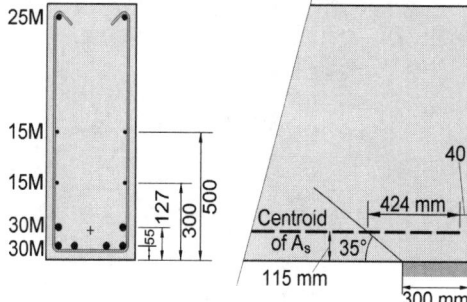

$$4800 \cdot 0.85 \cdot 400 \cdot 424/1080 = 641\,\text{kN}$$

As 641 > 496, Clause 11.3.9.5 is satisfied.

5   *Choose bar cut-off locations*

Shear causes additional tension in the longitudinal reinforcement which influences the locations where the area of longitudinal reinforcement can be reduced.   Clause 11.3.9.1 permits this effect to be accounted for by extending the bars a distance of $d_v\cot\theta$ beyond the location where they bars could be cut-off if only the tension due to flexure was considered.The factored moment resistance of the section with 6-30M bottom bars is 1285 kN·m. If the bending moment diagram shown is examined, it will be found that the applied factored moment in span BC exceeds 1285 kN·m at sections which are between 6520 mm and about 11920 mm from end A.   Hence if only tension due to flexure is considered, the 4 additional 30M bars would only need to be provided between these two locations.   That is, the 4 bars would be about 5400 mm long. Note that even when the development length of these bars is accounted for, they will provide a factored moment resistance which will exceed the applied factored moment at all sections (dashed line on figure).   However to account for the additional tensions caused by the shear forces, the four additional bars must be extended a distance of $d_v \cot\theta$ = 798 cot 35° = 1140 mm. Thus the 4 bars must be (5400 + 2 · 1140) = 7680 mm long and extend from 5380 mm from A to 13060 mm from A. Four more of the 30M bottom bars can be cut off $d_v\cot\theta$ beyond the point where the applied factored moments drops below 577 kN·m which is the factored moment resistance of the section containing two 30M bars near the bottom face and the four 15M "skin reinforcing" bars.   While it is calculated that these 4 - 30M bars could be cut-off 120 mm from the face of support B, they will be extended the extra short distance into the support. For the 25M top bars, ℓ_d =1170 mm and because the negative moment reduces quickly with distance away from support B, this development length controls the location where two of the four 25M bars can be cut off to meet the flexural demand alone.   The bars must then be extended $d_v \cot\theta$ = 788 cot 35° = 1125 mm beyond the flexural cut-off locations. The length of the two additional 25M bars centred on support B is 2·(1170+1125) = 4590 mm.

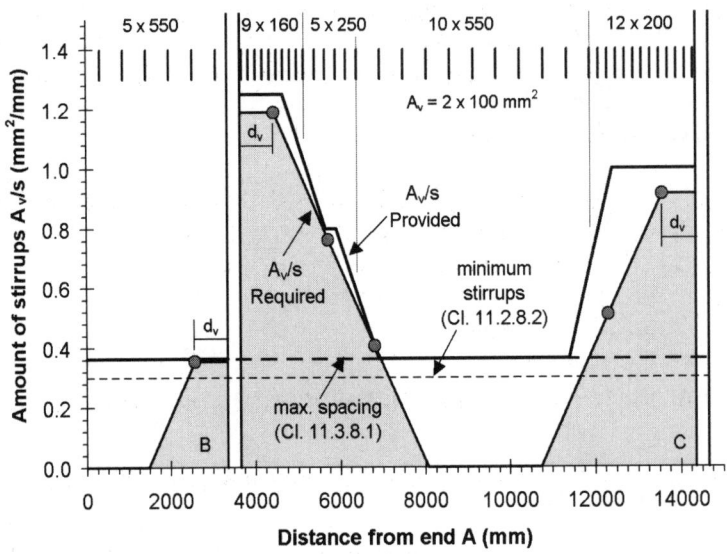

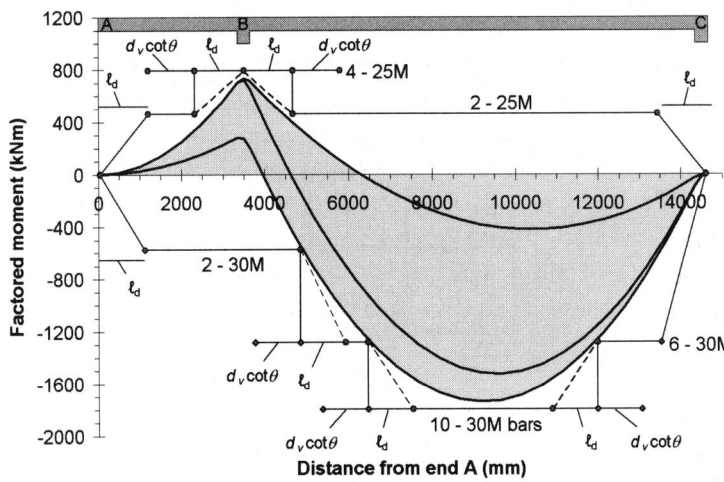

6   Summarize design

The figure shows the final design of the beam. The bars with cutoffs are drawn on different layers for clarity.

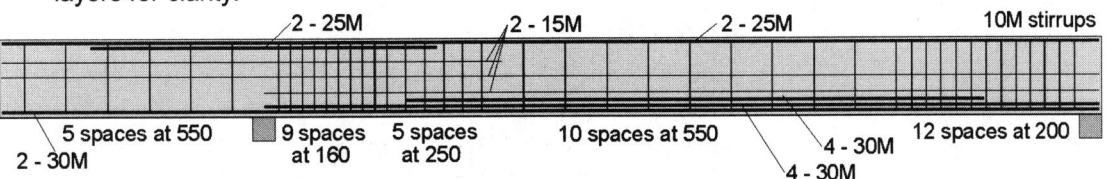

Example 4.4   Design Of Column For Shear

The ties in the ground storey columns of a high-rise building have been dimensioned to satisfy the column detailing requirements of Clause 7.6.5. Under wind loading, the leeward exterior columns are subjected to compression and the windward exterior columns are subjected to a tension. The two loading cases and the details of these columns are shown below. Check if the tie reinforcement is adequate for shear and if necessary, adjust the tie spacing.

1.   *Determine factored loads at critical section.*

For columns with a regular array of longitudinal steel A_s is the area of the bars in one-half of the column cross section. Hence, $A_s = 6 \cdot 1000 = 6000$ mm^2 and the centroid of these 6 bars is located at a distance x from the tension face, where

$$x = \frac{70 \cdot 4000 + 223 \cdot 2000}{6000} = 121\,\text{mm}$$

Therefore, d = 600 - 121 = 479 mm, and the effective shear depth $d_v = 0.9d = 0.9 \cdot 479 = 431$ mm.

At the critical section, d_v from the ends of the column, the factored loads are:

a)   Case I V_f = 522 kN N_f = -2000 kN M_f = 900 – 522 · 0.431 = 675 kN·m

b)   Case II V_f = 420 kN N_f = +300 kN M_f = 725 – 420 · 0.431 = 544 kN·m

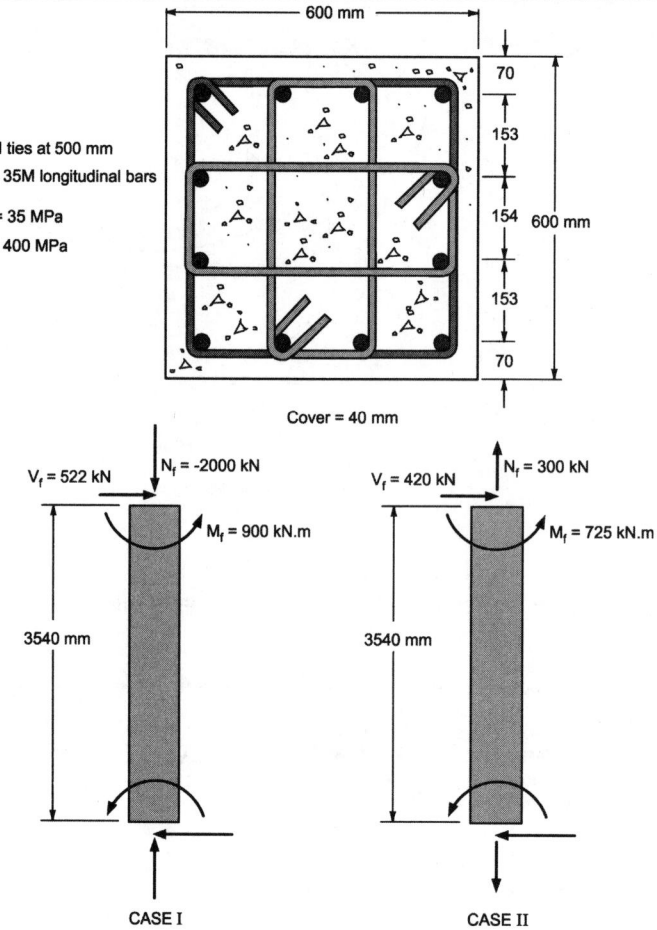

Cover = 40 mm

CASE I   CASE II

2.   *Determine required tie spacing for Case I.*

For this member, subjected to an axial force of -2000 kN, the longitudinal strain, ε_x, from Clause 11.3.6.4 is:

$$\varepsilon_x = \frac{M_f / d_v + 0.5N_f + V_f}{2A_sE_s} = \frac{675 \cdot 10^6 / 431 + 0.5 \cdot (-2000 \cdot 10^3) + 522 \cdot 10^3}{2 \cdot 200000 \cdot 6000} = 0.453 \cdot 10^{-3}$$

As this column will contain at least minimum ties, s_{ze} = 300 mm and substituting this into Eq 11-11 gives:

$$\beta = \frac{0.4}{1 + 1500\varepsilon_x} \cdot \frac{1300}{(1000 + s_{ze})} = \frac{0.4}{1 + 1500 \cdot 0.453 \cdot 10^{-3}} \cdot \frac{1300}{(1000 + 300)} = 0.238$$

Substitution into Eq. 11-12 produces:

$$\theta = 29° + 7000\varepsilon_x = 29° + 7000 \cdot 0.453 \cdot 10^{-3} = 32.2°$$

Thus from Eq. 11-6

$$V_c = \phi_c \lambda \beta \sqrt{f_c'} b_w d_v = 0.65 \cdot 1.0 \cdot 0.238 \cdot \sqrt{35} \cdot 600 \cdot 431 = 237 \text{ kN}$$

The shear to be carried by the ties is equal to V_s = 522 - 237 = 285 kN. From Eq. 11-7 the required spacing is:

$$s \leq \frac{\phi_s A_v f_y d_v \cot\theta}{V_s} = \frac{0.85 \cdot 4 \cdot 100 \cdot 400 \cdot 431 \cdot \cot 32.2°}{285 \cdot 10^3} \leq 327 \text{ mm}$$

3. *Determine required tie spacing for Case II.*

With an axial tension of 300 kN, ε_x is equal to:

$$\varepsilon_x = \frac{544 \cdot 10^6 / 431 + 0.5 \cdot (+300 \cdot 10^3) + 420 \cdot 10^3}{2 \cdot 200000 \cdot 6000} = 0.763 \cdot 10^{-3}$$

With s_{ze} = 300 mm:

$$\beta = \frac{0.4}{1 + 1500 \cdot 0.763 \cdot 10^{-3}} \cdot \frac{1300}{(1000 + 300)} = 0.186$$

and: $\theta = 29° + 7000\varepsilon_x = 29° + 7000 \cdot 0.763 \cdot 10^{-3} = 34.3°$

$$V_c = \phi_c \lambda \beta \sqrt{f'_c} b_w d_v = 0.65 \cdot 1.0 \cdot 0.186 \cdot \sqrt{35} \cdot 600 \cdot 431 \cdot 10^{-3} = 185 \text{ kN}$$

The shear to be carried by the ties is thus equal to V_s = 420-185 = 235 kN. Hence

$$s \leq \frac{0.85 \cdot 4 \cdot 100 \cdot 400 \cdot 431 \cdot \cot 34.3°}{235 \cdot 10^3} \leq 366 \text{ mm}$$

Note that the load case with high axial compression and high shear is more critical than the load case with axial tension and shear.

4. *Check maximum spacing requirements.*

Clause 11.3.8.3 reduces the maximum stirrup spacing by one-half if:

$$V_f > 0.125 \lambda \phi_c f'_c \cdot b_w d_v = 0.125 \cdot 1.0 \cdot 0.65 \cdot 35 \cdot 600 \cdot 431 = 735 \text{ kN}$$

As the maximum applied shear is less than this value, the maximum tie spacing is from Clause 11.3.8.1 as 600 mm or $0.7 d_v$ = 0.7·431 = 302 mm.
The minimum amount of shear reinforcement from Clause 11.2.8.2 requires a spacing of

$$s \leq \frac{A_v f_y}{0.06 \sqrt{f'_c} \cdot b_w} = \frac{4 \cdot 100 \cdot 400}{0.06 \sqrt{35} \cdot 600} \leq 751 \text{ mm}$$

5. *Final choice of tie spacing*

The tie spacing is governed by the maximum spacing for shear reinforcement. Thus use a tie spacing of 300 mm.

4

Shear and Torsion

Example 4.5 Design Of Spandrel Beam Supporting Balcony Slab

The balcony slab shown below is subjected to a specified live load of 3 kN/m². Design the longitudinal and transverse reinforcement required in the spandrel beam. Assume the beam is fully fixed against rotation at the column faces. Note that in this example the torsion is required for equilibrium and hence it is not a function of the torsional stiffness of the spandrel beam.

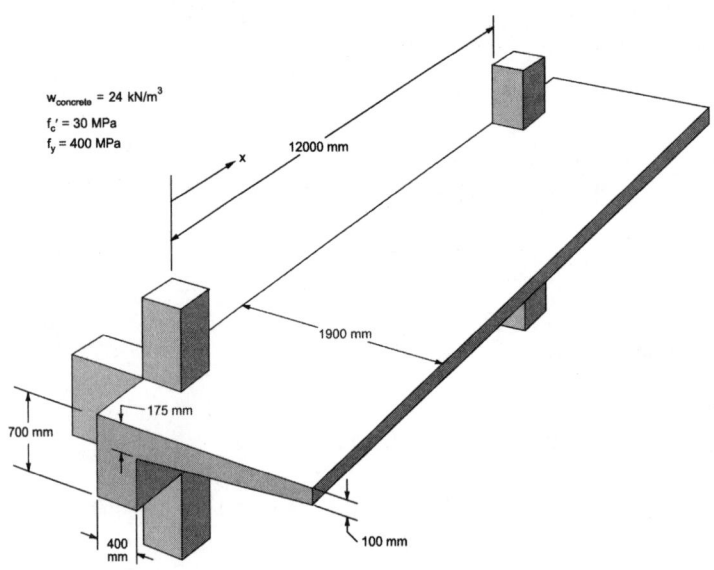

1. *Determine loads acting on spandrel beam.*

   Take a 1 m length of slab and beam.

   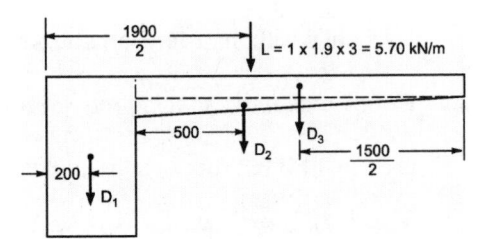

   $$w_f = 1.25D + 1.50L$$
   $$= 1.25 \cdot (6.72 + 1.35 + 3.60)$$
   $$+ 1.50 \cdot 5.70$$
   $$= 23.14 \text{ kN/m}$$
   $$D_1 = 0.4 \cdot 0.7 \cdot 24 = 6.72 \text{ kN/m}$$
   $$D_2 = 0.5 \cdot 1.5 \cdot 0.075 \cdot 24 = 1.35 \text{ kN/m}$$
   $$D_3 = 1.5 \cdot 0.10 \cdot 24 = 3.60 \text{ kN/m}$$
   $$m_f = 1.25 \cdot [1.35 \cdot (0.20 + 0.50) + 3.60 \cdot (0.2 + 0.75)]$$
   $$+ 1.50 \cdot 5.70 \cdot (0.95 - 0.20)$$
   $$= 11.87 \text{ kN/m}$$

2. *Determine M_f, T_f, V_f along spandrel.*

   See figure on next page

3. *Check if torsion significant.*

   From Clause 11.2.9.1

   $$T_{cr} = (A_c^2 / p_c) \cdot 0.38\lambda\phi_c \sqrt{f_c'} = \frac{(400 \cdot 700)^2}{2 \cdot (400 + 700)} 0.38 \cdot 1.0 \cdot 0.65 \cdot \sqrt{30} \cdot 10^{-6} = 48.2 \text{ kNm}$$

   At $T_f > 0.25T_{cr}$, torsion must be considered.

4. *Determine section parameters b_w, d_v, A_{oh}, p_h.*

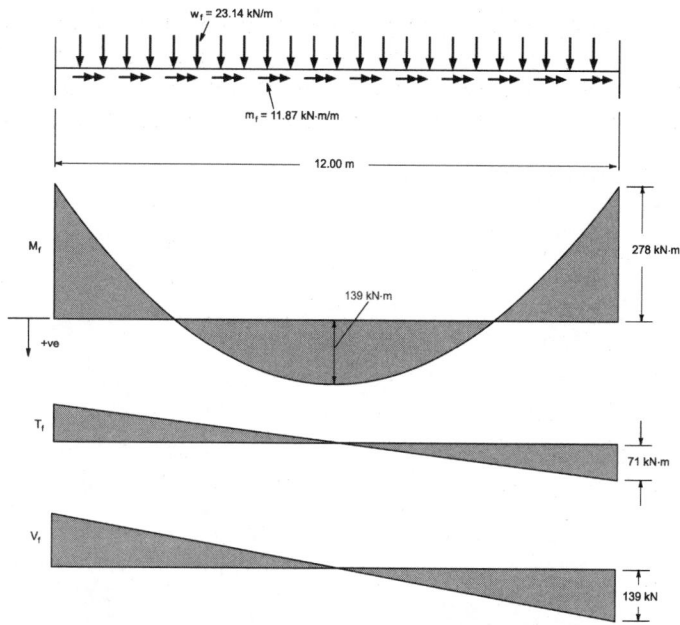

Assume cover = 40 mm and 25M longitudinal bars will be used.

b_w = 400 mm

d = 700 − 40 − 10 − 25/2 = 637.5 mm

d_v = 0.9d = 0.9·637.5 = 574 mm A_{oh} = 310·610 = 189·10³

p_h = 2·(310+610) = 1840 mm

5. *Design of closed stirrups near support*

At critical section d_v from the face of the support

$$V_f = 139 - 23.14 \cdot 0.574 = 125.7 \text{ kN}$$

$$T_f = 71 - 11.87 \cdot 0.574 = 64.2 \text{ kN}$$

$$M_f = -278 + \left(\frac{139 + 125.7}{2}\right)0.574$$

$$= -202 \text{ kNm}$$

The maximum shear stress limit is checked by Eq. 11-19.

$$\sqrt{\left(\frac{V_f}{b_w d_v}\right)^2 + \left(\frac{T_f p_h}{1.7 A_{oh}^{\ 2}}\right)^2} \le 0.25\lambda\phi_c f'_c$$

$$\sqrt{\left(\frac{125.7 \cdot 10^3}{400 \cdot 574}\right)^2 + \left(\frac{64.2 \cdot 10^6 \cdot 1840}{1.7 \cdot \left(189 \cdot 10^3\right)^2}\right)^2} \le 0.25 \cdot 1.0 \cdot 0.65 \cdot 30$$

$$\sqrt{\left(0.547\right)^2 + \left(1.945\right)^2} \le 4.88$$

$$2.02 \le 4.88 \text{ MPa}$$

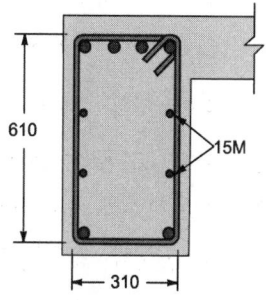

Since this equation is satisfied, the cross section is large enough to carry the combined shear and torsion.

Design the member with the simplified method whereby $\beta = 0.18$ and $\theta = 35°$ by Clause 11.3.6.3.

The shear carried by the concrete is:

$$V_c = \phi_c \lambda \beta \sqrt{f'_c} b_w d_v = 0.65 \cdot 1.0 \cdot 0.18 \cdot \sqrt{30} \cdot 400 \cdot 574 \cdot 10^{-3} = 147.1 \text{ kN}$$

As $V_c > V_f$, no stirrups are required to resist the shear in this beam. Had they been required, the parameter A_v/s would have been calculated by Clause 11.3.5 to provide the required stirrup area for shear.

The amount of closed stirrups required for torsion, from Eq. 11-17, is:

$$\frac{A_t}{s} = \frac{T_r}{2A_o \phi_s f_y \cot\theta}$$

where $A_o = 0.85 A_{oh}$. Hence:

$$\frac{A_t}{s} = \frac{64.2 \cdot 10^6}{2 \cdot 0.85 \cdot 189 \cdot 10^3 \cdot 0.85 \cdot 400 \cdot \cot 35°} = 0.412 \text{ mm}^2/\text{mm}$$

Thus while for this example stirrups are not needed for shear, they are required for resisting the applied torsion. According to Clause 11.3.10.1, the transverse reinforcement required shall be equal to the sum of that required for shear and the coexisting torsion, See Figure N11.3.10.1 in the explanatory notes. Recognizing that the term A_v is the area of two stirrup legs and A_t is the area of a single leg, the required spacing of the 10M closed stirrups can be found from:

$$\frac{A_t}{s} + 0.5 \frac{A_v}{s} = 0.412 + 0.5 \cdot 0.0 = 0.412 \text{ mm}^2/\text{mm}$$

Hence: 　　$$s \le \frac{100}{0.412} = 243 \text{ mm}$$

Clause 11.3.8.3 states that for all sections where $T_f > 0.25 T_{cr}$ the spacing of transverse reinforcement shall not exceed 300 mm nor $0.35 d_v = 0.35 \cdot 574 = 201$ mm.

The maximum spacing required to satisfy the minimum transverse reinforcement requirements of Clause 11.2.8.2 is:

$$s \le \frac{A_v f_y}{0.06\sqrt{f'_c} \cdot b_w} = \frac{2 \cdot 100 \cdot 400}{0.06\sqrt{30} \cdot 400} \le 609 \text{ mm}$$

Therefore provide closed 10M stirrups at a spacing of 200 mm at this location.

6. *Determine where stirrups are no longer required*

From step 5 it is clear that the stirrup spacing in this example is controlled by the maximum spacing of a 10M closed stirrup in a region where $T_f < 0.25\ T_{cr}$. To allow wider stirrup spacing, determine where this condition no longer applies. That is, determine where the following is true:

$$T_f = 0.25 T_{cr} = 0.25 \cdot 48.2 = 12.1 \text{ kN·m}$$

From the applied torsion diagram, this can be seen to occur 5.1 metres from the face of the support. As stirrups are not required for the applied shear force even d_v from the supports where the applied shear force is the highest, the stirrups are not required for a 2 m length near midspan.

4

7. *Design of longitudinal reinforcement at support face*

Torsion will increase the need for longitudinal reinforcement, even at sections of maximum moment. Torsion is resisted by diagonal compressive stresses that spiral around all faces of the section, which increases the demand for tensile capacity in the longitudinal reinforcement. In addition, the support reactions resisting torsion do not introduce direct compression into the flexural compression face of the member.

At the support face:

$$V_f = 139 \text{ kN} \qquad\qquad T_f = 71 \text{ kN·m} \qquad\qquad M_f = 278 \text{ kN·m}$$

From Clauses 11.3.9.2 and 11.3.10.6, the required tension force in the longitudinal reinforcement on the flexural tension side is:

$$F_{lt} = \frac{M_f}{d_v} + \cot\theta \sqrt{(V_f - 0.5V_s)^2 + \left(\frac{0.45 p_h T_f}{2A_o}\right)^2}$$

$$= \frac{278 \cdot 10^6}{574} + \cot 35° \sqrt{(139 \cdot 10^3 - 0.5 \cdot 0.0)^2 + \left(\frac{0.45 \cdot 1840 \cdot 71 \cdot 10^6}{2 \cdot 189 \cdot 10^3}\right)^2}$$

$$= 484 \cdot 10^3 + 297.9 \cdot 10^3 = 782 \text{ kN}$$

Therefore the required area of the fully developed longitudinal reinforcement in the top half of the beam is

$$A_s \geq \frac{782 \cdot 10^3}{0.85 \cdot 400} = 2300 \text{ mm}^2$$

With an overall depth of 700 mm, this spandrel beam is just below the size where longitudinal skin reinforcement is required for crack control by Clause 10.6.2. However, for such large beams subjected to torsion, it is good practice to provide some of the required longitudinal reinforcement as bars distributed down the sides. In this case use two intermediate layers each containing two 15M bars. Near the top face of the beam use 4-25M bars. Hence in the top half of the beam

$A_s = 4 \cdot 500 + 2 \cdot 200 = 2400 \text{ mm}^2$

At the bottom face of the beam, at the support, the compression from the flexure dominates and hence, we need only satisfy the requirements of Clause 12.11.1 that one-fourth of the bottom steel extend into the support.

In order to verify that the longitudinal reinforcement will yield, we will calculate the depth of compression, c, required to balance the total tensile force required, $T = 782$ kN. In calculating the stress block depth, a, the stress block factor $\alpha_1 = 0.85 - 0.0015 f'_c = 0.805$. Hence,

$$a = \frac{F_{lt}}{\alpha_1 \phi_c f'_c b} = \frac{782 \cdot 10^3}{0.805 \cdot 0.65 \cdot 30 \cdot 400} = 124 \text{ mm}$$

The stress block factor $\beta_1 = 0.97 - 0.0025 f'_c = 0.895$ and therefore the depth of compression, $c = a/\beta_1 = 124/0.895 = 139$ mm. The ratio $c/d = 139/637 = 0.218$ which is less than the yield limit given in Clause 10.5.2 as $700/(700 + f_y) = 0.636$. Therefore the longitudinal reinforcement will yield.

9   *Determine required reinforcement at point of contraflexure*

The point of contraflexure is located 2.54 m from the face of the support. At this location:

$$V_f = 80.2 \text{ kN} \qquad\qquad T_f = 41.0 \text{ kN·m} \qquad\qquad M_f = 0 \text{ kN·m}$$

The required tension force at this location is therefore:

$$F_{lc} = F_{lt} \geq \frac{0}{574} + \cot 35° \sqrt{\left(80.2 \cdot 10^3 - 0.5 \cdot 0.0\right)^2 + \left(\frac{0.45 \cdot 1840 \cdot 41 \cdot 10^6}{2 \cdot 189 \cdot 10^3}\right)^2} \geq 172.0 \text{ kN}$$

This tensile force is required for both the top and bottom halves of the beam, see Clause 11.3.9. The area of longitudinal reinforcement required for both the top and bottom halves of the beam is thus:

$$A_s \geq \frac{172.0 \cdot 10^3}{0.85 \cdot 400} = 506 \text{ mm}^2$$

Hence provide 2-25M bars, top and bottom, to support the stirrups, plus the 2-15M distributed bars in each half. Thus $A_s = 2 \cdot 500 + 2 \cdot 200 = 1400 \text{ mm}^2$.

Note that Clause 11.2.7 requires that the diameter of the longitudinal bars in the corners of the closed hoops required for torsion not be less than s/16 = 200/16 = 12.5 mm.

These bars will also satisfy the requirements of Clause 12.12.2 that at least one-third of the total tension reinforcement must extend beyond the point of inflection.

10   *Determined required longitudinal reinforcement at midspan*

At midspan the factored moment is 139 kN·m. We will estimate the required reinforcement assuming a lever arm of 0.9d = 574 mm. Hence, the required force is 139/0.574 = 242 kN and the required $A_s = 242 \cdot 10^3 / (0.85 \cdot 400) = 712 \text{ mm}^2$. Therefore use 2-25M bars. A check of the flexural capacity is carried out below.

$$a = \frac{\phi_s A_s f_y}{\alpha_1 \phi_c f'_c b} = \frac{0.85 \cdot 1000 \cdot 400}{0.805 \cdot 0.65 \cdot 30 \cdot 400} = 54 \text{ mm}$$

$$M_r = \phi_s A_s f_y (d - a/2) = 0.85 \cdot 1000 \cdot 400 \cdot (637 - 54/2) = 207 \text{ kNm} \geq M_f$$

$$c/d = \frac{(54/0.895)}{637} = 0.095 \leq 0.636$$

11   *Bar cut-off locations*

The figure shows the variations of required tensile force in the longitudinal reinforcement, as well as the factored resistance of the reinforcement provided. For this beam, with closed stirrups, the tensile development length for the bottom bars (from Table 12-1) is:

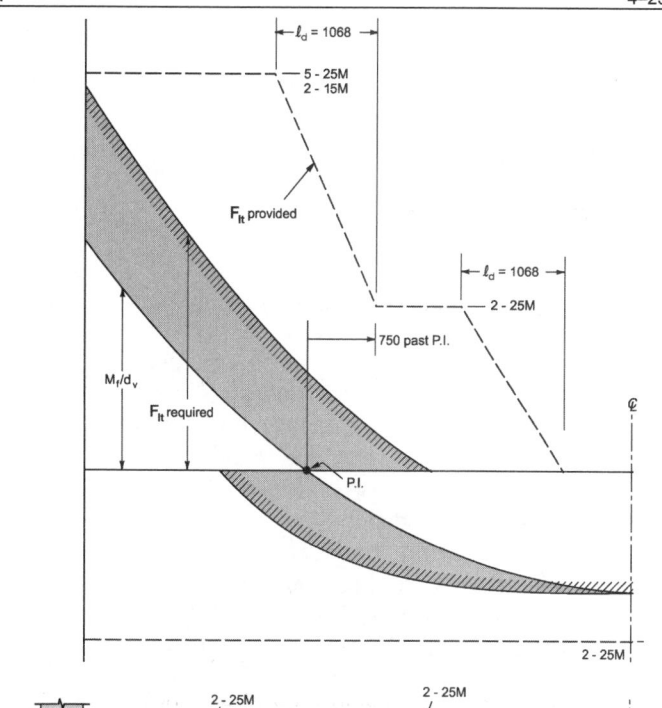

$$\ell_d = 0.45 k_1 k_2 k_3 k_4 \frac{f_y}{\sqrt{f'_c}} d_b$$

$$= 0.45 \cdot 1 \cdot 1 \cdot 1 \cdot 1 \frac{400}{\sqrt{30}} 25$$

$$= 822 \text{ mm}$$

For the top bars $\ell_d = 1.3 \cdot 822 = 1068$ mm.

The bar cut-offs are illustrated in the figure. In determining the factored tensile resistance of the steel, it has been assumed that the bar force varies linearly over the development length.

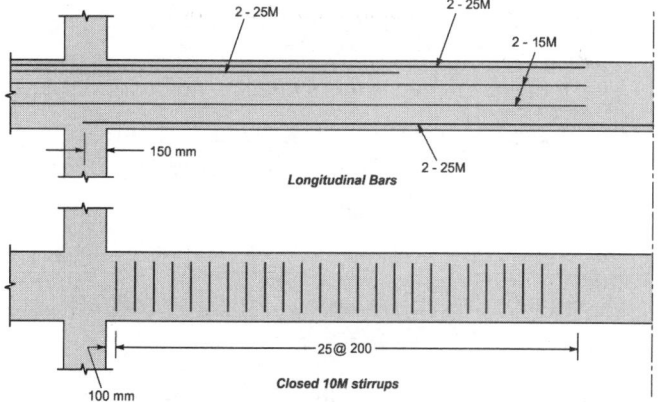

Example 4.6   Torsional Design Of Spandrel Beam In Two-Way Slab

The analysis of a two-way slab has resulted in a calculated factored moment at the edge of the slab of 17.57 kN·m/m. This moment causes torsions in the spandrel beam as shown in the figure. In addition, the spandrel beam has a factored moment, M_f, at the face of the column, of 135.3 kN·m, while the factored shear, d_v from the face of the column, is 83.5 kN.

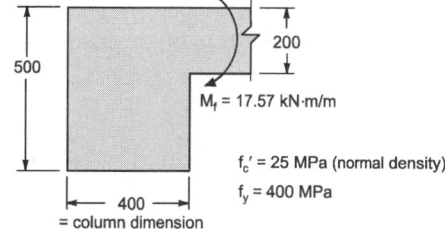

1.   *Determine torsions in spandrels having spans of 7500 mm*

2.   *Determine if torsion is significant*

The cracking torque, T_{cr}, from Clause 11.2.9.1 is:

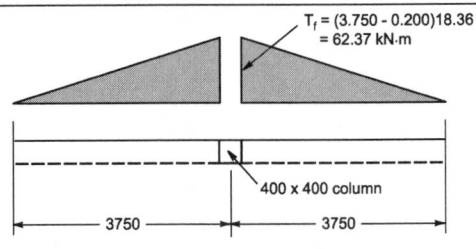

$$T_{cr} = \left(A_c^{\,2} / p_c\right) \cdot 0.38 \lambda \phi_c \sqrt{f_c'}$$

$$= \frac{(400 \cdot 500)^2}{2 \cdot (400 + 500)} 0.38 \cdot 1.0 \cdot 0.65 \cdot \sqrt{25} \cdot 10^{-6}$$

$$= 27.4 \text{ kNm}$$

Since T_f exceed $0.25T_{cr}$, torsion must be considered.

3. *Adjust torsion diagram to account for redistribution*

When a reinforced concrete beam cracks in torsion, there is a considerable loss of torsional stiffness. In statically indeterminate structures, where the magnitude of the torsion is a function of the torsional stiffness, considerable redistribution occurs after torsional cracking. Because of this, Clause 11.2.9.2 permits the maximum torsion at the face of the support to be reduced to $0.67T_{cr}$ provided that appropriate adjustments are made to the moments in adjoining members. The resulting torsions are illustrated in the figure below.

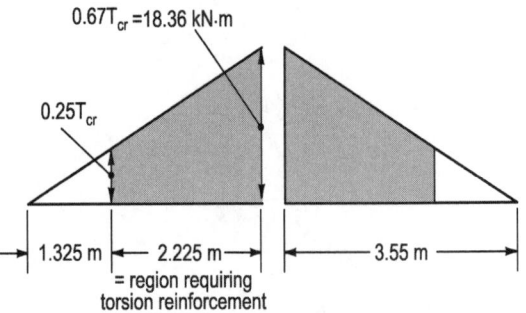

4. *Check if section size is adequate*

Determine required cross-sectional properties. Assuming 10M closed stirrups, 20M longitudinal bars, and a clear cover of 30 mm for interior exposure gives

$$d = 500 - 30 - 10 - 20/2 = 450 \text{ mm}$$

$$d_v = 0.9 \cdot 450 = 405 \text{ mm}$$

$$A_{oh} = (500 - 60 - 10)(400 - 60 - 10) = 141900 \text{ mm}^2$$

$$p_h = 2(430 + 330) = 1520 \text{ mm}$$

V_f at a distance d_v from the face of the support is 83.5 kN. T_f at d_v from the face of the support is:

$$T_f = \frac{(3.55 - 0.405)}{3.55} \cdot 18.36 = 16.27 \text{ kN·m}$$

Checking the maximum combined shear and torsion with Clause 11.10.4(b):

$$\sqrt{\left(\frac{V_f}{b_w d_v}\right)^2 + \left(\frac{T_f p_h}{1.7 A_{oh^2}}\right)^2} \le 0.25 \lambda \phi_c f_c'$$

$$\sqrt{\left(\frac{83.5 \cdot 10^3}{400 \cdot 405}\right)^2 + \left(\frac{16.27 \cdot 10^6 \cdot 1520}{1.7 \cdot (141900)^2}\right)^2} \le 0.25 \cdot 1.0 \cdot 0.65 \cdot 25$$

$$\sqrt{(0.515)^2 + (0.723)^2} \le 4.06$$

$$0.89 \le 4.88 \text{ MPa}$$

Therefore the section size is adequate.

5   *Design of transverse reinforcement for shear and torsion*

As this design will be performed with the simplified method, from Clause 11.3.6.3, $\beta = 0.18$, $\theta = 35°$. At the section d_v from the face of the support, the required amount of closed stirrups for torsion can be calculated from Clause 11.3.10.3 as:

$$\frac{A_t}{s} = \frac{T_r}{2A_o\phi_s f_y \cot\theta} = \frac{16.27 \cdot 10^6}{2 \cdot 0.85 \cdot 141900 \cdot 0.85 \cdot 400 \cdot \cot 35°} = 0.1389 \text{ mm}^2/\text{mm}$$

From Clause 11.3.5.1, the shear carried by the concrete, V_c, is:

$$V_c = \phi_c \lambda \beta \sqrt{f'_c} \cdot b_w d_v = 0.65 \cdot 1 \cdot 0.18 \cdot \sqrt{25} \cdot 400 \cdot 405 = 94.8 \text{ kN}$$

As V_f is less than V_c, no shear reinforcement is required to satisfy the strength requirement. Hence the total amount of closed stirrups required to provide the required shear and torsional strengths is:

$$\frac{A_t}{s} + 0.5\frac{A_v}{s} = 0.1389 + 0.5 \cdot 0.0 = 0.1389 \text{ mm}^2/\text{mm}$$

The required spacing of 10M closed stirrups is therefore 100/0.1389 = 720 mm.
Clause 11.2.8.1(c) requires that a minimum amount of transverse reinforcement be provided. The required spacing of 10M closed stirrups is:

$$s \le \frac{A_v f_y}{0.06\sqrt{f'_c} \cdot b_w} = \frac{2 \cdot 100 \cdot 400}{0.06\sqrt{25} \cdot 400} \le 667 \text{ mm}$$

As the factored torsion exceeds $0.25T_{cr}$, Clause 11.3.8.3 indicates that the maximum stirrup spacing shall not exceed 300 mm or $0.35d_v = 0.35 \cdot 405 = 142$ mm. Therefore provide stirrups at 140 mm.
According to Clause 11.2.9, no stirrups are required when the factored torque is less than $0.25T_{cr}$. This occurs at a distance of 2.225 m from the face of the column (see figure).

6   *Design of longitudinal reinforcement*

The factored moment at the face of the column $M_f = 135.3$ kN·m, $T_f = 18.36$ kN·m, and $V_f = 83.5$ kN. Checking the demand on the longitudinal reinforcement:

$$F_{lt} \ge \frac{M_f}{d_v} + \cot\theta\sqrt{(V_f - 0.5V_s)^2 + \left(\frac{0.45p_h T_f}{2A_o}\right)^2}$$

$$\ge \frac{135.3 \cdot 10^6}{405} + \cot 35°\sqrt{(83.5 \cdot 10^3 - 0.5 \cdot 0.0)^2 + \left(\frac{0.45 \cdot 1520 \cdot 18.36 \cdot 10^6}{2 \cdot 141900}\right)^2}$$

$$\ge 334 \cdot 10^3 + 140.5 \cdot 10^3$$

$$\ge 475 \text{ kN}$$

Thus the reinforcement on the flexural tension side must be able to resist a force of 475 kN. This requires an area of reinforcement of:

$$A_s \ge \frac{475 \cdot 10^3}{0.85 \cdot 400} = 1397 \text{ mm}^2$$

Hence use 3-25M as flexural tension reinforcement. From Clause 11.3.9.3 it can be determined that the flexural compression force is larger than the component due to torsion and shear. Provide 2-20M bars to anchor stirrup legs.

Note: The design of the spandrel beam assumed redistribution of moments after torsional cracking. This gives reduced torsions in the spandrel beam and therefore, the moments in the design strips perpendicular to the spandrel must be adjusted accordingly. That is, the end moments should be reduced and the positive moment increased.

Example 4.7   Design Of A Deep Beam Subjected To Uniform Load

Design the reinforcement for the laterally supported transfer girder shown below.

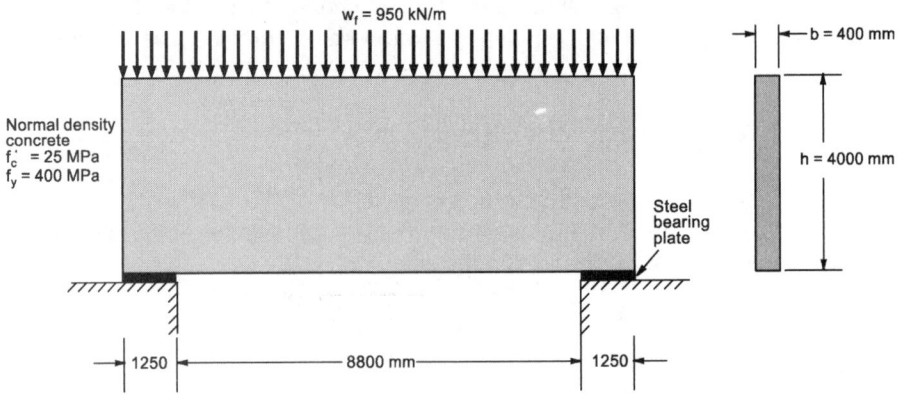

1.   *Idealize member by truss model*

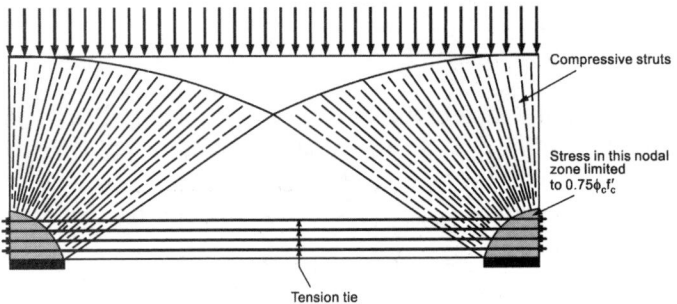

2.   *Check bearing stress.*

Support reaction = 950 · (4.4 + 1.25) = 5368 kN
Bearing stress = 5368 · 10³/(400 · 1250) = 10.74 MPa
Allowable bearing stress on nodal zone = 0.75 · 0.65 · 25 = 12.19 MPa
As 10.74 MPa < 12.19 MPa, bearing area is adequate.

3.   *Calculate required tension in tie of truss*

Consider free-body diagram shown. To limit stresses in the nodal zone the tension tie reinforcement must be distributed over a depth sufficient to produce an average stress of $0.75\phi_c\, f_c'$ by Clause 11.4.4.1(b). If the depth of the compression zone at mid-span is a, then since $C = T$, the depth over which the tie reinforcement is distributed is

$$\frac{0.85}{0.75}a = 1.13a$$

Therefore the lever arm $jd = h - a/2 - 1.13a/2 = h - 1.065a$. Equating the external moment with the internal moment, we have

$$5368 \cdot 10^3 \cdot (2.83 - 0.63) \cdot 10^3 = C \cdot j \cdot d = 0.85 \cdot 0.65 \cdot 25 \cdot a \cdot 400 \cdot (4000 - 1.065a)$$
$$\therefore a = 645 \text{ mm}$$

Hence: $C = T = 0.85 \cdot 0.65 \cdot 25 \cdot 400 \cdot 645 \cdot 10^{-3} = 3564 \text{ kN}$

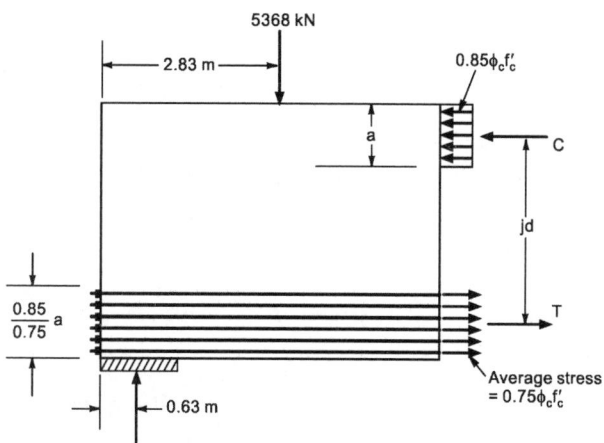

4.   *Choose reinforcement for tension tie*

Required area: $\phi_s A_s f_y = T = 3564 \text{ kN}$
Therefore: $A_s = 3564 \cdot 10^3/(0.85 \cdot 400) = 10480 \text{ mm}^2$

To satisfy Clause 11.4.4.2(b) this reinforcement must be distributed over a depth of $1.13 \cdot 645 = 729$ mm.

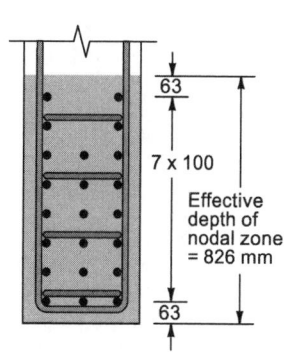

The distance over which this reinforcement must be developed is shown in the explanatory notes for the code in figure N11.4.3.2. In this case, 25M bars have been selected which are able to be developed within the nodal region.   Select 22 – 25M bars distributed as shown in the figure.

5.   *Calculate minimum shear reinforcement for crack control and ductility*

Using 2-leg 10M stirrups, $A_v = 2 \cdot 100 = 200 \text{ mm}^2$.
Required spacing of transverse reinforcement by Clause 11.4.5 is:

$$s \leq \frac{200}{0.002 \cdot 400} = 250 \text{ mm} \leq 300 \text{ mm}$$

Provide 10M U-stirrups at 250 mm.
To satisfy the minimum longitudinal requirements of Clause 11.4.5, provide pairs of 10M longitudinal bars at 250 mm centres.

6.   *Summarize design*

To provide some restraint against possible vertical splitting at the ends of the beam, 10M horizontal U-bars have been added as shown.

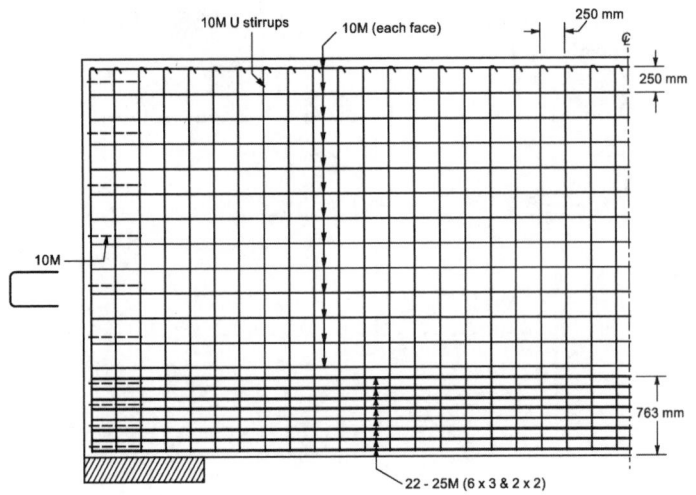

Example 4.8   Design Of A Deep Beam Subjected To A Concentrated Load

Design the reinforcement for the laterally supported transfer girder shown below. Use f'_c = 25 MPa and f_y = 400 MPa.

1.   *Check bearing stresses at supports and loading points*

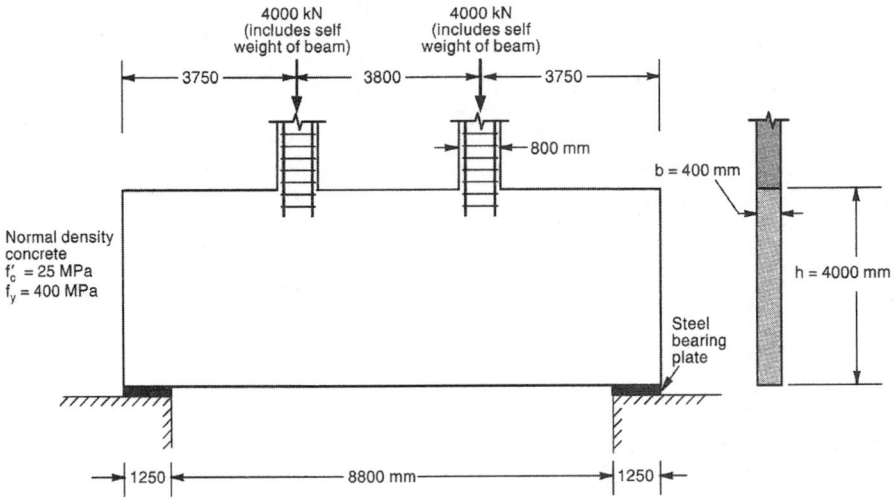

Support reaction = 4000 kN

Bearing stress:

= 4000 · 1000/(400 · 1250)

= 8.00 MPa

Allowable bearing stress:

$= 0.75 \cdot 0.65 \cdot 25$

$= 12.19$ MPa

(Clause 11.4.4.1(b) tension tie present)

Bearing stress < Allowable   O.K.

Bearing stress at loading point $= 4000 \cdot 1000 \cdot (400 \cdot 800) = 12.50$ MPa

Allowable bearing stress $= 0.85 \cdot 0.65 \cdot 25 = 13.81$ MPa   (Clause 11.4.4.1(a))

Bearing stress < Allowable   O.K.

2. *Calculate required tension in tie of truss*

Due to the presence of the tension tie, the maximum nodal zone stress at the support is $0.75\phi_c\, f'_c$ by Clause 11.4.4.1(b). Since $C = T$, the depth over which the tie reinforcement is distributed is

$$\frac{0.85}{0.75}a = 1.13a$$

Therefore the lever arm $jd = h - a/2 - 1.13a/2 = h - 1.065a$. Equating the external moment with the internal moment, we have

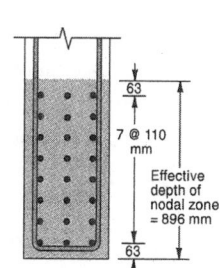

$4000 \cdot 10^3 \cdot 3215 = C \cdot j \cdot d$

$= 0.85 \cdot 0.65 \cdot 25 \cdot a \cdot 400 \cdot (4000 - 1.065a)$

$\therefore a = 720$ mm

Hence:

$C = T = 0.85 \cdot 0.65 \cdot 25 \cdot 400 \cdot 720 \cdot 10^{-3} = 3978$ kN

3. *Choose reinforcement for tension tie*

Required area

$$A_s \geq \frac{3978 \cdot 10^3}{0.85 \cdot 400} = 11700 \text{ mm}^2$$

Provide 24 - 25M bars, $A_s = 24 \cdot 500 = 12000$ mm^2. The minimum size over which to distribute this steel is $1.13 \cdot 720 = 814$ mm. If the 24 bars are placed in 8 layers of 3 bars, as shown in the figure, the effective nodal zone depth will be 896 mm. As the tension tie depth is somewhat greater than assumed, the lever arm will be somewhat reduced.

$jd = 4000 - 0.5 \cdot 720 - 0.5 \cdot 896 = 3192$ mm

Required tie force $= 4000 \cdot 3125 / 3192 = 3916$ kN. This causes a stress in the tie of

$$= \frac{3916 \cdot 10^3}{24 \cdot 500} = 326 \text{ MPa} \quad \leq \phi_s f_y = 0.85 \cdot 400 = 340 \text{ MPa} \qquad \text{OK}$$

As the development length for 25M bars is 900 mm, the tensile tie can be transferred to the nodal zone within the 1250 mm bearing length.

4.   *Sketch idealized truss model*

The idealized truss model is shown in the figure below.

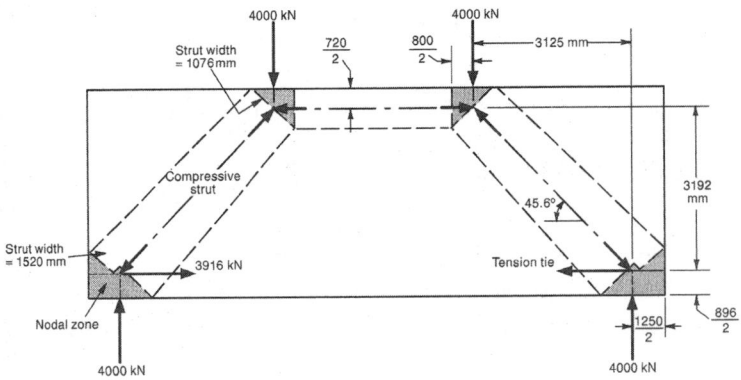

5.   *Check for compressive strut crushing*

The force in the strut is 4000/sin 45.6° = 5598 kN
At the top of the strut the compressive stress is

$$f_2 = \frac{5598 \cdot 10^3}{400 \cdot 1075} = 13.01 \, \text{MPa}$$

Since no tension ties cross the strut in this region (i.e., ε_1 is about zero) the permissible compressive stress near the top of the strut is calculated by Clause 11.4.2.3 as

$$\phi_c f_{cu} = \phi_c 0.85 f_c' = 0.65 \cdot 0.85 \cdot 25 = 13.8 \, \text{MPa}$$

Since $f_2 < \phi_c f_{cu}$, the compressive stresses at the top of the strut are acceptable.
At the bottom of the strut the stress in the strut is

$$f_2 = \frac{5598 \cdot 10^3}{400 \cdot 1520} = 9.21 \, \text{MPa}$$

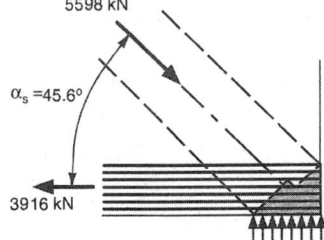

The compressive strut in this region is crossed by a tension tie and therefore the limiting stress, f_{cu} is reduced. Since the tie reinforcing bars are being developed in this region, assume an average strain, ε_s, in the tension tie at the centre of the strut to be equal to one half of the yield strain or 0.001. Thus the principal tensile strain from Eq. 11-23 is

$$\varepsilon_1 = \varepsilon_s + (\varepsilon_s + 0.002)\cot^2 \theta_s = 0.001 + (0.001 + 0.002)\cot^2 45.6° = 0.00388$$

And the limiting stress in the strut from Eq. 11-22 is therefore

$$\phi_c f_{cu} = \frac{\phi_c f_c'}{0.8 + 170\varepsilon_1} = \frac{0.65 \cdot 25}{0.8 + 170 \cdot 0.00388} = 11.1 \, \text{MPa}$$

As $f_2 < \phi_c f_{cu}$, the compressive stresses at the bottom of the strut are also acceptable.

6.   *Calculate minimum shear reinforcement required for crack control and ductility*

Using 10M U-stirrups, $A_v = 2 \cdot 100 = 200$ mm^2
Required spacing of transverse reinforcement by Clause 11.4.5 is:

$$s \le \frac{200}{0.002 \cdot 400} = 250 \text{ mm} \quad \le 300 \text{ mm}$$

Provide 10M U-stirrups at 250 mm.
To satisfy the minimum longitudinal requirements of Clause 11.4.5, provide pairs of 10M longitudinal bars at 250 mm centres.

7.   *Summarize design*

To provide some restraint against vertical splitting at the ends of the beam, 10M horizontal U-bars have been added as shown.

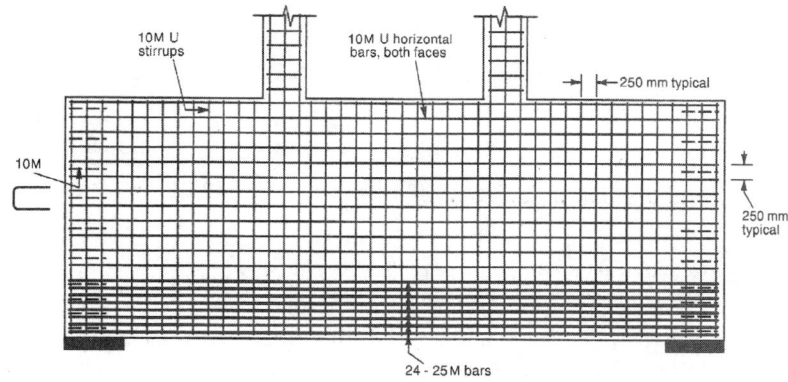

Example 4.9   Design Of Corbel For Exterior Column

As shown in the figure, a corbel projecting from a 350 mm x 350 mm column supports a precast girder. The corbel is subjected to a vertical specified dead load of 80 kN and a vertical specified live load of 100 kN. Calculations indicate that due to restraint of beam creep and shrinkage deformations, a horizontal force of 35 kN will develop. Design the corbel assuming $f_c' = 35$ MPa and $f_y = 300$ MPa.

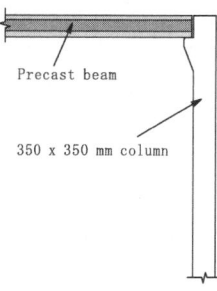

1.   *Determine factored loads.*

Vertical factored load:

$$V_f = \alpha_D D + \alpha_L L = 1.25 \cdot 80 + 1.5 \cdot 100 = 250 \text{ kN}$$

Horizontal factored load:

$$N_f = \alpha_T T = 1.25 \cdot 35 = 44 \text{ kN} \ge 0.2 V_f = 50 \text{ kN}$$

The second limitation is specified in Clause 11.64 and, in this case, controls so $N_f = 50$ kN.

2.   *Determining bearing plate dimensions*

Assume that bearing plate extends across a width of 350 - (2 40) = 270 mm. By Clause 11.44.1(b), the minimum width of the bearing plate is

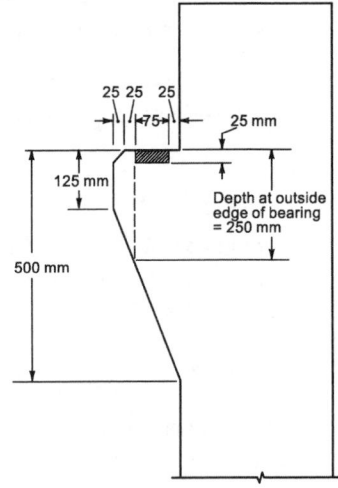

$$= \frac{V_f}{0.75 \cdot \phi_c \cdot f'_c \cdot b} = \frac{250 \cdot 10^3}{0.75 \cdot 0.65 \cdot 35 \cdot 270} = 54 \text{ mm}$$

Therefore, use a 270 x 75 x 25 mm bearing plate.

3. *Choose corbel dimensions*

    Choose an overall corbel depth at column face of 500 mm. If required reinforcement with this depth turns out to be excessive, this dimension may have to be increased.
    Choose the depth at the free end of the corbel to ensure that the depth at the outside of the bearing area is at least 0.5 x 500 mm = 250 mm to satisfy Clause 11.6.3.
    The external dimensions chosen for the corbel are summarized in the figure below.

4. *Determine geometry of strut-and-tie model*

    To allow for load eccentricities and erection tolerances, consider the vertical load to be placed 25 mm towards edge of corbel from centre of bearing plate. See Clause 16.4.4.3.

    The assumed compressive strut, tension tie and nodal zone model for the corbel is shown below. To clarify the geometry of the assumed truss, a separate line drawing of the truss is also given.

    Nodes A and B are located at the intersections of the centrelines of the tension ties. Node C is located at the intersection of the centreline of the upper tension tie and the line of action of the resultant applied load. Node D is located at the intersection of the centreline of the lower tension tie and the centreline of the vertical compressive strut below the corbel. The location of this strut centreline is found by calculating the strut width "a".
    The compressive force in the strut, N_c, can be found by taking moments about Node A

    $$250 \cdot 372 + 50 \cdot 467 = N_c \cdot (290 - a/2)$$

    As the stress on the nodal zone at D is to be limited by Clause 11.4.4.1(b) to $0.75 \phi_c f'_c = 17.1$ MPa, we have

    $$a = \frac{N_c \cdot 10^3}{17.1 \cdot 350}$$

    Solving these two equations gives
    $N_c = 463$ kN $a = 77$ mm

    This fixes the geometry of the truss and means that member CD has a horizontal projection of 82 + 77/2 = 121 mm, while member BD has a horizontal projection of 252 mm.

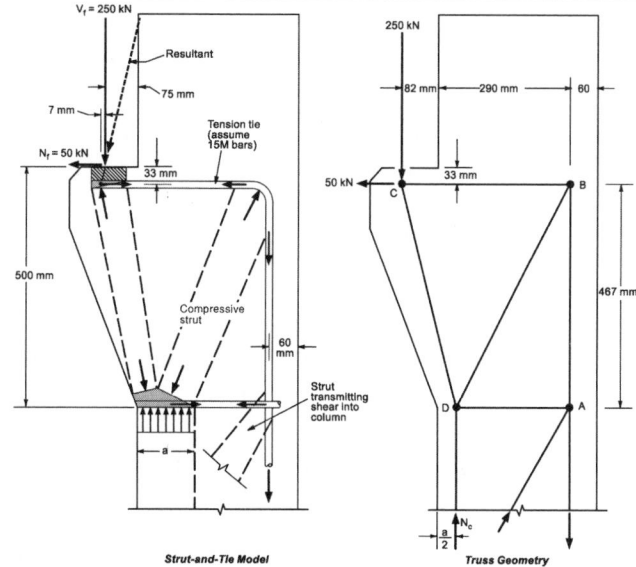

Strut-and-Tie Model   **Truss Geometry**

5. *Determine forces in truss by statics*

Member	CD	CB	BD	BA	DA
Force (kN)	-258	+115	-242	+213	+50

Positive indicates tension and negative is compression

6. *Design of tension ties*

The area of reinforcement required for tension tie CB is

$$= \frac{115 \cdot 1000}{0.85 \cdot 300} = 451\,\text{mm}^2$$

Hence, use 3 – 15M bars.

Although tie BA has a larger tension, it must be appreciated that the longitudinal reinforcement in the column, 2-30M bars on the tension face, will have been designed to resist this longitudinal tensile force. Hence, continue the 3 – 15M bars for a sufficient distance down the column to fully develop these bars.

The area of reinforcement required for tension tie DA is

$$= \frac{50 \cdot 1000}{0.85 \cdot 300} = 196\,\text{mm}^2$$

Hence, use one additional 10M column tie at location DA.

7. *Design of nodal zones*

The width "a" of nodal zone D was chosen in Step 4 to satisfy the stress limits on this nodal zone. The longitudinal column bars and the column ties will assist in anchoring the tension ties in nodal zones D, A and B. To anchor tension tie CB in nodal zone C, weld the 3 – 15M bars to the bearing plate and also weld a 15M cross bar to these bars as shown in the figure. To satisfy the nodal zone stress limits, Clause 11.4.4.2(b), the tension tie reinforcement must engage an effective depth of concrete at least equal to

$$= \frac{115 \cdot 10^3}{0.75 \cdot 0.65 \cdot 35 \cdot 270} = 25 \text{ mm} \le 57 \text{ mm} \quad \therefore \text{OK}$$

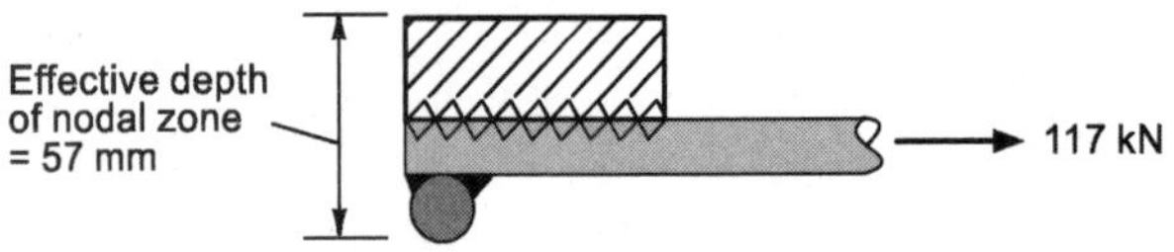

Effective depth of nodal zone = 57 mm → 117 kN

8.   *Checking compressive struts*

Compressive strut DC intersects tension tie CB at an angle of 75.5°. The tensile strain in tie CB is about $1.0 \cdot 10^{-3}$ and hence from Eq. 11-23, ε_1 is about $1.2 \cdot 10^{-3}$. For this low strain, f_{cu} is $0.85 \phi_c f_c'$. Since this exceeds the stress checked for in the nodal zone, the compressive stresses in strut DC will not be critical.

Compressive strut DB intersects tension tie BA at an angle of 28.4°. The tensile strain in tie BA is

$$\varepsilon_s = \frac{213 \cdot 10^3}{200000 \cdot (2 \cdot 700 + 3 \cdot 200)} = 0.533 \cdot 10^{-3}$$

Hence:

$$\varepsilon_1 = 0.533 \cdot 10^{-3} + (0.533 \cdot 10^{-3} + 2 \cdot 10^{-3}) \cot^2 28.4° = 9.19 \cdot 10^{-3}$$

Thus:

$$f_{cu} = \frac{35}{0.8 + 170 \cdot 9.19 \cdot 10^{-3}} = 14.81 \text{ MPa}$$

Strut DB is anchored by the 15M and 30M reinforcing bars at B. If in accordance with Fig. 11.3(a) we conservatively take ℓ_a as 12·15 = 180 mm then the thickness of the strut is 180sin28.4° = 86 mm. From Clause 11.4.2.1, the strength of the strut is then

$$\phi_c f_{cu} A_{cs} = 0.65 \cdot 14.81 \cdot 86 \cdot 350 = 290 \text{ kN}$$

as 290 kN > 242 kN the strength of strut DB is adequate.

9.   *Check minimum reinforcement requirements*

The area, A_{st}, of the primary tensile tie reinforcement must satisfy Clause 11.6.6 such that

$$A_{st} \ge 0.04 \frac{f_c'}{f_y} bd$$

$$\ge 0.04 \frac{35}{300} 350 \cdot 467$$

$$\ge 763 \text{ mm}^2$$

Hence, increase tension tie to 4 –15M bars. Having to increase the tie reinforcement to satisfy the minimum reinforcement requirement indicates that the 500 mm depth of the corbel could have been reduced.

To satisfy Clause 11.6.5, provide additional closed stirrups of area $A_{st}/2 = 400$ mm² over a depth of $2/3 \cdot 467 = 311$ mm. Use 2 – 10M closed stirrups.

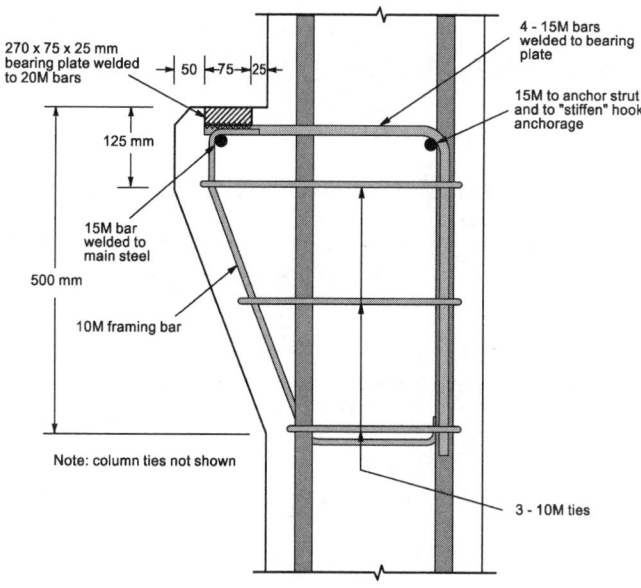

10. *Summarize design*

The final details of the corbel are shown on the figure.

Example 4.10   Design Of Beam With Dapped End

The beam shown below is subjected to a factored uniform load of 127 kN/m over a span of 6.3 m and a factored axial tension of 80 kN. Design the reinforcement for this beam.

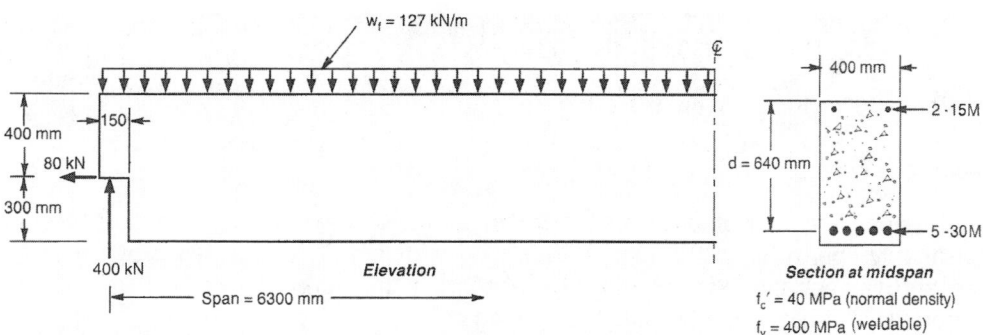

1. *Design flexural reinforcement at midspan*

Taking the axis of the beam to be on the line of the axial force, the factored moment at midspan is $M_f = 127 \cdot 6.3^2 / 8 = 630$ kN·m. If the tension reinforcement consists of 5 – 30M bars as shown above, the depth of the compressive stress block at the factored moment resistance, accounting for the tension of 80 kN, is

$$a = \frac{\phi_s A_s f_y - N_f}{\alpha_1 \phi_c f_c' b} = \frac{0.85 \cdot 5 \cdot 700 \cdot 400 - 80 \cdot 10^3}{0.79 \cdot 0.65 \cdot 40 \cdot 400} = 135.1 \text{ mm}$$

so that

$$M_r = 0.79 \cdot 0.65 \cdot 40 \cdot 135.1 \cdot 400 \cdot (400 - 135.1/2) \cdot 10^{-6} + 0.85 \cdot 400 \cdot 5 \cdot 700 \cdot (300 - 60) \cdot 10^{-6}$$
$$= 654.6 \text{ kN·m}$$

as $M_r > M_f$, the flexural reinforcement is OK at midspan.

2.   *Identify design regions of beam*

The design regions of the beam and some important components of the load-carrying path are identified in the figure below.

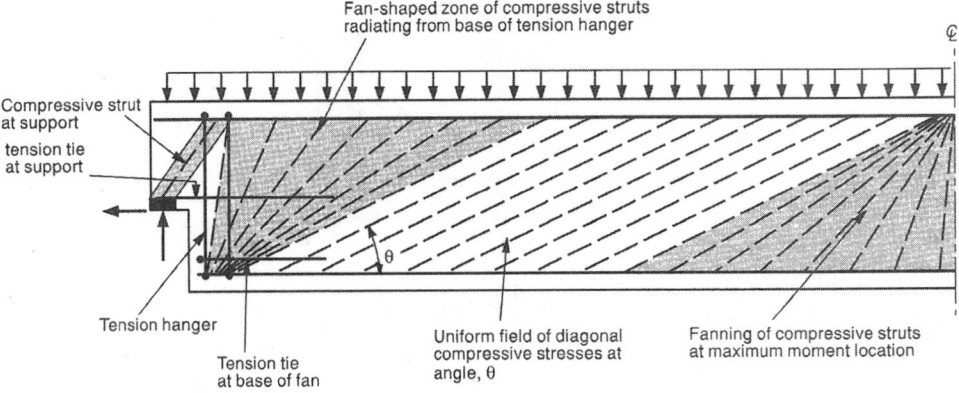

3.   *Determine bearing area at support*

Assuming that a 320 mm long steel angle across the width of the beam is to be used at the support, the required bearing length by Clause 11.4.4.1(b) is:

$$\ell_b = \frac{V_f}{0.75 \phi_c f'_c b} = \frac{400 \cdot 10^3}{0.75 \cdot 0.65 \cdot 40 \cdot 400} = 51 \text{ mm}$$

Provide a 100 x 100 x 16 mm thick angle

4.   *Determine geometry of strut and tie model*

A strut-and-tie model of one-half the beam is shown below. This truss was designed to reasonably approximate the flow of forces in the beam. This included providing a tension hanger BC near the face of the dap, anchoring the horizontal tie AD by two diagonal compressive struts, and modelling the fanning action at midspan and near the supports.

The specific geometry for this strut-and-tie model was chosen in the following manner. The bottom chord of the truss was located along the centreline of the bottom longitudinal reinforcement. The top chord was located at the level of the centroid of the compressive force due to flexure, at midspan. Nodes B and C, which define the centreline of the hanger, were located just far enough from the face of the dap to distribute the tension steel in the hanger over a region large enough to establish a nodal zone capable of resisting the applied strut and tie forces. Near the supports and at midspan, narrower frames were used to model the steep angle of the fanning compressive stresses in these regions. The remainder of the beam was divided into approximately square frames.

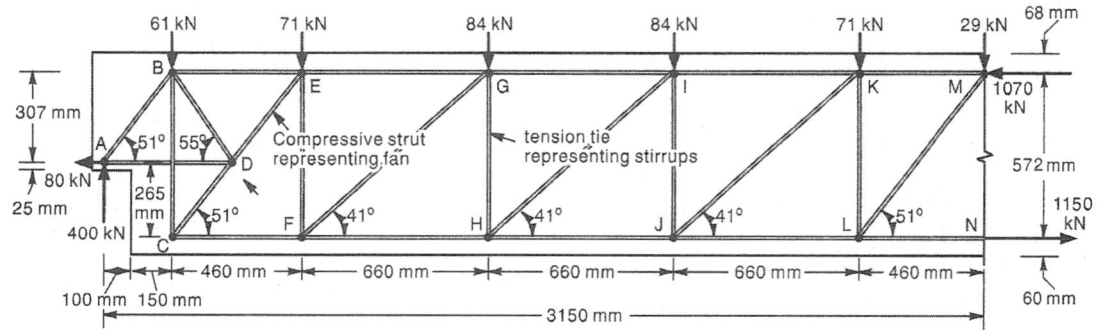

Truss Idealization

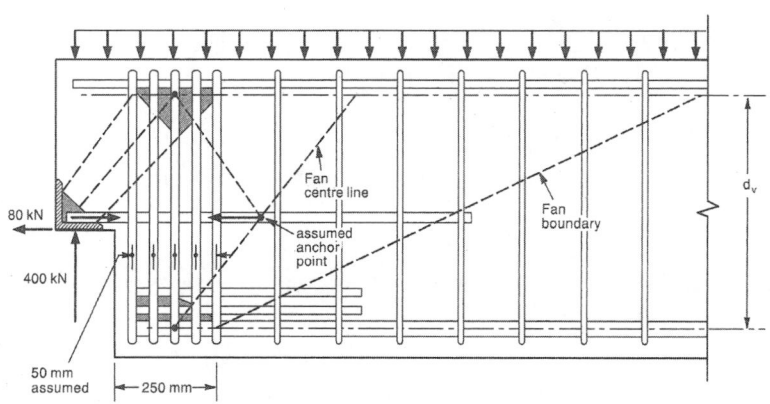

Strut and Tie Model

5   Determine forces in truss by statics

Member	Force (kN)
AB	-516
DB	-330
AD	406
CB	610
CD	-783
DE	-435

Member	Force (kN)
BE	-138
CF	491
EF	268
EG	-411
FG	-409
FH	800

Member	Force (kN)
GH	184
GI	-720
HI	-281
HJ	1012
IJ	100
IK	-932

Member	Force (kN)
JK	-152
JL	1127
KL	29
KM	-1047
LM	-37
LN	1150

Positive indicates tension, negative compression.

6.   Design of tension ties.

The following areas of reinforcement are required for the tension ties.

Tie AD: $A_s = \dfrac{406 \cdot 10^3}{0.85 \cdot 400} = 1194 \text{ mm}^2$ Use 5 – 20M bars

Hanger CB: $A_s = \dfrac{610 \cdot 10^3}{0.85 \cdot 400} = 1794 \text{ mm}^2$ Use 5 – 15M closed stirrups

Tie CF: $A_s = \dfrac{491 \cdot 10^3}{0.85 \cdot 400} = 1444 \text{ mm}^2$ 5-30M OK but need to check anchorage.

The forces in tension ties EF, GH, IJ, and KL determine the amount of shear reinforcement required in these regions (bands).

Stirrup Band EF: Tie force = 268 kN

Capacity of 10M closed stirrup is 2·100·0.85·400 = 68 kN. Therefore 268/68 = 3.94 stirrups are required over a width of 660 mm.

$$s \leq \frac{660}{3.94} = 167 \text{ mm}$$

Check minimum shear reinforcement requirements from Clause 11.2.8.2

$$s \leq \frac{A_v f_y}{0.06\sqrt{f_c'} \cdot b_w} = \frac{2 \cdot 100 \cdot 400}{0.06\sqrt{40} \cdot 400} = 527 \text{ mm}$$

Check maximum spacing requirements. The shear force at which the basic stirrup spacing limits of Clause 11.3.8.1 must be halved is

$$V_f \geq 0.125 \lambda \phi_c f_c' b_w d_v = 0.125 \cdot 1 \cdot 0.65 \cdot 40 \cdot 400 \cdot 640 \cdot 0.9 = 749 \text{ kN}$$

As the maximum V_f is less than this value, the maximum stirrup spacing is

$$s \leq 0.7 d_v = 0.7 \cdot 0.9 \cdot 640 = 403 \text{ mm}$$

The crack control requirements for strut-and-tie designs in Clause 11.4.5 also limit the stirrup spacing to:

$$s \leq 300 \text{ mm}$$

For stirrup band EF, therefore, the strength criterion governs. Use s = 150 mm.
Stirrup Band GH: Tie force = 184 kN
184/68 = 2.71 10M closed stirrups are required over 660 mm, or $s \leq$ 244 mm. Thus strength controls, use s = 240 mm.
Stirrup Band IJ: Tie force = 100 kN
100/68 = 1.47 10M closed stirrups are required over 660 mm, or $s \leq$ 449. Crack control reinforcement governs, so select s = 300 mm
Stirrup Band KL: Tie force = 29 kN
Crack control reinforcement governs, select s = 300 mm

7. *Design of nodal zones*

Nodal Zone A: The 100 mm horizontal leg length of the angle was chosen to satisfy the nodal stress limit in Step 3.
The required depth of the nodal zone from Clause 11.3.4.1(b)

$$= \frac{(406 - 80) \cdot 10^3}{0.75 \cdot 0.65 \cdot 40 \cdot 320} = 52 \text{ mm}$$

Thus the 100 mm provided by the angle is sufficient.

Nodal Zone B: Because of a concern about spalling of the concrete cover, neglect the concrete outside of the anchoring tie reinforcement. The required width of the nodal zone by Clause 11.4.4.1(b) is:

$$= \frac{610 \cdot 10^3}{0.75 \cdot 0.65 \cdot 40 \cdot 320} = 98 \text{ mm}$$

A spacing of 50 mm between the 5 –15M closed stirrups will provide a nodal zone width of at least 4 · 50 + 15 = 215 mm, which is conservative.

Nodal Zone C: This zone anchors two tension ties. Clause 11.4.4.1(c) requires a width of

$$= \frac{610 \cdot 10^3}{0.65 \cdot 0.65 \cdot 40 \cdot 320} = 113 \text{ mm}$$

Thus, 216 mm still O.K.
The require depth of the nodal zone to resist the tension in tie CF is:

$$= \frac{491 \cdot 10^3}{0.65 \cdot 0.65 \cdot 40 \cdot 320} = 91 \text{ mm}$$

To provide this nodal zone depth, provide 2 – 15M horizontal U-bars with 50 mm spacing above the layer of 30M bars.
Also check the anchorage of tension tie CF in Nodal Zone C. As the 30M bars emerge from Nodal Zone C, they can resist a tensile force of approximately

$$= \frac{216}{\ell_d} \cdot \phi_s A_s f_y = \frac{216}{854} \cdot 0.85 \cdot 3500 \cdot 400 \cdot 10^{-3} = 301 \text{ kN}$$

The 2-15M U-bars will be capable of resisting a tension of

$$0.85 \cdot 2 \cdot 2 \cdot 200 \cdot 400 \cdot 10^{-3} = 272 \text{ kN}$$

Hence the total tensile capacity at the face of the nodal zone is

= 301+272 = 573 kN

As 573 kN > 491 kN, the anchorage of the tension reinforcement at node C is OK.
Extend the 15M bars at least ℓ_d (= 426 mm) beyond the nodal zone and far enough for the 5 – 30M bars to be capable of carrying the 491 kN tie force on their own (i.e., 352 mm from the end of the 30M bars).
Although the addition of the 15M U-bars will raise the location of node C somewhat, this secondary effect will be neglected.

8. *Checking compressive struts*

As the compressive strut CD-DE represents a fan-shaped region of radiating struts and as the nodal zone stresses at the base of the fan have been checked, further checks are not required.
Check compressive stress in struts which meet at Node B. See drawing below.
Assuming the nodal zone is to be in equilibrium under a "hydrostatic" stress condition, the length of the faces of the nodal zone will be proportional to the loads applied to these faces and the faces will be perpendicular to the loads. Hence, the lengths of the compressive strut bearing surfaces at Nodal Zone B are

$$\ell_{AB} = \frac{516}{610 + 61} \cdot 215 = 165 \text{ mm} \quad \ell_{DB} = \frac{330}{610 + 61} \cdot 215 = 106 \text{ mm} \quad \ell_{EB} = \frac{138}{610 + 61} \cdot 215 = 44 \text{ mm}$$

Thus the stress in all struts at Nodal Zone B (neglecting the concrete cover) equals:

$$f_2 = \frac{(610+61)\cdot 10^3}{215\cdot 320} = 9.75 \text{ MPa}$$

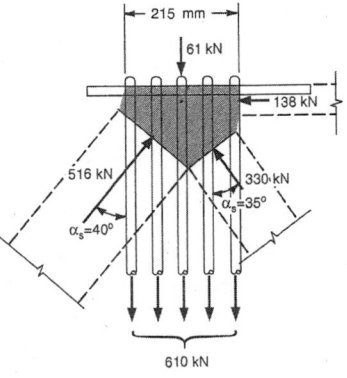

As the line of action of strut DB is closest to that of tie CB, strut DB will have the lowest diagonal crushing strength. The average tensile strain in tie CB can be estimated as

$$\varepsilon_s = \frac{610\cdot 10^3}{10\cdot 200\cdot 0.85\cdot 200\cdot 10^3} = 1.79\cdot 10^{-3}$$

From Clause 11.4.2.3, the strain, ε_1, perpendicular to the strut will be:

$$\varepsilon_1 = \varepsilon_s + (\varepsilon_s + 0.002)\cot^2 \theta_s = 0.00179 + (0.00179 + 0.002)\cot^2 35° = 0.00953$$

The diagonal crushing strength is

$$\phi_c f_{cu} = \frac{\phi_c f_c'}{0.8 + 170\varepsilon_1} = \frac{0.65\cdot 40}{0.8 + 170\cdot 0.00953} = 10.74 \text{ MPa}$$

As $f_2 < \phi_c f_{cu}$, the compressive stress in the strut is OK.
The other struts meeting at Node B will have the same compressive stress but smaller values of ε_1. Hence they will not be critical.

9.   *Other detailing considerations*

To improve crack control and ductility, provide a minimum amount of horizontal reinforcement parallel to the primary tensile tie reinforcement in the region above the support. If the dapped end were treated as a bracket, the required area of such additional reinforcement would be (Clause 11.6.5)

$$0.5\cdot A_s = 0.5\cdot 5\cdot 300 = 750 \text{ mm}^2$$

Use 2 – 15M horizontal U-bars distributed over two-thirds of the effective depth. Extend these bars at least ℓ_d beyond face of dap. To improve the support conditions for the highly stressed compressive struts AB and DB, use two additional 15M top longitudinal bars in the region of Node B.

10.   *Summarize design*

The final details of the dap ended beam are shown in the figure below

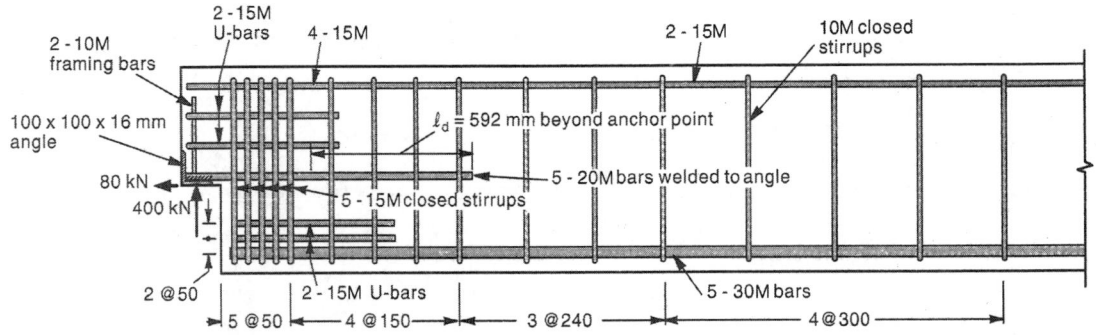

5

By S. Alexander

5

Slabs

Slabs

5.1   Introduction

Reinforced concrete slabs span either one-way or two-way, depending upon their support conditions. A one-way slab spans between parallel line supports such as walls or beams. At every point the axis of bending is parallel to the supports. A two-way slab spans in two directions and bends about two the axes. The orientation of the principle axes of bending change throughout the slab. There are many variations of two-way slabs, three of which are shown in Fig. 5.1.

One-way slabs are essentially wide beams and are designed following the same principles that apply to any beam. The behaviour of two-way slabs is more complex. They are highly statically indeterminate structures and a detailed prediction of their behaviour would require complex analysis. Fortunately, such an analysis is not essential for design. Most two-way slabs can be designed using procedures that uncouple strength and serviceability requirements. Provisions for the design of two-way slabs are provided in Clause 13 and Appendix B of the Standard.

Slabs must have sufficient strength to carry loads safely but must not deflect or crack excessively. The importance of these two serviceability factors cannot be overly emphasized. Barring blunder, providing sufficient strength in a slab rarely poses a difficult design problem. The success or failure of a design is almost always judged on the basis of serviceability.

The design of any slab system may be divided into the following steps: 1) select slab thickness; 2) obtain design moments; 3) choose flexural reinforcement; 4) check shear capacity; 5) design beams and/or other elements (if any). These steps are not independent and indeed may not be completed in the order listed. For example, it is usual to make at least a preliminary evaluation of shear capacity when selecting slab thickness. Nevertheless, these steps correspond to the grouping of the design calculations and are used as the major divisions in the remainder of this chapter and in the design examples.

Design examples are presented to assist in interpreting the provisions of specific clauses of the Standard. It should be pointed out that each example is an incomplete design in that only portions of the slab system are considered. Computations described in other chapters of this Handbook are usually omitted.

5.2   Selecting Slab Thickness

5.2.1   General

The slab thickness is the primary factor affecting serviceability and shear strength. In some instances, fire resistance requirements may govern both the cover and slab thickness.

Generally, the slab thickness is determined for serviceability by one of two methods. The first is to select a trial thickness and compute the expected deflections. Examples of such deflection computations are given in Chapter 6 of this Handbook. The trial thickness is revised as required until the calculated deflections satisfy the maximum permissible values given in Clause 9 of the Standard. The second is to select a thickness that is equal to or greater than the minimum thickness specified in the Standard. Slabs close to the minimum specified thickness should be chosen with caution since they are, as the name implies, minimally acceptable for typical dimensions and loading and require good workmanship and shoring practice. For many designs the optimum thickness will be greater than the specified minimum thickness.

The trial thickness must also be evaluated for shear strength. At this stage of the design, especially for two-way slabs without beams, only a preliminary check for shear capacity can be made since the moments to be transferred by eccentricity of shear are yet to be determined.

The increment of thickness used is a matter of designer judgment and local practice. Another consideration is the availability of "high chairs" for the top layers of reinforcement. In the examples of this Chapter an increment of 10 mm is used.

5.2.2   One-Way Slabs

The minimum thickness that may be used for one-way slabs not supporting or attached to partitions or other construction likely to be damaged by large deflections, without the need to compute deflections, is given in Table 9-2 of the Standard as a fraction of the clear span, ℓ_n , for different support conditions. If the slab is supporting construction likely to be damaged by large deflections, calculations are required to show that expected deflections, including time effects, will be satisfactory for the specific application.

For one-way slabs in buildings, it would be unusual for shear capacity to govern. Nonetheless, it must be checked.

5.2.3   Two-way Slabs

Clause 13.2 contains provisions for the minimum thickness of regular two-way slab systems as defined in Clause 2.2. The geometric limitations of a regular two-way slab system are a necessary prerequisite for applying the provisions of Clause 13.2. Deflection calculations are required for two-way slabs that cannot be classified as regular or for slabs that do not meet the minimums specified in Clauses 13.2.3 through 13.2.6.

The deflection, and hence minimum thickness, of slab panels with beams on all sides depends upon both the panel aspect ratio and the relative stiffness of the beams in the two directions. If beams in one direction are significantly stiffer than in the other, even for columns located on an essentially square grid, the slab will tend to act as a one-way slab spanning between the stiffer beams. Equation 13-3 gives the minimum thickness as a function of the longer clear span, ℓ_n, the panel aspect ratio, β, and the mean beam stiffness ratio, α_m. The beam stiffness ratio, α, is the ratio of the moment of inertia of the beam to that of the slab; the mean beam stiffness, α_m, is the average value of α for the beams along the four panel edges. The maximum effective value of α_m is limited to 2.0. Recognizing the approximations needed to develop Eqn (13-3), a simplified method of determining the beam moment of inertia, Eqn (13-4), is provided to ease the calculation of α.

For slabs with drop panels or slab bands, Clause 13.2.4 accounts for variations in the size of the drop panel. Note that slab bands are defined in Clause 2.2 as continuous extensions of drop panels. For those familiar with the previous edition of the Standard, Eqn (13-2) appears changed but this is not the case; it has simply been rearranged to make it more convenient for design.

With regard to slab bands, Clause 13.2.6 requires that the thickness of the slab band itself also satisfy the span to depth requirements for beams listed in Table 9.2. This additional stipulation is required for the lateral distribution of moments in 13.11.2.4 and 13.11.2.5.

The minimum specified thickness for slabs without drop panels (flat plates and slabs with column capitals only) is given in Clause 13.2.3. Such slabs have no interior beams and may or may not have edge beams.

The thickness of two-way slabs without beams may also be governed by the shear capacity of the slab at the supports. This is especially true for slabs supported on columns without capitals or drops and at exterior columns where there are significant moments in addition to shear to be transferred between the slab and column. Thus, although the slab thickness is generally selected for deflection considerations, it is prudent to make a preliminary shear capacity check before proceeding to the next design step. At this early stage of design, the total loading on the slab is known and the corresponding value of the factored shear force at each column, V_f, can be determined but the moments to be transferred are unknown and their effects can only be estimated. One procedure for doing this is to multiply the factored shear force by the following factors before comparing the factored shear stress to the maximum shear stress resistance (see Example 5.4).

interior column   1.2
edge column   1.6

5

Slabs

5.3   Slab Moments

5.3.1   General

For one-way slabs, it is usual to consider a strip of unit width spanning perpendicular to the supports and to analyze this strip for moments and shears as a continuous beam. When the loading and geometry satisfy the requirements of Clause 9.3.3, design moments and shears may be obtained directly from the coefficients given therein. Otherwise an elastic analysis is required.

There are many techniques that may be used to analyze and design two-way slabs. Clause 13.5.1 states "A slab may be designed by any procedure satisfying conditions of equilibrium and compatibility with the supports provided it is shown that the factored resistance at every section is at least equal to the effects of the factored loads, and that all serviceability conditions, including specified limits on deflections, are met". The Standard explicitly addresses analyses based on Elastic Plate Theory and on the Theorems of Plasticity. In addition, it provides details for modeling slab-column structures as elastic frames and it retains the Direct Design Method. Appendix B provides an analysis for two-way slabs with stiff supports on all sides.

5.3.2   Elastic Plate Theory

Finite difference or finite element techniques may be used to perform an elastic analysis of a two-way slab. All such analyses require some system of orthogonal coordinate axes, say x and y, to describe the slab. The coordinate axes are parallel to the flexural reinforcement. The analyses provide values of moment intensity, or moment per unit width, at various points on the slab. The points are usually arranged in some grid pattern that can be adjusted as the user sees fit. At each point, there are three components of moment intensity; two bending, m_x and m_y, and one from torsion or twisting, m_{xy}.

Twisting moments are non-zero whenever the principle bending axes are not parallel to the coordinate axes, x and y. By itself, a twisting moment will cause the two-way slab to deflect into a saddle shape, with the axes of bending skew to the coordinate axes. The saddle shape means that the slab is subject to negative bending about one skew axis in combination with positive bending about the other skew axis. Since the reinforcement is parallel to the coordinate axes, it follows that a twisting moment will require both top and bottom reinforcement to resist the skew negative and positive bending. This is reflected in the expressions for design moment in Clause 13.6.4 in which both the negative and positive design moments are increased by torsion. The corner reinforcement of Clause 13.12.5 is another example of reinforcing for torsion or twisting moments.

It is usually desirable to define bands within which the flexural reinforcement is uniformly spaced. The provisions in 13.6.4 produce design moment intensities at points on the slab. At any section across the width of the slab, the design moment intensities will vary substantially. Clause 13.6.5 provides a rule for defining reinforcing bands that will not place undue demands on ductility.

In column-supported slabs, shears are high in the vicinity of the column and the moments in the slab vary quite sharply. If the finite difference or finite element mesh is too coarse near the column, this variation may be missed. On the other hand, the shears are low near midspan and the variation in moments is gradual. A fine mesh here is unnecessary and may greatly increase run time of the numerical model. It is generally adequate to provide a relatively coarse mesh over most of the slab but a fine mesh for the slab within about 4 slab thicknesses of the column face.

Particular attention should be given to the effect of flexural cracking of the slab in the vicinity of column supports. Such cracking locally reduces the bending stiffness and results in significant transverse redistribution of slab moments. Consider additional comment on localized cracking

5.3.3   Theorems of Plasticity

These methods are concerned only with the ultimate strength of the slab and do not provide any check on serviceability. The Standard permits the analysis of a two-way slab to be based on either the upper or lower bound theorems of plasticity. An upper bound technique produces an estimate of the failure load of a slab that is greater than or equal to the correct failure load. Hence, the upper bound method approaches the correct solution from the "unsafe" side. A lower bound technique will always produce an estimate of failure load that is less than or equal to the correct failure load. Hence, the lower bound technique approaches the correct answer from the "safe" side. The most common upper and lower bound techniques used for two-way slabs are the yield line method and the strip method, respectively. These methods address the flexural strength of the slab only; neither addresses the shear strength.

In the yield line method, the factored moments are obtained by satisfying equilibrium for an assumed folding mechanism. The validity of the answer depends on finding the governing folding mechanism. Except in the simplest cases, finding the governing folding mechanism can be a far from trivial problem. Failing to find the correct folding mechanism will result in the slab being under-designed. There is no way of bounding the magnitude of the error.

With the strip method, the designer assumes a set of load paths that will carry all load to the supports of the slab. Each load path is analyzed for the load it is assumed to carry and is reinforced accordingly.

5.3.4   Elastic Frame Analogies

The concept behind the use of elastic frame analogies is that satisfactory values for average design moments and shears can be obtained by considering design strips (see Fig. 5.2) located along the support lines and bounded by the centre lines of the adjacent panels. These design strips are then analyzed as elastic plane frames. For gravity loading, the frame analysis may be simplified to consider only one level of slab at a time by assuming that the far ends of supports are fixed against rotation.

In a conventional plane frame analysis it is assumed that all members meeting at a joint undergo the same rotation. In a column-supported slab, the column provides only local restraint to the slab. As a result, across the full width of the design strip, the average rotation of the slab will not necessarily match the rotation of the column. For the case of gravity loading, the effective column stiffness is reduced to account for this added degree of flexibility between the slab and the column. The Standard provides two methods, prismatic and non-prismatic modelling, for estimating this reduced stiffness but it should be emphasized that these are for gravity loading only. Clause 13.6.3 suggests that a frame analogy may be used for lateral loads acting on an unbraced system provided the effects of cracking and reinforcement are taken into account in assigning member stiffness. The Standard contains no guidance for selecting these properties but, by analogy, would require reducing the effective stiffness of the beam (slab) members.

The use of elastic frame analogies is restricted to regular two-way slabs for two reasons. First, the definition of the design strips assumes that support lines and adjacent panels are readily identifiable. This is the case for slab systems supported on columns along lines to create essentially rectangular panels. Second, recommendations for assigning stiffness values to the members of the frame and the provisions for the lateral distribution of the design moments at the critical sections were all derived assuming rectangular panels.

Once the effective geometry of the frame has been selected using either prismatic or non-prismatic members, it is analyzed elastically for a number of defined patterned loadings to obtain the maximum effects at all critical sections in the slab and supporting members (see Fig. 5.4). When the live load is uniformly distributed and does not exceed three-quarters of the specified dead load, slab moments can be obtained assuming full factored design load on the entire slab

5

Slabs

system. This implies that pattern loadings are not required to compute unbalanced moments transferred at interior supports for this case.

The moments obtained from the analysis of the analogous frame are average values over the width of the design strip. The lateral distribution of these average design moments is addressed in Clause 13.11.

Non-prismatic modelling

Non-prismatic modelling of member stiffness uses the concept of an attached torsional member (see Fig. 5.3) to reduce the stiffness of the column. This approach, originally called the 'Equivalent Frame Method', was developed at the time when the only practical method for analyzing an elastic frame was by the 'moment distribution' procedure. Thus recommendations for assigning member stiffness to determine stiffness and carry-over-factors were made with that procedure in mind. The effective column stiffness is determined from the sum of the flexibilities of the attached torsional member and the column.

With this procedure the frame is modelled using member centrelines. As a result, the moments obtained at the beam member ends should be reduced to obtain the design moments at the critical sections at the face of supports. To use this method for electronic computation requires writing a special program that incorporates use of attached torsional members. The program PCASLAB^{TM}: Cement Association of Canada, is a complete slab design program that incorporates this procedure.

Prismatic Modelling

Today virtually every design office has a computer program for the elastic analysis of frames that is based on the direct stiffness method. So that these programs can be used for the analysis of slab systems, the Standard contains coefficients for reducing the effective stiffness of 'prismatic' column members. If the frame is modelled using only centreline dimensions, then centreline moments at the ends of the beam members must be reduced to obtain design moments at the critical sections as required with 'non-prismatic' modelling. However, with little effort, the designer may introduce joints at the critical sections to obtain design moments directly.

5.3.5   Direct Design Method

Over time the 'Direct Design Method' has gradually been reduced from a complete design method to a specialized simple elastic frame analogy that provides average design moments at the critical sections. The lateral distribution of the average design moments is addressed in Clause 13.11.

The same design strip is used as for the elastic frame analogy except that the columns are not included explicitly. Column dimensions are considered by using clear spans. The essence of the method is to distribute the total factored moment in each span of the frame to the critical sections using a set of coefficients. To ensure that the coefficients are applicable, additional restraints on the slab geometry are imposed. The unbalanced moments in interior columns and walls are determined from an expression involving partial loading on adjacent spans.

For slabs meeting the geometric requirements for use of the Direct Design Method, the curtailment of reinforcement may be obtained from Fig. 13-1 of the Standard.

5.3.6   Two-way Slabs with Stiff Supports

It is not uncommon for slab panels to be supported on all sides by walls or beams of sufficient stiffness that their curvature under load is much smaller than that required for the adjacent slab to develop significant moment resistance. Thus, for determining slab moments and shears, the panel boundaries may be considered as non-deflecting. One possible approach is to treat each panel separately with moments determined from tabulated coefficients obtained from classical plate theory. For continuous slab systems, any difference in negative moments in adjacent panels at their common support can be distributed. This is the basis for the method given in Appendix B of the Standard and is illustrated in Example 5.5.

Some criterion is required in the case of slabs with beams on all sides to determine whether the beam may be considered stiff. Appendix B defines a beam as stiff when the ratio $b_w h_b^3/(\ell_n h_s^3)$ is at least 2.0. Hence the determination as to whether the beam is stiff requires prior knowledge of the slab thickness, h_s. It should be noted that this ratio is different than the mean beam stiffness ratio, α_m, used previously. Notwithstanding this, a trial slab thickness can be obtained using Eqn (13-3) in Clause 13.2.5 of the Standard with $\alpha_m = 2.0$. This trial thickness must not be less than the perimeter of the panel divided by 160 in the case of fully continuous slabs or the perimeter of the panel divided by 140 in the case of slabs discontinuous on one or more edges.

The procedure described in Appendix B also uses the terms "middle" and "column" strips but the definitions are different from those used for reinforcement distribution in slabs analyzed using frame analogies. When the panel boundaries are prevented from deflecting, the larger moments are in the central portions of the panel or "middle" strips. Coefficients for determining design moments in these strips are given. The two portions of the slab outside this central half are referred to as "column" strips even though there may only be wall supports. Moments in these strips are determined from the "middle" strip moments. When slabs are designed using Appendix B, all other requirements of the Standard such as area of minimum reinforcement, etc. apply.

5.4   Slab Reinforcement

5.4.1   General

For all slabs, sufficient flexural reinforcement is required at each section to resist the factored moments at that section. The minimum area of reinforcement required in each direction is 0.002 Ag, however, for exposure conditions where crack control is essential, this minimum area of reinforcement must be increased (Clause 7.8.2). A general comment is that it is often beneficial to assess the flexural resistance provided by minimum reinforcement at an early stage in the design. In many cases, minimum reinforcement will satisfy the flexural requirements of the entire slab or at least large fractions of it. This allows the designer to focus attention on those regions that are most critical.

Positive moment reinforcement perpendicular to a discontinuous edge shall extend to the edge of the slab. Negative reinforcement perpendicular to a discontinuous edge shall be bent, hooked, or otherwise anchored to develop the calculated tension in the bar.

Other requirements pertain specifically to either one-way or two-way slabs and are discussed separately.

5.4.2   One-way Slabs

For solid one-way slabs, flexural reinforcement must be spaced not further than 3 times the slab thickness or 500 mm and cut-off points and development lengths are computed as for beams. In addition, to limit width of flexural cracks, spacing of the principal flexural reinforcement at critical sections shall be such that the crack control parameter, z, (Clause 10.6.1) does not exceed 30 000 N/mm for interior exposure and 25 000 N/mm for exterior exposure. Perpendicular to the span, minimum reinforcement must not be spaced further than 5 times the slab thickness or 500 mm.

Where the slab is considered as a T-beam flange and the principal reinforcement in the slab is parallel to that beam, Clause 10.5.3.2 requires flexural reinforcement perpendicular to this beam in the top of the slab. In this clause the phrase "clear distance between the webs of the T-beams" refers to the transverse beams supporting the one-way slab. This corresponds to the clear span of the one-way slab.

5.4.3   Two-way Slabs

Most methods of analyzing two-way slabs (finite difference and finite element methods being exceptions) provide average design moments across critical sections. Since the intensity of bending across these critical sections is generally not uniform, it follows that the distribution of the bending moments and hence the flexural reinforcement should not be uniform. Clauses 13.12 and 13.11 provide criteria for laterally distributing design moments in slabs with and without interior beams, respectively. The objective is to assign a greater fraction of the design moment to sections that have either greater flexural stiffness or greater curvature.

The provisions for the lateral distribution of design moments in slabs without interior beams, Clause 13.11, allow the designer to exercise some judgment in the placing of slab reinforcement. For a slab with no interior beams and rectangular panels, midspan bending for the long span will be more uniform than it is for the short span. As a result, bottom reinforcement for the long span should be more uniformly spaced than bottom steel for the short span.

For negative moment in slabs without beams or slab bands, the lateral distribution coefficients at interior columns have been revised slightly to place some top reinforcement in the middle strip. This was in response to concerns expressed about crack control in flat plates.

Clauses 13.11.2.4 and 13.11.2.5 provide guidance for the lateral distribution of reinforcement in slabs with slab bands. Perpendicular to the slab band, between 85% and 95% of the design moment is distributed uniformly over the entire design strip. The remaining 5% to 15% that is placed within a width b_b centred on the column is in addition to the uniformly distributed moment.

Clause 13.10 provides additional requirements for placement of slab reinforcement. Clauses 13.10.2 through 13.10.4 as well as 13.11.2.7 ensure a minimum amount of top reinforcement in close proximity to the column (within a width b_b centred on the column).

Unless beams containing shear reinforcement are provided in all spans framing into the column, integrity reinforcement is required to prevent progressive collapse. Clause 13.10.9 presents general requirements in terms of the total area of anchored bottom reinforcement on all faces of the periphery of the column.

Clause 13.10.9 requires top reinforcement at all free slab edges. Clearly, wherever a slab cantilevers beyond the face of support there is a need to provide at least minimum reinforcement throughout the entire cantilevering section to resist the cantilever moment. What may not be as obvious is the desirability of some top reinforcement at any free edge. Point loads near a free edge generate local negative moments in the slab about an axis parallel to the free edge. As well, hooking the top reinforcement, as required by 13.10.5.2, provides reinforcement for the effects of twisting moments at the free edge.

5.5   Shear and Moment Transfer

For slabs, one speaks of "beam" shear where the slab is considered to fail in shear as in a wide beam and "perimeter" or "two-way" shear where failure is considered to be a punching of the support through the slab (see Fig. 5.5). The resistances under beam and perimeter shear are given in Clauses 11.3 and 13.3, respectively.

One-way slabs are designed for beam shear only. Two-way slabs are also checked for beam shear although this is rarely critical. Slabs supported by beams are treated as unit strips spanning to the beams. For slabs without beams, the slab is considered as a wide beam extending across the entire width of the design strip.

Perimeter shear capacity in two-way slabs at interior and edge column supports is evaluated by comparing a factored shear stress computed at a critical section to a factored shear stress resistance. The critical section is located so that the perimeter is a minimum but need not approach closed than $d/2$ to the face of the support. Examples of critical sections are given in the Notes accompanying Clause 13.3.3. The factored shear resistance is a function of the concrete compressive strength and the shape and size of the support (Clause 13.3.4).

At interior and edge column-slab connections, the factored shear stress is computed from Eqn (13-9) and includes terms for unbalanced factored moments transferred to the support about the centroidal axes of the critical section. The centroidal axes to be used are parallel and perpendicular to the design strips framing into the column. This marks a return to the procedure in the editions prior to 1994. The 1994 edition required that principle axes be used. In certain cases, particularly corner column-slab connections, using principle axes increased both the complexity of the calculation and the magnitude of the calculated shear stress.

Eqn (13-9) may also be applied to corner column-slab connections; however, the Standard permits an alternative analysis in which the average shear stress on a critical section located $d/2$ from the support is limited to the one-way value defined in Eqn (13-10).

Expressions for evaluating b_o, γ_v, e and J in this equation for different column locations are given in Fig. 5.6. Because these terms are functions of c_1, c_2 and d only, Eqn (13-8) can be rewritten in the form

$$v_f = kv_f + k_1 M_1 + k_2 M_2$$

where values of the coefficients k, k_1 and k_2 can be obtained from design charts given in Tables 5.3 to 5.9.

Some judgment is required when assigning values for V_f, M_1 and M_2 in the above equation. Clause 13.3.5.5 indicates that the values used should be from a "consistent loading". For an interior column, the maximum factored shear force, V_f, occurs with all adjacent panels loaded whereas the maximum values of the unbalanced moments occur with selected partial loadings. Thus maximum values for all three terms cannot occur simultaneously and the consistent loading that would result in the sum of all three terms being a maximum is not easily determined. For an interior column, it is suggested that a satisfactory value of v_f can be obtained by adding the full V_f term to one of the unbalanced moment terms to obtain the larger sum. For an edge column, the maximum value of v_f will occur when both adjacent panels are loaded. Thus, for equal spans, the unbalanced moment about an axis perpendicular to the edge may be neglected.

For the first time, the Standard has added a factor to account for scale effect in two-way shear. Clause 13.3.4.3 provides a multiplier to be applied whenever the slab thickness exceeds 300 mm.

5.6   Examples

The following design examples are presented to assist in interpreting provisions in the Standard. They are incomplete designs in that only portions of the slab system are considered. Computations described elsewhere in this Handbook are generally omitted.

The first four examples deal with two-way slab variations that have the same column layout and the same design strip widths. The fifth example presents the design of an edge-supported two-way slab using the method presented in Appendix B. The sixth example demonstrates the calculation of design moments using the results of an elastic plate analysis (13.6). Finally, the seventh example is a one-way slab and beam system with the same column layout as the first four examples.

For all examples, the specified design strength of the concrete, f'_c is 25 MPa ($\alpha_1 = 0.81$) and the specified yield strength of the reinforcement, f_y, is 400 MPa. The density (unit weight) of reinforced concrete is assumed to be 24 kN/m^3.

Example 1   Two-way Slab without Beams (Flat Plate)

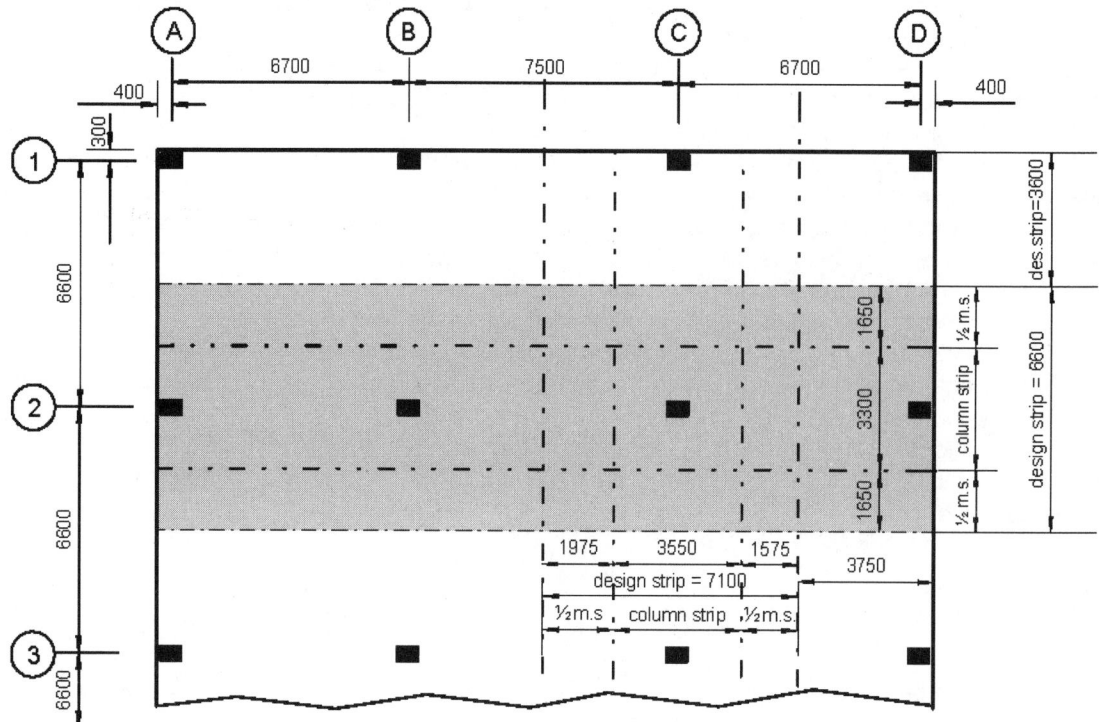

The preceding sketch shows a plan view of a portion of a typical floor in an apartment building. All columns measure 400 mm by 600 mm. The slab projects 100 mm beyond the exterior column face to support wall panels and assist with shear transfer. The slab supports a service live load of 1.9 kN/m^2 and a fixed partition allowance of 1.0 kN/m^2. The slab projection supports exterior precast panels weighing 2.4 kN/m.

Step 1 – Select Slab Thickness

a)   Deflection requirements (13.2.3)

Interior Panel

$\ell_n = 7500 - 300 - 300 = 6900 \, \text{mm}$

$h_s \geq \dfrac{\ell_n \left(0.6 + f_y / 1000\right)}{30} = \dfrac{6900 \times 1}{30} = 230 \, \text{mm}$

Exterior Panel

$\ell_n = 6600 - 200 - 200 = 6200 \, \text{mm}$

$h_s \geq 1.1 \times \dfrac{\ell_n \left(0.6 + f_y / 1000\right)}{30} = \dfrac{1.1 \times 6200 \times 1}{30} = 227 \, \text{mm}$

Try: h_s = 250 mm

Effective depths using 15M bars with 25 mm clear cover

        flexure (outer layer): d_{max} = 250 – 25 – 8 = 217 mm

        flexure (inner layer): d_{min} = 250 – 25 – 15 – 8 = 202 mm

        shear (centre of mat): d = 250 – 25 – 15 = 210 mm

Factored loading:

Load combination 1 (See Annex C)

$1.4 \times (0.25\ m \times 24\ kN/m^3 + 1.0\ kN/m^2) = 9.8\ kN/m^2$

Load combination 2

$1.5 \times 1.9\ kN/m^2 + 1.25 \times (0.25m \times 24\ kN/m^3 + 1.0\ kN/m^2) = 11.6\ kN/m^2$ **(governs)**

b) Preliminary shear check

i) interior column at C2

Shear perimeter (see sketch) defined in 13.3.3.

$b_o = 2 \times (400 + 600 + 2 \times 210) = 2840\ mm$

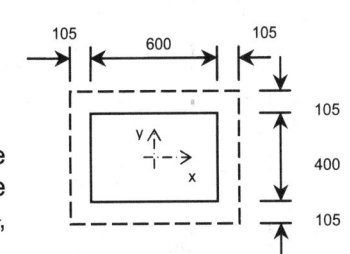

To account for the effect of unbalanced moment, the ratio of the resisting shear stress, v_r, to the average shear stress from the factored shear acting alone, v_f, should be at least 1.2.

v_r is the lesser of:

$$\left(1 + \frac{2}{\beta_c}\right)0.19\lambda\phi_c\sqrt{f_c'} = \left(1 + \frac{2}{1.5}\right)0.19 \times 1 \times 0.65 \times 5\ MPa = 1.44\ MPa \qquad (13\text{-}5)$$

$$\left(\frac{\alpha_s d}{b_o} + 0.19\right)\lambda\phi_c\sqrt{f_c'} = \left(\frac{4 \times 210}{2840} + 0.19\right) \times 1 \times 0.65 \times 5\ MPa = 1.58\ MPa \qquad (13\text{-}6)$$

$$0.38\lambda\phi_c\sqrt{f_c'} = 0.38 \times 1 \times 0.65 \times 5\ MPa = 1.23\ MPa \qquad (13\text{-}7)$$

$$v_f = \frac{V_f}{b_o d} = \frac{7.1 \times 6.6 \times 11.6\ kN/m^2}{2840 \times 210} = 0.911\ MPa$$

$$\frac{v_r}{v_f} = 1.35 > 1.2\ proceed$$

ii) edge columns at C1 and D2

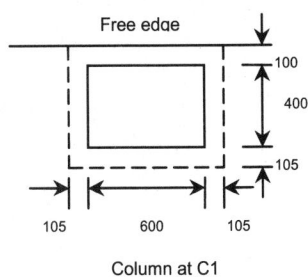

Column at C1

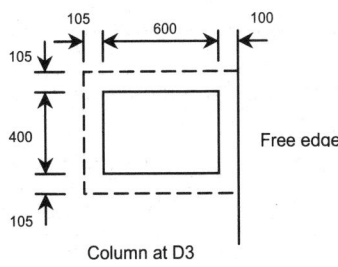

Column at D3

C1 (see sketch):

$b_o = 2 \times (400 + 100 + 105) + 600 + 210 = 2020\ mm$

$$v_f = \frac{V_f}{b_o d} = \frac{(3.3 + 0.2) \times 7.1 \times 11.6\ kN/m^2 + 7.1 \times 1.25 \times 2.4\ kN/m}{2020 \times 210} = 0.73\ MPa$$

$v_r = 1.23\ MPa.$ $\dfrac{v_r}{v_f} = 1.69 > 1.6\ proceed$

D3: (see sketch)

$b_o = 2 \times (600 + 100 + 105) + 400 + 210 = 2220\ mm$

$$v_f = \frac{V_f}{b_o d} = \frac{(3.35\,m + 0.3\,m) \times 6.6\,m \times 11.6\,kN/m^2 + 6.6\,m \times 1.25 \times 2.4\,kN/m}{2220\,mm \times 210\,mm} = 0.64\,MPa$$

$v_r = 1.23$ MPa. $\dfrac{v_r}{v_f} = 1.92 > 1.6$ proceed

iii)   corner column D1

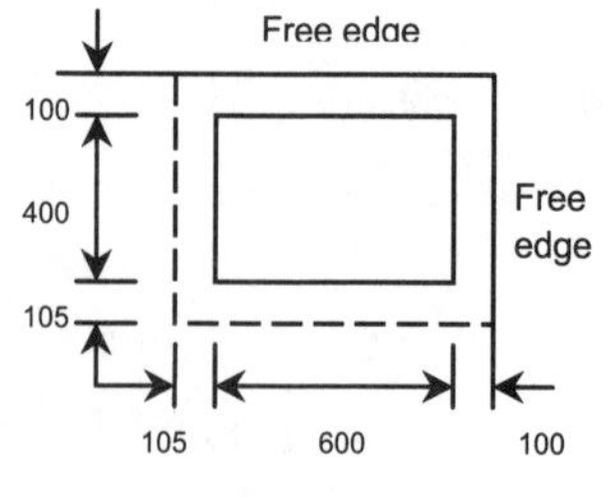

As with past editions of the Standard, the critical section for shear is located $\dfrac{d}{2}$ from the face of support (see sketch at right). The average stress on this section under vertical shear alone is limited to the one-way value for slabs. (13.3.6.2(a))

Column D1

$$v_c = \beta\lambda\phi_c\sqrt{f'_c} = 0.21 \times 1 \times 0.65 \times 5\,MPa = 0.68\,MPa$$

$$V_r = (400 + 600 + 210 + 200) \times 210 \times 0.68\,MPa = 201\,kN$$

$$V_f = \left(\frac{6.7}{2} + 0.3\right)\left(\frac{6.6}{2} + 0.2\right)11.6\,kN/m^2 + \left(\frac{6.7}{2} + \frac{6.6}{2} + 0.4 + 0.3\right)1.25 \times 2.4\,kN/m = 170\,kN$$

All preliminary shear checks are satisfactory.   **Use $h_s = 250$ mm**

Step 2 – Design Moments

Consider a design strip along gridline 2. Since the limitations of (13.9.1) are satisfied, use Direct Design Method.

	A			B			C			D	
ℓ_n		6100			6900			6100			(mm)
M_o (13.9.2.2)		356			456			356			(kN·m)
%M_o (13.9.3)	0.26	0.52	0.70	0.65	0.35	0.65	0.70	0.52	0.26		
M$_{DES}$	−93	185	−249	−296	160	−296	-2249	185	-93		(kN·m)

Step 3 – Select Reinforcement

Assume 15M bars: place   N-S reinf. in inner layer
                                 E-W reinf. in outer layer

Approximate moment resistance per bar (E-W design strips):

$$M_{r\,bar} \approx \phi_s A_{bar} f_y \times 0.9d_{max} = \frac{0.85 \times 200 \times 400 \times 0.9 \times 217}{10^6} = 13.28\ kN \cdot m$$

Minimum Reinforcement

$$A_{s\,min} = 0.002 A_g = 0.002 \times 250\ mm \times 1000\ mm/m = 500\ mm^2/m \quad \Rightarrow \quad \textbf{Use 15M @ 400 c/c}$$

Moment resistance with minimum reinforcement (E-W design strips)

$$m_{r\,min} = \frac{\phi_s A_{s\,min} f_y}{s}\left(d_{min} - \frac{\phi_s A_{s\,min} f_y}{2\alpha_1 \phi_c f'_c s}\right)$$

$$= \frac{0.85 \times 200 \times 400}{400}\left(217 - \frac{0.85 \times 200 \times 400}{2 \times 0.81 \times 0.65 \times 25 \times 400}\right) \times \frac{1}{10^3} = 35.8 \text{ kN} \cdot \text{m/m}$$

Positive moment (bottom) reinforcement

(13.11.2.2) requires that 55% to 65% of the positive moment in all spans be taken by the column strips, leaving 45% to 35% to be taken by the middle strips.

Consider moment intensities.

	A	B	C	
MDES	185	156	198	(kN·m)
$m_{DES\ col.st.}$	30.8 to 36.4	26.7 to 31.5	30.8 to 36.4	(kN·m/m)
$m_{DES\ mid.st.}$	25.2 to 17.7	21.8 to 17.0	25.2 to 17.7	(kN·m/m)

The resistance provided by minimum reinforcement, 35.8 kN·m/m, either exceeds or falls within the range of column strip design moment intensities and in all cases exceeds the range of middle strip design moment intensities. It follows that minimum reinforcement provides sufficient resistance for all spans.

Check Maximum spacing (13.10.4)

Positive moment reinforcement: $s \le 3h_s$ but not to exceed 500 mm   **OK**

Use 15M at 400 c/c bottom East-West

Negative moment (top) reinforcement: Column at C2

Design top East-West mat to be centred on column.

Total negative design moment: $M_{DES} = 296$ kN·m

Minimum total number of bars in top mat: $\dfrac{296 \text{ kN} \cdot \text{m}}{13.28 \text{ kN} \cdot \text{m/bar}} = 22.3 \text{ bars} \quad \Rightarrow \quad \text{say 24 bars}$

At least one third of these bars are to be placed within a width b_b (13.11.2.7).

Requires 8 bars within width b_b

Check moment transfer: for Direct Design, minimum unbalanced moment is (13.9.4)

$$M_f = 0.07\left[\left(w_{df} + 0.5w_{lf}\right)\ell_{2a}\ell_n^2 - w'_{df}\ell'_{2a}\left(\ell'_n\right)^2\right]$$
$$= 0.07\left[\left(8.75 + \frac{2.85}{2}\right)6.6 \times 6.9^2 - 8.75 \times 6.6 \times 6.1^2\right] = 73.4 \text{ kN} \cdot \text{m}$$

Fraction to be transferred by flexural reinforcement within width b_b (13.10):

$$\gamma_f = 1 - \gamma_v = \frac{1}{1 + \dfrac{2}{3}\sqrt{\dfrac{b_1}{b_2}}} = \frac{1}{1 + \dfrac{2}{3}\sqrt{\dfrac{810}{610}}} = 0.566$$

$$\gamma_f M_f = 0.566 \times 73.4 = 41.5 \text{ kN} \cdot \text{m}$$

This would require $41.5 \text{ kN} \cdot \text{m} \big/ 13.28 \text{ kN} \cdot \text{m/bar} = 3.1 \text{ bars}$

Requires 4 bars within width b_b. Does not govern

$b_b = c_2 + 3h_s = 400 + 3 \times 250 = 1150 \text{ mm} \quad \Rightarrow \quad say\ 1200 \text{ mm}$

Use: **24 – 15M bars. Place 8 bars in band 1200 wide centred on column.**
          Remaining 16 bars spaced at 200 c/c.

Check bars required in column strip (13.11.2.2):   from $0.70 \times 23 \text{ bars} = 16.1 \text{ bars}$

to $0.90 \times 23 \text{ bars} = 20.7 \text{ bars}$

# of bars provided in column strip = $8 + \dfrac{3300 - 1200}{200} = 18.5$ **OK**

Negative moment (top) reinforcement: Edge column at D2 and free edge of slab

From Direct Design on gridline 2, moment at face of support is 93 kN·m. 100% of this is to be transferred by reinforcement within width b_b. As before, b_b is 1200 mm.

Reinforcement required = $\dfrac{93 \text{ kN} \cdot \text{m}}{13.28 \dfrac{\text{kN} \cdot \text{m}}{\text{bar}}} = 7 \text{ bars} \quad \Rightarrow \quad say\ 8 \text{ bars}$

Use: **8 – 15M bars in band 1200 wide centred on column.**

The Standard calls for at least minimum top reinforcement perpendicular to the free edge of the slab (13.10.9). Close free edge with 180° hooks to provide reinforcement for edge shear resulting from torsional moments at free edge.

Use: **15M bars U-bars at 400 c/c at all slab edges.**

Structural Integrity (13.10.6)

$V_{se} = 7.1 \times 6.6 \times (1.9 + 1 + 0.25 \times 24) = 417 \text{ kN}$ but not less than

$V_{se} = 7.1 \times 6.6 \times 2 \times 0.25 \times 24 = 562 \text{ kN} \quad \Rightarrow \quad$ **governs**

$\Sigma A_{sb} = \dfrac{2 \times V_{se}}{f_y} = \dfrac{2 \times 562 \times 10^3}{400} = 2810 \text{ mm}^2$

Place 2 – 15M bars from bottom flexural steel through column in each direction. These bars must be continuous through the column. Add 1 – 15M extra bottom bar through column East-West and 2 – 15M extra bottom bars through column North-South. These extra bars must lap $2\ell_d$ with the bottom mat on either side of the column.

Step 4 – Check Shear

Interior column-slab connection at C-2

With the Direct Design Method, it is reasonable to check shear with moment acting about only one axis (x or y). Maximum vertical shear transfer and maximum moment transfer do not occur simultaneously.

For the East-West design strip (bending about the y-axis of the critical section shown above):

$c_1 = 600 \text{ mm}; c_2 = 400 \text{ mm}$

$b_1 = c_1 + d = 600 + 210 = 810 \text{ mm}; b_2 = c_2 + d = 400 + 210 = 610 \text{ mm}$

$$J = \frac{b_1^3 \times d + d^3 \times b_1}{6} + \frac{b_2 \times d \times b_1^2}{2}$$

$$= \frac{810^3 \times 210 + 210^3 \times 810}{6} + \frac{610 \times 210 \times 810^2}{2} = 61.87 \times 10^9 \, mm^4$$

$$e = \frac{b_1}{2} = 405 \, mm$$

From previous calculations:

$$\frac{V_f}{b_o d} = 0.911 \, MPa$$

$$M_f = 73.4 \, kN \cdot m$$

$$\gamma_v = 1 - \gamma_f = 1 - 0.566 = 0.434$$

$$v_r = 1.23 \, MPa$$

For moment about one axis only, Equation (13-9) simplifies to:

$$v_f = \frac{V_f}{b_o d} + \frac{\gamma_v M_f e}{J}$$

$$v_f = 0.911 \, MPa + \frac{0.434 \times 73.4 \times 10^6 \times 405}{61.87 \times 10^9} = 1.12 \, MPa$$

$$v_f < v_r \quad \Rightarrow \quad \textbf{OK}$$

For the North-South design strip (bending about the x-axis of the critical section shown above):

$$c_1 = 400 \, mm; \quad c_2 = 600 \, mm$$

$$b_1 = c_1 + d = 400 + 210 = 610 \, mm; \quad b_2 = c_2 + d = 600 + 210 = 810 \, mm$$

$$J = \frac{b_1^3 \times d + d^3 \times b_1}{6} + \frac{b_2 \times d \times b_1^2}{2}$$

$$= \frac{610^3 \times 210 + 210^3 \times 610}{6} + \frac{810 \times 210 \times 610^2}{2} = 40.53 \times 10^9 \, mm^4$$

$$e = \frac{b_1}{2} = 305 \, mm$$

$$M_f = 0.07 \left[\left(8.75 + \frac{2.85}{2} \right) 7.1 \times 6.2^2 - 8.75 \times 7.1 \times 6.2^2 \right] = 27.2 \, kN \cdot m$$

$$\gamma_v = 1 - \frac{1}{1 + \frac{2}{3}\sqrt{\frac{610}{810}}} = 0.366$$

$$v_f = 0.911 \, MPa + \frac{0.366 \times 34.9 \times 10^6 \times 305}{40.53 \times 10^9} = 0.99 \, MPa$$

$$v_f < v_r \quad \Rightarrow \quad \textbf{OK}$$

Edge column-slab connection at D-2

Consider moment about axis parallel to free edge. Equation 13-9 requires that moments be defined at the centroid of the critical section. Many analysis packages provide moments at the centroid of the column. The Direct Design Method gives moments at the face of the support. In either case, additional calculations are

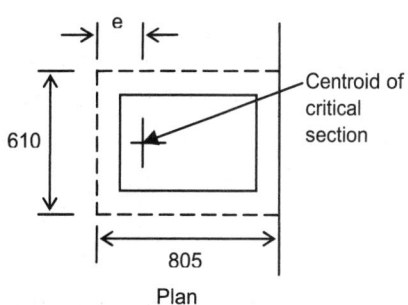

Plan

required to determine the moment to be used in Equation 13-9. With reference to the sketches at right:

$$e = \frac{805^2}{2 \times 805 + 610} = 292 \text{ mm}$$

From **Step 2**, the factored moment at the face of column support is 93 kN·m. The shears from span C-D, from the edge strip of slab between columns, and from the wall panels loading the edge are, respectively:

$$V_{SPAN} = 3.05 \text{ m} \times 6.6 \text{ m} \times 11.6 \text{ kN/m}^2 = 233.5 \text{ kN}$$

$$V_{EDGE} = 0.6 \text{ m} \times 6.6 \text{ m} \times 11.6 \text{ kN/m}^2 = 45.9 \text{ kN}$$

$$V_{WALL} = 6.6 \times 1.25 \times 2.4 \text{ kN/m}^2 = 19.8 \text{ kN}$$

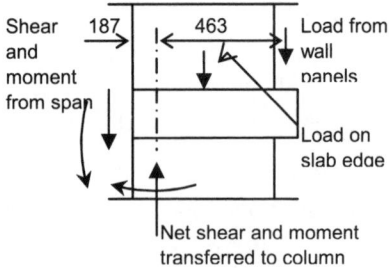

These shears have been overestimated a little. It would be reasonable to deduct load applied within the critical section. Also, the tributary area of an edge column does not extend to the midpoint of the span, as is usually assumed.

The net shear and moment acting at the centroid of the critical section are:

$$V_f = 233.5 + 45.9 + 19.8 = 299.2 \text{ kN}$$

$$M_f = 93 + 233.5 \times 0.187 - 45.9 \times (0.3 - 0.187) - 19.8 \times 0.463$$

$$= 93 + 44 - 5.2 - 9.2 = 122.6 \text{ kN} \cdot \text{m}$$

Geometric properties of the critical section for shear are:

$$b_1 = 805 \text{ mm}; \quad b_2 = 610 \text{ mm}; \quad b_o = 2220 \text{ mm}$$

$$J = 2\left(\frac{b_1^3 \times d}{3} + \frac{d^3 \times b_1}{12}\right) - b_o d e^2$$

$$= 2\left(\frac{805^3 \times 210}{3} + \frac{210^3 \times 805}{12}\right) - 2220 \times 210 \times 292^2 = 34.53 \times 10^9 \text{ mm}^4$$

$$\gamma_v = 1 - \frac{1}{1 + \frac{2}{3}\sqrt{\frac{805}{610}}} = 0.434$$

From preliminary shear check:

$$v_r = 1.23 \text{ MPa}$$

$$v_f = \frac{299.2 \times 10^3}{2220 \times 210} + \frac{0.434 \times 122.6 \times 10^6 \times 292}{34.53 \times 10^9} = 1.09 \text{ MPa}$$

$$v_f < v_r \quad \Rightarrow \quad \textbf{OK}$$

Edge column-slab connection at C-1

$$b_1 = 605 \text{ mm}; \quad b_2 = 810 \text{ mm}; \quad b_o = 2020 \text{ mm}$$

$$e = 181.2 \text{ mm}; \quad J = 18.01 \times 10^9 \text{ mm}^4; \quad \gamma_v = 0.366$$

$$V_{SPAN} = 255.3 \text{ kN}; \quad V_{EDGE} = 32.9 \text{ kN}; \quad V_{WALL} = 21.3 \text{ kN}$$

$$M_{face} = 0.26 \times 11.6 \times 7.1 \times \frac{6.2^2}{8} = 116.6 \text{ kN} \cdot \text{m}; \quad M_f = 124 \text{ kN} \cdot \text{m}$$

$$v_f = \frac{309.5 \times 10^3}{2020 \times 210} + \frac{0.366 \times 124 \times 10^6 \times 181}{18.01 \times 10^9} = 1.19 \text{ MPa}$$

$v_f < v_r \Rightarrow$ **OK**

Example 2 Two-way Slab with Drop Panels

Consider a floor with the same column layout as Example 1 that supports a higher live load of 3.6 kN/m^2, a partition load of 1.0 kN/m^2, and an additional mechanical services load of 1.0 kN/m^2. From the preliminary shear check in Example 1 we know that a 250 mm thick flat plate will not be satisfactory. **Try drop panels.**

Step 1 – Select Slab Thickness

a) Deflection requirements (13.2.4)

For economy, the projection of a drop panel below the underside of the slab, Δ_h, should be compatible with the forming system. This usually means being modular in some way with dimension lumber. Here the dimension Δ_h will be taken as the lumber dimension plus the thickness of one sheet of plywood (19 mm). Economical choices for Δ_h are:

$38 + 19 = 57$ mm or $89 + 19 = 98$ mm: **Try** $\Delta_h = 57$ mm

The value of x_d/ℓ_n is not known at this point. The upper limit is $\frac{1}{4}$. A reasonable preliminary estimate is $\frac{1}{6}$.

Interior Panel

$$h_s \geq \frac{\ell_n \left(0.6 + \frac{f_y}{1000}\right)}{30} - \frac{2x_d}{\ell_n} \Delta_h = \frac{6900}{30} - \frac{2}{6} \times 57 = 211 \text{ mm}$$

Try: $h_s = 220$ mm
$h_d = 277$ mm

Effective depths (to centre of mat) for shear using 15M bars with 25 mm clear cover
at column face: $d = 277 - 25 - 15 = 237$ mm
at face of drop: $d = 220 - 25 - 15 = 180$ mm

Factored loading:
1.5×3.6 kN/m^2 $+ 1.25 \times (0.22\text{m} \times 24$ kN/m^3 $+ 2.0$ kN/m^2) $= 14.5$ kN/m^2

b) Preliminary shear check

i) column at C3

Shear perimeter defined in 13.3.3.

$b_o = 2 \times (400 + 600 + 2 \times 237) = 2948$ mm

The final dimensions of the drop have not been decided but can be estimated as roughly 1/3 of the spans.

V_f = *factored uniformly distributed load* + *factored weight of drop projection*

$= 7.1 \times 6.6 \times 14.5$ kN/m^2 $+ 0.057 \times \dfrac{7.1}{3} \times \dfrac{6.6}{3} \times 24$ kN/m^2 $\times 1.25 = 688$ kN

$$v_f = \frac{V_f}{b_o d} = \frac{688\,kN}{2948 \times 237} = 0.985\,MPa \qquad \frac{v_r}{v_f} = 1.25 > 1.2 \; proceed$$

c)   Size drop panel

Re-arranging Equation (13-2),

$$x_d = \frac{\dfrac{\ell_n}{30} - h_s}{2\Delta_h} \times \ell_n = \frac{230 - 220}{2 \times 57} \times 6900 = 605 \; (east - west)\,; \; 2 \times 605 + 600 = 1810 \; mm$$

$$= \frac{230 - 220}{2 \times 57} \times 6200 = 544 \; (north - south)\,; \; 2 \times 544 + 400 = 1488 \; mm$$

Choose drop panel measuring 2000 x 2000.

Check shear around perimeter of drop. For a large shear perimeter, the resisting shear stress given by (13-6) will govern.

$$v_r = \left(\frac{\alpha_s d}{b_o} + 0.19 \right) \lambda \phi_c \sqrt{f_c'} = \left(\frac{4 \times 180}{4 \times (2000 + 180)} + 0.19 \right) \times 1 \times 0.65 \times 5 \; MPa = 0.886 \; MPa$$

$$v_f = \frac{(7.1 \times 6.6 - 2.0 \times 2.0) \times 14.5\,kN/m^2 \times 10^3}{4 \times (2000 + 180) \times 180} = 0.396 \; MPa < v_r \quad \Rightarrow OK$$

Use: h_s = 220 mm; h_d = 277 mm; drop measures 2000 x 2000

Step 2 – Design Moments

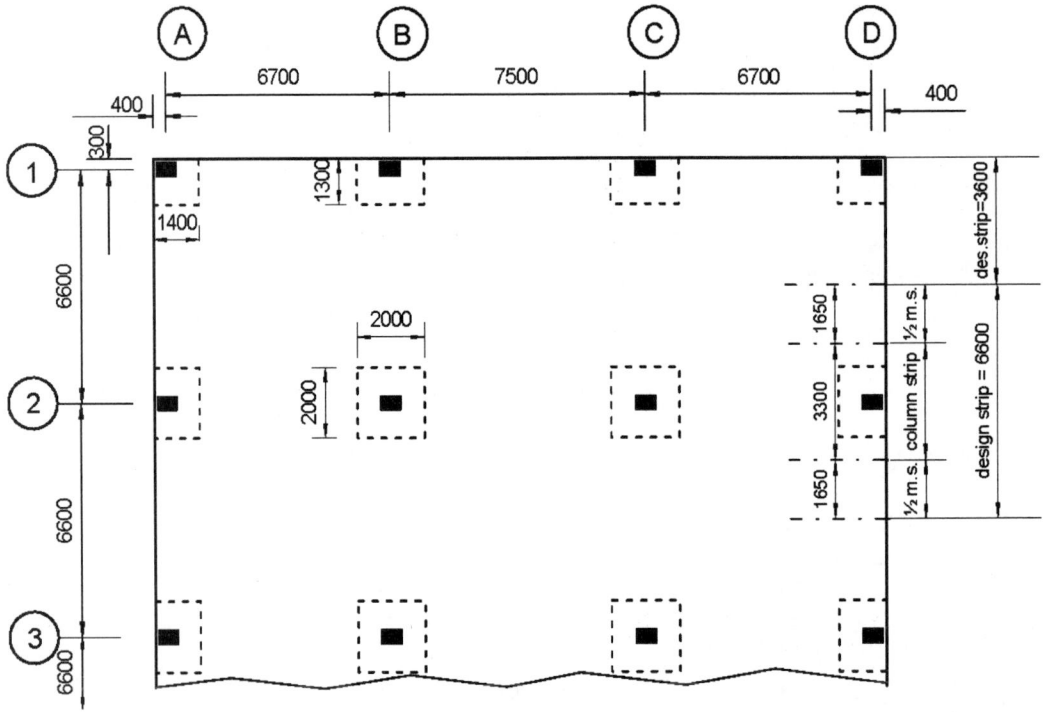

Consider a design strip along gridline 2. Since the limitations of (13.9.1) are satisfied, use Direct Design Method.

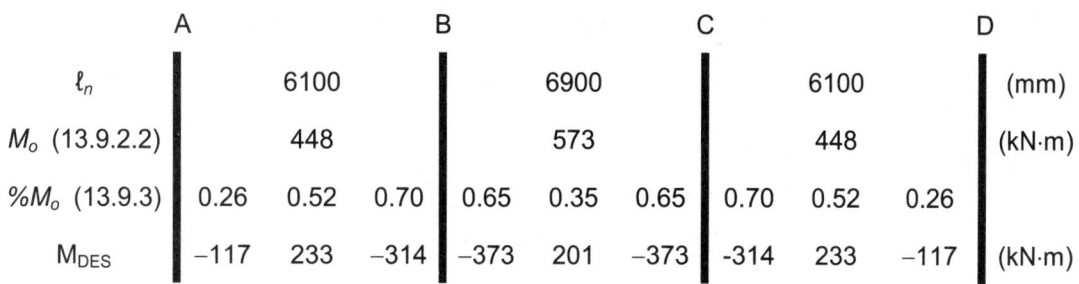

	A			B			C			D	
ℓ_n		6100			6900			6100			(mm)
M_o (13.9.2.2)		448			573			448			(kN·m)
%M_o (13.9.3)	0.26	0.52	0.70	0.65	0.35	0.65	0.70	0.52	0.26		
M_{DES}	−117	233	−314	−373	201	−373	-314	233	−117		(kN·m)

Step 3 – Select Reinforcement

Assume 15M bars: place   N-S reinf. in inner layer
                              E-W reinf. in outer layers
slab (outer layer): d_{max} = 220 – 25 – 8 = 187 mm
slab (inner layer): d_{min} = 220 – 25 – 15 – 8 = 172 mm

Approximate moment resistance per bar (E-W design strips):

$$M_{r\,bar} \approx \phi_s A_{bar} f_y \times 0.9 d_{min} = \frac{0.85 \times 200 \times 400 \times 0.9 \times 187}{10^6} = 11.44\ kN \cdot m$$

Minimum Reinforcement (in slab)

$$A_{s\,min} = 0.002 A_g = 0.002 \times 220\ mm \times 1000\ mm/m = 440\ mm^2/m \quad \Rightarrow \quad \textbf{Use 15M @ 400 c/c}$$

Moment resistance with minimum reinforcement (E-W design strips)

$$m_{r\,min} = \frac{\phi_s A_{s\,min} f_y}{s}\left(d_{min} - \frac{\phi_s A_{s\,min} f_y}{2\alpha_1 \phi_c f'_c s}\right)$$

$$= \frac{0.85 \times 200 \times 400}{400}\left(187 - \frac{0.85 \times 200 \times 400}{2 \times 0.81 \times 0.65 \times 25 \times 400}\right) \times \frac{1}{10^3} = 30.7\ kN \cdot m/m$$

Positive moment (bottom) reinforcement

(13.11.2.3) requires that 55% to 65% of the positive moment in all spans be taken by the column strips. This leaves 45% to 35% of the positive moment to be taken by the middle strips.

	A	B	C	
MDES	233	201	233	(kN·m)
$m_{DES\ col.st.}$	38.3 to 45.9	33.5 to 39.6	38.3 to 45.9	(kN·m/m)
$m_{DES\ mid.st.}$	31.8 to 24.7	27.4 to 21.3	31.8 to 24.7	(kN·m/m)

The resistance provided by minimum reinforcement, 30.7 kN·m/m, is not sufficient for the column strips but does satisfy the requirements of the middle strips. Try 15M at 400 c/c bottom and add bars in column strip as required.

Spans AB and CD

$$m_{r\,col.st.}(required) = \left(1 - \frac{30.7}{31.8} \times 0.45\right) \times \frac{233}{3.3} = 40.24\ kN \cdot m/m$$

Deficit within width of column strip $(3.3\ m) = 3.3 \times (40.24 - 30.7) = 31.5\ kN \cdot m$

$\dfrac{31.5}{11.44} = 2.75\ additional\ bars\quad \Rightarrow \qquad$ Add 3-15M bottom in column strip of spans AB and CD

Span BC

$m_{r\ col.st.}(required) = 33.5\ kN \cdot m/m$

Deficit within width of column strip $(3.3\ m) = 3.3 \times (33.5 - 30.7) = 9.24\ kN \cdot m$

$\dfrac{9.24}{11.44} = 0.8\ additional\ bars\quad \Rightarrow \qquad$ Add 1-15M bottom in column strip of spans BC

Check Maximum spacing (13.10.4)

Positive moment reinforcement: $s \leq 3h_s$ but not to exceed 500 mm **OK**

Use 15M at 400 c/c bottom East-West
Add 3-15M bottom in column strip of spans AB and CD
Add 1-15M bottom in column strip of spans BC

Negative moment (top) reinforcement: Column at C3

Design top East-West mat to be centred on column.

Effective depth of reinforcement for negative moment

In drop
East-West (outer layer): $d_{max} = 277 - 25 - 8 = 244$ mm
Outside drop
East-West (outer layer): $d_{max} = 220 - 25 - 8 = 187$ mm

Approximate moment resistance per bar **in drop** (E-W design strip):

$$M_{r\ bar} \approx \phi_s A_{bar} f_y \times 0.9 d_{max} = \dfrac{0.85 \times 200 \times 400 \times 0.9 \times 244}{10^6} = 14.93\ kN \cdot m$$

Approximate moment resistance per bar **outside drop** (E-W design strip):

From previous calculation, $M_{r\ bar} = 11.44\ kN \cdot m$

Total negative design moment: $M_{DES} = 373$ kN·m

Require moment resistance for $373/_3 = 124\ kN \cdot m$ within width b_b.

$b_b = c_2 + 3h_d = 400 + 3 \times 277 = 1231$ mm

Try extending same spacing throughout column strip.

# of bars in column strip $= \dfrac{124}{14.93} \times \dfrac{3300}{1231} = 22.3\quad \Rightarrow$ **Try 24 – 15M bars in column strip**

# of bars in drop $= \dfrac{2000}{3300} \times 24 = 14.5\ bars$

# of bars outside of drop $= \dfrac{1300}{3300} \times 24 = 9.5\ bars$

Moment resistance provided in column strip $= 14.5 \times 14.93 + 9.5 \times 11.44 = 325$ kN·m

Moment to be carried by middle strip $= 373 - 325 = 48$ kN·m

# of bars in middle strip $= \dfrac{48}{11.44} = 4.2\quad \Rightarrow$ **Try 3 – 15M in each half middle strip**

Check

Moment in column strip: $0.75 \times 373 = 280 \le 325 \le 0.9 \times 373 = 336$ kN·m **OK**

Use: 30 – 15M bars top. Place 24 in column strip and 3 in each half middle strip.

Step 3 – Check Shear

The procedure for checking shear and moment transfer at a drop panel is essentially identical to that for a flat plate. Shear is checked on a critical section located $d/_2$ from the face of the support. In this case, d is measured from the centre of the top mat to the bottom of the drop. Two-way shear should also be checked at the perimeter of the drop.

Example 3   Two-way Slab with Slab Bands

This example is the same as Example 2 except that slab bands will be used in lieu of drop panels. **Use edge beam on perimeter (same depth as slab bands).**

Step 1 – Select Slab Thickness

a) Deflection requirements (13.2.4)

Choose slab bands running east to west. Minimum thickness to satisfy Table 9.2 (13.2.6)

$$h_{band\ min} = \frac{6100}{18} = 339\ (end\ span) \qquad \textbf{governs}$$

$$h_{band\ min} = \frac{6900}{21} = 329 (interior\ span)$$

Try h_{band} = 350 mm

Taking $x_d/_{\ell_n} = 1/4$ and rearranging (13-2):

$$h_s \ge 2 \times \left(\frac{\ell_n}{30} - \frac{h_{band}}{2} \right) = 2 \times \left(\frac{6900}{30} - \frac{350}{2} \right) = 110 \qquad \text{Try } h_s = 150 \text{ mm}$$

b) Width of slab band

Re-arranging Equation (13-2),

$$x_d = \frac{\frac{\ell_{n\ max}}{30} - h_s}{2\Delta_h} \times \ell_n = \frac{6900/30 - 150}{2 \times 200} \times 6200 = 1240 \ ; 2 \times 1240 + 400 = 2880 \text{ mm}$$

Try width of slab band to be 3000.

c) Preliminary shear check

Factored loading (averaging slab band over entire panel is conservative) :

1.5×3.6 kN/m^2 + $1.25 \times (0.15$ m $\times 24$ kN/m^3 + 2.0 kN/m^2) = 12.4 kN/m^2

1.25×0.2 m $\times 3.0/6.6 \times 24$ kN/m^3 = 2.7 kN/m^2 (slab band projection below slab)

$w_f = 12.4 + 2.7 = 15.1$ kN/m^2.

$V_f = 6.6 \times 7.1 \times 15.1 = 708$ kN

Assume 15M bars.

$d = 350 - 25 - 15 = 310$ mm

$b_o = 2 \times (400 + 600 + 2 \times 310) = 3240$ mm

Since $d > 300$ mm, shear resistance modified for scale effect (13.3.4.3)

$$V_r = \frac{3240 \times 310 \times 1.23 \text{ MPa}}{10^3} \times \frac{1300}{1000 + 310} = 1226 \text{ kN}; \quad \frac{V_r}{V_f} = 1.73 > 1.2 \quad \Rightarrow \quad \textbf{OK}$$

Use: **Slab band running east-west**
h_s = 150 mm; h_{band} = 350 mm; width of band = 3000 mm

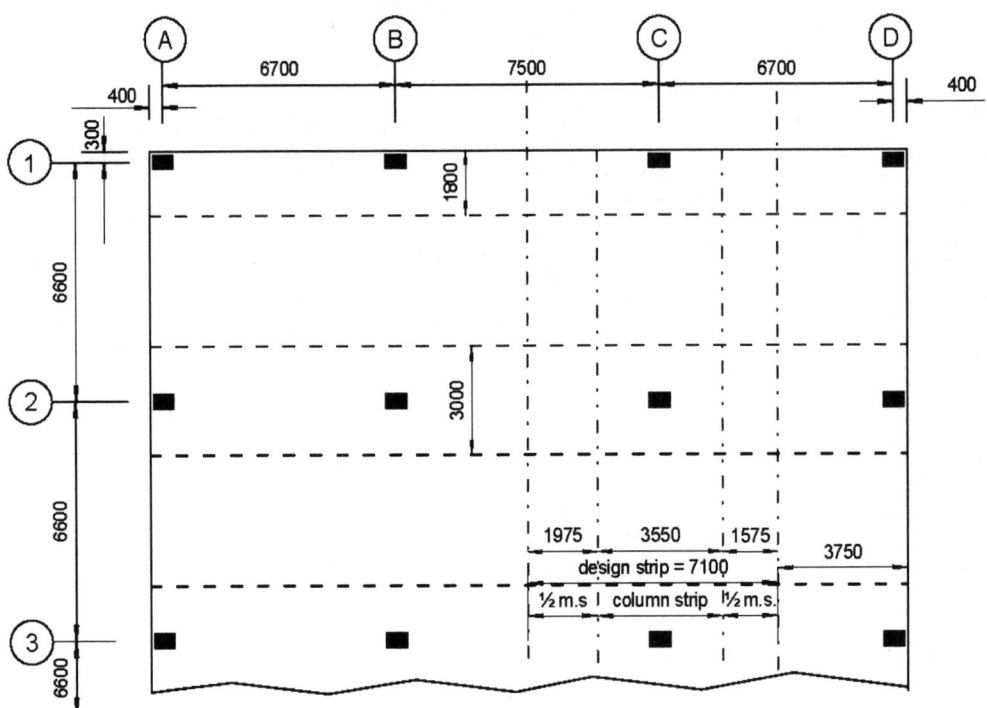

Step 2 – Design Moments

For moments in span parallel to slab band, the design process is much the same as it is for a slab with drop panels. Consider instead part of the design strip perpendicular to the slab band on gridline C. Use Direct Design Method.

		1			2			3	
ℓ_n		6200			6200				(mm)
M_o (13.9.2.2)		515			515				(kN·m)
$\%M_o$ (13.9.3)	0.26	0.52	0.70	0.65	0.35	0.65			
M_{DES}	−134	268	−361	−335	180	−335			(kN·m)

Step 3 – Select Reinforcement (perpendicular to slab band)

Assume 15M bars: place N-S bottom reinf. in outer layer
                                     place N-S top reinforcement in outer layer

Negative Moment

Check (13.10.7): distance from edge of band to face of support (1300 mm) is more than 4 times the projection of the slab band (200 mm). **Full depth of slab band can be used for negative moment.**

At slab band: d_{max} = 350 – 25 – 8 = 317 mm

Approximate negative moment resistance per bar:

$$M_{r\,bar} \approx \phi_s A_{bar} f_y \times 0.9d_{min} = \frac{0.85 \times 200 \times 400 \times 0.9 \times 317}{10^6} = 19.4 \text{ kN} \cdot \text{m}$$

# of bars required = $\dfrac{361}{19.4} = 18.6$ $\Rightarrow$ say 19 bars

Of these, 5% (1 bar) to 15% (2.9 bars) are added within width b_b. The remainder is uniformly distributed across the entire design strip (13.11.2.5).

$$b_b = 600 + 3 \times 350 = 1650 \text{ mm}$$

Use: 15M at 400 c/c top. Add 2 – 15 M in width b_b.

# of bars provided = $\dfrac{7100}{400} + 2 = 19.75$ **OK**

Positive Moment

In slab: d_{max} = 150 – 25 – 8 = 117 mm

Approximate positive moment resistance per bar:

$$M_{r\,bar} \approx \phi_s A_{bar} f_y \times 0.9d_{min} = \frac{0.85 \times 200 \times 400 \times 0.9 \times 117}{10^6} = 7.2 \text{ kN} \cdot \text{m}$$

# of bars required = $\dfrac{268}{7.2} = 37.2$

Try 15M at 200 c/c. # of bars in design strip = $\dfrac{7100}{200} = 35.5$

Add 2 – 15M in column strip.

Check:

$$M_r = 37.5 \times 0.85 \times 200 \times 400 \times \left(117 - \frac{37.5 \times 0.85 \times 200 \times 400}{2 \times 0.81 \times 0.65 \times 25 \times 7100} \right) \times \frac{1}{10^6} = 264 \text{ kN} \cdot \text{m}$$

$M_r \cong M_f$ **OK**

Use: 15M at 200 c/c. Add 2 – 15M bottom in column strip.

Example 4   Two-way Slab with Beams between All Supports

This slab has the same column layout as the three preceding examples but supports a higher service live load of 4.8 kN/m^2 and a superimposed dead load of 1.6 kN/m^2. A two-way slab and beam system will be used.

Step 1 – Select Slab Thickness (13.2.5)

Consider the interior panel bounded by gridlines B, C, 2, and 3.

$\beta = \dfrac{6900}{6600} = 1.04$; Assume $\alpha_m = 2$;

$$h_s \geq \frac{\ell_n}{30 + 8\beta\alpha_m} = \frac{6900}{30 + 8 \times 1.04 \times 2} = 180 \quad \Rightarrow \quad \text{Try } h_s = 200 \text{ mm}$$

Size beam

Table 9.2.   interior span: $h \geq \frac{6900}{21} = 320$

exterior span: $h \geq \frac{6200}{18} = 344$ **(governs)**

Try $h = 400$ mm

Determine required width of beam

$$\alpha = \frac{I_b}{I_s} \quad (\text{by definition})$$

$$= \frac{b_w}{\ell_2} \times 2.5 \times \left(\frac{h}{h_s}\right)^3 \times \left(1 - \frac{h_s}{h}\right) \quad (\text{combine with Equation 13 – 4})$$

The required beam width b_w is estimated as:

$$b_w = \frac{\alpha_m \times \ell_{2\,average}}{2.5 \times \left[\left(\frac{h}{h_s}\right)^3 - \left(\frac{h}{h_s}\right)^2\right]} = \frac{2 \times \left(\dfrac{7100 + 6600}{2}\right)}{2.5 \times \left[2^3 - 2^2\right]} = 1370 \text{ mm}$$

Try $b_w = 1400$ mm   for interior beams, $b_w = 800$ mm for perimeter beams.

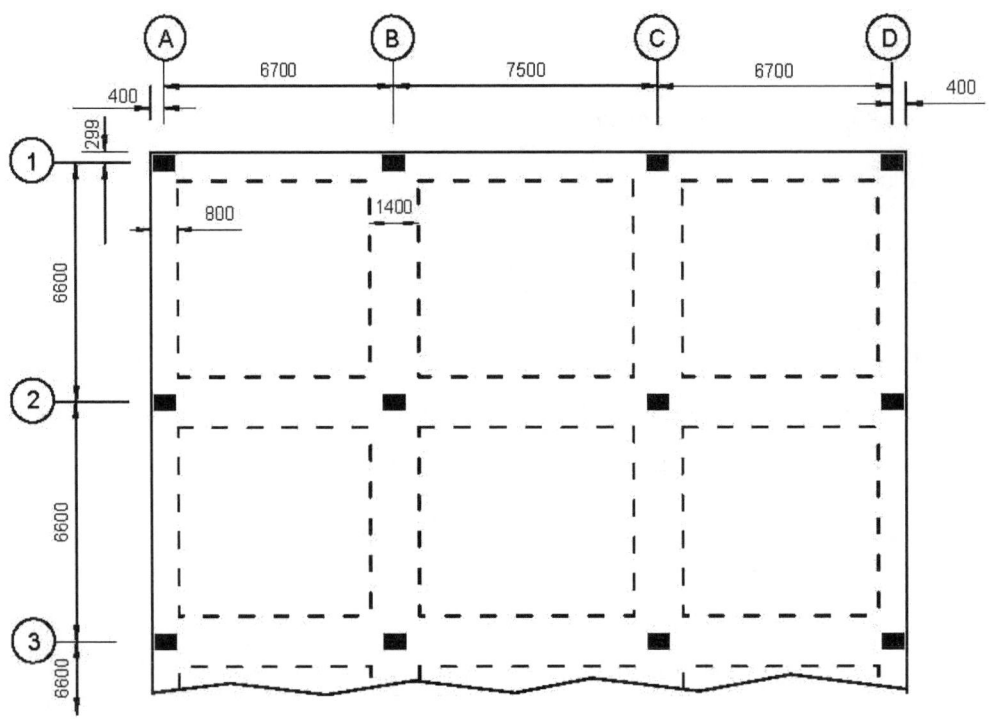

Step 2 – Design Moments

Loading:

$w_f = 1.5 \times 4.8 + 1.25 \times (0.2 \times 24 + 1.6) = 15.2$ kN/m^2

Beam stem: $1.25 \times 1.4 \times 0.2 \times 24 = 8.4$ kN/m

	A			B			C			D	
ℓ_n		6100			6900			6100			(mm)
M_o (13.9.2.2)		506			647			506			(kN·m)
%M_o (13.9.3)	0.16	0.59	0.70	0.65	0.35	0.65	0.70	0.59	0.16		(mm)
M_{DES}	−81	299	−354	−421	226	−421	-354	299	−81		(kN·m)

Step 3 – Select Reinforcement

Span AB

$$\alpha_1 = \frac{1400}{6600}\left(\frac{400}{200}\right)^3 \times 2.5 \times \left(1 - \frac{200}{400}\right) = 2.12$$

Portion of design moment resisted by beam (13.12.2.1)

$$\frac{\alpha_1}{0.3 + \alpha_1}\left(1 - \frac{\ell_2}{3\ell_1}\right) = \frac{2.12}{0.3 + 2.12}\left(1 - \frac{6600}{3 \times 6700}\right) = 0.59$$

Slab moment

$$M_{slab\ DES} = (1 - 0.59) \times M_{DES} = 0.41 M_{DES}$$

Span BC

Portion of design moment resisted by beam (13.12.2.1)

$$\frac{\alpha_1}{0.3 + \alpha_1}\left(1 - \frac{\ell_2}{3\ell_1}\right) = \frac{2.12}{0.3 + 2.12}\left(1 - \frac{6600}{3 \times 7500}\right) = 0.62$$

Slab moment

$$M_{slab\ DES} = (1 - 0.62) \times M_{DES} = 0.38 M_{DES}$$

Reinforcement for slab moments may be uniformly distributed over width of slab.

Step 4 – Shear Check (in slab)

$d = 200 - 25 - 15 = 160$ mm

$d_v = 0.9d = 144$ mm

$\quad = 0.76 h_s = 144$ mm

$V_r = \beta \phi_c \sqrt{f'_c}\, b_w d_v$

$\quad = 0.21 \times 0.65 \times 5 \times 1000 \times 144$

$\quad = 98.3$ kN

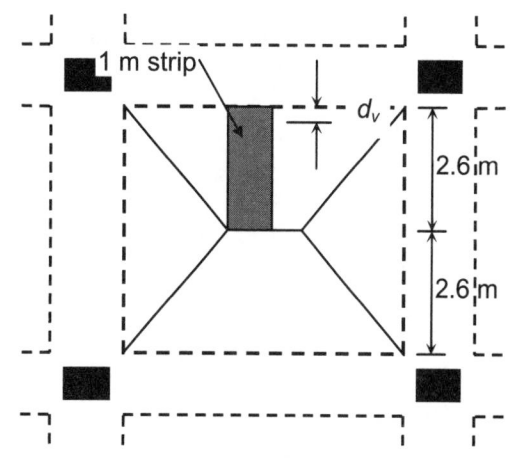

$V_f = 15.2 \times (2.6 - 0.144) \times 1 = 37.3 \text{ kN}$

$V_r > V_f \quad \Rightarrow \quad$ **OK**

Example 5   Two-way Slab with Stiff Supports (Appendix B)

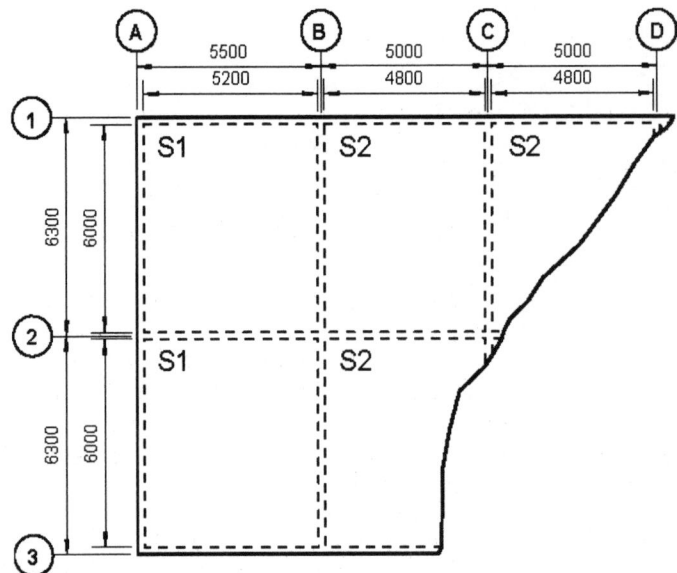

The roof of a storage facility supports a live load of 2.4 kN/m^2, a snow load of 1.6 kN/m^2, and a superimposed dead load of 1.44 kN/m^2. The roof slab is supported on all sides by stiff beams or masonry block walls.

Step 1 – Select Slab Thickness

Deflection requirements (13.2.5 and Appendix B)

Corner panel S1 governs: $\beta = {6000}/{5200} = 1.15$; assume $\alpha_m = 2$

$$h_{s\,min} = \frac{6000\left(0.6 + {400}/{1000}\right)}{(30 + 4 \times 2 \times 1.15)} = 153 \text{ mm}$$

(B.3.1) $h_{s\,min} = \dfrac{perimeter}{140} = \dfrac{2 \times (6000 + 5200)}{140} = 160 \text{ mm}$

Try h_s = 160 mm

Taking ${x_d}/{\ell_n} = {1}/{4}$ and rearranging (13-2):

$$h_s \geq 2 \times \left(\frac{\ell_n}{30} - \frac{h_{band}}{2}\right) = 2 \times \left(\frac{6900}{30} - \frac{350}{2}\right) = 110 \text{ mm} \qquad \textbf{Choose } \boldsymbol{h_s = 150 \text{ mm}}$$

Loading (Annex C), Load combination 2

$w_f = 1.5 \times 2.4 + 0.5 \times 1.6 + 1.25 \times (0.16 \times 24 + 1.44)$

$\quad = 3.6 + 0.8 + 6.6 = 11 \text{ kN/m}^2$

Step 2 – Design Moments

Middle strip moments

Panel S1; $\ell_a / \ell_b = 5200/6000 \approx 0.85$; Case 4

Negative moment at continuous edge (B.3.4):

$$m_{a\,neg} = 0.066(11)(5.2)^2 = 19.63 \text{ kN} \cdot \text{m/m}$$

$$m_{b\,neg} = 0.034(11)(6.0)^2 = 13.46 \text{ kN} \cdot \text{m/m}$$

Positive moments (B.3.5)

$$m_{a\,pos} = [0.043 \times (3.6 + 0.8) + 0.036 \times (6.6)] \times (5.2)^2 = 11.54 \text{ kN} \cdot \text{m/m}$$

$$m_{b\,pos} = [0.023 \times (3.6 + 0.8) + 0.019 \times (6.6)] \times (6.0)^2 = 8.16 \text{ kN} \cdot \text{m/m}$$

The remaining middle strip moments are as shown in the sketch. Negative moments at discontinuous edges are taken as ¾ of the positive moment (B.3.8). Bending moments in column strips are 2/3 of the adjacent middle strip (B.3.5). At all outside corners, special corner reinforcement to satisfy (13.12.5) is required (B.3.9). This special corner reinforcement matches the maximum positive moment in the panel.

The difference in negative moment at gridline B is not great enough to require balancing (B.3.10); nevertheless, they are balanced here to illustrate the process. Note that the positive moment in panel 1 requires adjustment.

$$m_{BA\,neg} = 19.63 - \frac{1/5200}{1/5200 + 1/4800} \times (19.63 - 19.01) = 19.33 \text{ kN} \cdot \text{m/m}$$

$$m_{BC\,neg} = 19.01 + \frac{1/4800}{1/5200 + 1/4800} \times (19.63 - 19.01) = 19.33 \text{ kN} \cdot \text{m/m}$$

$$m_{AB\,pos} = 11.54 + \frac{(19.63 - 19.331)}{2} = 11.69 \text{ kN} \cdot \text{m/m}$$

5

Slabs

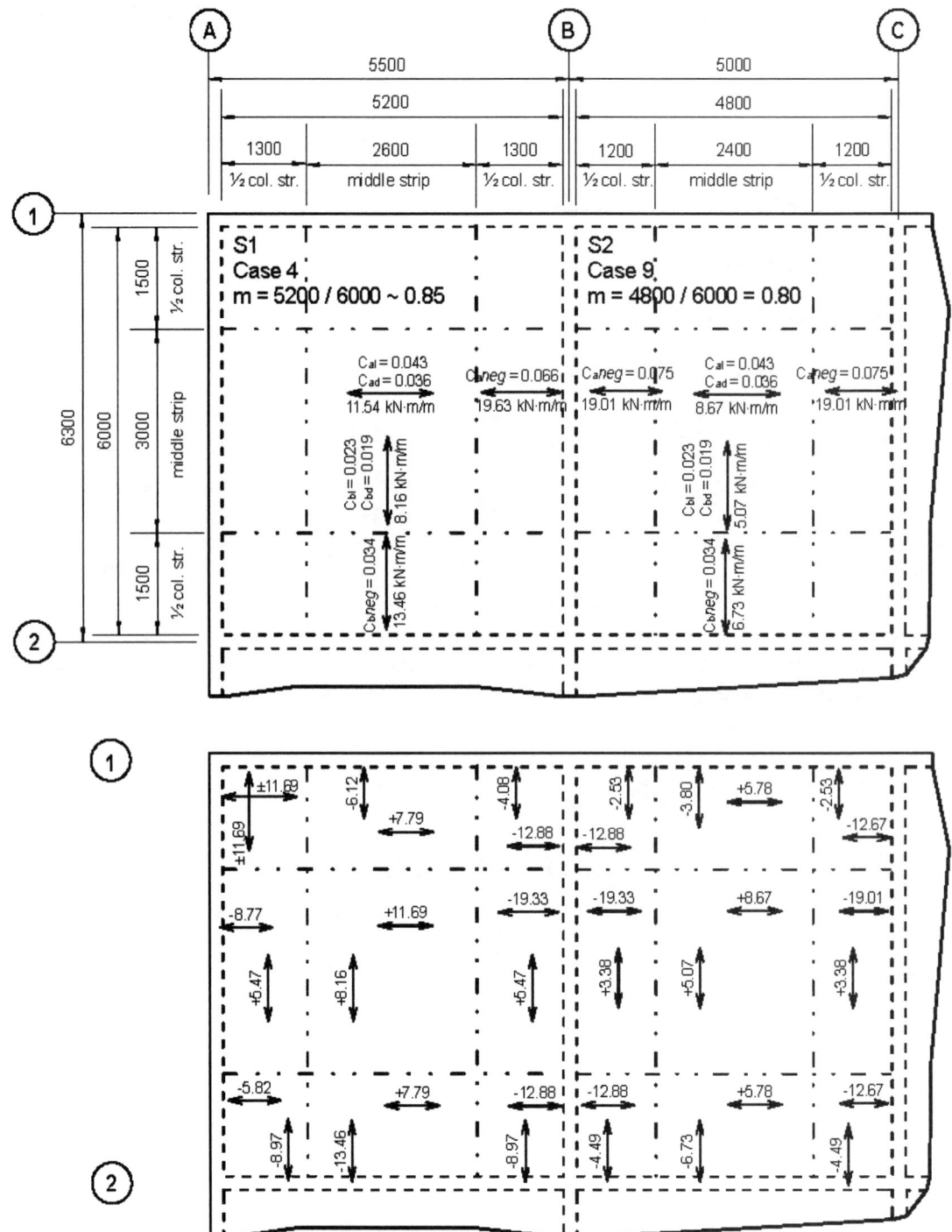

Steps 3 and 4 – Select Reinforcement and Check Shear

The procedure for selecting reinforcement is essentially the same as has been shown in earlier examples. Special attention should be given to the placing order so that reinforcement for the larger bending moments is given the larger flexural depth. As a general rule, it is usually economical to place minimum bottom reinforcement in both directions and add bars as required.

The procedure for checking shear is the same as was illustrated in step 4 of example 4 (two-way slab with beams).

Example 6   Reinforcing for Torsion (13.6)

The slab shown at right is continuous over two interior columns (500 × 500) and is simply-supported on the edges. It is 200 mm thick and supports a total factored load of 12 kN/m^2.

From a finite difference analysis, values of m_x, m_y, and m_{xy} were determined for each point on a regular grid covering the entire slab. Since the section in question will be crossed by reinforcement in the y-direction, we require values of m_y and m_{xy} along the section. These results are plotted below.

Determine Design Moments (13.6.4)

The distribution of my and m_{xy} are shown as dashed lines in the lower figure. The distributions of design moments, $m_{yDES}(pos)$ and $m_{yDES}(neg)$, form an envelope offset the absolute value of m_{xy} above and below my. The region filled with dashes is the negative design moment envelope and the region filled with crosses is the positive design moment envelope.

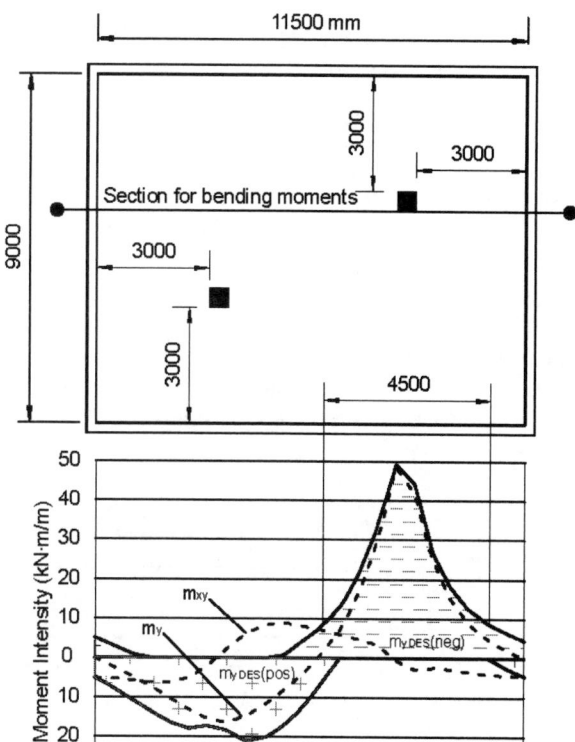

Lateral Distribution (13.6.5)

Minimum reinforcement

$$\frac{0.2}{100} \times 200 \times 1000 = 400 \text{ mm}^2/\text{m}$$

Use 15M at 500 c/c.

Assume minimum effective depth for reinforcement.

$d = 200 - 25 - 15 - 8 = 152$ mm

Moment resistance at minimum:

$$\frac{0.85 \times 200 \times 400}{500}\left(152 - \frac{0.85 \times 200 \times 400}{2 \times 0.81 \times 0.65 \times 25 \times 500}\right) = 20.0 \text{ kN} \cdot \text{m/m}$$

This is sufficient for all positive moment (bottom) reinforcement.

Total negative moment at column = shaded area = 132 kN·m. To simplify top reinforcement, try to design single band (i.e uniform spacing). The maximum negative design moment is 49.3 kN·m/m.

Minimum required moment intensity in band = 49.3 / 1.5 = 32.9 kN · m/m

Try 15M @ 300 c/c:

$$m_r = \frac{0.85 \times 200 \times 400}{300}\left(152 - \frac{0.85 \times 200 \times 400}{2 \times 0.81 \times 0.65 \times 25 \times 300}\right) = 32.5 \text{ kN} \cdot \text{m/m} \qquad \textbf{OK}$$

5

Slabs

Extend mat to uncracked concrete. From (13.2.7)

$$m_{cr} = \frac{h_s^2}{6} \times \frac{f_r}{2} = \frac{200^2}{6} \times 0.3\sqrt{25} = 10 \text{ kN} \cdot \text{m/m}$$

Region with design moment exceeding 10 kN·m/m is approximately 4.5 m wide (see sketch).

Try 15 – 15M at 300 top in band over column.

Check: $15 \times 0.3 \text{ m} \times 32.5 \text{ kN} \cdot \text{m/m} = 146 \text{ kN} \cdot \text{m} > 132 \text{ kN} \cdot \text{m}$ $\Rightarrow$ **OK**

Use: 15 – 15M at 300 c/c top in band over column.

Example 7   One-way Slab

An alternative slab and beam system supported by the same column grid as was used in Examples 1 through 4 is shown below. The slab supports a live load of 4.8 kN/m^2 and a superimposed dead load of 1.6 kN/m^2. Assume an exterior exposure.

Because the ratio of the long to short clear spans of the slab panels is 2 or more, the behaviour of the slab panels is essentially one-way, spanning in the short direction. One design approach is to use Appendix B with $m = 0.5$. An alternative to this is to design the slab as a continuous one-way beam.

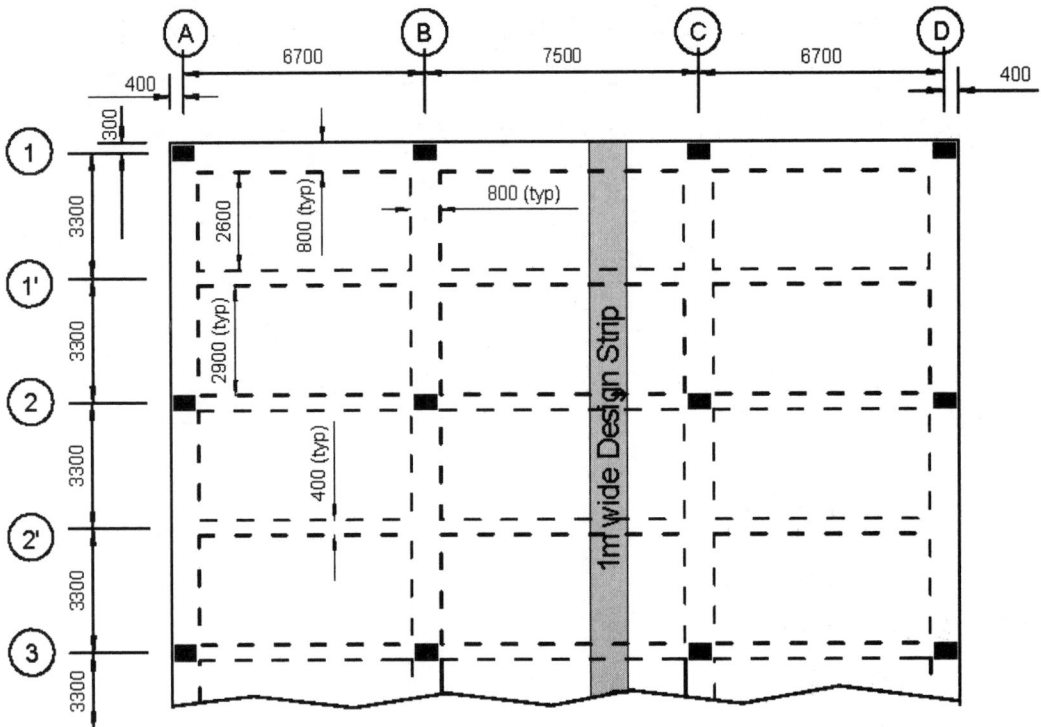

Step 1 – Slab Thickness (9.8.2.1)

Deflection requirements (Table 9-2)

Exterior span 1-1' $h_{s \, min} = {}^{\ell_n}\!/_{24} = {}^{2600}\!/_{24} = 108 \text{ mm}$

Interior span $h_{s \, min} = {}^{\ell_n}\!/_{28} = {}^{2900}\!/_{28} = 104 \text{ mm}$ $\Rightarrow$ Try $h_s = 125 \text{ mm}$

Step 2 – Design Moments

Factored Loading

$$w_f = 1.5 \times 4.8 + 1.25 \times (0.125 \times 24 + 1.6) = 12.95 \text{ kN/m}^2$$

For design strip 1 metre wide, $w_f = 12.95$ kN/m

Limitations for use of Clause 9.3.3 are satisfied;

use coefficients in Clause 9.3.3.

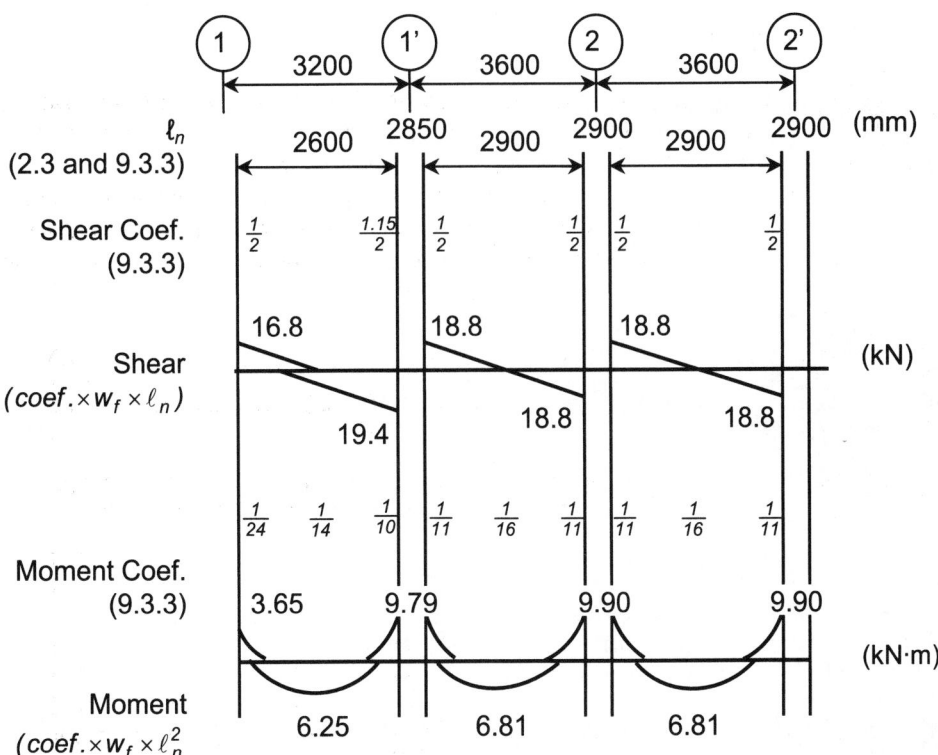

Step 3 – Select Reinforcement

Assume 10M reinforcement

Minimum Reinforcement

$0.002 \times 125 \times 1000 = 250$ mm^2/m $\Rightarrow$ Try 10M at 400 c/c

Check crack control:

At least minimum reinforcement will be provided for bottom steel in both directions. The principal reinforcement in the North-South direction will be in the outside layer. The reinforcement in the non-spanning East-West direction is more critical for crack control.

$d_c = 25 + 10 + 5 = 40$ mm

For $s = 400$ mm

$A = 400 \times 2 \times 40 = 32000$ mm^2

$$f_s = 0.6 \times 400 = 240 \, \text{MPa}$$

$$z = f_s \times \sqrt[3]{d_c A}$$

$$= 240 \times \sqrt[3]{40 \times 32000}$$

$$= 26060 \, \text{N/mm}$$

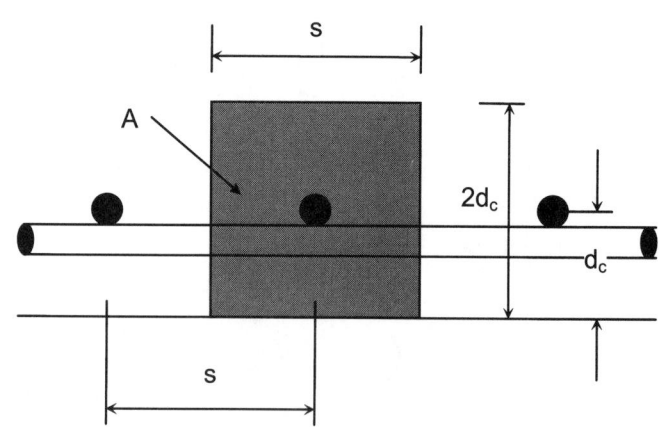

For an exterior exposure, z should be less than 25,000. this suggests that a spacing of 400 mm is too large. Revise spacing to 350 mm.

$$z = 240 \times \sqrt[3]{40 \times 350}$$

$$= 24,920 \, \text{N/mm}$$

Resisting moment at minimum reinforcement:

$$d = 125 - 25 - 5 = 95 \, \text{mm}$$

$$m_{r \, min} = \frac{\phi_s A_{s \, min} f_y}{s} \left(d_{min} - \frac{\phi_s A_{s \, min} f_y}{2 \alpha_1 \phi_c f'_c s} \right)$$

$$= \frac{0.85 \times 100 \times 400}{350} \left(95 - \frac{0.85 \times 100 \times 400}{2 \times 0.81 \times 0.65 \times 25 \times 350} \right) \times \frac{1}{10^3} = 8.87 \, \text{kN} \cdot \text{m/m}$$

This is adequate for all bottom steel requirements and for top steel on gridline 1. For top steel at interior supports try s = 300 mm.

$$m_r = \frac{0.85 \times 100 \times 400}{300} \left(95 - \frac{0.85 \times 100 \times 400}{2 \times 0.81 \times 0.65 \times 25 \times 300} \right) \times \frac{1}{10^3} = 10.3 \, \text{kN} \cdot \text{m/m}$$

This is sufficient at all interior supports.

Use: **10M at 350 c/c bottom each way.**
          10M at 350 c/c top North-South at perimeter beam.
          10M at 300 c/c top North-South at interior beams.

Transverse reinforcement over girders spanning parallel to slab is governed by (10.5.3.2).

$$A_{s \, min} = \frac{0.2 \sqrt{f'_c}}{f_y} b_t h = \frac{0.2 \times 5}{400} \times 1000 \times 125 = 313 \, \text{mm}^2/\text{m}$$

Use: **10M at 300 c/c top East-West over all girders.**

Step 4 – Check Shear

d_v is larger of:

$$0.9d = 85.5 \, \text{mm} \quad or \quad 0.72 h_s = 86.4 \, \text{mm} \; (governs)$$

$$V_r = \beta \lambda \phi_c \sqrt{f'_c} b_w d_v = 0.21 \times 1 \times 0.65 \times 5 \times 1000 \times 86.4 = 59.0 \, \text{kN} > V_f \quad \Rightarrow \quad \textbf{OK}$$

Step 5 – Design Supporting Beams

Beams and girders designed for vertical reaction from slab, self-weight of beam stem, and any other loads applied directly to beams. Edge beams also designed for torsion corresponding to negative support moments assumed in slab design.

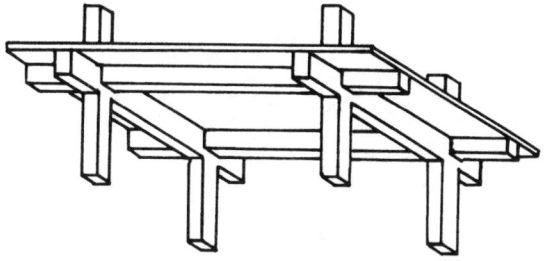

(a) 2-way slab with beams

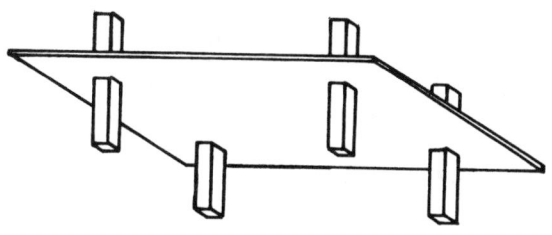

(b) 2-way slab without beams
(flat plate)

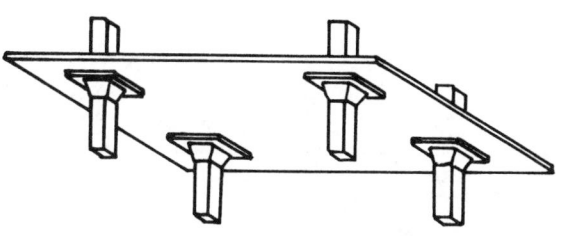

(c) 2-way slab without beams
(drop panels and column capitals)

Fig. 5.1   Types of 2-way Slabs

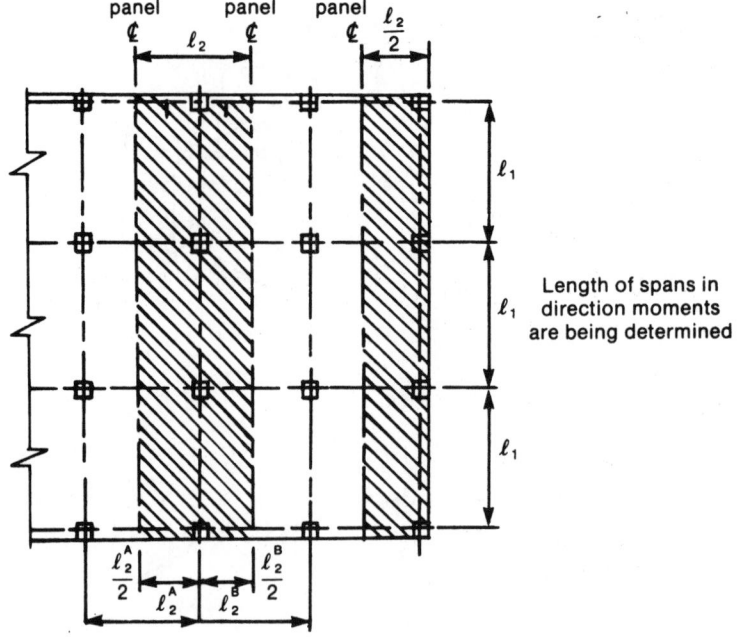

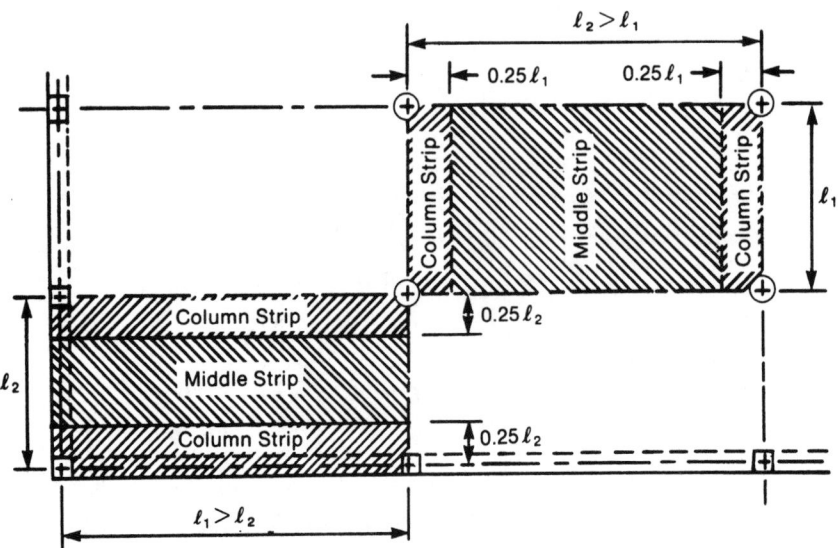

Fig. 5.2   Design Strips for Use with Direct Design and Elastic Frame Analogies

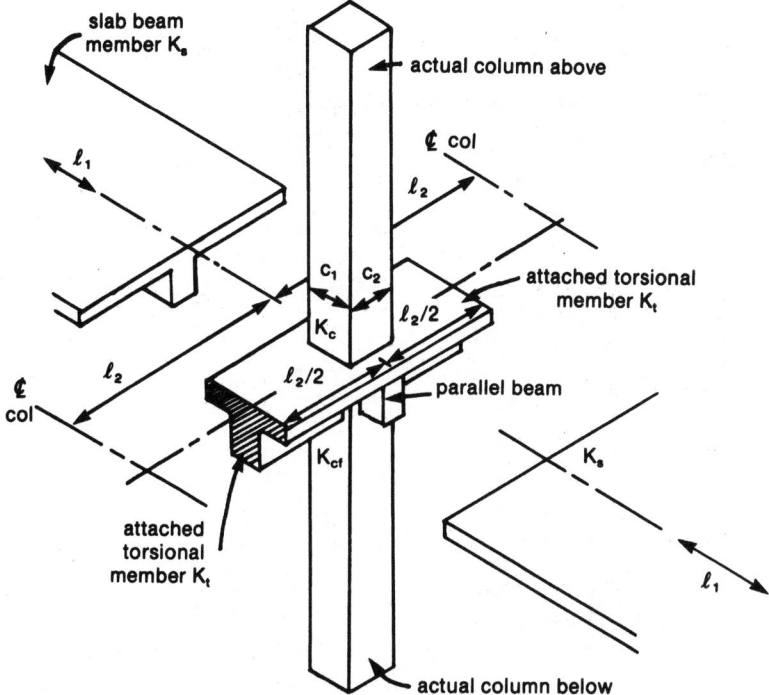

Fig. 5.3   Equivalent Column and Attached Torsional Members

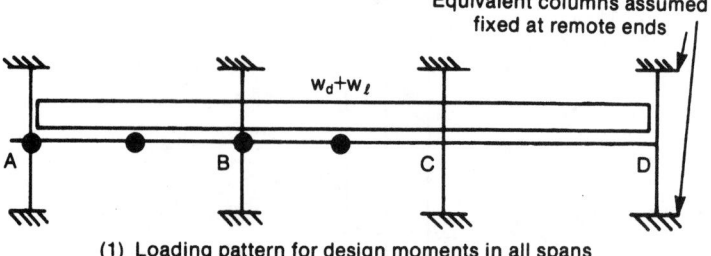

(1) Loading pattern for design moments in all spans
with L.L. ≦ ¾ D.L.

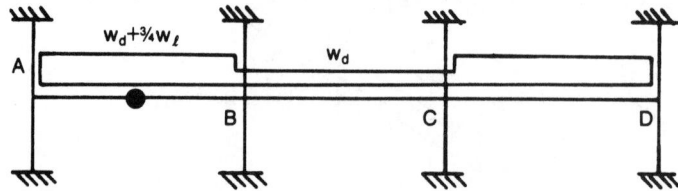

(2) Loading pattern for positive design moment in span AB*

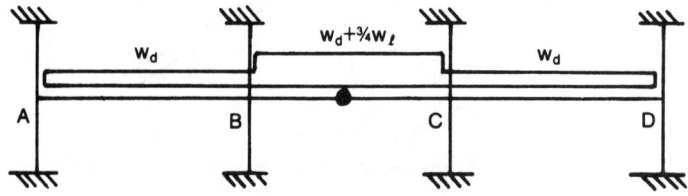

(3) Loading pattern for positive design moment in span BC*

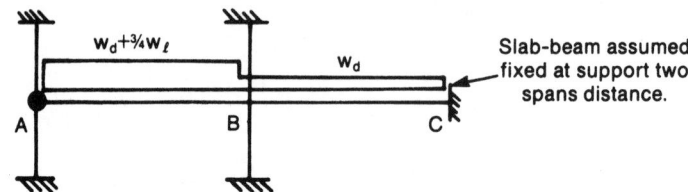

(4) Loading pattern for negative design moment at
support A*

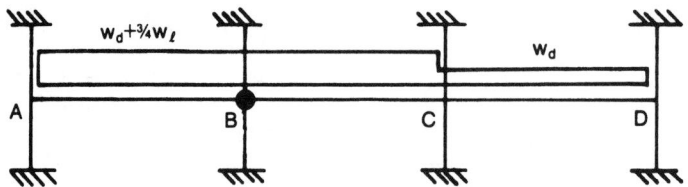

(5) Loading pattern for negative design moment at
support B*

*Design moments shall not be taken less than those
occurring for loading pattern (1).

Fig. 5.4   Partial Frame and Loading Patterns for Elastic Frame Analogies

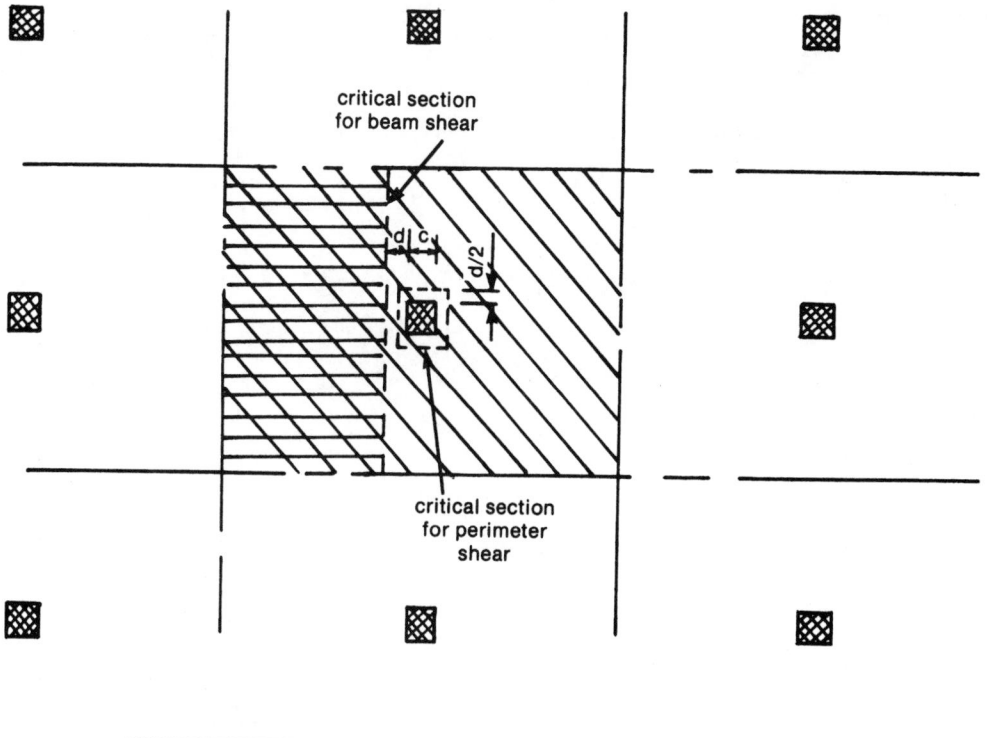

critical section
for beam shear

critical section
for perimeter
shear

Tributary area for beam shear

Tributary area for perimeter shear

Fig. 5.5   Critical Sections for Shear in Slabs

INTERIOR COLUMN

A $\quad = 2d(c_1 + c_2 + 2d)$

e $\quad = (c_1 + d)/2$

J $\quad = (c_1 + d)d^3/6 + (c_1 + d)^3 d/6$

$\quad\quad + d(c_2 + d)(c_1 + d)^2/2$

$\gamma_v \quad = 1 - \dfrac{1}{1 + \dfrac{2}{3}\sqrt{\dfrac{c_1 + d}{c_2 + d}}}$

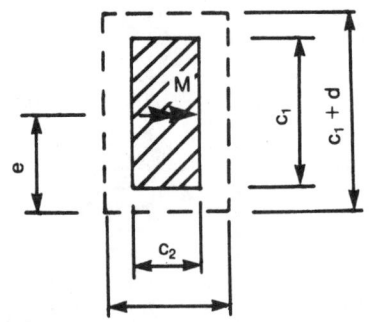

EDGE COLUMN

A $\quad = d(2c_1 + c_2 + 2d)$

$e_1 \quad = (c_1 + d/2)^2/(2c_1 + c_2 + 2d)$

$e_2 \quad = (c_2 + d)/2$

$J_1 \quad = [(c_1+d/2)d^3 + (c_1+d/2)^3 d]/6$

$\quad\quad + (c_2+d)d[e_1]^2 + 2(c_1+d/2)d[(c_1+d/2)/2 - e_1]^2$

$J_2 \quad = [(c_2+d)d^3 + (c_2+d)^3 d]/12 + 2(c_1+d/2)d[e_2]^2$

$\gamma_{v1} \quad = 1 - \dfrac{1}{1 + \dfrac{2}{3}\sqrt{\dfrac{c_1 + d/2}{c_2 + d}}}$

$\gamma_{v2} \quad = 1 - \dfrac{1}{1 + \dfrac{2}{3}\sqrt{\dfrac{c_2 + d}{c_1 + d/2}}}$

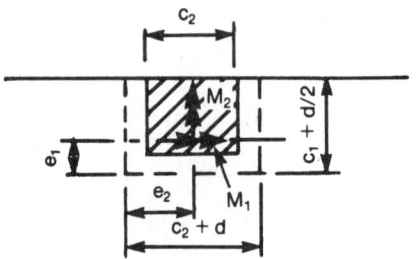

CORNER COLUMN

A $\quad = d(c_1 + c_2 + d)$

e $\quad = (c_1 + d/2)^2/[2(c_1 + c_2 + d)]$

J $\quad = [(c_1+d/2)d^3 + (c_1+d/2)^3 d]/12$

$\quad\quad + (c_2+d/2)de^2 + (c_1+d/2)d[(c_1+d/2)/2 - e]^2$

$\gamma_v \quad = 1 - \dfrac{1}{1 + \dfrac{2}{3}\sqrt{\dfrac{c_1 + d/2}{c_2 + d/2}}}$

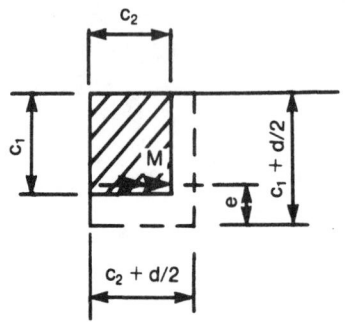

Fig. 5.6   Geometric Expressions for Shear-Moment Transfer

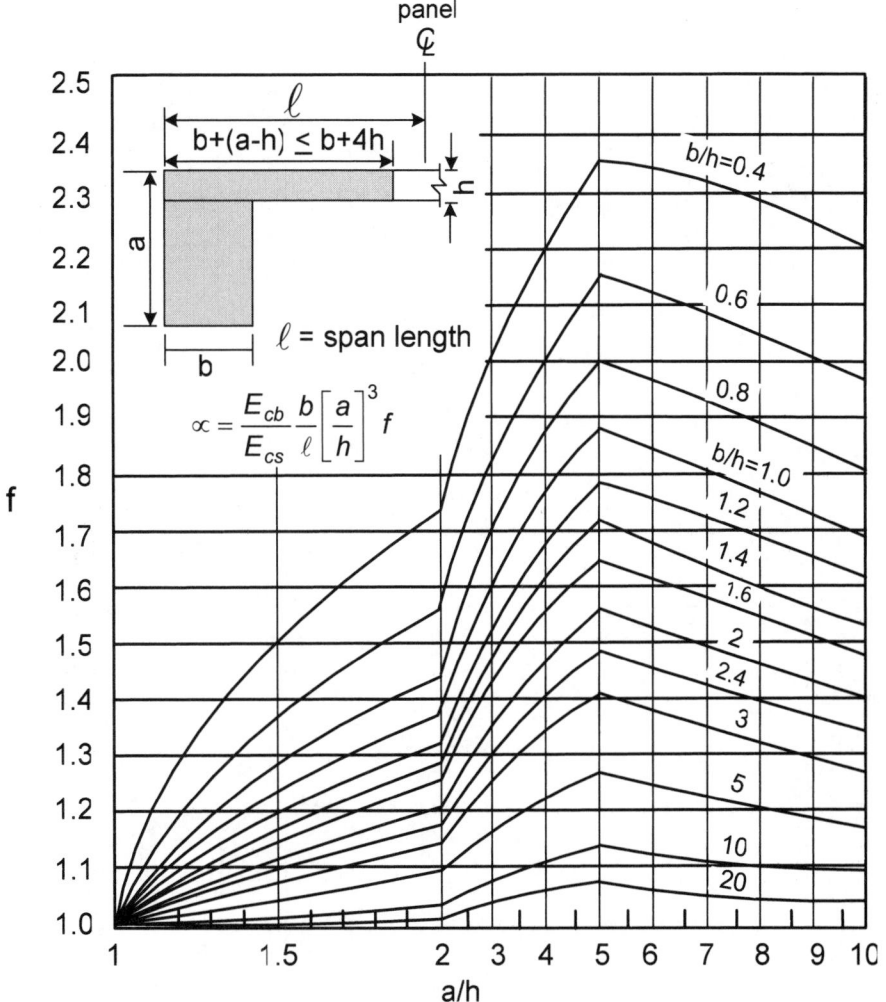

Table 5.1   Beam to Slab Ratio ∝ (Edge Beams)

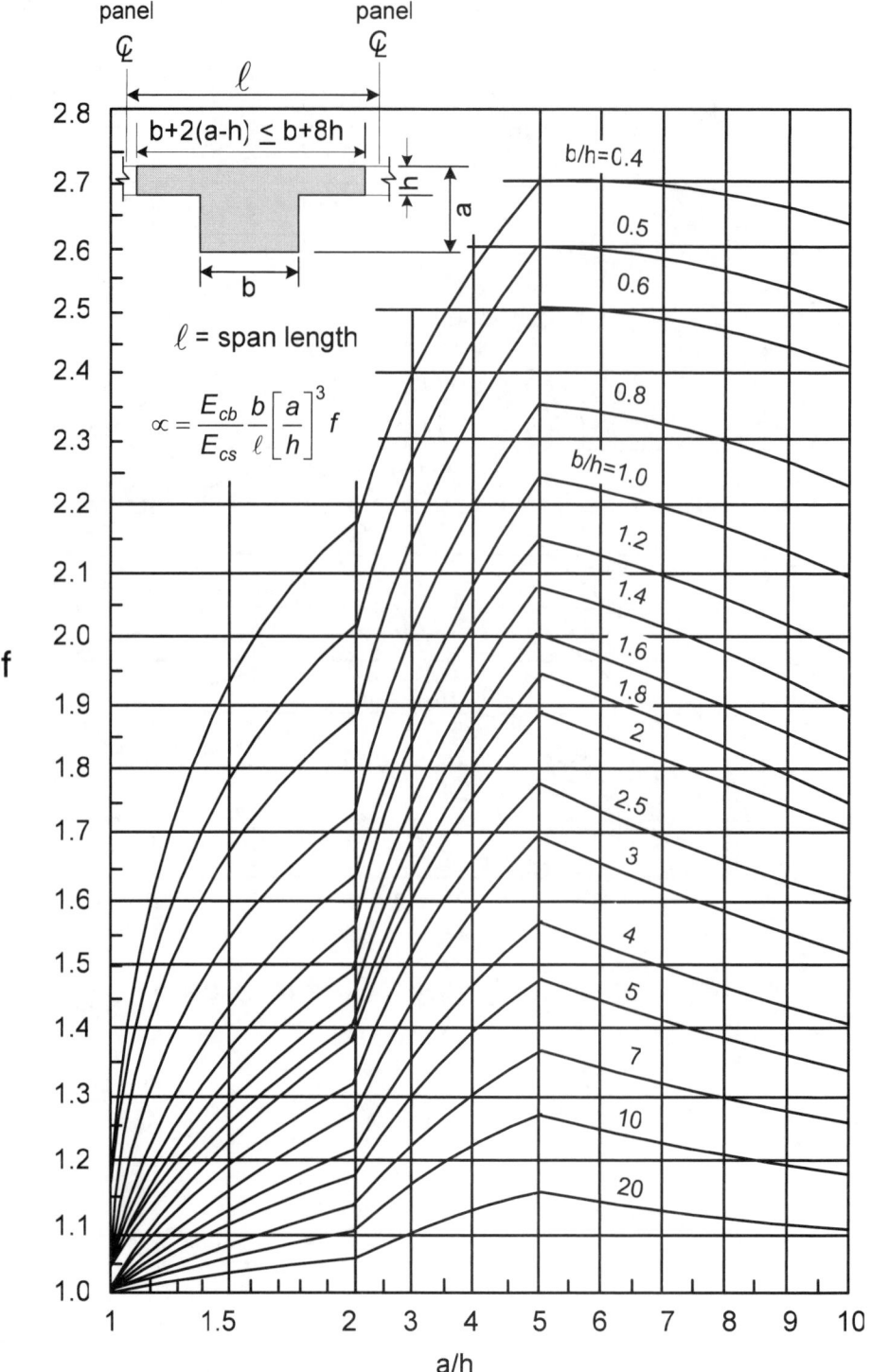

Table 5.2   Beam to Slab Ratio ∝ (Interior Beams)

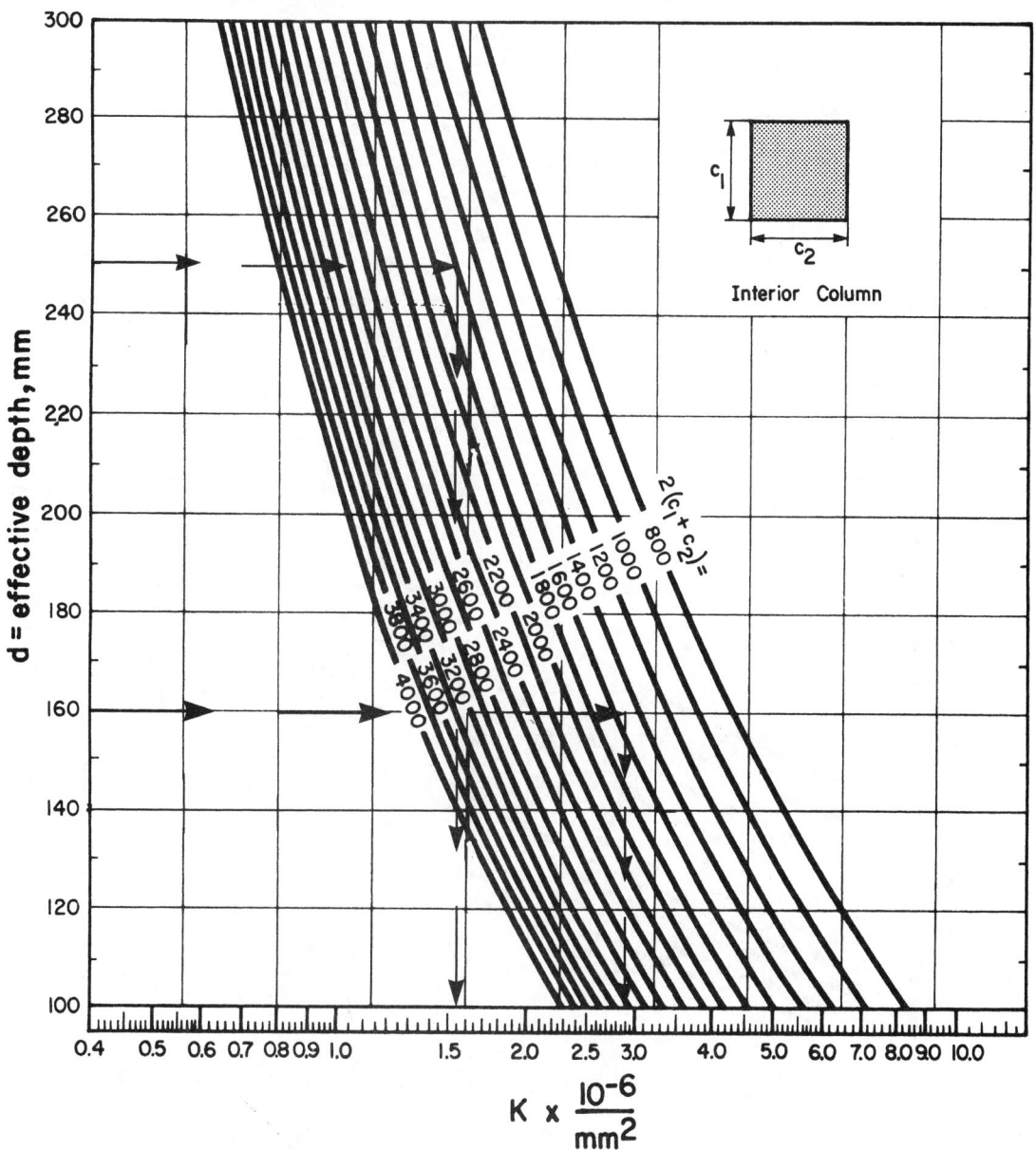

Table 5.3   Factor k, Shear-Moment Transfer, Interior Column

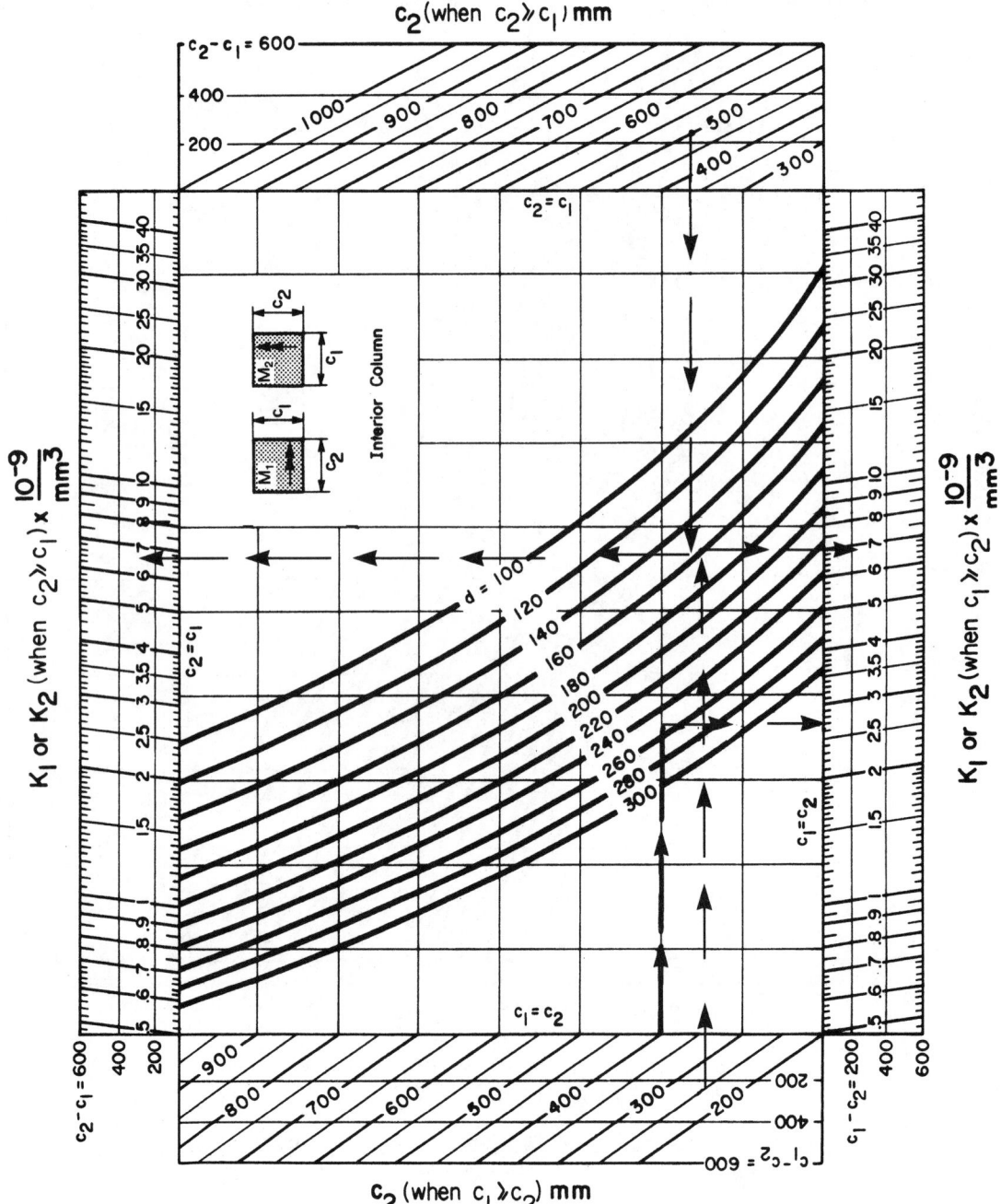

Table 5.4   Factor k_1 or k_2, Shear-Moment Transfer, Interior Column

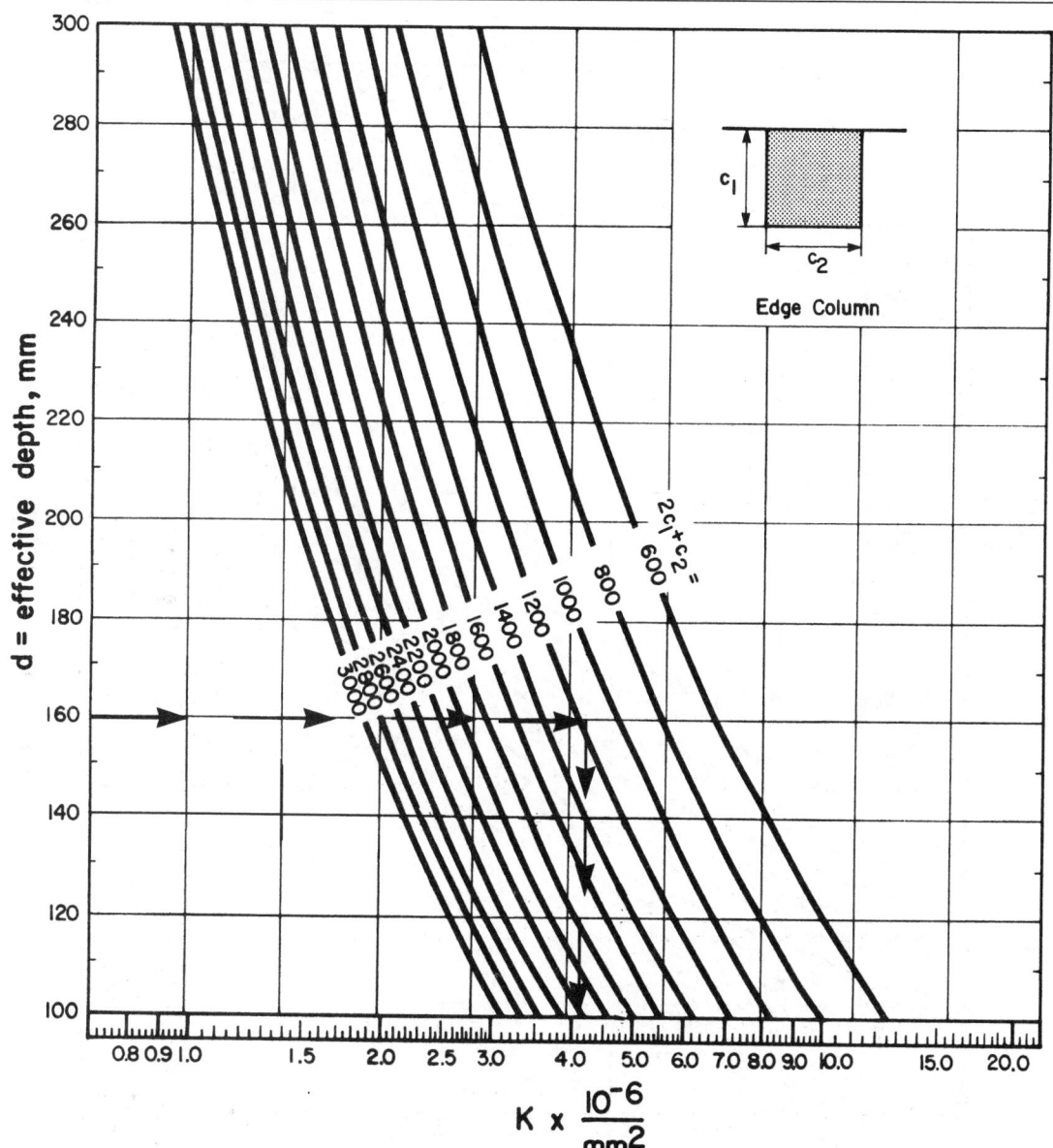

Table 5.5   Factor k, Shear-Moment Transfer, Edge Column

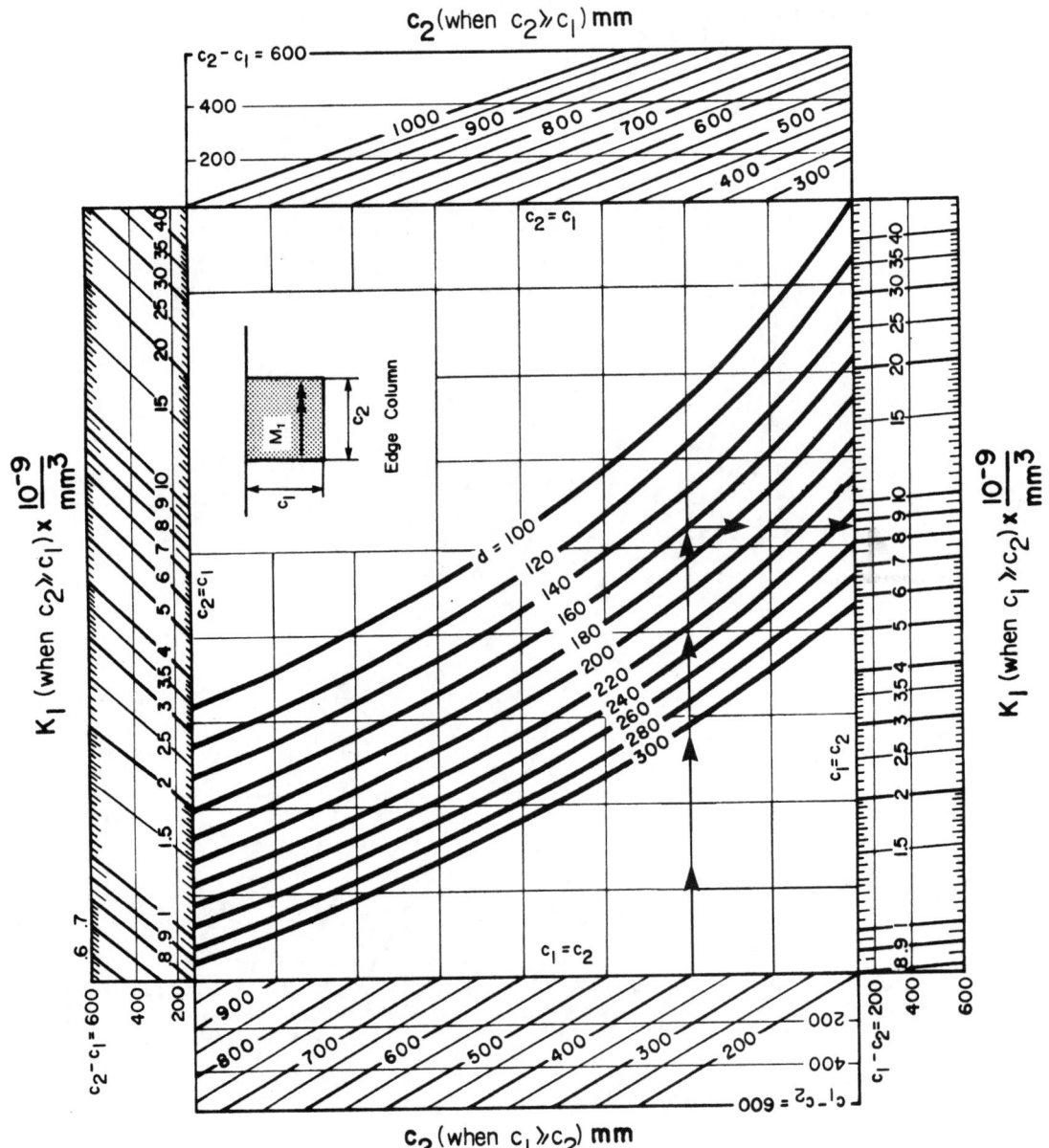

Table 5.6   Factor k_1, Shear-Moment Transfer, Edge Column

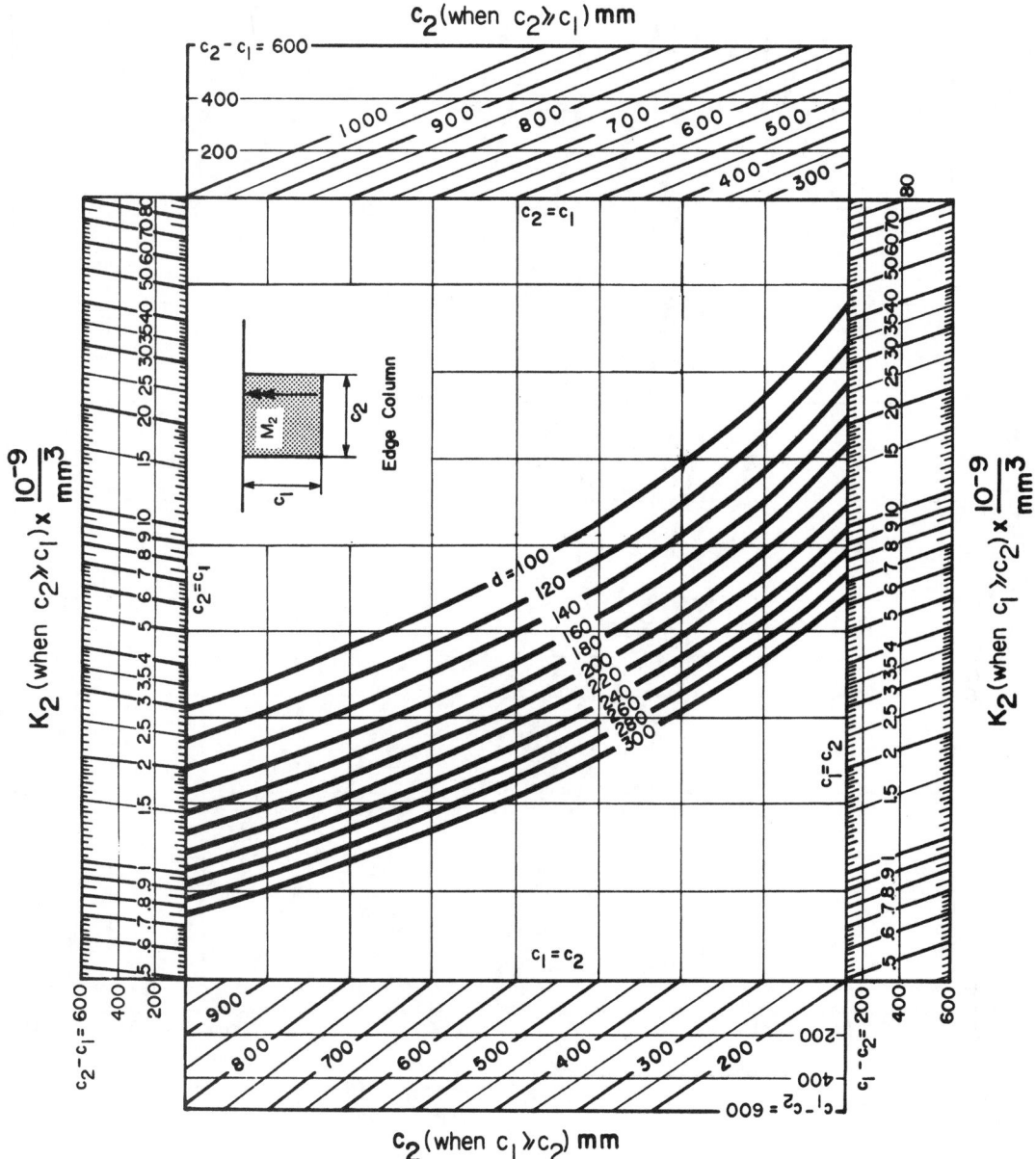

Table 5.7   Factor k_2, Shear-Moment Transfer, Edge Column

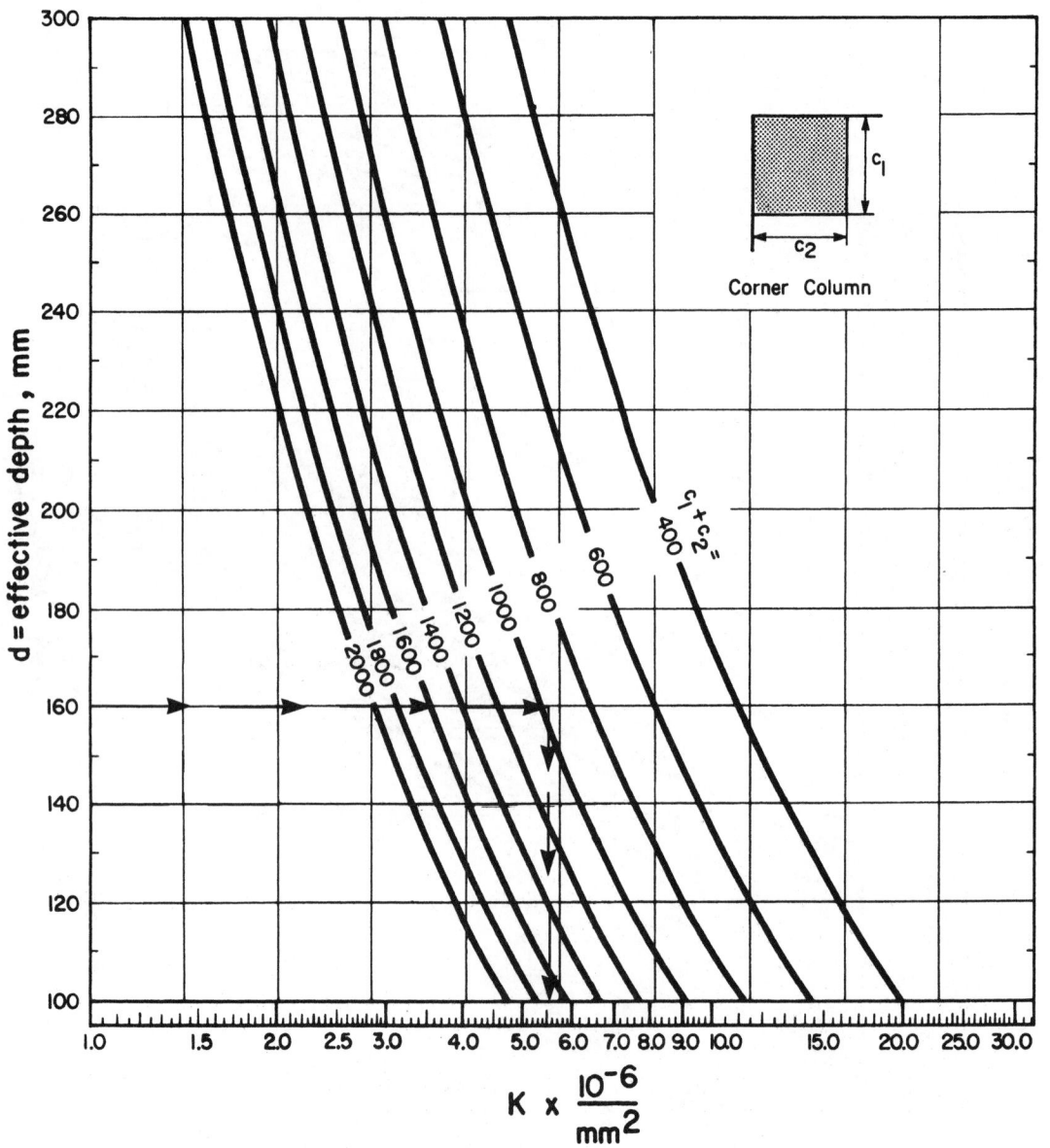

Table 5.8   Factor k, Shear-Moment Transfer, Corner Column

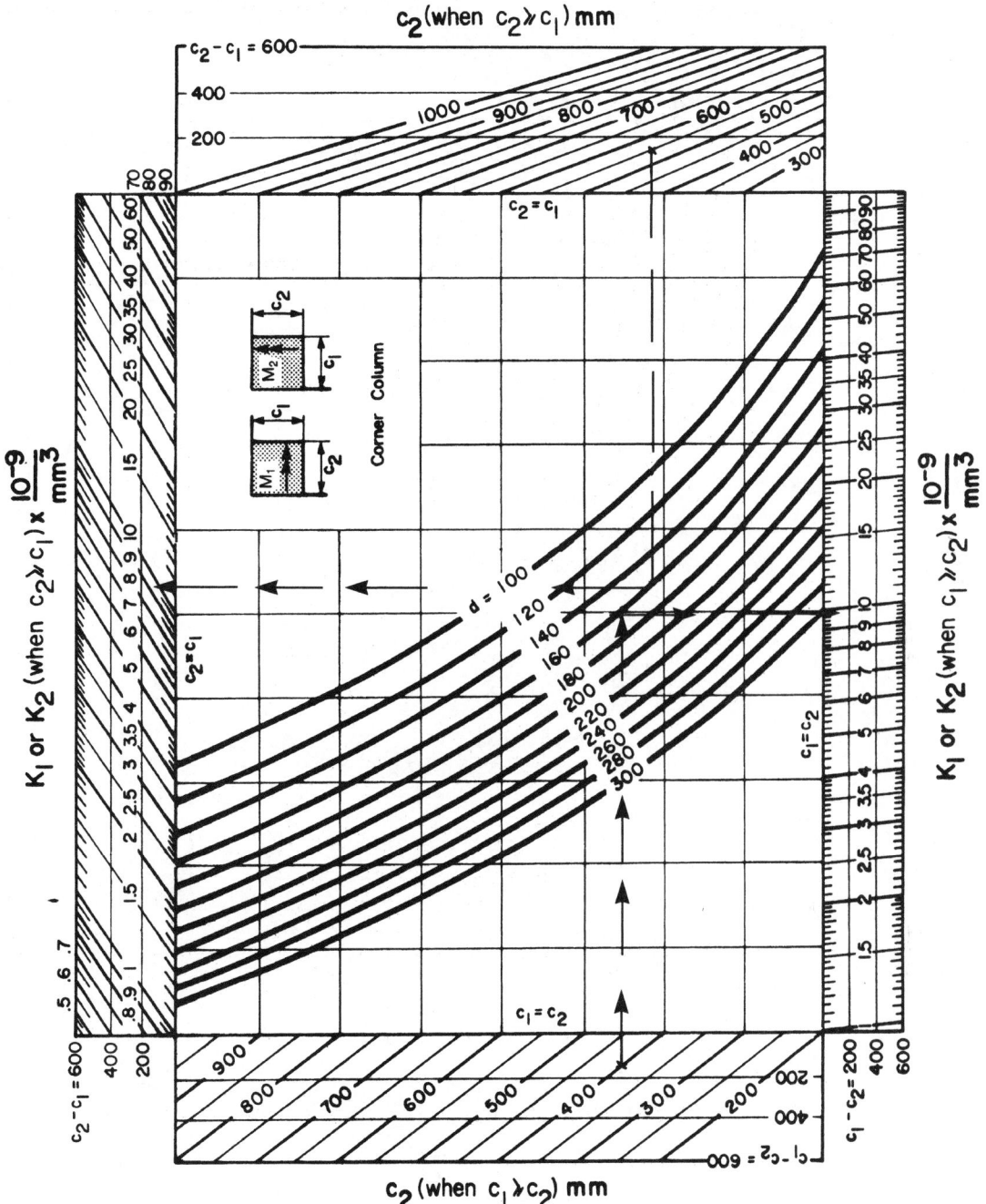

Table 5.9   Factor k_1 or k_2, Shear-Moment Transfer, Corner Column

Table 5.10   Area of Reinforcing Steel (A_s mm^2)
Per One Metre Strip

Bar Spacing mm	Bar Size (No.)					
	10	15	20	25	30	35
50	2000	4000	6000	10000	14000	20000
80	1250	2500	3750	6250	8750	12500
100	1000	2000	3000	5000	7000	10000
120	833	1667	2500	4167	5833	8333
150	667	1333	2000	3333	4667	6667
180	556	1111	1667	2778	3889	5556
200	500	1000	1500	2500	3500	5000
220	455	909	1364	2273	3182	4545
240	417	833	1250	2083	2917	4167
250	400	800	1200	2000	2800	4000
260	385	769	1154	1923	2692	3846
280	357	714	1071	1786	2500	3571
300	333	667	1000	1667	2333	3333
320	313	625	938	1563	2188	3125
340	294	588	882	1471	2059	2941
360	278	556	833	1389	1944	2778
380	263	526	789	1316	1842	2632
400	250	500	750	1250	1750	2500
420	238	476	714	1190	1667	2381
440	227	455	682	1136	1591	2273
460	217	435	652	1087	1522	2174

6

by A. Scanlon,
N. J. Gardner

Deflections

6

Deflections

6.1   Introduction

CSA Standard A23.3 Clause 9.8 requires that structures and structural members be designed to ensure that deflections are within acceptable limits for their intended use. Serviceability requirements for deflection are to be checked at specified load levels including effects of sustained load.

Deflections of concrete members depend on a large number of factors including the degree of cracking at specified load levels, cracking due to construction loads, creep and shrinkage characteristics of the concrete, modulus of elasticity, and support conditions. Because of the high degree of variability of factors affecting deformations, relatively simple procedures, as given in CSA Standard A23.3 may be used in deflection computations; however, undue reliance should not be placed on computed results.

Two approaches are available for control of deflections in one-way and two-way non-prestressed construction. In the first approach, deflection requirements are considered to be satisfied, under certain circumstances, by providing a member thickness equal to or exceeding a specified fraction of the span length. In the second approach, deflections must be calculated and compared with specified maximum permissible values. Situations not covered by the specified maximum permissible values must be considered on an individual basis.

ACI Special Publication SP 203 comparing Code Provisions for Deflection Control in Concrete Structure provides additional information.

6.2   Deflection Control by Span to Depth Ratios

6.2.1   One-way Construction (Non-prestressed)

For one-way construction *not* supporting or attached to partitions or other construction likely to be damaged by large deflections, deflections need not be computed if the member thickness equals or exceeds the value given in Table 6.1 (Table 9.1 of CSA Standard A23.3). If the member supports, or is attached to non-structural elements likely to be damaged by large deflections, the table of minimum thicknesses does not apply and deflections must be computed or otherwise shown to satisfy maximum permissible values.

6.2.2   Two-way Construction (Non-prestressed)

For two-way construction, if the slab thickness equals or exceeds the minimum thickness value given in Clauses 13.3.3 to 13.3.5, deflections need not be computed. These minimum thickness values apply whether or not the slab is supporting partitions or other construction likely to be damaged by large deflections.

CSA A23.3 equations specifying minimum thickness for two-way construction are given in Table 6.2.

Excessive deflections of two-way slabs present a serious serviceability problem not easily remedied, particularly after installation of non-structural elements and mechanical services. It is preferable, therefore, to err on the side of thicker rather than thinner slabs.

6.3   Deflection Limits

Computed deflections must not exceed the limits given in Table 6.3 (Table 9.2 of CSA Standard A23.3) expressed as fractions of the clear span length, ℓ_n.

Deflections to be considered are,

a)   immediate deflection due to specified live load, L

b)   deflection occurring after attachment of nonstructural elements (due to sustained load + live load).

Two conditions are considered in Table 6.3, namely, members either attached or not attached to non-structural elements. Requirements are more stringent for members attached to non-structural elements likely to be damaged by large deflections.

Other deflection criteria may have to be considered by the designer. For example, where excessive deflection may result in either aesthetic or functional problems, such as objectionable visual sagging, ponding of water, vibration, or improper operation of sliding doors, total deflection should be considered. Guidance on deflection limits for a range of design situations is given in Ref. 1.

6.4   Deflection Computations

6.4.1   Computation of Immediate Deflections for Beams and One-way Slabs (Non-prestressed)

For uniformly loaded members, immediate deflections can be computed using the expression:

$$\Delta = K \left(\frac{5}{48} \right) \frac{M \, \ell^2}{E_c \, I_e} \tag{6.1}$$

where M = support moment for cantilever, midspan moment for simple and continuous beams
    ℓ = span length
    E_c = modulus of elasticity of concrete
         $(3300 \sqrt{f_c'} + 6900) (\gamma_c/2300)^{1.5}$
         $(1500 \leq \gamma_c \leq 2500 \ kg/m^3)$
       = $4500 \sqrt{f_c'}$ for normal density concrete
    I_e = effective moment of inertia
    K = coefficient as follows

	K
Cantilevers (fixed end)*	2.400
Simple spans	1.0
Fixed-Hinged Beams	
–Midspan deflection	0.800
–Max deflection (when using max. moment)	0.738
Fixed-Fixed Beams	0.600
Continuous Spans	$1.20 - 0.20 M_o / M_m$

where $M_o = w\ell^2/8$ and M_m is the net midspan moment.

*In the case of cantilevers, the deflection due to the rotation at the support must also be included.

For loading other than uniformly distributed, the formulae given in Chapter 1 of this Handbook can be used.

The effective moment of inertia, I_e, is given by

$$I_e = \left(\frac{M_{cr}}{M_a}\right)^3 I_g + \left[1 - \left(\frac{M_{cr}}{M_a}\right)^3\right] I_{cr} \qquad (6.2)$$

where $M_{cr} = \dfrac{f_r I_g}{y_t}$ $\qquad\qquad\qquad\qquad\qquad\qquad\qquad$ (6.3)

$\qquad\quad f_r \;\; = \;\; 0.6\lambda\sqrt{f'_c}$ $\qquad\qquad\qquad\qquad\qquad\qquad$ (6.4)

$\qquad\quad \lambda \;\; = \;\; 1.00$ for normal density concrete

$\qquad\quad \lambda \;\; = \;\; 0.85$ for structural semi-low density concrete

$\qquad\quad \lambda \;\; = \;\; 0.75$ for structural low density concrete

$\qquad\quad M_a \;\; = \;\;$ moment at load level under consideration

The quantities I_g, I_{cr}, and y_t can be calculated for rectangular and T-sections using the equations and charts given in Tables 6-4 to 6-9. Use of the Design Aids is illustrated in the Design Examples. I_e should be evaluated based on moment at the support for cantilevers, and midspan moment for simply supported beams. For continuous beams average values of I_e based on support moments and midspan moments should be used. CSA A23.3 states that I_e may be taken as a weighted average as given by the following expressions:

One end continuous:

$$I_{e\,(avg)} = 0.85\,I_{e\,(pos)} \;+\; 0.15\,I_{e\,(neg)} \qquad (6.5)$$

Both ends continuous:

$$I_{e\,(avg)} = 0.70\,I_{e\,(pos)} \;+\; 0.30\,\frac{I_e(neg)_{left} + I_e(neg)_{right}}{2} \qquad (6.6)$$

For column supported end spans where partial fixity is provided by the exterior column the following expression could be considered:

$$I_{e\,(avg)} = 0.75\,I_{e\,(pos)} \;+\; 0.25\,I_{e\,(neg)} \qquad (6.7)$$

I_e should normally be calculated based on the load level under consideration. For example, dead load deflection should be calculated with I_e based on the dead load moment. Deflection under combined dead plus live load should be calculated with I_e based on total load moment. Live load deflection would then be taken as the difference between total load deflection and dead load deflection. The use of I_e based on total load moments to compute all terms would tend to overestimate the dead load deflections and underestimate the live load deflections.

When construction procedures are likely to result in high loads at early age, such as in multi-story floor construction, I_e for all cases should be based on the construction load level as discussed in Section 6.4.3.

6.4.2   Computation of Long-Time Deflection for Beams and One-Way Slabs (Non-prestressed)

Having calculated the immediate deflection Δ_i corresponding to the sustained load level, the additional long-time deflection, Δ_t, due to creep and shrinkage may be calculated using Eq. 6.8.

$$\Delta_t = \frac{S}{1 + 50\rho'}\,\Delta_i \qquad (6.8)$$

where $S \;\; = \;\; 2.0$ (5 years or more)

$\qquad\quad\;\; = \;\; 1.4$ (12 months)

$\qquad\quad\;\; = \;\; 1.0$ (3 months)

The variation of S with time is shown graphically in Fig. 6.1. The use of a single multiplier for both creep and shrinkage effects is sufficiently accurate for most situations. However, since creep is stress-dependent while shrinkage is not, it may be desirable in some cases to consider the two effects separately. For example, in lightly loaded slabs reinforced on one face only, it may be necessary to consider the effect of shrinkage warping separately from the creep deflection due to sustained load. To calculate the long-time deflection components due to creep and shrinkage separately, the following equations may be used.

$$\Delta_t = \Delta_{cp} + \Delta_{sh} \tag{6.9}$$

The creep deflection is given by

$$\Delta_{cp} = k_r C_t \Delta_t \tag{6.10}$$

where $k_r = \dfrac{0.85}{1 + 50\,\rho'}$

6

The ultimate value of C, may be taken as *1.6* for average conditions. For intermediate times,

$$C_t = \frac{1.6}{2.0} S \tag{6.11}$$

The shrinkage deflection is given by:

$$\Delta_{sh} = K_{sh}\,\phi_{sh}\,\ell^2 \tag{6.12}$$

$$\phi_{sh} = \frac{A_{sh}\,\varepsilon_{sh}}{h} \tag{6.13}$$

For this purpose, the ultimate value of ε_{sh} may be taken as *400 x 10^{-6}* for average conditions. For intermediate times

$$\varepsilon_{sh} = \frac{S}{2.0}\,400 \times 10^{-6} \tag{6.14}$$

The term A_{sh} is obtained from Table 6.10. The steel percentages used in determining A_{sh} refer to the support section of cantilevers and the midspan section of simple and continuous spans. For T-beams, use $\rho = 100\,(\rho + \rho_w)/2$ in determining A_{sh}, where $\rho_w = A_s/(b_w d)$.

The following values of K_{sh} can be used in Eq. 6.12.

	K_{sh}
Cantilevers	0.500
Simple beams	0.125
Beams continuous at one end only	0.090
Beams continuous at both ends	0.065

Design Example 6.1

Required: Calculate midspan deflections for exterior span of Tee Beam shown. Compare calculated deflections with CSA Standard A23.3 Maximum Permissible Values.

1. Loads

   Dead Load
Slab:	=	16.5 kN/m
Wall:	=	8.6
Beam:	=	2.4
Superimposed:	=	4.6
Total Dead Load w_D	=	32.1 kN/m

Deflections

Live Load

Total Live Load w_L	=	8.4 kN/m
(Assume 20% sustained)	=	1.7 kN/m)

Total Load

$w_D + w_L$ = 40.5 kN/m

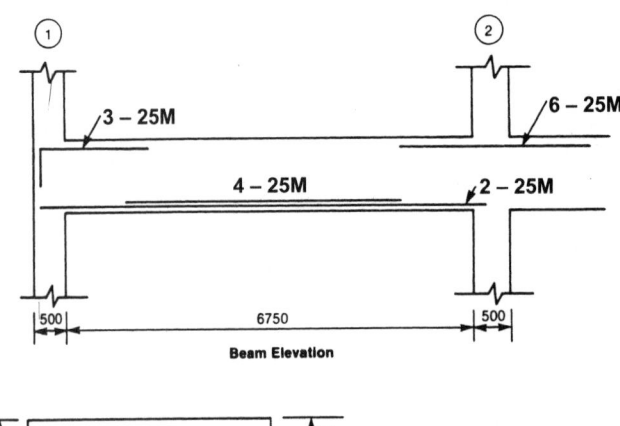

Beam Elevation

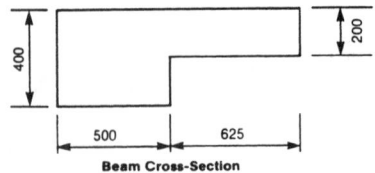

Beam Cross-Section

2.   Bending Moments

	Exterior Support	Midspan	Interior Support	
Clear span (ℓ_n)	6750	6750	6875	mm
Moment Coeff. (C_m)	1/16	1/14	1/10	
$M_D = C_m w_D \ell_n^2$	91.4	104.5	151.7	x 10^6 N·mm
$M_{D+L} = C_m(w_D + w_L) \ell_n^2$	115.3	131.8	191.4	x 10^6 N·mm

3.   Modulus of rupture, modulus of elasticity, modular ratio

$$f_r = 0.6\sqrt{25} = 3 \text{ MPa}$$
$$E_c = 4500\sqrt{25} = 22,500 \text{ MPa}$$
$$n = E_s/E_c = 200,000/22,500 = 8.89$$

4.   Gross Moment of Inertia, I_g

a)   Using chart: Table 6.7
$b/b_w = 1125/500 = 2.25$, $h_f/h = 200/400 = 0.5$
Read $I_g/(bh^3) = 0.054$

b)   Alternatively, using equations from Table 6.6

$$A_r = \frac{200}{400}\left(\frac{1125}{500} - 1\right) = 0.625$$

$$C_T = \frac{4(0.625)\left(1 - \dfrac{200}{400}\right)^2 + \left(1 + 0.625\,\dfrac{200}{400}\right)^2}{12\left(\dfrac{1125}{500}\right)(1 + 0.625)} = 0.0535$$

$I_g = 0.0535\,(1125)(400^3) = \underline{3852 \times 10^6 \text{ mm}^4}$

5. Cracking Moment, M_{cr}

(i)   Positive Moment Region: tension on bottom face

   a)   Using Chart Table 6.8

   $b/b_w = 1125/500 = 2.25$ $h_f/h = 200/400 = 0.5$

   Read $y_{tb}/h = 0.6$ i.e. $y_{tb} = 0.6(400) = \underline{240 \text{ mm}}$

   $$M_{cr} = \frac{3(3852 \times 10^6)}{240} = \underline{48.2 \times 10^6 \text{ N·mm}}$$

   b)   Alternatively, using Equation: Table 6.6

   $$\frac{y_{tb}}{h} = \frac{\dfrac{1125}{500}\left(\dfrac{200}{400}\right)\left(1 - \dfrac{1}{2}\dfrac{200}{400}\right) + \dfrac{1}{2}\left(1 - \dfrac{200}{400}\right)^2}{\dfrac{1125}{500}\left(\dfrac{200}{400}\right) + \left(1 - \dfrac{200}{400}\right)} = 0.60$$

   i.e. $y_{tb} = 0.60(400) = \underline{240 \text{ mm}}$

(ii) Negative Moment Region, Interior Support: tension top face

   $y_{tt} = h - y_{tb} = 400 - 240 = 160 \text{ mm}$

   $$M_{cr} = \frac{3(3852 \times 10^6)}{160} = 72.2 \times 10^6 \text{ N·mm}$$

6. Cracked Transformed Moment of Inertia, I_{cr}

(i)   Positive Moment Region

   Assume N.A. in flange: treat as rectangular section.

   b = 1125 mm
   b_w = 500 mm
   A_s = 2000 mm^2
   d = 336 mm

   a)   Using Chart: Table 6.5

   $$\rho' = 0 : \rho n = \frac{A_s n}{bd} = \frac{2000(8.89)}{1125\,(336)} = 0.047$$

   Read $I_{cr}/(bd^3) = 0.031$

   i.e. $I_{cr} = 0.031(1125)\,(336)^3 = \underline{1323 \times 10^6 \text{ mm}^4}$

   b)   Alternatively using equations from Table 6.4

   $$B = \frac{1125}{8.89\,(2000)} = 0.0633$$

6

Deflections

$$kd = \frac{\sqrt{2(336)(0.0633)+1} - 1}{0.0633} = 88.4 \text{ mm} < 200$$

∴ N.A. in flange

$$I_{cr} = \frac{1125(88.4)^3}{3} + 8.89(2000)(336 - 88.4)^2 = \underline{1349 \times 10^6 \text{ mm}^4}$$

(ii)   Negative Moment Region - Interior Support

Treat as rectangular section

b = 500 mm
A_s = 3000 mm^2
A'_s = 1000 mm^2

Note: Since the bottom bars are not developed as compression bars, their contribution could be neglected as a conservative assumption. We will include them here to illustrate the calculation procedure for compression steel.

d = 336 mm
d' = 64 mm

a) Using Chart: Table 6.5

$$\rho'n'(1 - d'/d) = \frac{1000(7.89)}{500(336)}\left(1 - \frac{64}{336}\right) = 0.0380$$

$$\rho n + \rho'n' = \frac{3000(8.89)}{500(336)} + \frac{1000(7.89)}{500(336)} = 0.206$$

Read $I_{cr}/(bd^3)$ = 0.086

d'/d = 64/336 = 0.19

Read $I_{cr}/(bd^3)$ = 0.006

Net value of $I_{cr}/(bd^3)$ = 0.086 - 0.006 = 0.080

i.e. I_{cr} = 0.080(500)(336)^3 = $\underline{1517 \times 10^6 \text{ mm}^4}$

b) Alternatively using Equations from Table 6.4

$$B = \frac{500}{8.89(3000)} \qquad\qquad r = \frac{7.89(1000)}{8.89(3000)}$$

$$= 0.0187 \qquad\qquad\qquad = 0.296$$

$$kd = \frac{\sqrt{2(336)(0.0187)\left(1 + \frac{0.296(64)}{336}\right) + (1 + 0.296)^2} - (1 + 0.296)}{0.0187} = 137 \text{ mm}$$

$$I_{cr} = \frac{500(137)^3}{3} + 8.89(3000)(336 - 137)^2 + 7.89(1000)(137 - 64)^2$$

$$= \underline{1527 \times 10^6 \text{ mm}^4}$$

7.   Effective Moment of Inertia, I_e

(i)   Positive Moment Region

a) Dead Load Level $(I_e)_D$

$$(I_e)_D = \left[\left(\frac{48.2}{104.5}\right)^3 3852 + \left(1 - \left(\frac{48.2}{104.5}\right)^3\right)1349\right] \times 10^6 \text{ mm}^4$$

$$= 378 + 1217 = \underline{1595 \times 10^6 \text{ mm}^4}$$

b) Dead + Live Load Level $(I_e)_{D+L}$

$$(I_e)_{D+L} = \left[\left(\frac{48.2}{131.8}\right)^3 3852 + \left(1 - \left(\frac{48.2}{131.8}\right)^3\right)1349\right] \times 10^6 \text{ mm}^4$$

$$= 188 + 1283 = \underline{1471 \times 10^6 \text{ mm}^4}$$

(ii) Negative Moment Region, Interior Support

a) Dead Load Level $(I_e)_D$

$$(I_e)_D = \left[\left(\frac{72.2}{151.7}\right)^3 3852 + \left(1 - \left(\frac{72.2}{151.7}\right)^3\right)1527\right] \times 10^6 \text{ mm}^4$$

$$= 415 + 1362 = \underline{1777 \times 10^6 \text{ mm}^4}$$

b) Dead + Live Load Level

$$(I_e)_{D+L} = \left[\left(\frac{72.2}{191.4}\right)^3 3852 + \left(1 - \left(\frac{72.2}{191.4}\right)^3\right)1527\right] \times 10^6 \text{ mm}^4$$

$$= 207 + 1445 = \underline{1652 \times 10^6 \text{ mm}^4}$$

(iii) Average I_e (Eq. 6.7)

a) Dead Load Level

$$(I_e) = [0.75(1595) + 0.25(1777)] \times 10^6 \text{ mm}^4$$
$$= \underline{1641 \times 10^6 \text{ mm}^4}$$

b) Dead + Live Load Level

$$(I_e)_{D+L} = [0.75(1471) + 0.25(1652)] \times 10^6 \text{ mm}^4$$
$$= \underline{1516 \times 10^6 \text{ mm}^4}$$

8. Immediate Deflection

$$\Delta = K\left(\frac{5}{48}\right)\frac{M\ell^2}{E_c I_e} \qquad\qquad M_o = \frac{w_D \ell^2}{8} = \frac{32.1\left(6750^2\right)}{8} = 183 \times 10^6 \text{ N·mm}$$

a) Dead Load

$$K = 1.20 - 0.2\, M_o/M_m = 1.20 - 0.2\,(183/104.5) = 0.85$$

$$\Delta_D = 0.85\left(\frac{5}{48}\right)\frac{104.5\left(6.75^2\right)}{22,500\,(1641)} \times 10^6$$

$$= 11.4 \text{ mm}$$

b) Dead + Live Load

$$\Delta_{D+L} = 0.85\left(\frac{5}{48}\right)\frac{131.8\left(6.75^2\right)}{22,500\,(1516)} \times 10^6 = 15.6 \text{ mm}$$

6

Deflections

c)   Live Load

$\Delta_L = 15.6 - 11.4 = 4.2$ mm

d)   Permissible Deflection (Table 6.3)

(i) $\ell_n/180 = 6750/180 = 37.5$ mm > 4.2 mm   OK

(ii) $\ell_n/360 = 6750/360 = 18.8$ mm > 4.2 mm   OK

9.   Long-Time Deflection

$1 + 50\rho'$ $= 1$ for positive moment

$$= 1 + 50\frac{1000}{500(336)}$$

$= 1.30$ for negative moment

Average $= 0.75(1.0) + 0.25(1.30) = 1.08$

Assume nonstructural elements installed after 1 month.

Sustained Load Deflection at one month, $S = 0.5$

$$\Delta_{1\,mo.} = \left(1 + \frac{0.5}{1.08}\right)11.4 + \left(1 + \frac{0.5}{1.08}\right)(0.2)(4.2) = 16.7 + 1.2 = 17.9 \text{ mm}$$

Sustained Load Deflection at 5 years, $S = 2.0$

$$\Delta_{5\,yrs.} = \left(1 + \frac{2.0}{1.08}\right)11.4 + \left(1 + \frac{2.0}{1.08}\right)(0.2)(4.2) = 32.5 + 2.4 = 34.9 \text{ mm}$$

Incremental Deflection = 34.9 - 17.9 =   17.0 mm
Add Live Load Deflection = 0.8(4.2) =   <u>3.4 mm</u>
                                          20.4 mm

Permissible Deflection (Table 6.3)

$\ell_n/240 = 6750/240 = 28.1$ mm > 20.4 mm   OK
$\ell_n/480 = 6750/480 = 14.0$ mm < 20.4 mm   NOT OK

6.4.3   Computation of Immediate Deflection for Non-Prestressed Two-way Construction

An approximate procedure using the equations developed in Section 6.4.1 for one-way construction can be used to calculate deflections for two-way slab system designed by the Direct Design Method or Equivalent Frame Method of Clause 13 of CSA Standard A23.3. The basis for the procedure is illustrated in Fig. 6.2 where parts (a) and (b) of the figure were drawn assuming the edges parallel to ℓ_y and ℓ_x, respectively, do not deflect. The deflection, Δ_{mp}, at midpanel of a two-way slab can be considered as the sum of the column strip deflection Δ_c, and the perpendicular middle strip deflection, Δ_m.

$$\Delta_{mp} = \Delta_{cx} + \Delta_{my} = \Delta_{cy} + \Delta_{mx} \tag{6.15}$$

Both the column strip and middle strip can be treated as continuous beams for which the end moments and midspan moments are M_1, M_2, and M_m. These moments will have been calculated at factored load levels for proportioning flexural reinforcement. To calculate deflections the factored moments must be scaled down to the appropriate specified load level. Column and middle strip deflections can then be calculated using Eq. 6.1. However, in determining the coefficient K, the total static moment M_o should be calculated on the basis of the end moments and midspan moment, rather than the uniformly distributed applied load, w.

i.e.

$$M_o = \frac{1}{2}(M_1 + M_2) + M_m \qquad\qquad (6.16)$$

where M_1, M_2 = end moments
         M_m = midspan moment.

For irregular panel layouts and non-uniform loading conditions, computer based procedures such as the finite element method should be considered for calculating deflections.

As suggested in Ref. 2, effects of cracking may be included by applying the effective moment of inertia concept to element stiffness values in orthogonal reinforcement directions. Using a linear elastic plate bending program, bending moments in orthogonal reinforcement directions can be calculated ignoring effects of cracking. A second analysis can then be made with reduced stiffness values reflecting the ratio of cracking moment to applied moment in each element. This procedure can be automated as described in Ref. 3. It should be emphasized that a finite element or other type of analysis that does not include the effect of reduced stiffness due to cracking is likely to underestimate deflections by a significant amount.

Effective Moment of Inertia

I_e can be calculated for column and middle strips using the expressions given in Section 6.4.1 for beams. However, since slabs are generally lightly reinforced, with design moments in many cases less than the theoretical cracking moment, M_{cr}, the effects on deflection of cracking due to construction loads and shrinkage restraint must be considered (2, 3, 4, 5). Normal shoring and re-shoring procedures may induce construction loads in excess of twice the slab dead load at early age. Thus, the loads during construction may exceed the specified design loads leading to a greater degree of cracking than would be expected based on design loads alone. For multi-story construction it is suggested that I_e for all load cases be based on moments due to construction loads. A construction load of 2.0 to 2.2 times the slab dead load is suggested. Detailed procedures for calculating construction loads when the construction procedure is known are provided in Refs. 22, 23, and 24. To account for the effect of shrinkage restraint cracking, a reduced effective modulus of rupture of one-half the value given in CSA Standard A23.3 is used.

6.4.4   Computation of Long-Time Deflection for Two-Way Construction

The same procedures as outlined in Section 6.4.2 for one way systems can be used, by applying the long-time multipliers to immediate column and middle strip deflections.

6.4.5   Deflection Limits for Two-Way Construction

Deflection limits referred to in Table 6.3 apply to two-way as well as one-way construction. In two-way construction, three components of deflection should be considered, namely, column strip, middle strip, and mid-panel deflection. Span lengths to be used are the column strip span for column strip deflection, middle strip span for middle strip deflection, and length of span measured diagonally between columns for mid-panel deflection.

Design Example 6.2

Required: Deflection calculations for a two-way slab system with drop panels. Calculations based on specified loads and $f_r = 0.3\sqrt{f'_c}$ MPa.

Slab Thickness, h_s = 170 mm
Drop Panel Thickness, h_d = 290 mm

$\Delta h = h_d - h_s = 290 - 170 = 120$ mm

Minimum thickness, h_s (min):

$$h_s(min) = \frac{\ell_n(0.6 + f_y/1000)}{30} - \left(\frac{2x_d}{\ell_n}\right)\Delta h$$

ℓ_n = 7000 - 400 = 6600 mm

x_d = 1170 - 200 = 970 mm

$$h_s(min) = \frac{6600\,(0.6 + 0.4)}{30} - \frac{2(970)}{6600}120 = 185\ mm > 170\ mm$$

∴ Deflection calculations required

Concrete compressive strength: $f_c' = 25$ MPa $E_c = 4500\sqrt{f_c'} = 4500\sqrt{25} = 22\,500$ MPa

Steel yield strength: $f_y = 400$ MPa $n = E_s/E_c = 20\,0000/22\,500 = 8.89$

Deflection Limits:

a) Deflection due to live load: $\ell_n/360$
b) Deflection after attachment of non-structural elements: $\ell_n/480$

1.   Slab design moments and reinforcement

Design slab flexural reinforcing using h_s = 170 mm and h_d = 290 mm

Loads

$$
\begin{array}{lll}
w_{slab} & = (170/1000)(2.4)(9.81) & = 4.0\ \text{kN/m}^2\\
w_{drop} & = (120/1000)(2.4)(9.81)(6.25/51.06) & = 0.4\ \text{kN/m}^2\\
w_{SDL} & & = \underline{1.3\ \text{kN/m}^2}\\
w_D & & = 5.7\ \text{kN/m}^2\\
\\
w_L & & = \underline{2.4\ \text{kN/m}^2}\\
w_{D+L} & & = \underline{8.1\ \text{kN/m}^2}
\end{array}
$$

Total Static Moment, M_o (Span 1) under factored loads

w_f = 1.25(5.7) + 1.5(2.4) = 10.7 kN/m²

$$M_o = \frac{10.7(7400)(6.4)^2}{8}10^3 = 405\ x\ 10^6\ \text{N}\cdot\text{mm}^2$$

Distribute M_o to Positive and Negative Moment, Column and Middle Strips by Direct Design Method. See Clause 13.11.2.3. M_{COL} for positive moment must be 55% to 65% of M_{DES}. M_{COL} for interior negative moment must be 75% to 90% of M_{DES}.

	A				B	
M_o			405			x 10^6 N·mm
		M_1	M_m	M_2		
M_{DES}		(26%M_o)105	(52%M_o)211	(70%M_o)284		x 10^6 N·mm
M_{COL}		(100%M_{DES})105	(60%M_{DES})127	(75%M_{DES})213		x 10^6 N·mm
M_{MID}		0	84	71		x 10^6 N·mm
$A_{s(Col)}$		15 – 15M	16 – 15M	15 – 15M		
		(3000)	(3200)	(3000)		mm²
$A_{s(Mid)}$		10 – 15M	11 – 15M	10 – 15M		
		(2000)	(2200)	(2000)		mm²

2. Gross Moment of Inertia, I_g

    a) Column Strip b = 3450. (Average of b for spans A-B and B-C.)

                 Midspan: I_g = 1/12 (3450)(170)^3 = 1412 x 10^6 mm^4

                 Interior Support: $b/b_w = 3450/2500 = 1.38$ $h_f/h = 170/290 = 0.59$

                 From Table 6.7 $K = 0.071$
                                  $I_g = 0.071(3450)(290)^3$
                                    $= 5970$ x 10^6 mm^4

    b) Middle Strip $b = 3950$

                 Midspan: I_g = 1/12 (3950)(170)^3 = 1617 x 10^6 mm^4
                 Interior Support: I_g = 1617 x 10^6 mm^4

3. Cracking Moment: $M_{cr} = \dfrac{f_r I_g}{y_t}$ $f_r = 0.3\sqrt{25}$ = 1.5 MPa

    Column Strip

                 Midspan: $M_{cr} = \dfrac{1.5(1412) \times 10^6}{85} = 25$ x 10^6 N·mm

                 Interior Support: $M_{cr} = \dfrac{1.5(5970) \times 10^6}{133} = 67.3$ x 10^6 N·mm

    Middle Strip

                 Midspan: $M_{cr} = \dfrac{1.5(1617) \times 10^6}{85} = 28$ x 10^6 N·mm

                 Interior Support: M_{cr} = 28 x 10^6 N·mm

4. Moments at Specified Load Level (Unfactored)

    a) Dead Load: w_D/w_f = 5.7/10.7 = 0.53
                          M_o = 216 x 10^6 N·mm

    b) Dead + Live Load: w_{D+L}/w_f = 8.1/10.7 = 0.76
                          M_o = 307 x 10^6 N·mm

Scale factored design moment to specified load level

			M_1	M_m	M_2		
a)	Dead Load						
	M_{COL}		56	67	113		x 10^6 N·mm
	M_{MID}		0	45	38		x 10^6 N·mm
b)	Dead + Live Load						
	M_{COL}		80	97	162		x 10^6 N·mm
	M_{MID}		0	64	54		x 10^6 N·mm

(columns headed A ... B)

5. Moment of Inertia of Cracked Transformed Section, I_{cr}

    a) Column Strip

        Midspan: A_s = 3200 mm^2, b = 3450 mm, d = 128 mm

$$\rho_n = \frac{3200(8.89)}{3450(128)} = 0.064$$

From Table 6.5 Read $I_{cr}/(bd^3) = 0.040$

$I_{cr} = 0.040(3450)(128)^3 = \underline{289 \times 10^6 \text{ mm}^4}$

Interior Support: $A_s = 3000 \text{ mm}^2$, $b = 2500 \text{ mm}$, $d = 248 \text{ mm}$

$$\rho_n = \frac{3000(8.89)}{2500(248)} = 0.043$$

From Table 6.5 Read $I_{cr}/(bd^3) = 0.029$

$I_{cr} = 0.029(2500)(248)^3 = \underline{1106 \times 10^6 \text{ mm}^4}$

b)   Middle Strip: calculated as for column strip

Midspan: $I_{cr} = \underline{215 \times 10^6 \text{ mm}^4}$

Interior Support: $I_{cr} = \underline{190 \times 10^6 \text{ mm}^4}$

6.   Effective Moment of Inertia

Dead Load

Column Strip

Midspan:

$I_e = [(25/67)^3(1412) + (1 - (25/67)^3)(289)] \times 10^6 \text{ mm}^4$

$= 73 + 274 = \underline{347 \times 10^6 \text{ mm}^4}$

Interior Support:

$I_e = [(67.3/113)^3(5970) + (1 - (67.3/113)^3)(1106)] \times 10^6 \text{ mm}^4$

$= 1261 + 872 = 2133 \times 10^6 \text{ mm}^4$

Average $I_e = 0.75(347) + 0.25(2133)$

$= 794 \times 10^6 \text{ mm}^4$

Middle Strip

Midspan:

$I_e = [(28/45)^3(1617) + (1 - (28/45)^3)(215)] \times 10^6 \text{ mm}^4$

$= 390 + 163 = 553 \times 10^6 \text{ mm}^4$

Interior Support:

$I_e = [(28/38)^3 \, 1617 + (1 - (28/38)^3) \, 190] \times 10^6 \text{ mm}^4$

$= 647 + 114 = 761 \times 10^6 \text{ mm}^4$

Average $I_e = 0.75(553) + 0.25(761)$

$= 605 \times 10^6 \text{ mm}^4$

Similarly for other cases:

Dead + Live Load

Column Strip

Average $I_e = \underline{595 \times 10^6 \text{ mm}^4}$

Middle Strip

Average $I_e = \underline{346 \times 10^6 \text{ mm}^4}$

7. Column Strip Deflections

a) Dead Load Deflection

M_o = 1/2 $(M_1 + M_2)$ + M_m = 1/2 (56 + 113) + 67
    = 152 x 10^6 N·mm
M_m = 67 x 10^6 N·mm
K = 1.20 - 0.20(152/67) = 0.75
E_c = 22,500 MPa
I_e = 794 x 10^6 mm^4

$$\Delta_D = 0.75\left(\frac{5}{48}\right)\frac{(67 \times 10^6)(6.4)^2(\times 10^6)}{22,500(794 \times 10^6)}$$
    = 12 mm

b) Dead + Live Load Deflection

M_o = 1/2 (80 + 162) + 97 = 218 x 10^6 N·mm
M_m = 97 x 10^6 N·mm
K = 1.20 - 0.20(218/97) = 0.75
I_e = 595 x 10^6 mm^4

$$\Delta_{D+L} = 0.75\left(\frac{5}{48}\right)\frac{(97 \times 10^6)(6.4)^2(\times 10^6)}{22,500(595 \times 10^6)}$$
    = 23 mm

c) Live Load Deflection

Δ_L = 23 - 12 = 11 mm

d) Permissible Live Load Deflection

ℓ_n/360 = 6400/360 = 17.8 > 11 mm   OK

e) Long Time Deflection

$\rho' = 0$

Assume non-structural elements installed after 1 month, and 20% live load sustained.

Sustained Load Deflection at 1 month: $S = 0.5$

Δ_{1mo} = (1 + 0.5)(12) + (1 + 0.5)(0.2)(11)
    = 18.0 + 3.3 = 21.3 mm

Sustained Load Deflection at ≥ 5 years: $S = 2.0$

Δ_{5yr} = (1 + 2)(12) + (1 + 2)(0.2)(11)
    = 36 + 6.6 = 42.6 mm

Incremental Deflection = 42.6 – 21.3 =   21.3
Add Live Load Deflection = 0.8(11) =   <u>8.8</u>
                            30.1 mm

f) Permissible Long-Time Deflection

ℓ_n/480 = 6400/480 = 13.3 mm < 30.1 mm   NOT OK

6

Deflections

8.   Middle Strip Deflections

a)   Dead Load Deflection

K = 0.80 (Assume fixed-hinged condition)

M_m = 45 x 10^6 N·mm

I_e = 605 x 10^6 mm^4

$$\Delta_D = 0.80\left(\frac{5}{48}\right)\frac{(45 \times 10^6)(6.4)^2 \times 10^6}{22,500(605 \times 10^6)}$$

= 11.3 mm

b)   Dead + Live Load Deflection

M_m = 64 x 10^6 N·mm

I_e = 346 x 10^6 mm^4

$$\Delta_{D+L} = 0.80\left(\frac{5}{48}\right)\frac{(64 \times 10^6)(6.4)^2 \times 10^6}{22,500(346 \times 10^6)}$$

= 28.1 mm

c)   Live Load Deflection

Δ_L = 28.1 - 11.3 = 16.8 mm

d)   Permissible Live Load Deflection

ℓ_n/360 = 17.8 > 16.8 mm   OK

e)   Long Time Deflection

Δ_{1mo} = (1 + 0.5)(11.3) + (1 + 0.5)(0.2)(16.8) = 22.0 mm

Δ_{5yr} = (1 + 2)(11.3) + (1 + 2)(0.2)(16.8) =   44.0 mm

Incremental Deflection = 44.0 – 22.0 =   22.0 mm

Add Live Load Deflection = 0.8(16.8) =   13.4 mm

                                                 35.4 mm

f)   Permissible Long-Time Deflection

ℓ_n/480 = 13.3 < 35.4 mm   NOT OK

9.   Mid Panel Deflections

Midpanel deflection is obtained by superimposing orthogonal column and middle strip deflections

$\Delta_{mp} = \Delta_c + \Delta_m$

In this example, deflections were calculated for parallel column and middle strip deflections. However, these calculated deflections will be used, assuming orthogonal strips, to illustrate the calculation of mid-panel deflections.

a)   Span length = $\sqrt{6.4^2 + 6.4^2} = \sqrt{81.9} = 9.0$ m

(Measured diagonally between columns)

b)   Dead Load Deflection

Δ_{mp} = 12 + 11.3 = 23.3 mm

c)   Dead + Live Load Deflection

        $\Delta_{mp} = 23 + 28.1 = 51.1$ mm

d)   Live Load Deflection

        $\Delta_{mp} = 51.1 - 23.3 = 27.8$ mm

e)   Permissible Live Load Deflection

        $\ell_n /360 = 9000/360 = 25$ mm < 27.8 mm   NOT OK

f)   Long Time Deflection

        $\Delta_{mp} = 30.1 + 35.4 = 65.5$ mm

g)   Permissible Long Time Deflection

        $\ell_n /480 = 9000/480 = 18.8$ mm < 65.5 mm   NOT OK

Design Example 6.3

Required: Repeat Example 6.2 using construction loads and $f_r = 0.3 \sqrt{f'_c}$ MPa.

1.   See design example 6.2 for calculation of I_g, I_{cr}, and deflection limits

2.   Loads

    $w_{slab} = $ 4.0 kN/m^2
    $w_{drop} = $ <u>0.4 kN/m^2</u>
                4.4 kN/m^2

    Allowance for Construction Loads x 2.2 = 9.7 kN/m^2

    (ie. max load on slab during construction is 2.2 x (slab dead load))

3.   Moments

    Factored D + L from Example 6.2 = 10.7 kN/m^2. Scale factored moments from Design Example 6.2 by 9.7/10.7 = 0.907

             A   B

	M_1	M_m	M_2	
M_{col}	95	115	193	x 10^6 N·mm
M_{cr}		25	67	x 10^6 N·mm
I_g		1412	5970	x 10^6 mm^4
I_{cr}		289	1106	x 10^6 mm^4
I_e				
(See step 4 below)		<553>		x 10^6 mm^4
M_{mid}	0	76	64	x 10^6 N·mm^4
M_{cr}		28	28	x 10^6 N·mm
I_g		1617	1617	x 10^6 mm^4
I_{cr}		215	190	x 10^6 mm^4
I_e				
(See step 4 below)		<291>		x 10^6 mm^4

4.   Effective Moment of Inertia (See Example 6.2, step 6 for calculation procedure)

    Column Strip
        Average $I_e = $ <u>553 x 10^6 mm^4</u>

Middle Strip
Average I_e = <u>291 x 10^6 mm^4</u>

5.   Column Strip Deflection (due to construction load)

M_o = 1/2(95 + 193) + 115 = 259 x 10^6 N·mm
M_m = 115 x 10^6 N·mm
K = 0.75
E_c = 22,500 MPa
I_e = 553 x 10^6 mm^4

$\Delta_{const} = 0.75\left(\dfrac{5}{48}\right)\dfrac{(115 \times 10^6)(6.4)^2(x\,10^6)}{22500(553 \times 10^6)}$ = 29.6 mm

Δ_D = 29.6 (5.7/9.7) = 17.4 mm
Δ_L = 29.6 (2.4/9.7) = 7.3 mm

ℓ_n /360 = 6400/360 = 17.8 > 7.3 mm   OK

Long-time Deflection

Δ_{1mo} = (1 + 0.5) (17.4) + (1 + 0.5)(0.2)(7.3)
     = 28.3 mm

Δ_{5yr} = (1 + 2) (17.4) + (1 + 2)(0.2)(7.3)
     = 56.6 mm

Incremental Deflection = 56.6 – 28.3 =   28.3
Add Live Load Deflection = 0.8(7.3) =   <u>5.8</u>
                                                34.1 mm

ℓ_n /480 = 6400/480 = 13.3 < 34.1 mm   NOT OK

6.   Middle Strip Deflection

M_o = 1/2 (0 + 64) + 76 = 108 x 10^6 N·mm
K = 0.80
M_m = 76 x 10^6 N·mm
E_c = 22,500 MPa
I_e = 291 x 10^6 mm^4

$\Delta_{const} = 0.80\left(\dfrac{5}{48}\right)\dfrac{(76 \times 10^6)(6.4)^2(x10^6)}{22,500(291 \times 10^6)} = 39.6$ mm

          Δ_D = 39.6(5.7/9.7) = 23.3 mm
Δ_L = 39.6(2.4/9.7) = 9.8 mm

ℓ_n /360 = 6400/360 = 17.8 > 9.8 mm   OK

Long Term Deflection

Δ_{1mo} = (1 + 0.5)(23.3) + (1 + 0.5)(0.2)(9.8) = 37.9 mm

Δ_{5yr} = (1 + 2)(23.3) + (1 + 2)(0.2)(9.8)   = 75.8 mm

Incremental Deflection = 75.8 – 37.9 =   37.9
Add Live Load Deflection =   <u>9.8</u>
                                                47.7 mm

$\ell_n/480 = 6400/480 = 13.3 < 47.7$ mm   NOT OK

7.   Mid-Panel Deflections

$\Delta_L = 7.3 + 9.8 = 17.1 < 25.0$ mm   OK
$\Delta_{LT} = 34.1 + 47.7 = 81.8 > 18.8$ mm   NOT OK

8.   Discussion

Calculated deflections and deflection limits for the two-way slab examples 6.2 and 6.3 are summarized in Table A. The sensitivity of calculated deflections to effects of construction loads is evident from the significant differences between calculated deflections occurring after attachment of non-structural elements for the two cases considered. For these examples the slab did not meet minimum thickness requirements and specified deflection limits were exceeded.

6.5   Non-Prestressed Composite Members [*]

6.5.1   Minimum Thickness

In the case of shored composite members, the minimum thicknesses in Table 6.1 (CSA Standard A23.3 Table 9.1) apply as for monolithic T-beams. In the case of unshored construction, if the thickness of a non-prestressed precast member meets the requirements of Table 6.1, deflections need not be computed, according to Clause 9.8.5.1. Clause 9.8.5.2 also states that, if the thickness of an unshored non-prestressed composite member meets the requirements of Table 6.1, deflections occurring after the member becomes composite, need not be calculated. However, the long-time deflection of the precast members should be investigated for the magnitude and duration of load prior to the beginning of effective composite action. It should be noted that these comments refer only to the conditions in Table 6.1.

6.5.2   Computation of Deflection

The ultimate (in time) deflection of unshored and shored composite members is computed by Eqs. (6-17) to (6-20).[**] Subscripts 1 and 2 are used to refer to the slab (or effect of the slab under dead load) and precast beam, respectively.

These procedures are illustrated for a composite beam in which both unshored and shored construction is assumed. Examples 6.4 and 6.5 demonstrate the beneficial effect of shoring on deflections.

Unshored Composite Members

$$\Delta_u = \underset{(1)}{(\Delta_i)_2} + \underset{(2)}{0.70 k_r (\Delta_i)_2} + \underset{(3)}{0.90 k_r (\Delta_i)_2 \frac{I_2}{I_c}} + \underset{(4)}{0.20 \Delta_{sh}} + \underset{(5)}{0.80 \Delta_{sh} \frac{I_2}{I_c}} + \underset{(6)}{(\Delta_i)_1}$$

$$+ \underset{(7)}{1.40 k_r (\Delta_i)_1 \frac{I_2}{I_c}} + \underset{(8)}{\Delta_{DS}} + \underset{(9)}{(\Delta_i)_L} + \underset{(10)}{(\Delta_{cp})_L} \qquad\qquad (6\text{-}17)$$

---

[*]   Note: Section 6.5 was originally prepared by Professor Dan E. Branson for a previous edition of the CPCA Metric Design Handbook

[**]   Derived in detail in References 6 and 7.

When $k_r = 0.85$ (no compression steel in precast beam) and Δ_{DS} is assumed to be equal to 0.50 $(\Delta_i)_1$, Eq. (6-17) reduces to Eq. (6-18).

$$
\overset{(1\;+\;2\;+\;3)}{\Delta_u \;=\; \left(1.6+0.77\,{}^{I_2}\!\big/_{\!I_c}\right)(\Delta_i)_2} \;+\; \overset{(4\;+\;5)}{\left(0.20+0.80\,{}^{I_2}\!\big/_{\!I_c}\right)\Delta_{sh}} \;+\; \overset{(6\;+\;7\;+\;8)}{\left(1.50+1.19\,{}^{I_2}\!\big/_{\!I_c}\right)(\Delta_i)_1}
$$

$$
\overset{(9)}{+\;(\Delta_i)_L} \;+\; \overset{(10)}{(\Delta_{cp})_L} \tag{6-18}
$$

Term (1) is the initial dead load deflection of the precast beam using Eq. (6.1).

> In Eq. (6.1) $M = M_2 =$ midspan moment due to precast beam dead load. For computing $(I_e)_2$ in Eq. (6.2), M_a refers to the precast beam dead load and M_{cr}, I_g, I_{cr}, to the precast beam.

Term (2) is the dead load creep deflection of the precast beam up to the time of slab casting ($C_t = 0.70$ part of 1.60).

> From Eq. (6-10), $k_r = 0.85/(1 + 50\rho')$, where ρ' refers to the compressive steel in the precast beam at midspan.

Term (3) is the creep deflection of the composite beam following slab casting due to the precast beam dead load ($C_t = 0.90$ part of 1.60).

> The ratio, I_2/I_c, modifies the initial stress (strain) and accounts for the effect of the composite section in restraining additional creep curvature (strain) after the composite section becomes effective. As a simple approximation, use $I_2/I_c = [(I_2/I_c)_g + (I_2/I_c)_{cr}]/2$.

Term (4) is the deflection due to shrinkage warping of the precast beam up to the time of slab casting (20% of total shrinkage), using Eqs. (6-12) and (6-13).

Term (5) is the shrinkage deflection of the composite beam following slab casting due to the shrinkage of the precast beam concrete (80% of total shrinkage), but not including the effect of differential shrinkage and creep which is given by Term (8).

Term (6) is the initial deflection of the precast beam under slab dead load. For incremental deflections, $(\Delta_i)_1 = [(\Delta_i)_1 + (\Delta_i)_2] - (\Delta_i)_2$, where $[(\Delta_i)_1 + (\Delta_i)_2] =$ Eq. (6-1), with $M = M_1 + M_2(\Delta_i)_2$ is from Term (1), and $M_1 =$ midspan moment due to the slab dead load. For computing $(I_e)_{1+2}$ in Eq. (6-2), M_a refers to the precast beam plus slab dead load and M_{cr}, I_g, I_{cr}, to the precast beam. When partitions, roofing, etc., are placed at the same time as the slab, or soon thereafter, their dead load is also included in M_1 and M_a.

Term (7) is the creep deflection of the composite beam due to slab dead load.

> $C_t = 1.40$ (instead of 1.60) is used because of the later loading age.

Term (8) is the deflection due to differential shrinkage and creep.[*]

> As an approximation, use $\Delta_{DS} = 0.50(\Delta_i)_1$, where $(\Delta_i)_1$ is based on the slab dead load deflection only in Term (6).

---

[*] Details can be found in References 6 and 7.

Term (9) is the initial live load (plus other loads applied to the composite beam and not included in Term (6) deflection of the composite beam using Eq. (6-1) with $M = M_L$ and $I_e = (I_c)_{cr}$.

This is a simple approximation used instead of the usual incremental deflection calculation with I_e, since the incremental loads are resisted by different sections (members).

Term (10) is the partial live load creep deflection for any sustained live load (and other loads) applied to the composite beam, using Eq. (6-10) in which ρ' refers to any slab compression steel that may be taken into account.

Shored Composite Beams
(assuming the composite beam supports all dead and live load).

$$\underset{(1)}{\Delta_u} = \underset{}{(\Delta_i)_{1+2}} + \underset{(2)}{1.80\,k_r\,(\Delta_i)_{1+2}} + \underset{(3)}{\Delta_{sh}\frac{l^2}{l_c}} + \underset{(4)}{\Delta_{DS}} + \underset{(5)}{(\Delta_i)_L} + \underset{(6)}{(\Delta_{cp})_L} \tag{6-19}$$

When $k_r = 0.85$ (neglecting any effect of slab compression steel) and Δ_{DS} is assumed to be equal to $(\Delta_i)_{1+2}$, Eq. (6-19) reduces to Eq. (6-20).

$$\underset{(1+2+4)}{\Delta_u} = 3.53(\Delta_i)_{1+2} + \underset{(3)}{\Delta_{sh}\frac{l^2}{l_c}} + \underset{(5)}{(\Delta_i)_L} + \underset{(6)}{(\Delta_{cp})_L}$$

Term (1) is the initial deflection of the composite beam due to slab plus precast beam dead load (plus partitions, roofing, etc.) using Eq. (6-1), with $M = M_1 + M_2$ = midspan moment due to span plus precast beam (etc.) dead load.

For computing $(I_e)_{1+2}$ in Eq. (6-2), M_a refers to the moment, $M_1 + M_2$, and M_{cr}, I_g, I_{cr}, to the composite section.

Term (2) is the creep deflection of the composite beam due to the dead load in Term (1).

$C_t = 1.80$ (instead of 1.60) because of a typical loading age for the slab concrete when the shores are removed.

From Eq. (6-10), $k_r = 0.85/(1 + 50\rho')$, where ρ' refers to any slab compression steel that may be taken into account.

Term (3) is the shrinkage deflection of the composite beam after the shores are removed due to the shrinkage of the precast beam concrete, but not including the effect of differential shrinkage and creep which is given by Term (4).

Eqs. (6-12) and (6-13) may be used with $\Delta_{sh} = 300 \times 10^{-6}$. The ratio, l_2/l_c, is explained in Term (3) of Eq. (6-17).

Term (4) is the deflection due to differential shrinkage and creep.[*]

As an approximation, use $\Delta_{DS} = (\Delta_1)_{1+2}$, where $(\Delta_i)_{1+2}$ is based on the slab plus precast beam dead load deflection only in Term (1).

---

[*]   Details can be found in References 6 and 7.

Term (5) is the initial live load deflection of the composite beam using Eq. (6-1).

The calculation for the incremental live load deflection follows the same procedure as that for a monolithic beam.

Term (6) is the partial live load creep deflection for any sustained live load.

This is the same as Term (10) of Eq. (6-17).

The calculation of deflection for the shored composite beam is essentially the same as for a monolithic beam, except for the deflection due to shrinkage warping of the precast beam which is resisted by the composite section, and the deflection due to differential shrinkage and creep of the composite beam. These effects are represented by Terms (3) and (4) in Eq. (6-19).

6.5.3   Permissible Deflection

The maximum permissible computed deflections are given in Table 6.3.

Example 6.4   Unshored Non-Prestressed Composite Beam, Normal Density Concrete

Given:

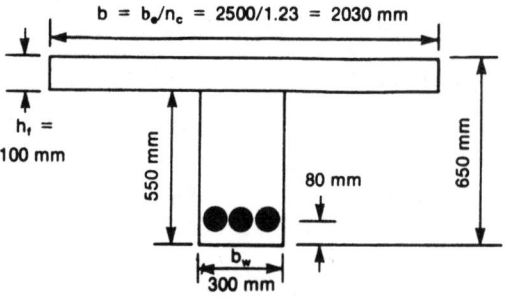

$$b = b_e/n_c = 2500/1.23 = 2030 \text{ mm}$$

Slab: $(f_c')_1 = 20$ MPa

Precast Beam: $(f_c')_2 = 30$ MPa

$f_y = 350$ MPa

Simple span = 10 m

Beam spacing = 2.5 m

Live load = 3.5 kN/m^2

$A_s = 3 - 30M = 2100$ mm^2

$b_e = 0.4(10,000) + 300 = 4300$ mm

        or spacing = 2500 mm Use

        or 24(100) + 300 = 2700 mm

Required: Deflection analysis

1.   Loads and moments:

w_1 = (2400 kg/m^3) (1.04 for steel) x (0.00981 kN/m^3 per kg/m^3) x (0.100 x 2.500)
        = 6.12 kN/m

w_2 = 2400(1.04) (0.00981) (0.300 x 0.550) = 4.04 kN/m

w_L = (3.5 kN/m^2) (2.500 m) = 8.75 kN/m

M_1 = $w_1\ell^2/8 = 6.12(10)^2/8 = 76.5$ kN·m

M_2 = $w_2\ell^2/8 = 4.04(10)^2/8 = 50.5$ kN·m

M_L = $w_L\ell^2/8 = 8.75(10)^2/8 = 109.4$ kN·m

2.   Minimum thickness:

Min. $h = \ell/16 = 10,000/16 = 625$ mm, which is met by the composite beam, but not by the precast beam. Hence, for members not supporting or attached to partitions or other construction likely to be damaged by deflections (condition in Table 6.3), only the long-time deflection of the precast beam before composite action is effective need be investigated. However, deflections will be calculated and compared with all limiting values in CSA Standard A23.3, Table 6.3.

3. Modulus of rupture, modulus of elasticity, modular ratios:

$(E_c)_1$ = 20,100 MPa
$(f_r)_2$ = 3.29 MPa
$(E_c)_2$ = 24,700 MPa
n_c = $(E_c)_2/(E_c)_1$ = 24,600/20,100 = 1.23
E_s = 200,000 MPa, $n = E_s/(E_c)_2$ = 200/24.7 = 8.1

4. Gross and cracked section moments of inertia:

Precast Section
I_g = $bh^3/12$ = $300(550)^3/12$ = 4159×10^6 mm^4
I_{cr} = 2014×10^6 mm^4 (Table 6.4)
Check by Table 6.5, OK

Composite Section

y_t = 454 mm (Table 6.6), I_g = $13,940 \times 10^6$ mm^4 (Table 6.6). Check by Table 6.9, OK
I_{cr} = 4412×10^6 mm^4 (Table 6.4 since $a < h_f$). Check by Table 6.5, OK
I_2/I_c = $[(I_2/I_c)_g + (I_2/I_c)_{cr}]/2$ (Term 3 of Eq. (6-16) = $[(4159/13,940) + (2014/4412)]/2$ = 0.377

5. Effective moments of inertia:

In Term (1), Eq. (6-17) - Precast section,

M_{cr} = $f_r I_g/y_t$ = $3.29(4159 \times 10^6)(10)^{-6}/275$ = 49.8 kN·m

M_{cr}/M_2 = 49.8/50.5 = 0.986 $0.986^3 = 0.959$

$(I_e)_2$ = $(M_{cr}/M_2)^3 I_g + [1 - (M_{cr}/M_2)^3] I_{cr}$ = $0.959(4159 \times 10^6) + [1 - 0.959](2014 \times 10^6)$
            = 4070×10^6 mm^4

In Term (6), Eq. (6-17) - Precast section,

$M_{cr}/(M_1 + M_2)$ = 49.8/(76.5 + 50.5) = 0.392, $(0.392)^3 = 0.060$

$(I_e)_{1+2}$ = $0.06(4159 \times 10^6) + (1 - 0.060)(2014 \times 10^6)$ = 2140×10^6 mm^4

6. Deflections:

Solution by Eq. (6-17)

Term (1), $(\Delta_i)_2$ = $\dfrac{K(5/48)M_2\ell^2}{(E_{c2})(I_c)_2}$

   = $\dfrac{1(5/48)(50.5)(10)^2 \times 10^{12}}{24,700(4070 \times 10^6)}$ = 5.2 mm

Term (2), k_r = 0.85 (no precast beam compression steel)
$0.70k_r (\Delta_i)_2$ = 0.70(0.85)(5.2)
            = 3.1 mm

Term (3), $0.90k_r (\Delta_i)_2 \dfrac{I_2}{I_c}$ = 0.90(0.85)(5.2)(0.377) = 1.5 mm

Term (4), K_{sh} = 0.125, $\rho' = 0$
ρ = 100 (2100)/(300(470)) = 1.49%

From Table 6.10, $A_{sh} = 0.80$

$\phi_{sh} = A_{sh}\varepsilon_{sh}/h = 0.80(400 \times 10^{-6})/550$
$= 0.582 \times 10^{-6}$

$\Delta_{sh} = K_{sh}\phi_{sh}\ell^2 = 0.125(0.582 \times 10^{-6})(10,000)^2$
$= 7.3$ mm

$0.20\Delta_{sh} = 0.20(7.3) = 1.5$ mm

Term (5), $0.80 \Delta_{sh} \dfrac{l_2}{l_c} = 0.80(7.25)(0.377) = 2.2$ mm

Term (6), $(\Delta_i)_1 = \dfrac{K(5/48)(M_1 + M_2)\ell^2}{(E_c)_2(I_e)_{1+2}} - (\Delta_i)_2$

$= \dfrac{1(5/48)(76.5 + 50.5)(10)^2(10)^{12}}{24,700(2140 \times 10^6)} - 5.2$

$= 19.8$ mm

Term (7), $1.40\, k_r\, (\Delta_i)_1 \dfrac{l_2}{l_c} = 1.40(0.85)(19.8)(0.377)$

$= 8.9$ mm

Term (8), $\Delta_{DS} = 0.50(\Delta_i)_1 = 0.50(19.8)$
$= 9.7$ mm (rough estimate)

Term (9), $(\Delta_i)_L = \dfrac{K(5/48)M_L\ell^2}{(E_c)_2(I_c)_{cr}}$

$= \dfrac{1(5/48)(109.4)(10)^2(x\,10^{12})}{24,700(4412 \times 10^6)}$

$= 10.5$ mm

$$
\begin{array}{ccccccccc}
(1) & (2) & (3) & (4) & (5) & (6) & (7) & (8) & (9)
\end{array}
$$

$\Delta_u = 5.2 + 3.1 + 1.5 + 1.5 + 2.2 + 19.8 + 8.9 + 9.7 + 10.5$
$= 62.4$ mm (Solution by Eq. (6-17))

Checking solution by Eq. (6-18)

$\Delta_u = \left(1.60 + 0.77\left(\dfrac{l_2}{l_c}\right)\right)(\Delta_i)_2 + \left(0.20 + 0.80\left(\dfrac{l_2}{l_c}\right)\right)\Delta_{sh}$

$\quad + \left(1.50 + 1.19\left(\dfrac{l_2}{l_c}\right)\right)(\Delta_i) + (\Delta_i)_L$

$= (1.60 + 0.77 \times 0.377)(5.2) + (0.20 + 0.80 \times 0.377)(7.25)$
$+ (1.50 + 1.19 \times 0.377)(19.8) + 10.5$
$= 62.5$ mm   OK

Assuming non-structural elements are installed after the composite slab has hardened, $\Delta_t + \Delta_L =$ Terms (3) + (5) + (7) + (8) + (9) = 1.5 + 2.2 + 8.9 + 9.7 + 10.5 = 32.8 mm should be a reasonable estimate.

Comparison with allowable deflections in CSA Standard A23.3: Flat roofs not supporting or attached to non-structural elements likely to be damaged by large deflections - $(\Delta_i)_L \le \ell_n /180 = 10,000/180 = 56$ mm versus 10 mm.   OK

Floors not supporting or attached to non-structural elements likely to be damaged by large deflections - $\Delta_t + (\Delta_i)_L \le \ell_n /360 = 10,000/360 = 28$ mm versus 10 mm.   OK

Roof or floor construction supporting or attached to non-structural elements likely to be damaged by large deflections $\Delta_t + (\Delta_i)_L \le \ell_n / 480 = 10{,}000/480 = 21$ mm versus 33 mm.   NOT OK

Roof or floor construction supporting or attached to non-structural elements not likely to be damaged by large deflections - $\Delta_t + (\Delta_i)_L \le \ell_n / 240 = 10{,}000/240 = 42$ mm versus 33 mm.   OK

Example 6.5   Shored Non-Prestressed Composite Beam, Normal Density Concrete

Given: Same as Example 6.4, except using shored construction.

Required: Deflection analysis

1. Effective moments of inertia:
   In Term (1), Eq. (6-19) - Composite section,

   $M_{cr} = f_r I_g / y_t = 3.29(13{,}940 \times 10^6)(10^{-6})/454 = 101.0$ kN·m

   $M_{cr}/(M_1 + M_2) = 101.0/(76.5 + 50.5) = 0.795$ $0.795^3 = 0.502$

   $(I_e)_{1+2} = (M_{cr}/M_{1+2})^3 I_g + [1 - (M_{cr}/M_{1+2})^3] I_{cr}$
   $= 0.502(13{,}490 \times 10^6) + [1 - 0.502](4412 \times 10^6) = 8970 \times 10^6$ mm^4

   In Term (5), Eq. (6-19) - Composite section.

   $M_{cr}/(M_1 + M_2 + M_L) = 101.0/(76.5 + 50.5 + 109.4) = 0.427$ $0.427^3 = 0.078$

   $(I_e)_{D+L} = 0.078(13{,}940 \times 10^6) + (1 - 0.078)(4412 \times 10^6) = 5120 \times 10^6$ mm^4

2. Deflections:

   Solution by Eq. (6-19)

   Term (1), $(\Delta_i)_{1+2} = \dfrac{K(5/48)(M_1 + M_2)\ell^2}{(E_c)_2 (I_e)_{1+2}}$

   $= \dfrac{1(5/48)(76.5 + 50.5)(10)^2(10^{12})}{24{,}700(8970 \times 10^6)} = 6.0$ mm

   Term (2), $k_r = 0.85$ (neglecting effect of any slab compression steel)

   $1.80 k_r (\Delta_i)_{1+2} = 1.80(0.85)(6.0) = 9.2$ mm

   Term (3), using $\varepsilon_{sh} = 300 \times 10^{-6}$ instead of 400×10^{-6}

   From Ex. 6.5, $\Delta_{sh} = 7.25(300/400) = 5.4$ mm

   $\Delta_{sh} \dfrac{l_2}{l_c} = 5.44(0.377) = 2.1$ mm

   Term (4), $\Delta_{DS} = (\Delta_i)_{1+2} = 6.0$ mm (rough estimate)

   Term (5), $(\Delta_i)_L = \dfrac{K(5/48)(M_{D+L})\ell^2}{(E_c)_2 (I_e)_{D+L}} - (\Delta_i)_{1+2}$

   $= \dfrac{1(5/48)(76.5 + 50.5 + 109.4)(10)^2(10^{12})}{24{,}700(5120 \times 10^6)} - 6.0 = 13.5$ mm

6

Deflections

$$\begin{array}{ccccc}(1) & (2) & (3) & (4) & (5)\end{array}$$
$$\Delta_u = 6.0 + 9.2 + 2.1 + 6.0 + 13.5 = 36.8 \text{ mm}$$

(Solution by Eq. (6-19) versus *62.5* mm in Ex. 6.4 Step 6 for the unshored case.

Checking solution by Eq. (6-20)

$$\Delta_u = 3.53 \left(\Delta_i \right)_{1+2} + \Delta_{sh} \frac{l_2}{l_c} + \left(\Delta_i \right)_L$$
$$= 3.53(6.0) + 2.1 + 13.5 = 36.8 \text{ mm} \hspace{4cm} \text{OK}$$

Assuming non-structural elements are installed after the shores are removed, $\Delta_t + (\Delta)_L$ will be taken as $\Delta_u - (\Delta_i)_{1+2} = 36.8 - 6.0 = 30.8$ mm versus *32.8* mm in Ex. 6.5 for the unshored case. In both the unshored (Ex. 6.4) and shored (Ex. 6.5) cases, three of the four deflection criteria in CSA Standard A23.3, Table 5, are met, but not the most stringent limitation of $\Delta_t + (\Delta_i)_L \le \ell /480 = 10{,}000/480 = 21$ mm versus *31* mm in Ex. 6.5 and *33* mm in Ex. 6.4.

6.6   Concluding Remarks

For additional information on deflections of concrete members the reader is referred to the references listed in Section 6.7.

6.7   References

1.   Subcommittee 1, ACI Committee 435, "Allowable Deflections," ACI Journal, Proceedings V. 65, No. 6, June 1968, pp. 433-444. Also ACI Manual of Concrete Practice, Part 2.

2.   Scanlon, A. and Murray, D. W., "Practical Calculation of Two-Way Slab Deflections," Concrete International, November 1983, pp. 43-50.

3.   Graham, C. J., and Scanlon, A., "Deflection of Reinforced Concrete Slabs under Construction Loading," Structural Engineering Report No. 117, The University of Alberta, August, 1984, 201 pp.

4.   Sbarounis, J. A., "Multi-story Flat Plate Buildings: Effect of Construction Loads on Long-Term Deflections," Concrete International, Vol. 6, No. 4, April 1984, pp. 62-70.

5.   Jokinsen, E. P. and Scanlon, A., "Field-Measured Two-Way Slab Deflections," Proceedings of Annual Conference, Canadian Society for Civil Engineering, Saskatoon, Saskatchewan, May, 1985.

6.   Branson, D. E. Deformation of Concrete Structures, McGraw-Hill Advanced Book Program, 1977, pp. 1-546.

7.   Branson, D. E., Chapter 4 - "Reinforced Concrete Composite Flexural Members," Handbook of Composite Construction Engineering, Editor, G. M. Sabnis, Van Nostrand Reinhold Co., 1978.

8.   ACI Committee 435, "Deflections of Reinforced Concrete Flexural Members," ACI Journal, Proceedings V. 63, No. 6, June 1966, pp. 637-674. Also ACI Manual of Concrete Practice, Part 2.

9.   American Concrete Institute, "Designing for Effects of Creep, Shrinkage, and Temperature in Concrete Structures," ACI Publication SP 27, 1970, pp. 1-430.

10. Subcommittee 2, ACI Committee 435, "Variability of Deflections of Simply Supported Reinforced Concrete Beams," ACI Journal, Proceedings, V. 69, No. 1, Jan. 1972, pp. 29-35, Discussion in ACI Journal, Proceedings, V 69, No. 7, July 1972, pp. 449-451, Also ACI Manual of Concrete Practice, Part 2.

11. Subcommittee 5, ACI Committee 435, "State-of-the-Art Report: Deflection of Two-Way Reinforced Concrete Floor Systems," ACI Publication SP-43, 1974, pp. 55-81.

12. Subcommittee 7, ACI Committee 435, "Deflections of Continuous Concrete Beams," ACI Journal, Proceedings V. 70, No. 12, Dec. 1973, pp. 781-787. Also ACI Manual of Concrete Practice, Part 2.

13. American Concrete Institute, "Deflections of Concrete Structures," ACI Publication SP 43, 1974, pp. 1-637.

14. Building Code Subcommittee, ACI Committee 435, "Proposed ACI Code and Commentary Provision on Deflections," Nov. 1975, April 1977, pp. 1-25.

15. Branson, D. E., "Instantaneous and Time-Dependent Deflections of Simple and Continuous Reinforced Concrete Beams," HPR Report No. 7, Part 1, Alabama Highway Department, Bureau of Public Roads, Aug. 1963., p. 1-78.

16. Lutz, L. A. "Graphical Evaluation of the Effective Moment of Inertia for Deflection," ACI Journal, Proceedings, V. 70, No. 3 March 1973, pp. 207-213.

17. Fling, R. S., Chapter 2 - "Deflections," Handbook of Concrete Engineering, M. Fintel, Editor, Van Nostrand Reinhold Co., 1974, pp. 44-54.

18. Branson, D. E., "Compression Steel Effect on Long-Time Deflections," ACI Journal, Proceedings V. 68, No. 8, August 1971, pp. 555-559.

19. Nilson, A. H., and Walters, D. B., "Deflection of Two-Way Floor Systems by the Equivalent Frame Method," ACI Journal, Proceedings V. 72, No. 5, May 1975, pp. 210-218.

20. Kripanarayanan, K. M., and Branson, D. E., "Short-Time Deflections of Flat Plates, Flat Slabs, and Two-Way Slabs," ACI Journal, Proceedings V. 73, No. 12, Dec. 1976, pp. 686-690.

21. Neville, A. M., Dilger, W. H. and Brooks, J. J., "Creep of Plain and Structural Concrete," Construction Press, London, New York, 1983, 351 pp.

22. Grundy, R., and Kabaila, A., "Construction Loads on Slabs with Shored Formwork in Multistory Buildings," ACI Journal, Proceedings V. 60, No. 12, Dec. 1963, pp. 1729-1738.

23. Agarwal, R. K., and Gardner, N. J., "Form and Shore Requirements for Multistory Flat Slab Type Buildings," ACI Journal Proceedings V. 71, No. 11, Nov. 1974, pp. 559-569.

24. Gardner, N. J., "Design and Construction Interdependence," Concrete International, Nov. 1990, pp. 32-38.

6

Deflections

Table A Summary of Calculated Deflections for Two-Way Slab Examples

Design Example	Location of Deflection	Live Load Deflection		Deflection After Attachment of Non-Structural Elements	
		Calculated (mm)	Permissible (mm)	Calculated (mm)	Permissible (mm)
Example (6.2) Specified Loads $f_r = 0.3\sqrt{f_c'}$ MPa	Column Strip Middle Strip Mid-Panel	11.0 16.8 27.8	17.8 17.8 25.0	30.1 35.4 65.5	13.3 13.3 18.8
Example (6.3) Construction Loads $f_r = 0.3\sqrt{f_c'}$ MPa	Column Strip Middle Strip Mid-Panel	7.3 9.8 17.1	17.8 17.8 25.0	34.1 47.7 81.8	13.3 13.3 18.8

Table 6.1 –   Thickness Below Which Deflections Must be Computed for Non Prestressed Beams or One-Way Slabs Not Supporting or Attached to Partitions or Other Construction Likely to be Damaged by Large Deflections

Member Type	Minimum thickness, h			
	Simply supported	One end continuous	Both ends continuous	Cantilever
Solid one-way slabs	$\ell_n/20$	$\ell_n/24$	$\ell_n/28$	$\ell_n/10$
Beams or ribbed one-way slabs	$\ell_n/16$	$\ell_n/18.5$	$\ell_n/21$	$\ell_n/8$

Values given shall be used directly for members with normal density concrete ($\gamma_c > 2150$ kg/m^3) and Grade 400 reinforcement. For other conditions, the values shall be modified as follows:

(a) For structural low density concrete and structural semi-low density concrete, the values shall be multiple by $(1.65 - 0.0003\gamma_c)$, but not less than 1.00, where γ_c is the density in kg/m^3.

(b) For f_y other than 400 MPa, the values shall be multiplied by $(0.4 + f_y/670)$.

---

*   This table also appears in CSA Standard A23.3 as Table 9.1.

Table 6.2 – CSA Standard A23.3 Minimum Thickness for Two-Way Construction Expressed as a Fraction of the Longer Span Length, ℓ_n

a)   Flat Plates and Slabs with Column Capitals

$$h_s \geq \frac{\ell_n(0.6 + f_y/1000)}{30} \qquad \text{(Eq. 13-1)}$$

At discontinuous edges, an edge beam shall be provided with a stiffness ratio, α, of not less than 0.8 or the thickness required by Equation (13.1) shall be multiplied by 1.1 in the panel with the discontinuous edge or edges.

b)   Slabs with Drop Panels

$$h_s \geq \frac{\ell_n(0.6 + f_y/1000)}{30} - \left(\frac{2x_d}{\ell_n}\right)\Delta h \qquad \text{(Eq. 13-2)}$$

c)   Slabs with beams between all supports

$$h_s \geq \frac{\ell_n (0.6 + f_y/1000)}{30 + 4\,\beta\,\alpha_m} \qquad \text{(Eq. 13-3)}$$

where α_m in equation (13.3a) shall not be taken greater than *2.0* and the value α may be determined taking l_b equal to

$$l_b = \frac{b_w h^3}{12}\left[2.5\left(1 - \frac{h_s}{h}\right)\right] \qquad \text{(Eq. 13-4)}$$

Notes: 1) Ratio of long to short span (β) not exceeding 2.

2) Stiffness ratio, α, for beam at discontinuous edge must not be less than *0.8*, or increase minimum thickness by at least *10%*. A beam with $h \geq 2\,h_s$ and $b_w h \geq 4(h_s)^2$ will always give $\alpha = 0.8$ or greater.

Table 6.3 – Maximum Permissible Computed Deflections[*]

Type of Member	Deflections to be Considered	Deflection Limitation
Flat roofs not supporting or attached to non-structural elements likely to be damaged by large deflections	Immediate deflection due to the specified live load, L, or snow load, S	$\ell_n /180$[**]
Floors not supporting or attached to non-structural elements likely to be damaged by large deflections	Immediate deflection due to the specified live load, L	$\ell_n /360$
Roof or floor construction supporting or attached to non-structural elements likely to be damaged by large deflections	That part of the total deflection which occurs after attachment of the non-structural elements, the sum of the long-time deflection due to all sustained loads and the immediate deflection due to any additional live load[+]	$\ell_n /480$[++]
Roof or floor construction supporting or attached to non-structural elements not likely to be damaged by large deflections	That part of the total deflection which occurs after attachment of the non-structural elements, the sum of the long-time deflection due to all sustained loads and the immediate deflection due to any additional live load[+]	$\ell_n /240$[&]

[*]   This table is identical to Table 9.3 of CSA Standard A23.3

[**] This limit is not intended to safeguard against ponding, ponding should be checked by suitable calculations of deflection including the added deflections due to ponded water, and considering long-time effects of all sustained loads, camber construction tolerances, and reliability of provisions for drainage.

[+]   Long-time deflections shall be determined in accordance with Clause 9.8.2.5 or 9.8.4.4 of CSA Standard A23.3 but may be reduced by the amount of deflection calculated to occur before attachment of non-structural elements.

[++] This limit may be exceeded if adequate measures are taken to prevent damage to supported or attached elements.

[&]   But not greater than the tolerance provided for the non-structural elements. This limit may be exceeded if camber is provided so that the total deflection minus the camber does not exceed the limitation.

Note: For two-way construction ℓ_n shall be taken as the clear span in the long direction, measured face-to-face of supports in slabs without beams, and face-to-face of beams or other supports in other cases.

Table 6.4   Section Properties for Rectangular Cross-Section

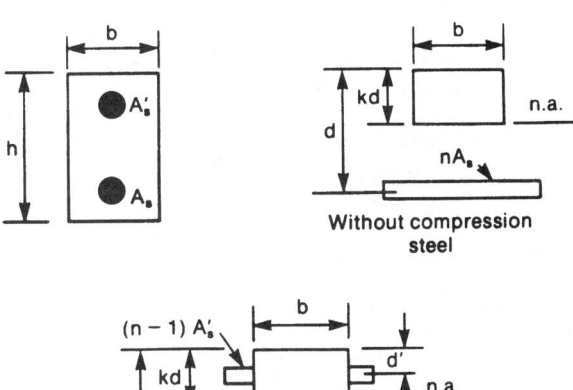

Moment of Inertia of Gross Section, I_g

$$I_g = \frac{1}{12}\, b\, h^3$$

Cracking Moment, M_{cr}

$$M_{cr} = \frac{f_r I_g}{y_t} \qquad y_t = \frac{h}{2}$$

Moment of Inertia of Cracked Transformed Section, I_{cr}

$$B = \frac{b}{n\,A_s} \qquad r = \frac{(n-1)A_s'}{n\,A_s}$$

a)   Without compression Steel

$$kd = \frac{\sqrt{2dB + 1} - 1}{B}$$

$$I_{cr} = \frac{1}{3} b(kd)^3 + nA_s\,(d - kd)^2$$

b)   With Compression Steel

$$kd = \frac{\sqrt{2dB\left(1 + \dfrac{rd'}{d}\right) + (1+r)^2} - (1+r)}{B}$$

$$I_{cr} = \frac{1}{3} b(kd)^3 + nA_s\,(d - kd)^2 + (n-1)A_s'(kd - d')^2$$

(Note: See Table 6.5 for graphical evaluation of I_{cr})

Table 6.5   Cracked Section Moment of Inertia, I_{cr} for Rectangular Section [16]

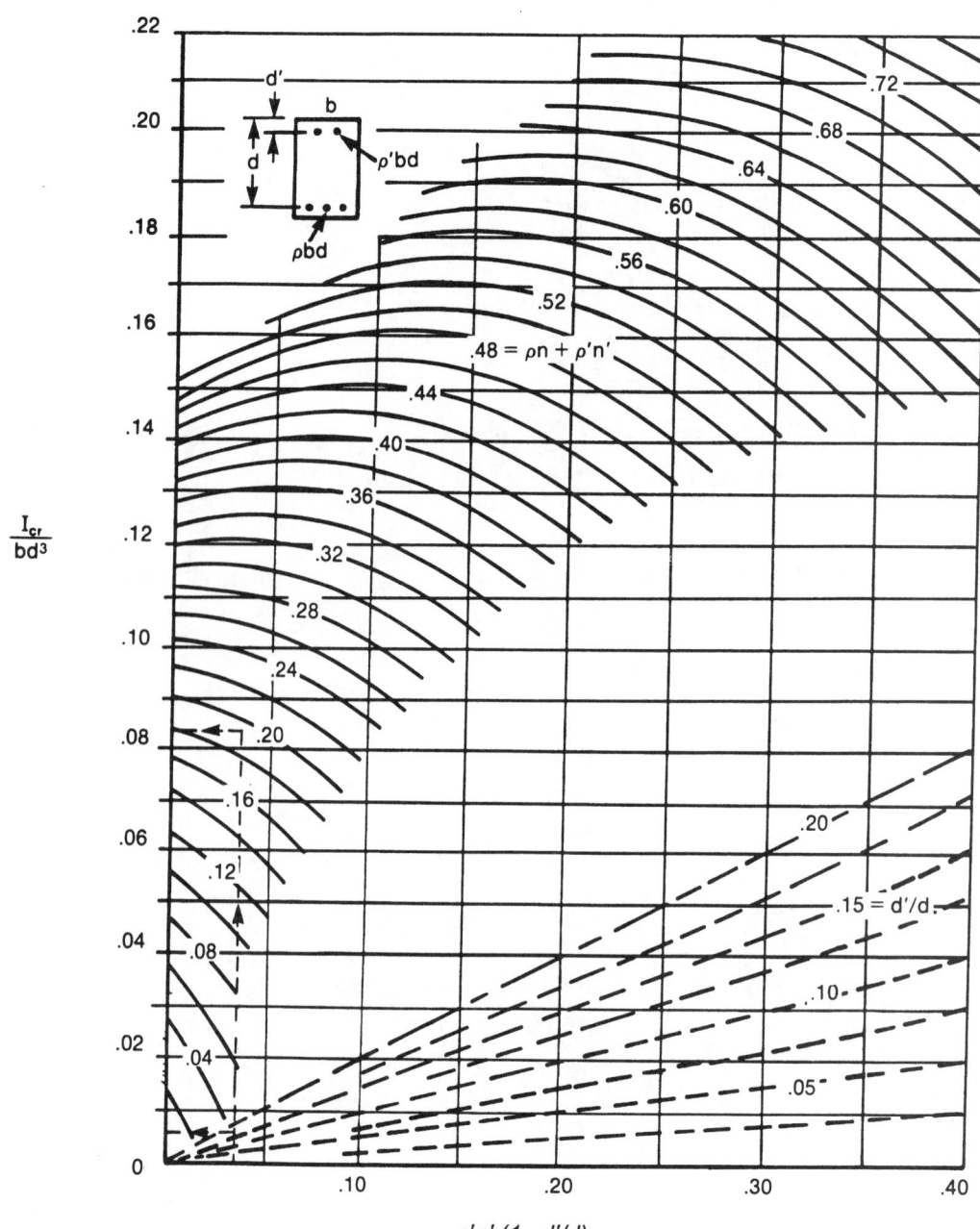

Table 6.6   Section Properties for Tee Cross-Section

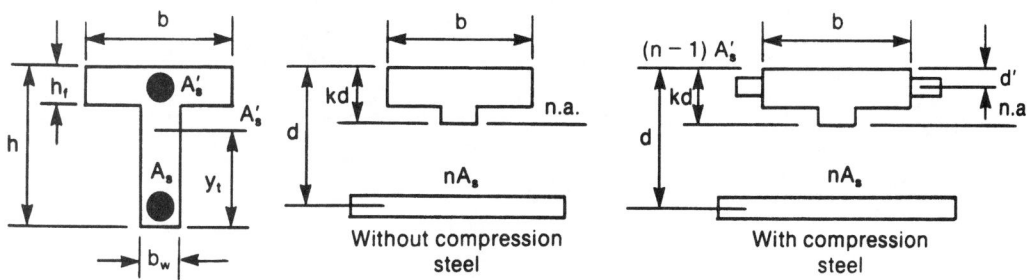

Moment of Inertia of Gross Section, I_g

$$A_r = \frac{h_f}{h}\left(\frac{b}{b_w} - 1\right) \qquad\qquad I_g = C_T bh^3$$

$$C_T = \frac{4A_r\left(1 - \frac{h_f}{h}\right)^2 + \left(1 + A_r\frac{h_f}{h}\right)^2}{12\frac{b}{b_w}(1 + A_r)}$$

(Note: See Table 6.7 for graphical evaluation of I_g)

Cracking Moment, M_{cr}

a)   Tension at bottom face

$$\frac{y_{tb}}{h} = \frac{\frac{b}{b_w}\left(\frac{h_f}{h}\right)\left(1 - \frac{1}{2}\frac{h_f}{h}\right) + \frac{1}{2}\left(1 - \frac{h_f}{h}\right)^2}{\frac{b}{b_w}\left(\frac{h_f}{h}\right) + \left(1 - \frac{h_f}{h}\right)}$$

$$M_{cr} = \frac{f_r I_g}{y_{tb}}$$

(Note: See Table 6.8 for graphical evaluation of y_{tb})

b)   Tension at top face

$$y_{tt} = h - y_{tb} \qquad\qquad M_{cr} = \frac{f_r I_g}{y_{tt}}$$

Moment of Inertia of Cracked Transformed Section, I_{cr} (without compression steel)

a)   Tension at bottom face

$$C = \frac{b_w}{nA_s} \qquad\qquad f = \frac{h_f(b - b_w)}{nA_s}$$

$$kd = \frac{\sqrt{C(2d + h_f f) + (1 + f)^2} - (1 + f)}{C}$$

$$I_{cr} = \frac{(b - b_w)h_f^3}{12} + \frac{b_w(kd)^3}{3} + (b - b_w)h_f\left(kd - \frac{h_f}{2}\right)^2 + nA_s(d - kd)^2$$

(Note: See Table 6.9 for graphical evaluation of I_{cr})

b)   Tension at top face: same as rectangular section with width $b = b_w$

Table 6.7   Gross Moment of Inertia, I_g[16]

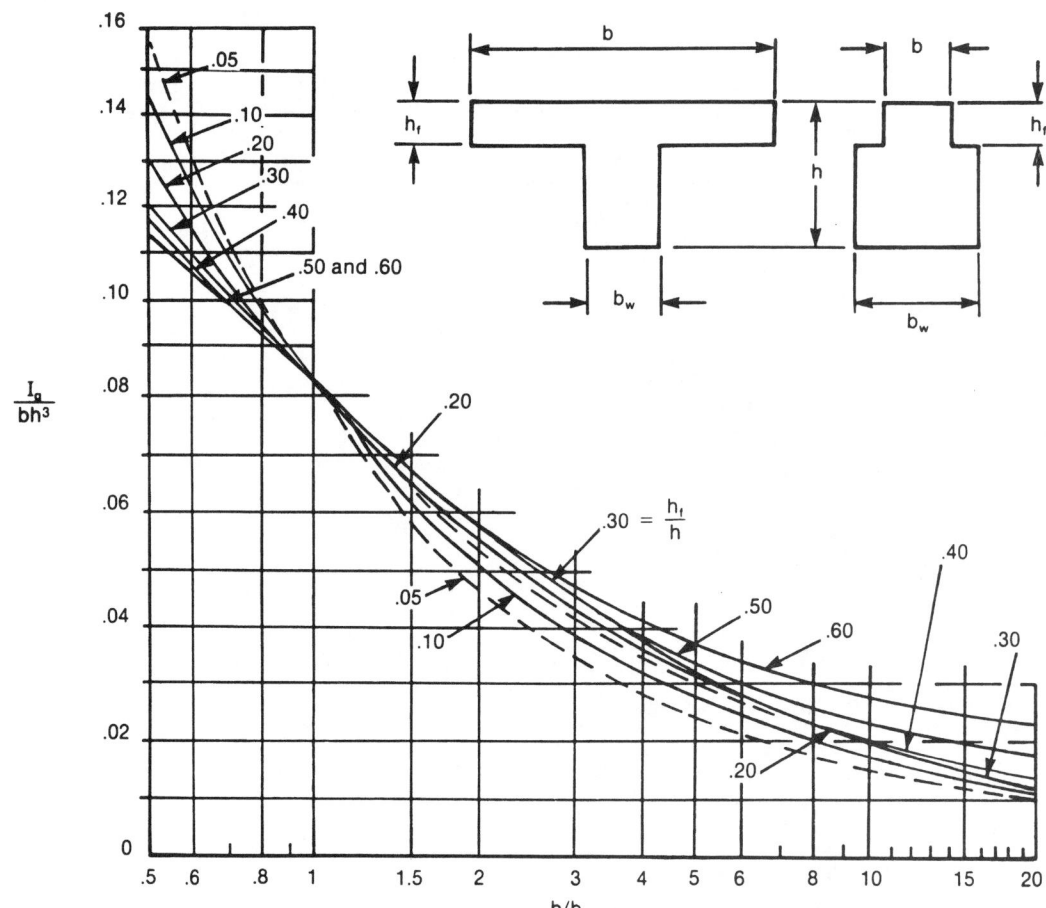

Table 6.8   Distance from centroid to bottom fibre

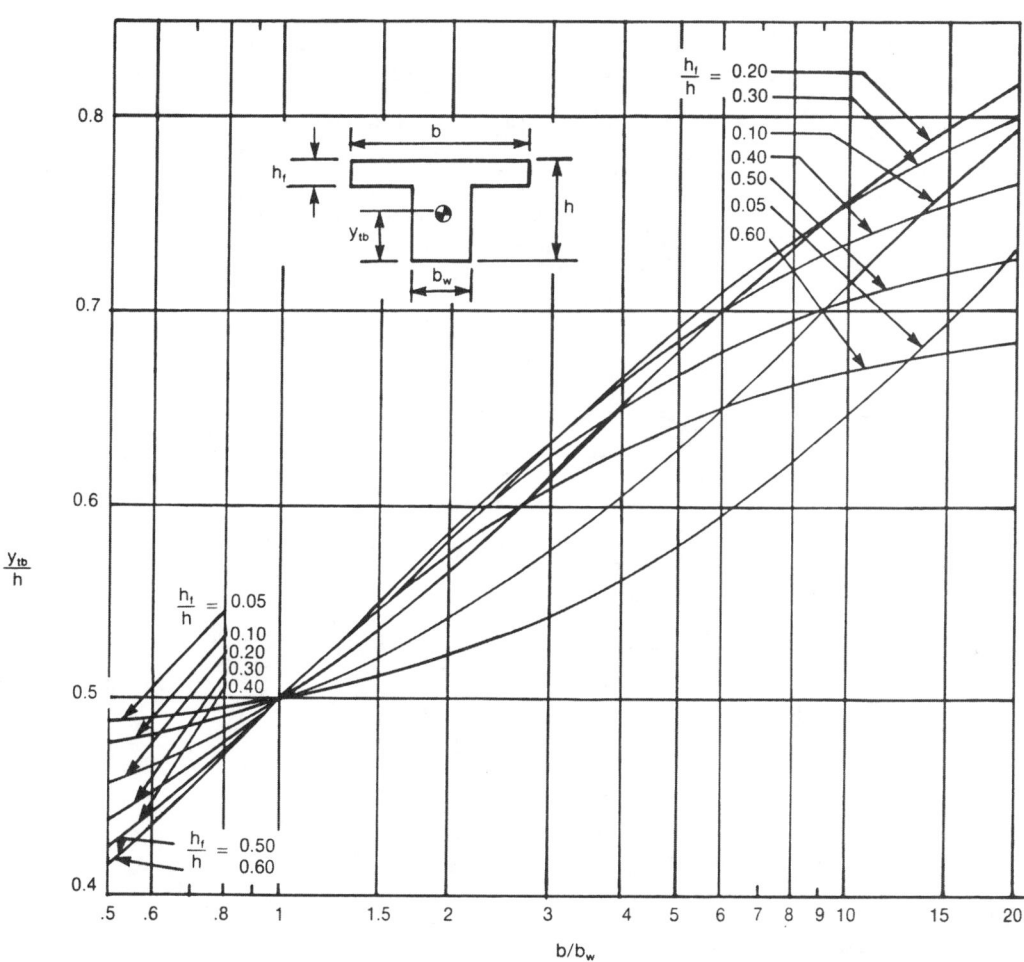

Table 6.9   Cracked Section Moment of Inertia, I_{cr} for T-Section[16]

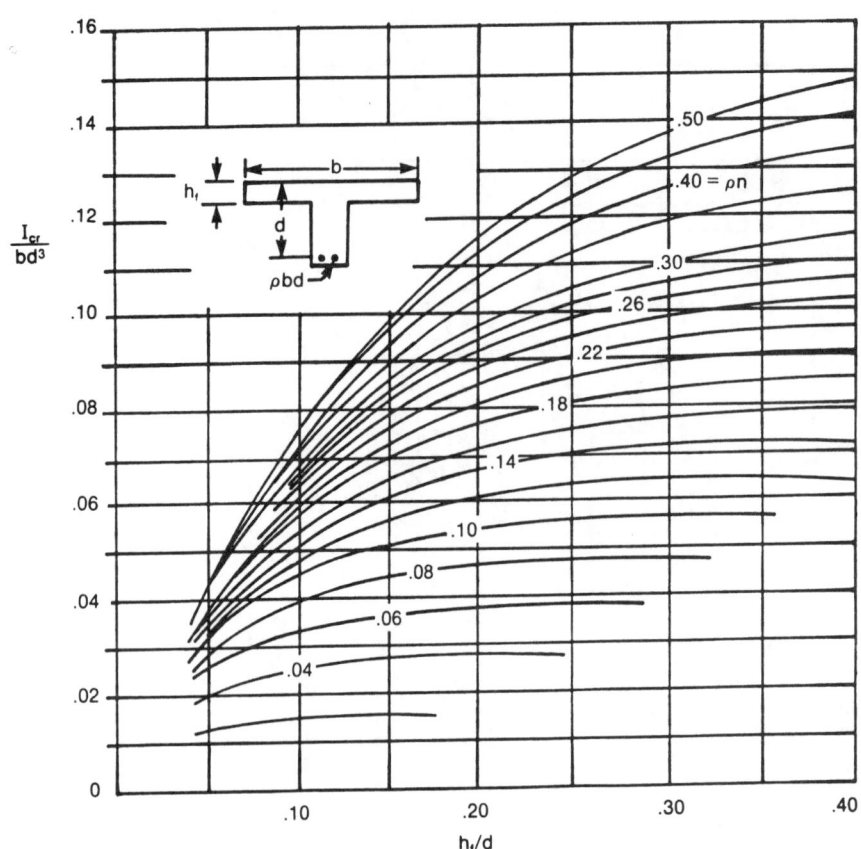

Table 6.10   Values of A_{sh} for Calculating Shrinkage Curvature in Eq. (6.12)*

ρ' \ ρ	0.00	0.25	0.50	0.75	1.00	1.25	1.50	1.75	2.00	2.25	2.50	2.75	3.00
0.25	0.44	0.00	-	-	-	-	-	-	-	-	-	-	-
0.50	0.56	0.31	0.00	-	-	-	-	-	-	-	-	-	-
0.75	0.64	0.45	0.25	0.00	-	-	-	-	-	-	-	-	-
1.00	0.70	0.55	0.39	0.22	0.00	-	-	-	-	-	-	-	-
1.25	0.75	0.63	0.49	0.35	0.20	0.00	-	-	-	-	-	-	-
1.50	0.80	0.69	0.57	0.45	0.32	0.18	0.00	-	-	-	-	-	-
1.75	0.84	0.74	0.64	0.57	0.42	0.30	0.17	0.00	-	-	-	-	-
2.00	0.88	0.79	0.69	0.64	0.50	0.39	0.28	0.16	0.00	-	-	-	-
2.25	0.92	0.83	0.74	0.69	0.56	0.47	0.37	0.26	0.15	0.00	-	-	-
2.50	0.95	0.87	0.79	0.74	0.62	0.53	0.44	0.35	0.25	0.14	0.00	-	-
2.75	0.98	0.91	0.83	0.79	0.67	0.59	0.51	0.42	0.33	0.24	0.13	0.00	-
3.00	1.00	0.94	0.87	0.83	0.72	0.64	0.57	0.49	0.40	0.32	0.23	0.13	0.00
3.25	1.00	0.97	0.90	0,87	0.76	0.69	0.62	0.54	0.47	0.39	0.31	0.22	0.12
3.50	1.00	1.00	0.94	0.90	0.80	0.74	0.67	0.60	0.52	0.45	0.37	0.29	0.32
3.75	1.00	1.00	1.00	0.94	0.84	0.78	0.71	0.64	0.58	0.52	0.44	0.36	0.28
4.00	1.00	1.00	1.00	1.00	0.88	0.81	0.75	0.69	0.62	0.56	0.49	0.42	0.35

* $\rho = 100 A_s/(bd)$ $\rho' = 100 A'_s/(bd)$. When $\rho' > \rho$, interchange ρ' and ρ to obtain corresponding solution in opposite direction.

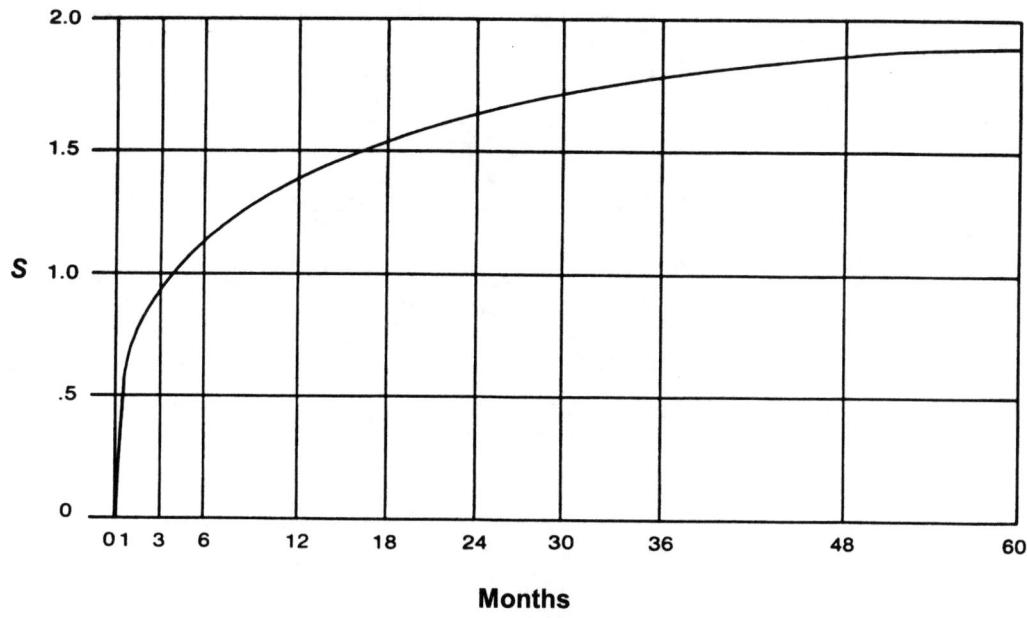

Months

Figure 6.1 Variation of *S* with Load Duration

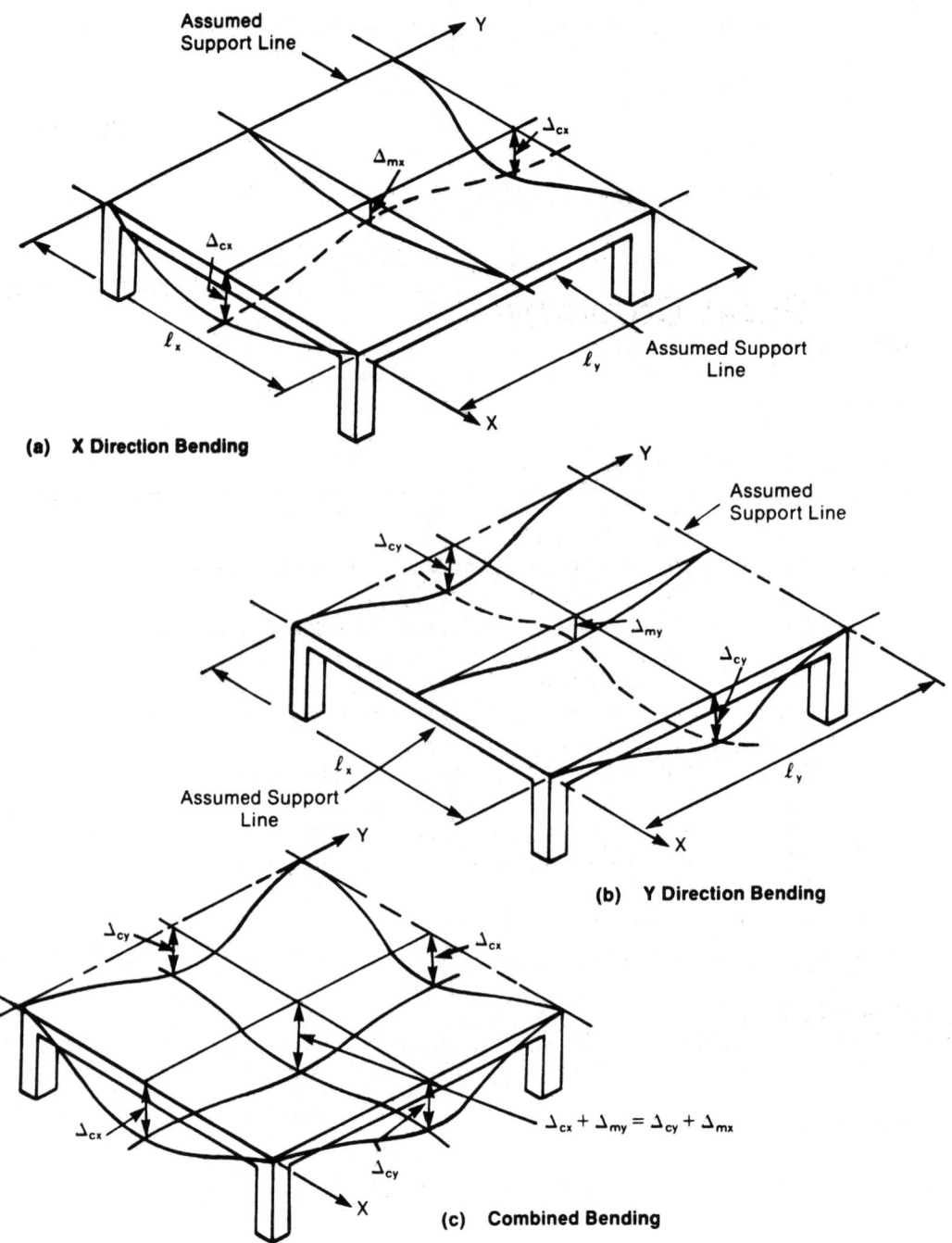

(a) X Direction Bending

(b) Y Direction Bending

$$\Delta_{cx} + \Delta_{my} = \Delta_{cy} + \Delta_{mx}$$

(c) Combined Bending

Figure 6.2 Basis of Equivalent Frame Method for Deflection Analysis

7

By Robert Loov

Short Columns

7

Short Columns

7.1   General Remarks

Columns must be proportioned to resist bending moment as well as axial load. The capacity of column cross sections is described using interaction diagrams (Tables 7.4 through 7.7).

Clause 10.15.2 of CSA A23.3* defines a limiting slenderness ratio $k\ell_u/r$ below which slenderness effects will be insignificant for non-sway frames. (See Table 8.1 for description of ℓ_u.)

The design of slender columns is covered in chapter 8 of this handbook.

7.2   Maximum Axial Resistance Under Small Moments

Column cross sections can resist more axial load when moments are small. Clause 10.10.4 of CSA A23.3 sets a maximum axial load resistance based on the assumption that some moment is inevitable. Values of the maximum axial load, $P_{r,\,max}$, for tied columns are shown in Tables 7.1.1 to 7.1.5 for common sizes of cross sections, concrete strengths of 25, 30, 35, 40 and 45 MPa and steel strengths of 400 MPa and 500 MPa. The material resistance factors $\phi_c = 0.65$ and $\phi_s = 0.85$ are incorporated into the graphs. Precast concrete columns for which $\phi_c = 0.70$ will have slightly higher capacities.

These graphs can be used as an estimating design aid as each displays the possible square column sizes appropriate for a specific axial load. They can also be used for rectangular and circular tied columns by choosing comparable areas. The diameter of a circular column is 1.128 times the size of a square column of the same area.

The capacity, $P_{r,\,max}$ of spiral columns will be 6.25% larger than the tied columns shown because the upper limit is based on $0.85P_{ro}$ rather than $0.80P_{ro}$ (see Clause10.10.4). This difference exists only for small eccentricities. (See Tables 7.7.1 to 7.7.16.) The remaining portions of the interaction curves are the same

When ρ_t exceeds 4%, welded splices, mechanical connections, or end-bearing splices have to be staggered to satisfy Clause 12.17.2 of CSA A23.3. Columns with lapped splices can seldom have much more than 4% steel while, even with end-bearing splices, ρ_t will seldom exceed 6%.

Steeper lines correspond to ρ_t ratios between 0.5 and 1%. Columns with these low steel ratios may be useful in upper storeys to reduce the number of size changes in a column stack. The sharp change in capacity is based on the application of Clause 10.10.5. This Clause has been revised to permit a somewhat larger capacity than before.

7.3   Values of Gamma for Columns

Table 7.2 provides values of γ for common sizes of columns, with 40 mm and 50 mm cover to 10M ties or spirals. The value γ is the ratio of the centre-to-centre distance between the outermost reinforcing bars (measured perpendicular to the axis of bending) to the overall depth of the column, h. For other covers $\gamma = \gamma_{40} + 2(40 - c)/h$.

7.4   Minimum Column Sizes and Covers for Fire and Durability

Table 7.3 summarizes the requirements for minimum column size and cover for different fire ratings, column lengths, steel ratios, concrete type, and overdesign factor, P_r/P_f. Concrete types and requirements for fire resistance are discussed in Section 1 of this handbook.

Cover requirements for durability as specified in Clause 6.6.6.2 of CSA A23.1-04 "Concrete Materials and Methods of Concrete Construction", are also shown in this table.

---

* CSA Standard A23.3-04 "Design of Concrete Structures." From here on referred to as CSA A23.3.

Section 1 of this handbook provides information on construction intended for a de-icer salt environment. Bearing walls and columns that support slabs and ramps may be splashed with de-icers and are hence subject to corrosion. Such supporting elements should be constructed using at least the same quality of concrete and cover recommended for slabs and ramps.

7.5   Interaction Diagrams

The strength of column cross sections can be determined using interaction diagrams with the factored axial resistance as the ordinate and the factored moment resistance as abscissa. To make the graphs applicable to all column sizes, P_r has been divided by A_g and M_r has been divided by $A_g h$. The material resistance factors $\phi_c = 0.65$ and $\phi_s = 0.85$ have been included in the calculation of the factored resistances so the charts give P_r/A_g, and $M_r/(A_g h)$ without modification. The charts are conservative for precast columns for which $\phi_c = 0.70$.

Four graphs with different values of γ are included for each concrete strength, column shape and reinforcing pattern. The interaction diagrams are plotted for 3 reinforcement patterns for rectangular cross sections and for circular sections with circular or helical ties, or spirals.

Tied rectangular column cross sections include those with equal amounts of reinforcement in each of the four faces (Tables 7.4.1 to 7.4.20); equal amounts of reinforcement in the two faces parallel to the axis of bending (Tables 7.5.1 to 7.5.20); and columns with equal amounts of reinforcement in the two side faces perpendicular to the axis of bending (Tables 7.6.1 to 7.6.20). Tables 7.5.1 to 7.5.20 should be used for columns with 4 bars since all 4 bars are located the same distance from the axis of the column.

The charts for circular columns have been plotted using P_r/h^2 and M_r/h^3. The capacities of circular tied and spiral columns differ only at small eccentricities when Clause 10.10.4 governs. The charts in Tables 7.7.1 to 7.7.16 can be used for both cases. A shaded line shows the additional capacity of spiral columns.

Three radial lines in each diagram give the tensile stress ratio in the steel layer closest to the tensile face of the column. These are used to determine the type of column splices required. See Clause 12.17 of CSA A23.3

Some description of the assumptions incorporated into the calculation of these interaction curves may be of interest. Calculations have been based on a limiting strain of 0.0035 in the extreme compression fibre. The interaction curves have been based on an equivalent rectangular concrete stress block of depth $\beta_1 c$ with a uniform stress, $\phi_c \alpha_1 f'_c$. The effect of the concrete displaced by the area of steel in regions of compressed concrete has been taken into account by deducting ϕ_c times the concrete stress from the stress in the compressed reinforcement. For this purpose the concrete stress was assumed to be εE_c at low compressive strains and $\alpha_1 f'_c$ at high strains.

In situations with a small moment with $c > h$, the graphs have been approximated by a straight line from P_{ro} to the P_r and M_r corresponding to $c = h$.

The interaction curves in Table 7.5.1 to 7.5.20 were developed for equal reinforcement in the two end faces. All of the other charts for rectangular columns have been based on 6 layers of steel. The curves for circular columns have been based on 8 bars with 2 bars located directly on the axis of bending as shown in the sketches on Tables 7.7.1 to 7.7.16 and the remaining bars uniformly spaced around the column. These curves are reasonably conservative for any number of longitudinal bars ranging down to the minimum of 6 allowed for spirals and even the 4 allowed for circular ties.

Gamma, γ, is the ratio of the distance between the centres of the outermost reinforcing bars and the overall column depth, h. Gamma does not affect the column capacity $P_{r, max}$ with low moment. It has maximum effect at balanced conditions $(f_s/f_y = 1.0)$ and with higher values of ρ_t. It is conservative to use an interaction chart with γ smaller than the expected value. Only when γ approaches that of the next higher graph and $f_s/f_y > 0$ is it worthwhile to interpolate between graphs with different γ.

7

Short Columns

7.5.1   Column stiffness

As an aid in determining slenderness effects, the values of EI are given on each strength interaction graph.

Equation 10-19

If the effective stiffness of cross sections is determined without the influence of reinforcement,

$$EI_{19} = \frac{0.4E_c I_g}{1 + \beta_d} \quad \text{(Eq. 10-19 of CSA A23.3)}$$

The modulus of elasticity has been based on Eq. 8-1 of A23.3 with a concrete density of 2400 kg/m³.

$$E_c = \left(3300\sqrt{f'_c} + 6900\right)\left(\frac{\gamma_c}{2300}\right)^{1.5}$$

For rectangular columns $I_g = bh^3/12$. The value of EI_{19} is given with each set of interaction graphs as a constant times bh^3.

For circular columns $I_g = \pi h^4/64$ so EI_{19} is shown as a constant times h^4.

Equation 10-18

The alternate equation for EI includes the influence of longitudinal reinforcement

$$EI_{18} = \frac{0.2E_c I_g + E_s I_{st}}{1 + \beta_d} \quad \text{(Eq. 10-18 of CSA A23.3)}$$

The values of I_{st} are different for each pattern of reinforcing.

Reinforcing on End Faces Only

For rectangular columns with the reinforcing on the two end faces that are parallel to the axis of bending, all of the reinforcing is centred a distance $\frac{1}{2}\gamma h$ from the column centreline

$$\therefore I_{st} = A_{st}\gamma^2 h^2/4 = \rho_t \gamma^2 bh^3/4$$

$$EI_{18} = (0.2\, E_c I_g + E_s\rho_t\gamma^2 bh^3/4)/(1 + \beta_d)$$

$$EI_{18} = \left(\frac{E_c}{60} + \frac{E_s\, \rho_t\gamma^2}{4}\right)bh^3 \, /(1 + \beta_d) = kbh^3 \, /(1 + \beta_d)$$

where $k = E_c/60 + E_s\rho_t\gamma^2/4$

The value of k has been shown for each value of ρ_t on each interaction chart.

Reinforcing on Side Faces

With reinforcing on the side faces that are perpendicular to the axis of bending, the value of I_{st} reduces as the number of bars/side is increased:

$$\text{for 3 bars} \quad I_{st} = \frac{2}{3} A_{st} \gamma^2 h^2 \left(\frac{1}{4} \right) = \frac{\rho_t \gamma^2 bh^3}{6}$$

$$\text{for 4 bars} \quad I_{st} = \frac{2}{4} A_{st} \gamma^2 h^2 \left(\frac{1}{4} + \frac{1}{36} \right) = \frac{\rho_t \gamma^2 bh^3}{7.2}$$

$$\text{for 5 bars} \quad I_{st} = \frac{2}{5} A_{st} \gamma^2 h^2 \left(\frac{1}{4} + \frac{1}{16} \right) = \frac{\rho_t \gamma^2 bh^3}{8}$$

$$\text{for 6 bars} \quad I_{st} = \frac{2}{6} A_{st} \gamma^2 h^2 \left(\frac{1}{4} + \frac{9}{100} + \frac{1}{100} \right) = \frac{\rho_t \gamma^2 bh^3}{8.57}$$

The chosen value of I_{st} of $\rho_t \gamma^2 bh^3 / 8.57$ has been based on 6 bars/face, which will be conservative for columns with less than 6 bars/face;

Therefore $k = E_c/60 + E_s \rho_t \gamma^2 / 8.57$

Equal Reinforcement on all 4 Faces

When there are an equal number of bars on each face, the number of bars/face still affects I_{st}, but the variation is not as pronounced as for reinforcement only on the side faces.

$$\text{for 3 bars} \quad I_{st} = \frac{2}{8} A_{st} \gamma^2 h^2 \left(\frac{3}{4} \right) = \frac{\rho_t \gamma^2 bh^3}{5.33}$$

$$\text{for 4 bars} \quad I_{st} = \frac{2}{12} A_{st} \gamma^2 h^2 \left(\frac{4}{4} + \frac{2}{36} \right) = \frac{\rho_t \gamma^2 bh^3}{5.68}$$

$$\text{for 5 bars} \quad I_{st} = \frac{2}{16} A_{st} \gamma^2 h^2 \left(\frac{5}{4} + \frac{2}{16} \right) = \frac{\rho_t \gamma^2 bh^3}{5.82}$$

$$\text{for 6 bars} \quad I_{st} = \frac{2}{20} A_{st} \gamma^2 h^2 \left(\frac{6}{4} + \frac{2(9)}{100} + \frac{2}{100} \right) = \frac{\rho_t \gamma^2 bh^3}{5.88}$$

A moment of inertia based on 6 bars/side gives $k = E_c/60 + E_s \rho_t \gamma^2 / 5.88$

Circular Columns

For circular columns I_g is $\pi h^4/64$ and I_{st} varies depending upon both the number and orientation of the bars relative to the axis of bending. For 4, 8 or an infinite number of bars $I_{st} = A_s \gamma^2 h^2 / 8$. Using this value for I_{st}:

$$EI_{18} = kh^4/(1 + \beta_d)$$

where $k = \frac{\pi}{4} (E_c / 80 + E_s \rho_t \gamma^2 / 8)$

7.5.2   Steel or concrete strengths which differ from charted values

The interaction curves have been based on 400 MPa reinforcement. For locations in the interaction diagrams where the steel strains in the compression or tension reinforcement are higher than *0.002*, the interaction curves can be used for other steel strengths by using ρ_t adjusted by multiplication by $400/f_y$. This adjustment is appropriate for the region near $P_{r,\,max}$ and is also applicable for low values of P_r/A_g up to approximately 3/4 of the value at $f_s/f_y = 1.0$. In other regions of the interaction diagram there will be little benefit from the increased steel strength.

Interaction curves have been produced for concrete strengths of 25, 30, 35, 40 and 45 MPa. The curves for $f_c' = 25$ MPa can be used for lower concrete strengths by modifying P_r/A_g, $M_r/(A_g h)$ and ρ_t as follows:

Enter the curves with adjusted values of P_r/A_g and $M_r/(A_g h)$.

$$\left(\frac{P_r}{A_g}\right)_{25} \approx \left(\frac{P_r}{A_g}\right)_{f_c'}\left(\frac{25}{f_c'}\right)$$

$$\left(\frac{M_r}{A_g h}\right)_{25} \approx \left(\frac{M_r}{A_g h}\right)_{f_c'}\left(\frac{25}{f_c'}\right)$$

The required ρ_t determined from the interaction curves must be adjusted by the ratio $f_c'/25$. The variation of α_1 and β_1 as f_c' is reduced does not have a significant effect and the prediction is conservative.

Using adjustments similar to those indicated above, the curves for 45 MPa may be used to estimate the strength of columns with higher concrete strengths. In this case the reduction in α_1 should be included.

$$\left(\frac{P_r}{A_g}\right)_{45} \approx \left(\frac{P_r}{A_g}\right)_{f_c'}\left(\frac{45}{f_c'}\right)\left(\frac{\alpha_{1(45)}}{\alpha_{1(f_c')}}\right)$$

$$\left(\frac{M_r}{A_g h}\right)_{45} \approx \left(\frac{M_r}{A_g h}\right)_{f_c'}\left(\frac{45}{f_c'}\right)\left(\frac{\alpha_{1(45)}}{\alpha_{1(f_c')}}\right)$$

The required ρ_t found from the 45 MPa interaction curves must then be adjusted to $\rho_{t(f_c')} = \rho_{t(45)}\left(f_c'/45\right)$.

7.5.3   Biaxial Bending

Rectangular cross sections subjected to biaxial bending and axial compression must be checked to ensure adequate strength under this combination of loads. A common way of estimating the column strength under biaxial bending is the reciprocal load method suggested by Bresler[*]:

$$\frac{1}{P_r/A_g} = \frac{1}{P_{rx}/A_g} + \frac{1}{P_{ry}/A_g} - \frac{1}{P_{ro}/A_g}$$

---

[*] Bresler, Boris, "Design Criteria for Reinforced Columns under Axial Load and Biaxial Bending", ACI Journal, Proceedings V. 57, No. 11, Nov. 1960, pp. 481-490.

where:

P_{rx} = factored axial load resistance if the load were applied at the eccentricity e_x with $e_y = 0$.

P_{ry} = factored axial load resistance if the load were applied at the eccentricity e_y with $e_x = 0$.

P_{ro} = factored axial load resistance if e_x and e_y were 0.

(P_{ro} is 1.25 times $P_{r, max}$ shown as a horizontal line on the interaction curves.)

Design for biaxial bending can be started by augmenting the larger bending moment by about 10 percent. The cross section dimensions and reinforcement can be selected and then checked using the above equation.

Circular columns can be designed directly by computing $M_f = (M_{fx}^2 + M_{fy}^2)^{\frac{1}{2}}$. A column is then chosen which has $M_r \geq M_f$ and $P_r \geq P_f$.

7.6 Bars Required to Obtain Desired Steel Ratios

Construction costs can be minimized if column forms are reused as often as possible without readjustment during the construction of successive storeys. The ground floor columns of multi-storey frames should therefore normally be constructed with high strength concrete and proportioned for relatively high steel ratios. The reinforcement ratio can usually be increased to approximately 4 percent before the splicing of longitudinal steel creates clearance problems. After a high steel ratio has been used at the ground floor columns, the reduction of axial load at each higher floor permits the use of successively lower concrete strengths and steel ratios without changes in the column forms.

Tables 7-8 to 7-10 are provided to assist in the choice of column reinforcement. All bar combinations shown may be spliced with welded splices, mechanical connections or bearing type slices. If $\rho_t > 4\%$, splice locations must be staggered by at least 750 mm (see Clause 12.17.2).

The bar combinations above the solid zigzag line may be spliced using either tangential splices or radial splices.

When a reinforcing ratio, ρ_t, less than 0.01 is used as permitted by Clause 10.10.5, the column resistance shall be based on the factored resistance calculated for a steel ratio of ρ_t multiplied by the ratio $0.5(1+\rho_t/0.01)$.

Blank values in the tables correspond to ρ_t less than 0.5% or greater than 8% or to combinations of bars which would violate the minimum or maximum bar spacing requirements or would result in γ less than about 0.5.

7.6.1 Reinforcement For Rectangular Columns

Tables 7.8 and 7.9 give the reinforcing ratios $\rho_t = A_{st}/(bh)$ for a wide range of b and h values for rectangular columns with various bar sizes and placement patterns.

7.6.2 Reinforcement for Circular Columns

Table 7.10 gives reinforcing ratios when various numbers of reinforcing bars are used in circular columns.

Table 7.11 indicates the maximum pitch, s, for 10M or 15M spirals with 25, 30, 35, 40, 45, or 50 MPa concrete. The table includes spirals made with 400 MPa and 500 MPa reinforcement. Clause 6.6.5.2 of CSA A23.1 limits the nominal maximum aggregate size to $(s - d_b)/1.4$. Spirals must have a clear spacing greater than 1.4 times the maximum nominal aggregate size but not less than 30 mm.

7

Short Columns

7.7   Compression Development and Lap Lengths

Table 7.12 is a tabulation of compression development lengths for deformed bars with $f_y = 400$ MPa.

Table 7.13 is a tabulation of lap lengths for 400 MPa reinforcement in normal density concrete.

7.8   Notation

A_g	=	gross area of concrete cross section
A_{st}	=	total area of longitudinal reinforcing bars
b	=	width of compression face of member
c	=	distance from extreme compression fibre to neutral axis
c	=	cover to surface of reinforcement
d_b	=	diameter of bar
EI	=	flexural stiffness of compression member
E_c	=	modulus of elasticity of concrete
E_s	=	modulus of elasticity of reinforcement
f_c'	=	specified compressive strength of concrete
f_s	=	calculated stress in reinforcement under factored load
f_y	=	specified yield strength of reinforcement
h	=	overall thickness of member
I_g	=	moment of inertia of gross concrete section about centroidal axis, neglecting reinforcement
I_{st}	=	moment of inertia of reinforcement about centroidal axis of member cross section
k	=	effective length factor for compression members
k	=	factor equal to $(0.2 E_c I_g + E_s I_{st})/bh^3$
ℓ_d	=	development length
ℓ_u	=	unsupported length of compression member
M_f	=	factored moment
M_r	=	factored moment resistance
P_f	=	factored axial load
P_r	=	factored axial load resistance
$P_{r, max}$	=	maximum factored axial load resistance
P_{ro}	=	factored axial load resistance if e_x and e_y were zero
P_{rx}	=	factored axial load resistance if the load were applied at eccentricity e_x with $e_y = 0$
P_{ry}	=	factored axial load resistance if the load were applied at eccentricity e_y with $e_x = 0$
r	=	radius of gyration of cross section of a compression member
R	=	required fire-resistance rating in hours
s	=	pitch or distance between turns of a spiral
α_1	=	ratio of average stress in rectangular stress block to the specified concrete strength
β_1	=	ratio of depth of rectangular compression block to depth to the neutral axis
β_d	=	factor defined in Clause 10.14.1.2 of CSA A23.3 to account for effects of sustained loads
γ	=	ratio of centre to centre distance between the outermost reinforcing bars to the overall depth
γ_c	=	density of concrete
ε	=	strain in concrete
ρ_t	=	ratio of A_{st}/A_g
ϕ_c	=	resistance factor for concrete
ϕ_s	=	resistance factor for steel

7.9 Examples

Estimate of Column Loads for Examples
Given:

350×350 mm edge columns spaced at 7.5 m with a 200 mm two-way flat slab spanning 6.8 m to the interior columns.

350 mm wide edge beam projecting 300 mm below the slab.

Wall load averaging 2.35 kN/m^2.   Floor-to-floor height of 3.6 m.

Roof dead load of (0.2 m)(24 kN/m^3) plus 2.2 kPa for roofing, insulation and an allowance for mechanical equipment.

Floor dead load of (0.2 m)(24 kN/m^3) plus 1.2 kPa for flooring and partitions.

Tributary area: (6.8/2 + 0.175)(7.5) = 27 m^2

Dead Load (Roof)

Roofing + slab	7.0(27)	= 189
Edge Beam + column	28	= 28
include ≈ ½ of wall depending on wall support details?		= 32
		249 kN

Dead Load (typical floor)

Floor load	6.0(27)	= 162
Edge Beam + column	28	= 28
Wall (2.35 kN/m^2)	2.35(3.6)(7.5)	= 64
		254 kN

Snow Load on Roof

3.0 kPa for chosen location	0.8(3)(27)	= 65 kN

Live Load on Floor

Office loading (2.4 kPa)	(2.4)(27)	= 65 kN

Reduce live floor load by the tributary area reduction factor = $0.3 + (9.8/B)^{\frac{1}{2}}$ where B is the tributary area supported by the member (m^2).

Shear walls provide lateral support so the columns can be designed as non-sway frames and wind loads don't need to be considered.

The factored axial load, P_f, is the largest of the loads obtained from the factored load combinations specified in NBCC 2005. (See Table C-1 in CSA A23.3)

		Unfactored loads						Factored Loads			
Level Supported	Snow kN	Cumulative Dead kN	Cumulative Live kN	Cumulative Area m^2	Area Reduction Factor	Reduced Live kN	1.4D MN	1.25D +1.5L +0.5S MN	1.25D +1.5S +0.5L MN	P_f MN
Roof	65	249					0.35	0.34	0.41	0.41
8		503	65	27	0.902	59	0.70	0.75	0.76	0.76
7		757	130	54	0.726	94	1.06	1.12	1.09	1.12
6		1011	195	81	0.648	126	1.42	1.49	1.42	1.49
5		1265	260	108	0.601	156	1.77	1.85	1.76	1.85
4		1519	325	135	0.569	185	2.13	2.21	2.09	2.21
3		1773	390	162	0.546	213	2.48	2.57	2.42	2.57
2		2027	455	189	0.528	240	2.84	2.93	2.75	2.93

7

Short Columns

Moment

Assume edge moment from 2-way flat floor slab with edge beams but no interior beams:

$$M_f = 0.26(7.5)\left(\frac{1.25(6.0)+1.5(2.4)}{8}\right)6.8^2 = 0.125 \; MN \cdot m$$

The moment for equal size columns will be split evenly between the upper and lower column, therefore $M_f = 0.063$ MN·m

Example 7.1   Tied Column Design

Given:

$f_c' = 40$ MPa, $f_y = 400$ MPa.

All steel lap spliced (Clause 10.9.2) and bar size $\leq$ 35M (See Clause 12.14.2.1).

Storey height 3600 mm

Slab thickness 200 mm.

Three hour fire rating with Type S concrete and columns exposed to weather.

From Table 7.3 it can be seen that columns with their smaller dimension equal to at least 320 mm do not need to be overdesigned. They may also have $k\ell_u$ as large as 7.3 m and have any reinforcement ratio. A minimum cover of 50 mm to the main steel is required for a 3 h fire rating (Table 7.3).

Minimum of 40 mm cover required to ties and main steel 25M and smaller (Table 7.3) for columns exposed to weather.

A cover of 40 mm to 10M ties will satisfy both fire and durability requirements.

$\ell_u = 3600 - 200 = 3400$ mm (clause 10.14.3.1).

Condition is elastic + at both the top and bottom of the column (Fig. N10.15.2 of Handbook).

$k \approx 0.9$ $k\ell_u \approx 0.9(3400) = 3060$ mm

$r = 0.3h = 0.3(350) = 105$ mm (Clause 10.14.2) $k\ell_u/r = 3060/105 = 29.1$

Column Supporting 2nd Floor

$P_f = 2.93$ MN $M_f = 0.063$ MN·m

From Table 7.1.4 a 350×350 mm column with $\rho_t \approx 2.9\%$ will be adequate if the effects of moment are negligible.

Try 350×350 mm column, $A_g = 0.1225$ m^2

Equation 10-15 indicates the limiting $k\ell_u/r$ that can be used in non-sway frames without considering slenderness. The column being designed may be considered fixed at the far ends under the given loads (Clause 9.3.2). The column moment at the far end will thus have the opposite sign to the column moment at the floor where the moment is applied. M_1/M_2 will be approximately -0.5. The maximum value of $k\ell_u/r$ that permits a column to be designed as a short column is therefore:

$$\frac{k\ell_u}{r} \leq \frac{25 - 10(-0.5)}{\sqrt{2.99/\left(40(0.1225)\right)}} = 38.4 \qquad \text{Slenderness may therefore be neglected.}$$

From Table 7.8, 8-25M bars giving $\rho_t = 3.27$ will be needed to get $\rho_t > 2.9\%$.

From Table 7.2 $\gamma = 0.63$ for 25M bars.

$P_f/A_g = 2.93/0.1225 = 23.9$ MPa $M_f/(A_g h) = 0.063/(0.35^3) = 1.47 \; MPa$

From Table 7.4.13, $\rho_t \geq 2.9\%$

8-25M bars giving $\rho_t = 3.27$ O.K.
From Table 7.4.13 $f_s/f_y < 0.0$ ∴ compression splice
From Clause 12.16.1, Table 7.13 a splice length of 880 mm is required.

Column supporting 3rd floor

$P_f = 2.57$ MN, $M_f = 0.063$ MN·m
Try 350×350 mm column with $\rho_t > 1.9\%$ (Table 7.1.4)
Concentrate reinforcement on interior and exterior faces, 6 - 25M bars, $\rho_t = 2.45\%$ (Table 7.9)
$P_f/A_g = 2.57/0.1225 = 21.0$ MPa $M_f/A_g h = 1.47$ MPa
For $\gamma = 0.60$, required $\rho_t = 1.9\%$ (Table 7.5.14)
Use 6-25M bars giving $\rho_t = 2.45\%$

Capacity of Column with Minimum Reinforcing

Determine minimum and maximum axial loads P_r for a 350×350 mm column with
$M_f = 0.063$ MN·m and $\rho_t = 1\%$.
Use 4-20M bars $\rho_t = 0.98\%$ (Table 7.9), $\gamma = 0.65$
For $\gamma = 0.60$, $M_r/(A_g h) = 1.47$ MPa and $\rho_t = 1\%$,
$P_r/A_g \leq 19.0$ MPa (Table 7.5.13)
$P_r \leq 19.0(0.1225) = 2.33$ MN
A 350×350 mm column with 4-20M bars is adequate for supporting floor 4 through 8.

Column Supporting Roof

The column supporting the roof is subjected to a low axial load and a moment roughly twice as high as for the floors. This is a situation where the lowest axial load is critical.

$P_f = 0.41$ MN $M_f = 0.26(7.5)\left(\dfrac{1.25(7.0) + 1.5(2.4)}{8}\right) 6.8^2 = 0.139\ MN \cdot m$

Check Table 7.5.13 with 0.98% reinforcing as above.
$P_f/A_g = 0.41/0.1225 = 3.35$ MPa $M_f/h^3 = 0.139/0.35^3 = 3.24$ MPa
This point is near the bottom of the graph where the interaction curves show a reduced moment capacity as the axial load is reduced. Four 20M bars are inadequate. Approximately twice as much reinforcement is needed. Use a total of 8-20M bars in the inside and outside faces of the column supporting the roof.

Example 7.1(a)   Tied Column with Uncharted Material Strengths

Assume $f_c' = 50$ MPa, $f_y = 500$ MPa, $P_f = 2.99$ MN, $M_f = 0.100$ MN·m
Try 350×350 mm column with $\gamma = 0.6$
Use Table 7.5.18 for $f_c' = 45$ MPa, $f_y = 400$ MPa
Adjust values

$$\left(\frac{P_r}{A_g}\right)_{45} = \frac{2.99}{0.35^2}\left(\frac{45}{50}\right)\left(\frac{0.7825}{0.775}\right) = 22.2\ MPa \qquad \left(\frac{M_r}{A_g h}\right)_{45} = \frac{0.100}{0.35^3}\left(\frac{45}{50}\right)\left(\frac{0.7825}{0.775}\right) = 2.12\ MPa$$

$\rho_{t(45,400)} \approx 1.5\%$ (Table 7.5.18)   Adjust $\rho_{t(50,500)} \approx 1.5\left(\dfrac{400}{500}\right)\left(\dfrac{50}{45}\right) = 1.33\%$

Use 4 - 25M bars, $\rho_t = 1.63\%$ (Table 7.9) $\gamma = 0.63$ (Table 7.2)

7

Short Columns

Example 7.2(a)   Circular Tied Column

Assume:

P_f = 4.8 MN M_f = 0.12 MN·m
f_c' = 40 MPa, f_y = 400 MPa, $\rho_t \approx$ 4.0%

From Table 7.1.4, A_g required $\approx$ 0.19 m^2 $h \approx [(4/\pi)\,0.19]^{1/2}$ = 0.49 m

Try h = 500 mm P_f/h^2 = 4.8/0.5^2 = 19.2 MPa M_f/h^3 = 0.12/0.5^3 = 0.96 MPa

ρ_t = 3.1% (Table 7.7.10)

Use 9-30M, ρ_t = 3.21% (Table 7.10),

Determine maximum spacing using 10M ties

   $s \leq$ 16(30) = 480 mm

   $s \leq$ 48(10) = 480 mm $\leftarrow$ governs (Clause 7.6.5.2)

   $s \leq$ 500 mm

   Use 10M helical ties @ 480 mm pitch.

Note: this is a tied column. The helical ties don't need to meet the steel volume requirements of Clause 10.9.4, or the spacing requirements of clause 7.6.4.

Example 7.2(b)   Circular Spiral Column

Redesign the above circular column as a spiral column using upper shaded lines in Table 7.7.10.
Use $\rho_t \geq$ 2.6 % Use 8-30M, ρ_t = 2.85% (Table 7.10)
Use 10M spiral (Clause 7.6.4), Pitch = 50 mm (Clause 10.9.4, Table 7.11)

Example 7.3   Biaxial Bending

Assume the following loads:

P_f = 1.75 MN

M_{fy} = 0.10 MN·m

and M_{fx} = 0.06 MN·m

Consider a 350×350 mm column with corner reinforcing only (4 bars) (Table 7.9)

P_f/A_g = 1.75/0.1225 = 14.3 MPa

$M_{fy}/(A_gh)$ = 0.10/0.35^3 = 2.33 MPa

$M_{fx}/(A_gh)$ = 0.06/0.35^3 = 1.40 MPa

Try 4 - 25M bars,

ρ_t = 1.63% (Table 7.9)

γ = 0.63 (Table 7.2)

Determine P_{ro}/A_g

$$\frac{P_{r,max}}{A_g} \approx 20.5 \; MPa \; (Table \; 7.5.14)$$

$$P_{ro}/A_g = \frac{20.5}{0.8} \approx 25.6 \; MPa$$

(Clause 10.10.4(b))

P_{rx}/A_g and P_{ry}/A_g are obtained from Table 7.5.14.

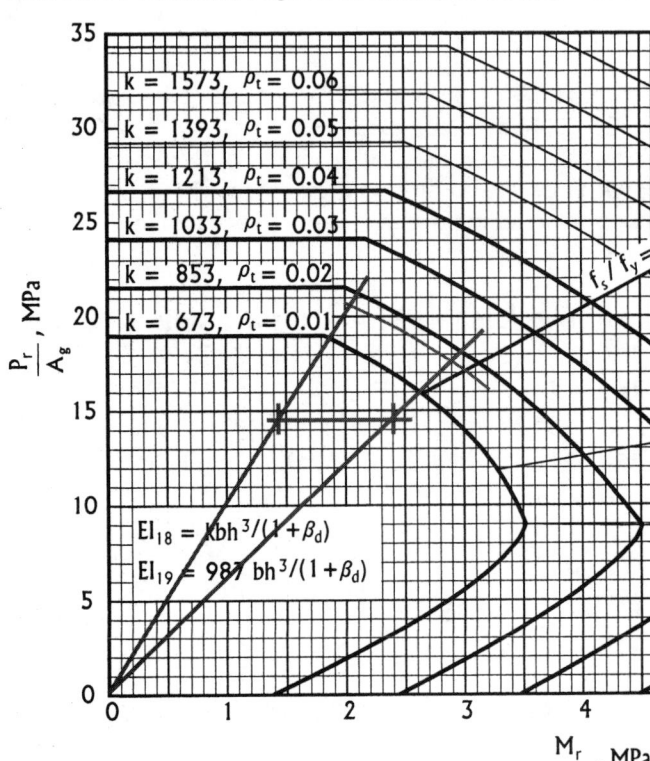

Table 7.5.14 Interaction Diagrams for Rectangular Columns With Bar:

Extend lines from the origin through points 1.4, 14.3 and 2.33, 14.3 until they cross the line for $\rho_t = 1.63\%$ at 20.5 MPa and 17.4 MPa.

These intersection points are P_{rx}/A_g and P_{ry}/A_g.

$$\frac{1}{P_r/A_g} = \frac{1}{P_{rx}/A_g} + \frac{1}{P_{ry}/A_g} - \frac{1}{P_{ro}/A_g}$$

$$\frac{1}{P_r/A_g} = \frac{1}{20.5} + \frac{1}{17.4} - \frac{1}{25.6}$$

$P_r/A_g = 14.9$ $P_r = 14.9(0.35_2) = 1.83$ MN.

O.K. because $P_r > P_f$

(Capacity is actually slightly greater than 1.83 MN because $\gamma = 0.63$.)

7

Short Columns

Table 7.1.1   Axial Load Limit $P_{r,max}$ for Tied Columns, $f'_c = 25$ MPa

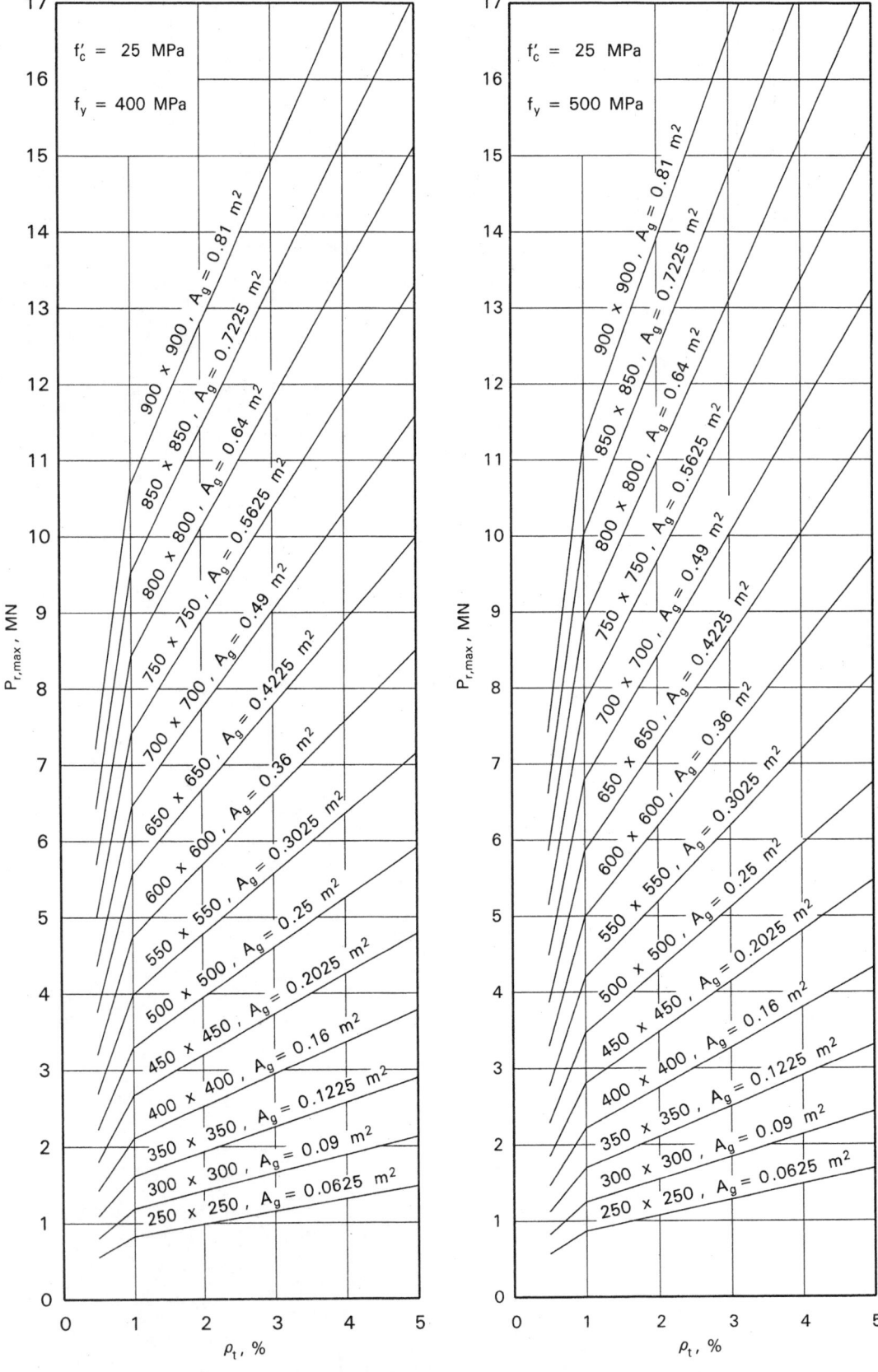

Table 7.1.2   Axial Load Limit $P_{r,max}$ for Tied Columns, $f'_c = 30$ MPa

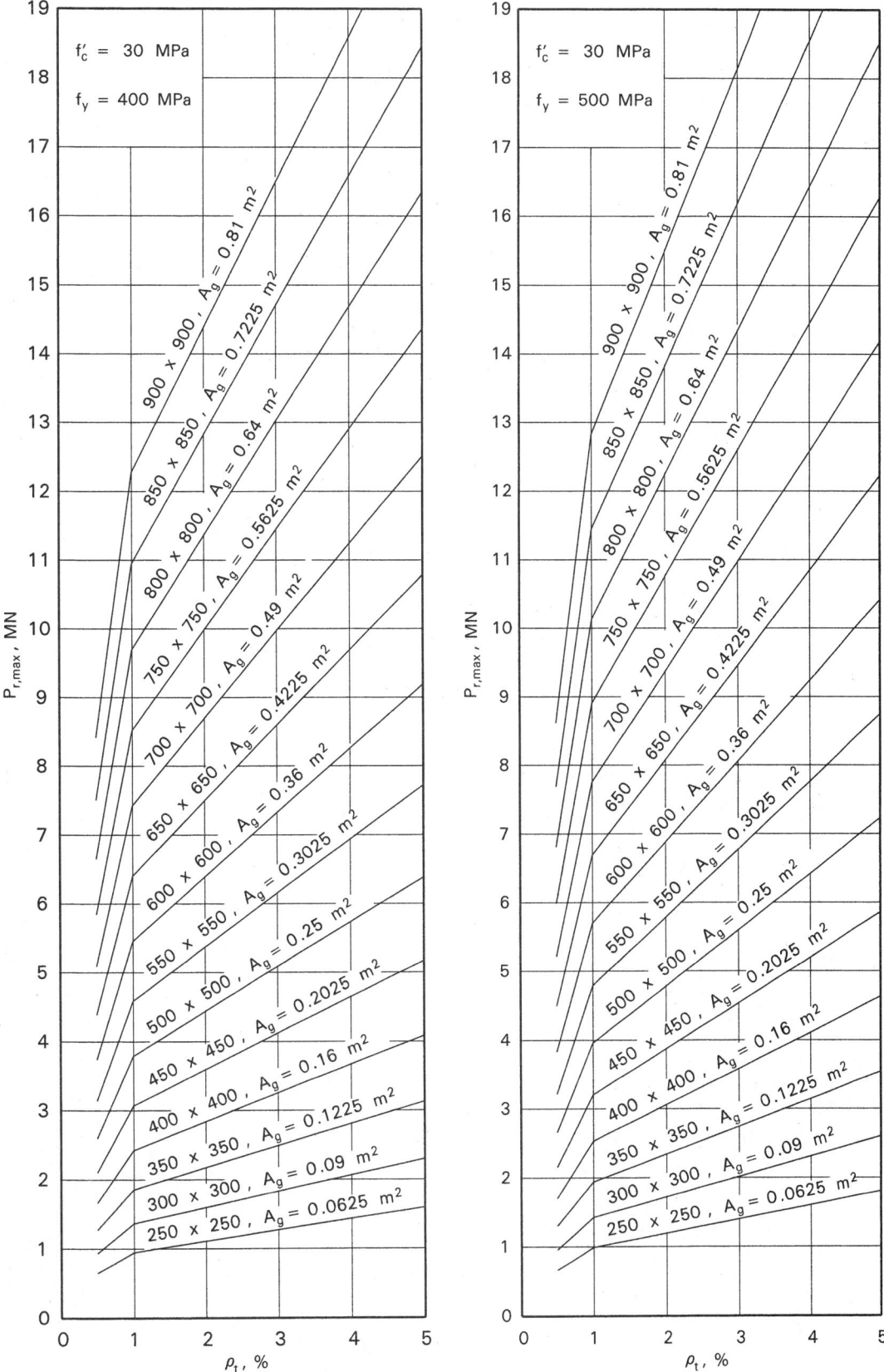

Table 7.1.3   Axial Load Limit $P_{r,max}$ for Tied Columns, $f'_c = 35$ MPa

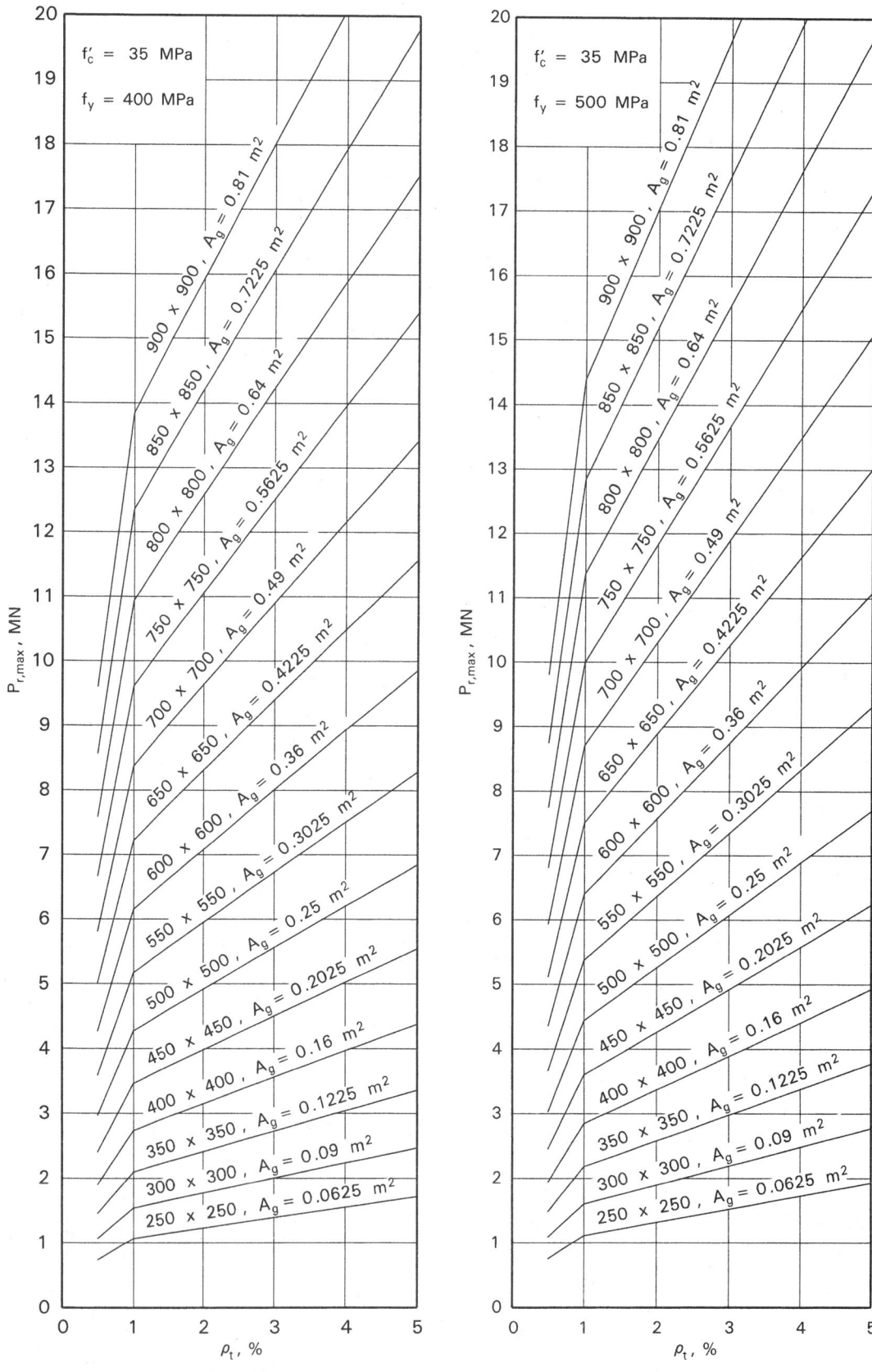

Table 7.1.4   Axial Load Limit $P_{r,max}$ for Tied Columns, $f'_c = 40$ MPa

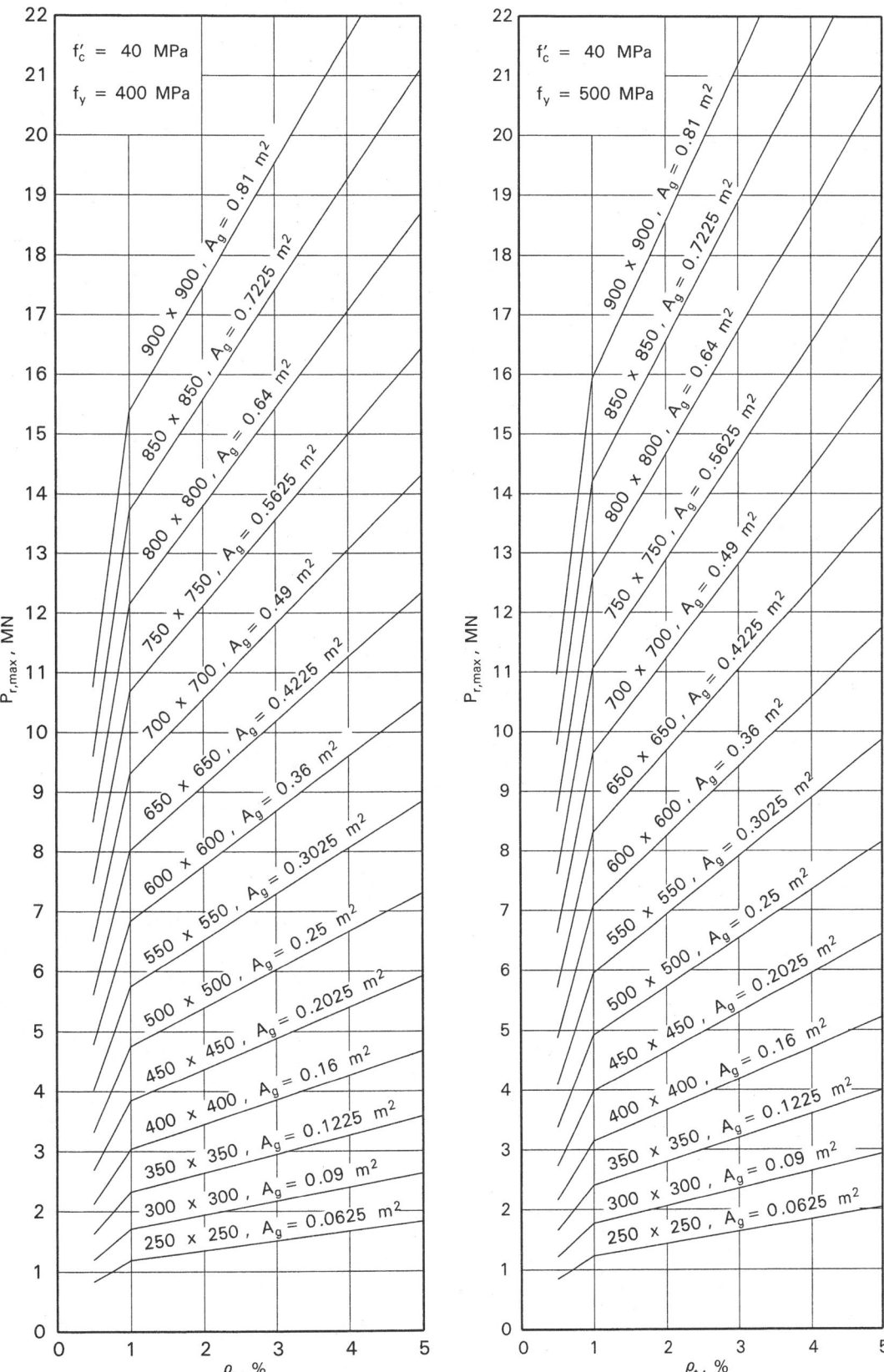

Table 7.1.5   Axial Load Limit $P_{r,max}$ for Tied Columns, $f'_c = 45$ MPa

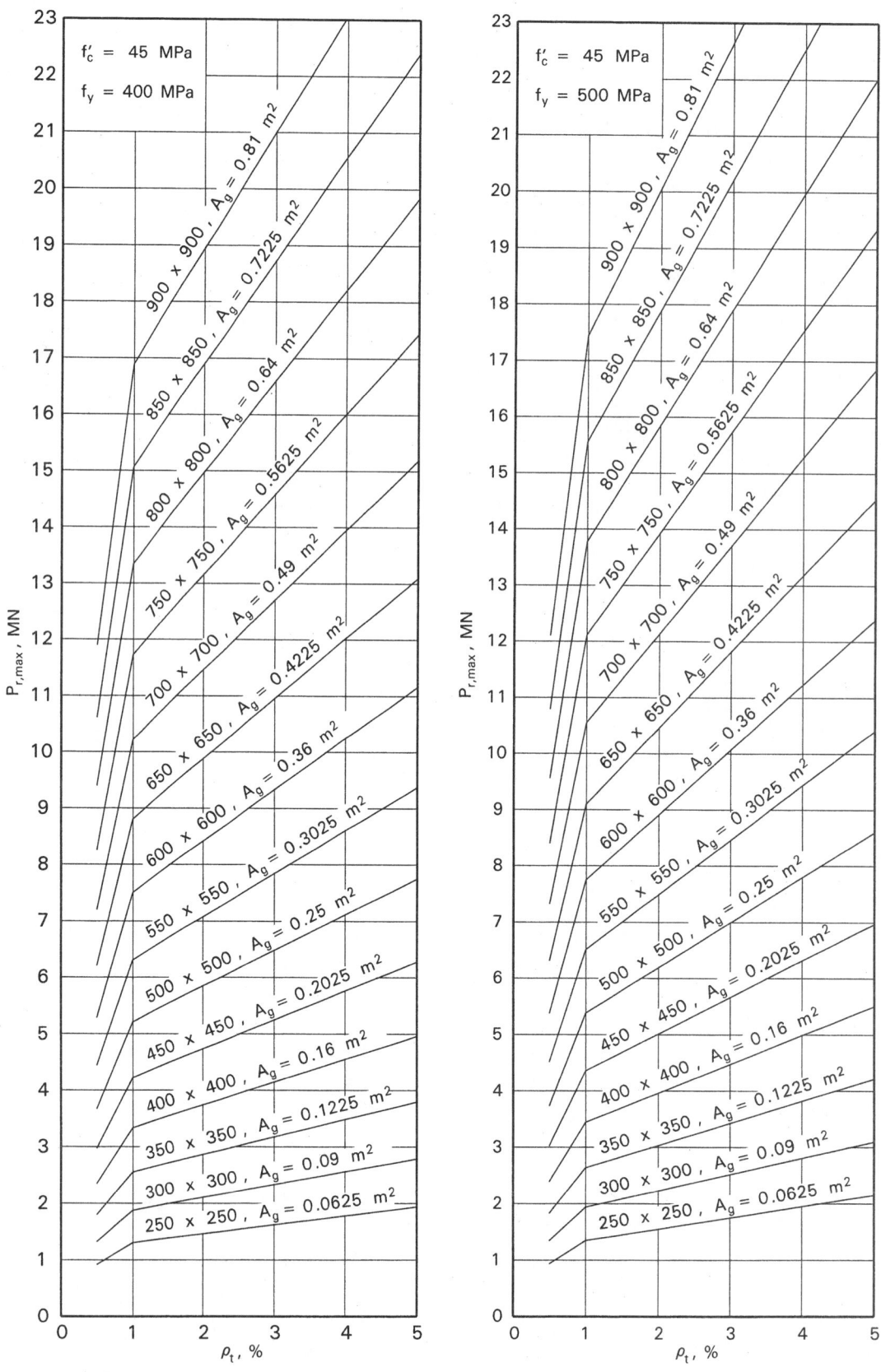

Table 7.2 Values of gamma, γ, for Columns

h mm	15M	20M	25M	30M	35M	45M	55M
	40 mm cover to 10M ties						
250	0.53	0.51	0.49	0.47			
300	0.60	0.59	0.57	0.56	0.54	0.51	
350	0.66	0.65	0.63	0.62	0.60	0.58	
400	0.70	0.69	0.68	0.67	0.65	0.63	
450	0.74	0.73	0.72	0.71	0.69	0.67	
500	0.76	0.76	0.74	0.73	0.72	0.71	
550	0.78	0.78	0.77	0.76	0.75	0.73	
600	0.80	0.80	0.79	0.78	0.77	0.76	
650	0.82	0.81	0.80	0.80	0.79	0.77	
700	0.83	0.83	0.82	0.81	0.80	0.79	
750	0.84	0.84	0.83	0.82	0.82	0.80	
800	0.85	0.85	0.84	0.83	0.83	0.82	
850	0.86	0.86	0.8566	0.84	0.84	0.83	
900	0.87	0.86	0.86	0.85	0.85	0.84	
950	0.88	0.87	0.87	0.86	0.85	0.85	
1000	0.88	0.88	0.87	0.87	0.86	0.85	
1100	0.89	0.89	0.88	0.88	0.87	0.87	
1200	0.90	0.90	0.89	0.89	0.88	0.88	
1300	0.91	0.91	0.90	0.90	0.89	0.89	
1400	0.92	0.91	0.91	0.91	0.90	0.90	
1500	0.92	0.92	0.91	0.91	0.91	0.90	
1600	0.93	0.92	0.92	0.92	0.91	0.91	
	50 mm cover to 10M ties						
300	0.54	0.53	0.51	0.49			
350	0.60	0.59	0.58	0.56	0.55	0.52	0.49
400	0.65	0.64	0.63	0.62	0.60	0.58	0.55
450	0.69	0.68	0.67	0.66	0.65	0.63	0.60
500	0.72	0.72	0.70	0.69	0.68	0.67	0.64
550	0.75	0.74	0.73	0.72	0.71	0.70	0.67
600	0.77	0.76	0.75	0.75	0.74	0.72	0.70
650	0.79	0.78	0.77	0.77	0.76	0.74	0.72
700	0.80	0.80	0.79	0.78	0.77	0.76	0.74
750	0.82	0.81	0.80	0.80	0.79	0.78	0.76
800	0.83	0.82	0.82	0.81	0.80	0.79	0.78
850	0.84	0.83	0.83	0.82	0.81	0.80	0.79
900	0.85	0.84	0.84	0.83	0.82	0.82	0.80
950	0.85	0.85	0.84	0.84	0.83	0.82	0.81
1000	0.86	0.86	0.85	0.85	0.84	0.83	0.82
1100	0.87	0.87	0.87	0.86	0.86	0.85	0.84
1200	0.88	0.88	0.88	0.87	0.87	0.86	0.85
1300	0.89	0.89	0.89	0.88	0.88	0.87	0.86
1400	0.90	0.90	0.89	0.89	0.89	0.88	0.87
1500	0.91	0.91	0.90	0.90	0.89	0.89	0.88
1600	0.91	0.91	0.91	0.90	0.90	0.90	0.89

Table 7.3 Minimum Column Dimensions and Cover for Rectangular or Circular* Columns with $k\ell_u \leq 7.3$ m

Condition	Concrete Type	Over-design Factor	Fire Rating, R Hours 1	2	3
$3.7 < k\ell_u \leq 7.3$ and $\rho_t \leq 3\%$	L or L40S	1	180	270	300
		1.25	165	248	300
		1.5	150	225	300
	S	1	240	300	320
		1.25	220	300	300
		1.5	200	300	300
	N	1	240	300	300
		1.25	220	300	300
		1.5	200	300	300
Other Conditions	L or L40S	1	150	225	300
		1.25	135	203	270
		1.5	125	187	249
	S	1	160	240	320
		1.25	144	216	288
		1.5	133	199	266
	N	1	140	220	300
		1.25	126	198	270
		1.5	116	183	249
Cover to Principal Reinforcement for fire			25	50	50

Cover to Principal Reinforcement for Corrosion Protection based on CSA A23.1[#]

Not exposed to earth or weather
30M bars & smaller	30
35M bars & larger	$1.0d_b$

Exposed to earth or weather
25M bars & smaller	40
30M bars & larger	$1.5d_b$

Exposed to chlorides
30M bars & smaller	60
35M bars & larger	$2.0d_b$

Cast against earth
all sizes	75

*Circular columns must have a diameter at least 1.2 times the size shown in the table.

The column sizes and cover requirements for fire are in accordance with Appendix D of supplement to NATIONAL BUILDING CODE OF CANADA, 2005

[#]For parking structures, bridges, and offshore structures see CSA Standards S413, S6, and S474

Table 7.4.1   Interaction Diagrams for Rectangular Columns With an Equal Number of Bars on all Four Faces.

$\gamma = 0.60$
$\phi_c = 0.65$
$\phi_s = 0.85$
$f'_c = 25$ MPa
$f_y = 400$ MPa

k = 1150, $\rho_t = 0.06$
k = 1028, $\rho_t = 0.05$
k = 906, $\rho_t = 0.04$
k = 783, $\rho_t = 0.03$
k = 661, $\rho_t = 0.02$
k = 538, $\rho_t = 0.01$

$f_s / f_y = 0.0$
$f_s / f_y = 0.5$
$f_s / f_y = 1.0$

$EI_{18} = kbh^3/(1+\beta_d)$
$EI_{19} = 831\, bh^3/(1+\beta_d)$

$\dfrac{P_r}{A_g}$, MPa

$\dfrac{M_r}{A_g h}$, MPa

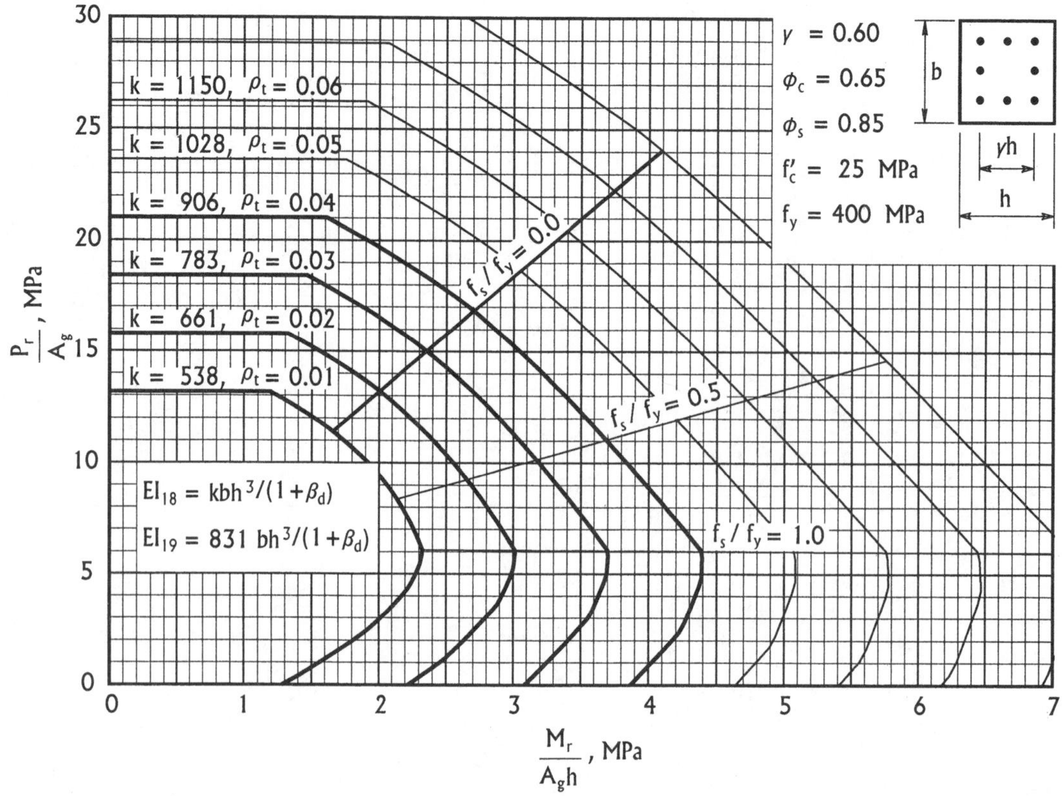

Table 7.4.2   Interaction Diagrams for Rectangular Columns With an Equal Number of Bars on all Four Faces.

$\gamma = 0.70$
$\phi_c = 0.65$
$\phi_s = 0.85$
$f'_c = 25$ MPa
$f_y = 400$ MPa

k = 1416, $\rho_t = 0.06$
k = 1249, $\rho_t = 0.05$
k = 1082, $\rho_t = 0.04$
k = 916, $\rho_t = 0.03$
k = 749, $\rho_t = 0.02$
k = 582, $\rho_t = 0.01$

$f_s / f_y = 0.0$
$f_s / f_y = 0.5$
$f_s / f_y = 1.0$

$EI_{18} = kbh^3/(1+\beta_d)$
$EI_{19} = 831\, bh^3/(1+\beta_d)$

$\dfrac{P_r}{A_g}$, MPa

$\dfrac{M_r}{A_g h}$, MPa

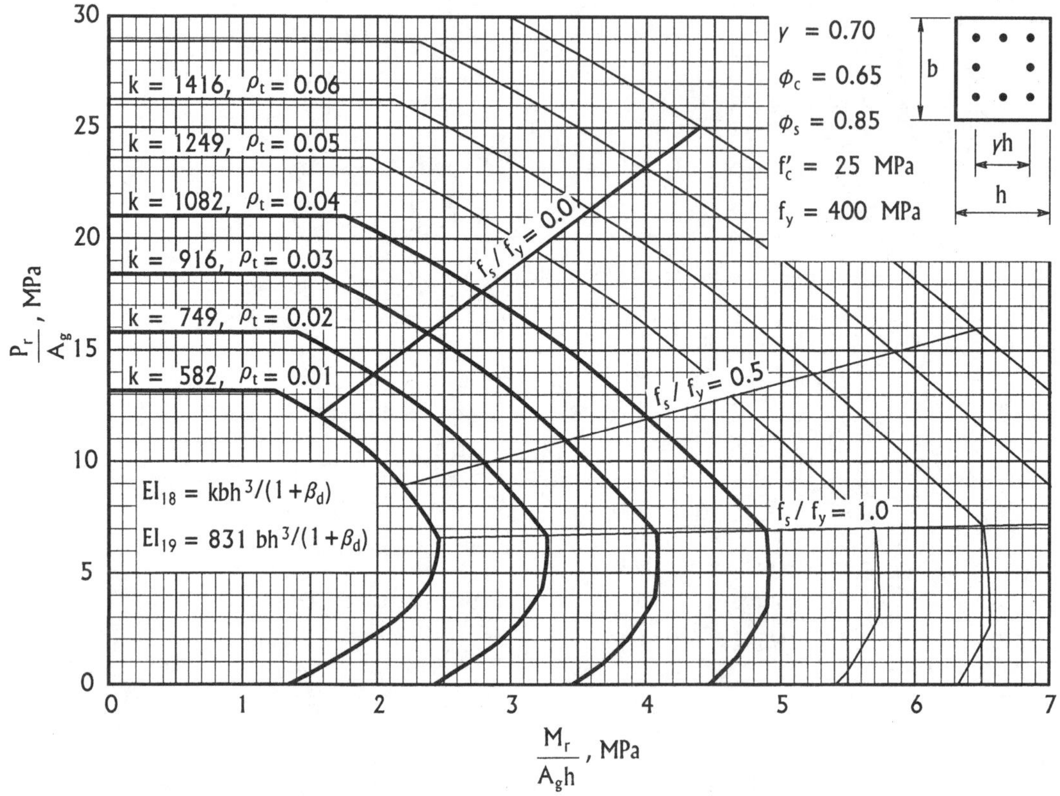

Table 7.4.3 Interaction Diagrams for Rectangular Columns With an Equal Number of Bars on all Four Faces.

$$\gamma = 0.80$$
$$\phi_c = 0.65$$
$$\phi_s = 0.85$$
$$f_c' = 25 \text{ MPa}$$
$$f_y = 400 \text{ MPa}$$

$k = 1722, \rho_t = 0.06$
$k = 1504, \rho_t = 0.05$
$k = 1286, \rho_t = 0.04$
$k = 1069, \rho_t = 0.03$
$k = 851, \rho_t = 0.02$
$k = 633, \rho_t = 0.01$

$f_s / f_y = 0.0$
$f_s / f_y = 0.5$
$f_s / f_y = 1.0$

$$EI_{18} = kbh^3/(1+\beta_d)$$
$$EI_{19} = 831\ bh^3/(1+\beta_d)$$

$\dfrac{P_r}{A_g}$, MPa

$\dfrac{M_r}{A_g h}$, MPa

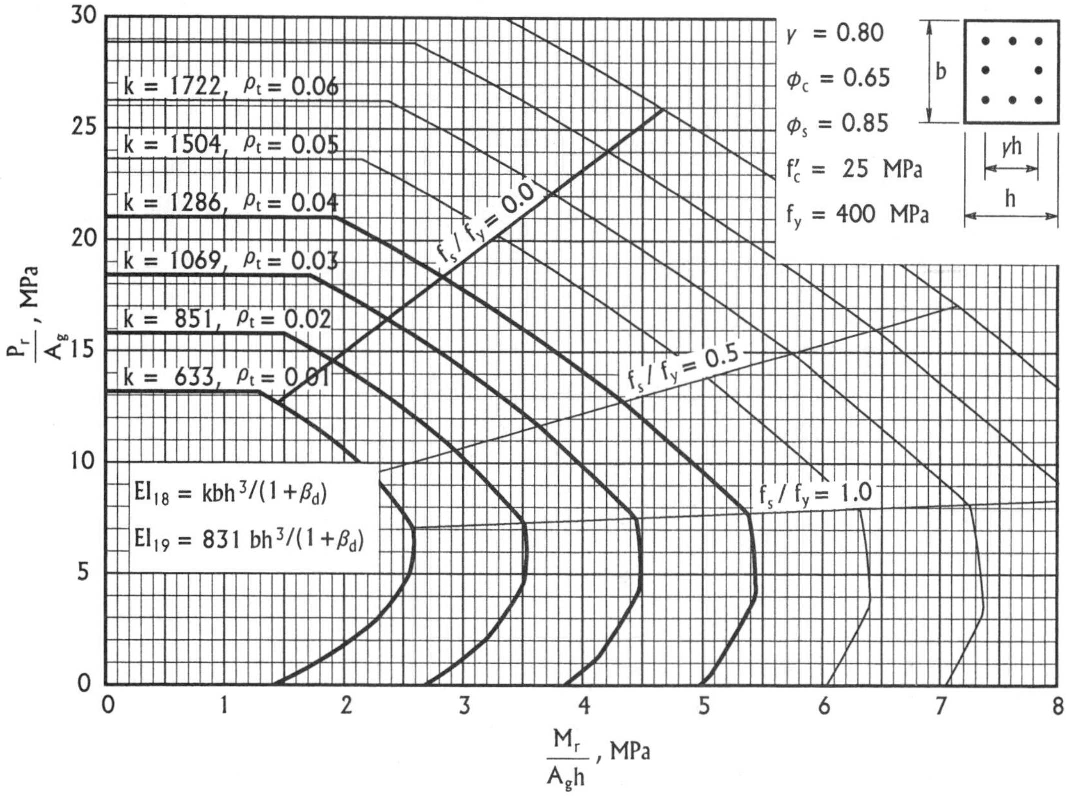

Table 7.4.4 Interaction Diagrams for Rectangular Columns With an Equal Number of Bars on all Four Faces.

$$\gamma = 0.90$$
$$\phi_c = 0.65$$
$$\phi_s = 0.85$$
$$f_c' = 25 \text{ MPa}$$
$$f_y = 400 \text{ MPa}$$

$k = 2069, \rho_t = 0.06$
$k = 1793, \rho_t = 0.05$
$k = 1518, \rho_t = 0.04$
$k = 1242, \rho_t = 0.03$
$k = 967, \rho_t = 0.02$
$k = 691, \rho_t = 0.01$

$f_s / f_y = 0.0$
$f_s / f_y = 0.5$
$f_s / f_y = 1.0$

$$EI_{18} = kbh^3/(1+\beta_d)$$
$$EI_{19} = 831\ bh^3/(1+\beta_d)$$

$\dfrac{P_r}{A_g}$, MPa

$\dfrac{M_r}{A_g h}$, MPa

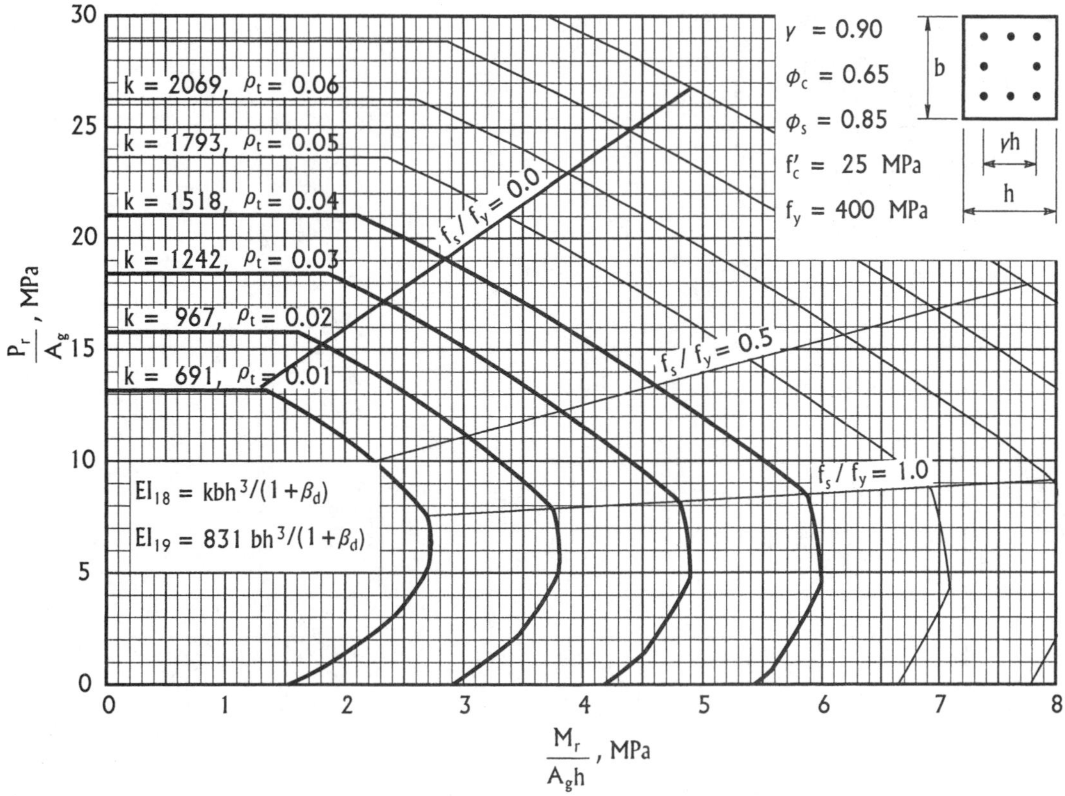

Table 7.4.5   Interaction Diagrams for Rectangular Columns With an Equal Number of Bars on all Four Faces.

$k = 1178, \; \rho_t = 0.06$

$k = 1056, \; \rho_t = 0.05$

$k = 933, \; \rho_t = 0.04$

$k = 811, \; \rho_t = 0.03$

$k = 689, \; \rho_t = 0.02$

$k = 566, \; \rho_t = 0.01$

$f_s / f_y = 0.0$

$f_s / f_y = 0.5$

$f_s / f_y = 1.0$

$\gamma = 0.60$

$\phi_c = 0.65$

$\phi_s = 0.85$

$f_c' = 30$ MPa

$f_y = 400$ MPa

$EI_{18} = kbh^3/(1+\beta_d)$

$EI_{19} = 887 \, bh^3/(1+\beta_d)$

$\dfrac{P_r}{A_g}$, MPa

$\dfrac{M_r}{A_g h}$, MPa

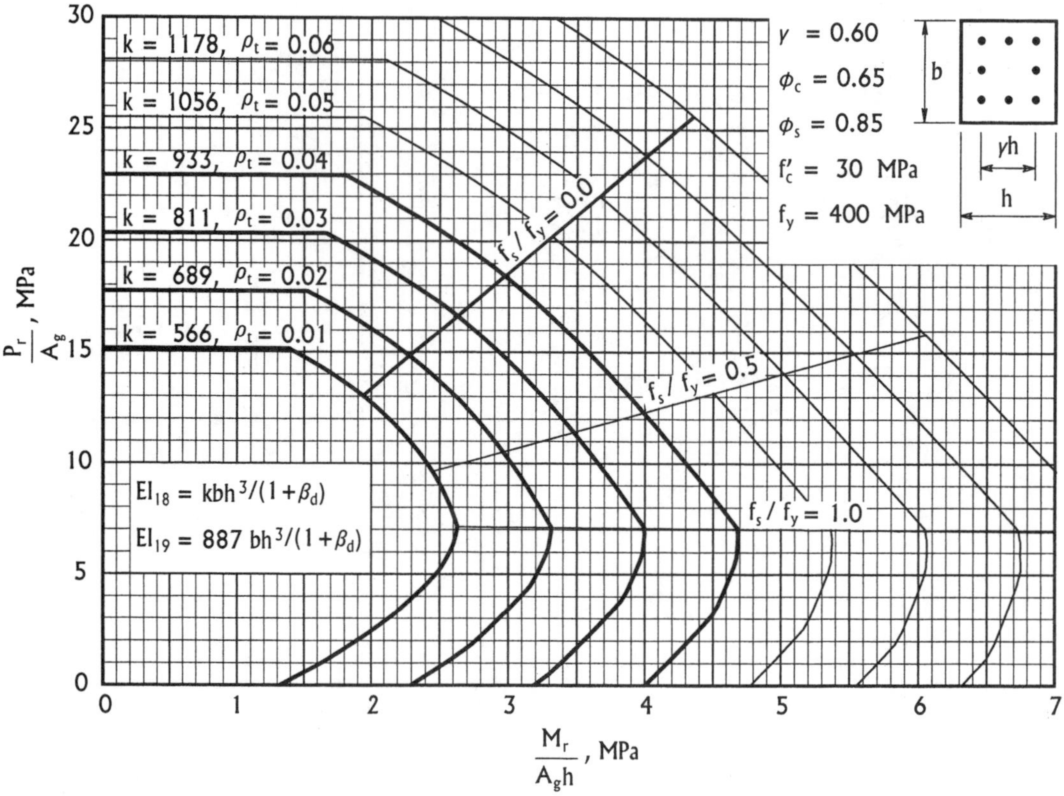

Table 7.4.6   Interaction Diagrams for Rectangular Columns With an Equal Number of Bars on all Four Faces.

$k = 1444, \; \rho_t = 0.06$

$k = 1277, \; \rho_t = 0.05$

$k = 1110, \; \rho_t = 0.04$

$k = 944, \; \rho_t = 0.03$

$k = 777, \; \rho_t = 0.02$

$k = 610, \; \rho_t = 0.01$

$f_s / f_y = 0.0$

$f_s / f_y = 0.5$

$f_s / f_y = 1.0$

$\gamma = 0.70$

$\phi_c = 0.65$

$\phi_s = 0.85$

$f_c' = 30$ MPa

$f_y = 400$ MPa

$EI_{18} = kbh^3/(1+\beta_d)$

$EI_{19} = 887 \, bh^3/(1+\beta_d)$

$\dfrac{P_r}{A_g}$, MPa

$\dfrac{M_r}{A_g h}$, MPa

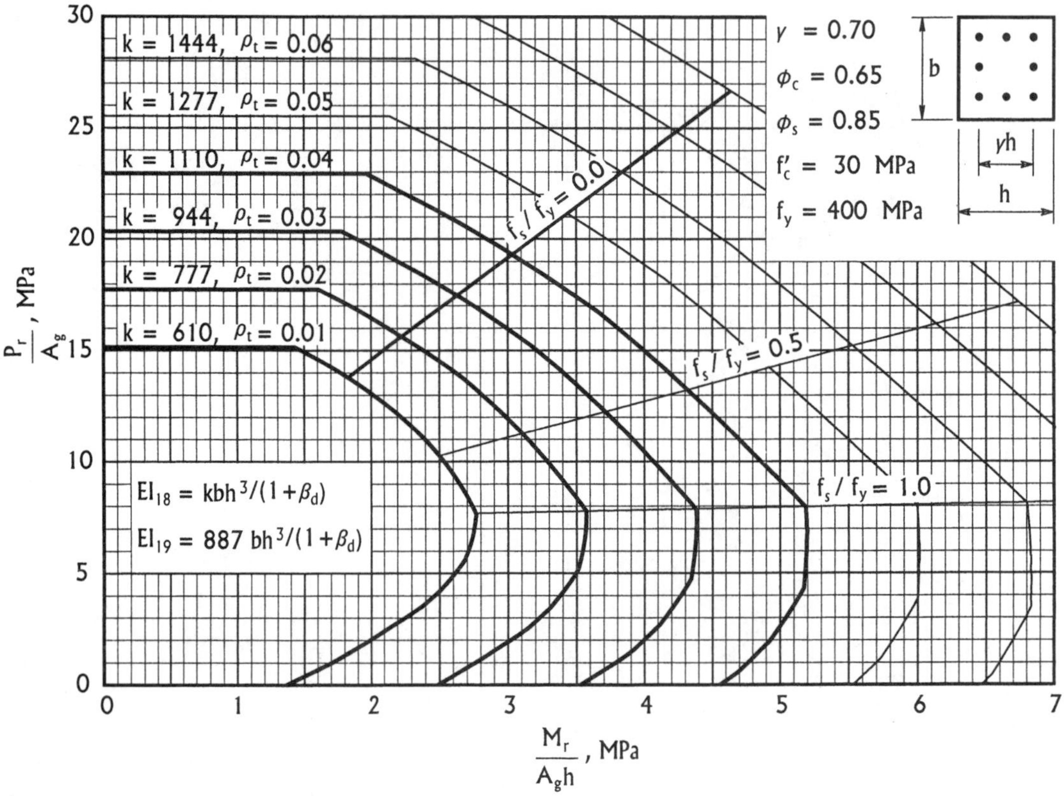

Table 7.4.7   Interaction Diagrams for Rectangular Columns With an Equal Number of Bars on all Four Faces.

$\gamma = 0.80$
$\phi_c = 0.65$
$\phi_s = 0.85$
$f'_c = 30$ MPa
$f_y = 400$ MPa

$k = 1750, \ \rho_t = 0.06$
$k = 1532, \ \rho_t = 0.05$
$k = 1314, \ \rho_t = 0.04$
$k = 1097, \ \rho_t = 0.03$
$k = 879, \ \rho_t = 0.02$
$k = 661, \ \rho_t = 0.01$

$f_s/f_y = 0.0$
$f_s/f_y = 0.5$
$f_s/f_y = 1.0$

$EI_{18} = kbh^3/(1+\beta_d)$
$EI_{19} = 887\ bh^3/(1+\beta_d)$

$\dfrac{P_r}{A_g}$, MPa

$\dfrac{M_r}{A_gh}$, MPa

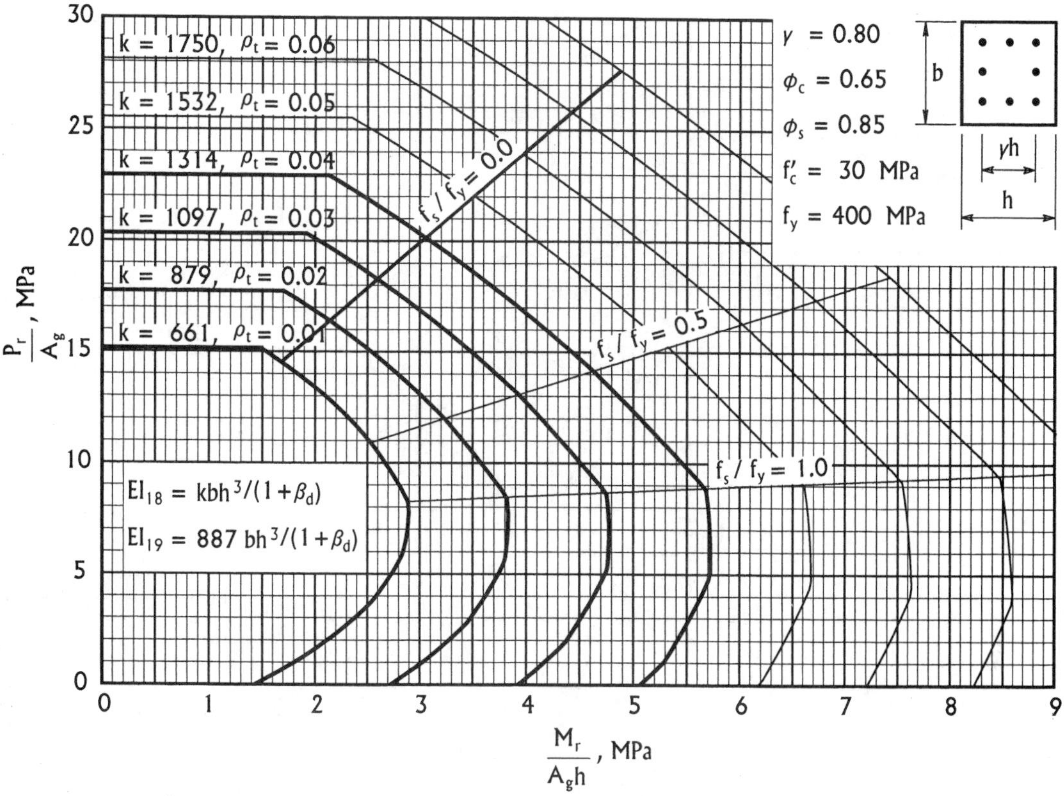

Table 7.4.8   Interaction Diagrams for Rectangular Columns With an Equal Number of Bars on all Four Faces.

$\gamma = 0.90$
$\phi_c = 0.65$
$\phi_s = 0.85$
$f'_c = 30$ MPa
$f_y = 400$ MPa

$k = 2097, \ \rho_t = 0.06$
$k = 1821, \ \rho_t = 0.05$
$k = 1546, \ \rho_t = 0.04$
$k = 1270, \ \rho_t = 0.03$
$k = 995, \ \rho_t = 0.02$
$k = 719, \ \rho_t = 0.01$

$f_s/f_y = 0.0$
$f_s/f_y = 0.5$
$f_s/f_y = 1.0$

$EI_{18} = kbh^3/(1+\beta_d)$
$EI_{19} = 887\ bh^3/(1+\beta_d)$

$\dfrac{P_r}{A_g}$, MPa

$\dfrac{M_r}{A_gh}$, MPa

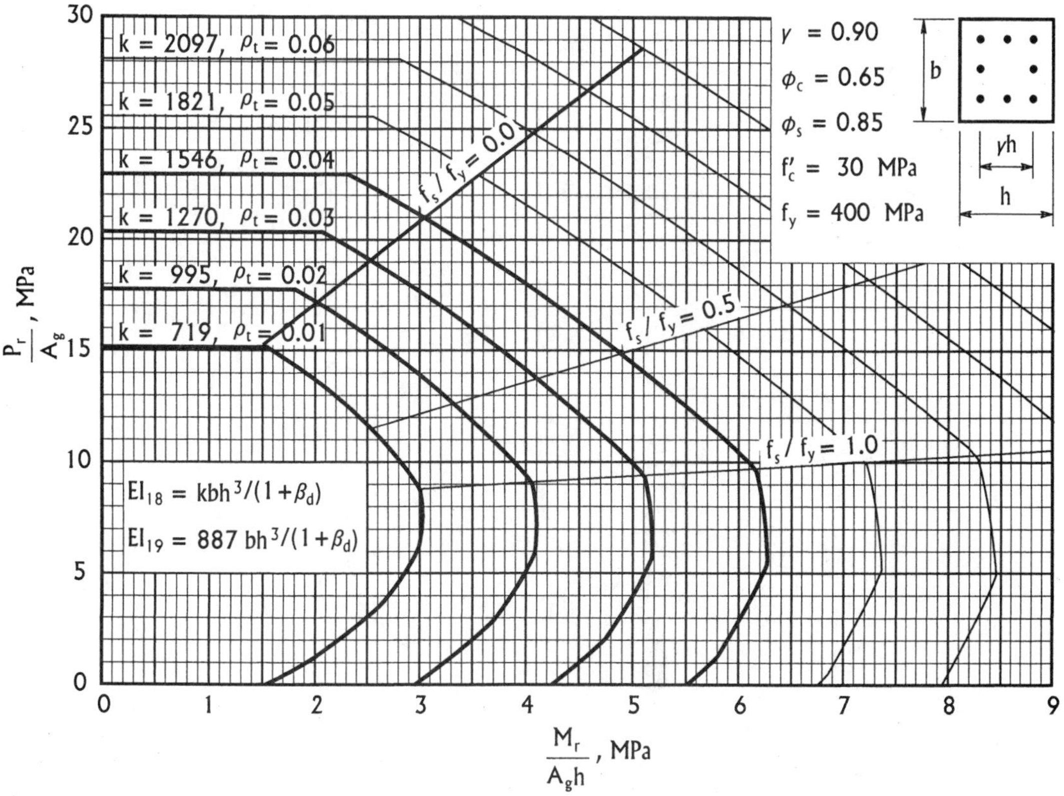

Table 7.4.9   Interaction Diagrams for Rectangular Columns With an Equal Number of Bars on all Four Faces.

$$k = 1082, \; \rho_t = 0.05$$
$$k = 959, \; \rho_t = 0.04$$
$$k = 837, \; \rho_t = 0.03$$
$$k = 714, \; \rho_t = 0.02$$
$$k = 592, \; \rho_t = 0.01$$

$$\gamma = 0.60$$
$$\phi_c = 0.65$$
$$\phi_s = 0.85$$
$$f'_c = 35 \text{ MPa}$$
$$f_y = 400 \text{ MPa}$$

$$f_s / f_y = 0.0$$
$$f_s / f_y = 0.5$$
$$f_s / f_y = 1.0$$

$$EI_{18} = kbh^3/(1+\beta_d)$$
$$EI_{19} = 939 \, bh^3/(1+\beta_d)$$

$\dfrac{P_r}{A_g h}$, MPa

$\dfrac{M_r}{A_g h}$, MPa

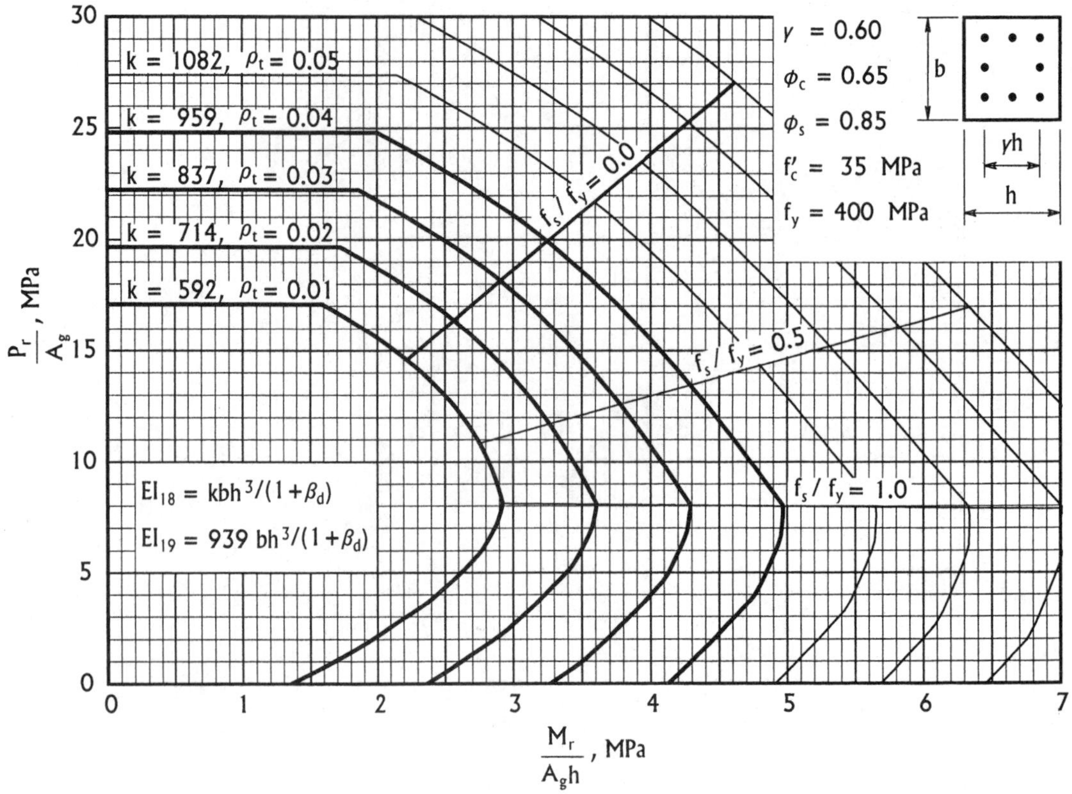

Table 7.4.10   Interaction Diagrams for Rectangular Columns With an Equal Number of Bars on all Four Faces.

$$k = 1303, \; \rho_t = 0.05$$
$$k = 1136, \; \rho_t = 0.04$$
$$k = 969, \; \rho_t = 0.03$$
$$k = 803, \; \rho_t = 0.02$$
$$k = 636, \; \rho_t = 0.01$$

$$\gamma = 0.70$$
$$\phi_c = 0.65$$
$$\phi_s = 0.85$$
$$f'_c = 35 \text{ MPa}$$
$$f_y = 400 \text{ MPa}$$

$$f_s / f_y = 0.0$$
$$f_s / f_y = 0.5$$
$$f_s / f_y = 1.0$$

$$EI_{18} = kbh^3/(1+\beta_d)$$
$$EI_{19} = 939 \, bh^3/(1+\beta_d)$$

$\dfrac{P_r}{A_g h}$, MPa

$\dfrac{M_r}{A_g h}$, MPa

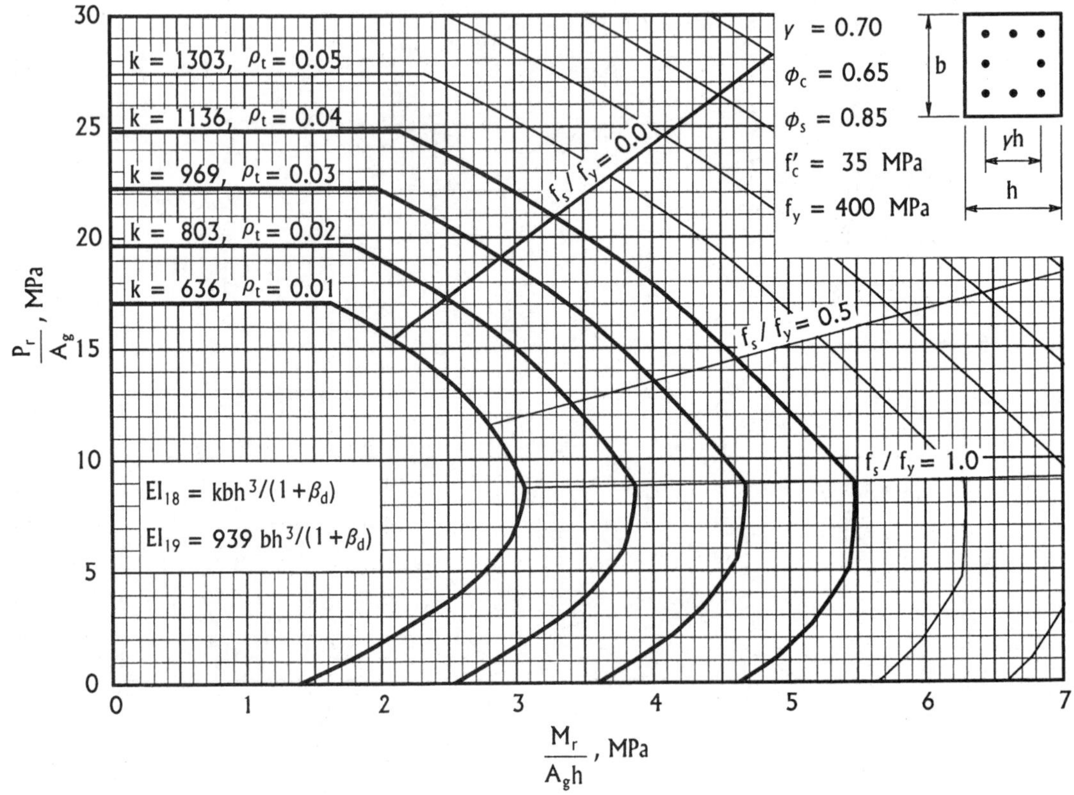

Table 7.4.11 Interaction Diagrams for Rectangular Columns With an Equal Number of Bars on all Four Faces.

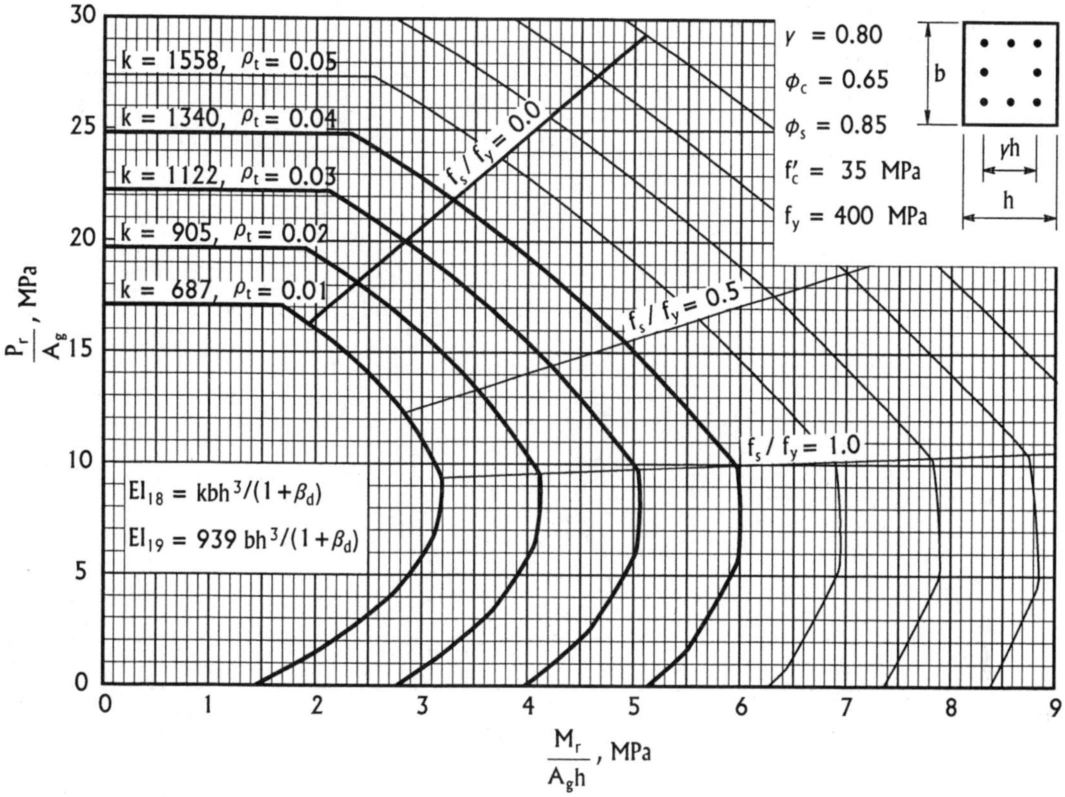

k = 1558, ρt = 0.05
k = 1340, ρt = 0.04
k = 1122, ρt = 0.03
k = 905, ρt = 0.02
k = 687, ρt = 0.01
fs / fy = 0.0
fs / fy = 0.5
fs / fy = 1.0
γ = 0.80
φc = 0.65
φs = 0.85
f'c = 35 MPa
fy = 400 MPa
b
γh
h
EI18 = kbh3/(1+βd)
EI19 = 939 bh3/(1+βd)
Pr/Ag, MPa
Mr/Agh, MPa

Table 7.4.12 Interaction Diagrams for Rectangular Columns With an Equal Number of Bars on all Four Faces.

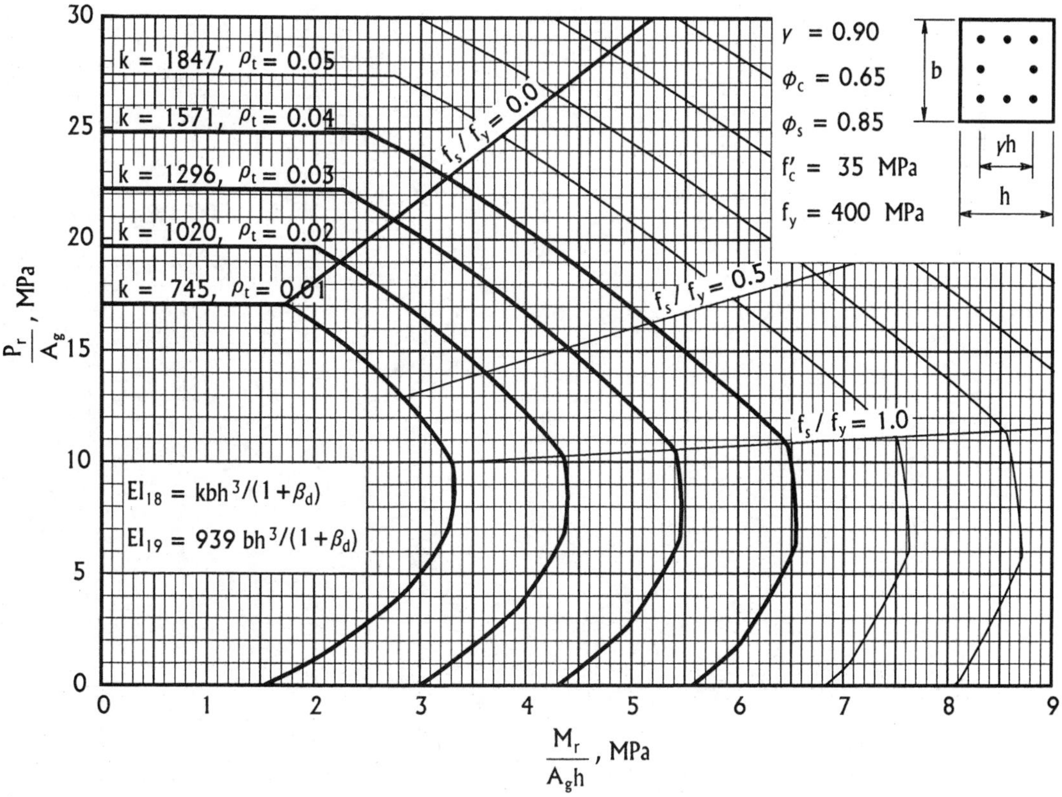

k = 1847, ρt = 0.05
k = 1571, ρt = 0.04
k = 1296, ρt = 0.03
k = 1020, ρt = 0.02
k = 745, ρt = 0.01
fs / fy = 0.0
fs / fy = 0.5
fs / fy = 1.0
γ = 0.90
φc = 0.65
φs = 0.85
f'c = 35 MPa
fy = 400 MPa
b
γh
h
EI18 = kbh3/(1+βd)
EI19 = 939 bh3/(1+βd)
Pr/Ag, MPa
Mr/Agh, MPa

Table 7.4.13 Interaction Diagrams for Rectangular Columns With an Equal Number of Bars on all Four Faces.

$$\gamma = 0.60$$
$$\phi_c = 0.65$$
$$\phi_s = 0.85$$
$$f'_c = 40 \text{ MPa}$$
$$f_y = 400 \text{ MPa}$$

$k = 1228, \; \rho_t = 0.06$
$k = 1106, \; \rho_t = 0.05$
$k = 983, \; \rho_t = 0.04$
$k = 861, \; \rho_t = 0.03$
$k = 738, \; \rho_t = 0.02$
$k = 616, \; \rho_t = 0.01$

$f_s / f_y = 0.0$
$f_s / f_y = 0.5$
$f_s / f_y = 1.0$

$$EI_{18} = kbh^3/(1+\beta_d)$$
$$EI_{19} = 987 \, bh^3/(1+\beta_d)$$

$\dfrac{P_r}{A_g}$, MPa

$\dfrac{M_r}{A_g h}$, MPa

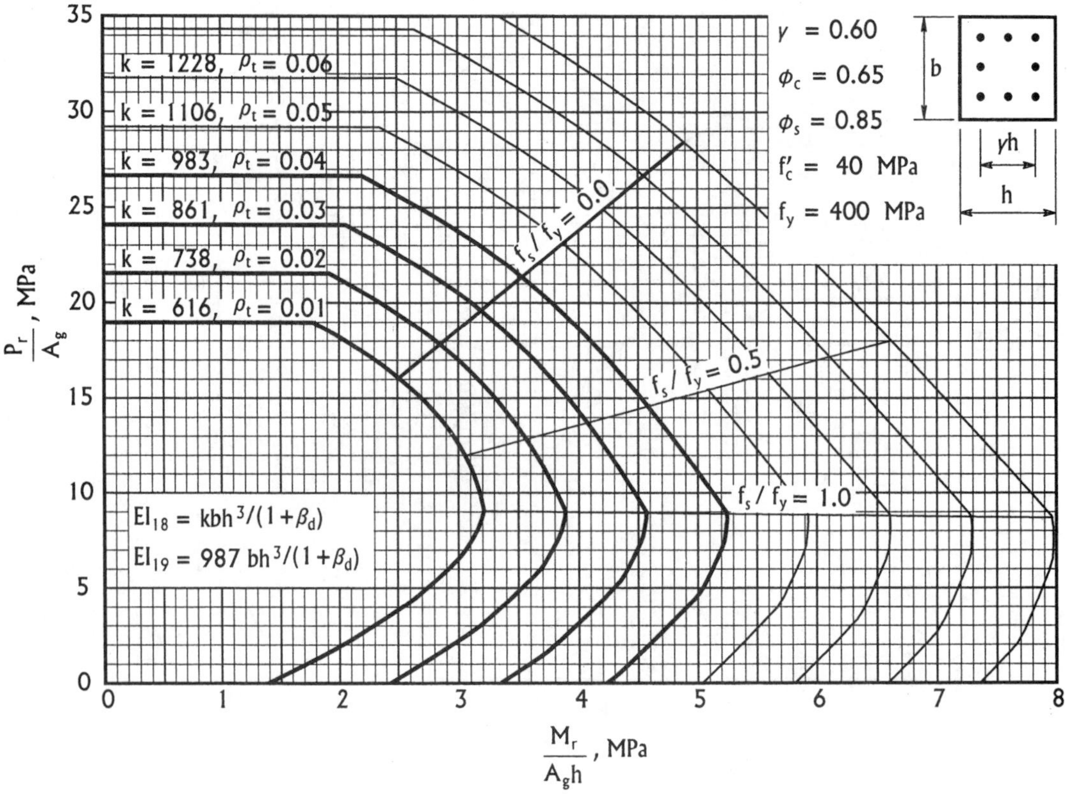

Table 7.4.14 Interaction Diagrams for Rectangular Columns With an Equal Number of Bars on all Four Faces.

$$\gamma = 0.70$$
$$\phi_c = 0.65$$
$$\phi_s = 0.85$$
$$f'_c = 40 \text{ MPa}$$
$$f_y = 400 \text{ MPa}$$

$k = 1493, \; \rho_t = 0.06$
$k = 1327, \; \rho_t = 0.05$
$k = 1160, \; \rho_t = 0.04$
$k = 993, \; \rho_t = 0.03$
$k = 827, \; \rho_t = 0.02$
$k = 660, \; \rho_t = 0.01$

$f_s / f_y = 0.0$
$f_s / f_y = 0.5$
$f_s / f_y = 1.0$

$$EI_{18} = kbh^3/(1+\beta_d)$$
$$EI_{19} = 987 \, bh^3/(1+\beta_d)$$

$\dfrac{P_r}{A_g}$, MPa

$\dfrac{M_r}{A_g h}$, MPa

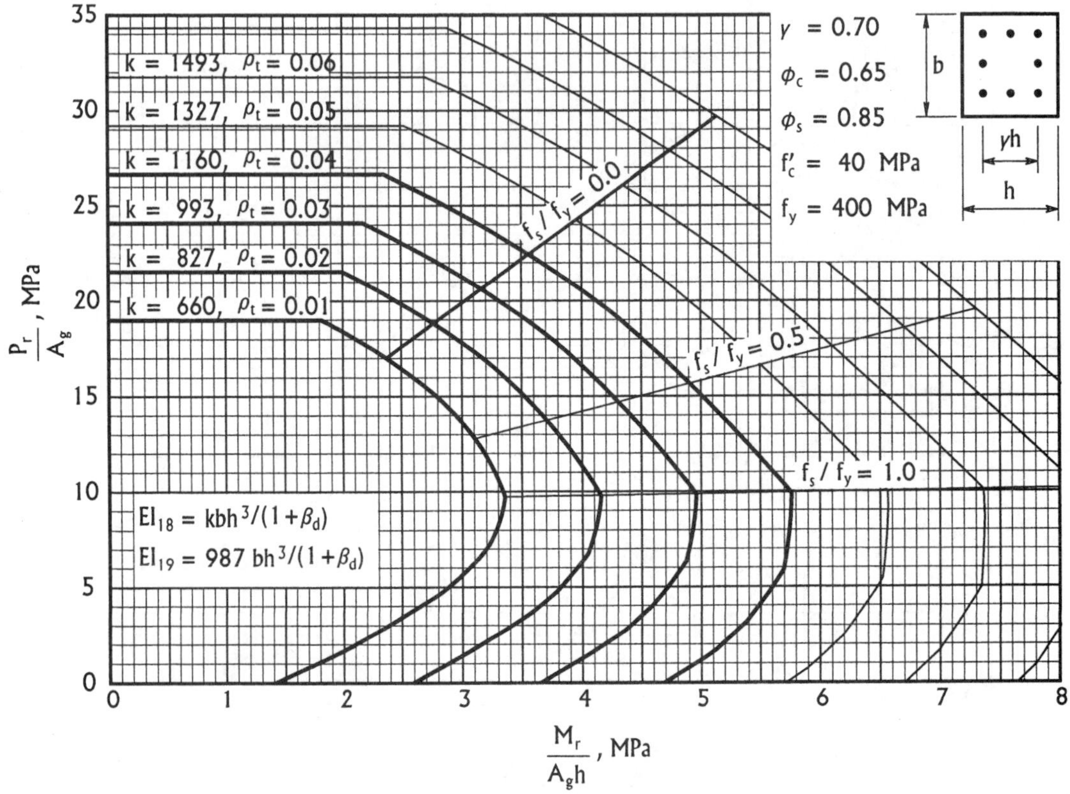

Table 7.4.15 Interaction Diagrams for Rectangular Columns With an Equal Number of Bars on all Four Faces.

$\gamma = 0.80$
$\phi_c = 0.65$
$\phi_s = 0.85$
$f'_c = 40$ MPa
$f_y = 400$ MPa

k = 1799, ρ_t = 0.06
k = 1582, ρ_t = 0.05
k = 1364, ρ_t = 0.04
k = 1146, ρ_t = 0.03
k = 929, ρ_t = 0.02
k = 711, ρ_t = 0.01

$f_s / f_y = 0.0$
$f_s / f_y = 0.5$
$f_s / f_y = 1.0$

$EI_{18} = kbh^3/(1+\beta_d)$
$EI_{19} = 987\ bh^3/(1+\beta_d)$

$\frac{P_r}{A_g}$, MPa

$\frac{M_r}{A_g h}$, MPa

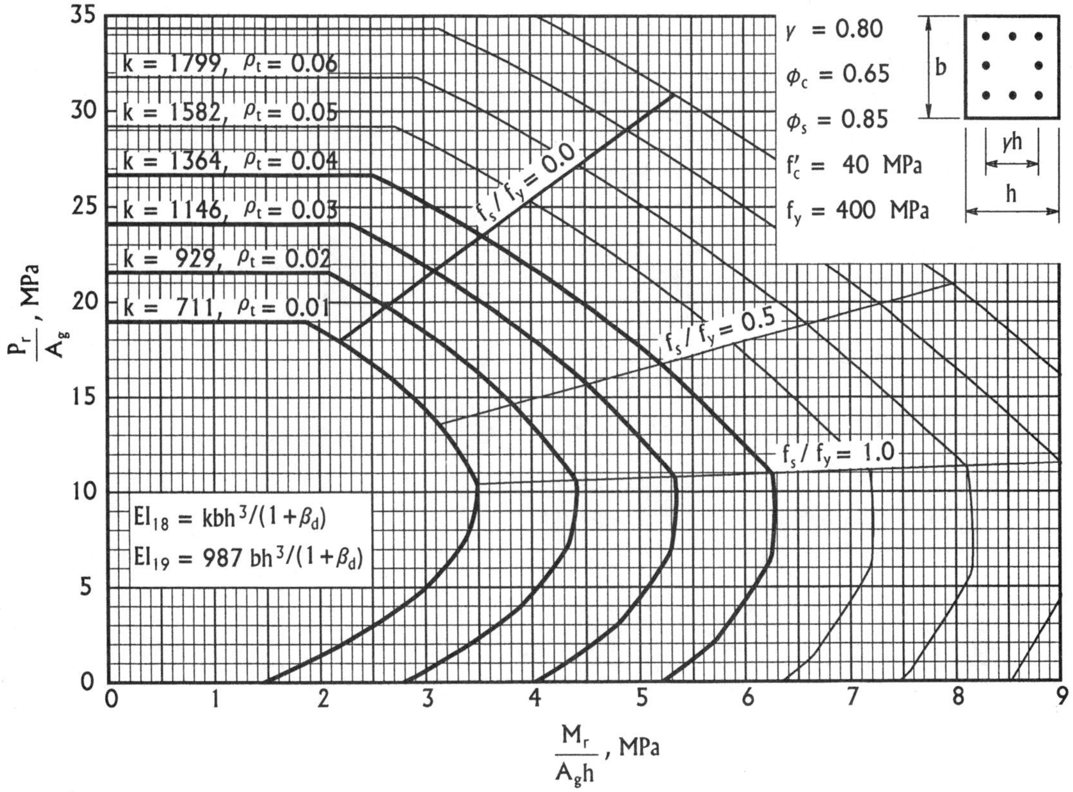

Table 7.4.16 Interaction Diagrams for Rectangular Columns With an Equal Number of Bars on all Four Faces.

$\gamma = 0.90$
$\phi_c = 0.65$
$\phi_s = 0.85$
$f'_c = 40$ MPa
$f_y = 400$ MPa

k = 2146, ρ_t = 0.06
k = 1871, ρ_t = 0.05
k = 1595, ρ_t = 0.04
k = 1320, ρ_t = 0.03
k = 1044, ρ_t = 0.02
k = 769, ρ_t = 0.01

$f_s / f_y = 0.0$
$f_s / f_y = 0.5$
$f_s / f_y = 1.0$

$EI_{18} = kbh^3/(1+\beta_d)$
$EI_{19} = 987\ bh^3/(1+\beta_d)$

$\frac{P_r}{A_g}$, MPa

$\frac{M_r}{A_g h}$, MPa

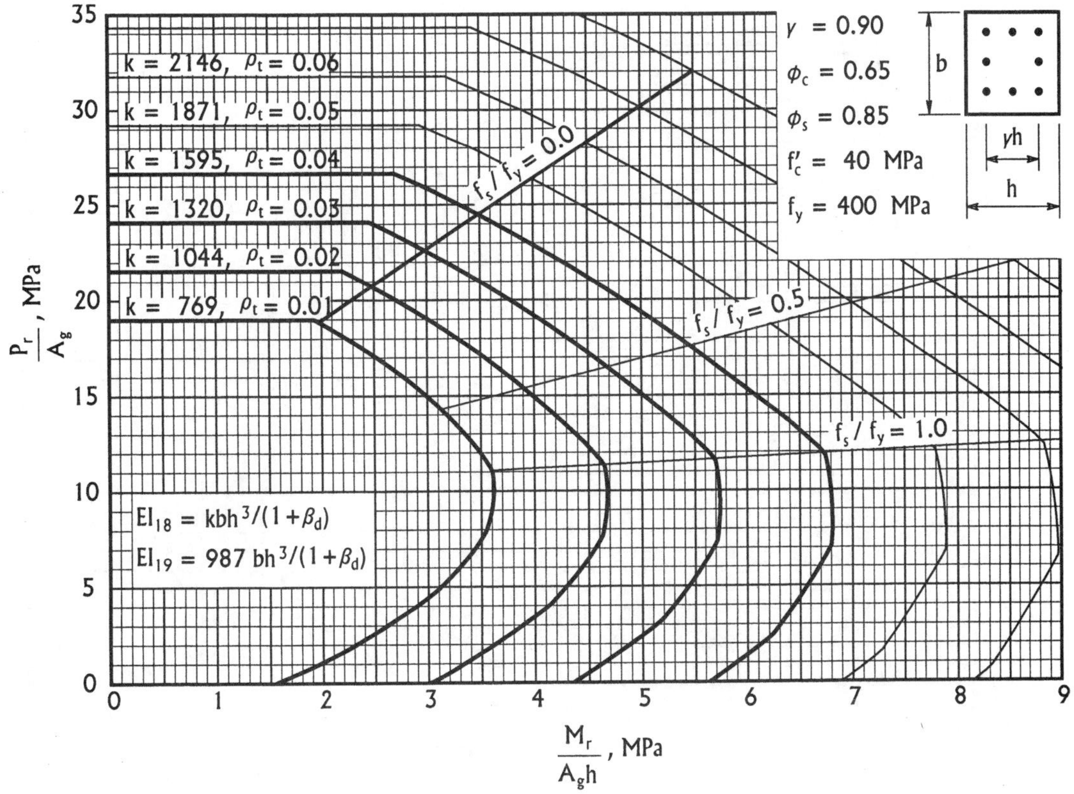

Table 7.4.17 Interaction Diagrams for Rectangular Columns With an Equal Number of Bars on all Four Faces.

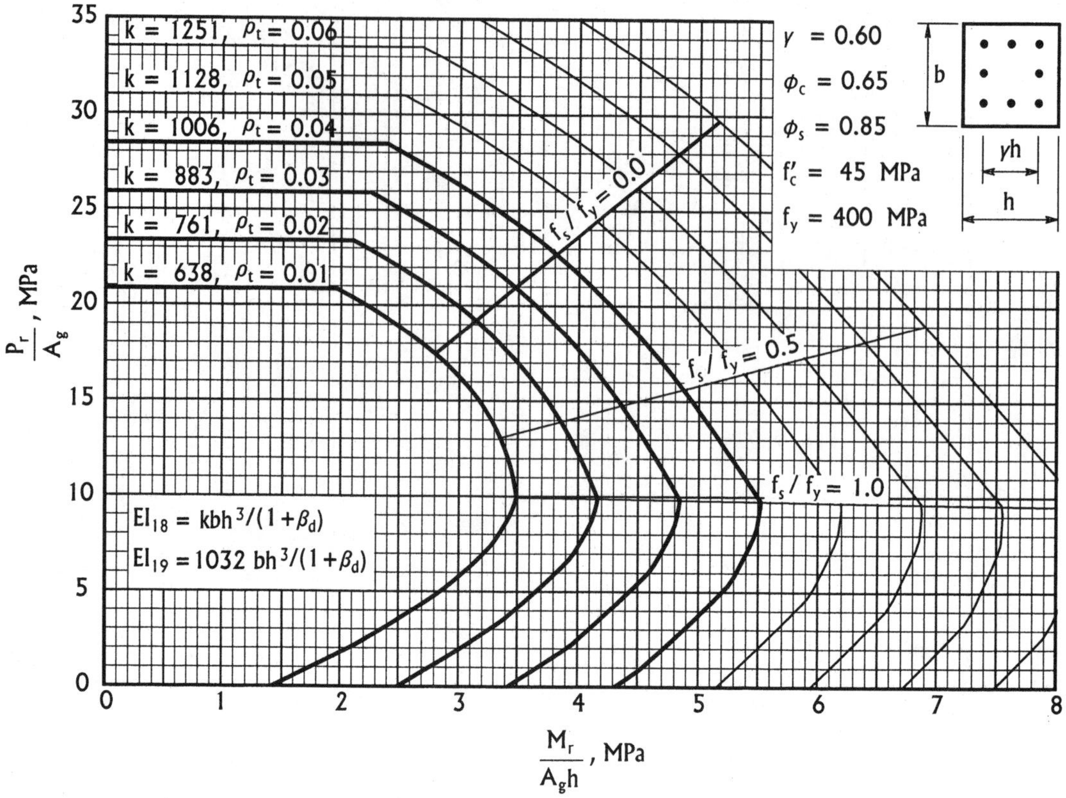
k = 1251, ρ_t = 0.06
k = 1128, ρ_t = 0.05
k = 1006, ρ_t = 0.04
k = 883, ρ_t = 0.03
k = 761, ρ_t = 0.02
k = 638, ρ_t = 0.01
γ = 0.60
ϕ_c = 0.65
ϕ_s = 0.85
f'_c = 45 MPa
f_y = 400 MPa
b
γh
h
$f_s / f_y = 0.0$
$f_s / f_y = 0.5$
$f_s / f_y = 1.0$
$EI_{18} = kbh^3/(1+\beta_d)$
$EI_{19} = 1032\ bh^3/(1+\beta_d)$
$\frac{P_r}{A_g}$, MPa
$\frac{M_r}{A_g h}$, MPa
0 5 10 15 20 25 30 35
0 1 2 3 4 5 6 7 8

Table 7.4.18 Interaction Diagrams for Rectangular Columns With an Equal Number of Bars on all Four Faces.

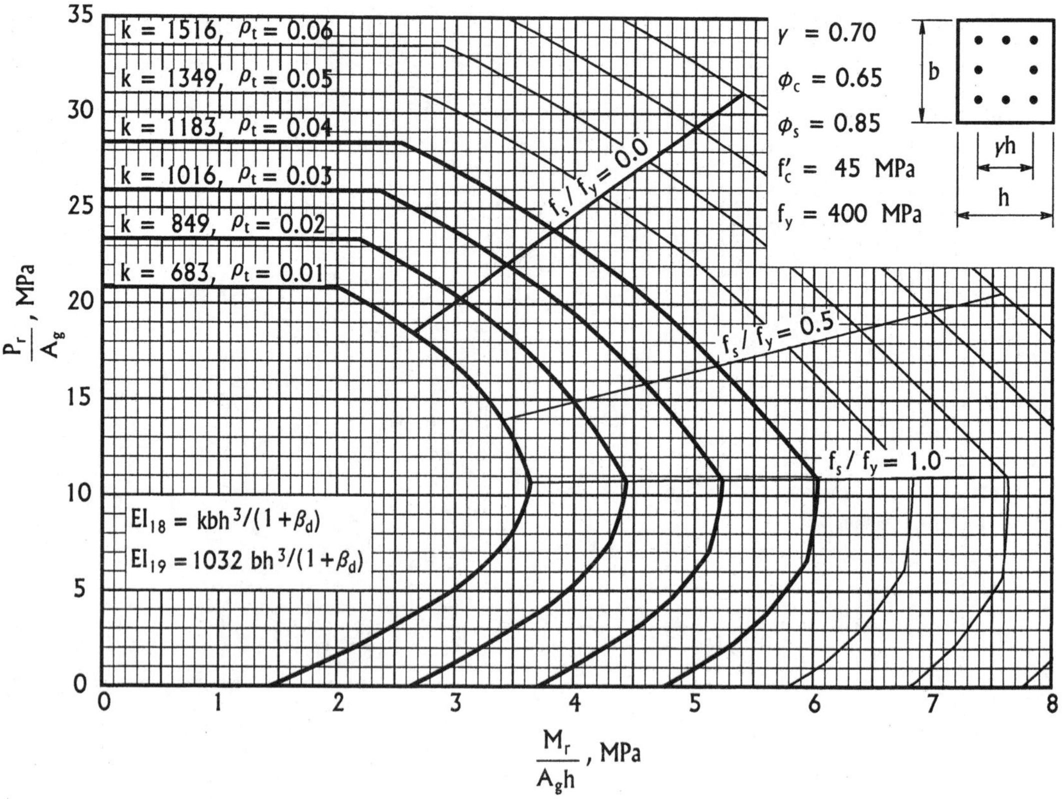
k = 1516, ρ_t = 0.06
k = 1349, ρ_t = 0.05
k = 1183, ρ_t = 0.04
k = 1016, ρ_t = 0.03
k = 849, ρ_t = 0.02
k = 683, ρ_t = 0.01
γ = 0.70
ϕ_c = 0.65
ϕ_s = 0.85
f'_c = 45 MPa
f_y = 400 MPa
b
γh
h
$f_s / f_y = 0.0$
$f_s / f_y = 0.5$
$f_s / f_y = 1.0$
$EI_{18} = kbh^3/(1+\beta_d)$
$EI_{19} = 1032\ bh^3/(1+\beta_d)$
$\frac{P_r}{A_g}$, MPa
$\frac{M_r}{A_g h}$, MPa
0 5 10 15 20 25 30 35
0 1 2 3 4 5 6 7 8

Table 7.4.19 Interaction Diagrams for Rectangular Columns With an Equal Number of Bars on all Four Faces.

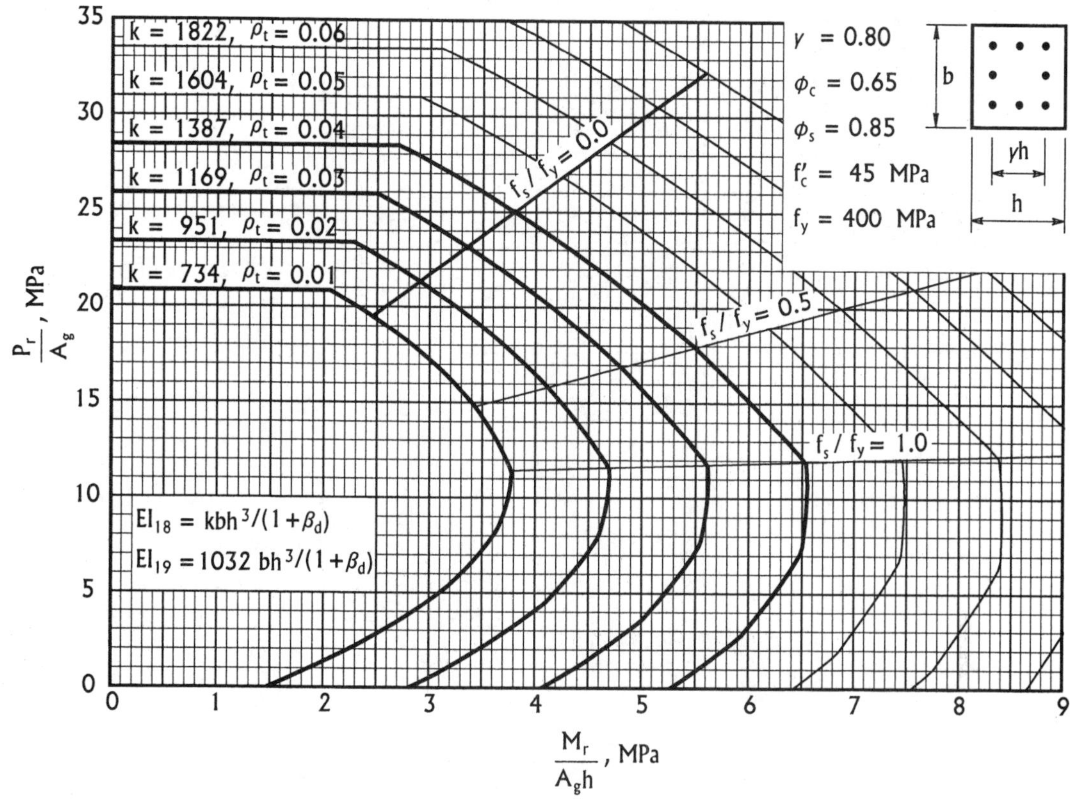

Table 7.4.20 Interaction Diagrams for Rectangular Columns With an Equal Number of Bars on all Four Faces.

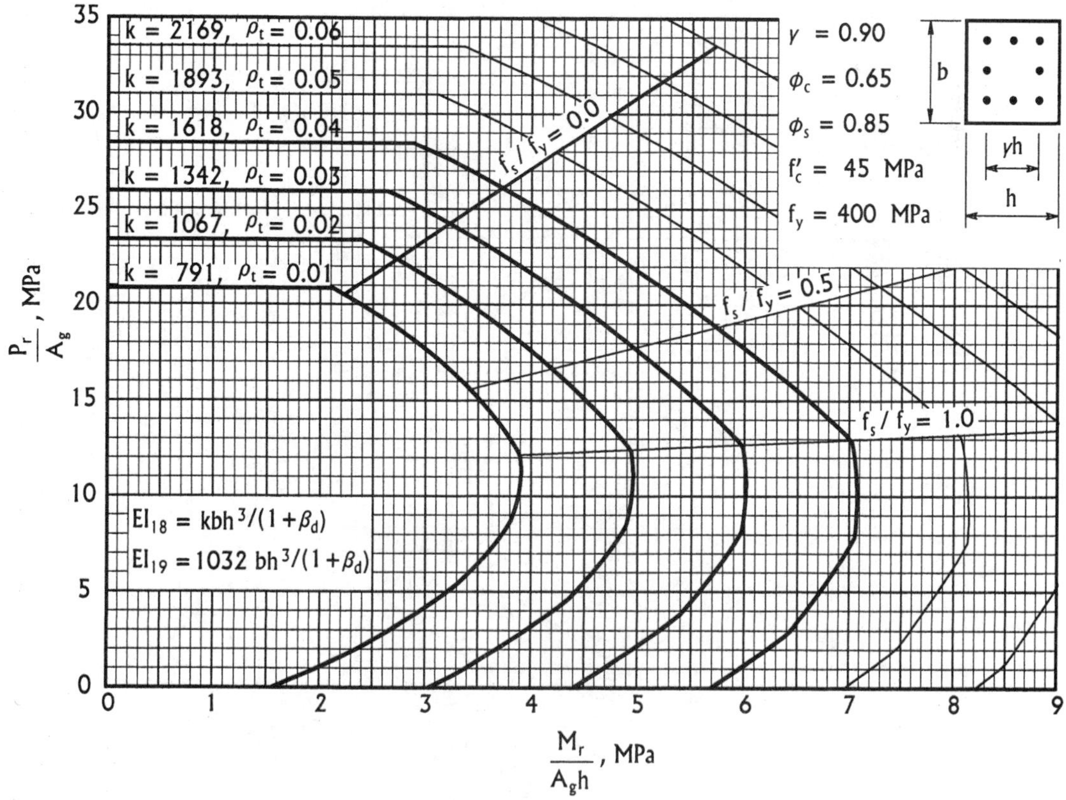

Table 7.5.1   Interaction Diagrams for Rectangular Columns With Bars in Two End Faces Only.

Graph, vertical axis $\frac{P_r}{A_g}$, MPa from 0 to 30; horizontal axis $\frac{M_r}{A_gh}$, MPa from 0 to 7.

Parameters:
- $\gamma = 0.50$
- $\phi_c = 0.65$
- $\phi_s = 0.85$
- $f'_c = 25$ MPa
- $f_y = 400$ MPa

Curves:
- $k = 1166, \; \rho_t = 0.06$
- $k = 1041, \; \rho_t = 0.05$
- $k = 916, \; \rho_t = 0.04$
- $k = 791, \; \rho_t = 0.03$
- $k = 666, \; \rho_t = 0.02$
- $k = 541, \; \rho_t = 0.01$

$f_s/f_y = 0.0$
$f_s/f_y = 0.5$
$f_s/f_y = 1.0$

$EI_{18} = kbh^3/(1+\beta_d)$
$EI_{19} = 831\, bh^3/(1+\beta_d)$

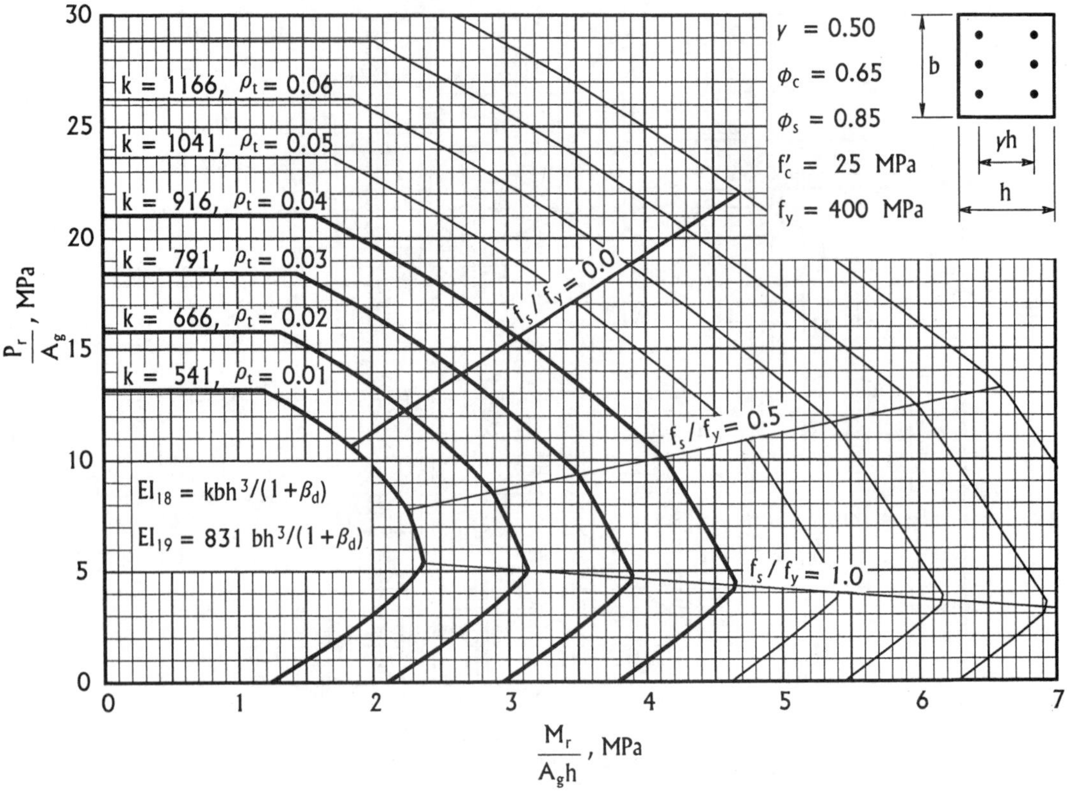

Table 7.5.2   Interaction Diagrams for Rectangular Columns With Bars in Two End Faces Only.

Graph, vertical axis $\frac{P_r}{A_g}$, MPa from 0 to 30; horizontal axis $\frac{M_r}{A_gh}$, MPa from 0 to 7.

Parameters:
- $\gamma = 0.60$
- $\phi_c = 0.65$
- $\phi_s = 0.85$
- $f'_c = 25$ MPa
- $f_y = 400$ MPa

Curves:
- $k = 1496, \; \rho_t = 0.06$
- $k = 1316, \; \rho_t = 0.05$
- $k = 1136, \; \rho_t = 0.04$
- $k = 956, \; \rho_t = 0.03$
- $k = 776, \; \rho_t = 0.02$
- $k = 596, \; \rho_t = 0.01$

$f_s/f_y = 0.0$
$f_s/f_y = 0.5$
$f_s/f_y = 1.0$

$EI_{18} = kbh^3/(1+\beta_d)$
$EI_{19} = 831\, bh^3/(1+\beta_d)$

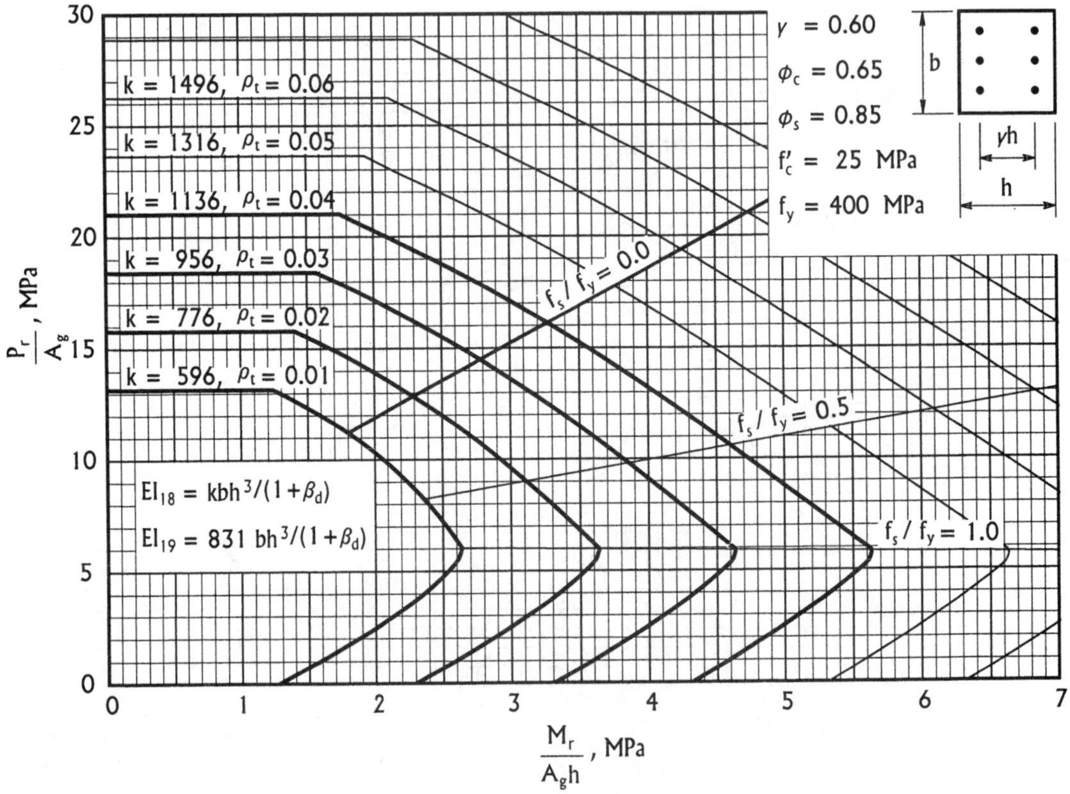

Table 7.5.3   Interaction Diagrams for Rectangular Columns With Bars in Two End Faces Only.

$$\gamma = 0.70$$
$$\phi_c = 0.65$$
$$\phi_s = 0.85$$
$$f'_c = 25 \text{ MPa}$$
$$f_y = 400 \text{ MPa}$$

$k = 1886, \ \rho_t = 0.06$
$k = 1641, \ \rho_t = 0.05$
$k = 1396, \ \rho_t = 0.04$
$k = 1151, \ \rho_t = 0.03$
$k = 906, \ \rho_t = 0.02$
$k = 661, \ \rho_t = 0.01$

$EI_{18} = kbh^3/(1+\beta_d)$
$EI_{19} = 831 \ bh^3/(1+\beta_d)$

$f_s/f_y = 0.0$
$f_s/f_y = 0.5$
$f_s/f_y = 1.0$

$\dfrac{P_r}{A_g}$, MPa

$\dfrac{M_r}{A_g h}$, MPa

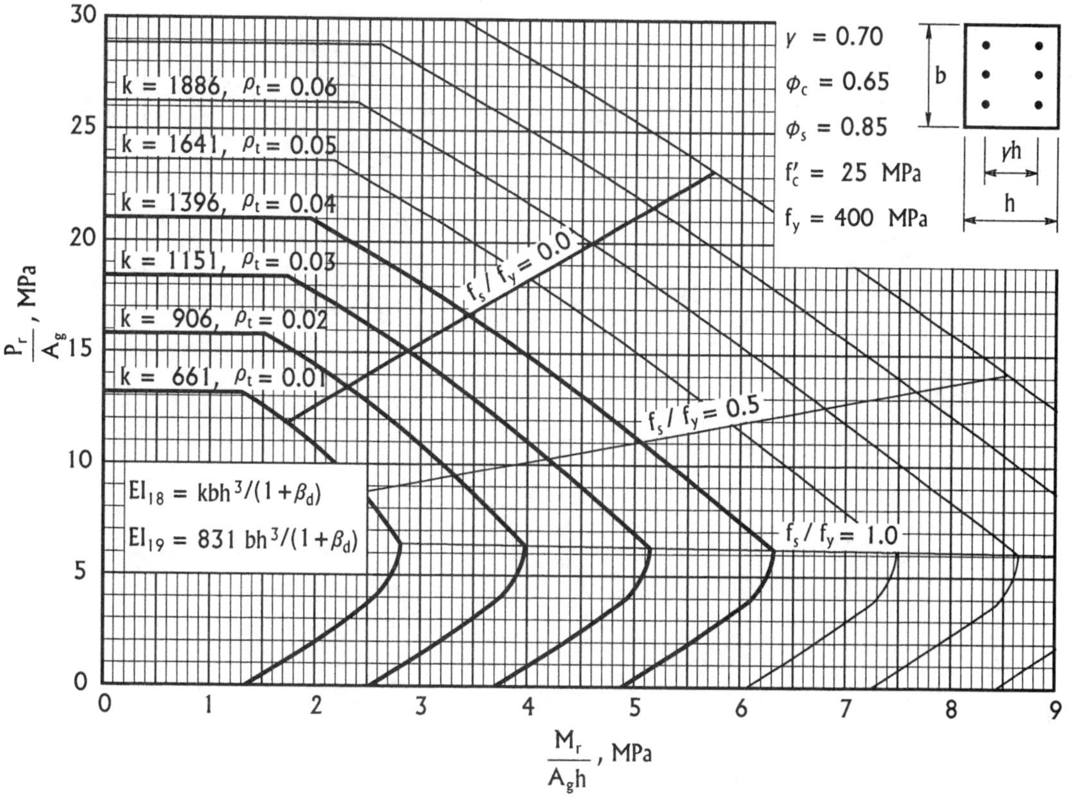

Table 7.5.4   Interaction Diagrams for Rectangular Columns With Bars in Two End Faces Only.

$$\gamma = 0.80$$
$$\phi_c = 0.65$$
$$\phi_s = 0.85$$
$$f'_c = 25 \text{ MPa}$$
$$f_y = 400 \text{ MPa}$$

$k = 2336, \ \rho_t = 0.06$
$k = 2016, \ \rho_t = 0.05$
$k = 1696, \ \rho_t = 0.04$
$k = 1376, \ \rho_t = 0.03$
$k = 1056, \ \rho_t = 0.02$
$k = 736, \ \rho_t = 0.01$

$EI_{18} = kbh^3/(1+\beta_d)$
$EI_{19} = 831 \ bh^3/(1+\beta_d)$

$f_s/f_y = 0.0$
$f_s/f_y = 0.5$
$f_s/f_y = 1.0$

$\dfrac{P_r}{A_g}$, MPa

$\dfrac{M_r}{A_g h}$, MPa

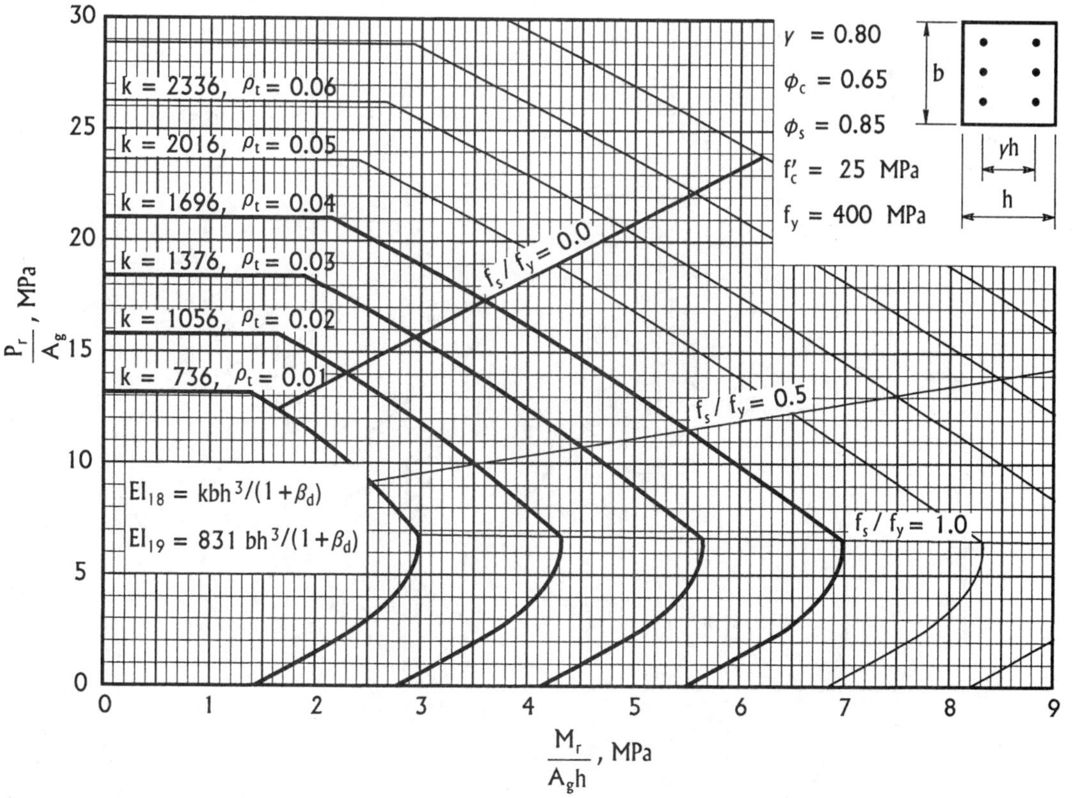

Table 7.5.5   Interaction Diagrams for Rectangular Columns With Bars in Two End Faces Only.

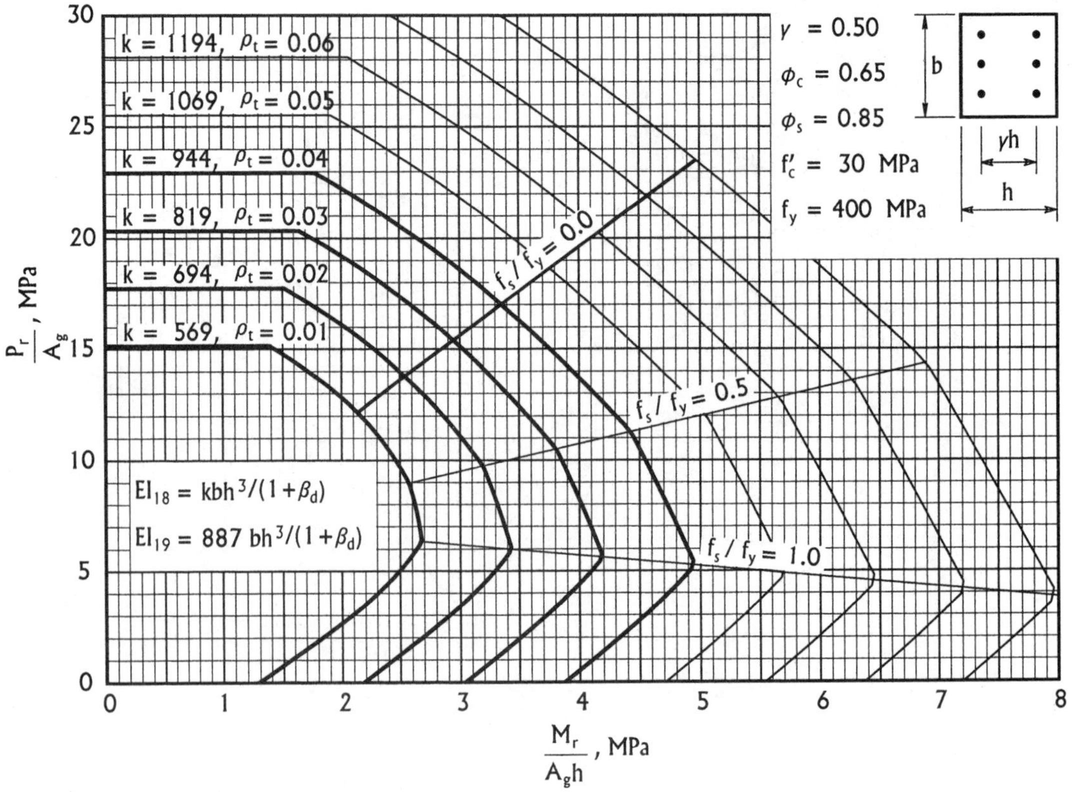

Table 7.5.6   Interaction Diagrams for Rectangular Columns With Bars in Two End Faces Only.

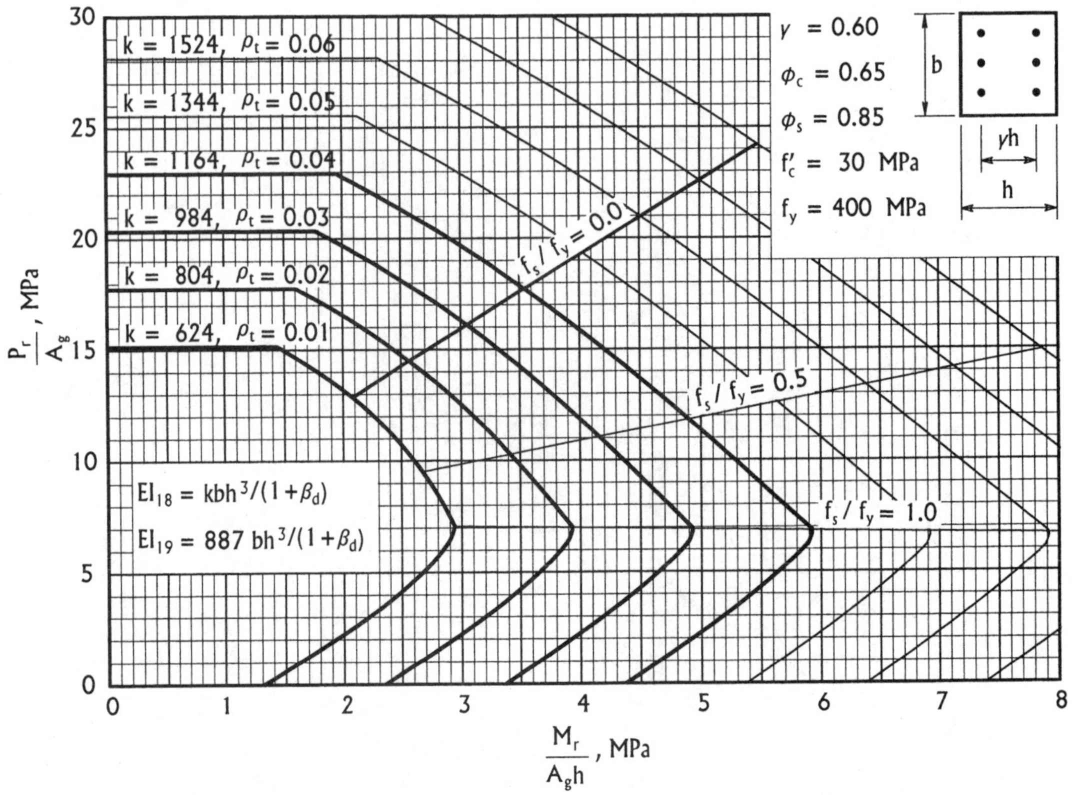

Table 7.5.7 Interaction Diagrams for Rectangular Columns With Bars in Two End Faces Only.

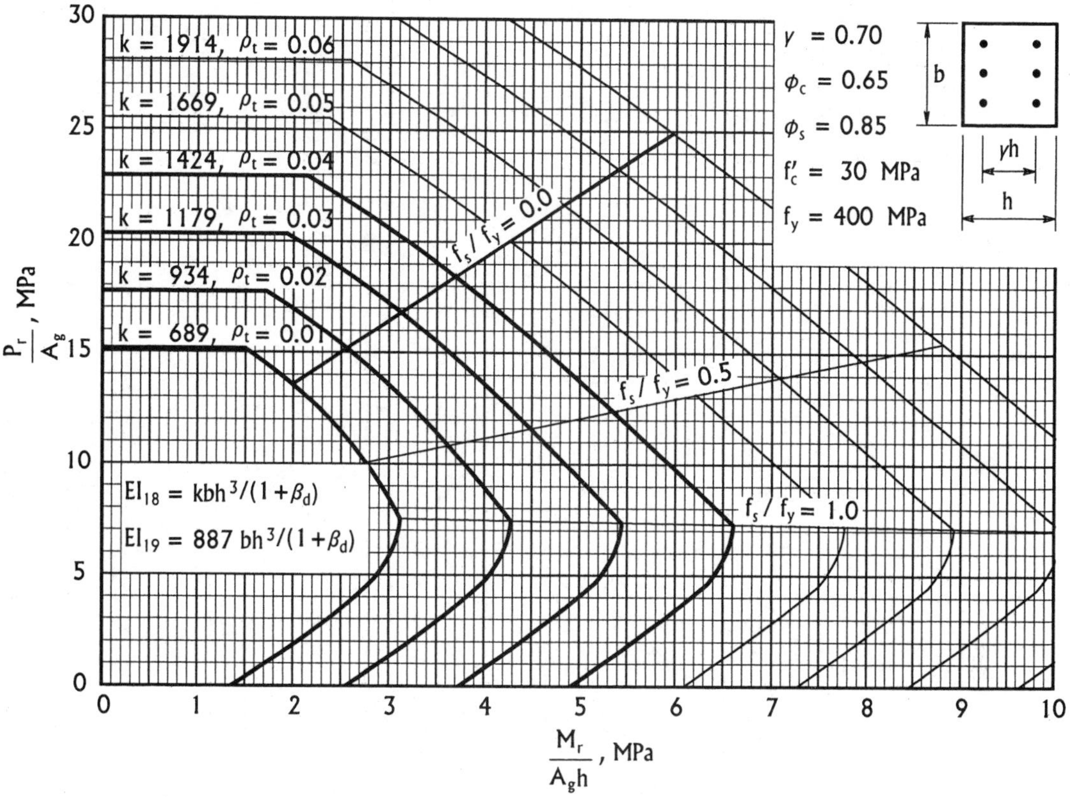

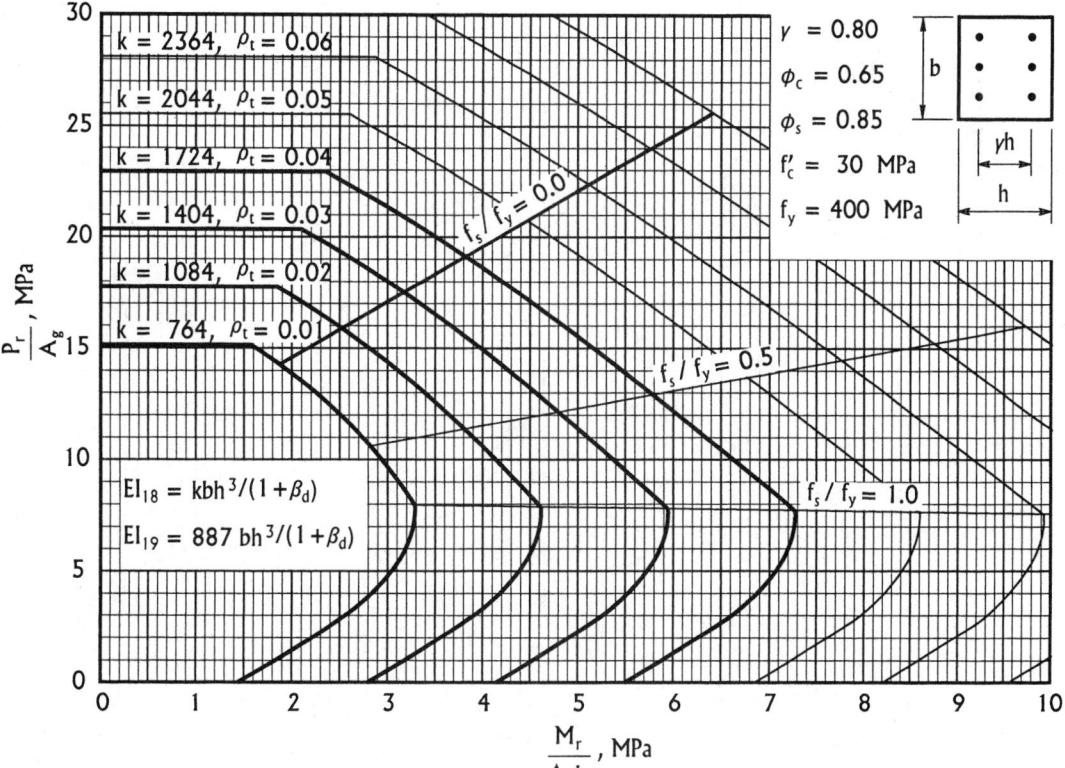

Table 7.5.8 Interaction Diagrams for Rectangular Columns With Bars in Two End Faces Only.

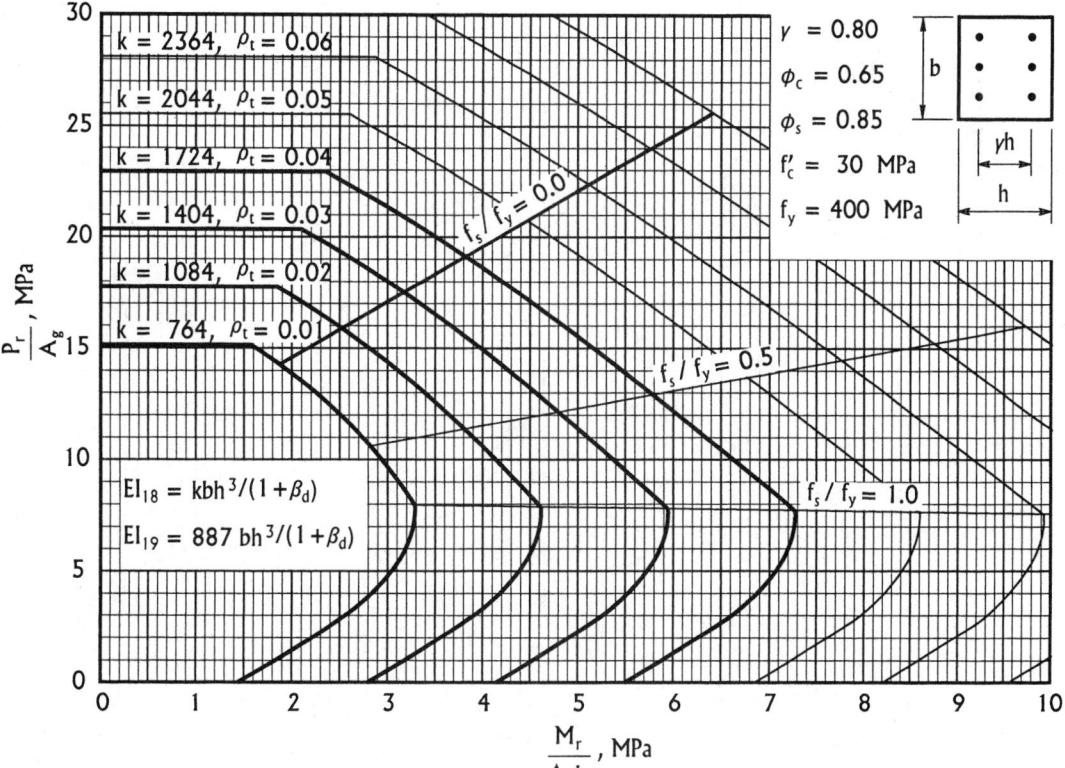

Table 7.5.9   Interaction Diagrams for Rectangular Columns With Bars in Two End Faces Only.

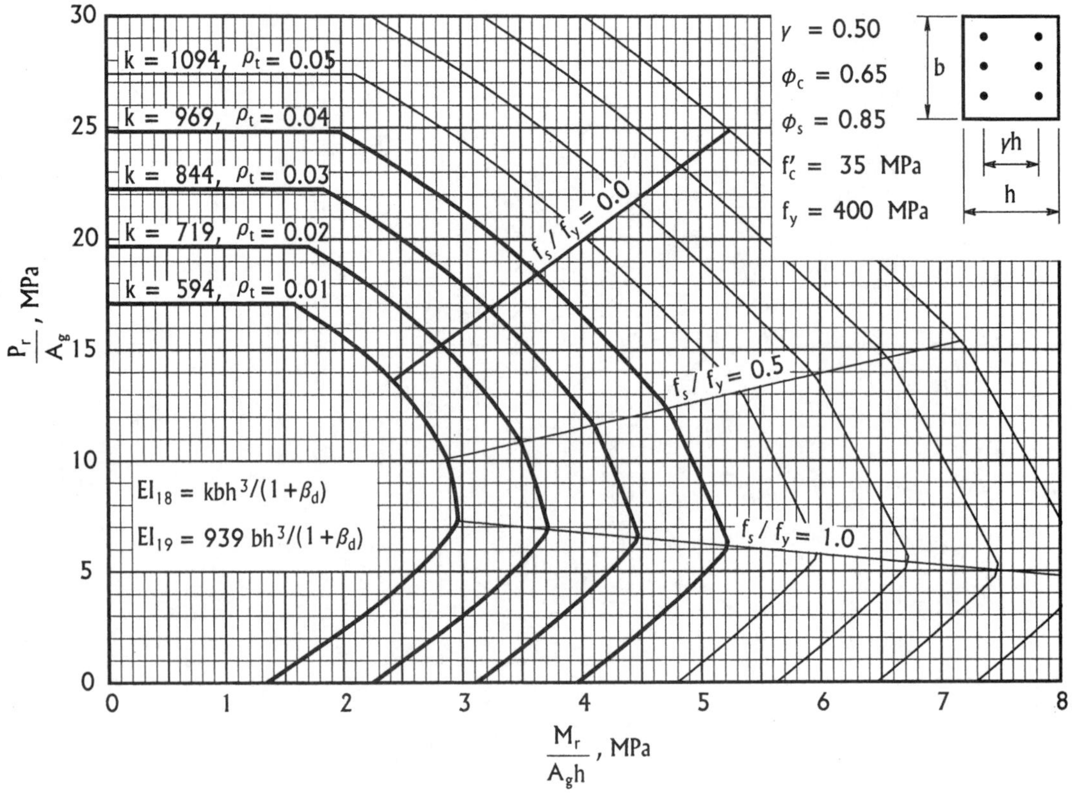

Table 7.5.10 Interaction Diagrams for Rectangular Columns With Bars in Two End Faces Only.

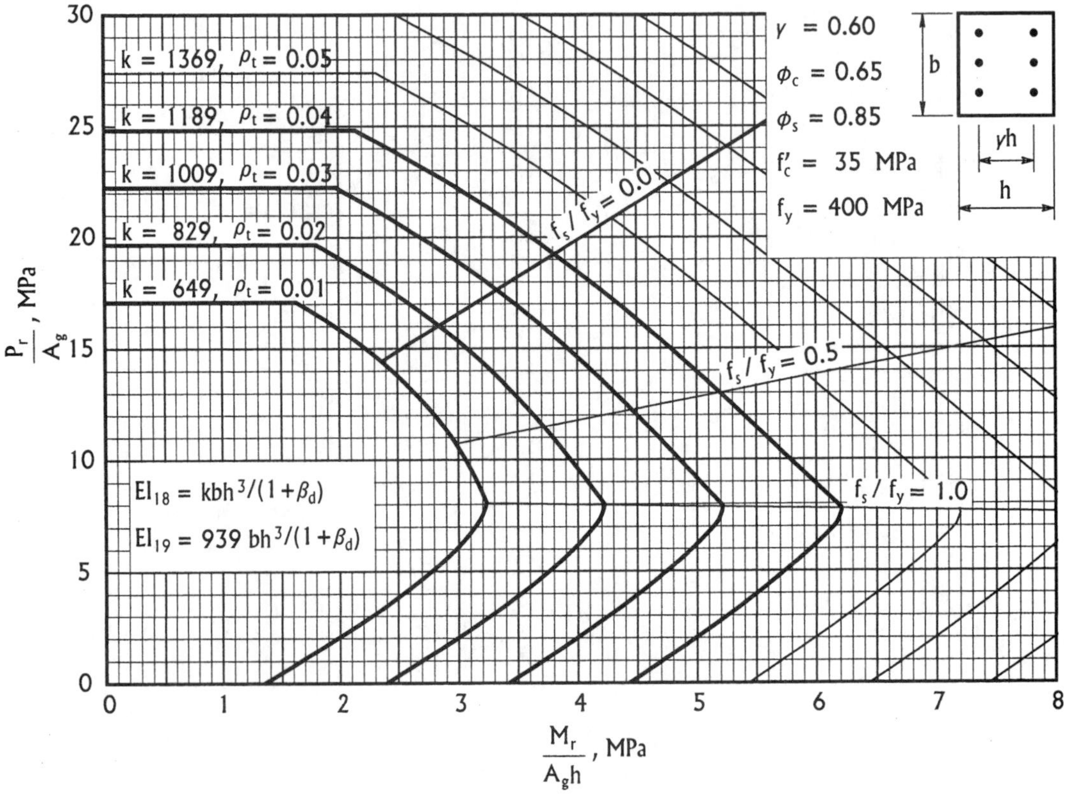

Table 7.5.11 Interaction Diagrams for Rectangular Columns With Bars in Two End Faces Only.

$\gamma = 0.70$
$\phi_c = 0.65$
$\phi_s = 0.85$
$f'_c = 35$ MPa
$f_y = 400$ MPa

$k = 1694, \rho_t = 0.05$
$k = 1449, \rho_t = 0.04$
$k = 1204, \rho_t = 0.03$
$k = 959, \rho_t = 0.02$
$k = 714, \rho_t = 0.01$

$f_s / f_y = 0.0$
$f_s / f_y = 0.5$
$f_s / f_y = 1.0$

$EI_{18} = kbh^3/(1+\beta_d)$
$EI_{19} = 939 \, bh^3/(1+\beta_d)$

$\dfrac{P_r}{A_g}$, MPa

$\dfrac{M_r}{A_g h}$, MPa

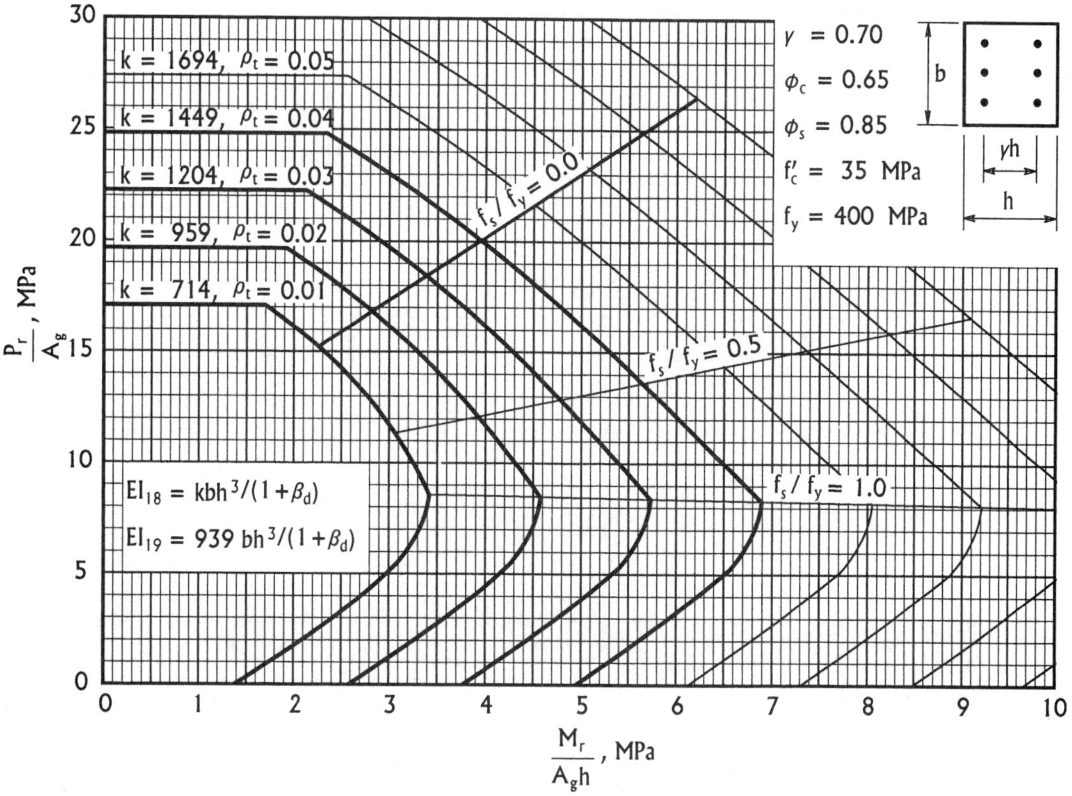

Table 7.5.12 Interaction Diagrams for Rectangular Columns With Bars in Two End Faces Only.

$\gamma = 0.80$
$\phi_c = 0.65$
$\phi_s = 0.85$
$f'_c = 35$ MPa
$f_y = 400$ MPa

$k = 2069, \rho_t = 0.05$
$k = 1749, \rho_t = 0.04$
$k = 1429, \rho_t = 0.03$
$k = 1109, \rho_t = 0.02$
$k = 789, \rho_t = 0.01$

$f_s / f_y = 0.0$
$f_s / f_y = 0.5$
$f_s / f_y = 1.0$

$EI_{18} = kbh^3/(1+\beta_d)$
$EI_{19} = 939 \, bh^3/(1+\beta_d)$

$\dfrac{P_r}{A_g}$, MPa

$\dfrac{M_r}{A_g h}$, MPa

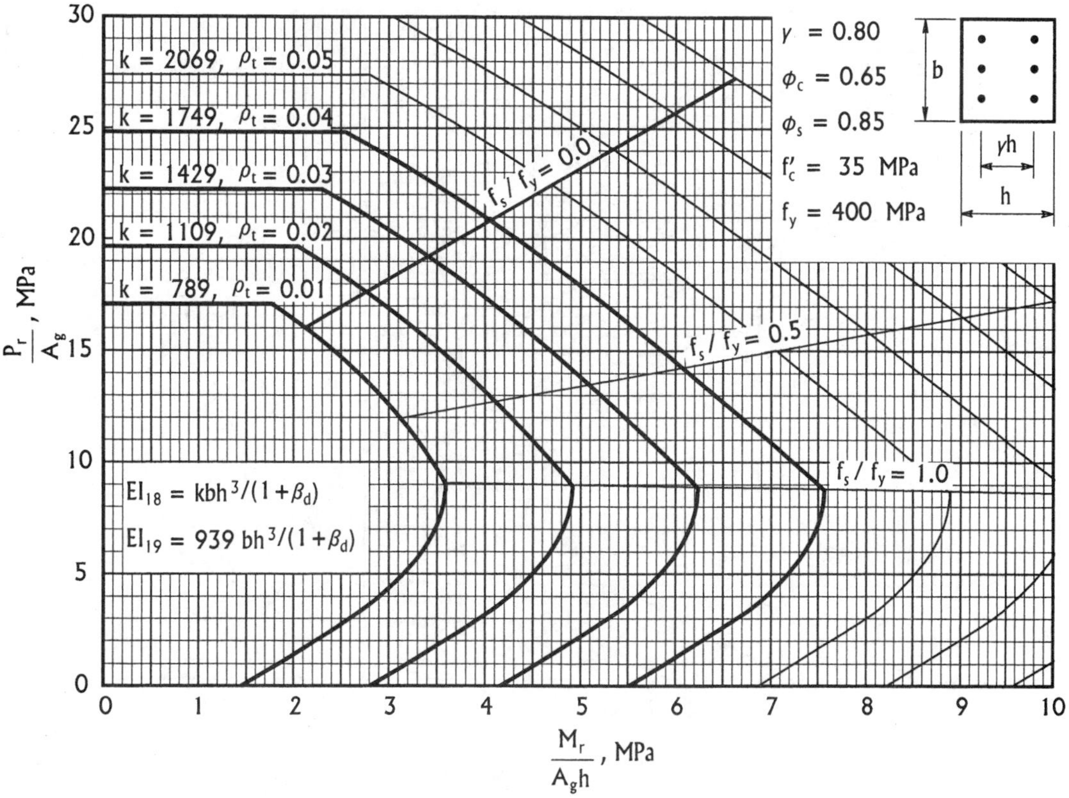

Table 7.5.13 Interaction Diagrams for Rectangular Columns With Bars in Two End Faces Only.

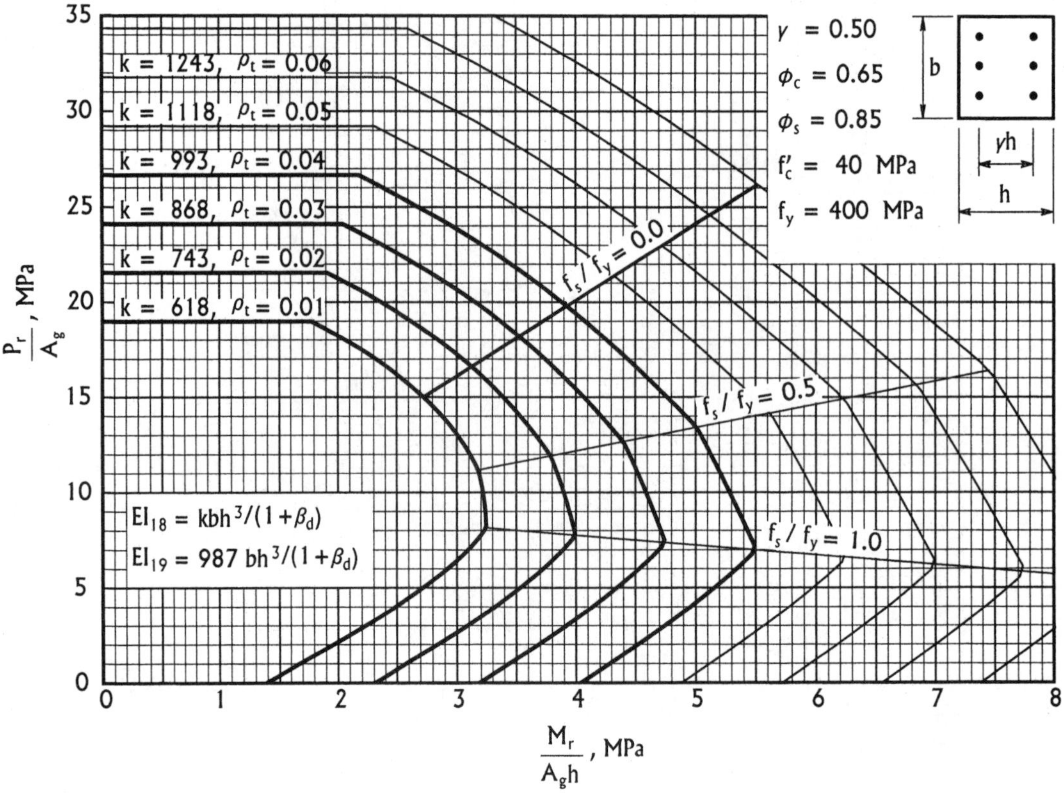

Table 7.5.14 Interaction Diagrams for Rectangular Columns With Bars in Two End Faces Only.

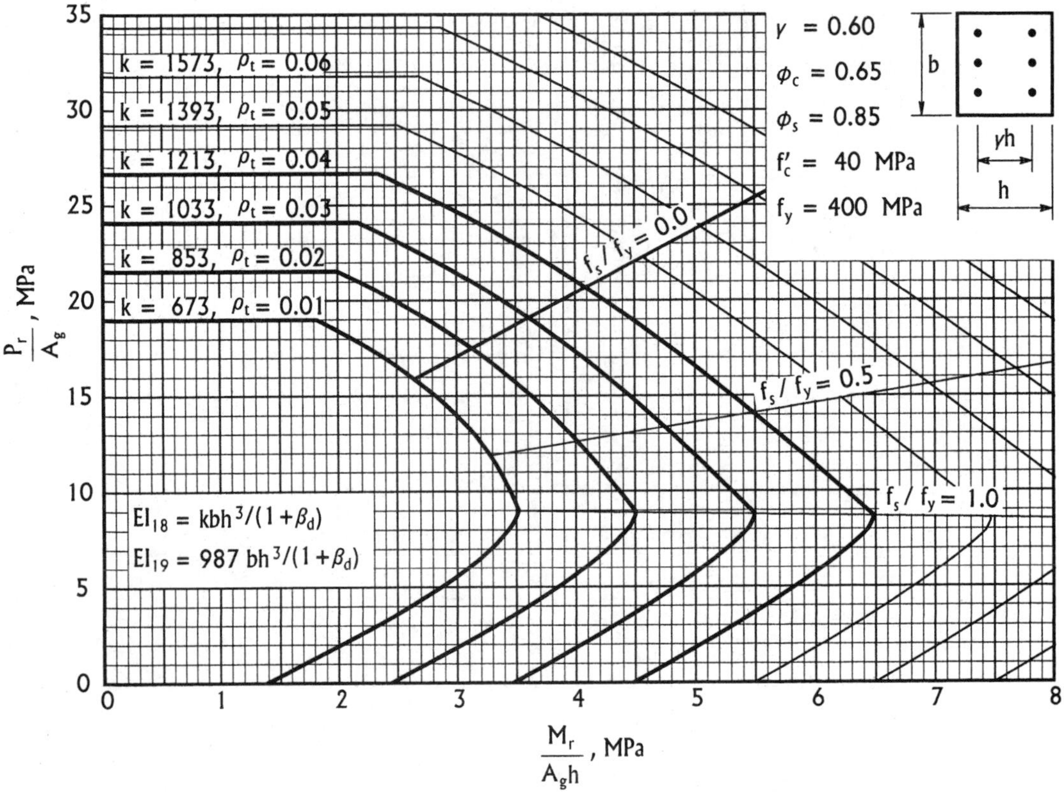

Table 7.5.15 Interaction Diagrams for Rectangular Columns With Bars in Two End Faces Only.

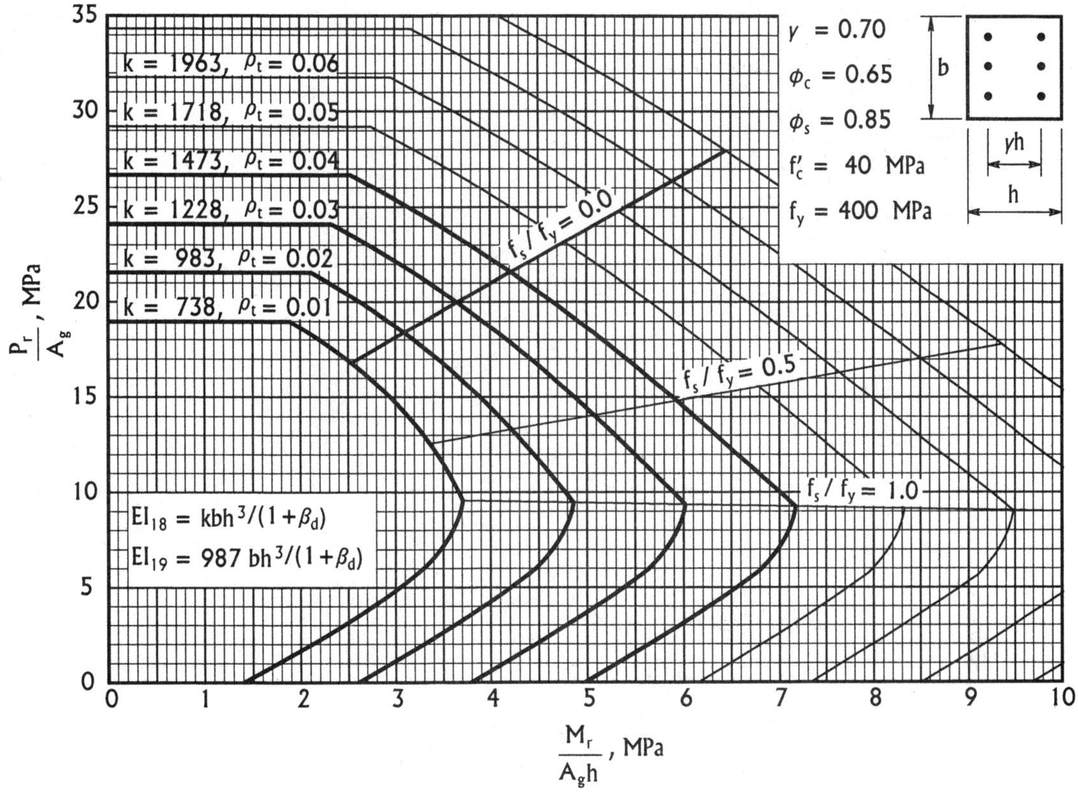
γ = 0.70
ϕ_c = 0.65
ϕ_s = 0.85
f'_c = 40 MPa
f_y = 400 MPa
b
γh
h
k = 1963, ρ_t = 0.06
k = 1718, ρ_t = 0.05
k = 1473, ρ_t = 0.04
k = 1228, ρ_t = 0.03
k = 983, ρ_t = 0.02
k = 738, ρ_t = 0.01
f_s / f_y = 0.0
f_s / f_y = 0.5
f_s / f_y = 1.0
$EI_{18} = kbh^3/(1+\beta_d)$
$EI_{19} = 987\ bh^3/(1+\beta_d)$
$\frac{P_r}{A_g}$, MPa
$\frac{M_r}{A_g h}$, MPa
0 5 10 15 20 25 30 35
0 1 2 3 4 5 6 7 8 9 10

Table 7.5.16 Interaction Diagrams for Rectangular Columns With Bars in Two End Faces Only.

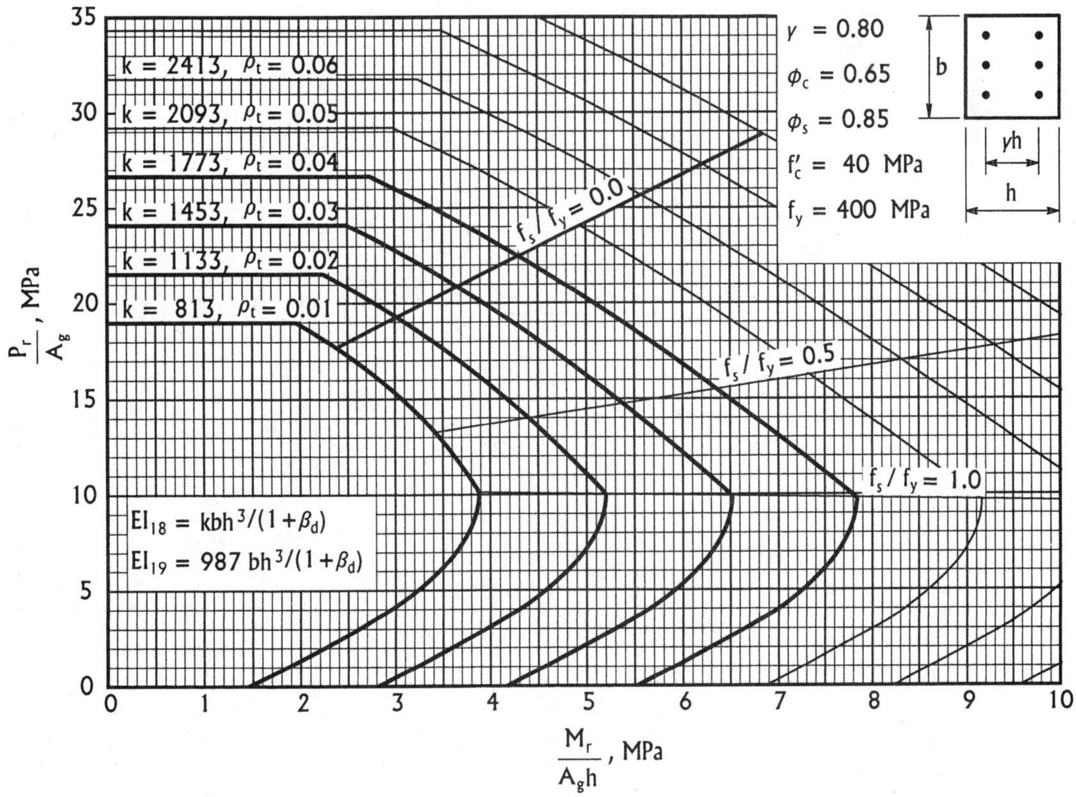
γ = 0.80
ϕ_c = 0.65
ϕ_s = 0.85
f'_c = 40 MPa
f_y = 400 MPa
b
γh
h
k = 2413, ρ_t = 0.06
k = 2093, ρ_t = 0.05
k = 1773, ρ_t = 0.04
k = 1453, ρ_t = 0.03
k = 1133, ρ_t = 0.02
k = 813, ρ_t = 0.01
f_s / f_y = 0.0
f_s / f_y = 0.5
f_s / f_y = 1.0
$EI_{18} = kbh^3/(1+\beta_d)$
$EI_{19} = 987\ bh^3/(1+\beta_d)$
$\frac{P_r}{A_g}$, MPa
$\frac{M_r}{A_g h}$, MPa
0 5 10 15 20 25 30 35
0 1 2 3 4 5 6 7 8 9 10

Table 7.5.17 Interaction Diagrams for Rectangular Columns With Bars in Two End Faces Only.

$EI_{18} = kbh^3/(1+\beta_d)$
$EI_{19} = 1032\ bh^3/(1+\beta_d)$

$k = 1266,\ \rho_t = 0.06$
$k = 1141,\ \rho_t = 0.05$
$k = 1016,\ \rho_t = 0.04$
$k = 891,\ \rho_t = 0.03$
$k = 766,\ \rho_t = 0.02$
$k = 641,\ \rho_t = 0.01$

$\gamma = 0.50$
$\phi_c = 0.65$
$\phi_s = 0.85$
$f'_c = 45$ MPa
$f_y = 400$ MPa

$f_s/f_y = 0.0$
$f_s/f_y = 0.5$
$f_s/f_y = 1.0$

$\dfrac{P_r}{A_g}$, MPa

$\dfrac{M_r}{A_gh}$, MPa

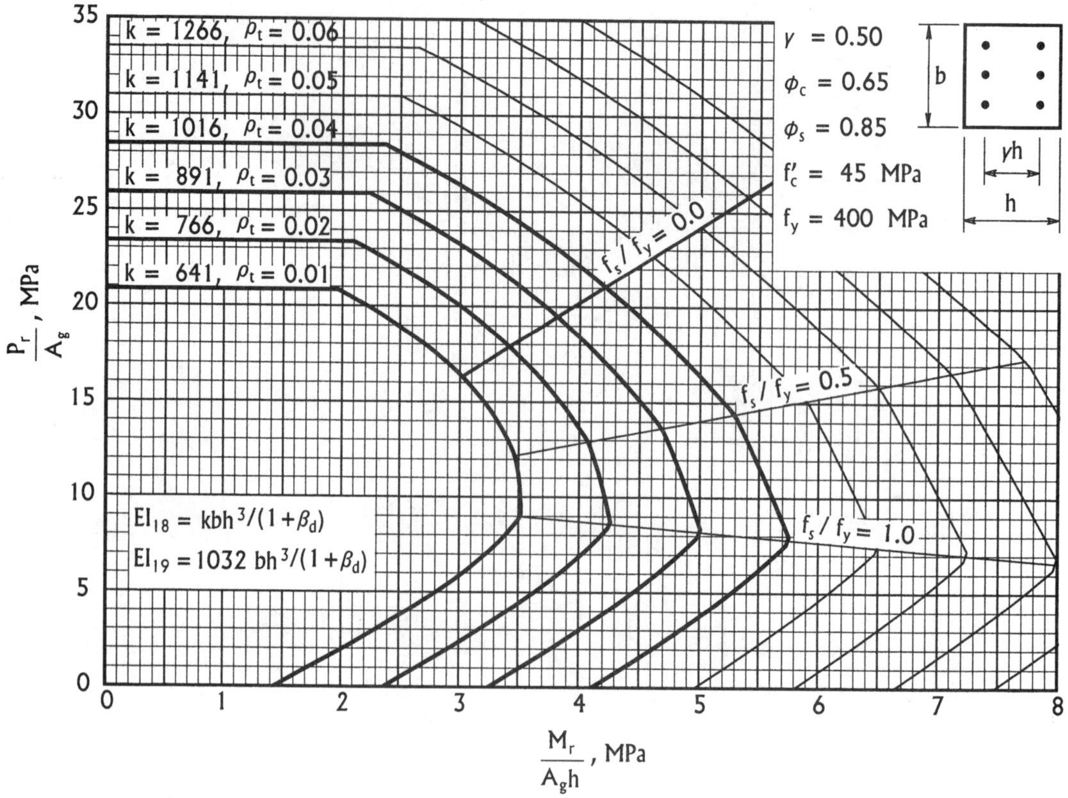

Table 7.5.18 Interaction Diagrams for Rectangular Columns With Bars in Two End Faces Only.

$EI_{18} = kbh^3/(1+\beta_d)$
$EI_{19} = 1032\ bh^3/(1+\beta_d)$

$k = 1596,\ \rho_t = 0.06$
$k = 1416,\ \rho_t = 0.05$
$k = 1236,\ \rho_t = 0.04$
$k = 1056,\ \rho_t = 0.03$
$k = 876,\ \rho_t = 0.02$
$k = 696,\ \rho_t = 0.01$

$\gamma = 0.60$
$\phi_c = 0.65$
$\phi_s = 0.85$
$f'_c = 45$ MPa
$f_y = 400$ MPa

$f_s/f_y = 0.0$
$f_s/f_y = 0.5$
$f_s/f_y = 1.0$

$\dfrac{P_r}{A_g}$, MPa

$\dfrac{M_r}{A_gh}$, MPa

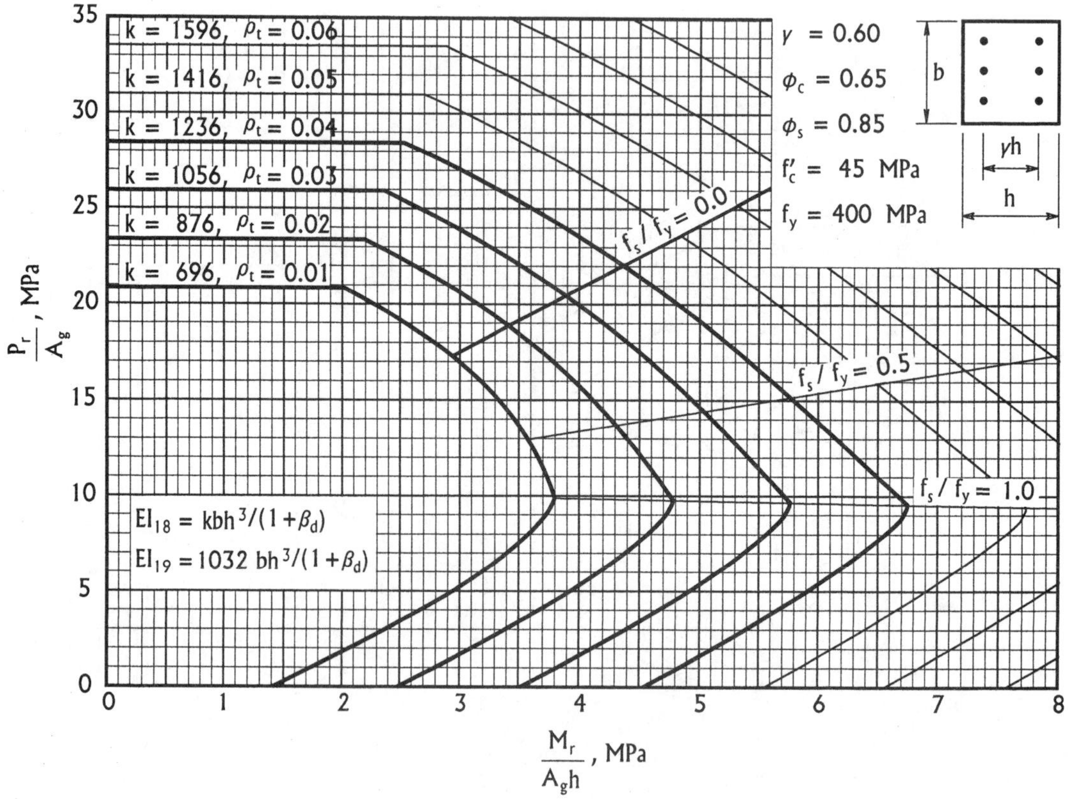

Table 7.5.19 Interaction Diagrams for Rectangular Columns With Bars in Two End Faces Only.

$\gamma = 0.70$
$\phi_c = 0.65$
$\phi_s = 0.85$
$f'_c = 45$ MPa
$f_y = 400$ MPa

$k = 1986, \ \rho_t = 0.06$
$k = 1741, \ \rho_t = 0.05$
$k = 1496, \ \rho_t = 0.04$
$k = 1251, \ \rho_t = 0.03$
$k = 1006, \ \rho_t = 0.02$
$k = 761, \ \rho_t = 0.01$

$f_s / f_y = 0.0$
$f_s / f_y = 0.5$
$f_s / f_y = 1.0$

$EI_{18} = kbh^3/(1+\beta_d)$
$EI_{19} = 1032 \ bh^3/(1+\beta_d)$

$\dfrac{P_r}{A_g}$, MPa

$\dfrac{M_r}{A_g h}$, MPa

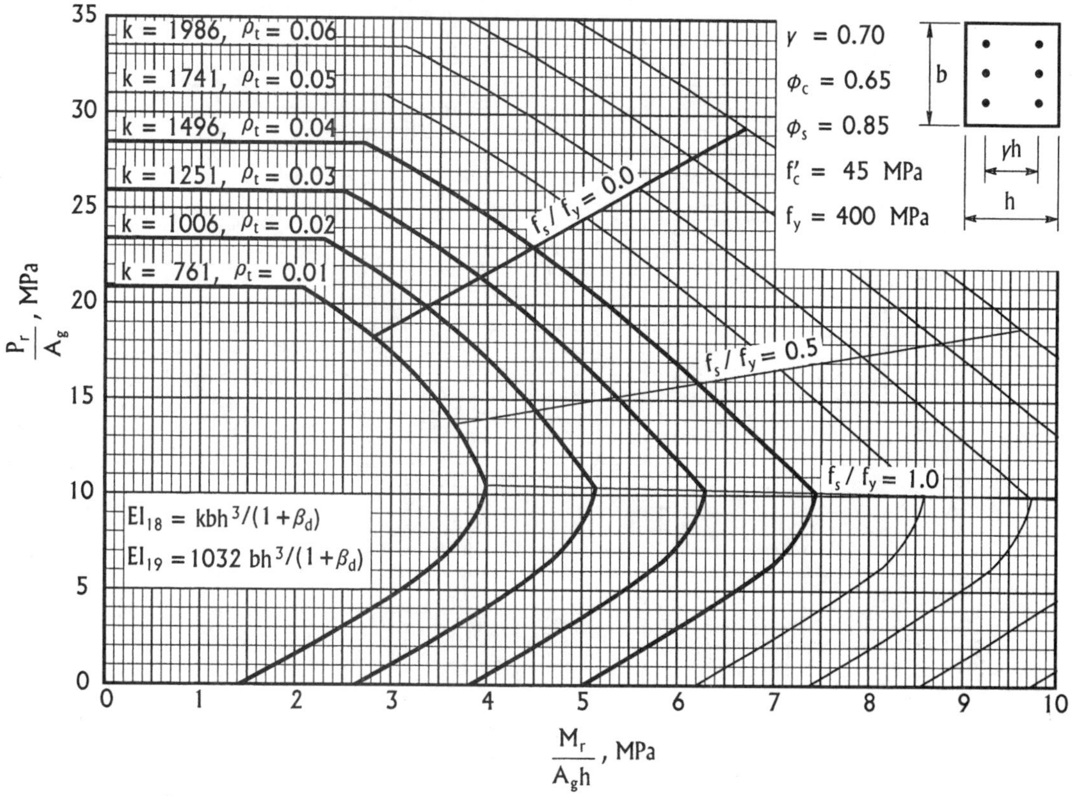

Table 7.5.20 Interaction Diagrams for Rectangular Columns With Bars in Two End Faces Only.

$\gamma = 0.80$
$\phi_c = 0.65$
$\phi_s = 0.85$
$f'_c = 45$ MPa
$f_y = 400$ MPa

$k = 2436, \ \rho_t = 0.06$
$k = 2116, \ \rho_t = 0.05$
$k = 1796, \ \rho_t = 0.04$
$k = 1476, \ \rho_t = 0.03$
$k = 1156, \ \rho_t = 0.02$
$k = 836, \ \rho_t = 0.01$

$f_s / f_y = 0.0$
$f_s / f_y = 0.5$
$f_s / f_y = 1.0$

$EI_{18} = kbh^3/(1+\beta_d)$
$EI_{19} = 1032 \ bh^3/(1+\beta_d)$

$\dfrac{P_r}{A_g}$, MPa

$\dfrac{M_r}{A_g h}$, MPa

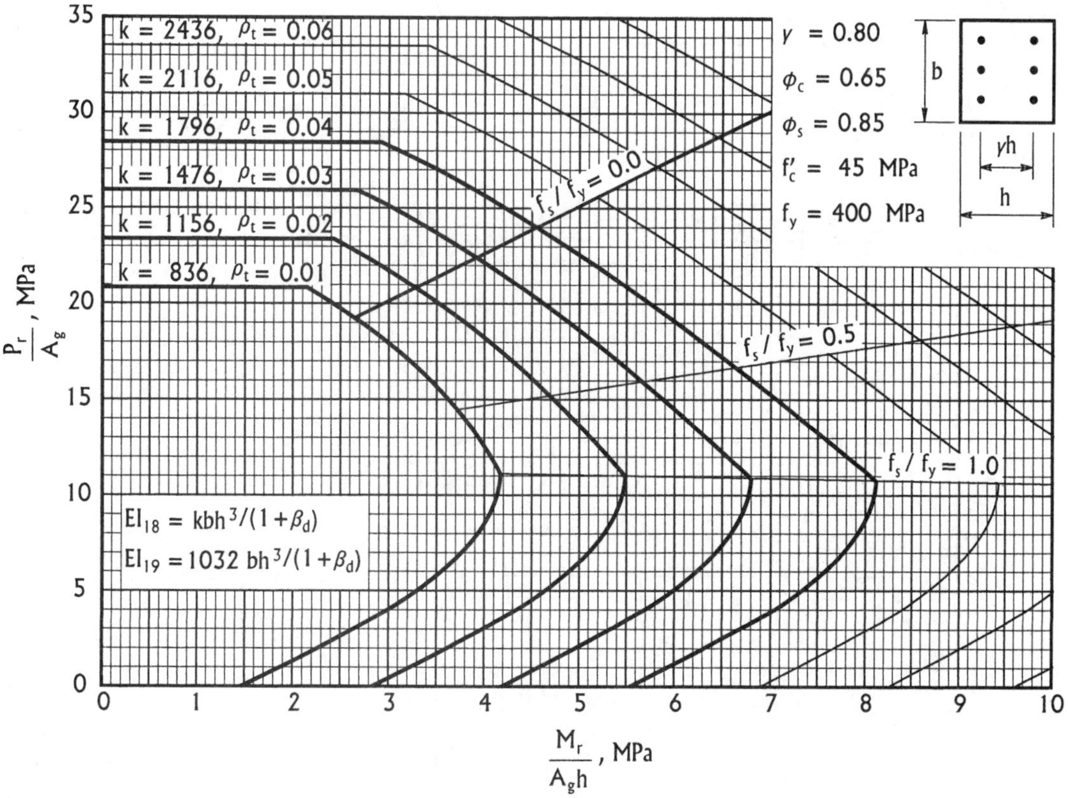

Table 7.6.1   Interaction Diagrams for Rectangular Columns With Bars in Two Side Faces Only.

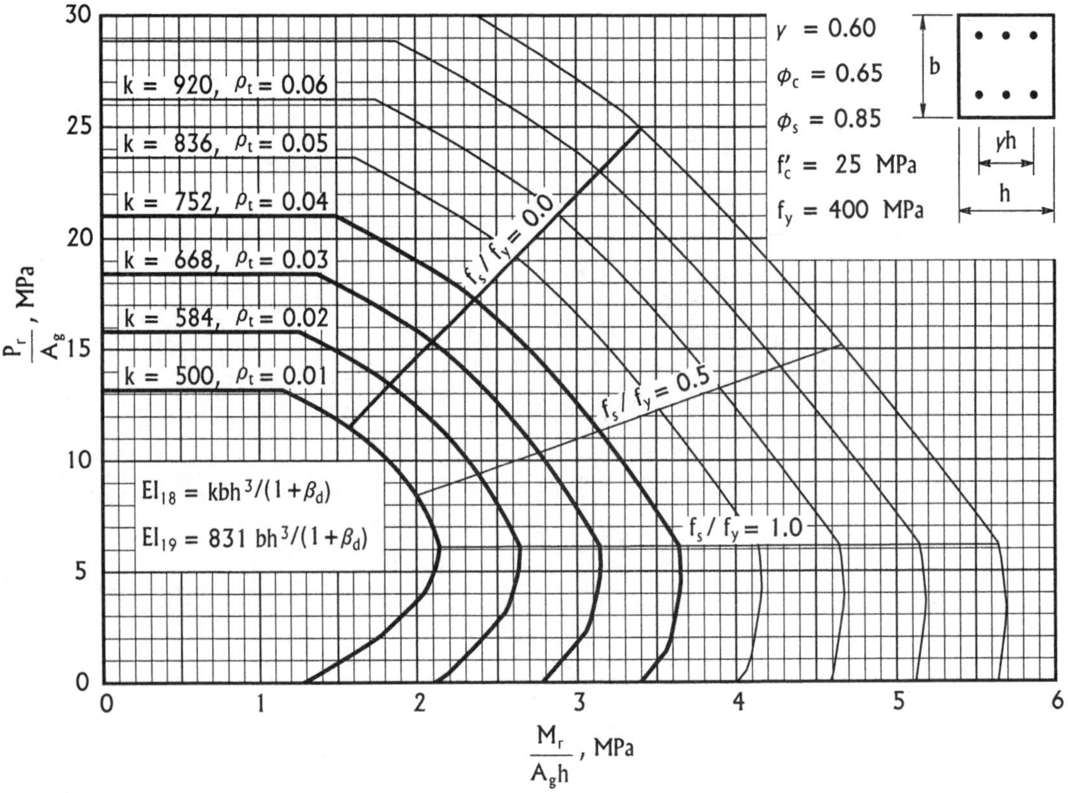

Table 7.6.2   Interaction Diagrams for Rectangular Columns With Bars in Two Side Faces Only.

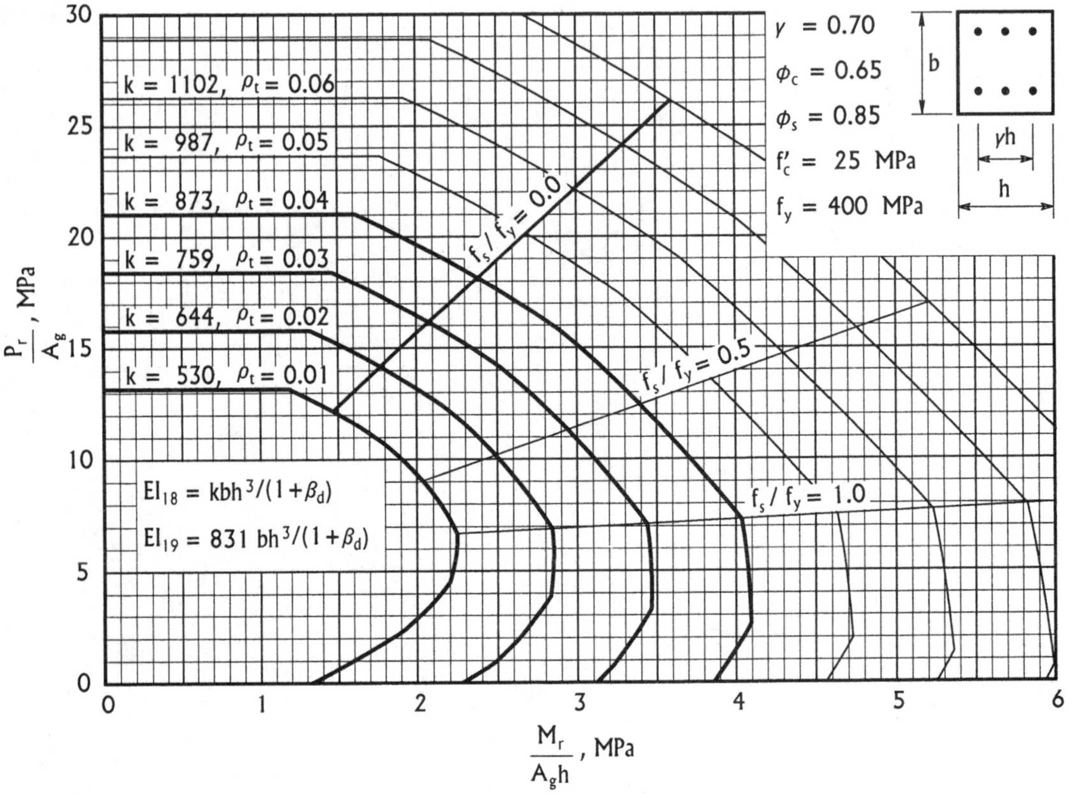

Table 7.6.3   Interaction Diagrams for Rectangular Columns With Bars in Two Side Faces Only.

$$EI_{18} = kbh^3/(1+\beta_d)$$

$$EI_{19} = 831\, bh^3/(1+\beta_d)$$

$\gamma = 0.80$
$\phi_c = 0.65$
$\phi_s = 0.85$
$f'_c = 25$ MPa
$f_y = 400$ MPa

$k = 1312, \rho_t = 0.06$
$k = 1163, \rho_t = 0.05$
$k = 1013, \rho_t = 0.04$
$k = 864, \rho_t = 0.03$
$k = 714, \rho_t = 0.02$
$k = 565, \rho_t = 0.01$

$f_s/f_y = 0.0$
$f_s/f_y = 0.5$
$f_s/f_y = 1.0$

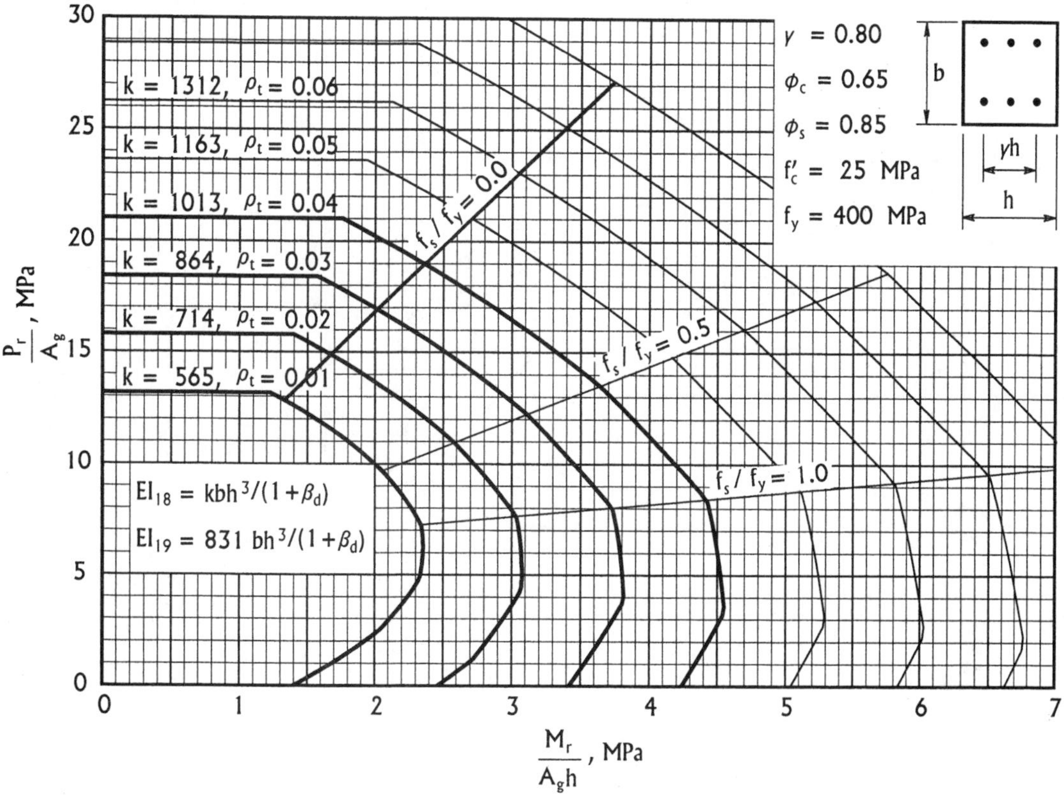

Table 7.6.4   Interaction Diagrams for Rectangular Columns With Bars in Two Side Faces Only.

$$EI_{18} = kbh^3/(1+\beta_d)$$

$$EI_{19} = 831\, bh^3/(1+\beta_d)$$

$\gamma = 0.90$
$\phi_c = 0.65$
$\phi_s = 0.85$
$f'_c = 25$ MPa
$f_y = 400$ MPa

$k = 1550, \rho_t = 0.06$
$k = 1361, \rho_t = 0.05$
$k = 1172, \rho_t = 0.04$
$k = 983, \rho_t = 0.03$
$k = 794, \rho_t = 0.02$
$k = 605, \rho_t = 0.01$

$f_s/f_y = 0.0$
$f_s/f_y = 0.5$
$f_s/f_y = 1.0$

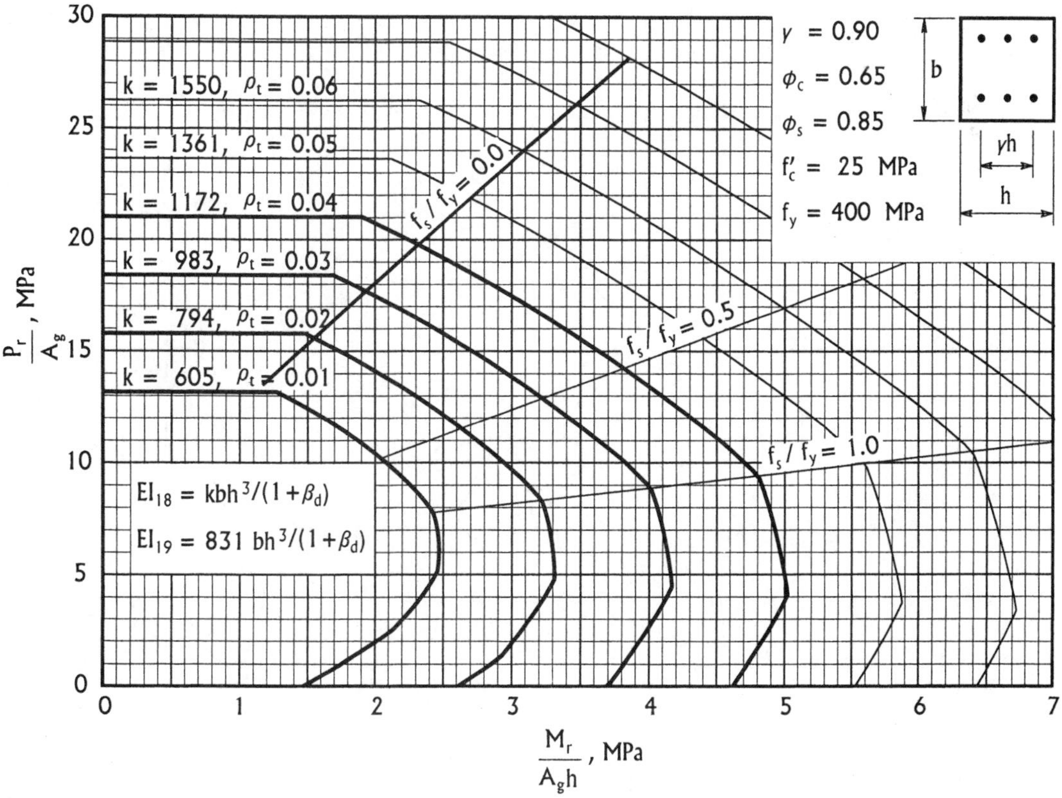

Table 7.6.5   Interaction Diagrams for Rectangular Columns With Bars in Two Side Faces Only.

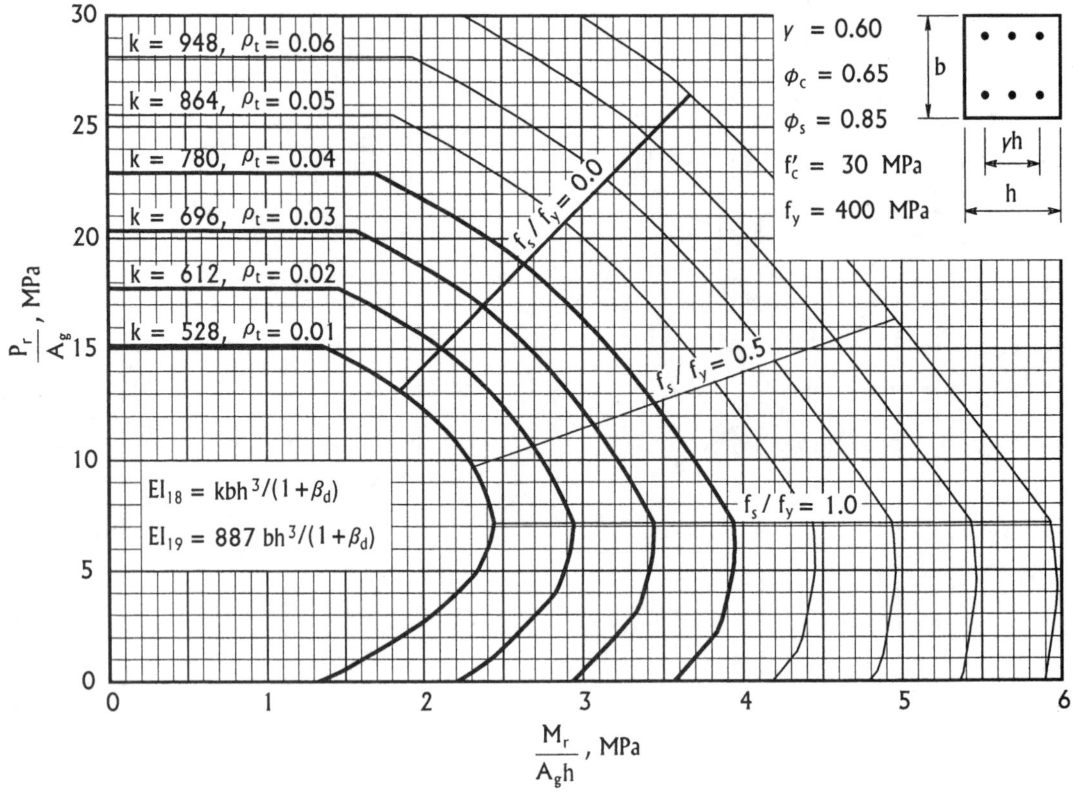

Table 7.6.6   Interaction Diagrams for Rectangular Columns With Bars in Two Side Faces Only.

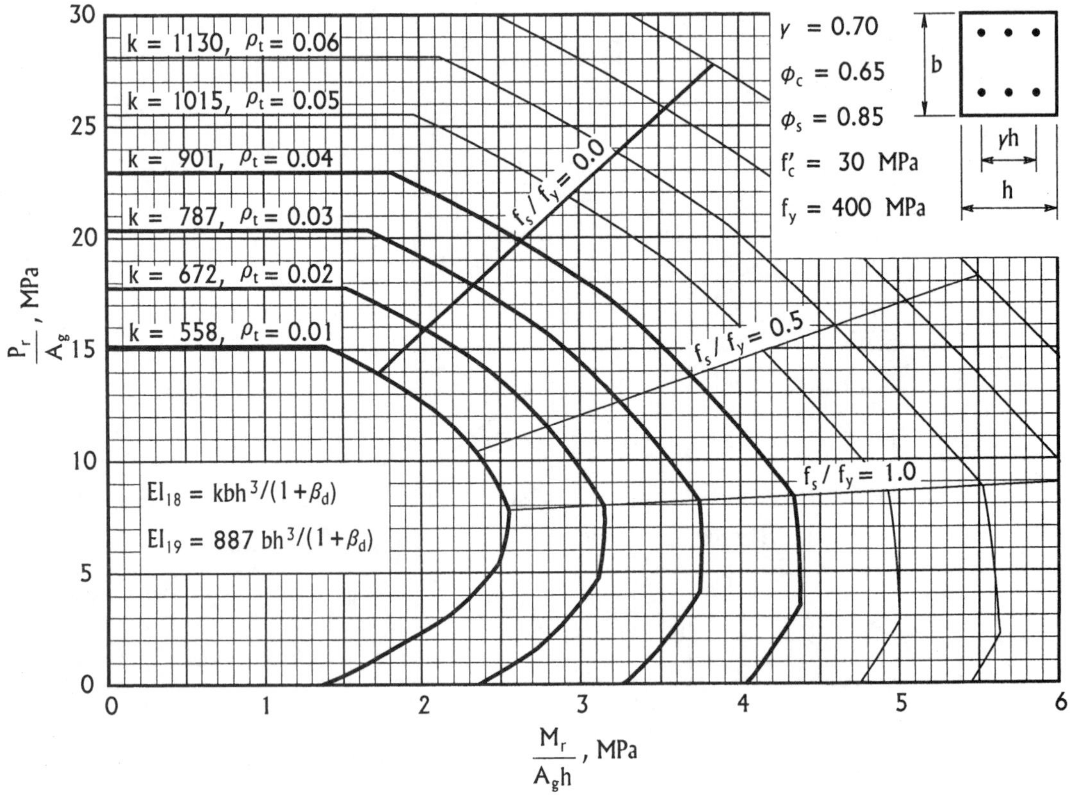

Table 7.6.7 Interaction Diagrams for Rectangular Columns With Bars in Two Side Faces Only.

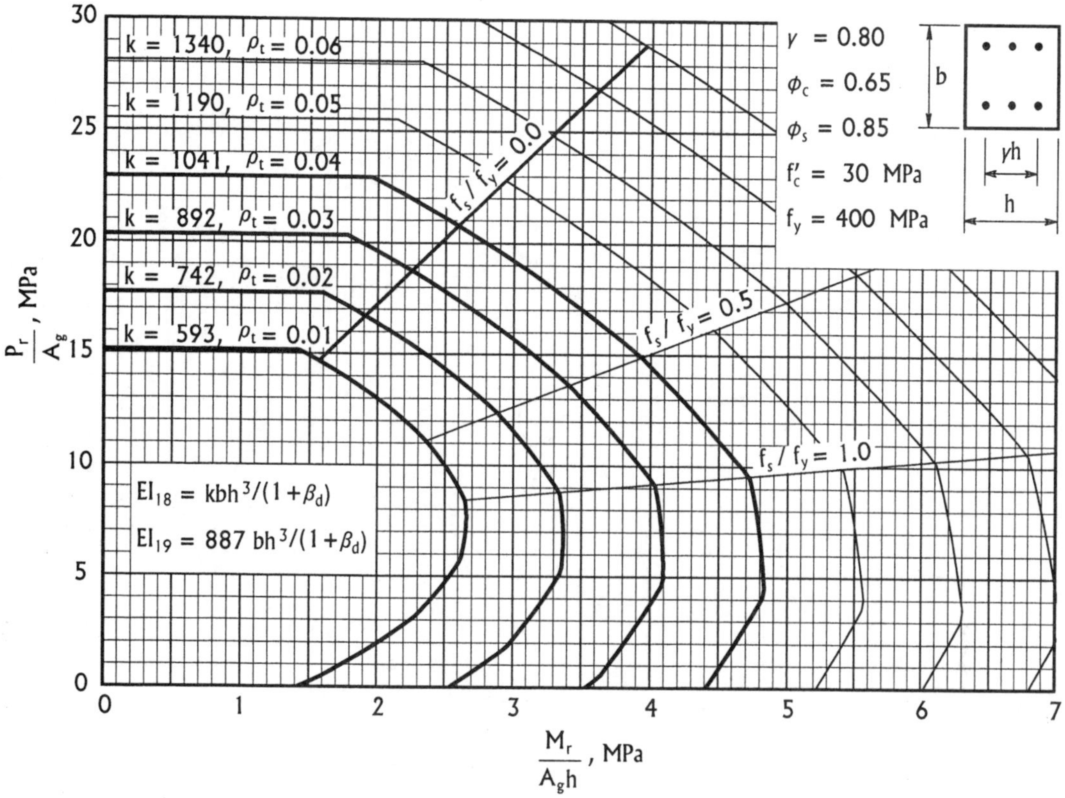
k = 1340, ρ_t = 0.06
k = 1190, ρ_t = 0.05
k = 1041, ρ_t = 0.04
k = 892, ρ_t = 0.03
k = 742, ρ_t = 0.02
k = 593, ρ_t = 0.01
$f_s / f_y = 0.0$
$f_s / f_y = 0.5$
$f_s / f_y = 1.0$
$EI_{18} = kbh^3/(1+\beta_d)$
$EI_{19} = 887\ bh^3/(1+\beta_d)$
γ = 0.80
ϕ_c = 0.65
ϕ_s = 0.85
f'_c = 30 MPa
f_y = 400 MPa
b
γh
h
$\frac{P_r}{A_g}$, MPa
$\frac{M_r}{A_g h}$, MPa
0
5
10
15
20
25
30
0
1
2
3
4
5
6
7

Table 7.6.8 Interaction Diagrams for Rectangular Columns With Bars in Two Side Faces Only.

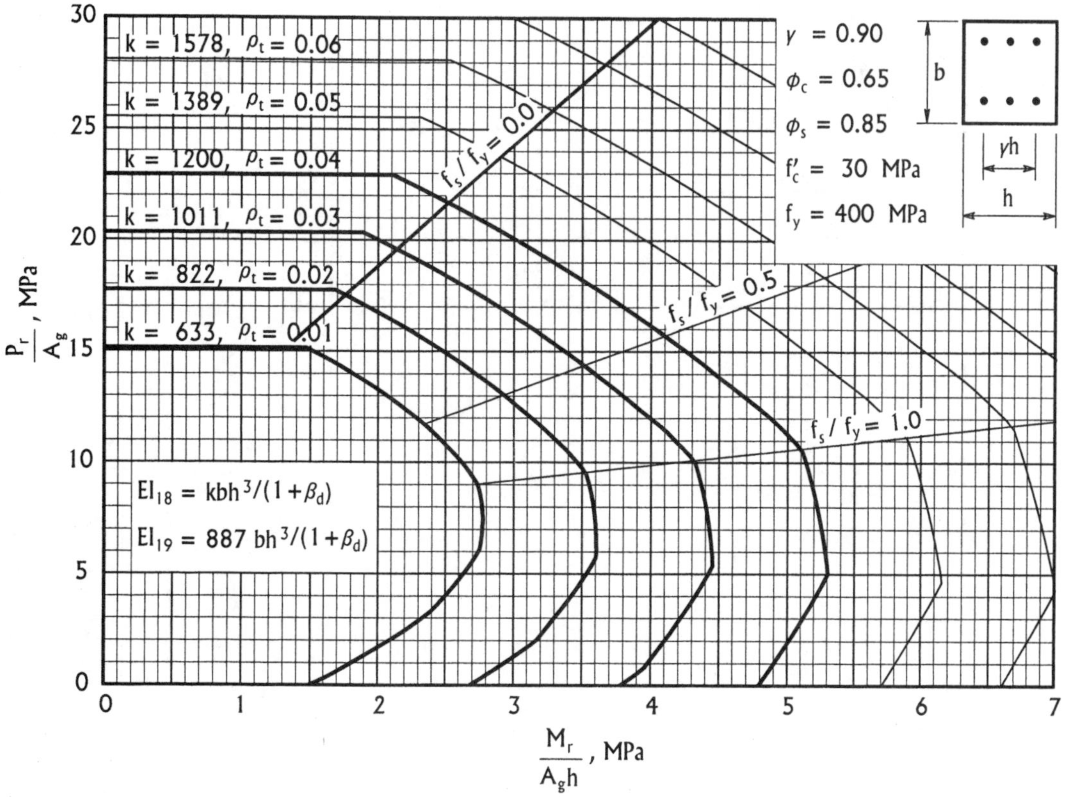
k = 1578, ρ_t = 0.06
k = 1389, ρ_t = 0.05
k = 1200, ρ_t = 0.04
k = 1011, ρ_t = 0.03
k = 822, ρ_t = 0.02
k = 633, ρ_t = 0.01
$f_s / f_y = 0.0$
$f_s / f_y = 0.5$
$f_s / f_y = 1.0$
$EI_{18} = kbh^3/(1+\beta_d)$
$EI_{19} = 887\ bh^3/(1+\beta_d)$
γ = 0.90
ϕ_c = 0.65
ϕ_s = 0.85
f'_c = 30 MPa
f_y = 400 MPa
b
γh
h
$\frac{P_r}{A_g}$, MPa
$\frac{M_r}{A_g h}$, MPa
0
5
10
15
20
25
30
0
1
2
3
4
5
6
7

Table 7.6.9   Interaction Diagrams for Rectangular Columns With Bars in Two Side Faces Only.

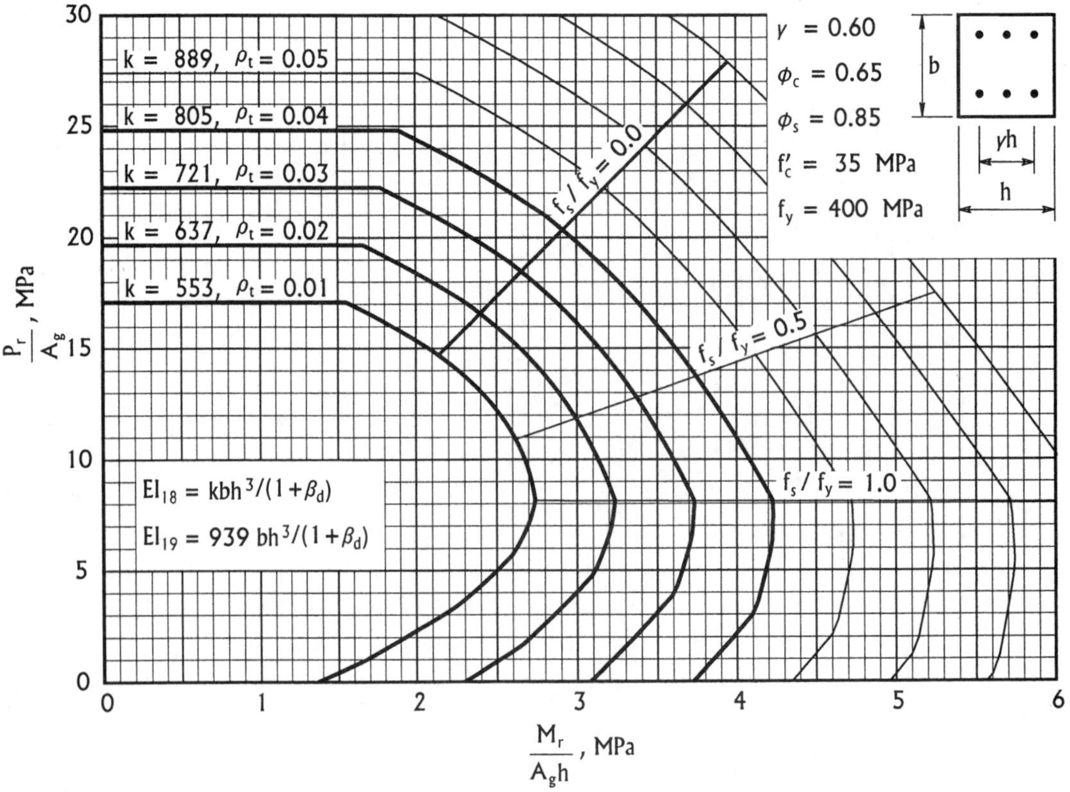

Table 7.6.10 Interaction Diagrams for Rectangular Columns With Bars in Two Side Faces Only.

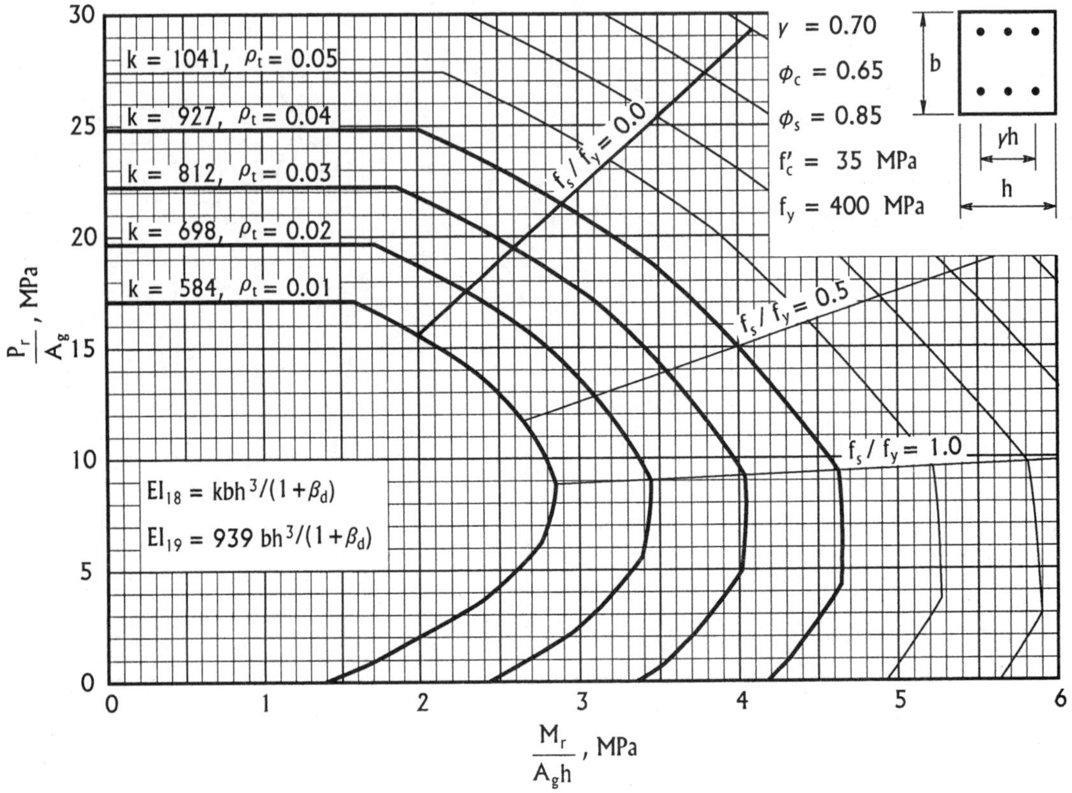

Table 7.6.11 Interaction Diagrams for Rectangular Columns With Bars in Two Side Faces Only.

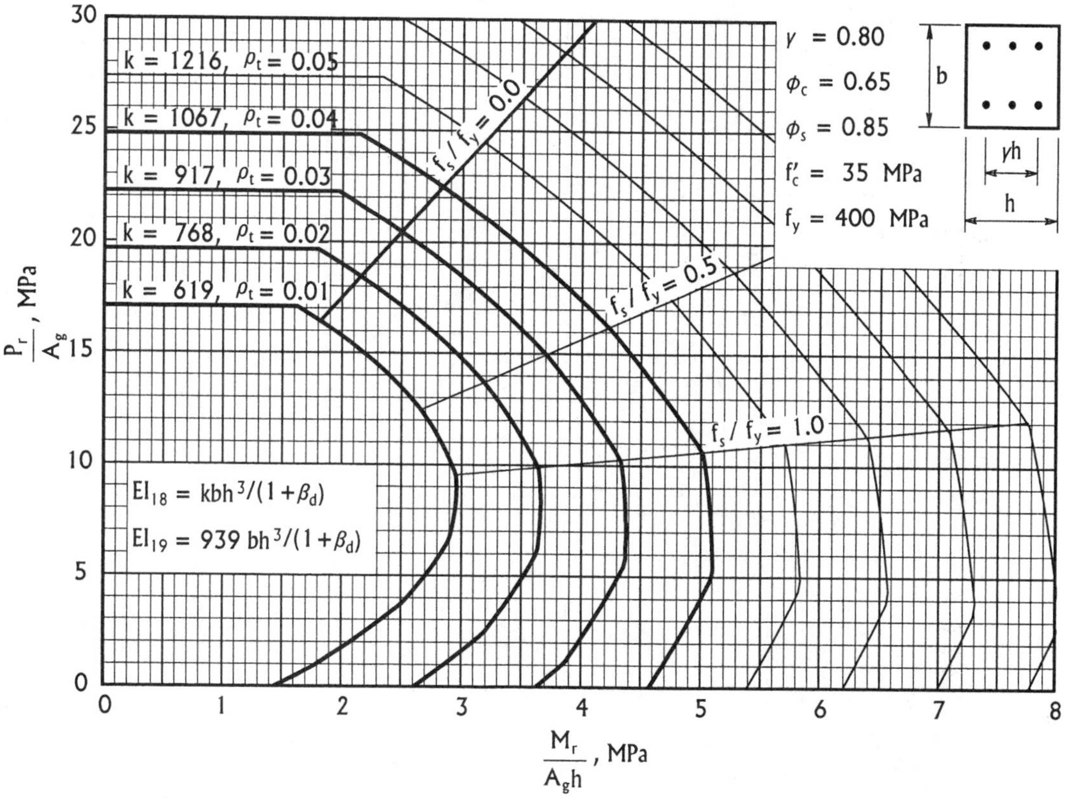
k = 1216, ρ_t = 0.05
k = 1067, ρ_t = 0.04
k = 917, ρ_t = 0.03
k = 768, ρ_t = 0.02
k = 619, ρ_t = 0.01
f_s / f_y = 0.0
f_s / f_y = 0.5
f_s / f_y = 1.0
γ = 0.80
ϕ_c = 0.65
ϕ_s = 0.85
f'_c = 35 MPa
f_y = 400 MPa
b
γh
h
$EI_{18} = kbh^3/(1+\beta_d)$
$EI_{19} = 939\ bh^3/(1+\beta_d)$
$\frac{P_r}{A_g}$, MPa
$\frac{M_r}{A_g h}$, MPa
0
5
10
15
20
25
30
1
2
3
4
6
7
8

Table 7.6.12 Interaction Diagrams for Rectangular Columns With Bars in Two Side Faces Only.

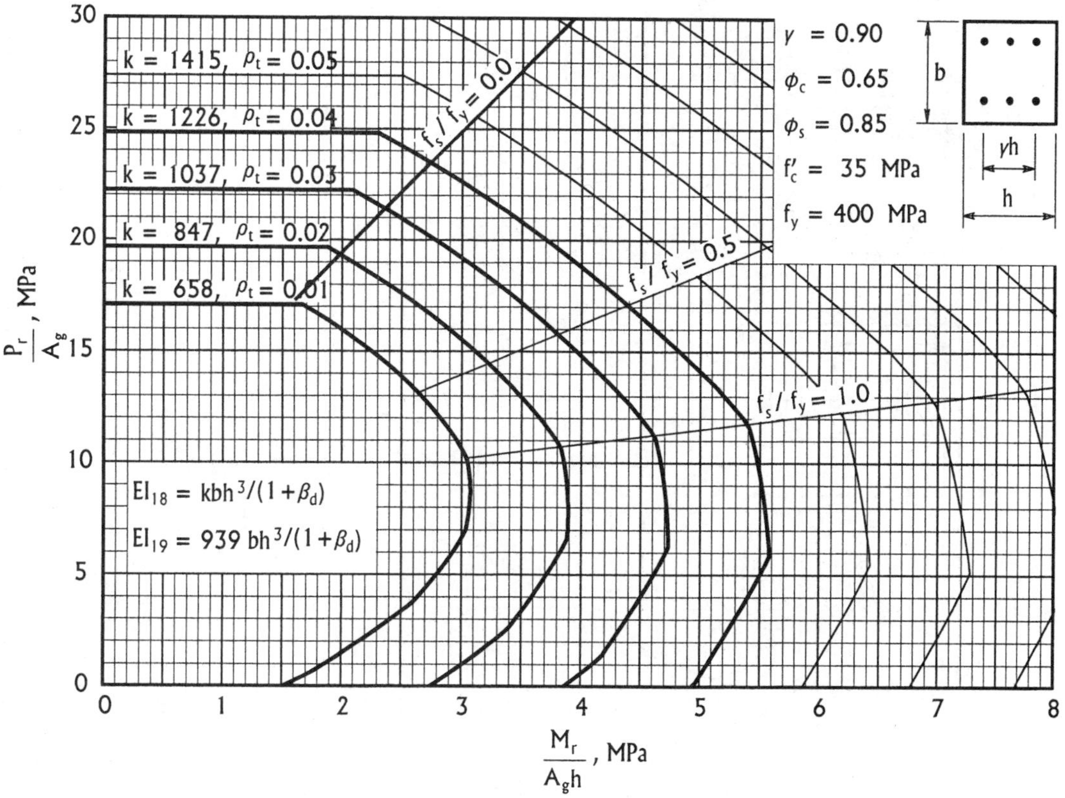
k = 1415, ρ_t = 0.05
k = 1226, ρ_t = 0.04
k = 1037, ρ_t = 0.03
k = 847, ρ_t = 0.02
k = 658, ρ_t = 0.01
f_s / f_y = 0.0
f_s / f_y = 0.5
f_s / f_y = 1.0
γ = 0.90
ϕ_c = 0.65
ϕ_s = 0.85
f'_c = 35 MPa
f_y = 400 MPa
b
γh
h
$EI_{18} = kbh^3/(1+\beta_d)$
$EI_{19} = 939\ bh^3/(1+\beta_d)$
$\frac{P_r}{A_g}$, MPa
$\frac{M_r}{A_g h}$, MPa
0
5
10
15
20
25
30
1
2
3
4
6
7
8

Table 7.6.13 Interaction Diagrams for Rectangular Columns With Bars in Two Side Faces Only.

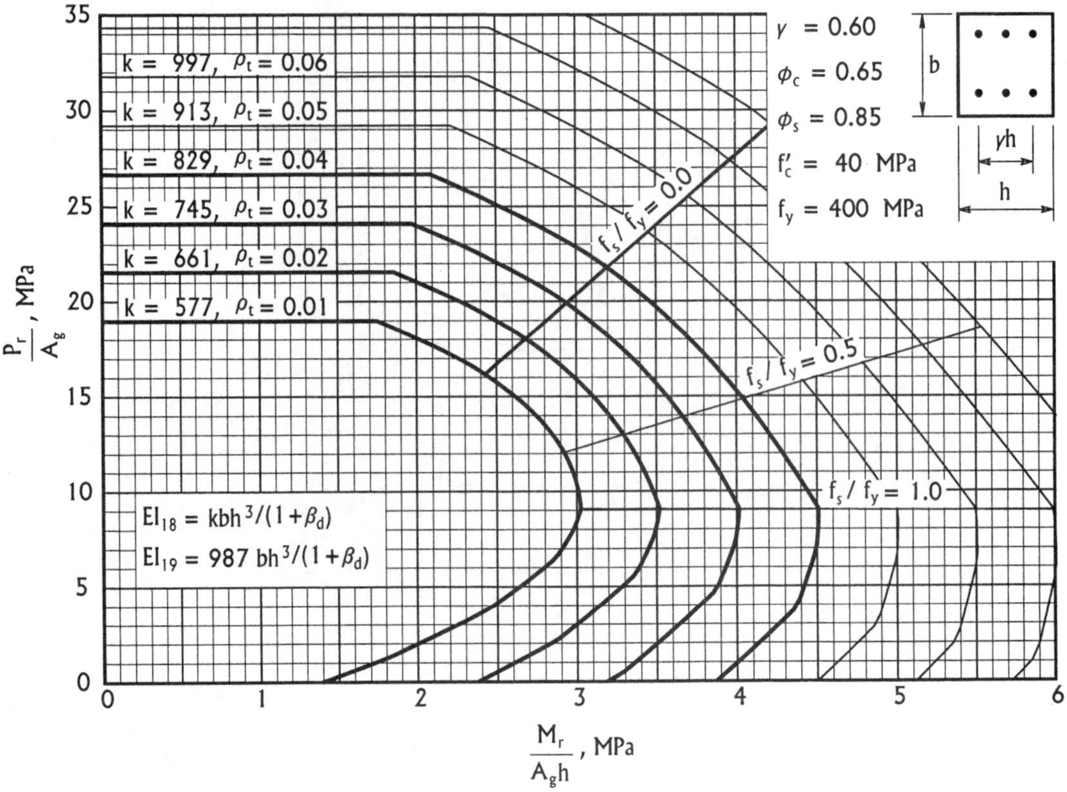
γ = 0.60
φc = 0.65
φs = 0.85
f'c = 40 MPa
fy = 400 MPa
b
γh
h
k = 997, ρt = 0.06
k = 913, ρt = 0.05
k = 829, ρt = 0.04
k = 745, ρt = 0.03
k = 661, ρt = 0.02
k = 577, ρt = 0.01
fs / fy = 0.0
fs / fy = 0.5
fs / fy = 1.0
EI18 = kbh3/(1+βd)
EI19 = 987 bh3/(1+βd)
Pr/Ag, MPa
Mr/(Ag h), MPa
0
5
10
15
20
25
30
35
1
2
3
4
5
6

Table 7.6.14 Interaction Diagrams for Rectangular Columns With Bars in Two Side Faces Only.

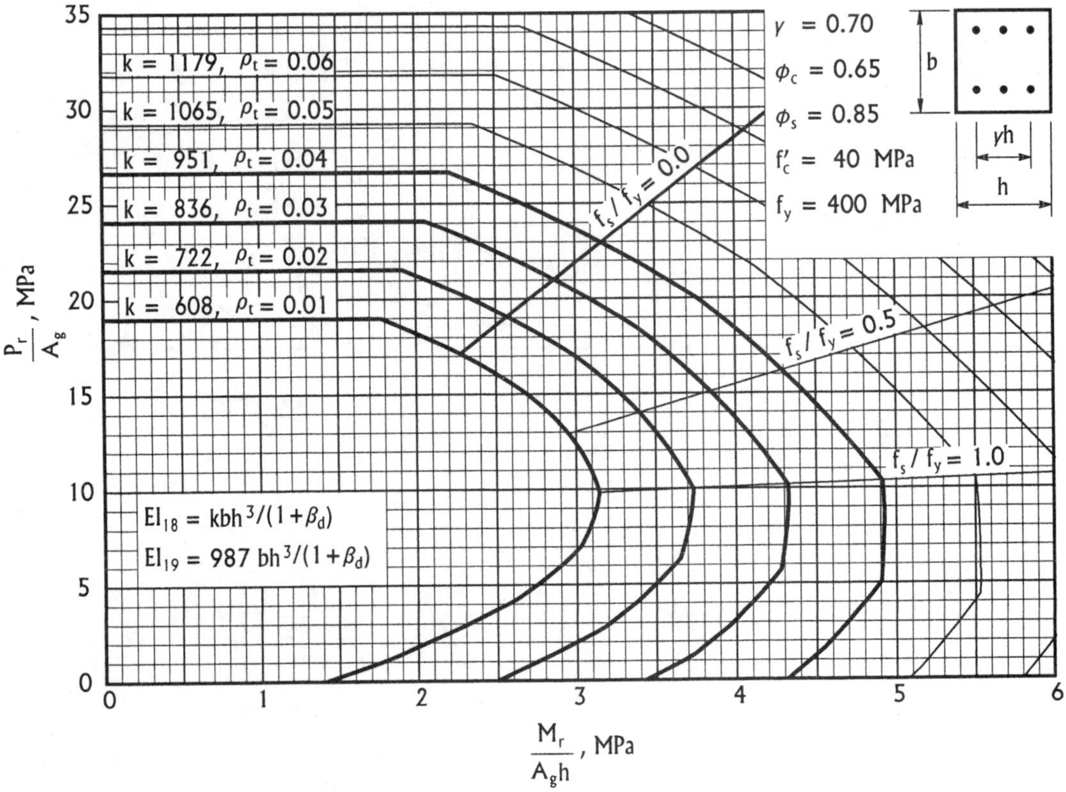
γ = 0.70
φc = 0.65
φs = 0.85
f'c = 40 MPa
fy = 400 MPa
b
γh
h
k = 1179, ρt = 0.06
k = 1065, ρt = 0.05
k = 951, ρt = 0.04
k = 836, ρt = 0.03
k = 722, ρt = 0.02
k = 608, ρt = 0.01
fs / fy = 0.0
fs / fy = 0.5
fs / fy = 1.0
EI18 = kbh3/(1+βd)
EI19 = 987 bh3/(1+βd)
Pr/Ag, MPa
Mr/(Ag h), MPa
0
5
10
15
20
25
30
35
1
2
3
4
5
6

Table 7.6.15 Interaction Diagrams for Rectangular Columns With Bars in Two Side Faces Only.

Chart parameters:
- $k = 1390, \; \rho_t = 0.06$
- $k = 1240, \; \rho_t = 0.05$
- $k = 1091, \; \rho_t = 0.04$
- $k = 941, \; \rho_t = 0.03$
- $k = 792, \; \rho_t = 0.02$
- $k = 643, \; \rho_t = 0.01$

$f_s / f_y = 0.0$
$f_s / f_y = 0.5$
$f_s / f_y = 1.0$

$\gamma = 0.80$
$\phi_c = 0.65$
$\phi_s = 0.85$
$f'_c = 40 \text{ MPa}$
$f_y = 400 \text{ MPa}$

$EI_{18} = kbh^3/(1+\beta_d)$
$EI_{19} = 987 \, bh^3/(1+\beta_d)$

Vertical axis: $\dfrac{P_r}{A_g}$, MPa

Horizontal axis: $\dfrac{M_r}{A_g h}$, MPa

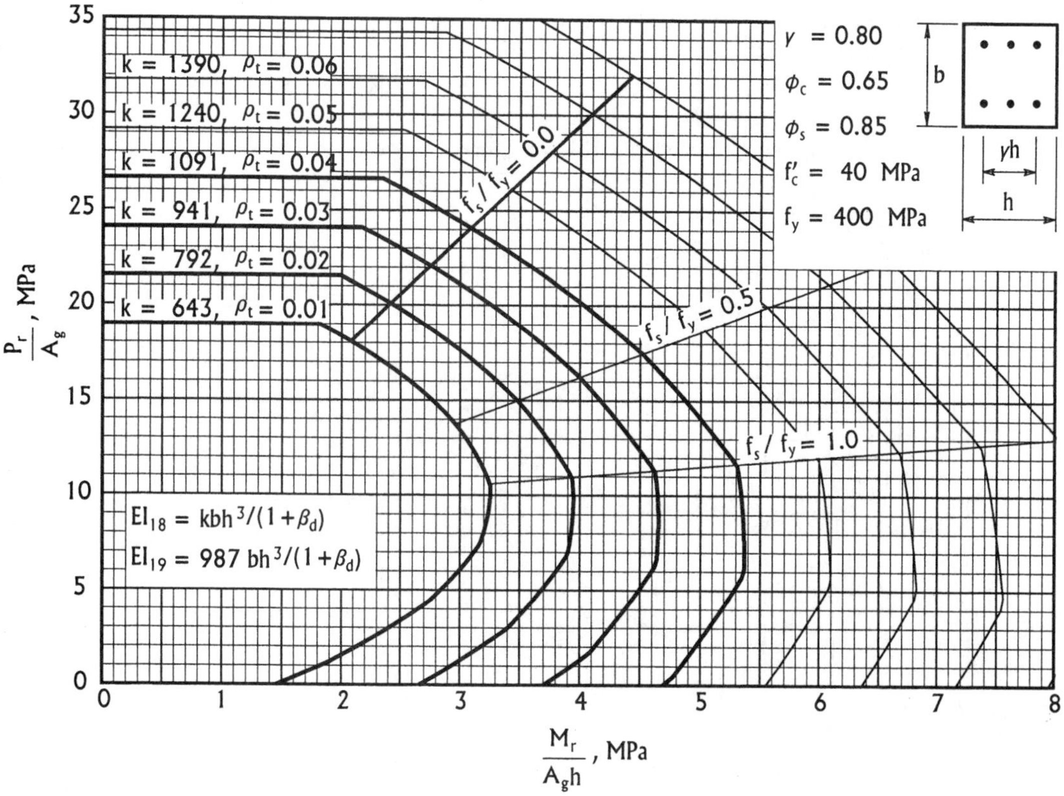

Table 7.6.16 Interaction Diagrams for Rectangular Columns With Bars in Two Side Faces Only.

Chart parameters:
- $k = 1628, \; \rho_t = 0.06$
- $k = 1439, \; \rho_t = 0.05$
- $k = 1249, \; \rho_t = 0.04$
- $k = 1060, \; \rho_t = 0.03$
- $k = 871, \; \rho_t = 0.02$
- $k = 682, \; \rho_t = 0.01$

$f_s / f_y = 0.0$
$f_s / f_y = 0.5$
$f_s / f_y = 1.0$

$\gamma = 0.90$
$\phi_c = 0.65$
$\phi_s = 0.85$
$f'_c = 40 \text{ MPa}$
$f_y = 400 \text{ MPa}$

$EI_{18} = kbh^3/(1+\beta_d)$
$EI_{19} = 987 \, bh^3/(1+\beta_d)$

Vertical axis: $\dfrac{P_r}{A_g}$, MPa

Horizontal axis: $\dfrac{M_r}{A_g h}$, MPa

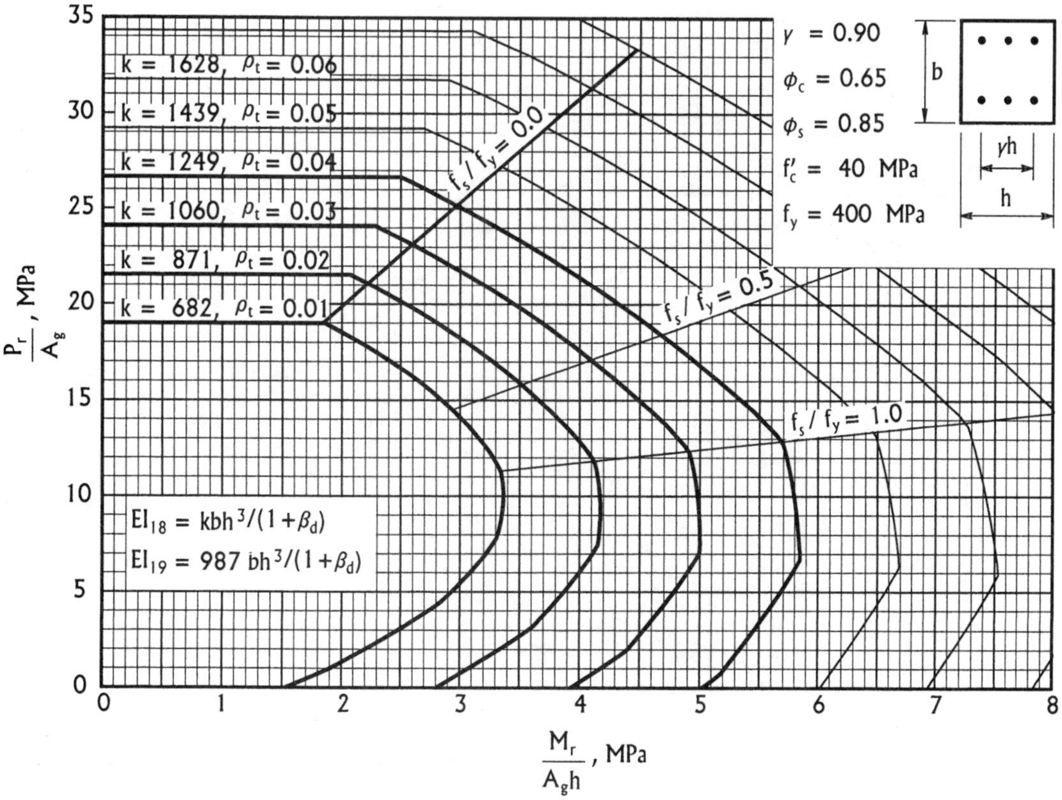

Table 7.6.17 Interaction Diagrams for Rectangular Columns With Bars in Two Side Faces Only.

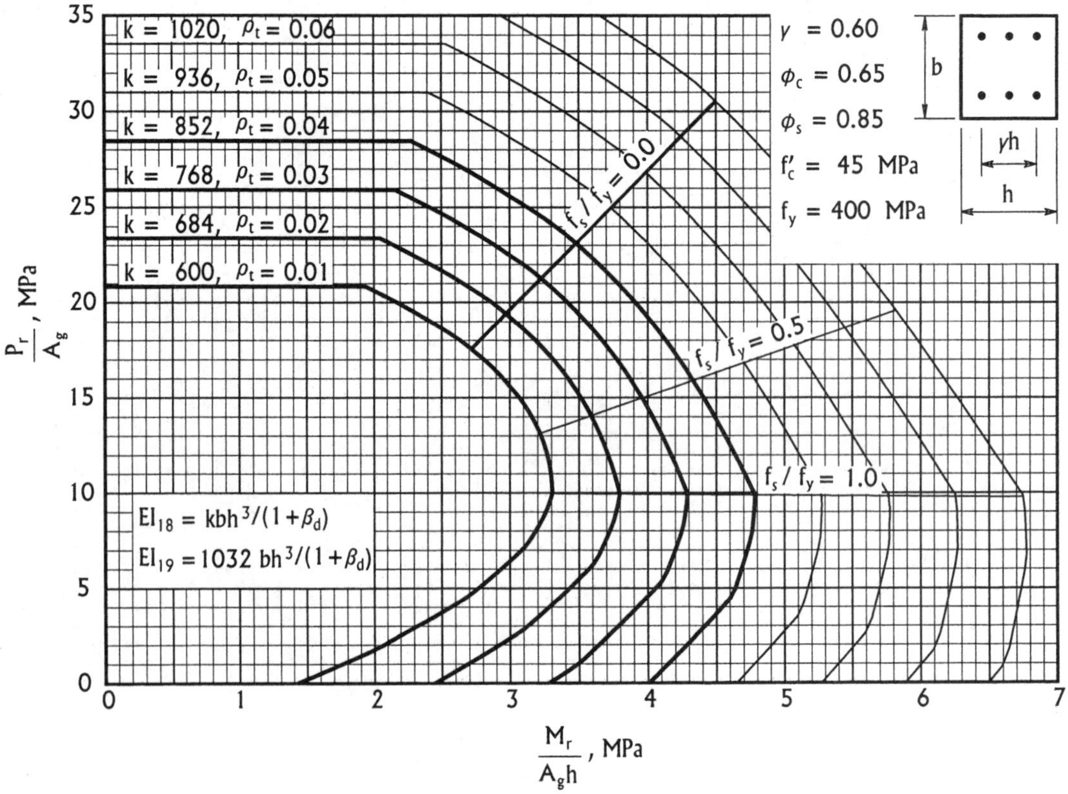
k = 1020, ρt = 0.06
k = 936, ρt = 0.05
k = 852, ρt = 0.04
k = 768, ρt = 0.03
k = 684, ρt = 0.02
k = 600, ρt = 0.01
γ = 0.60
φc = 0.65
φs = 0.85
f′c = 45 MPa
fy = 400 MPa
b
γh
h
fs / fy = 0.0
fs / fy = 0.5
fs / fy = 1.0
EI18 = kbh3/(1 + βd)
EI19 = 1032 bh3/(1 + βd)
Pr / Ag , MPa
Mr / Agh , MPa
0
5
10
15
20
25
30
35
0
1
2
3
4
5
6
7

Table 7.6.18 Interaction Diagrams for Rectangular Columns With Bars in Two Side Faces Only.

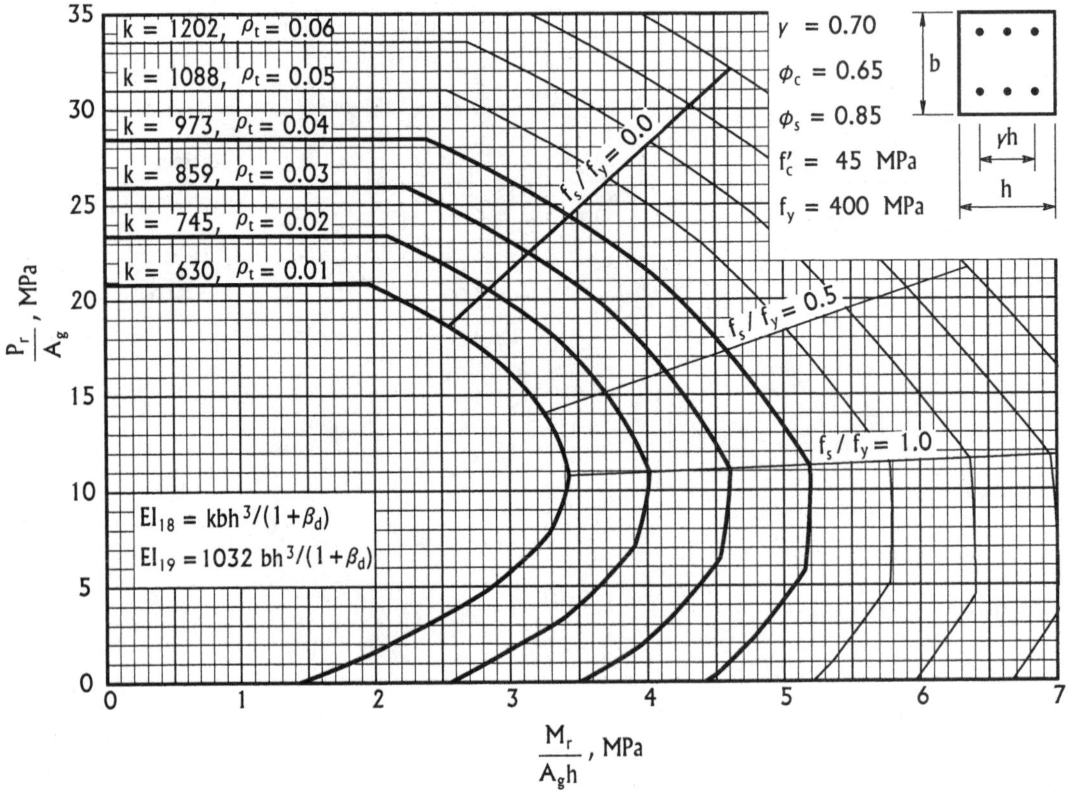
k = 1202, ρt = 0.06
k = 1088, ρt = 0.05
k = 973, ρt = 0.04
k = 859, ρt = 0.03
k = 745, ρt = 0.02
k = 630, ρt = 0.01
γ = 0.70
φc = 0.65
φs = 0.85
f′c = 45 MPa
fy = 400 MPa
b
γh
h
fs / fy = 0.0
fs / fy = 0.5
fs / fy = 1.0
EI18 = kbh3/(1 + βd)
EI19 = 1032 bh3/(1 + βd)
Pr / Ag , MPa
Mr / Agh , MPa
0
5
10
15
20
25
30
35
0
1
2
3
4
5
6
7

Table 7.6.19 Interaction Diagrams for Rectangular Columns With Bars in Two Side Faces Only.

$\dfrac{P_r}{A_g}$, MPa

$k = 1412,\ \rho_t = 0.06$
$k = 1263,\ \rho_t = 0.05$
$k = 1113,\ \rho_t = 0.04$
$k = 964,\ \rho_t = 0.03$
$k = 815,\ \rho_t = 0.02$
$k = 665,\ \rho_t = 0.01$

$f_s / f_y = 0.0$
$f_s / f_y = 0.5$
$f_s / f_y = 1.0$

$\gamma = 0.80$
$\phi_c = 0.65$
$\phi_s = 0.85$
$f'_c = 45$ MPa
$f_y = 400$ MPa

$EI_{18} = kbh^3/(1+\beta_d)$
$EI_{19} = 1032\,bh^3/(1+\beta_d)$

$\dfrac{M_r}{A_g h}$, MPa

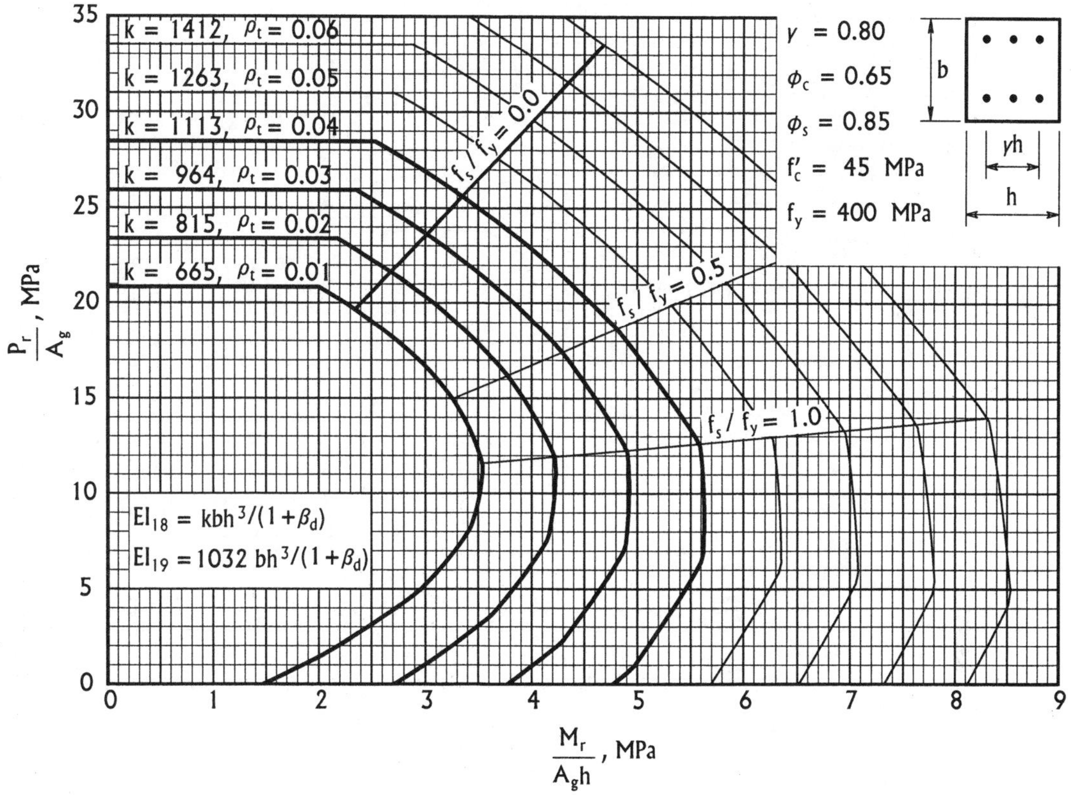

Table 7.6.20 Interaction Diagrams for Rectangular Columns With Bars in Two Side Faces Only.

$\dfrac{P_r}{A_g}$, MPa

$k = 1650,\ \rho_t = 0.06$
$k = 1461,\ \rho_t = 0.05$
$k = 1272,\ \rho_t = 0.04$
$k = 1083,\ \rho_t = 0.03$
$k = 894,\ \rho_t = 0.02$
$k = 705,\ \rho_t = 0.01$

$f_s / f_y = 0.0$
$f_s / f_y = 0.5$
$f_s / f_y = 1.0$

$\gamma = 0.90$
$\phi_c = 0.65$
$\phi_s = 0.85$
$f'_c = 45$ MPa
$f_y = 400$ MPa

$EI_{18} = kbh^3/(1+\beta_d)$
$EI_{19} = 1032\,bh^3/(1+\beta_d)$

$\dfrac{M_r}{A_g h}$, MPa

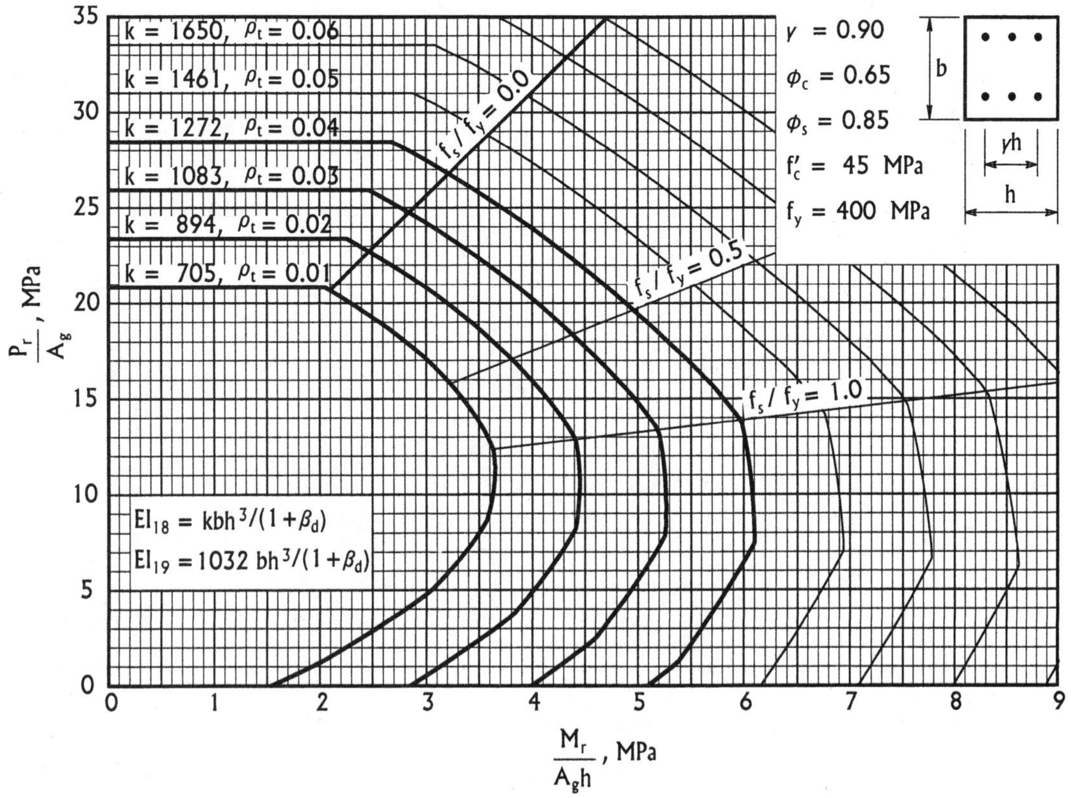

Table 7.7.1   Interaction Diagrams for Circular Tied or Spiral Columns.

$$\gamma = 0.60$$
$$\phi_c = 0.65$$
$$\phi_s = 0.85$$
$$f'_c = 30 \text{ MPa}$$
$$f_y = 400 \text{ MPa}$$

$k = 685, \ \rho_t = 0.06$
$k = 615, \ \rho_t = 0.05$
$k = 544, \ \rho_t = 0.04$
$k = 473, \ \rho_t = 0.03$
$k = 403, \ \rho_t = 0.02$
$k = 332, \ \rho_t = 0.01$

$$EI_{18} = kh^4/(1+\beta_d)$$
$$EI_{19} = 523 \, h^4/(1+\beta_d)$$

$f_s/f_y = 0.0$
$f_s/f_y = 0.5$
$f_s/f_y = 1.0$

$\frac{P_r}{h^2}$, MPa

$\frac{M_r}{h^3}$, MPa

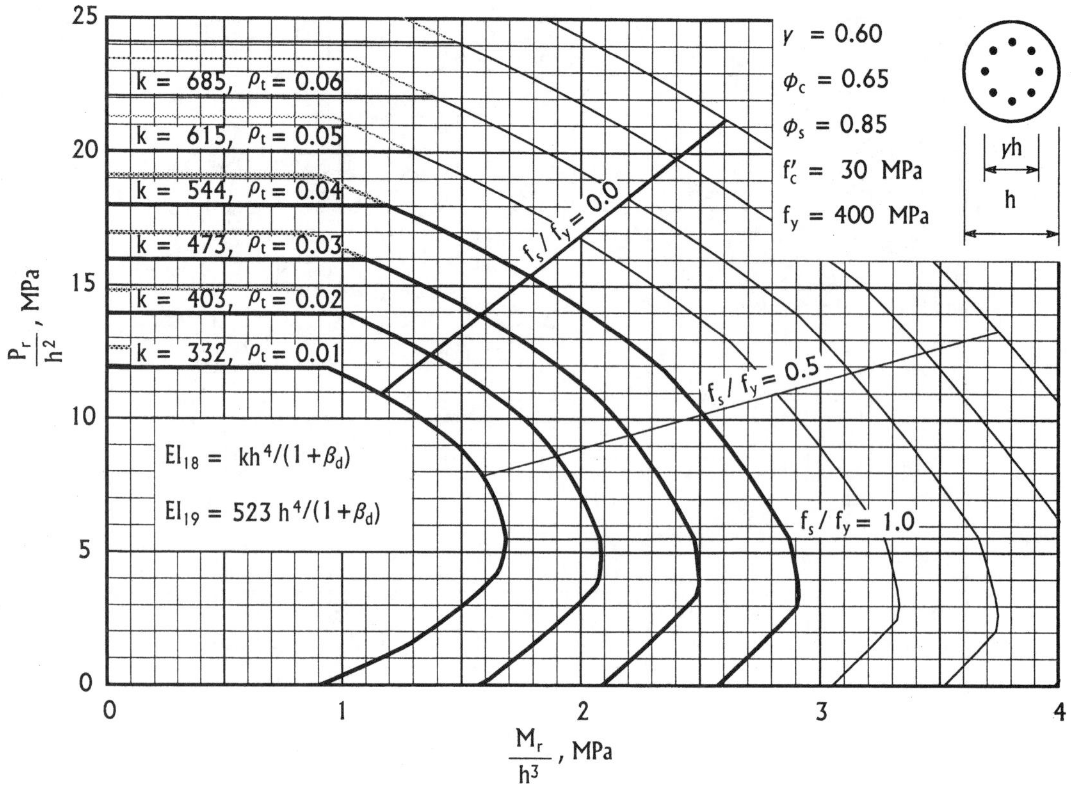

Table 7.7.2   Interaction Diagrams for Circular Tied or Spiral Columns.

$$\gamma = 0.70$$
$$\phi_c = 0.65$$
$$\phi_s = 0.85$$
$$f'_c = 30 \text{ MPa}$$
$$f_y = 400 \text{ MPa}$$

$k = 839, \ \rho_t = 0.06$
$k = 742, \ \rho_t = 0.05$
$k = 646, \ \rho_t = 0.04$
$k = 550, \ \rho_t = 0.03$
$k = 454, \ \rho_t = 0.02$
$k = 358, \ \rho_t = 0.01$

$$EI_{18} = kh^4/(1+\beta_d)$$
$$EI_{19} = 523 \, h^4/(1+\beta_d)$$

$f_s/f_y = 0.0$
$f_s/f_y = 0.5$
$f_s/f_y = 1.0$

$\frac{P_r}{h^2}$, MPa

$\frac{M_r}{h^3}$, MPa

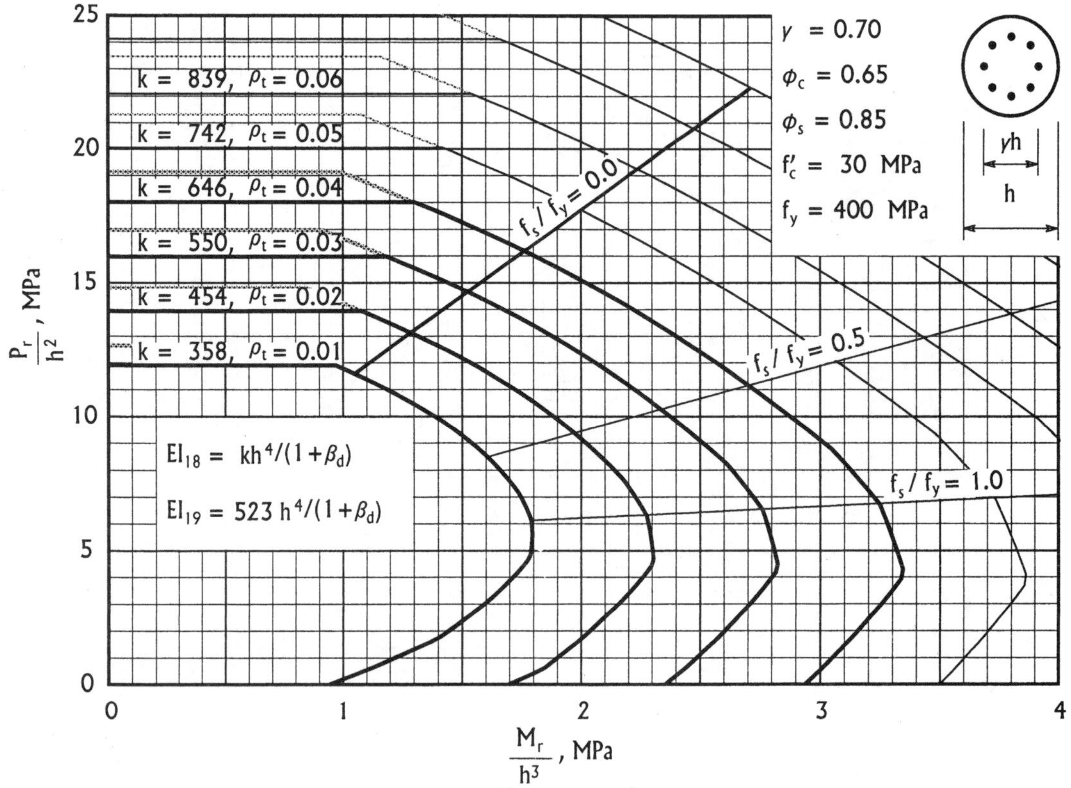

Table 7.7.3 Interaction Diagrams for Circular Tied or Spiral Columns.

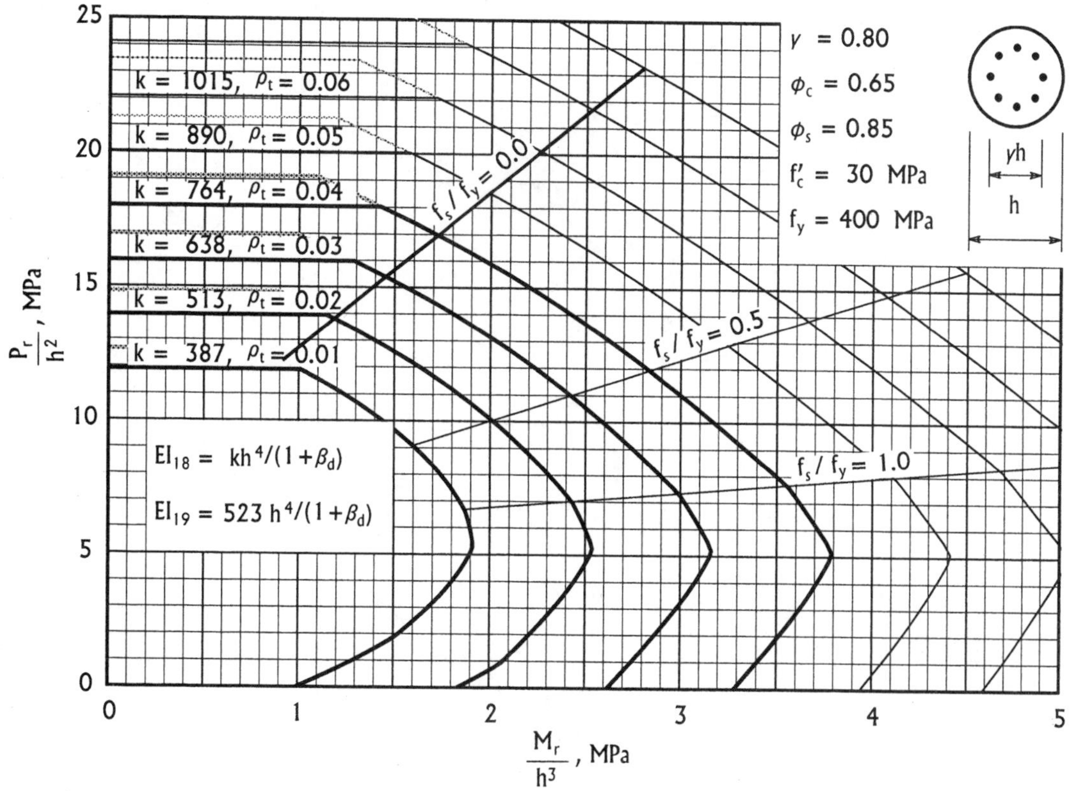

γ = 0.80
φc = 0.65
φs = 0.85
f'c = 30 MPa
fy = 400 MPa
γh
h
k = 1015, ρt = 0.06
k = 890, ρt = 0.05
k = 764, ρt = 0.04
k = 638, ρt = 0.03
k = 513, ρt = 0.02
k = 387, ρt = 0.01
fs / fy = 0.0
fs / fy = 0.5
fs / fy = 1.0
EI18 = kh4/(1 + βd)
EI19 = 523 h4/(1 + βd)
Pr / h2, MPa
Mr / h3, MPa

Table 7.7.4 Interaction Diagrams for Circular Tied or Spiral Columns.

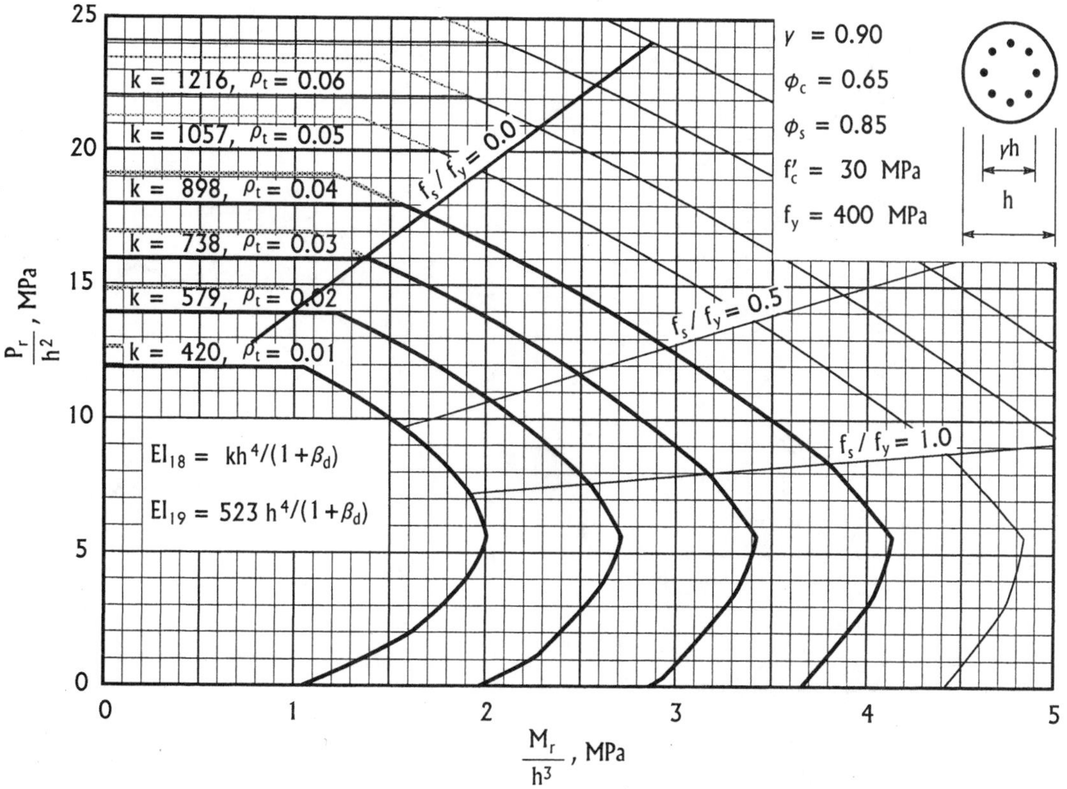

γ = 0.90
φc = 0.65
φs = 0.85
f'c = 30 MPa
fy = 400 MPa
γh
h
k = 1216, ρt = 0.06
k = 1057, ρt = 0.05
k = 898, ρt = 0.04
k = 738, ρt = 0.03
k = 579, ρt = 0.02
k = 420, ρt = 0.01
fs / fy = 0.0
fs / fy = 0.5
fs / fy = 1.0
EI18 = kh4/(1 + βd)
EI19 = 523 h4/(1 + βd)
Pr / h2, MPa
Mr / h3, MPa

Table 7.7.5   Interaction Diagrams for Circular Tied or Spiral Columns.

Within the chart:

$k = 701, \ \rho_t = 0.06$
$k = 630, \ \rho_t = 0.05$
$k = 559, \ \rho_t = 0.04$
$k = 489, \ \rho_t = 0.03$
$k = 418, \ \rho_t = 0.02$
$k = 347, \ \rho_t = 0.01$

$f_s/f_y = 0.0$
$f_s/f_y = 0.5$
$f_s/f_y = 1.0$

$EI_{18} = kh^4/(1+\beta_d)$

$EI_{19} = 553\, h^4/(1+\beta_d)$

$\gamma = 0.60$
$\phi_c = 0.65$
$\phi_s = 0.85$
$f_c' = 35$ MPa
$f_y = 400$ MPa

Vertical axis: $\dfrac{P_r}{h^2}$, MPa

Horizontal axis: $\dfrac{M_r}{h^3}$, MPa

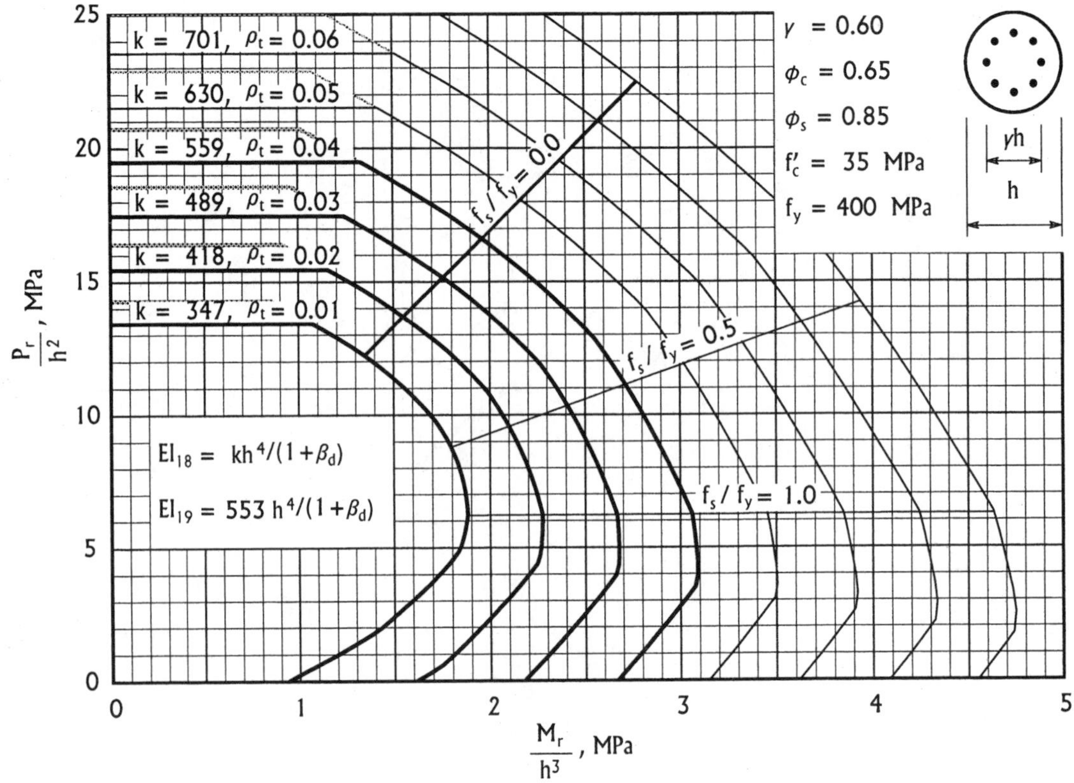

Table 7.7.6   Interaction Diagrams for Circular Tied or Spiral Columns.

Within the chart:

$k = 854, \ \rho_t = 0.06$
$k = 758, \ \rho_t = 0.05$
$k = 661, \ \rho_t = 0.04$
$k = 565, \ \rho_t = 0.03$
$k = 469, \ \rho_t = 0.02$
$k = 373, \ \rho_t = 0.01$

$f_s/f_y = 0.0$
$f_s/f_y = 0.5$
$f_s/f_y = 1.0$

$EI_{18} = kh^4/(1+\beta_d)$

$EI_{19} = 553\, h^4/(1+\beta_d)$

$\gamma = 0.70$
$\phi_c = 0.65$
$\phi_s = 0.85$
$f_c' = 35$ MPa
$f_y = 400$ MPa

Vertical axis: $\dfrac{P_r}{h^2}$, MPa

Horizontal axis: $\dfrac{M_r}{h^3}$, MPa

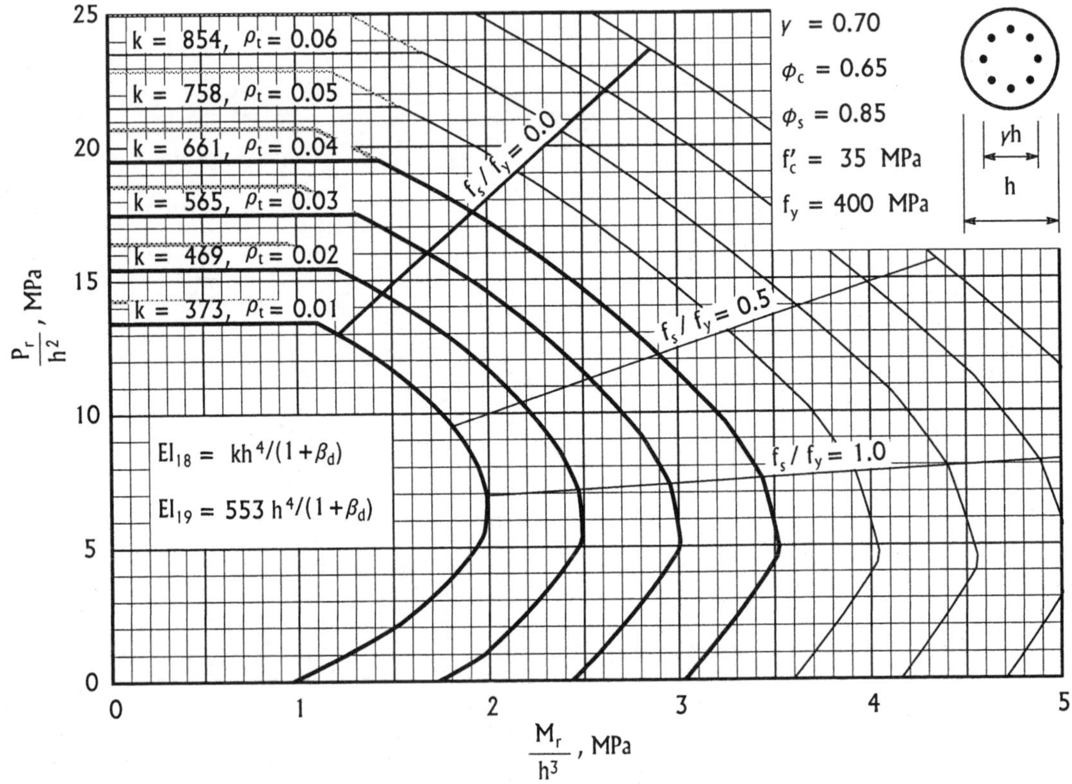

Table 7.7.7 Interaction Diagrams for Circular Tied or Spiral Columns.

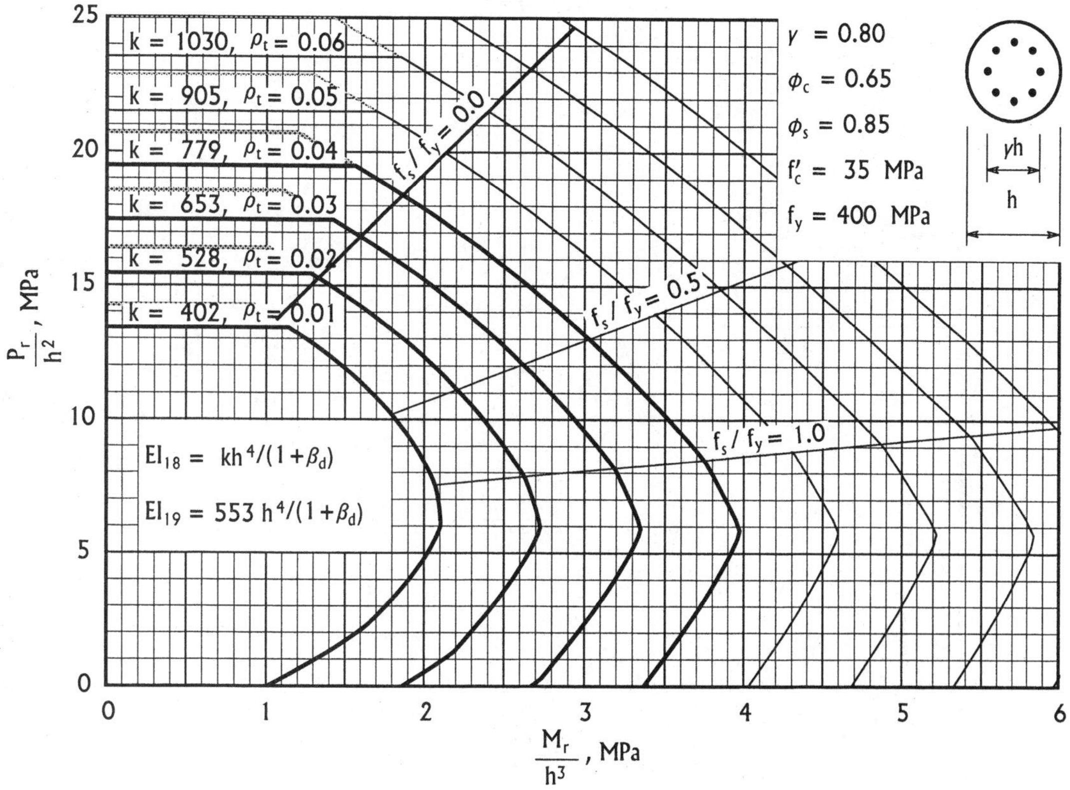
k = 1030, ρt = 0.06
k = 905, ρt = 0.05
k = 779, ρt = 0.04
k = 653, ρt = 0.03
k = 528, ρt = 0.02
k = 402, ρt = 0.01
fs / fy = 0.0
fs / fy = 0.5
fs / fy = 1.0
EI18 = kh4/(1+βd)
EI19 = 553 h4/(1+βd)
γ = 0.80
φc = 0.65
φs = 0.85
f'c = 35 MPa
fy = 400 MPa
γh
h
Pr/h2, MPa
Mr/h3, MPa
0
5
10
15
20
25
1
2
3
4
5
6

Table 7.7.8 Interaction Diagrams for Circular Tied or Spiral Columns.

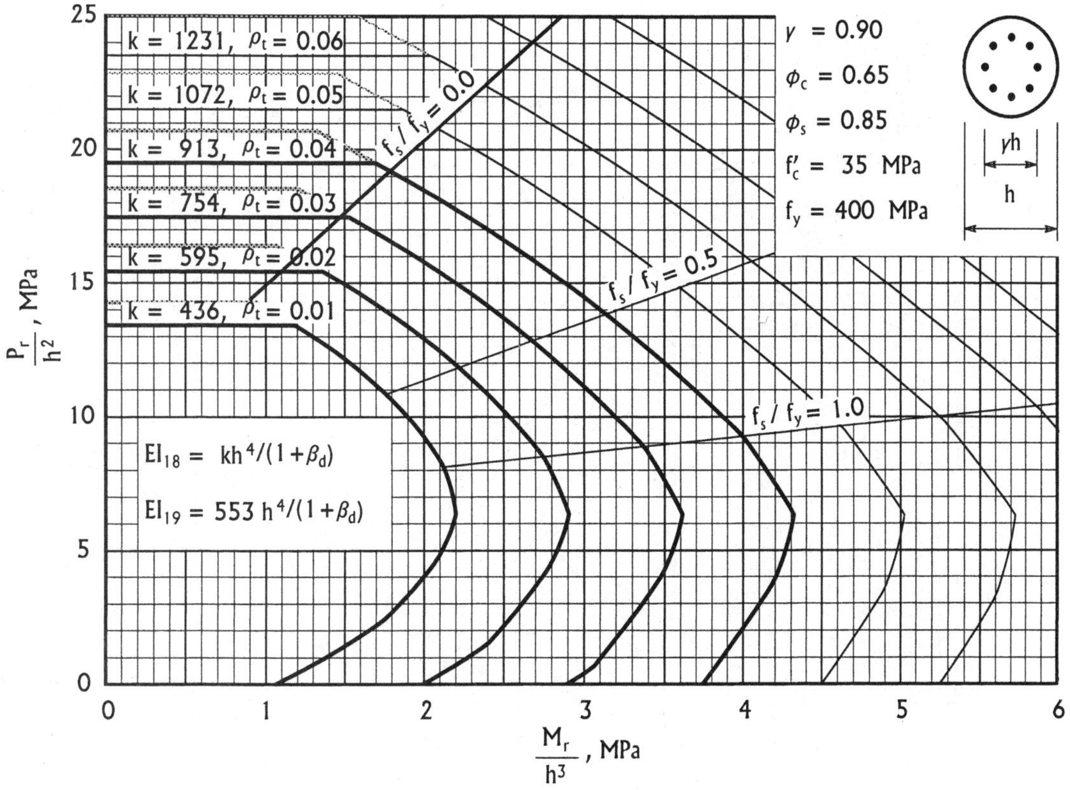
k = 1231, ρt = 0.06
k = 1072, ρt = 0.05
k = 913, ρt = 0.04
k = 754, ρt = 0.03
k = 595, ρt = 0.02
k = 436, ρt = 0.01
fs / fy = 0.0
fs / fy = 0.5
fs / fy = 1.0
EI18 = kh4/(1+βd)
EI19 = 553 h4/(1+βd)
γ = 0.90
φc = 0.65
φs = 0.85
f'c = 35 MPa
fy = 400 MPa
γh
h
Pr/h2, MPa
Mr/h3, MPa
0
5
10
15
20
25
1
2
3
4
5
6

Table 7.7.9   Interaction Diagrams for Circular Tied or Spiral Columns.

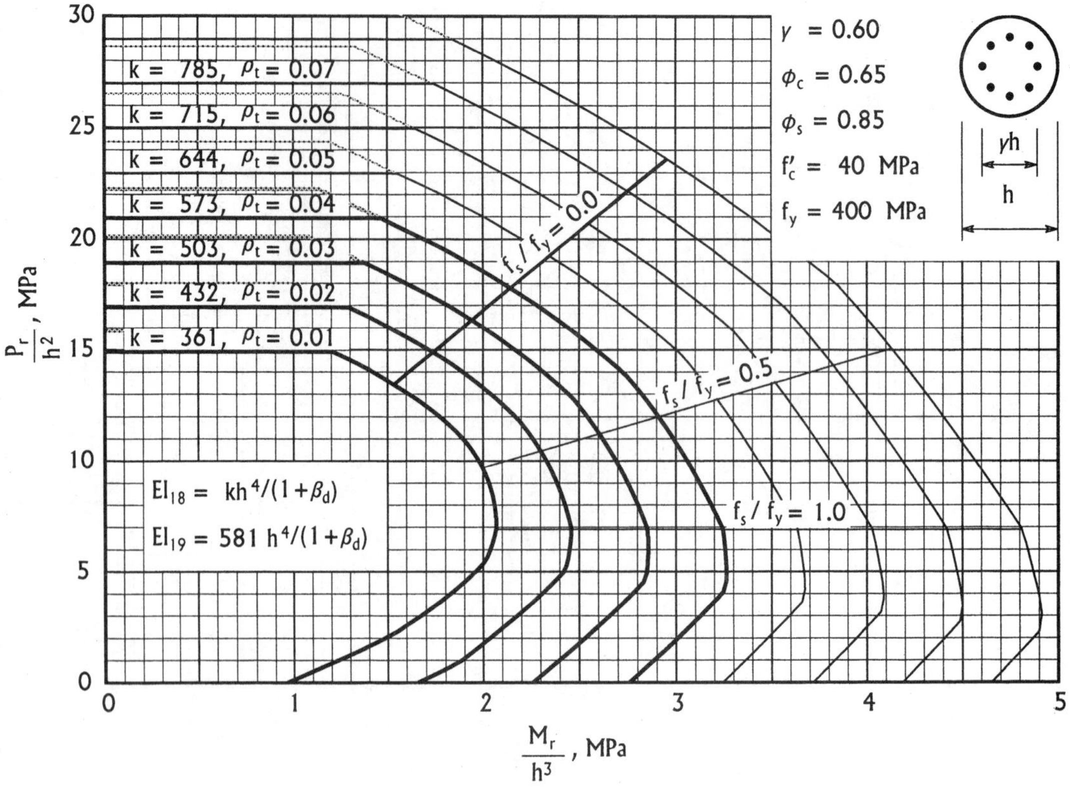

Table 7.7.10 Interaction Diagrams for Circular Tied or Spiral Columns.

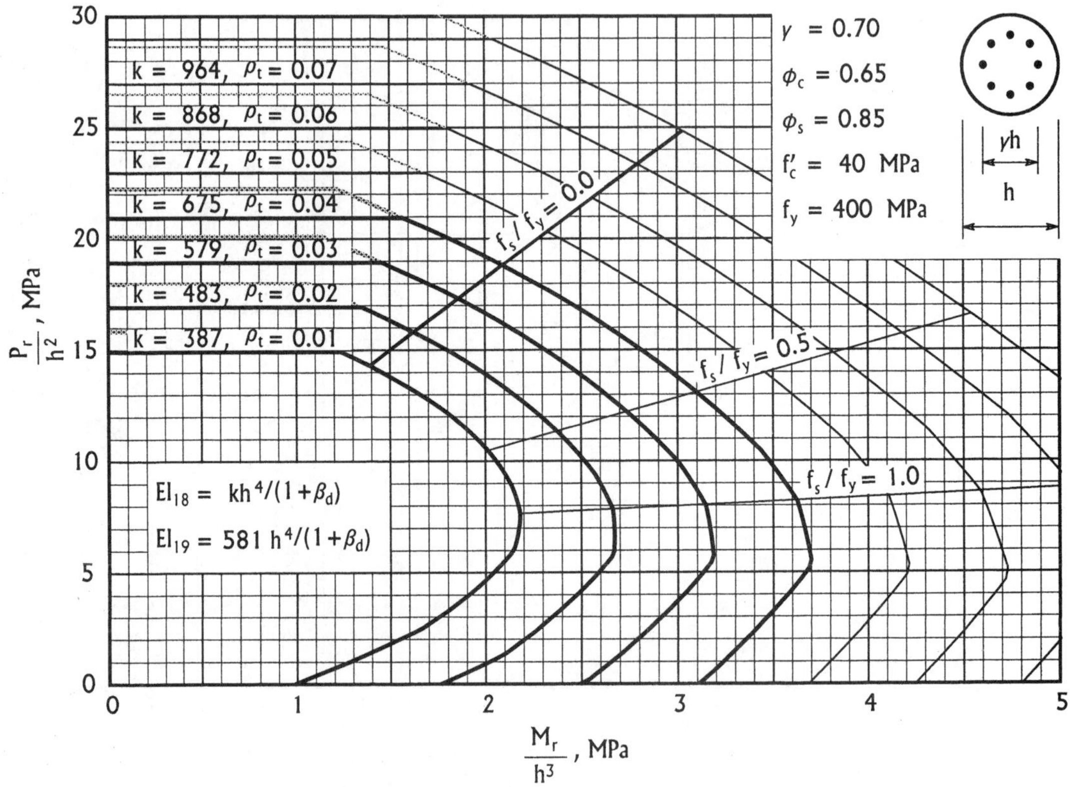

Table 7.7.11 Interaction Diagrams for Circular Tied or Spiral Columns.

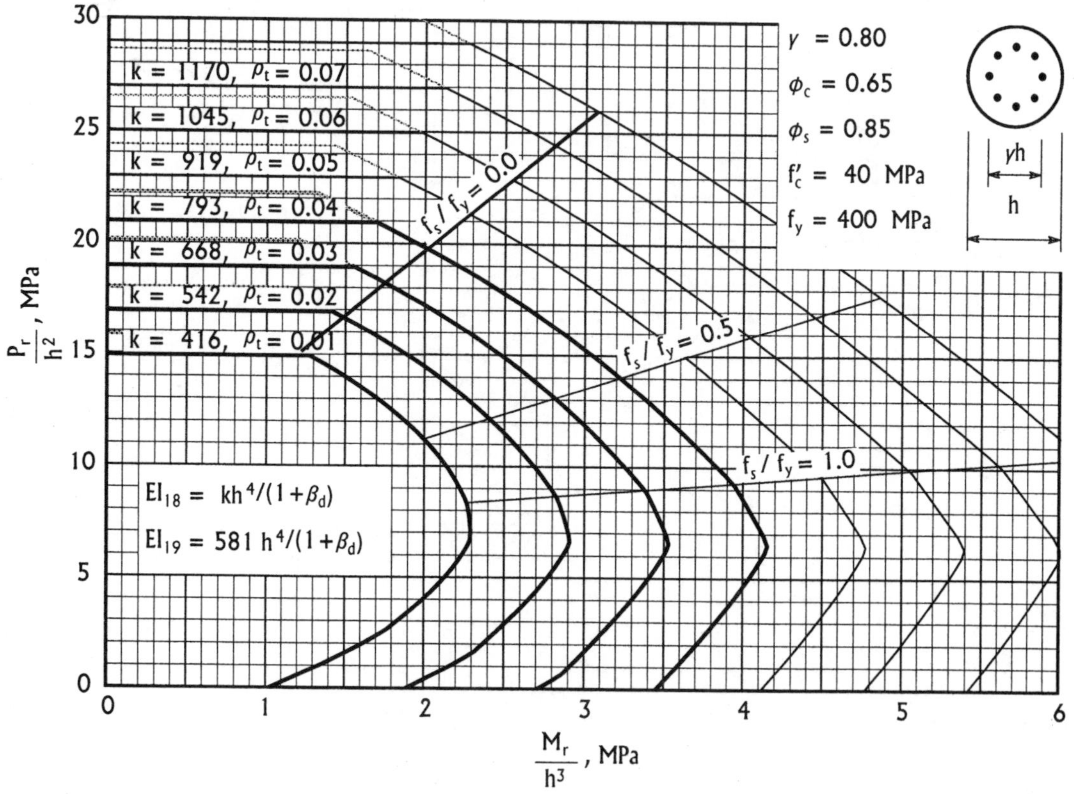
γ = 0.80
ϕ_c = 0.65
ϕ_s = 0.85
f'_c = 40 MPa
f_y = 400 MPa
γh
h
k = 1170, ρ_t = 0.07
k = 1045, ρ_t = 0.06
k = 919, ρ_t = 0.05
k = 793, ρ_t = 0.04
k = 668, ρ_t = 0.03
k = 542, ρ_t = 0.02
k = 416, ρ_t = 0.01
f_s / f_y = 0.0
f_s / f_y = 0.5
f_s / f_y = 1.0
$EI_{18} = kh^4/(1+\beta_d)$
$EI_{19} = 581\ h^4/(1+\beta_d)$
$\frac{P_r}{h^2}$, MPa
$\frac{M_r}{h^3}$, MPa
0
5
10
15
20
25
30
1
2
3
4
5
6

Table 7.7.12 Interaction Diagrams for Circular Tied or Spiral Columns.

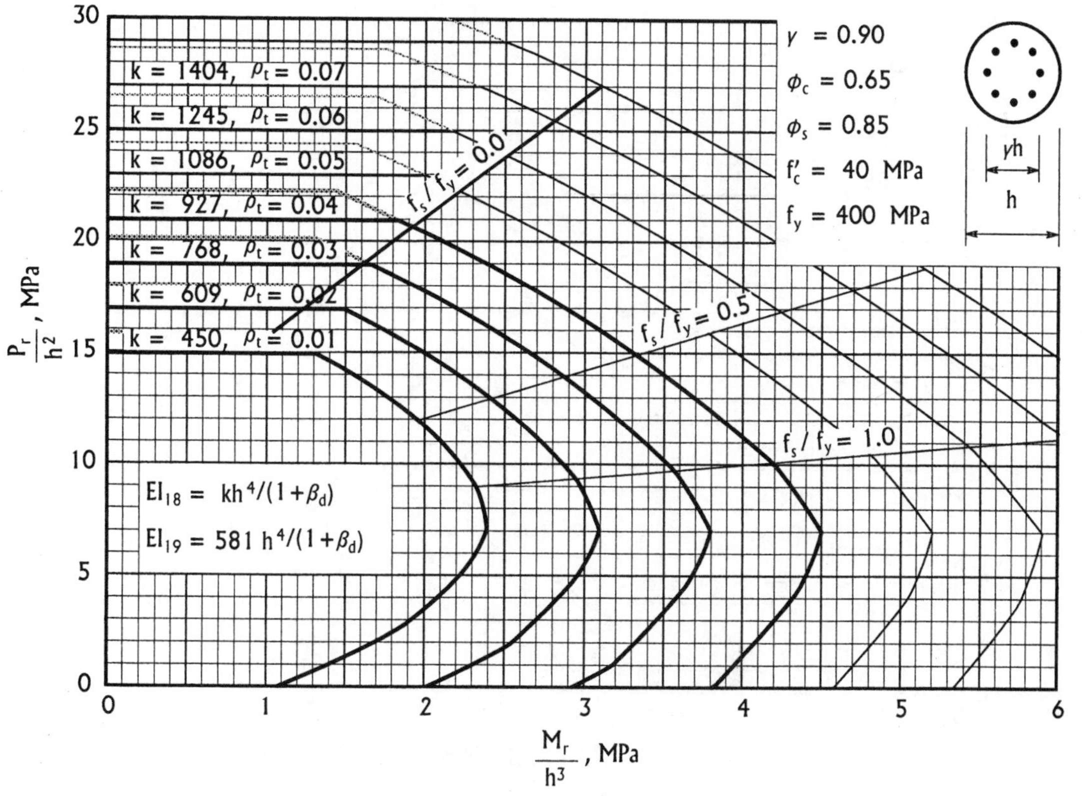
γ = 0.90
ϕ_c = 0.65
ϕ_s = 0.85
f'_c = 40 MPa
f_y = 400 MPa
γh
h
k = 1404, ρ_t = 0.07
k = 1245, ρ_t = 0.06
k = 1086, ρ_t = 0.05
k = 927, ρ_t = 0.04
k = 768, ρ_t = 0.03
k = 609, ρ_t = 0.02
k = 450, ρ_t = 0.01
f_s / f_y = 0.0
f_s / f_y = 0.5
f_s / f_y = 1.0
$EI_{18} = kh^4/(1+\beta_d)$
$EI_{19} = 581\ h^4/(1+\beta_d)$
$\frac{P_r}{h^2}$, MPa
$\frac{M_r}{h^3}$, MPa
0
5
10
15
20
25
30
1
2
3
4
5
6

Table 7.7.13 Interaction Diagrams for Circular Tied or Spiral Columns.

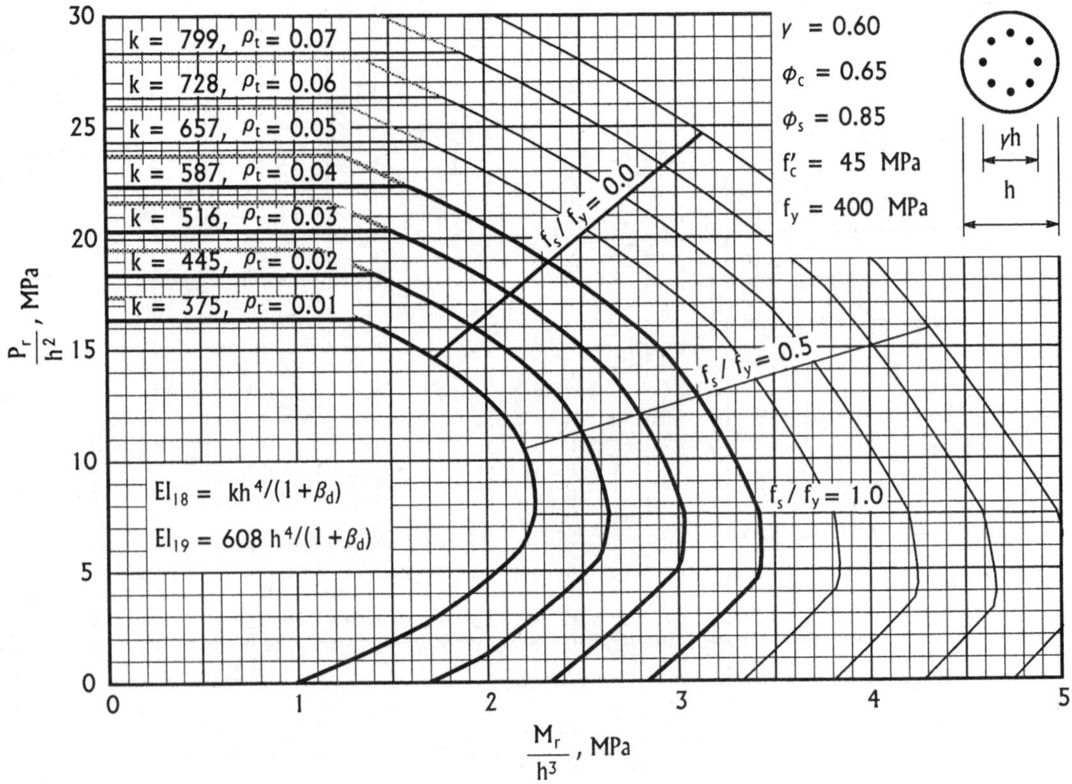

Table 7.7.14 Interaction Diagrams for Circular Tied or Spiral Columns.

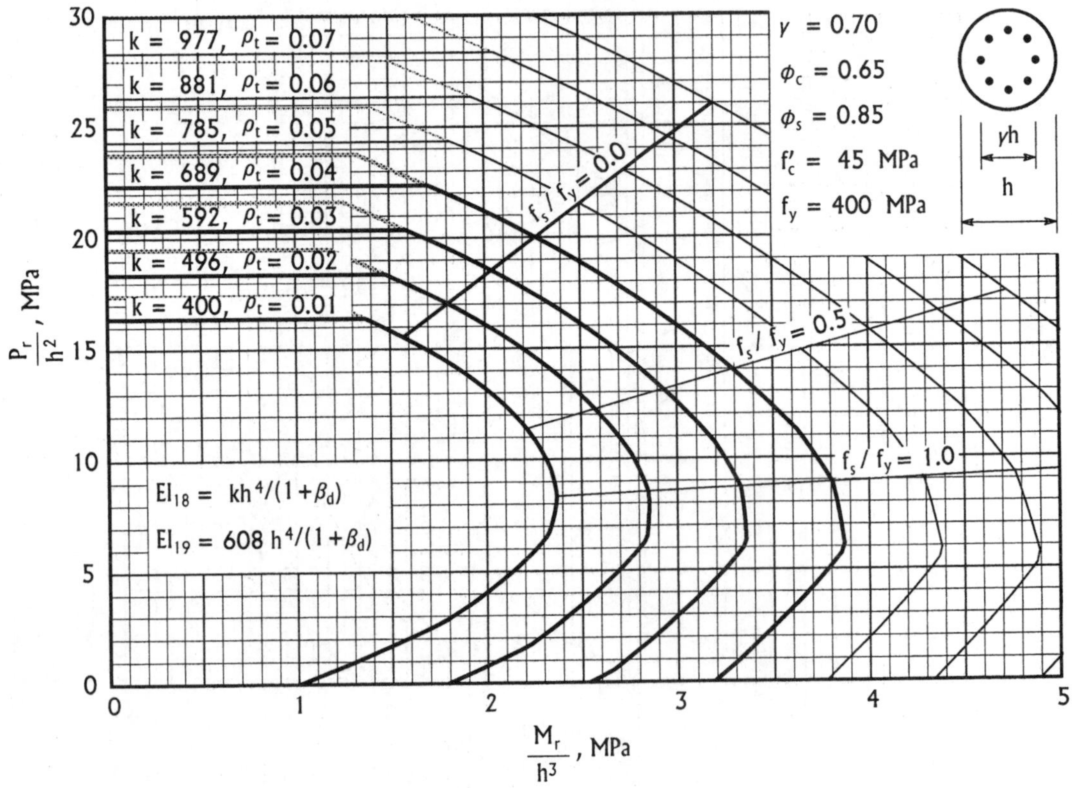

Table 7.7.15 Interaction Diagrams for Circular Tied or Spiral Columns.

Chart parameters:
- $k = 1184$, $\rho_t = 0.07$
- $k = 1058$, $\rho_t = 0.06$
- $k = 932$, $\rho_t = 0.05$
- $k = 807$, $\rho_t = 0.04$
- $k = 681$, $\rho_t = 0.03$
- $k = 555$, $\rho_t = 0.02$
- $k = 430$, $\rho_t = 0.01$

$\gamma = 0.80$
$\phi_c = 0.65$
$\phi_s = 0.85$
$f'_c = 45$ MPa
$f_y = 400$ MPa

$f_s / f_y = 0.0$
$f_s / f_y = 0.5$
$f_s / f_y = 1.0$

$EI_{18} = kh^4/(1+\beta_d)$
$EI_{19} = 608\, h^4/(1+\beta_d)$

Vertical axis: $\dfrac{P_r}{h^2}$, MPa

Horizontal axis: $\dfrac{M_r}{h^3}$, MPa

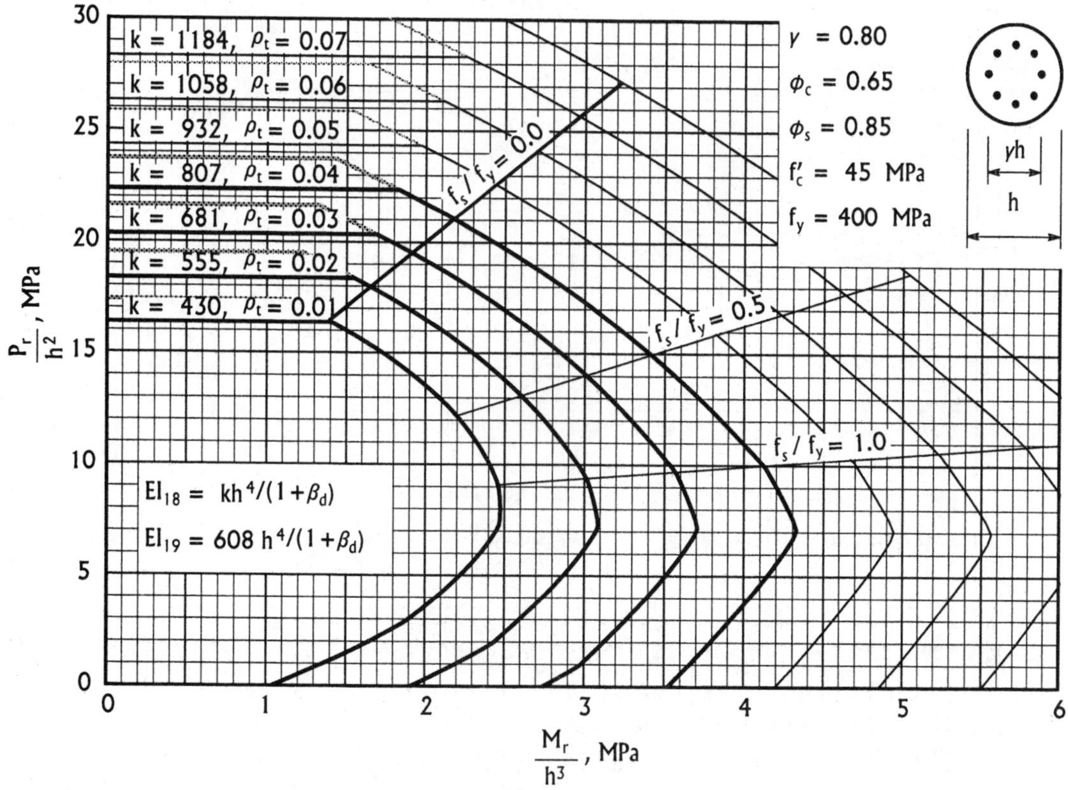

Table 7.7.16 Interaction Diagrams for Circular Tied or Spiral Columns.

Chart parameters:
- $k = 1417$, $\rho_t = 0.07$
- $k = 1258$, $\rho_t = 0.06$
- $k = 1099$, $\rho_t = 0.05$
- $k = 940$, $\rho_t = 0.04$
- $k = 781$, $\rho_t = 0.03$
- $k = 622$, $\rho_t = 0.02$
- $k = 463$, $\rho_t = 0.01$

$\gamma = 0.90$
$\phi_c = 0.65$
$\phi_s = 0.85$
$f'_c = 45$ MPa
$f_y = 400$ MPa

$f_s / f_y = 0.0$
$f_s / f_y = 0.5$
$f_s / f_y = 1.0$

$EI_{18} = kh^4/(1+\beta_d)$
$EI_{19} = 608\, h^4/(1+\beta_d)$

Vertical axis: $\dfrac{P_r}{h^2}$, MPa

Horizontal axis: $\dfrac{M_r}{h^3}$, MPa

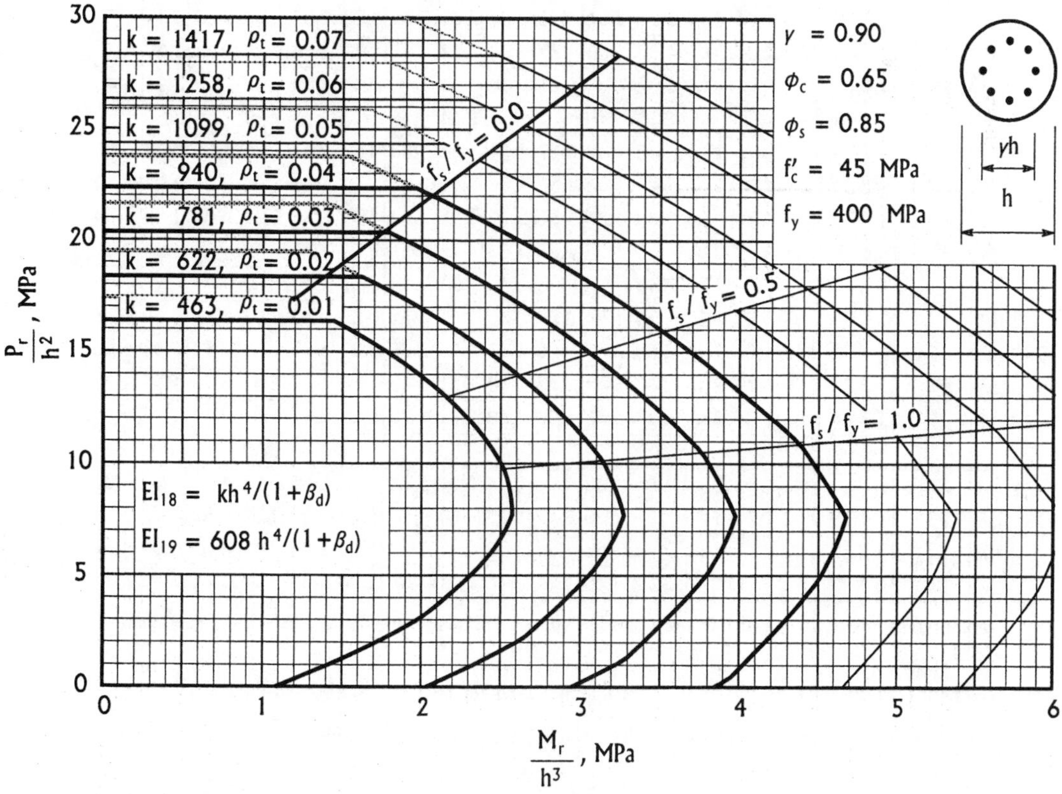

Table 7.8 Reinforcement Ratios for Rectangular Columns Reinforced on Four Faces, 40 mm Cover to 10M ties.

Bars	Total	8	12	16	20	8	12	16	20	8	12	16	20	8	12	16	20	8	12	16	20
	Size	b or h 300				350				400				450				500			
b or h 300	15M	1.78	2.67			1.52	2.29			1.33	2.00			1.19	1.78			1.07	1.60		
	20M	2.67	4.00			2.29	3.43			2.00	3.00			1.78	2.67			1.60	2.40		
	25M	4.44				3.81				3.33				2.96				2.67			
	30M	6.22				5.33				4.67				4.15				3.73			
		350				400				450				500				550			
350	15M	1.31	1.96	2.61		1.14	1.71	2.29		1.02	1.52	2.03		0.91	1.37	1.83		0.83	1.25	1.66	
	20M	1.96	2.94	3.92		1.71	2.57	3.43		1.52	2.29	3.05		1.37	2.06	2.74		1.25	1.87	2.49	
	25M	3.27	4.90			2.86	4.29			2.54	3.81			2.29	3.43			2.08	3.12		
	30M	4.57				4.00				3.56				3.20				2.91			
	35M	6.53				5.71				5.08				4.57				4.16			
		400				450				500				550				600			
400	15M	1.00	1.50	2.00	2.50	0.89	1.33	1.78	2.22	0.80	1.20	1.60	2.00	0.73	1.09	1.45	1.82	0.67	1.00	1.33	1.67
	20M	1.50	2.25	3.00	3.75	1.33	2.00	2.67	3.33	1.20	1.80	2.40	3.00	1.09	1.64	2.18	2.73	1.00	1.50	2.00	2.50
	25M	2.50	3.75	5.00		2.22	3.33	4.44		2.00	3.00	4.00		1.82	2.73	3.64		1.67	2.50	3.33	
	30M	3.50	5.25			3.11	4.67			2.80	4.20			2.55	3.82			2.33	3.50		
	35M	5.00				4.44				4.00				3.64				3.33			
		450				500				550				600				650			
450	15M	0.79	1.19	1.58	1.98	0.71	1.07	1.42	1.78	0.65	0.97	1.29	1.62	0.59	0.89	1.19	1.48	0.55	0.82	1.09	1.37
	20M	1.19	1.78	2.37	2.96	1.07	1.60	2.13	2.67	0.97	1.45	1.94	2.42	0.89	1.33	1.78	2.22	0.82	1.23	1.64	2.05
	25M	1.98	2.96	3.95	4.94	1.78	2.67	3.56	4.44	1.62	2.42	3.23	4.04	1.48	2.22	2.96	3.70	1.37	2.05	2.74	3.42
	30M	2.77	4.15	5.53		2.49	3.73	4.98		2.26	3.39	4.53		2.07	3.11	4.15		1.91	2.87	3.83	
	35M	3.95	5.93			3.56	5.33			3.23	4.85			2.96	4.44			2.74	4.10		
		500				550				600				650				700			
500	20M	0.96	1.44	1.92	2.40	0.87	1.31	1.75	2.18	0.80	1.20	1.60	2.00	0.74	1.11	1.48	1.85	0.69	1.03	1.37	1.71
	25M	1.60	2.40	3.20	4.00	1.45	2.18	2.91	3.64	1.33	2.00	2.67	3.33	1.23	1.85	2.46	3.08	1.14	1.71	2.29	2.86
	30M	2.24	3.36	4.48	5.60	2.04	3.05	4.07	5.09	1.87	2.80	3.73	4.67	1.72	2.58	3.45	4.31	1.60	2.40	3.20	4.00
	35M	3.20	4.80	6.40		2.91	4.36	5.82		2.67	4.00	5.33		2.46	3.69	4.92		2.29	3.43	4.57	
		550				600				650				700				750			
550	20M	0.79	1.19	1.59	1.98	0.73	1.09	1.45	1.82	0.67	1.01	1.34	1.68	0.62	0.94	1.25	1.56	0.58	0.87	1.16	1.45
	25M	1.32	1.98	2.64	3.31	1.21	1.82	2.42	3.03	1.12	1.68	2.24	2.80	1.04	1.56	2.08	2.60	0.97	1.45	1.94	2.42
	30M	1.85	2.78	3.70	4.63	1.70	2.55	3.39	4.24	1.57	2.35	3.13	3.92	1.45	2.18	2.91	3.64	1.36	2.04	2.72	3.39
	35M	2.64	3.97	5.29		2.42	3.64	4.85		2.24	3.36	4.48		2.08	3.12	4.16		1.94	2.91	3.88	
		600				650				700				750				800			
600	20M	0.67	1.00	1.33	1.67	0.62	0.92	1.23	1.54	0.57	0.86	1.14	1.43	0.53	0.80	1.07	1.33	0.50	0.75	1.00	1.25
	25M	1.11	1.67	2.22	2.78	1.03	1.54	2.05	2.56	0.95	1.43	1.90	2.38	0.89	1.33	1.78	2.22	0.83	1.25	1.67	2.08
	30M	1.56	2.33	3.11	3.89	1.44	2.15	2.87	3.59	1.33	2.00	2.67	3.33	1.24	1.87	2.49	3.11	1.17	1.75	2.33	2.92
	35M	2.22	3.33	4.44	5.56	2.05	3.08	4.10	5.13	1.90	2.86	3.81	4.76	1.78	2.67	3.56	4.44	1.67	2.50	3.33	4.17
		650				700				750				800				850			
650	20M	0.57	0.85	1.14	1.42	0.53	0.79	1.05	1.32		0.74	0.98	1.23		0.69	0.92	1.15		0.65	0.87	1.09
	25M	0.95	1.42	1.89	2.37	0.88	1.32	1.76	2.20	0.82	1.23	1.64	2.05	0.77	1.15	1.54	1.92	0.72	1.09	1.45	1.81
	30M	1.33	1.99	2.65	3.31	1.23	1.85	2.46	3.08	1.15	1.72	2.30	2.87	1.08	1.62	2.15	2.69	1.01	1.52	2.03	2.53
	35M	1.89	2.84	3.79	4.73	1.76	2.64	3.52	4.40	1.64	2.46	3.28	4.10	1.54	2.31	3.08	3.85	1.45	2.17	2.90	3.62

All bar combinations shown may be spliced with bearing splices. Values above the line may be spliced with tangential or radial splices.

If a reinforcement ratio greater than 4% is used, the splice location must be staggered by at least 750 mm.

If reinforcement ratios less than 1% are used, the factored resistance must be reduced as specified in Clause 10.10.5.

Table 7.9 Reinforcement Ratios for Rectangular Columns Reinforced on Two Faces, 40 mm Cover to 10M Ties.

Bars b=	Total Size	h = 250					300					350					400				
		4	6	8	10	12	4	6	8	10	12	4	6	8	10	12	4	6	8	10	12
b = 250	15M	1.28	1.92				1.07	1.60				0.91	1.37				0.80	1.20			
	20M	1.92	2.88				1.60	2.40				1.37	2.06				1.20	1.80			
300	15M	1.07	1.60	2.13			0.89	1.33	1.78			0.76	1.14	1.52			0.67	1.00	1.33		
	20M	1.60	2.40	3.20			1.33	2.00	2.67			1.14	1.71	2.29			1.00	1.50	2.00		
	25M	2.67	4.00				2.22	3.33				1.90	2.86				1.67	2.50			
	30M						3.11	4.67				2.67	4.00				2.33	3.50			
350	15M	0.91	1.37	1.83	2.29	2.74	0.76	1.14	1.52	1.90	2.29	0.65	0.98	1.31	1.63	1.96	0.57	0.86	1.14	1.43	1.71
	20M	1.37	2.06	2.74	3.43		1.14	1.71	2.29	2.86		0.98	1.47	1.96	2.45		0.86	1.29	1.71	2.14	
	25M	2.29	3.43	4.57			1.90	2.86	3.81			1.63	2.45	3.27			1.43	2.14	2.86		
	30M						2.67	4.00	5.33			2.29	3.43	4.57			2.00	3.00	4.00		
	35M						3.81	5.71				3.27	4.90				2.86	4.29			
400	15M	0.80	1.20	1.60	2.00	2.40	0.67	1.00	1.33	1.67	2.00	0.57	0.86	1.14	1.43	1.71	0.50	0.75	1.00	1.25	1.50
	20M	1.20	1.80	2.40	3.00	3.60	1.00	1.50	2.00	2.50	3.00	0.86	1.29	1.71	2.14	2.57	0.75	1.13	1.50	1.88	2.25
	25M	2.00	3.00	4.00	5.00		1.67	2.50	3.33	4.17		1.43	2.14	2.86	3.57		1.25	1.88	2.50	3.13	
	30M						2.33	3.50	4.67			2.00	3.00	4.00			1.75	2.63	3.50		
	35M						3.33	5.00	6.67			2.86	4.29	5.71			2.50	3.75	5.00		
450	15M	0.71	1.07	1.42	1.78	2.13	0.59	0.89	1.19	1.48	1.78	0.51	0.76	1.02	1.27	1.52		0.67	0.89	1.11	1.33
	20M	1.07	1.60	2.13	2.67	3.20	0.89	1.33	1.78	2.22	2.67	0.76	1.14	1.52	1.90	2.29	0.67	1.00	1.33	1.67	2.00
	25M	1.78	2.67	3.56	4.44	5.33	1.48	2.22	2.96	3.70	4.44	1.27	1.90	2.54	3.17	3.81	1.11	1.67	2.22	2.78	3.33
	30M						2.07	3.11	4.15	5.19		1.78	2.67	3.56	4.44		1.56	2.33	3.11	3.89	
	35M						2.96	4.44	5.93			2.54	3.81	5.08			2.22	3.33	4.44		
500	15M	0.64	0.96	1.28	1.60	1.92	0.53	0.80	1.07	1.33	1.60		0.69	0.91	1.14	1.37		0.60	0.80	1.00	1.20
	20M	0.96	1.44	1.92	2.40	2.88	0.80	1.20	1.60	2.00	2.40	0.69	1.03	1.37	1.71	2.06	0.60	0.90	1.20	1.50	1.80
	25M	1.60	2.40	3.20	4.00	4.80	1.33	2.00	2.67	3.33	4.00	1.14	1.71	2.29	2.86	3.43	1.00	1.50	2.00	2.50	3.00
	30M						1.87	2.80	3.73	4.67	5.60	1.60	2.40	3.20	4.00	4.80	1.40	2.10	2.80	3.50	4.20
	35M						2.67	4.00	5.33	6.67		2.29	3.43	4.57	5.71		2.00	3.00	4.00	5.00	
550	15M	0.58	0.87	1.16	1.45	1.75		0.73	0.97	1.21	1.45		0.62	0.83	1.04	1.25		0.55	0.73	0.91	1.09
	20M	0.87	1.31	1.75	2.18	2.62	0.73	1.09	1.45	1.82	2.18	0.62	0.94	1.25	1.56	1.87	0.55	0.82	1.09	1.36	1.64
	25M	1.45	2.18	2.91	3.64	4.36	1.21	1.82	2.42	3.03	3.64	1.04	1.56	2.08	2.60	3.12	0.91	1.36	1.82	2.27	2.73
	30M						1.70	2.55	3.39	4.24	5.09	1.45	2.18	2.91	3.64	4.36	1.27	1.91	2.55	3.18	3.82
	35M						2.42	3.64	4.85	6.06		2.08	3.12	4.16	5.19		1.82	2.73	3.64	4.55	
600	20M	0.80	1.20	1.60	2.00	2.40	0.67	1.00	1.33	1.67	2.00	0.57	0.86	1.14	1.43	1.71	0.50	0.75	1.00	1.25	1.50
	25M	1.33	2.00	2.67	3.33	4.00	1.11	1.67	2.22	2.78	3.33	0.95	1.43	1.90	2.38	2.86	0.83	1.25	1.67	2.08	2.50
	30M						1.56	2.33	3.11	3.89	4.67	1.33	2.00	2.67	3.33	4.00	1.17	1.75	2.33	2.92	3.50
	35M						2.22	3.33	4.44	5.56	6.67	1.90	2.86	3.81	4.76	5.71	1.67	2.50	3.33	4.17	5.00
650	20M		1.11	1.48	1.85	2.22		0.92	1.23	1.54	1.85		0.79	1.05	1.32	1.58		0.69	0.92	1.15	1.38
	25M		1.85	2.46	3.08	3.69		1.54	2.05	2.56	3.08		1.32	1.76	2.20	2.64		1.15	1.54	1.92	2.31
	30M							2.15	2.87	3.59	4.31		1.85	2.46	3.08	3.69		1.62	2.15	2.69	3.23
	35M							3.08	4.10	5.13	6.15		2.64	3.52	4.40	5.27		2.31	3.08	3.85	4.62
700	20M		1.03	1.37	1.71	2.06		0.86	1.14	1.43	1.71		0.73	0.98	1.22	1.47		0.64	0.86	1.07	1.29
	25M		1.71	2.29	2.86	3.43		1.43	1.90	2.38	2.86		1.22	1.63	2.04	2.45		1.07	1.43	1.79	2.14
	30M							2.00	2.67	3.33	4.00		1.71	2.29	2.86	3.43		1.50	2.00	2.50	3.00
	35M							2.86	3.81	4.76	5.71		2.45	3.27	4.08	4.90		2.14	2.86	3.57	4.29

All bar combinations shown may be spliced with bearing splices. Values above the line may be spliced with tangential or radial splices.

If a reinforcement ratio greater than 4% is used, the splice location must be staggered by at least 750 mm.

If reinforcement ratios less than 1% are used, the factored resistance must be reduced as specified in Clause 10.10.5.

Table 7.10 Reinforcement Ratios for Circular Columns, 40 mm Cover to 10M Ties or Spirals

Bars	Total Size	6	7	8	9	10	11	12	13	14	15	16	17	18	19	20	21	22	23
Column diameter 300	15M	1.70	1.98	2.26	2.55	2.83	3.11	3.40											
	20M	2.55	2.97	3.40	3.82	4.24	4.67												
	25M	4.24	4.95	5.66															
	30M	5.94	6.93																
350	15M	1.25	1.46	1.66	1.87	2.08	2.29	2.49	2.70	2.91	3.12								
	20M	1.87	2.18	2.49	2.81	3.12	3.43	3.74	4.05	4.37									
	25M	3.12	3.64	4.16	4.68	5.20	5.72												
	30M	4.37	5.09	5.82	6.55														
	35M	6.24	7.28																
400	15M	0.95	1.11	1.27	1.43	1.59	1.75	1.91	2.07	2.23	2.39	2.55	2.71	2.86	3.02				
	20M	1.43	1.67	1.91	2.15	2.39	2.63	2.86	3.10	3.34	3.58	3.82	4.06						
	25M	2.39	2.79	3.18	3.58	3.98	4.38	4.77	5.17	5.57									
	30M	3.34	3.90	4.46	5.01	5.57	6.13												
	35M	4.77	5.57	6.37	7.16														
450	15M	0.75	0.88	1.01	1.13	1.26	1.38	1.51	1.63	1.76	1.89	2.01	2.14	2.26	2.39	2.52	2.64	2.77	
	20M	1.13	1.32	1.51	1.70	1.89	2.07	2.26	2.45	2.64	2.83	3.02	3.21	3.40	3.58	3.77			
	25M	1.89	2.20	2.52	2.83	3.14	3.46	3.77	4.09	4.40	4.72	5.03							
	30M	2.64	3.08	3.52	3.96	4.40	4.84	5.28	5.72										
	35M	3.77	4.40	5.03	5.66	6.29	6.92												
500	20M	0.92	1.07	1.22	1.38	1.53	1.68	1.83	1.99	2.14	2.29	2.44	2.60	2.75	2.90	3.06	3.21	3.36	3.51
	25M	1.53	1.78	2.04	2.29	2.55	2.80	3.06	3.31	3.57	3.82	4.07	4.33	4.58	4.84				
	30M	2.14	2.50	2.85	3.21	3.57	3.92	4.28	4.63	4.99	5.35								
	35M	3.06	3.57	4.07	4.58	5.09	5.60	6.11	6.62										
550	20M	0.76	0.88	1.01	1.14	1.26	1.39	1.52	1.64	1.77	1.89	2.02	2.15	2.27	2.40	2.53	2.65	2.78	2.90
	25M	1.26	1.47	1.68	1.89	2.10	2.31	2.53	2.74	2.95	3.16	3.37	3.58	3.79	4.00	4.21	4.42		
	30M	1.77	2.06	2.36	2.65	2.95	3.24	3.54	3.83	4.12	4.42	4.71	5.01	5.30					
	35M	2.53	2.95	3.37	3.79	4.21	4.63	5.05	5.47	5.89									
600	20M	0.64	0.74	0.85	0.95	1.06	1.17	1.27	1.38	1.49	1.59	1.70	1.80	1.91	2.02	2.12	2.23	2.33	2.44
	25M	1.06	1.24	1.41	1.59	1.77	1.95	2.12	2.30	2.48	2.65	2.83	3.01	3.18	3.36	3.54	3.71	3.89	4.07
	30M	1.49	1.73	1.98	2.23	2.48	2.72	2.97	3.22	3.47	3.71	3.96	4.21	4.46	4.70	4.95			
	35M	2.12	2.48	2.83	3.18	3.54	3.89	4.24	4.60	4.95	5.31	5.66							
650	20M	0.54	0.63	0.72	0.81	0.90	0.99	1.08	1.18	1.27	1.36	1.45	1.54	1.63	1.72	1.81	1.90	1.99	2.08
	25M	0.90	1.05	1.21	1.36	1.51	1.66	1.81	1.96	2.11	2.26	2.41	2.56	2.71	2.86	3.01	3.16	3.31	3.47
	30M	1.27	1.48	1.69	1.90	2.11	2.32	2.53	2.74	2.95	3.16	3.38	3.59	3.80	4.01	4.22	4.43	4.64	
	35M	1.81	2.11	2.41	2.71	3.01	3.31	3.62	3.92	4.22	4.52	4.82	5.12	5.42					
700	20M		0.55	0.62	0.70	0.78	0.86	0.94	1.01	1.09	1.17	1.25	1.33	1.40	1.48	1.56	1.64	1.71	1.79
	25M	0.78	0.91	1.04	1.17	1.30	1.43	1.56	1.69	1.82	1.95	2.08	2.21	2.34	2.47	2.60	2.73	2.86	2.99
	30M	1.09	1.27	1.46	1.64	1.82	2.00	2.18	2.36	2.55	2.73	2.91	3.09	3.27	3.46	3.64	3.82	4.00	4.18
	35M	1.56	1.82	2.08	2.34	2.60	2.86	3.12	3.38	3.64	3.90	4.16	4.42	4.68	4.94	5.20			
750	20M			0.54	0.61	0.68	0.75	0.81	0.88	0.95	1.02	1.09	1.15	1.22	1.29	1.36	1.43	1.49	1.56
	25M	0.68	0.79	0.91	1.02	1.13	1.24	1.36	1.47	1.58	1.70	1.81	1.92	2.04	2.15	2.26	2.38	2.49	2.60
	30M	0.95	1.11	1.27	1.43	1.58	1.74	1.90	2.06	2.22	2.38	2.54	2.69	2.85	3.01	3.17	3.33	3.49	3.64
	35M	1.36	1.58	1.81	2.04	2.26	2.49	2.72	2.94	3.17	3.40	3.62	3.85	4.07	4.30	4.53	4.75	4.98	5.21

All bar combinations shown may be spliced with bearing splices. Values above the line may be spliced with tangential or radial splices.

If a reinforcing ratio greater than 4% is used the splice location must be staggered by at least 750 mm.

If reinforcing ratios less than 1% are used the factored resistance must be reduced as specified in Clause 10.10.5.

Table 7.11 Maximum Allowable Spiral Pitch for Circular Spiral Columns, 40 mm Cover to Spiral

Column	Column Diameter	Concrete Strength, MPa					
		25	30	35	40	45	50
10M Spiral f_y = 400 MPa	300 mm	35	35	35	35	35	35
	350	45	45	45	45	40	35
	400	55	55	55	50	40	40
	450	60	60	55	50	45	40
	500	70	65	55	50	45	40
	550	80	65	55	50	45	40
	600	80	65	60	50	45	40
	650-950	80	70	60	50	45	40
	1000-1200	85	70	60	55	45	40
	1250-1350	85	70	60	55	45	45
	1400-2450	85	70	60	55	50	45
15M Spiral f_y = 400 MPa	350 mm	45	45	45	45	45	45
	400	55	55	55	55	55	55
	450	60	60	60	60	60	60
	500	70	70	70	70	70	70
	550	80	80	80	80	80	80
	600	85	85	85	85	85	80
	650-800	90	90	90	90	90	80
	850-3600	90	90	90	90	90	85
10M Spiral f_y = 500 MPa	300 mm	35	35	35	35	35	35
	350	45	45	45	45	45	45
	400	55	55	55	55	55	50
	450	60	60	60	60	55	50
	500	70	70	70	60	55	50
	550	80	80	70	60	55	50
	600	85	85	70	65	55	50
	650-750	85	85	75	65	55	50
	800-950	85	85	75	65	60	50
	1000-1850	85	85	75	65	60	55
	1900-2200	85	85	75	70	60	55
15M Spiral f_y = 500 MPa	350 mm	45	45	45	45	45	45
	400	55	55	55	55	55	55
	450	60	60	60	60	60	60
	500	70	70	70	70	70	70
	550	80	80	80	80	80	80
	600	85	85	85	85	85	85
	650 +	90	90	90	90	90	90

Table 7.12 Compression Development Lengths, ℓ_d, for Deformed Bars with f_y = 400 MPa*

f'_c MPa	Bar Size						
	15M	20M	25M	30M	35M	45M	55M
20	320	430	540	640	750	970	1180
25	290	380	480	580	670	860	1060
$f'_c \geq 30$	260	350	440	530	620	790	970

* For f_y of 500 MPa multiply lengths by 1.25.
See Clause 12.4 for additional lengths for bundled bars.
See Clause 12.3.3 for reduced lengths with additional transverse reinforcement

Table 7.13 Lap lengths for Uncoated[†] Reinforcement[‡] with f_y = 400 MPa in Normal Density Concrete[†]

Category	f'_c MPa	Bar size				
		15M	20M	25M	30M	35M
Compression only*		440	580	730	880	1020
Class A Tension splice[#] 0<(f_s/f_y)$_{max}$<0.5 with less than 50% spliced within required lap length	20	480	640	1010	1210	1410
	25	430	580	900	1080	1260
	30	390	530	820	990	1150
	35	370	490	760	910	1060
	40	340	460	710	850	1000
	45	320	430	670	800	940
	50	310	410	640	760	890
Class B Tension splice[#] for all other situations	20	630	840	1310	1570	1830
	25	560	750	1170	1400	1640
	30	510	680	1070	1280	1500
	35	470	630	990	1190	1380
	40	440	590	920	1110	1290
	45	420	560	870	1050	1220
	50	400	530	830	990	1160

* For f_y of 500 MPa multiply compression lap by 1.46.
# For f_y of 500 MPa multiply tension lap length by 1.25.
† See Clause 12.2.4 for increased lengths for epoxy-coating and for concrete with lower densities.
‡ See Clause 12.14.2.2 for increased lap lengths for bundled bars.
See Clause 12.17.3 for reduced lap lengths with additional transverse reinforcement.

8

By Murat Saatcioglu

Slender Columns

8

Slender Columns

8.1   Introduction

The majority of reinforced concrete columns are subjected to primary stresses caused by flexure, axial force, and shear. Secondary stresses associated with deformations are usually very small in most columns used in practice. These columns are referred to as "short columns." Short columns are designed using the interaction diagrams presented in Chapter 7. The capacity of a short column is the same as the capacity of its section under primary stresses, irrespective of its length.

Long columns, columns with small cross-sectional dimensions, and columns with little end restraints may develop secondary stresses associated with column deformations, especially if they are not braced laterally. These columns are referred to as "slender columns". Fig. 8.1 illustrates secondary moments generated in a slender column by P-Δ effect. Consequently, slender columns resist lower axial loads than short columns with the same cross-section. This is illustrated in Fig. 8.1. Failure of a slender column is initiated either by the material failure of a section, or instability of the column as a member, depending on the level of slenderness. The latter is known as column buckling.

It is clear from the foregoing discussion that slender columns are subjected to higher bending moments than those computed by a first-order structural analysis that engineers conduct routinely for design purposes. This increase in moment due to secondary effects should be accounted for in design if the interaction diagrams given in Chapter 7 are to be used for design purposes.

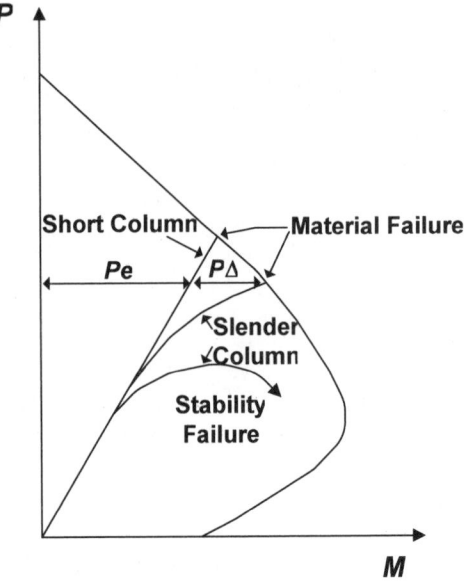

Fig. 81 Failure Modes in Short and Slender Columns

8.2   Slenderness Ratio

The degree of slenderness in a column is expressed in terms of "slenderness ratio" as defined below:

Slenderness Ratio: $k\ell_u/r$

where, ℓ_u is the unsupported column length; k is the effective length factor reflecting the end restraint and lateral bracing conditions of a column; and r is the radius of gyration reflecting the size and shape of a column cross-section.

8.2.1   Unsupported Length, ℓ_u

The unsupported length ℓ_u of a column is measured as the clear distance between the underside of the beam, slab, or column capital above, and the top of the beam or slab below. The unsupported length of a column may be different in two orthogonal directions depending on the supporting elements in respective directions. Table 8.1 provides examples of different support conditions and corresponding unsupported lengths (ℓ_u).

8.2.2   Effective Length Factor, k

The effective length factor k reflects end restraint (support) and lateral bracing conditions of a column relative to a pin-ended and laterally braced "reference column." The reference column, shown in Fig. 8.2(a), follows a half sine wave when it buckles, and is assigned a k factor of 1.0. Therefore, the effective length $k\ell_u$ for this column is equal to the unsupported column length ℓ_u. A column with fully restrained end conditions develops the deflected shape illustrated in Fig. 8.2(b). The portion of the column between the points of contraflexure follows a half sign wave, the same deflected shape as that of the reference column. This segment is equal to 50% of the unsupported column length ℓ_u. Therefore, the effective length factor k for this case is equal to 0.5. Effective length factors for columns with idealized supports can be determined from Fig. 8.2. It may be of interest to note that k varies between 0.5 and 1.0 for laterally braced columns, and 0.5 and ∞ for unbraced columns. A discussion of lateral bracing is provided in Sec. 8.3 to establish whether a given column can be considered to be as part of a sway or a non-sway frame.

Most columns have end restraints that are neither perfectly hinged nor fully fixed. The degree of end restraint depends on the stiffness of adjoining beams relative to that of the columns. Jackson and Moreland alignment charts, given in Tables 8.2 and 8.3 can be used to determine the effective length factor k for different values of relative stiffnesses at column ends. The stiffness ratios ψ_A and ψ_B used in Tables 8.2 and 8.3 should reflect concrete cracking, and the effects of sustained loading. Beams and slabs are flexure dominant members and may crack significantly more than columns which are compression members. The reduced stiffness values recommended by CSA A23.3-04 are given in Table 8.4, and should be used in determining k. Alternatively, Table 8.5 may be used to establish conservative values of k for braced columns.

8.2.3   Radius of Gyration, r

The radius of gyration reflects the effect of cross-sectional size and shape on slenderness. For the same cross-sectional area, a section with higher moment of inertia produces a more stable column with a lower slenderness ratio. The radius of gyration r is defined below.

$$r = \sqrt{\frac{I}{A}}\tag{8.1}$$

It is permissible to use the approximations of $r = 0.3h$ for square and rectangular sections, and $r = 0.25d$ for circular sections.

8

Slender Columns

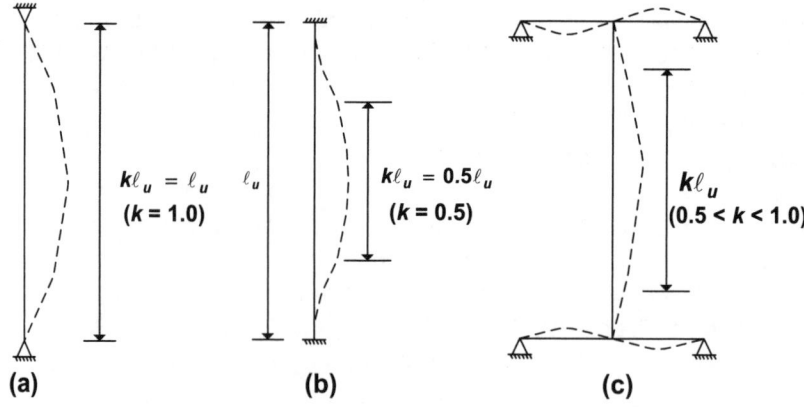

Columns in Non-Sway Frames

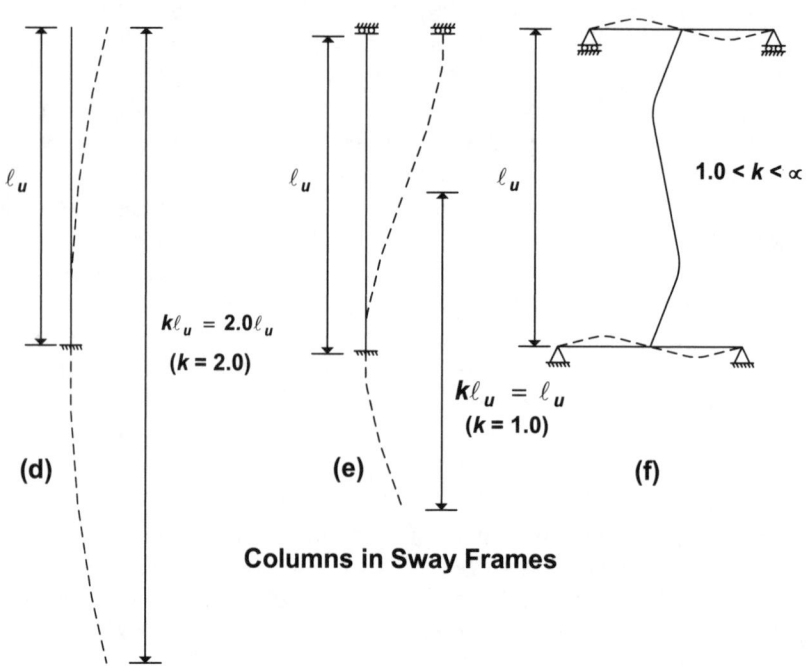

Columns in Sway Frames

Fig. 8.2 Effective Length Factor (k) for Columns in Non-Sway Frames

8.3   Lateral Bracing and Designation of Frames as Non-Sway

A frame is considered to be "non-sway" if it is sufficiently braced by lateral bracing elements like structural walls. Otherwise, it may be designated as a "sway" frame. Frames that provide resistance to lateral loads by columns only are considered to be sway frames. Structural walls that appear in the form of elevator shafts, stairwells, partial building enclosures or simply used as interior stiffening elements provide substantial drift control and lateral bracing. In most cases, even a few structural walls may be sufficient to brace a multi-storey multi-bay building. The designer can usually decide whether the frame is non-sway or sway by inspecting the floor plan. Frames with lateral bracing elements, where the total lateral stiffness of the bracing elements exceeds six times the summation of the stiffnesses of all the columns, may be classified as non-sway. A more accurate approach is specified in CSA A23.3-04 [Clause 10.14.4] based on the stability index "Q" defined in Eq. 8.2. Accordingly, if $Q \leq 0.05$ the frame may be designated as non-sway and the columns of the frame as braced.

$$Q = \frac{\sum P_f \Delta_o}{V_f \ell_c} \qquad\qquad (8.2)$$

where $\sum P_f$ is the total factored axial load acting on all the columns in a storey, V_f is the total factored storey shear, Δ_0 is the lateral storey drift (deflection of the top of the storey relative to the bottom of that storey) due to V_f. The storey drift Δ_0 should be computed using the modified EI values given in Table 8.4 with β_d defined as the ratio of the maximum factored sustained shear within a storey to the maximum factored shear in that storey. If Q exceeds approximately 0.2, the structure may have to be stiffened laterally to provide overall structural stability.

8.4   Design of Slender Columns

Design of a slender column should be based on a second-order analysis which incorporates member curvature and lateral drift effects, as well as material non-linearity and sustained load effects. An alternative approach is specified in CSA A23.3-04 for columns with slenderness ratios not exceeding 100. This approach is commonly referred to as the "Moment Magnification Method," and is based on magnifying the end moments to account for secondary stresses. The application of this procedure is outlined in the following sections.

8.4.1   Slender Columns in Non-Sway Frames

Slenderness effects may be ignored for columns in non-sway frames if the following inequality is satisfied:

$$\frac{k\ell_u}{r} \leq \frac{25 - 10(M_1 / M_2)}{\sqrt{P_f /(f' A_g)}} \qquad\qquad (8.3)$$

where M_1/M_2 is the ratio of smaller to larger end moments, with a negative value when the column is bent in double curvature, and a positive value when it is bent in single curvature. Fig. 8.3 illustrates columns in double and single curvatures. Columns are more stable, and the secondary effects are smaller, in double curvature than in single curvature. This is reflected in Eq. 8.3 through the sign of M_1/M_2 ratio. For negative values of this ratio the limit of slenderness, specified in Eq. 8.3 increases, allowing a wider range of columns to be treated as short columns. The M_1/M_2 ratio is not to be taken less than -0.5 when used in Eq. 8.3.

8

Slender Columns

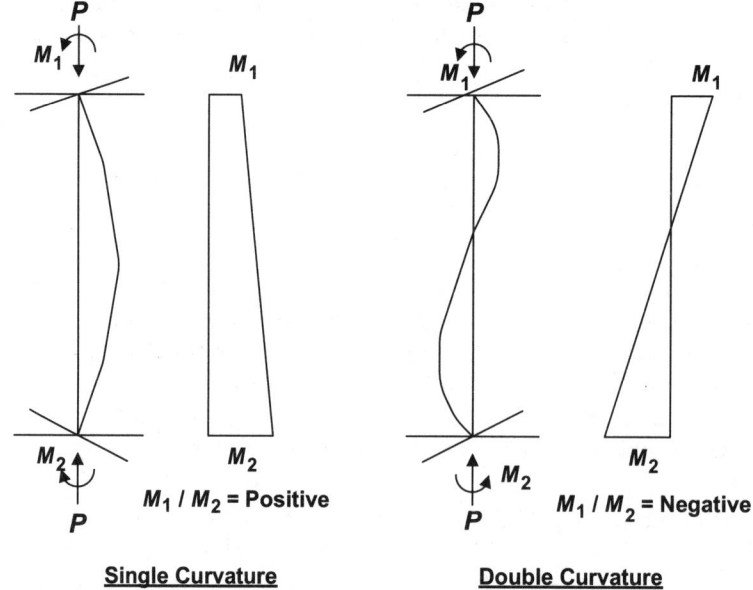

Single Curvature   Double Curvature

Fig. 8.3 Columns in Single and Double Curvature

Slender columns in non-sway frames are designed for factored axial force P_f and amplified moment M_c. The amplified moment is obtained by magnifying the larger of the two end moments (M_2) to account for member curvature and resulting secondary moments between the supports, while the supports are braced against sidesway. If M_c computed for the curvature effect between the ends is smaller than the larger end moment M_2, the design is carried out for M_2.

$$M_c = \frac{C_m M_2}{1 - \dfrac{P_f}{\phi_m P_c}} \geq M_2 \tag{8.4}$$

where, $\phi_m = 0.75$, and the critical column load, P_c (Euler buckling load) is;

$$p_c = \frac{\pi^2 EI}{(k\ell_u)^2} \tag{8.5}$$

EI in Eq. 8.5 is computed either with due considerations given to the presence of reinforcement in the section, as specified in Eq. 8.6, or approximately using Eq. 8.7.

$$EI = \frac{0.2 E_c I_g + E_s I_{st}}{1 + \beta_d} \tag{8.6}$$

where β_d is the ratio of the maximum factored axial dead load to the total factored axial load. The moment of inertia of reinforcement about the cross-sectional centroid (I_{st}) can be computed using Table 8.6.

$$EI = \frac{0.4 E_c I_g}{1 + \beta_d} \tag{8.7}$$

Coefficient C_m is equal to 1.0 for members with transverse loads between the supports. For the more common case of columns without transverse loads between the supports;

$$C_m = 06 + 0.4 \frac{M_1}{M_2} \geq 0.4 \qquad (8.8)$$

Furthermore, the product $C_m M_2$ should not be less than the moment associated with minimum eccentricity.

$$C_m M_2 \geq P_f (15 + 0.03h) \qquad (8.9)$$

where h is the cross-sectional dimension in mm in the direction of eccentricity. Once the amplified moment M_c is obtained, the designer can use the appropriate interaction diagram from Chapter 7 to determine the required percentage of longitudinal reinforcement.

8.4.2   Slender Columns in Sway Frames

Columns in sway frames are designed for the factored axial load P_f and the combination of factored gravity load moments and magnified sway moments. This is specified below, and illustrated in Table 8.7.

$$M_1 = M_{1ns} + \delta_s M_{1s} \qquad (8.10)$$

$$M_2 = M_{2ns} + \delta_s M_{2s} \qquad (8.11)$$

where, M_{1ns} and M_{2ns} are end moments due to factored gravity loads; and M_{1s} and M_{2s} are sway moments normally caused by factored lateral loads. All of these moments can be obtained from a first-order elastic frame analysis. Magnified sway moments $\delta_s M_{1s}$ and $\delta_s M_{2s}$ are obtained either from a second order frame analysis, with member stiffnesses as specified in Table 8.4, or by magnifying the end moments by sway magnification factor δ_s.

$$\delta_s = \frac{1}{1 - \dfrac{\sum P_f}{\phi_m \sum P_c}} \qquad (8.12)$$

In a sway frame, all the columns of a given storey participate in sway mechanism and the stability of columns. Therefore, Eq. 8.12 includes $\sum P_f$ and $\sum P_c$ which give the summations of factored axial loads and critical loads for all the columns in the storey, respectively. The critical column load P_c can be computed using Eqs. 8.5 through 8.7 with the effective length factor k computed for unbraced columns (for sway frames), and β_d as the ratio of the maximum factored sustained shear within the storey to the maximum total factored shear in the storey.

Eq. 8.12 provides an average δ_s for all the columns in a storey. Therefore, it yields acceptable results if all the columns in a storey undergo the same storey drift. When significant torsion is anticipated under lateral loading, a second order analysis is recommended for finding the amplified sway moment, $\delta_s M_s$.

An alternative to Eq. 8.12 is given below for cases where Q has been computed from Eq. 8.2 to be less than or equal to 1/3.

$$\delta_s = \frac{1}{1 - Q} \qquad (8.13)$$

The sidesway magnification discussed above is intended to amplify the end moments associated with lateral drift. Although the amplified end moment is commonly the critical moment for most sway columns, additional magnification may become necessary due to the curvature of

8

Slender Columns

the column between the ends. This occurs if the slenderness ratio is high. The magnification of moment due to the curvature of column between the ends is similar to that discussed for braced columns in non-sway frames. This additional magnification is required for columns that satisfy the following condition:

$$\frac{\ell_u}{r} > \frac{35}{\sqrt{P_f / (f'_c A_g)}} \tag{8.14}$$

The larger of the end moments computed by Eqs. 8.10 and 8.11, for the load combination used in computing P_f, is then magnified using Eqs 8.4 through 8.8. As in the case of braced columns, the effective length factor k used in Eq. 8.5 is computed as if the column were a braced column, from Table 8.2, and β_d used in Eq. 8.6 is taken as the ratio of the factored axial dead load to the total factored axial load.

Sometimes columns of a sway frame may buckle under gravity loads alone, without the effects of lateral loading. In this case one of the gravity load combinations may govern the stability of columns. The reduction of EI under sustained gravity loads may be another factor contributing to the stability of sway columns under gravity loads. Therefore, an additional provision is provided in CSA A23.3-04 (Clause 10.16.5) to safeguard against column buckling in sway frames under gravity loads alone. Accordingly, the strength and stability of structure is reconsidered depending on the method of amplification used for sway moments. If a second order analysis has been conducted to find $\delta_s M_{2s}$, two additional analyses are necessary using the reduced stiffness values given in Table 8.4 with β_d taken as the ratio of the factored sustained axial dead load to total factored axial load. First, a second-order analysis is conducted under combined factored gravity loads and lateral loads equal to 0.5% of the gravity loads. Second, a first-order analysis is conducted under the same loading condition. The ratio of lateral drift obtained by the second-order analysis to that obtained by the first-order analysis is required to be limited to 2.5.

If the sway moment has been amplified by computing the sway magnification factor (as opposed to conducting second order analysis), then δ_s computed by using gravity loads is required to be positive and less than or equal to 2.5 to ensure the stability of the column.

8.5   Design Examples

Example 8.1 - Design of an interior column braced against sidesway

Consider a 10-storey office building, laterally braced against sidesway by an elevator shaft (Q is computed to be much less than 0.05). The building has an atrium opening at the second floor level with a two-storey high column in the middle of the opening to be designed. Design the column for the design forces given below, obtained from a first-order analysis. The framing beams are 400 mm wide and 500 mm deep with 7.0 m (canter-to-centre) spans. The beam depth includes a slab thickness of 150 mm. The storey height is 4.3 m, and 40 MPa concrete is used in all beams and columns. f_y = 400 MPa. (See figure for Example 8.1). It is assumed that the bracing elements provide full resistance to lateral loads and the columns only resist gravity loads.

Unfactored Loads	Dead Load	Live Load
Axial load (kN):	1776	1320
Top moment (kN.m):	-130	-79
Bottom moment (kN.m)	-15	-8

Note: Moments are positive if counterclockwise at column ends. The column is bent in double curvature.

1.   Determine factored design forces:
     Note: M_1 is the lower, and M_2 is the higher end moment

    i) U = $1.4D$
           P_f = $1.4\,P_D$ = 1.4 (1776) = 2486 kN
           M_2 = $1.4\,M_{D2}$ = 1.4 (130) = 182 kN.m
           M_1 = $1.4\,M_{D1}$ = 1.4 (15) = 21 kN.m

    ii) U = $1.25\,D + 1.5\,L$
           P_f = $1.25\,P_D + 1.50\,P_L$ = 1.25 (1776) + 1.50 (1320) = 4200 kN
           M_2 = $1.25\,M_{D2} + 1.50\,M_L$ = 1.25 (130) + 1.50 (79) = 281 kN.m
           M_1 = $1.25\,M_{D1} + 1.5\,M_L$ = 1.25 (15) + 1.50 (8) = 31 kN.m

Note: Load Combination (ii) governs the design

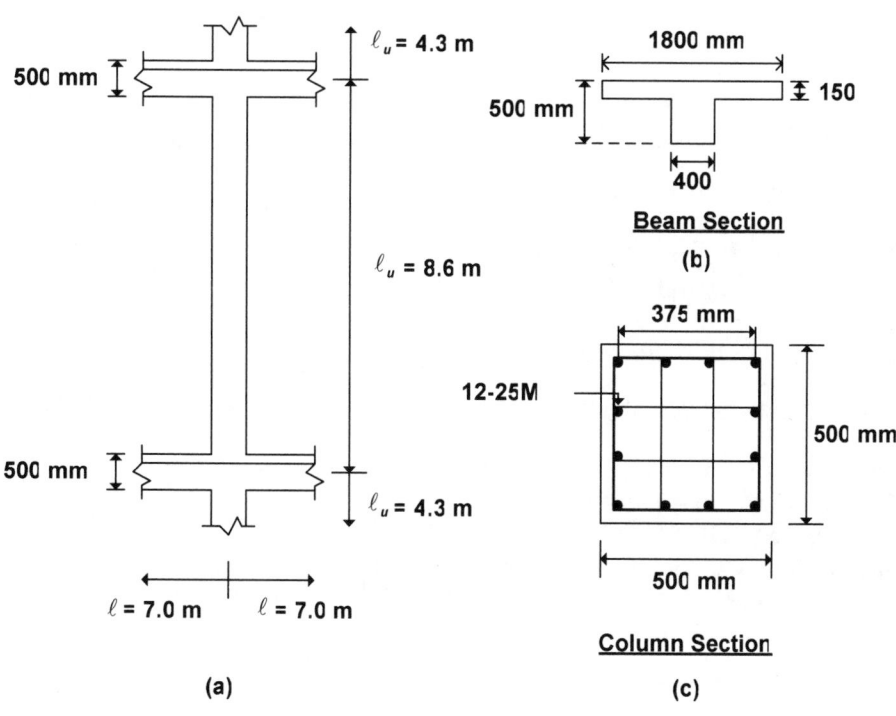

Example 8.1

2.   Estimate the column size:

    For P_f = 4200 kN, select 500 x 500 mm from Table 7.1.4.

3.   Calculate slenderness ratio $k\ell_u/r$.

    The unsupported column length (Table 8.1); ℓ_u = 8600 - 250 - 250 = 8100 mm
    The radius of gyration for a square column; r = 0.3 h = 0.3 (500) = 150 mm
    Compute the effective length factor "k" from Table 8.2.

First find stiffness ratios at the ends.

Beam moment of inertia (T-section): $I_g = 7.7 \times 10^9$ mm^4

Column moment of inertia: $I_g = bh^3/12 = (500)(500)^3/12 = 5.2 \times 10^9$ mm^4

Find reduced EI values as per Table 8.4;

$(EI)_{beam} = (10361)(7.7 \times 10^9) = 8.0 \times 10^{13}$ N.mm^2

$(EI)_{col} = (20721)(5.2 \times 10^9) = 1.1 \times 10^{14}$ N.mm^2

$(EI/\ell)_{beam} = (8.0 \times 10^{13}) / (7000) = 1.1 \times 10^{10}$ for both left and right beams

$(EI/\ell_c)_{col} = (1.1 \times 10^{14}) / (8600) = 1.3 \times 10^{10}$ for the atrium column to be designed

$(EI/\ell_c)_{col} = (1.1 \times 10^{14}) / (4300) = 2.6 \times 10^{10}$ for columns above and below

$\psi = (\Sigma EI/\ell_c)_{col} / (\Sigma EI/\ell)_{beam} = [(EI/\ell_c)_{col,\,above} + (EI/\ell_c)_{col,\,below}] / [(EI/\ell)_{beam,\,left} + (EI/\ell)_{beam,\,right}]$

$\psi_A = (2.6 \times 10^{10} + 1.3 \times 10^{10}) / (1.1 \times 10^{10} + 1.1 \times 10^{10}) = 1.8$

for $\psi_B = \psi_A = 1.8$;   select $k = 0.84$ from Table 8.2

(Note that Table 8.5 gives a conservative value of $k = 0.90$)

$k\ell_u/r = 0.84 \, (8100) / 150 = 45.4$

4. Check if slenderness can be neglected:

From Eq. 8.3; if $k\ell_u / r \le [25 - 10(M_1 / M_2)] / \sqrt{P_f /(f'_c \, A_g)}$ then slenderness can be neglected. *Note:* M_1/M_2 can not be less than -0.5. In this problem $M_1/M_2 = -31/281 = -0.11$

$k\ell_u / r = 45.4 > [25 - 10(M_1 / M_2)] / \sqrt{P_f /(f'_c \, A_g)} =$

$$[25 - 10(-0.11)] / \sqrt{4200 \times 10^3 /(40 \times 500 \times 500)} = 40.3$$

Therefore, consider slenderness.

5. Compute critical load, P_c from Eq. 8.5 and associated EI from Eq. 8.6 or 8.7:

EI from Eq. 8.6 for assumed reinforcement ratio of $\rho_t = 0.025$, equally distributed on all faces with $\gamma = 0.75$;

$E_c = 29602$ MPa (from Table 8.4); $E_s = 200,000$ MPa; $I_g = 5.2 \times 10^9$ mm^4

$I_{st} = 0.18 \, \rho_t \, b \, h^3 \gamma^2$ (from Table 8.6);

$I_{st} = 0.18 \,(0.025)(500)(500)^3 (0.75)^2 = 1.6 \times 10^8$ mm^4

$\beta_d = 2220 / 4200 = 0.53$ $EI = (0.2E_c I_g + E_s I_{st}) / (1 + B_d)$

$EI = [(0.2 \times 29602 \times 5.2 \times 10^9) + (200000 \times 1.6 \times 10^8)] / (1 + 0.53)$

$EI = 4.1 \times 10^{13}$ N.mm^2

Alternatively, EI from Eq 8.7;

$EI = 0.25 \, E_c I_g = 0.25 \times 29602 \times 5.2 \times 10^9 = 3.8 \times 10^{13}$ N.mm^2

From Eq. 8.5; $P_c = \pi^2 \, EI / (k \, \ell_u)^2$

$P_c = \pi^2 \times 4.1 \times 10^{13} / (0.84 \times 8100)^2 = 8741 \times 10^3$ N

6. Compute C_m from Eq. 8.8 :

$C_m = 0.6 + 0.4 \, M_1/M_2 \ge 0.4$ $C_m = 0.6 + 0.4 \,(-0.11) = 0.56$

7. Compute magnified moment M_c from Eq. 8.4 :

$M_c = C_m \, M_2 / [1 - P_f / (\phi_m \, P_c)] = 0.56 \,(281) / [1 - 4200 / (0.75 \times 8741)]$

$M_c = 1.56 \times 281 = 438$ kN.m (magnified moment)

Check against minimum design moment as per Eq. 8.9;

$C_m M_2 \ge P_f \,(15 + 0.03h) = 4200 \times 10^3 \,(15 + 0.03 \times 500) = 126 \times 10^6$ N.mm; O.K.

8.   Select reinforcement ratio and design the column section:

Select the appropriate interaction diagram from Chapter 7. For f'_c = 40 MPa; f_y = 400 MPa, γ = 0.75 (assumed in step 5), and equal reinforcement on all four sides. Select Tables 7.4.14 and 7.4.15, and interpolate between the two:

P_f / A_g = 4200 x 10^3 / $(500)^2$ = 16.8 MPa
$M_c / A_g h$ = 438 x 10^6 / $[(500)^2(500)]$ = 3.5 MPa

From Table 7.4.14 for γ = 0.7; ρ_t = 0.025
From Table 7.4.15 for γ = 0.8; ρ_t = 0.022

Interpolating for γ = 0.75; ρ_t = 0.0235
$A_{st} = \rho_t A_g$ = 0.0235 $(500)^2$ = 5875 mm^2 try 25M bars (A_{st} = 500 mm^2);
5250 / 500 = 11.75

Use 12-25M longitudinal reinforcement, equally distributed on all sides.
Note: For further details of cross-sectional design refer to Chapter 7.

Example 8.2 - Design of an exterior column in a sway frame

A typical floor plan and a section through a four-storey apartment building is shown in the figure (See figure for Example 8.2). Design column 3-A at the ground level for combined gravity and east-west wind loading.

f'_c = 40 MPa; f_y = 400 MPa.

1.   Consider the applicable load combinations:

The structure is not braced against sidesway. Therefore, the column will be designed considering the loads that cause sidesway. Note that sidesway in this structure is caused by wind loading. No significant sidesway is anticipated due to the gravity loads since the structure is symmetric.

a)   The load combinations that include wind loading;
       Load Combination I: U = 1.25D + 1.5L + 0.4W
       Load Combination II: U = 1.25D + 0.5L + 1.4W
b)   The Load combinations for gravity loading;
       Load Combination III: U = 1.4D
       Load Combination IV: U = 1.25D + 1.5L

Note: The column may be critical under gravity loading only, even if it is part of a sway frame (CSA A23.3-04, Clause 10.16.5).

Conduct a frame analysis to determine first-order design forces. Use the stiffness values given in Table 8.4 for the analysis.

8

Slender Columns

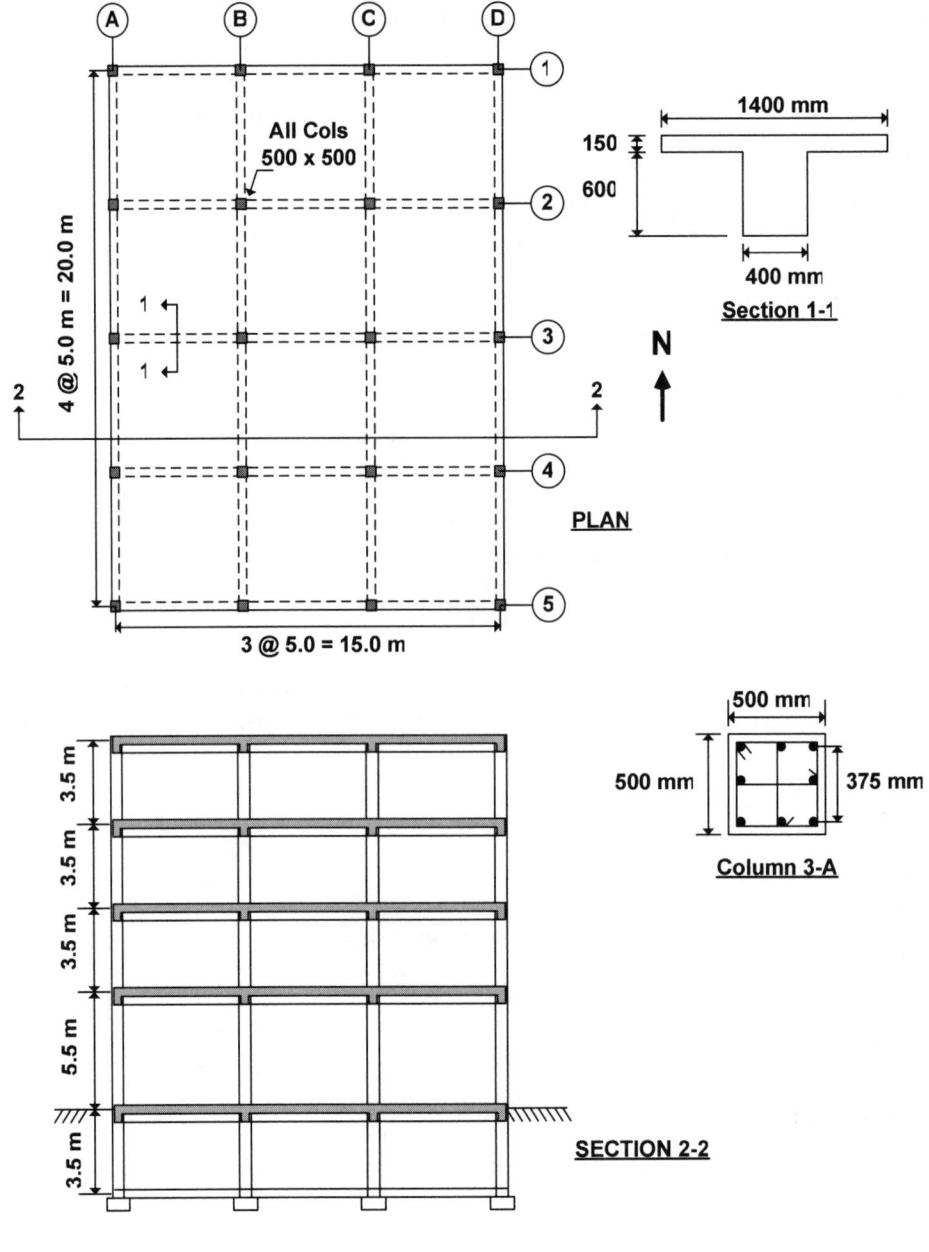

Example 8.2

Try the preliminary column section given in the figure.

2.   Determine the effective length factor k for all columns at the ground level:

Note: All columns have the same geometry.
$I_{beam} = 2.3 \times 10^{10}$ mm^4 (for T-section)
$I_{col} = (500)(500)^3/12 = 5.2 \times 10^9$ mm^4

Find reduced *EI* values from Table 8.4 for 40 MPa concrete;
$(E_c I)_{beam} = 10361\ I_{beam} = 10361\ (2.3 \times 10^{10}) = 2.4 \times 10^{14}$ N.mm^2

$(E_cI)_{col} = 20721\ I_{col} = 20721\ (5.2 \times 10^9) = 1.1 \times 10^{14}$ N.mm^2
$(EI/\ell)_{beam} = 2.4 \times 10^{14} / 5000 = 4.8 \times 10^{10}$ N.mm
$(EI/\ell_c)_{col,\ above} = 1.1 \times 10^{14} / 3500 = 3.1 \times 10^{10}$ N.mm
$(EI/\ell_c)_{col,\ below} = 1.1 \times 10^{14} / 5500 = 2.0 \times 10^{10}$ N.mm

$\psi = (\Sigma EI/\ell_c)_{col} / (\Sigma EI/\ell)_{beam} = [(EI/\ell_c)_{col,\ above} + (EI/\ell_c)_{col,\ below}] / [(EI/\ell)_{beam,\ left} + (EI/\ell)_{beam,\ right}]$

i) For exterior columns (columns on lines A and D):

$\psi_A = (3.1 \times 10^{10} + 2.0 \times 10^{10}) / 4.8 \times 10^{10} = 1.06$
$\psi_B = \psi_A = 1.06$; from Table 8.3; $k = 1.35$ (for unbraced frame)
$k = 0.78$ from Table 8.2 for a braced column. This value is computed for further magnification of moments, if necessary, for column 3-A as per CSA A23.3-04, Clause 10.16.4.

ii) For interior columns (columns on lines B and C):

$\psi_A = (3.1 \times 10^{10} + 2.0 \times 10^{10}) / (4.8 \times 10^{10} + 4.8 \times 10^{10}) = 0.53$
$\psi_B = \psi_A = 0.53$; from Table 8.3 $k = 1.15$ (for unbraced frame)

8

Slender Columns

3. Compute critical load P_c from Eq. 8.5, and associated EI from Eq. 8.6 or 8.7 :

Note: P_c for all load combinations can be computed to be the same if Eq. 8.7 is used in computing EI, since this expression is independent of β_d.
$E_c = 29602$ MPa for $f'_c = 40$ MPa (from Table 8.4)

From Eq. 8.7; $EI = 0.25\ E_cI_g = 0.25\ (29602)(5.2 \times 10^9) = 3.8 \times 10^{13}$ N.mm^2
$\ell_u = 5500 - 750 = 4750$ mm

i) For exterior columns (columns on lines A and D):

$P_c = \pi^2\ EI / (k\ell_u)^2 = \pi^2\ (3.8 \times 10^{13})/(1.35 \times 4750)^2 = 9{,}121 \times 10^3$ N for a sway frame.
$P_c = \pi^2\ EI / (k\ell_u)^2 = \pi^2\ (3.8 \times 10^{13})/(0.78 \times 4750)^2 = 27{,}322 \times 10^3$ N for braced columns.

P_c for braced columns may be needed if further magnification of moments is required as per Clause 10.16.4 of CSA A23.3-04 for column 3-A.

ii) For interior columns (columns on lines B and C):

$P_c = \pi^2\ EI / (k\ell_u)^2 = \pi^2\ (3.8 \times 10^{13}) / (1.15 \times 4750)^2 = 12{,}569 \times 10^3$ N for a sway frame.

4. Compute magnified sway moment $\delta_s M_s$:

i) Load Combination I: U = 1.25D + 1.5L + 0.4W
Consider factored axial loads and bending moments obtained from first-order frame analysis conducted using the stiffness coefficients in Table 8.4.

Load	1.25D + 1.5L	0.4W
P_f (kN) – Corner Column	2359	±18
P_f (kN) – Edge Column	3375	±26
P_f (kN) – Interior Column	5287	±6
$(M_f)_{top}$ kN.m – Column 3-A	-226	±43
$(M_f)_{bot}$ kN.m – Column 3-A	-239	±63

Note: Counterclockwise moment at column end is positive.

a)   Sway magnification factor δ_s from Eq. 8.12.

$\Sigma P_f = 4\ (2359 + 18) + 10\ (3375 + 26) + 6\ (5287 + 6) = 75276$ kN

From Step 3; $\Sigma P_c = 10\ (9121) + 10\ (12569) = 216900$ kN

$\delta_s = 1\ /\ [1 - \Sigma P_f\ /\ (\phi_m \Sigma P_c\ )] = 1\ /\ [1 - 75276\ /\ (0.75 \times 216900)] = 1.86$
$\delta_s\ M_{1s} = 1.86 \times 43 = 80$ kN.m
$\delta_s\ M_{2s} = 1.86 \times 63 = 117$ kN.m

b)   Compute design moments M_1 and M_2 from Eqs. 8.10 and 8.11, and Table 8.7.
$M_1 = M_{1ns} + \delta_s\ M_{1s} = 226 + 80 = 306$ kN.m
$M_2 = M_{2ns} + \delta_s\ M_{2s} = 239 + 117 = 356$ kN.m

c)   Check if further magnification of moments is required due to the curvature of the columns between the ends using Eq. 8.14.

$$\frac{\ell_u}{r} > \frac{35}{\sqrt{P_f\ /(f'_c\ A_g\ )}}$$

$P_f = 3375 + 26 = 3401$ kN
$k\ell_u/r = 4750\ /\ (0.3 \times 500) = 31.7\ < 35\ /\ \sqrt{3401 \times 10^3\ /(40 \times (500)^2\ )} = 60.0$
Therefore, no further magnification is required.

ii) Load Combination II : U = 1.25D + 0.5L + 1.4W
Consider factored axial loads and bending moments obtained from first-order frame analysis conducted using the stiffness coefficients in Table 8.4.

Load	1.25D + 0.5L	1.4W
P_f (kN) – Corner Column	1850	±64
P_f (kN) – Edge Column	2646	±91
P_f (kN) – Interior Column	4143	±21
$(M_f)_{top}$ kN.m – Column 3-A	-177	±152
$(M_f)_{bot}$ kN.m – Column 3-A	-188	±220

Note: Counterclockwise moment at column end is positive.

a)   Sway magnification factor δ_s and magnified sway moments $\delta_s\ M_{1s}$ and $\delta_s\ M_{2s}$

$\Sigma P_f = 4\ (1850 + 64) + 10\ (2646 + 91) + 6\ (4143 + 21) = 60010$ kN

From Step 3:
$\Sigma P_c = 10\ (9121) + 10\ (12569) = 216900$ kN
$\delta_s = 1\ /\ [1 - \Sigma P_f\ /\ (\phi_m \Sigma P_c\ )] = 1\ /\ [1 - 60010\ /\ (0.75 \times 216900)] = 1.58$
$\delta_s\ M_{1s} = 1.58 \times 152 = 240$ kN.m
$\delta_s\ M_{2s} = 1.58 \times 220 = 348$ kN.m

b)   Compute design moments M_1 and M_2 from Eqs. 8.10 and 8.11, and Table 8.7.

$M_1 = M_{1ns} + \delta_s\ M_{1s} = 177 + 240 = 417$ kN.m
$M_2 = M_{2ns} + \delta_s\ M_{2s} = 188 + 348 = 536$ kN.m

c) Check if further magnification of moments is required due to the curvature of the columns between the ends using Eq. 8.14.

$$\frac{\ell_u}{r} > \frac{35}{\sqrt{P_f /(f'_c A_g)}}$$

$P_f = 2646 + 91 = 2737$ kN

$k\ell_u /r = 4750 / (0.3 \times 500) = 31.7 \; < 35 / \sqrt{2737 x10^3 /(40x(500)^2)} \; = 66.9$

Therefore, no further magnification is required.

5. Check the stability of column under gravity loads only (Load Combinations III and IV) as per CSA A23.3-04, Clause 10.16.5:

Consider factored axial loads and bending moments obtained from a first-order frame analysis, conducted using the stiffness coefficients given in Table 8.4.

i) Load Combination III : U = 1.4D

Load	1.4D
P_f (kN) – Corner Column	1788
P_f (kN) – Edge Column	2555
P_f (kN) – Interior Column	4000
$(M_f)_{top}$ kN.m – Column 3-A	-171
$(M_f)_{bot}$ kN.m – Column 3-A	-183

Note: Counterclockwise moment at column end is positive.

Compute the sway magnification factor δ_s

$\Sigma P_f = 4\,(1788) + 10\,(2555) + 6\,(4000) = 56702$ kN
From Step 3; $\Sigma P_c = 10\,(9121) + 10\,(12569) = 216900$ kN

$\delta_s = 1 / [1 - \Sigma P_f / (\phi_m \Sigma P_c)] = 1 / [1 - 56702 / (0.75 \times 216900)] = 1.54$

$\delta_s = 1.54 < 2.5$ O.K.

ii) Load Combination IV : U = 1.25D + 1.5L

Load	1.25D + 1.5L
P_f (kN) – Corner Column	2359
P_f (kN) – Edge Column	3375
P_f (kN) – Interior Column	5287
$(M_f)_{top}$ kN.m – Column 3-A	-226
$(M_f)_{bot}$ kN.m – Column 3-A	-239

Note: Counterclockwise moment at column end is positive.

8

Slender Columns

Compute the sway magnification factor δ_s

$\Sigma P_f = 4\,(2359) + 10\,(3375) + 6\,(5287) = 74908$ kN
From Step 3;
$\Sigma P_c = 10\,(9121) + 10\,(12569) = 216900$ kN

$\delta_s = 1\,/\,[1 - \Sigma P_f\,/\,(\phi_m \Sigma P_c\,)] = 1\,/\,[1 - 74908\,/\,(0.75 \times 216900)] = 1.85$
$\delta_s = 1.85 < 2.5$ O.K.

6.   Design the column for the governing load combination:

Summary of Design Loads:

Load Combinations	P_f (kN)	(M_f) (kN.m)
I - U = 1.25D + 1.5L + 0.4W	3401	356
II - U = 1.25D + 0.5L + 1.4W	2737	536
III - U = 1.4D	2555	183
IV - U = 1.25D + 1.5L	3375	239

Select the interaction diagrams given in Table 7.4.15 from Chapter 7.
For Load Combination II;
$P_f/A_g = 2737 \times 10^3\,/\,(500)^2 = 11.0$ MPa
$M_f/A_g h = 536 \times 10^6\,/\,(500)^3 = 4.3$ MPa
Select $\rho_t = 0.02$. $A_{st} = 0.02\,(500)^2 = 5000$ mm^2. Try 30M bars ($A_{st} = 700$ mm^2);
5000 / 700 = 7.14. Use 8-30M bars equally distributed on all four faces.

Check the capacity for Load Combination I;
$P_f/A_g = 3401 \times 10^3\,/\,(500)^2 = 13.6$ MPa
$M_f/A_g h = 356 \times 10^6\,/\,(500)^3 = 2.8$ MPa
the point lies inside the interaction diagram, O.K.
Note: For further details of cross-sectional design refer to Chapter 7.

8.6 Design Aids

Table 8.1 Unsupported Column Length, ℓ_u

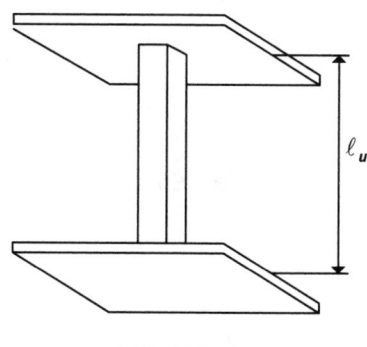

a) Flat Plate

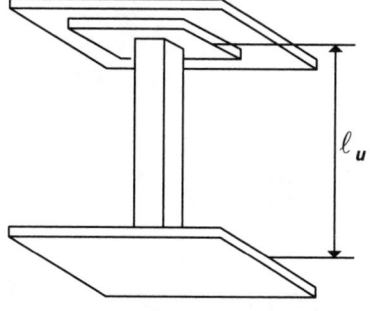

b) Flat Slab

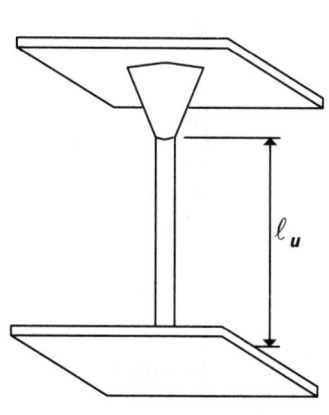

c) Column Capital

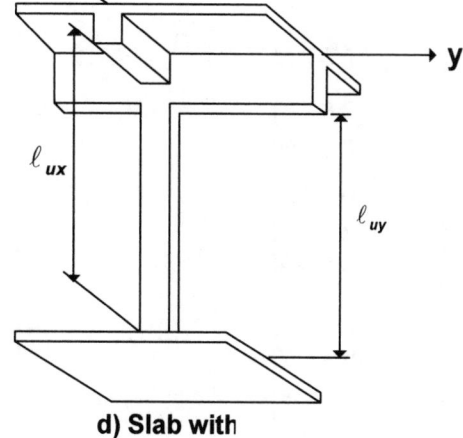

d) Slab with Beams

Table 8.2 Effective Length Factor – Alignment Chart for Columns in Braced Frames

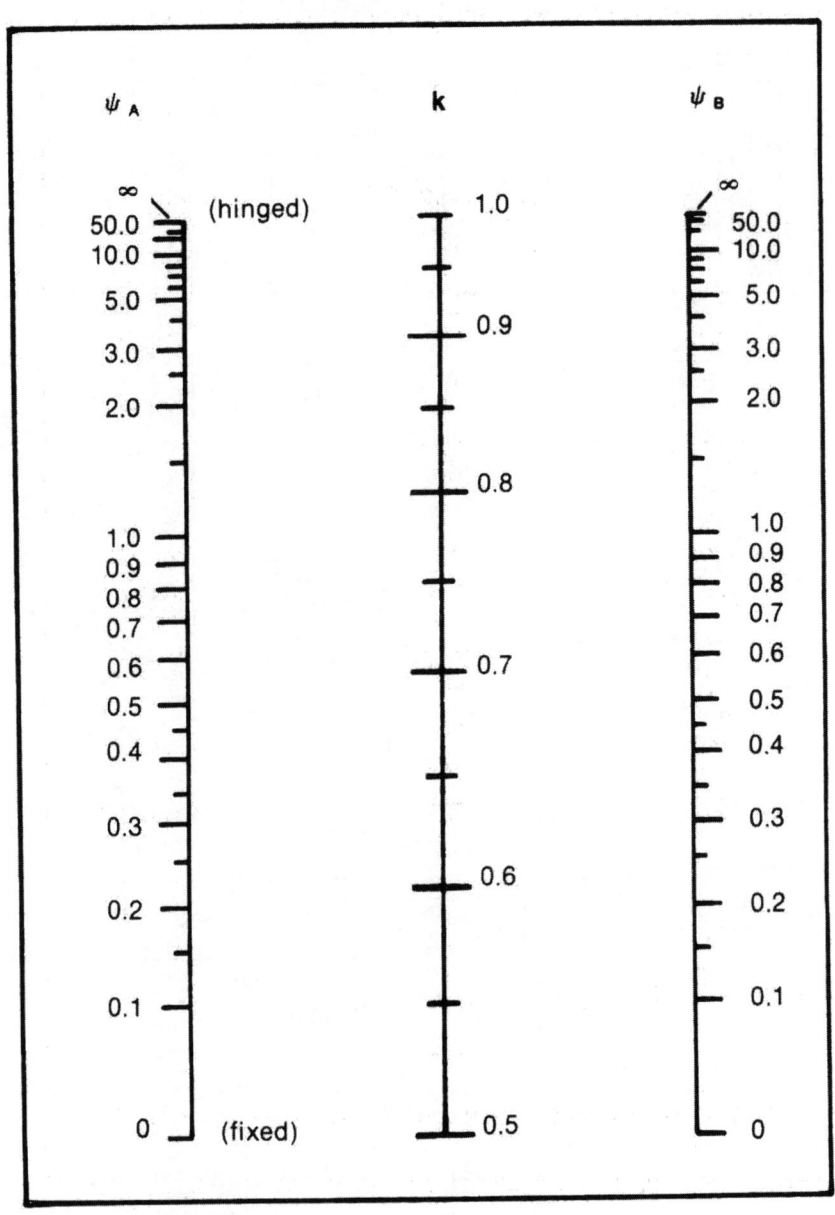

$$\psi_i = \frac{(\Sigma EI/\ell_c)_{\text{columns}}}{(\Sigma EI/\ell)_{\text{beams}}} \quad \text{at end i of column}$$

Table 8.3 Effective Length Factor – Alignment Chart for Columns in Unbraced Frames

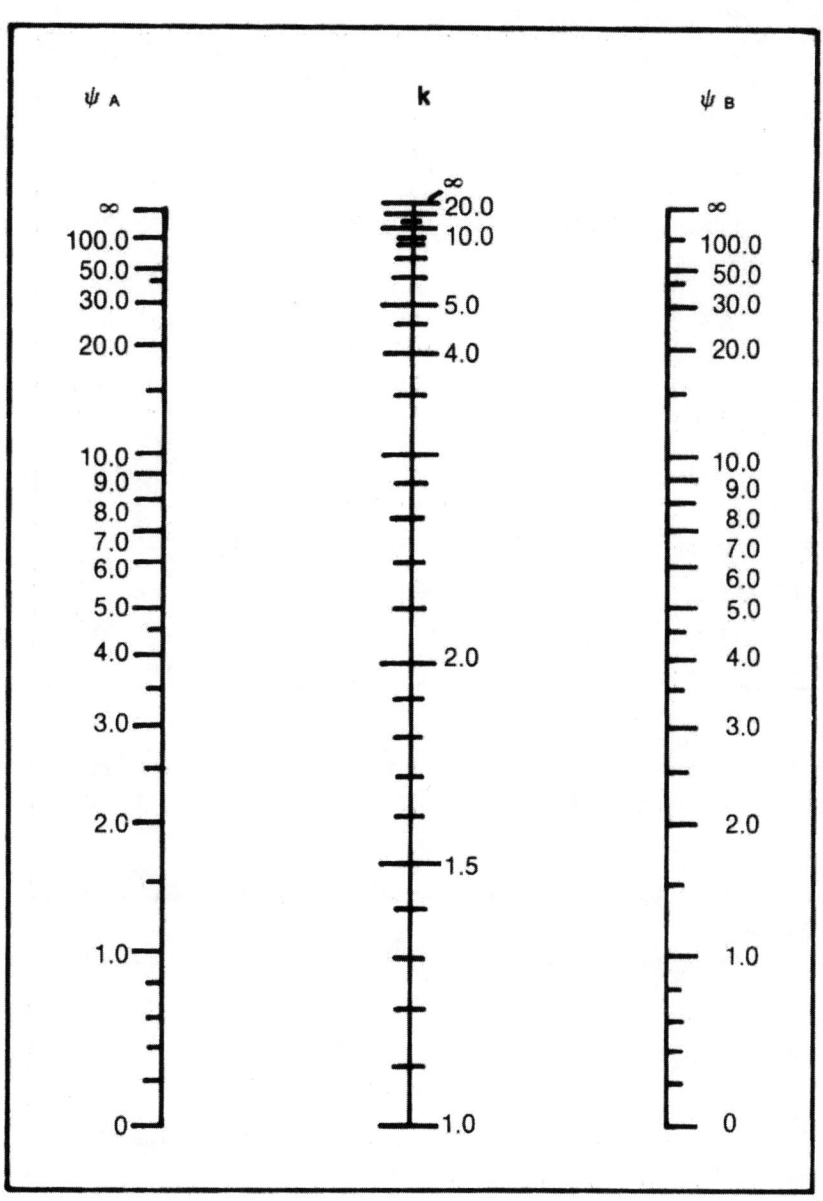

$$\psi_i = \frac{(\Sigma EI/\ell_c)_{columns}}{(\Sigma EI/\ell)_{beams}} \quad \text{at end i of column}$$

Table 8.4 Recommended Flexural Rigidities (*EI*) for use in First-Order and Second Order Analyses of Frames for Design of Slender Columns

	$E_c I / I_g$ (MPa)							
f'_c (MPa):	20	30	40	50	60	70	80	
E_c (MPa):	23,085	26,621	29,602	32,228	34,602	36,785	38,817	I / I_g
Beams:	8,080	9,317	10,361	11,280	12,111	12,875	13,586	0.35
Columns:	16,160	18,635	20,721	22,560	24,221	25,750	27,172	0.70
Walls Uncracked:	16,160	18,635	20,721	22,560	24,221	25,750	27,172	0.70
Cracked:	8,080	9,317	10,361	11,280	12,111	12,875	13,586	0.35
Flat Plates Flat Slabs:	5,771	6,655	7,400	8,057	8,651	9,196	9,704	0.25

Notes:

The walls will be analyzed with uncracked flexural rigidities until the analysis indicates cracking based on the modulus of rupture, in which case the analysis will be repeated with cracked rigidities.

The above values will be divided by $(1+\beta_d)$, when applicable as per CSA A23.3-04.

The above values are applicable to normal-density concrete with $\gamma_c = 2400$ kg/m^3.

Table 8.5 Effective Length Factor "*k*" for Columns in Braced Frames

TOP		*k*			
Hinged		0.81	0.91	0.95	1.00
Elastic		0.77	0.86	0.90	0.95
Elastic		0.74	0.83	0.86	0.91
Stiff		0.67	0.74	0.77	0.81
		Stiff	Elastic	Elastic	Hinged
		BOTTOM			

Table 8.6 Moment of Inertia of Reinforcement About Sectional Centroid

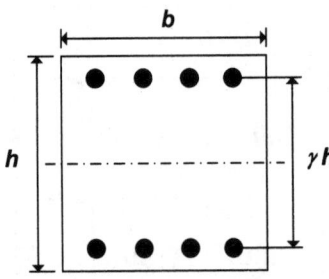

Bars in two end faces

$$I_{st} = 0.25\, \rho_t b\, h^3 \gamma^2$$

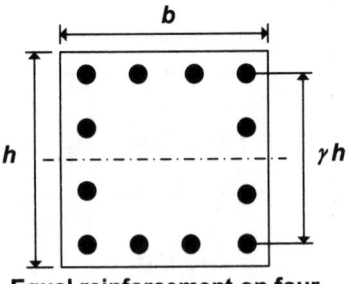

Equal reinforcement on four sides

$$I_{st} = 0.18\, \rho_t b\, h^3 \gamma^2$$

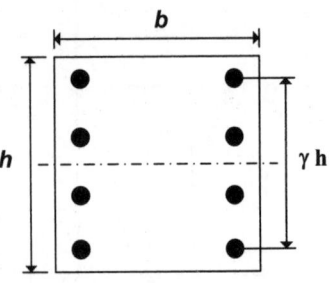

Bars in two side faces

$$I_{st} = 0.17\, \rho_t b\, h^3 \gamma^2 \quad \text{(3 bars per face)}$$
$$I_{st} = 0.12\, \rho_t b\, h^3 \gamma^2 \quad \text{(6 bars per face)}$$

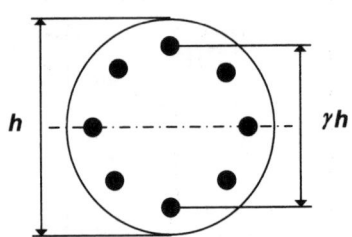

Uniformly distributed reinforcement

$$I_{st} = 0.10\, \rho_t\, h^4 \gamma^2$$

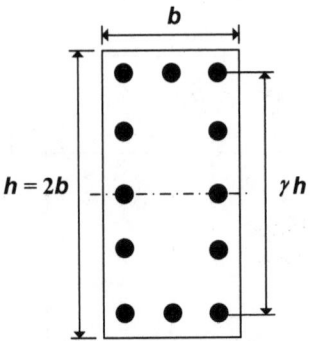

Bars uniformly spaced on all sides

$$I_{st} = 0.13\, \rho_t b\, h^3 \gamma^2$$

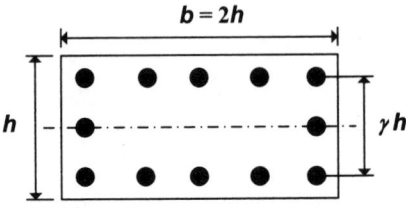

Bars uniformly spaced on all sides

$$I_{st} = 0.22\, \rho_t b\, h^3 \gamma^2$$

Note: This table is based on Table 12-1 of MacGregor, J.G., Second Edition, Prentice Hall, Englewood Cliffs, New Jersey, 1992.

Table 8.7 Design Moments in Sway Frames

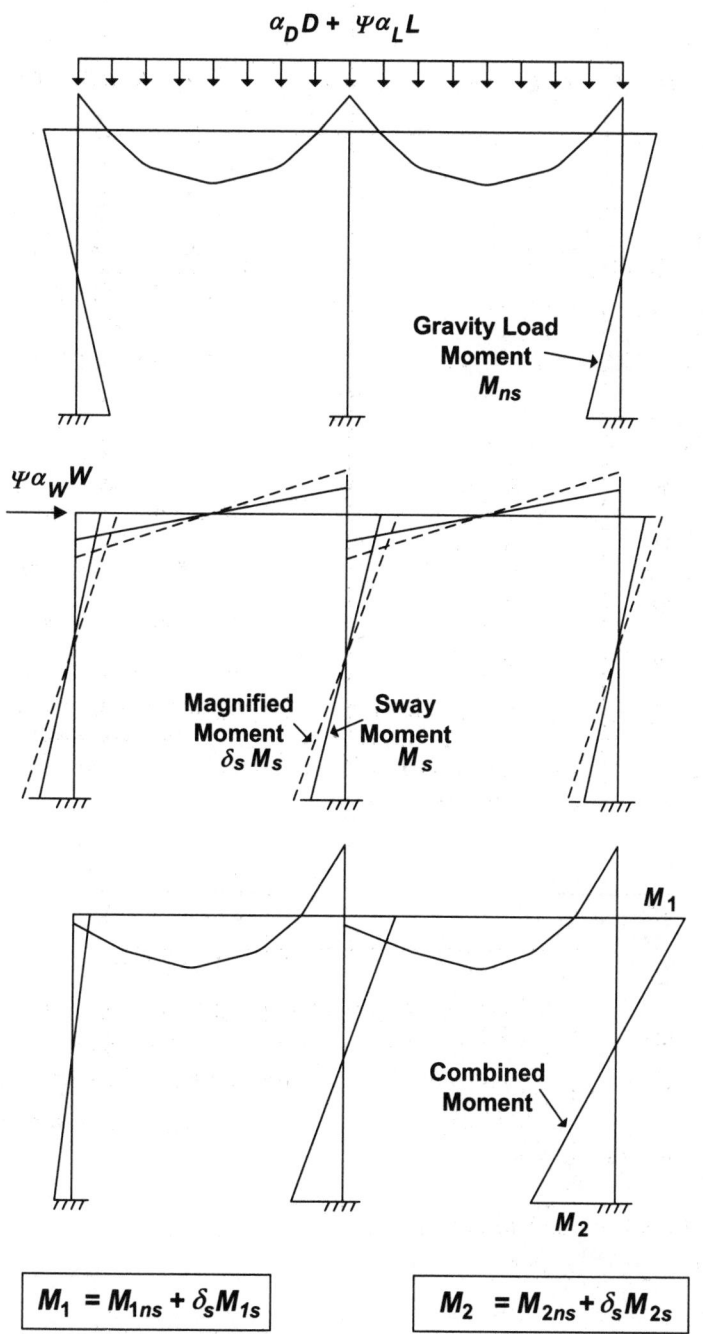

$$M_1 = M_{1ns} + \delta_s M_{1s}$$

$$M_2 = M_{2ns} + \delta_s M_{2s}$$

9

By Tibor Kokai

Foundations

9.1 Introduction

In this handbook, spread footings are addressed similarly to the previous edition. Design examples are presented for the strut-and-tie method and for spread footings supporting shear walls.

For the first time the 2004 edition of the CSA A23.3 Design of Concrete Structures Standard addresses deep foundations. Sample calculations are presented for drilled piles and pile caps.

9.2 Special Loading Conditions

The sample calculations presented, focus on the shear and flexural design of critical sections. To reduce the complexity of the design examples and to demonstrate the design procedure, usually just the gravity loads are considered. Practitioners must consider other load cases such as differential settlements, and unbalanced soil pressures acting on the structure, as specified in the National Building Code of Canada (NBCC 2005).

Unbalanced soil pressures (in the case of a sloping grade, or an excavation near an existing building) often result in higher shear forces and overturning moments than those calculated from wind or earthquake actions.

9.3 Selecting the Foundation Type

The foundation type used (spread footings vs. deep foundations) depends largely on the soil parameters/conditions, such as: bearing capacity, closeness of the bearing strata, water table level, and settlements. It is always prudent to consult the geotechnical engineer and cost consultant when deciding on the foundation type to be used.

Spread footings are utilized when the bearing stratum is close to the lowest basement level and the soil capacity is adequate, otherwise deep foundations are used. When the use of both spread and deep foundations is possible, the deciding factor is usually the cost of construction. While spread footings are usually more economical than deep foundations, in special circumstances (such as winter construction) the reverse may be true.

9.4 Spread Footings

Spread footings are shallow structural elements that transfer loads from the superstructure to the bearing strata – see definition in CSA A23.3 Clause 2.2.

9.4.1 Design Procedure

The design procedure can be broken into two general steps: 1. defining the shape and type of spread footings; and 2. design of cross sections.

1. Shape and type of spread footings: There are four basic types of spread footings: individual spread footings, wall (or strip) footings, continuous footings and mats (or combined footings). The type of spread footings to be used is a function of the supported structure and its geometry (column and wall spacing, load intensity, etc.).

In the case of continuous footings (supporting columns along a single line/grid) or mats (supporting columns and walls along several lines/grids) special care is needed when assessing the soil-footing structure interaction. The soil spring constant is load dependent, thus non-linear analysis is required or an iterative linear analysis can be used to converge to an acceptable stress/deflection equilibrium state.

9

Foundations

2.   Design of cross sections: The main design steps are as follows:

a)   Calculate minimum footing area and thickness.

b)   Calculate or obtain settlements from the geotechnical consultant and assess the effects of settlements on the structure.

c)   Calculate required flexural and if necessary shear reinforcement.

d)   Check development of reinforcement.

e)   Check bearing stresses at the column-footing interface.

9.4.2   Footing Area

The loads acting on a spread footing are depicted in Figure 9.1. Note that in the following equations, buoyancy due to the water table and moment at the column base are not considered.

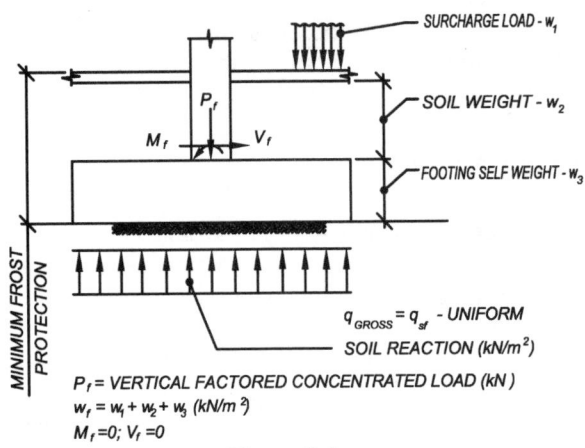

Figure 9.1

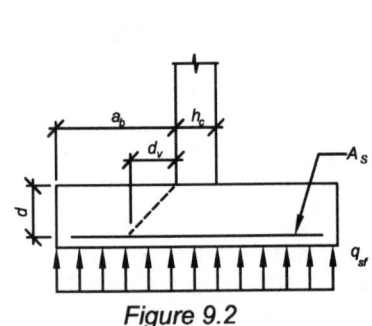

Figure 9.2

The total factored soil pressure (q_{sf}), also referred to as factored "gross soil pressure" (q_{GROSS}), has to be less than or equal to the factored soil bearing resistance (q_{sr}):

$$q_{sf} = P_f / A_f + w_f \le q_{sr} \qquad (9.1.a)$$

$$A_f = P_f / (q_{sf} - w_f) \qquad (9.1.b)$$

The minimum required footing area is therefore calculated from the factored gross soil pressure (total factored load) acting on the subgrade.

There are no deformations or internal stresses in the footing from the load w_f. Only the P_f / A_f component, the factored "net soil pressure", causes internal forces in the footing. Thus the footing depth and reinforcement is established based on the factored net soil pressure.

The structural design of a footing is usually based on Equation (9.1.a) by neglecting w_f since in most practical cases it is negligible.

It was common practice to establish the required footing area based on service loads and service soil bearing capacity, q_s. In this case, assuming that (w_f) is negligible, the required footing base was defined as:

$$A_s = P_s / q_s \qquad (9.1.c)$$

The NBCC 2005 does not specify any service load combinations for foundation design, thus this design practice is obsolete.

9.4.3   Shear – Minimum Footing Thickness

It is common practice to design footings without shear reinforcement. Therefore the minimum thickness is usually governed by one-way or two-way shear, although, in some cases, it can be governed by the compression or tension development length of the reinforcement from the supported structure.

The minimum depth of footings above the flexural reinforcement is specified at 150 mm – see Clause 15.7.

If necessary, shear reinforcement may be provided as defined in Clauses 11 and 13.

The minimum thickness defined in 9.4.3.1 and 9.4.3.2 is based on the assumption that the soil pressure is uniform and thus only vertical load is acting on the footing. See 9.4.3.3 for footings with vertical loads and moments.

9.4.3.1   One-way Shear

The minimum thickness of continuous strip/wall footings and some rectangular footings is governed by one-way (or beam) shear as defined in Clause 11.3.3. Since these shallow structural elements are usually constructed without shear reinforcement, the factored shear resistance is defined by Clause 11.3.4. The minimum effective shear depth, d_v, of the critical section (located d_v from the face of the support – see Clause 11.3.2 and Figure 9.2) is thus a function of β (the factor accounting for shear resistance of cracked concrete), which is defined in Clauses 11.3.6.2, 11.3.6.3 and 11.3.6.4.

The β value defined in Clause 11.3.6.2 is always larger than the value from Clause 11.3.6.3 (simplified method), hence Tables 9.1 to 9.3 for one-way shear include both conditions (Clauses 11.3.6.2 and 11.3.6.3), as described below. Note, that Clause 11.3.6.4 (general method) was not considered for the above tables and that the β values from Clause 11.3.6.4 could be even larger than the value from Clause 11.3.6.2 for cases involving significant prestress.

From Clause 11.3.6.2 the minimum shear depth can be derived, by equating the factored shear stress to the shear resistance (Clause 11.3.4) at the critical section:

$$d_v = q_{sf}a_b /(q_{sf} + \phi_c \lambda \beta \sqrt{f_c'}) \qquad ; \text{where: } \beta = 0.21,\ q_{sf}\ (\text{MPa}),\ f_c'\ (\text{MPa}) \text{ and } a_b(\text{m}). \qquad (9.2)$$

From Clause 11.3.6.3 the minimum depth can be derived as described above, resulting in a quadratic equation. Assuming that the specified nominal maximum size of coarse aggregate is not less than 20 mm (Clause 11.3.6.3(b)), the quadratic equation takes the following form:

$$d_v{}^2 + d_v(230\phi_c \lambda \sqrt{f_c'} / q_{sf} + 1000 - a_b) - 1000a_b = 0 \qquad (9.3)$$

This can be solved directly or an iterative solution can be used for establishing the required minimum effective shear depth of a spread footing.

Tables 9.1 to 9.3 consider all conditions set out in Clauses 11.3.6.2, 11.3.6.3 and 15.7. When $3d < a_b$ the smallest d value was used calculated based on Clause 11.3.6.3.(b) and $a_b/3$.

9.4.3.2   Two-way Shear

The effective thickness of square or almost square isolated footings is usually governed by two-way shear, as specified in Clause15.5.1 and Clause13.3.4. The critical section is $d/2$ away from the face of the support as per Clause15.5.2 and Clause13.3.3. The minimum footing depth is established based on the criteria set in Clause 13.3.4.1.

Tables 9.4 to 9.6 have been derived based on Equation (13-5), (13-6) and (13-7) and assuming square columns, thus $h_e = \sqrt{A_c}$, where $\beta_c \le 2.0$. Equation (13-5) does not govern over

Equation (13-7) for any $\beta_c \leq 2.0$. Equation (13-6) also gives higher shear stress resistance values than Equation (13.7), thus tables 9.4 to 9.6 are based on Equation (13-7). For consideration of Clause 13.3.4.4 see note under Table 9.4.

By equating the maximum shear stress in the critical section with the maximum factored shear resistance from Equation (13-7), one obtains the following equation:

$$v_c = 0.38\lambda\phi_c\sqrt{f_c'} = (A_f q_{sf} - q_{sf}h_e^2 - 2q_{sf}h_e d - q_{sf}d^2)/(4h_e d + 4d^2); \qquad (9.4)$$

Rearranging the above equation one gets a quadratic equation for d:

$$d^2(4v_c + q_{sf}) + d(4h_e v_c + 2q_{sf}h_e) - q_{sf}(A_f - h_e^2) = 0; \qquad (9.5)$$

where: q_{sf} (MPa), v_c (MPa), h_e (m), $A_f(m^2)$

In the above equation A_f denotes the footing area.
Tables 9.4 to 9.6 give d/h_e values for the specified q_{sf} values.

9.4.3.3   Footings supporting Vertical Loads, Moments and Shear Forces

Vertical load with moment: When the moment acting at the base of the column is not negligible, the footing design must account for this condition.

The footing size that will ensure that the factored soil stresses do not exceed the factored soil capacity needs to be chosen, thus:

$$q_{sf} = P_f / A_f + M_f / S \leq q_{sr} \qquad (9.6)$$

One-way shear is checked considering the soil stress distribution given by Equation (9.6).

Two-way shear must be checked by considering direct shear and the shear stresses from the unbalanced moment, as defined in Clause 13.3.5. Obviously, the shear depth will be increased by the presence of the moment. (See reference 2).

Effect of horizontal shear force: The horizontal shear force, acting at the top of the footing, has to be transferred to the subgrade by utilizing the passive soil resistance and the friction between the subgrade and the footing surface. The geotechnical consultant can provide the soil parameters defining the friction and passive resistance.

Overturning and sliding must be checked in accordance with the NBCC. (Reference 1).

9.4.4   Flexure

Minimum reinforcement in a spread footing is governed by Clause 10.5.1, which refers to Clause 7.8 through Clause 10.5.1.2 (a). As specified in Clause 7.8, this minimum reinforcement must be provided in each direction of the spread footings.

Flexural reinforcement is designed in accordance with Clauses 10 and 11.4 where applicable (see Clause 10.7). Based on the above clauses and Clause 10.5.2, reinforcement areas for various values of $q_{sf}a_b^2$ are provided in tables 9.7 to 9.9 for a 1.0 m width of footing. Since the selected $q_{sf}a_b^2$ values in these tables are independent of the footing depth and the footing overhang, these tables cannot account for the criteria defining deep flexural members. Therefore when designing, one always needs to check for deep beam action (see 9.4.5 of this Chapter).

9.4.4.1   Development of Tension Reinforcement

When the clear cover to the reinforcement is greater than d_b, where d_b is the nominal bar diameter in mm, and when the clear spacing between bars is greater than $1.4d_b$, then the development length specified by Clause 12.2.3 may be used. Assuming that only straight bars will be used ending 75 mm from the edge of the footing, the maximum bar diameter, for a given a_b, can be found from

$$max\, d_b = \sqrt{f_c'}\,(a_b - 0.075)1000\,/(0.45k_1k_2k_3k_4f_y) \qquad (9.7)$$

where the parameters k_1, k_2, k_3 and k_4 are as specified by Clause 12.2.4. For uncoated bars, normal density concrete, and distance between the reinforcement and base of the footing less than 300 mm, $k_1 = k_2 = k_3 = 1.0$. For 20M and smaller bars, $k_4 = 0.8$, otherwise $k_4 = 1.0$. Table 9.10 lists the development lengths required under these conditions for various bar sizes.

Table 9.11 gives the compression development lengths of bars based on Clause 12.3

9.4.4.2   Distribution of Reinforcement

According to Clause 15.4.4, a certain percentage of the total reinforcement in the short direction of rectangular spread footings must be concentrated over the width equal to the length of the short side of the footing or equal to the length of the supported wall or column, whichever is greater. This percentage is *100 x 2/(β+1)* where β is the ratio of the long to short side of the footing. The remainder of the reinforcement is to be placed outside of this strip.

When it is desirable to space the bars in the short direction uniformly to expedite fieldwork and minimize the possibility of error, increase the amount of reinforcement accordingly.

9.4.5   Strut-and-Tie Model – Deep Flexural Members

Flexural members with clear span to overall depth ratios less than 2 are designed as deep flexural members – see Clause 10.7. In lieu of more accurate procedures a strut-and-tie model may be used as defined in Clause 11.4.

Alternatively, for flexural analysis of deep beams, Park & Paulay suggest (see reference 3) the use of a reduced level arm, z, such that

$$z = 0.4\,(d + M_f/V_f) \qquad \text{for } dV_f/M_f \geq 1.0 \qquad (9.8a)$$

$$z = 1.2\,M_f/V_f \qquad \text{for } dV_f/M_f = \frac{2d}{a_b} \geq 2.0 \qquad (9.8b)$$

where M_f and V_f are the moment and shear acting at the face of the column. The required steel area is then obtained from

$$A_s = M_f/(\phi_s f_y z) \qquad (9.9)$$

In the case of deep beam action, additional anchorage requirements apply since the arching action results in steel stresses significantly higher than predicted by the flexural model. In lieu of a detailed analysis accounting for the reduction in steel stress along the development length, it is recommended that standard hooks be provided at the outside edge of the footing whenever the spread footing acts as a deep beam. If standard hooks are not practical, welded plates can be used to anchor the reinforcement (see Chapter 4 Shear and Torsion of this Design Handbook).

9.4.6   Plain Concrete Spread Footings

In plain (unreinforced) concrete footings the flexural stresses are limited by Clause 22.6.5 and the shear stresses by Clause 22.6.6. The total thickness of footing is calculated by adding 50 mm to the minimum depth required by the flexural and shear criteria. Clause 22.6.2 specifies the minimum footing depth as 200 mm.

9

Foundations

9.4.7   Spread Footings with Caps or Pedestals

Spread footings with caps: Caps are used with spread footings to reduce the cantilever (a_b) of the footing – see Fig 9.3.a. Using caps the factored shear force and bending moments are reduced in the critical sections, therefore the volume of concrete and reinforcement is reduced. Caps are also justified and practical to use when bearing elevations vary. While there is a saving on the materials used, constructing a footing with a cap is more complex than constructing a spread footing without one.

Bearing and minimum reinforcement (Clause 15.9) must be checked at sections 1 and 2 – see Figure 9.3.a. Reinforcement for compression must be developed from section 1, for tension from section 2.

Caps typically have a 1:1 to 1:2 overhang to depth ratio. Caps with greater depth ratios are considered pedestals. See Figure 9.3.b and c for cap reinforcement as a function of arrangement of the column verticals and dowels.

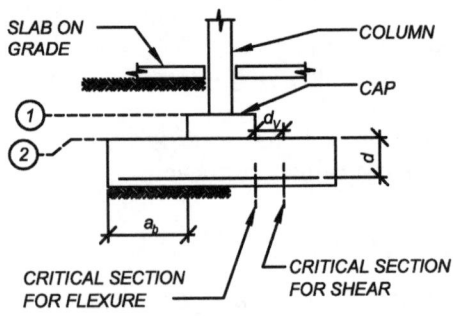

Figure 9.3a

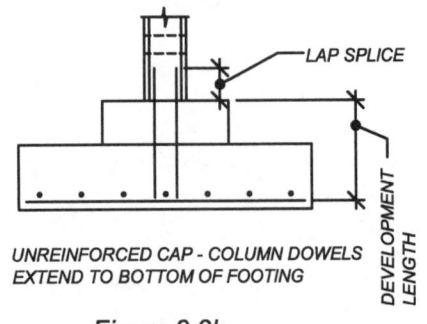

Figure 9.3b

Spread footings with pedestals: Pedestals are used when the bearing stratum is deep below the slab-on-grade and the superstructure (column) is not extended to the top of the footing – see Figure 9.3.d.

The pedestal is designed as a column, while checking bearing and the minimum reinforcement requirements (Clause 15.9) in sections 1 and 2 – see Figure 9.3.d. Lateral support of the pedestal is usually provided by the slab-on-grade and the surrounding soil.

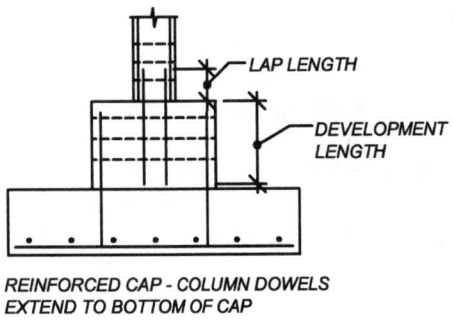

Figure 9.3c

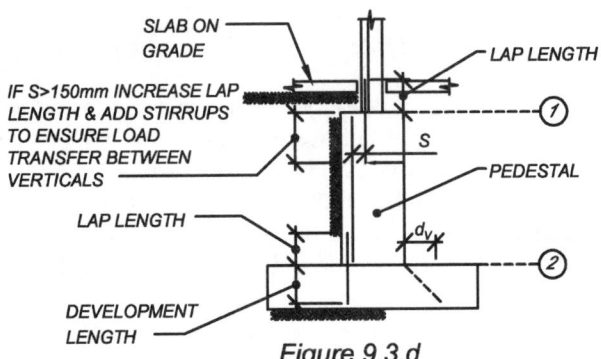

Figure 9.3.d

9.4.8   Combined Footings and Mats

Combined footings: Combined footings support more than one column located along a single grid line – see Figure 9.4.

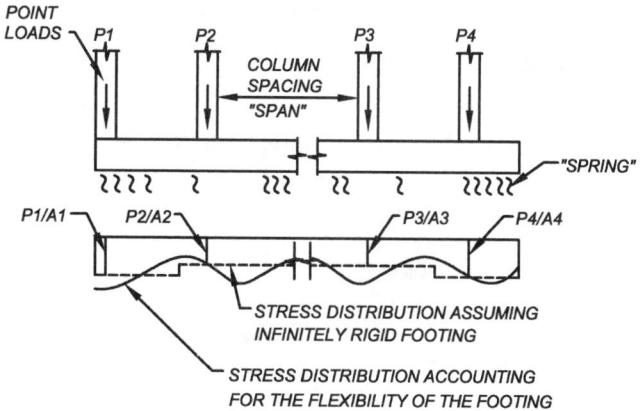

Figure 9.4

For approximate analysis, it may be assumed that the footing is infinitely rigid thus resulting in a uniform soil stress distribution. The resultant of the subgrade reaction and the resultant of the acting loads must be in equilibrium with each other. This can be achieved by selecting an appropriate footing geometry – see references 2 and 4.

The assumption of an infinitely rigid footing (uniform soil stress distribution) is acceptable for combined footings where the column spacing to footing shear depth ratio does not exceed approximately 4:1.

For combined footings where the uniform stress distribution criterion is not fulfilled, the above-described approximate analysis is not acceptable. To establish a more accurate stress distribution and cross sectional forces, the theory of beams on elastic foundations should be applied as described by the following differential equation:

$$EI\frac{d^4y(x)}{dx^4} + ky = q(x)$$

(9.10)

where: EI – stiffness of the combined footing (beam element)
$y(x)$ – deflection of the beam/footing element
k – Winkler coefficient (spring constant/modulus or subgrade reaction) – (units kN/m or MN/m) defined by the geotechnical consultant
$q(x)$ – loading (kN/m)

A closed form solution of the above differential equation exists for only a few load cases, however, it is relatively easy to solve any particular problem by using the finite element method (FEM).

The above Winkler solution can be further refined by assuming that the supporting springs do not deform independently of each other (see references 4 and 5).

Mat foundations: Mat foundations are large reinforced concrete slabs supporting columns and/or walls located along several grid lines. It becomes a matter of definition as to when a spread or combined footing becomes a mat. A mat foundation is used when piles are not economical to use or when the individual spread footings are too large.

The design of mats is based on the theory of slabs supported on an elastic foundation. There is a significant resemblance between the design of flat slabs and mats. Using FEM the designer can assess the soil-stress distribution and the cross sectional forces in the slab. It is very important to consider that the modulus of subgrade reaction is not a linear function of the soil deformation. If a linear spring constant is used, several iterations may be required to arrive to an acceptable soil-stress distribution. For more complex analysis methods, see references 4, 5 and 6.

The following issues need to be considered during design and construction of mats:

• Constructability: Simplicity of the top and bottom reinforcement arrangement is important since mats can be quite thick. The stability of the reinforcing cage during concreting needs to be ensured.

• Shear reinforcement: Stirrups or headed studs may be used if necessary.

• Concrete temperature control: In placement of mass concrete, the heat of hydration, which continues to build for several days, is a major cause for concern. As the concrete surface cools, a thermal gradient is formed across the concrete section, which can cause the concrete to crack. Controlling the initial and maximum concrete temperatures and the temperature gradient, is key to avoiding excessive thermal stresses – for available techniques and required parameters, see CSA A23.1.

9.5   Deep Foundations

Deep foundations are elongated structural elements that transfer loads from the superstructure to the bearing strata, by utilizing end bearing, friction or both.

There are a great variety of deep foundations in use; they vary based on the materials (timber, structural steel, reinforced, unreinforced and prestressed concrete and combinations of these) and the construction methods (drilled or driven piles, excavated systems, etc.) used.

This edition of the Design Handbook addresses driven or drilled piles.

9.5.1   Piles

For definition of piles see Clause 2.2 of CSA A23.3-04.
Piles are usually used for the following purposes:

1.   To carry axial compression forces.

2.   To carry tension uplift forces by utilizing side friction or anchors.

3.   To carry horizontal shear forces. All piles have some lateral load carrying capacity, but when piles are driven at an angle to the vertical (batter piles) they can carry significant horizontal loads. Usual slopes for batter piles vary from *1H:12V* to *5H:12V*.

4.   To control deflections and improve the capacity of a mat foundation. Sometimes it is necessary to augment the mat with piles to create a combined system which is superior to the mat foundation alone.

9.5.1.1   Pile Type Selection Criteria

The decision on the type of piles to be used and the method of construction to be utilized is based on local economic and geotechnical (site-specific) considerations. It is always prudent to consult the geotechnical engineer and the pile contractor for the methods of construction and the desired types of piles.

See reference 4 for the variety of piles in use and the associated details.

9.5.1.2   Pile Design Criteria

The design of piles consists of two steps: 1. determination of the cross sectional forces in individual piles; and 2. design of pile cross sections.

9.5.1.2.1   Determination of the Cross Sectional Forces in Individual Piles

CSA A23.3 has the following new design criteria:

1. Clause 15.2.3 accounts for the construction tolerance. It specifies that the calculated reactions (refer to Clause 15.2.2) must act at the larger of a minimum eccentricity of 50 mm or the construction tolerance (in any direction) when designing the pile.

2. Clause 22.8.1 sets the minimum eccentricity criterion at $0.1d_p$ for plain concrete piles.

3. Clause 15.8.1 indicates that the pile-soil interaction and the non-linear soil behaviour must be considered for determining the cross sectional forces. In references 4 and 7 there are numerous methods presented for determining the pile-soil interaction. The most common approach is to use finite element analysis software to model the pile as a beam on elastic foundation. This approach can easily consider the changes in soil constants along the height of the pile. The subgrade response characteristics (spring constants) are normally established by the geotechnical engineer. See Figure 9.5.

    If linear spring constants are used, the process becomes iterative, since the spring constant is a function of the soil stresses.

4. Clauses 15.8.2.2 and 22.8.2 require that the outer 25 mm of uncased drilled piles be ignored when establishing end bearing and side friction. This reduction in diameter must also be considered when the pile-soil interaction is assessed. Thus the inertia and area of the pile is based on the reduced diameter when determining the cross sectional forces.

    This requirement is based on past visual inspections of exposed uncased drilled piles. It accounts for the fact that the concrete quality is questionable near the pile surface due to the interaction of the wet concrete with the soil during concreting.

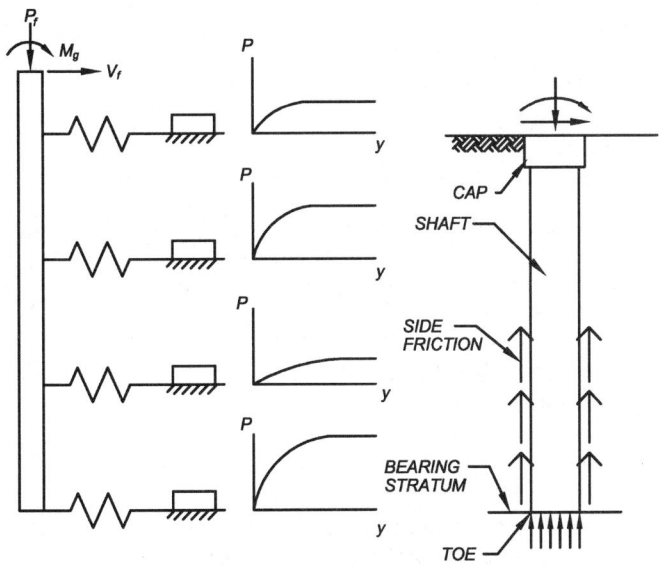

STRUCTURAL MODEL OF A DRILLED PILE,
WITH NON-LINEAR SOIL RESPONSE.

Figure 9.5

9.5.1.2.2   Design of Pile Cross Sections

Independently of the pile type (precast, structural steel, cast-in-place concrete, timber, etc.), the following new criteria is set by CSA A23.3:

1. Clauses 15.8.2.2 and 22.8.2 require that the outer 25 mm of uncased drilled piles be ignored. Thus the factored resistance of the cross sections is based on the reduced cross section.

2. Clause 15.8.2.3 for uncased drilled piles specifies an additional reduction factor of 0.9 applied to the factored resistances specified in Clauses 10 and 11. This factor was introduced to account for construction techniques used and the fact that the concrete in the drilled pile is usually not vibrated.

3. Clause 22.8.3 for plain concrete uncased drilled piles specifies the use of an additional reduction factor of 0.8 for maximum factored stresses specified in Clause 22.8.5.

4. Clause 22.1.1 specifies a minimum concrete strength of 15 MPa for plain concrete.

5. Clause 22.1.2 prohibits the use of plain concrete piles where ductility is required.

6. Additional relevant pile design issues are addressed in Clause 15.8.2 and Clause 22.

7. Assessment of the lateral support conditions must be done in accordance with Clause 15.8.2.1.

9.5.2   Pile Caps

Pile caps transfer loads from the superstructure to piles or a group of piles – see pile cap definition in Clause 2.2.

Single drilled piles may support walls or columns without a pile cap provided that the bearing stresses and the interface reinforcement/connection meet the code criteria.

The use of pile caps is warranted by the fact that the construction tolerance for piles is larger than the construction tolerance for the superstructure; hence it plays a role as a "transitional element" between the less and more accurately located/constructed structural elements. Example: Placing column dowels accurately into the top of a drilled pile is much harder than into a pile cap.

9.5.2.1   Selection of Pile Cap Types

The pile cap type is usually determined by the number of piles used and a variety of geometrical constraints such as site issues, interference with other pile caps, and pile spacing limits. Provide a sufficient number of piles to support the loads and to ensure that the pile-cap and cap-superstructure system is structurally stable – see Figure 9.6 (reference 15). In case of a two-pile system, a column load may be eccentric perpendicular to the line connecting the two piles, resulting in an unstable system. Thus a three-pile system is more appropriate for supporting a single column. A two-pile system however can easily support a wall since the eccentricity (in any direction) does not induce extra moments into the piles.

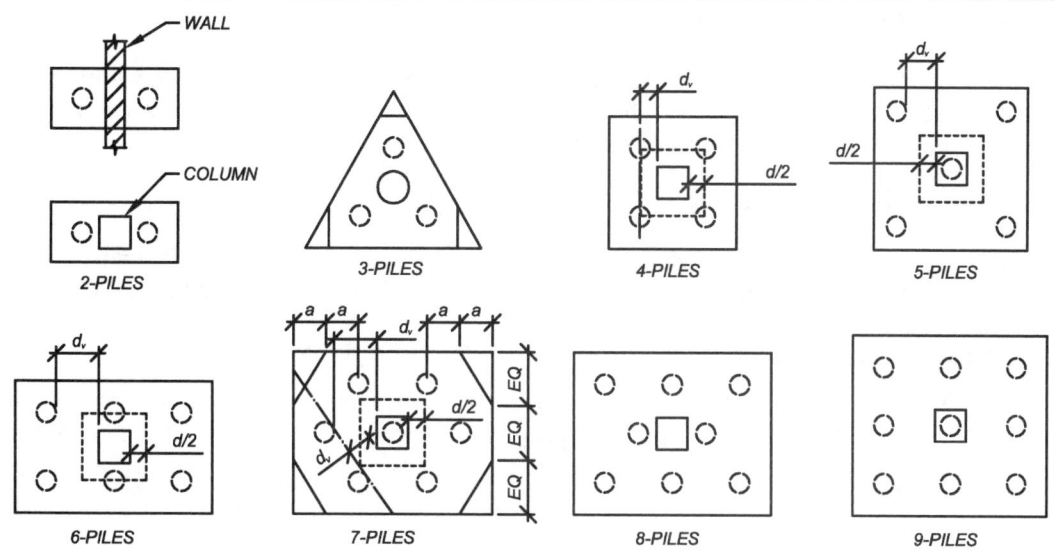

PILE ARRANGEMENTS AND CRITICAL SECTIONS

Figure 9.6

9.5.2.2 Main Design Issues

Pile caps are usually thick structural concrete elements where beam theory (plane sections assumption) is not applicable. For such members Clause 10.7.1 recommends the use of the strut-and-tie (S&T) method described in Clause 11.4. While the S&T method accurately describes the behaviour of the discontinuous/disturbed regions (D-regions), the provisions presented in Clause 11.4 were developed for two-dimensional elements only, with minimum reinforcement used – Clause 11.4.5 (reference 9). When defining the nodal stresses, Clause 11.4.4.1 allows for the beneficial effects of three-dimensional confinement if substantiated by test results.

The modified S&T method, as proposed by Adebar et al (see references 10, 11, 12 and 17) accounts for the beneficial effects of the three-dimensional confinement, while not using minimum reinforcement. The depths of pile caps are selected to satisfy both the traditional sectional shear limits (ignoring any pile loads within the critical sections) and the nodal/bearing stress limits (as specified in the modified strut-and-tie method). That is, the nodal stress limits replace the shear design for deep pile caps where a large portion of the pile loads do not intercept the critical shear sections at d_v or $d/2$ from the column face. Since no shear reinforcement is provided (similarly to the spread footings), pile caps usually contain only bottom tension reinforcement (unless there is a top tension due to net uplift load conditions).

Pile caps, which do not qualify as deep pile caps, may be designed based on Clauses 10, 11 and 13 of CSA A23.3. While it is not a common practice, pile caps may be reinforced for shear utilizing stirrups or shear studs using beam or slab design techniques and theories.

9.5.2.3 Description of the Design Procedure

Only those pile caps which utilize a bottom mat for tension/flexural reinforcement and do not require shear reinforcement are addressed.

The design steps are as follows:

1. Establish the pile cap depth based on the sectional method – see 9.5.2.3.1.

2. For deep pile caps, for the established depth from step 1, check the compressive struts and bearing stresses in accordance with the modified strut-and-tie method and determine the required reinforcement – see 9.5.2.3.2.

9.5.2.3.1   Sectional Method

While the sectional method does not accurately describe the behavior of a typical "deep" pile cap, it is still appropriate for designing "shallow" pile caps and pile caps for shear walls (supporting axial, shear and in-plane overturning moments).

9.5.2.3.1.1   Shallow Pile Caps

The behavior of shallow pile caps is very similar to the behavior of spread footings, thus the sectional method can be applied, using Clauses 10, 11 and 13. Figure 9.7 shows the definition of shallow pile caps based on Clause 11.3.6.2 (b).

Sectional design of shallow pile caps involves the following steps:

1. Determine the required effective shear depth 'd_v' based on one-way shear criteria using Clause 11.3.4 or Clause 11.3.6 at the critical section defined by Clauses 11.3.2, 15.2.3 and 15.5.3. See Figure 9.6.

2. Determine the depth "d" based on two-way shear criteria from Clause 13.3.4 at the critical section defined by Clauses 13.3.3.1, 15.2.3 and 15.5.3. See Figure 9.6.

3. Perform corner pile shear checks for shallow caps only as per Clause 13.3.6.2. Corner column shear checks need not be performed for deep pile caps since the corner pile in a deep pile cap behaves very differently from a corner column supporting a slab. This check is only necessary if the corner pile (in case of a three-pile cap) is enclosed by a pile cap corner that is less than 90 degrees.

4. Use the larger pile cap depth from steps 1 to 3.

5. Determine flexural reinforcement for the critical sections based on Clauses 10 and 15.

6. Check the bearing stresses for the superstructure columns and the piles – Clause 10.8. Note: See bearing details in 9.5.2.4.

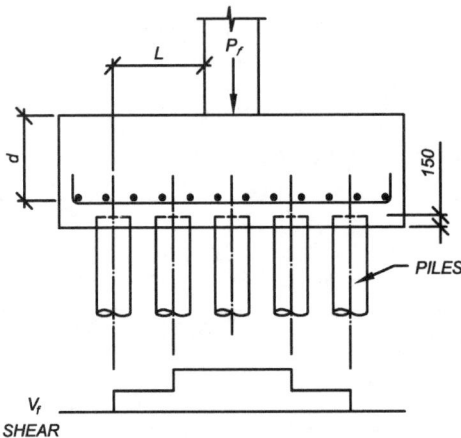

Figure 9.7

L - DISTANCE OF POINT OF ZERO
SHEAR TO FACE OF COLUMN

9.5.2.3.1.2   Pile Caps Supporting Shear Walls

Pile reactions are established based on Clause 15.2.2 and the pile cap is designed based on the steps described for "shallow" pile caps (see 9.5.2.3.1.1).

The strut-and-tie method for pile caps was developed for simple geometries and for concentric loads only, inducing compression into piles. For more complex geometries and loads, which include moments and shears, the strut-and-tie method would become too complex for practical engineering use. Hence the design of pile caps supporting shear walls or columns with significant moments/shears should be based on the sectional method.

The design steps to use are listed below (see Figure 9.8):

1. Determine the pile reactions (assuming rigid body behavior) by using the formula: $R = P/A + M/S$, where A is the total area of piles, S is the sectional moment of all piles about the neutral axis, and P and M are the acting loads. Any other method may be used that considers the relative stiffness of the interconnected elements (shear wall, pile cap and piles).

2. Assess the minimum pile cap depth as described in 9.5.2.3.1.1.

3. Determine the required flexural reinforcement in both directions. Since the sectional method underestimates the pile cap flexural reinforcement (see 9.5.2.3.3 and example 9.7.7), the calculated reinforcement needs to be adjusted accordingly.

4. Assess the load path for the horizontal shear. The horizontal shear may be resisted by the sum of the shear resistances of: individual piles, batter piles, slab-on-grade reaction and passive resistance of the earth (if approved by the geotechnical engineer). Not all of the above act simultaneously.

5. In case of uplift, care should be taken about the proper anchorage of the piles into the pile cap and proper top tension reinforcement.

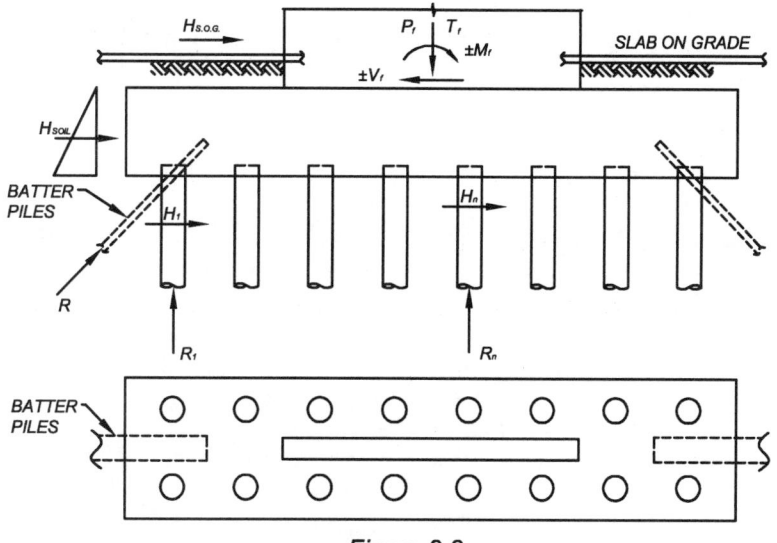

Figure 9.8

9.5.2.3.2 Strut-and-Tie Method for Deep Pile Caps

9.5.2.3.2.1 Experimental Results

For deep pile caps it was observed (see references 10, 11 and 12) that:

1. Even with symmetrical pile layouts, pile reactions deviated significantly.

2. "Banded" tie reinforcement resulted in 20% or higher failure loads than uniformly spaced bottom reinforcement. The uniformly spaced reinforcement from the sectional method does

not follow the internal flow of forces appropriately – see 9.5.2.3.3. However, pile caps with only banded reinforcement had poor crack control.

3.   Pile compressive struts did not fail by crushing but by splitting longitudinally. Longitudinal splits occurred due to transverse spreading of the compression stresses – (Figure 9.9).

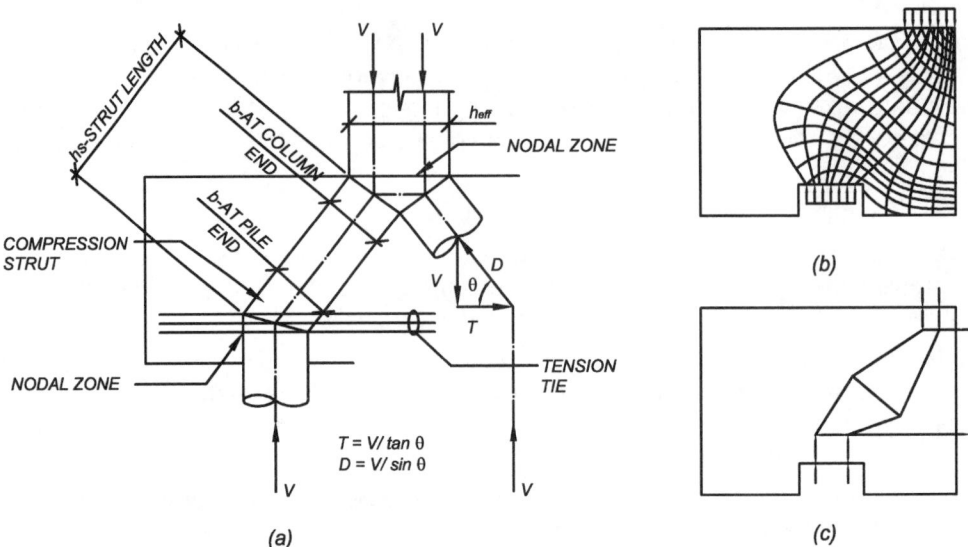

STRUT-AND-TIE MODEL FOR A DEEP BEAM OR PILE CAP: (a) IDEALIZED LOAD-RESISTING TRUSS; (b) LINEAR
ELASTIC STRESS TRAJECTORIES WITH TRANSVERSE TENSION DUE TO SPREADING OF COMPRESSION;
(c) REFINED TRUSS MODEL WITH CONCRETE TENSION TIE TO RESIST TRANSVERSE TENSION

Figure 9.9

9.5.2.3.2.2   Bearing Stress Limits

Based on the above and other experiments, the strut forces must be limited to avoid diagonal tensional failure. Rather than employing a refined strut-and-tie model (Figure 9.9.a and c) a simplistic truss model was proposed to depict the force flow but with modified bearing stress limits to ensure that diagonal splitting would not occur (see Figures 9.11 and 9.7.7.4). Note that Adebar's method uses a S&T method where the compressive struts are defined by the pile top-pile cap and column bottom-pile cap planes (see Figure 9.11), as opposed to the S&T model described in Clause 11.4 and shown in Figures 9.9.a and c.

The shear check for deep piles is therefore replaced with a bearing stress check at the two ends of each compressive strut.

Adebar et al. suggested that in D-regions, without minimum reinforcement (for crack control) in two directions, the bearing stresses should be limited to:

$$f_b = 0.6\varphi_c f_c' + 6\alpha\beta\,\varphi_c\sqrt{f_c'} \ \ \text{[MPa]} \tag{9.11}$$

Where: α accounts for confinement:

$$\alpha = \frac{1}{3}\left(\sqrt{\frac{A_2}{A_1}} - 1\right) \le 1\,; \ \text{thus} \ \sqrt{\frac{A_2}{A_1}} \le 4 \tag{9.11a}$$

where: A_1 and A_2 are defined similarly to Clause 10.8.1
        and β accounts for the aspect ratio of the strut (see examples 9.7.7 and 9.7.8).

$$0.0 \leq \beta = 0.33 \ (h_s/b_s - 1) \leq 1.0 \qquad\qquad\qquad (9.11b)$$

h_s/b_s is the aspect ratio of the strut, which can be approximated at the column as $h_s/b_s \cong 2d/h_{eff}$ and at piles, where only one compressive strut acts, as $h_s/b_s \cong d/d_p$. See Figure 9.9 for definitions of dimensions.

For the purpose of the bearing stress check, circular, polygonal or rectangular sections can be transformed into a square pile of equal area, ($h_{eff} = \sqrt{A_{pile}}$).

For the purpose of the S&T method the bearing area of an H–pile is defined by the depth of the section and the width of the flange.

9.5.2.3.2.3   Strut-and-Tie Method Design Steps

The following main steps are necessary to complete the strut-and-tie design of a deep pile cap:

1.   Establish the pile layout – see Figure 9.10.

2.   Establish the pile cap depth by the sectional method – see 9.5.2.3.1.

3.   Define the strut-and-tie geometry and calculate the tie forces – see Figure 9.7.7.4.

4.   Check strut bearing stresses – see 9.5.2.3.2.2 and 9.5.2.4.

5.   Calculate minimum tie reinforcement, minimum pile cap reinforcement and minimum reinforcement required for interfaces – Clause 15.9.2.

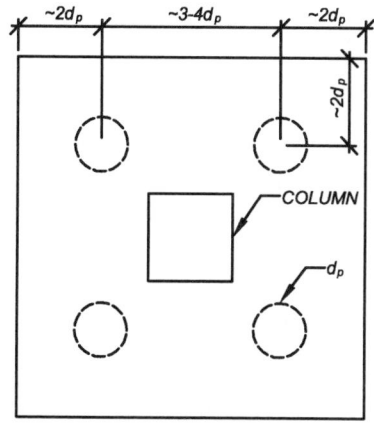

* PILE SPACING TO BE CONFIRMED BY
  GEOTECHNICAL CONSULTANT. USUALLY
  ~3d_p IS USED.
* EDGE DISTANCE OF 2d_p REQUIRED FOR
  CONFINEMENT
* EMBED PILES MINIMUM 150mm INTO PILE
  CAPS.

Figure 9.10

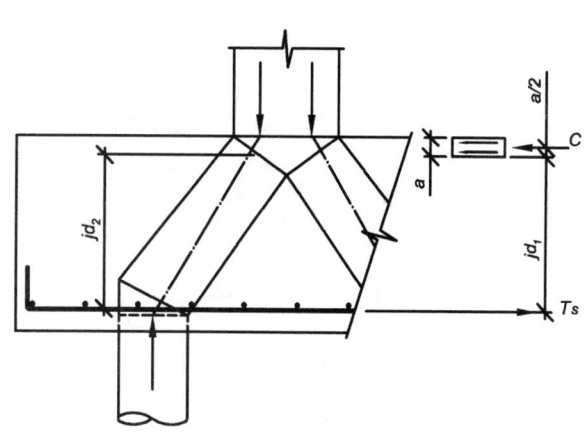

- $jd_1 > jd_2$
- jd_1 - INTERNAL LEVER ARM FOR SECTIONAL METHOD
- jd_2 - INTERNAL LEVER ARM FOR S & T METHOD

Figure 9.11

9.5.2.3.3   Comparison of the Sectional and Strut-and-Tie Methods

Figure 9.11 shows the internal lever arms' relationship for the S&T and sectional methods. Since the sectional method utilizes the full width of the pile cap, usually the compression block depth 'a' is very shallow resulting in a relatively large jd_1, as opposed to a smaller jd_2 for the S&T method. This explains why the sectional method underestimates the required tension reinforcement, thus resulting in an unsafe design. See example 9.7.7.

9.5.2.4   Bearing Details

Bearing stresses must be checked at the interfaces of the pile cap and the superstructure and the pile cap and the piles as described previously.

In construction practice the following typical cases/details occur:

1.   Bearing on cast-in-place, precast or concrete filled steel pipe piles:

For these pile types the bearing surface is easily definable and meeting Clause 15.9.2 is easily done. In the case of net uplift, proper anchorage and detail of reinforcement must be provided.

2.   Bearing on H-piles:

For H-piles the bearing stresses can be significant, especially if the pile load induces a typical stress level of about $0.3f_y$. At these pile stress levels the concrete stresses are in the range of $6f_c'$. (Similar concrete stresses occur under the heads of headed studs). These stress levels are acceptable if the H-pile is well confined (see Figure 9.10 – edge distance) and embedded at least 150 mm into the pile cap. Based on reference 16, a cap plate is not required in these cases.

Mitigating the above stress concentrations is a good practice, but placing cap plates on H piles is very costly. Other methods of concrete confinement could be: a) spiral reinforcement over the H-piles; b.) shear studs welded to the H-piles; c) horizontal bottom steel placed over the H-piles or through them. H-piles in net tension must have adequate tension anchorage in accordance with the Standard.

9.6   Acknowledgements

Sincere thanks to Mr. Alex Mandel and Dr. Perry Adebar for their valuable comments and thorough review of this chapter. Special thanks to Mr. Alex Mandel for preparation of the design tables and for his practical engineering suggestions.

I also wish to express my thanks to Mr. Rick McGrath, Dr. Michael P. Collins, Dr. R. E. Loov, and Yolles Partnership Inc. for their support of this work.

9.7   Design Examples

Example 9.7.1 - Wall Footing

Determine footing depth and reinforcement for the wall footing shown. Also compute the required depth for a plain footing. Use a factored soil reaction of q_{sr} = 450 kPa,

f_c' = 20 MPa, and f_y = 400 MPa.

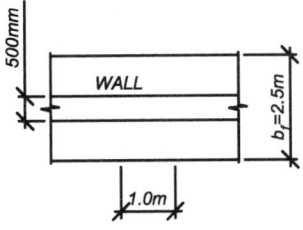

Figure 9.7.1-1

Calculations and Discussions:

1.   Reinforced one-way footing

1.1   Determine minimum effective shear depth, d_v, required by one-way shear:
      a_b = 1.0 m; From Table 9.1 d_v = 424 mm, thus $d = d_v/0.9 = 471$ mm

1.2   Determine required flexural reinforcement:
      Check deep beam action in accordance with Clause 10.7.1.

$a_b/d = 1000/471 = 2.12 > 2.0$, therefore no deep beam action.

$q_{sf} a_b^2 = 450$ kN, from Table 9.7a:

$A_s = 1465 + (1556 - 1465)(4/25) = 1480$ mm^2/m

Minimum reinforcement based on Clauses 10.5.1.2 (a) and 7.8, assuming total depth of footing as $t_f = 471 + 15$ (half bar diameter) + 75 (cover) = 561 mm and using $t_f = 575$ mm, is: $A_{s, min} = 1150$ mm^2/m, which is less than the calculated A_s. ($A_{s, min}$ must be provided in both directions.)

1.3   Find maximum bar size that can be developed in distance $a_b - 0.075 = 0.925$ m.
From Table 9.10 max $d_b = 20M$.

1.4   Reinforcement summary:
Short direction: Use 20M bars @ 200 mm c/c BLL (bottom lower layer)
Long direction – $A_{s,min}$: Use 20M @ 260 mm c/c BUL (bottom upper layer).

1.5   Total footing depth:
$t_f = 471+10$ (half bar diameter) + 75 (cover) = 556 mm. Round up this value to the next 25 mm and use a total footing depth of $t_f = 575$ mm - as assumed in 1.2.
Transfer of wall forces at wall base and development of wall reinforcement into the footing is not checked in this example – see Clause 15.9.

2.0   Unreinforced one-way footing

2.1   Minimum depth required for flexure (Clause 22.6.5)
$M_f = q_{sf} a_b^2/2 = 225$ kN•m/m, maximum stress in tension $f_t = 0.37 \lambda \phi_c \sqrt{f_c'} = 1.08$ MPa

From $f_t = M/S$; $d = \sqrt{6M_f/(f_t b)}$ = 1.12 m, where $b = 1.0$ m.
Use a total depth of $h = 1.12 + 0.050 \approx 1.2$ m.
Clause 22.6.3 requires the addition of 50 mm because of the irregular soil surface.

2.2   Minimum depth required for shear (Clause 22.6.6.1):
The critical section is 'h' away from the face of the wall. Since $h > a_b$ shear does not govern.

Example 9.7.2 - Wall Footing

Determine footing width, depth and reinforcement for the wall shown in Figure 9.7.2-1. Use factored rock reaction of $q_{sf} = 2000$ kPa, $f_c' = 35$ MPa, and $f_y = 400$ MPa.

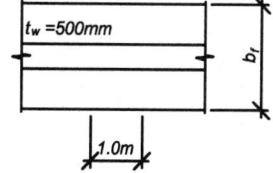

Factored wall load $P_f = 4500$ kN/m of wall.

Calculations and Discussions:

Figure 9.7.2-1

1.   Required footing width: Assuming w_f is negligible $b_f = 4500/2000 = 2.25$ m

2.   Calculation of effective shear depth: $a_b = (2.25 - 0.5)/2 = 0.875$ m
Assuming that $a_b < 3d_v$, (Clause 11.3.6.2 (b)) $\beta = 0.21$. The concrete shear resistance is

$v_r = \phi_c \lambda \beta \sqrt{f_c'}$, thus $v_r = 0.81$ MPa.

Factored shear at the critical section: $V_f = q_{sf} (a_b - d_v)$
Minimum shear depth from the maximum shear stress condition at the critical section is:
$v_f = V_f/(1.0d_v) = (q_{sf} a_b - q_{sf} d_v)/(1.0d_v);$ thus the effective shear depth is

9

Foundations

$d_v = (q_{sf}a_b)/(v_f + q_{sf}) = 0.623$ m – thus the assumption of $a_b < 3d_v$ was correct.
Therefore $d = d_v/0.9 = 0.692$ m – use $d = 0.7$ m.
(Clause 11.3.6.3 would give a $\beta = 0.14$ value with the above d_v.)

3.   Flexural design: Check for deep beam action – Clause 10.7.
      $a_b/d = 0.875/0.7 = 1.25 < 2.0$ thus deep beam action needs to be considered.
      The deep beam action will be assessed by two methods: Park and Paulay's reduced lever
      arm method and the Strut-and-tie method.

3.1   Park and Paulay's reduced lever arm method
      Lever arm:
      $dV_f/ M_f = 2d/a_b = 2(0.7)/0.875 = 1.6$, thus
      $z = 0.4(d + M_f/V_f) = 0.4 (d + a_b/2) = 0.45$ m
      Required reinforcement:
      $A_s = M_f /(\phi_s f_y z) = (0.5(0.875^2)(2000 \times 10^3)/(0.85(400)(0.45)) = 5004$ mm^2/m
      Minimum reinforcement:
      Based on Clauses 10.5.1.2 (a) and 7.8, and assuming the total depth of footing as
      $t_f = 700 + 75$ (cover) + 15 (assumed half bar diameter) = 790 mm, thus use
      $t_f = 800$, the required minimum reinforcement is: $A_{s,min} = 1600$ mm^2/m, which is less than the
      calculated A_s.
      Maximum rebar size that can be developed into $a_b - 0.075 = 0.8$ m from Table 9.10 is
      max $d_b = 25$M.
      Reinforcement: Use:
      25M @ 100 mm c/c BLL - HH (bottom lower layer, hooked-hooked) – short direction
      20M @ 175 mm c/c BUL (bottom upper layer) – long direction
      Transfer of wall forces at wall base and development of wall reinforcement into the footing
      has not been checked in this example – see Clause 15.9.

3.2   Design Flexural steel based on strut-and-tie method
      Based on $d = 0.7$ m the total depth of $t_f = 700 + 75 + 15$(half bar diameter) = ~800 mm, from
      steps 1 and 2, will be used for further design.
      Based on the force diagram on Figure 9.7.2-2, the compressive factored strut forces and
      their corresponding tension (horizontal) components are summarized below.

Strut	Angle (°)	Compression - C - in strut kN	Tension -T - kN
A-J; I-L	$\alpha_A = 40$	$C_A = 500/\sin\alpha_A = 778$	$T_A = 500/\tan\alpha_A = 596$
B-J; H-L	$\alpha_B = 50.2$	651	417
C-J; G-L	64.5	554	238
D-K; F-K	70.3	531	179
E-K	90	500	0

- Resultant tension forces in the tension reinforcement are therefore:

Nodes	Factored tension force - T - kN
A, I	596
B, H	596 + 417 = 1013
C, G	1013 + 238 = 1251
D, F	1251+179 = 1430
E	1430

Required tension reinforcement:

$$A_s = T_f /(\phi_s f_y) = 1.43 \times 10^6 /(0.85(400)) = 4206 \text{ mm}^2/m$$

This is 84% of the reinforcement by Park and Paulay's reduced lever arm method.
Reinforcement:
Based on the reinforcement development considerations in item 3.1, use:
25M @ 110 mm c/c BLL - HH (bottom lower layer, hooked-hooked) – short direction
20M @ 175 mm c/c BUL (bottom upper layer) – long direction

Check capacity of struts:

Strut A-J:
h_A = 250 sin40 = 161 mm; C_A = 778 kN; T_A = 596 kN
Strain along the tension reinforcement in point A: See Figure 9.7.2-4
$$\varepsilon_x = T_A /(EA_s) = 0.596/(200000(500\times 10^{-6})/0.11) = 0.656 \times 10^{-3}$$

Principle tensile strain in the strut – Clause 11.4.2.3:
$$\varepsilon_1 = \varepsilon_x + (\varepsilon_x + 0.002)\cot^2 \alpha_s = 0.656 \times 10^{-3} + (0.656 \times 10^{-3} + 0.002)\cot^2 40 = 4.43 \times 10^{-3}$$

Limiting compressive stress in the strut – Clause 11.4.2.3:
$$f_{cu} = f_c' /(0.8 + 170\varepsilon_1) \le 0.85 f_c'$$
f_{cu} = 35/(0.8 + 170(4.43×10⁻³)) = 22.5 MPa < 29.7 MPa   therefore stress level is acceptable.
Strut resistance:
$$P_r = \phi_c A_c f_{cu} = 0.65(1)(0.161)(22.5) = 2.35 \text{ MN} > 0.812 \text{ MN, thus strut capacity is adequate.}$$

The other struts can be checked in a similar way; however strut A-J governs for f_{cu} limit.

Check nodal stresses:

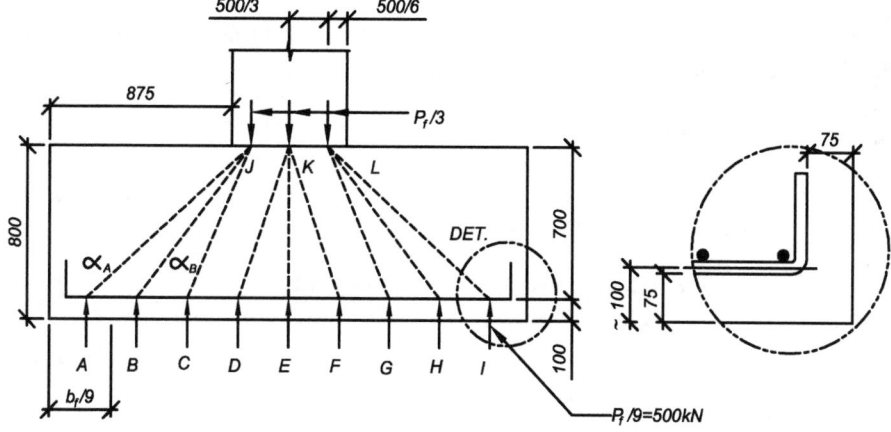

Figure 9.7.2-2

9

Foundations

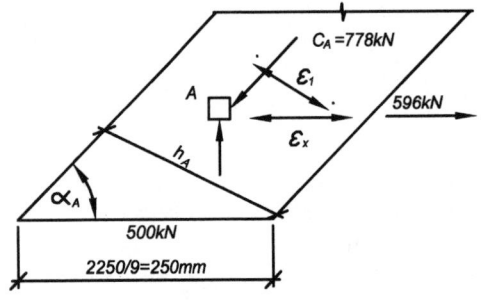

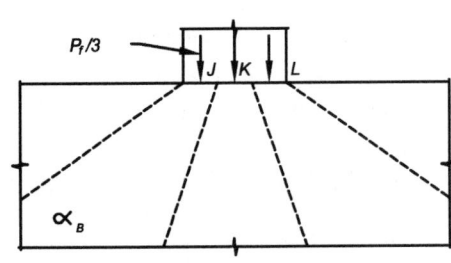

Figure 9.7.2-3   Figure 9.7.2-4

Node K:
P_f = 1500 kN; A_c = 1(0.167) = 0.167 m^2 thus concrete stress is f_c = 1.5/0.167 = 8.98 MPa.
Limiting stress based on Clause 11.4.4.1 is 0.85$\phi_c f_c'$ = 19.3 MPa > f_c. OK.

Concrete area (A_c) in node K was taken at the wall and footing interface.

Nodes J and L:
Acting compressive force (vector sum of strut forces C_A, C_B, C_C) with angle α_B is
C_J = 1500/sinα_B = 1952 kN.
Strut depth h_J = (500/3)sin α_B = 128 mm.
Concrete stress is f_c = 1.952/0.128 = 15.24 MPa < 19.3 MPa.
The above calculated nodal stress levels are the function of the assumed strut widths. For strain compatibility one could have assumed different strut widths at the column-footing interface, thus lowering or increasing the nodal stress levels. The strut widths could be adjusted to achieve equal stresses at nodes J, K and L.
Ultimately Clause 10.8 may be used for checking the stresses at the column-footing interface.

Transfer of wall forces at wall base and development of wall reinforcement into the footing is not checked in this example.

Example 9.7.3 - Square Footing

For the square footing and square column with factored load as indicated, select the total required thickness for footing size of 2.5 x 2.5 m.

P_f = 1875 kN f_c' = 20 MPa w_f is negligible
h_c = 500 mm f_y = 400 MPa

Calculations and Discussions:

1. Compute factored reaction:
    q_{sf} = 1875/2.5^2 = 300 kPa

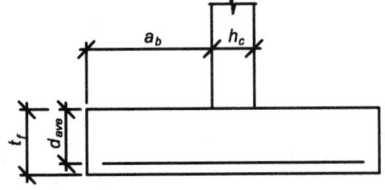

2. Minimum effective shear depth – one-way shear:
    a_b = (2.5 - 0.5)(½) = 1.0 m
    From Table 9.1 d_v = 333 mm, thus d = d_v/0.9 = 370 mm

    Figure 9.7.3-1

3. Minimum depth – two-way shear:
    From Table 9.4 establish d/h_e based on A_f/A_c.

$A_f/A_c = 2.5^2/0.5^2 = 25$
From interpolation $d/h_e = 0.8 + 0.1(25 - 24.5)/(28.8 - 24.5) = 0.812$, resulting in
$d_{ave} = h_c(0.812) = 406$ mm.
Since $3d_{ave} = 3(0.406) = 1.22$ m $> a_b = 1.0$ m, Clause 13.3.4.4 is not applicable.
Thus two-way shear governs.

4. Total footing depth assuming 20M bars in both directions: $t_f = 406 + 75 + 20 = 501$ mm.
    Use $t_f = 525$ mm (rounding it up to the next 25 mm).
    Note that the d_{ave} will be used for calculating the flexural reinforcement in both directions.

5. Flexural reinforcement:
    Check deep beam action in accordance with Clause 10.7.1.
    $a_b/d = 1.0/(0.525 - 0.075 - 0.02) = 1.0/0.43 = 2.3 > 2.0$, therefore no deep beam action.
    $q_{sf}a_b^2 = 300$ kN, from Table 9.7a
    $A_s = 1082 + (1100 - 1082)(430 - 425)/(450 - 425) = 1086$ mm^2/m,
    Thus the total reinforcement is:
    $A_s = 2.5(1086) = 2715$ mm$^2 > A_{s, min} = 0.002(2500)(525) = 2625$ mm^2.

6. Find maximum bar size that can be developed in distance $a_b - 0.075 = 0.925$ m.
    From Table 9.7 max $d_b = 20M$.
    Number of bars = $2715/300 = 9.05 - 20M$ bars, thus
    Use: 9 – 20M bars BEW (bottom each way).

Example 9.7.4 - Square Footing

Determine the minimum footing thickness and required reinforcement for the spread footing shown. Assume a square footing concentrically loaded and that w_f is negligible.

Service loads:
Dead load $D_s = 3800$ kN $h_c = 500$ mm
Live load $L_s = 600$ kN $f'_c = 30$ MPa
Snow load $S_s = 380$ kN $f_y = 400$ MPa
                                         $q_{sr} = 625$ kPa

Calculations and Discussions:

1. Factored column load:
    $P_f = 1.25(3800) + 1.5(600) + 0.5(380) = 5840$ kN

2. Required footing area:
    $A_f = 5840/625 = 9.34$ m^2, $b_f = 3.06$ m, use $b_f = 3.1$ m square footing for further calculations.

3. Minimum footing thickness:

3.1 One-way shear: $a_b = (3.1 - 0.5)/2 = 1.3$ m, $q_{sf} = 5840/3.1^2 = 608$ kPa
    Values considered for interpolation for $q_{sf} = 608$ kPa from Table 9.3:
    For $q_{sf} = 600$ kPa and $a_b = 1.3$ m: $d_v = (534 + 623)/2 = 578$ mm
    For $q_{sf} = 650$ kPa and $a_b = 1.3$ m: $d_v = (558 + 651)/2 = 604$ mm
    thus $d_v = 578 + (604 - 578)(8/50) = 583$ mm.
    Therefore minimum depth from one-way shear stress condition is:
    $d = d_v/0.9 = 648$ mm.

3.2   Two-way shear: $A_f/A_c = 3.1^2/0.5^2 = 38.4$

Values considered for interpolation for $q_{sf} = 608$ kPa from Table 9.6:

for $d/h_c = 1.4$, $A_f/A_c = 33.8 + (36.1 - 33.8)(42/50) = 35.7$

for $d/h_c = 1.5$, $A_f/A_c = 37.5 + (40.1 - 37.5)(42/50) = 39.7$

thus for $A_f/A_c = 38.4$ $d/h_c = 1.4 + 0.1(38.4 - 35.7)/(39.7 - 35.7) = 1.46$

Therefore the minimum depth from the two-way stress condition is $d \geq 1.46(0.5) = 0.73$ m.

Since $3(0.73) = 2.19$ m $> a_b = (3.1 - 0.5)/2 = 1.3$ m, Clause 13.3.4.4 is not applicable.

Conclusion: The two-way shear stress condition governs, thus use $d_{ave} = 0.75$ m (by rounding up to the next 25 mm).

3.3   From Table 9.11 the maximum reinforcement diameter in a column supported by a footing with $d = 750$ mm is 35M (assuming no net tension in the column).

4.   Flexural design:

Check for deep beam action in accordance with Clause 10.7.1:

$a_b/d = 1.3/0.75 = 1.73 < 2$, therefore deep beam action needs to be considered.

4.1   Park and Paulay's reduced lever arm method:

Lever arm:

$dV_f/M_f = 2d/a_b = 2(0.75/1.3) = 1.15$ $1 < 1.15 < 2$ thus

$z = 0.4(d + M_f/V_f) = 0.4(d + a_b/2) = 0.56$ m

Required reinforcement:

$A_s = M_f /(\phi_s f_y z) = (608(1.3^2)(0.5)(3.1)) \times 10^3/(0.85(400)(0.56)) = 8365$ mm^2

Minimum reinforcement:

Based on Clause 10.5.1.2 (a) and Clause 7.8, and the total depth of footing of $t_f = 750 + 75 + 25 = 850$ mm. Use $t_f = 850$ mm

$A_{s, min} = 5270$ mm$^2 < 8365$ mm^2

Reinforcement:

Use: 17-25M BEW HH (bottom each way, hooked-hooked)

4.2   Design flexural steel based on strut-and-tie method:

Based on the $d = 0.75$ m the total depth of $t_f = 750 + 75 + 25 = 850$ mm will be used for further design.

Based on the force diagram (See Figure 9.7.2-2 for the strut layout and node designation) the compressive factored strut forces and their corresponding tension (horizontal) components are summarized below.

Strut	Angle (°)	Compression - C - in strut kN	Tension - T - kN
A-J; I-L	$\alpha_A = 32$	$C_A = 649/\sin \alpha_A = 1225$	$T_A = 649/\tan \alpha_A = 1039$
B-J; H-L	$\alpha_B = 41$	989	747
C-J; G-L	55	792	454
D-K; F-K	65	716	303
E-K	90	649	0

Resultant tension forces in the tension reinforcement are therefore:

Nodes	Factored tension force - T - kN
A, I	1039
B, H	1039 + 747 = 1786
C, G	2240
D, F	2543
E	2543

Required tension reinforcement:

$A_s = T_f /(\phi_s f_y) = 2543 \times 10^3/(0.85(400)) = 7479$ mm^2

Note: This is 89% of the reinforcement by the Park and Paulay's reduced lever arm method.

Reinforcement to be developed in a_b - 0.075 = 1.225 m:
Maximum bar size from Table 9.10 is; 35M.

Reinforcement:
Use: 15–25M BEW HH (bottom each way, hooked-hooked).

Check capacity of struts: See Figure 9.7.2-3
$\alpha_A = \theta_A$
$h_A = 344 \sin 32 = 183$ mm
$C_A = 1225$ kN; $T_A = 1039$ kN
Strain along the tension reinforcement in point A:
$\varepsilon_x = T_A /(EA_s) = 1.039/(200000(15)(500 \times 10^{-6})) = 0.691 \times 10^{-3}$
Principle tensile strain in the strut – Clause 11.4.2.3:
$\varepsilon_1 = \varepsilon_x + (\varepsilon_x + 0.002)\cot^2 \alpha_s = 0.691 \times 10^{-3} + (0.691 \times 10^{-3} + 0.002)\cot^2 32 = 7.58 \times 10^{-3}$
Limiting compressive stress in the strut – Clause 11.4.2.3:
$f_{cu} = f_c'/(0.8 + 170\varepsilon_1) \leq 0.85 f_c'$
$f_{cu} = 30/(0.8 + 170(7.58 \times 10^{-3})) = 14.35$ MPa $< 0.85 f_c' = 25.5$ MPa - acceptable stress level.

Strut resistance:
$P_r = \phi_c A_c f_{cu} = 0.65(3.1)(0.183)(14.35) = 5.29$ MN > 1.22 MN, thus strut capacity adequate.
(The other struts can be checked in the similar way; however strut A-J governs for f_{cu} limit.)

Check nodal stresses: See Figure 9.7.2-3
Limiting stress based on Clause 11.4.4.1 is $0.85\phi_c f_c' = 0.85(0.65)(30) = 16.6$ MPa.

Nodes J and L:
Acting compressive force (vector sum of strut forces C_A, C_B, C_C) with angle α_B
$C_J = 3(649/\sin 41) = 2968$ kN.
Strut depth $h_J = (500/3)\sin \alpha_B = 109$ mm.
Concrete stress is $f_c = 2.97/(3.1)(0.109) = 8.8$ MPa < 16.6 MPa. Stress is acceptable.

Example 9.7.5 Rectangular Footing

Determine the required thickness and reinforcement for the column and footing shown.

Footing: 4.6 x 3.0 m $f_c' = 20$ MPa
Column: 1000 x 600 mm $q_{sr} = 300$ kPa
$f_y = 400$ MPa w_f is negligible

Calculations and Discussions:

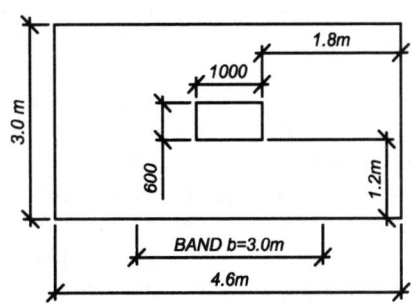

Figure 9.7.5-1

1.   Minimum effective shear depth – one-way shear:
     a_b = 1.8 m,
     q_{sf} = 300 kPa, from Table 9.1 d_v = 600 mm and $d = d_v/0.9 = 667$ mm.

2. Minimum depth – two-way shear:
    From Table 9.4 establish d/h_e based on $A_f/A_c = 4.6(3)/((1.0)(0.6)) = 23$
    $d/h_e = 0.7 + 0.1(23 - 20.45)/(24.5 - 20.4) = 0.76$
    Since tables 9.4 to 9.6 were calculated for $\beta_c \leq 2$ this condition has to be checked:

    $h_e = \sqrt{A_c} = 0.77$ thus $\beta_c = 1.67 < 2$ O.K.

    thus $d = 0.76(0.77) = 0.585$ m.
    Clause 13.3.4.4 is not applicable since $3(0.585) = 1.76$ m $\cong a_b = 1.8$ m.

    Since the one-way shear governs use $d = 659$ mm, which by rounding up results in $d = 675$ mm. Assuming 25M bars the total depth is then: $t_f = 675 + 25 + 75 = 775$ mm.

3. Compute A_s required in the long direction:
    Check deep beam action: $a_b/d = 1800/675 = 2.67 > 2$ – thus no deep beam action.
    $q_{sf}a_b^2 = 300(1.8^2) = 972$ kN,   from Table 9.7b with $d = 675$ mm.
    $A_s = 3(2061 + (2304 - 2061)(972 - 900)/(1000 - 900)) = 6708$ mm^2
    $A_{s,min} = 0.002(3000)(775) = 4650$ mm$^2 < 6708$ mm^2
    From Equation (9.7) of this Design Handbook the maximum diameter bar to be developed is max $d_b = 42.8$ mm, thus use 14 – 25M BLL.

4. Compute A_s required in the short direction:
    Check deep beam action: $a_b/d = 1200/675 = 1.78 < 2$ thus deep beam action needs to be considered.
    Using Park and Paulay's reduced lever arm method:
    $d\,V_f/M_f = 0.675(2)/1.2 = 1.125 > 1$
    thus, $z = 0.4 (d + M_f/V_f) = 0.4 (d + a_b/2) = 0.51$ m
    $A_s = M_f /(\phi_s f_y z) = (300(1.2^2)(0.5)(4.6)) \times 10^3/(0.85(400)(0.51)) = 5730$ mm^2
    $A_s = 5730$ mm$^2 / 4.6$ m
    $A_{s,\,min} = 7130$ mm$^2 > 5730$ mm^2
    From Equation (9.7) of this Design Handbook the maximum diameter bar to be developed is max $d_b = 28$ mm, thus
    Use 15 – 25M BUL HH.
    Check bar distribution - Clause 15.4.4.1 (b).
    $\beta = 4.6/3 = 1.53$; Reinforcing in band/Total reinforcing $= 2/(\beta + 1) = 0.79$
    Reinforcing required in band: $A_{sb} = 0.79(5730) = 4527$ mm^2
    In the bandwidth of 3.0 m, the reinforcement is $7500(3.0/4.6) = 4891$ mm$^2 > 4527$ mm^2, thus O.K.

Reinforcement summary:

Long way: 14–25M BLL HH (bars hooked since the other direction is a deep beam).
Short way: use 15–25M BUL HH.

Example 9.7.6 Footings Supporting Shear Walls

Determine the required footing size (width, b, and length, L), depth and reinforcement supporting the wall with length of 4 m and width of $t_w = 0.25$ m.

$f_c' = 30$ MPa w_f is negligible
$f_y = 400$ MPa $P_f = 6500$ kN
$q_{sr} = 350$ kPa $M_f = \pm 2500$ kN•m (wind)

Assume 20M zone bars at the wall ends (tension and compression).

Calculations and Discussions:

Note: As described in 9.4.3.3 of this Design Handbook, Clause 13.3.5 is used for designing footings supporting axial loads and moments. Equations (13-8) and (13-9) in Clause 13.3.5 are used for slabs supported by columns and not for walls, hence these equations cannot be used for footings supporting shear walls. Due to the significant size and stiffness of the shear walls and the associated footings, additional shear stresses cannot be justified in the footings using Equation (13-9) of Clause 13.3.5. For defining the critical shear depth of the footings supporting shear walls, a linear soil stress distribution is used as defined by Equation (9.6) of this handbook.

1. Establish footing size:

   An iterative method is used for establishing the required footing dimensions. The footing dimensions are a function of the maximum factored soil stresses, q_{sf}, with the assumption that the cantilever, a_b, is equal in both directions.

   In the first step of the iteration the footing size is calculated by assuming that $M = 0$ and increasing the axial load by 35%:

   $A_{min} = 1.35(6500)/350 = 25$ m^2. Using the same cantilever in both directions:

   $25 = (2a_b + 0.25)(4 + 2a_b)$ yields $a_b = 1.61$ m.

   Thus use $a_b = 1.6$ m and re-check soil stresses. Footing dimensions are thus:

   $b = 3.45$ m and $L = 7.2$ m.

   Soil stresses:

   $q_{sf\,max/min} = P_f/A_f \pm M_f/S = 6500/(3.45(7.2)) \pm 2500/29.8$

   $q_{sf\,max} = 346$ kPa < 350 kPa and $q_{sf\,min} = 178$ kPa < 350 kPa. Thus the footing dimensions meet the soil stress requirements and no further iteration is required – See Figure 9.7.6.-1.

2. Minimum depth required at point B (corners of the wall) – one-way shear (checking overhang/cantilever in direction perpendicular to the wall):

   $a_b = 1.6$ m

   Maximum soil pressure within the length of the wall at point B from Figure 9.7.6-1:

   $q_{sf} = 308$ kPa.

   From Table 9.3: $d_v = 533$ mm, thus $d = d_v/0.9 = 592$ mm.

3. Minimum depth at point A (end faces of the wall):

3.1 One-way shear (checking overhang in direction of the wall):

   $a_b = 1.6$ m

   Average factored soil pressure in the cantilevered portion

   $q_{sf} = 0.5(346 + 308) = 327$ kPa.

   From Table 9.3: $d_v = 533$ mm, thus $d = 533/0.9 = 592$ mm.

3.2 Two-way shear at point A:

   Ends of walls are considered as columns with side proportions of 1:2 for establishing minimum footing thickness. The footing is assumed to be concentric with this fictitious column with the long side 250 mm longer than the short side. Therefore the column dimensions are 250 x 500 mm and the footing dimensions are 3450 × 3700 mm.

   $A_f/A_c = 3.45(3.7)/((0.25)(0.5)) = 102.1$ and the maximum average stress is 327 kPa. Using Table 9.6, the following values are considered for interpolation:

9

Foundations

for $d/h_c = 1.9$, $A_f/A_c = 93.7 + (107.8 - 93.7)(23.2)/50 = 100.2$

for $d/h_c = 2.0$, $A_f/A_c = 101.8 + (117.3 - 101.8)(23.2)/50 = 109$

thus for $A_f/A_c = 102.1$, $d/h_c = 1.9 + 0.1(102.1 - 100.2)/(109 - 100.2) = 1.92$

Since $h_e = \sqrt{A_c} = \sqrt{250(500)} = 354$ mm thus $d = 1.92(354) = 679$ mm > 592 mm, thus two-way shear governs. Use minimum $d = 700$ mm. Note: Clause 13.3.4.4 is therefore not applicable.

4.   Flexural reinforcement

Check deep beam action in accordance with Clause 10.7.1.

$a_b/d = 1.6/0.7 = 2.29 > 2$, thus no deep beam action.

4.1 Flexural reinforcement within the length of wall (based on the maximum stresses within the wall length) – reinforcement perpendicular to the wall:

$q_{sf}a_b{}^2 = 308(1.6^2) = 789$ kN, from Table 9.9b with $d = 700$ mm and $h = 800$ mm

$A_s = 1600 + (1727 - 1600)(89)/100 = 1713$ mm^2/m

$A_{s,min} = 1600$ mm^2/m < 1713

Reinforcement:

20M vertical wall reinforcement can be developed for tension in the footing with depth of

$800 – 75 = 725$ mm.

Based on Table 9.10, 25M bars can be developed in the footing cantilever perpendicular to the wall, thus use: 25M @ 290 c/c BLL

4.2 Flexural reinforcement at the ends of wall – reinforcement parallel to the wall:

$q_{sf}a_b{}^2 = 327(1.6^2) = 837$ kN, from Table 9.9b with $d = 700$ mm

$A_s = 1727 + (1950 - 1727)(36.6)/100 = 1808$ mm^2/m – BUL

$A_{s,\ min} = 1600$ mm^2/m < 1808 mm^2/m

Main reinforcement in the cantilevers parallel to the walls:

Use 25M @275 mm c/c BUL (13-25M)

For minimum reinforcement parallel to the walls use: 25M @300 mm BUL (11-25M)

Reinforcement summary:

Short way perpendicular to the wall: full length of the footing: 25M @290 mm c/c BLL.

Long way parallel to the wall:

Use 11 – 25M for full length of footing plus 2 – 25M with a length of 3.3 m under each end of the wall.

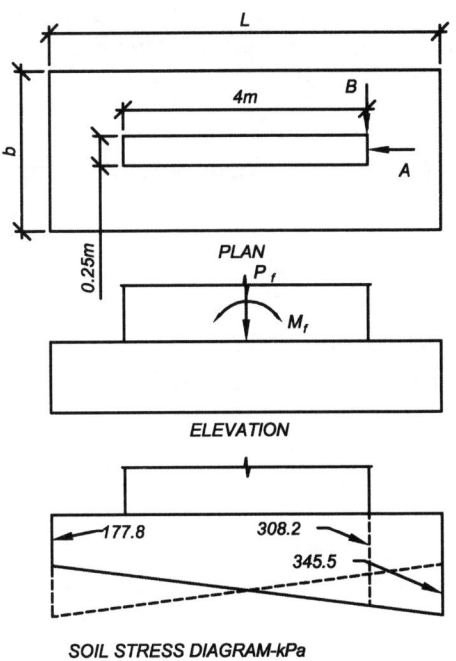

SOIL STRESS DIAGRAM-kPa

Figure 9.7.6-1

Example 9.7.7 Square Pile Cap Design

Determine the pile cap dimensions and reinforcement for the given column load and piles.

Factored column load: $P_f = 4800$ kN (No moment acts at the base of column).
Column size: 500 x 500 mm; $f'_c = 35$ MPa.
Factored pipe pile capacity (by the geotechnical consultant) is $P_r = 1300$ kN.
Pipe pile: DN300; Ø323, 9 x 9.52, spaced at 4 pile diameters.
Pile cap concrete strength at 28 days: $f'_c = 30$ MPa.
Pile location tolerance is 50 mm in any direction.

1. Number of piles required:
    $n = 4800/1300 = 3.7$ thus use 4 piles.
    Maximum factored pile reaction is: $R_f = 4800/4 = 1200$ kN.

2. Preliminary depth based on sectional method
    Since the pile cap will be ultimately designed by the S&T method, Clause 11.3.2 (b) can be ignored. For pile cap designs where the S&T method is not used, the above clause needs to be considered. The plan geometry is shown on 9.7.7-1.a.

2.1 One-way shear
    Calculation of V_f is described on Figure 9.7.7-2.a. Stress limits are set by Clause 11.3.6.2 and Equation (11-6) from Clause 11.3.4.

    Equating $V_c = V_f$; $(0.65)(1)(0.21)\sqrt{30}\,(2.6)d_v = 2(1.2)\dfrac{0.288 + 0.324 - d_v}{0.324}$;

    where: $b_w = 2.6$ m; $\beta = 0.21$; $\phi_c = 0.65$; $R_f = 1.2$ MN;
    $c = 562 - 324 + 50$(construction tolerance) $= 288$ mm.

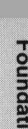

Thus, $d_v = 0.48$ m and $d = 0.53$ m. See Figure 9.7.7-3.a for the variation of V_f as a function of d_v. $V_f = 0$ at the outer edge of the pile at: $562 + 50$ (tolerance) $= 612$ mm.
In the above equation $0 \leq V_f \leq 2400$ kN.

2.2 Two-way shear

Determination of V_f is described in Figure 9.7.7-2.b. Stress limits are set by Clause 13.3.4.1.c.

Equating $V_r = V_f$; $0.38(1)(0.65)\sqrt{30}\ (4)(0.5 + d)d = 4(1.2)\left\{1 - \left(1 - \dfrac{0.288 + 0.324 - d/2}{0.324}\right)^2\right\}$

where the area of critical section $b_o d = 4(0.5 + d)d$; $\phi_c = 0.65$; and $R_f = 4(1.2) = 4.8$ MN;
Calculation of c_1, with 50 mm tolerance considered:

$c_1 = 400 - \dfrac{324}{2} + 50 = 288$ mm

From the $V_r = V_f$ equation $d = 0.705$ m ~ 0.7 m. Note: Clause 13.3.4.4 is therefore not applicable.
See Figure 9.7.7-3.b for variation of V_f as a function of d. $V_f = 0$ at outer edge of pile (see Figure 9.7.7.2-b and c), which is 612 mm from the face of column.
In the above equation $0 \leq V_f \leq 4800$ kN.

For the S&T method $d = 700$ mm will be used; thus the total depth of the pile cap is $h = 700 + 30$ (assumed rebar diameter) $+ 150 \cong 900$ mm. Based on Clause 11.3.6.2 (b) This is a deep pile cap.

3. Strut-and-tie method

Bearing resistance, based on Equation (9.11) above is:

$f_b = 0.6\phi_c\ (30) + 6\alpha\ \beta\ \phi_c \sqrt{30}\ = 11.7 + 21.4\ \alpha\ \beta$;(MPa)

At column: A_2 - pile cap area, A_1 - column area

$\sqrt{\dfrac{A_2}{A_1}} = \sqrt{\dfrac{2.6^2}{0.5^2}} = 5.2 > 4$ thus $\alpha = 1.0$; $\beta = 0.33 \left(\dfrac{2(0.7)}{0.5} - 1\right) = 0.6$, thus

$f_b = 11.7 + 21.4(1.0)(0.6) = 24.5$ MPa – bearing resistance
Factored bearing stress under the column is:
$f_{bf} = P_f/A_c = 4.8/0.5^2 = 19.2$ MPa < 24.5 MPa.

At pile:

$\sqrt{\dfrac{A_2}{A_1}} = \sqrt{\dfrac{650^2 \pi}{162^2 \pi}} = 4.01 > 4$ thus $\alpha = 1.0$; $\beta = 0.33 \left(\dfrac{700}{324} - 1\right) = 0.39$

$f_b = 11.7 + 21.4\ (1.0)(0.39) = 20$ MPa

Factored bearing stress is: $f_{bf} = R_f/A_p = 1.2/(0.162^2 \pi) = 14.6$ MPa < 20.0 MPa.

4. Internal forces and reinforcement

See Figure 9.7.7-5 for arrangement of reinforcement.

4.1 Tie force and tie reinforcement (see Figure 9.7.7-4):

$T_{diag} = R_f/\tan\theta = 1200/\tan 43.3 = 1273$ kN

$T_f = T_{diag}\ /\sqrt{2} = 900$ kN – factored tension.
$A_{s,required} = 1000 T_f/(0.85 f_y) = 2648$ mm^2.

4.2 Minimum reinforcement:

$A_{s,min} = 0.002A_g = 0.002(1000)(900) = 1800$ mm^2/m, thus a total of $A_{s,min} = 4680$ mm^2 is required in each direction. Since the total tension tie reinforcement (in each direction) is $2 \times 2648 = 5296$ mm^2 is almost equal to $A_{s,min}$, distribute all reinforcement uniformly, thus use 11-25M BEW. In case of significant difference between the tension tie and the minimum reinforcement, place the minimum reinforcement uniformly and concentrate the difference in the ties over the piles.

4.3 Dowels from piles into the pile cap:

Add dowels from piles into pile cap as per Clause 15.9.2.1.

$A_{dowel} = 0.005(324/2)^2 \pi = 412$ mm^2

It is a good practice to provide a minimum of 4 vertical dowels, tied.

Thus use: 4 -15M verticals with 15M @240 mm ties, extend dowels into cap and pile for the tension development length. (Piles are filled with 25 MPa concrete.)

5.0 Comparing the Strut-and-Tie method with the sectional method

Bottom reinforcement by sectional method:

Factored moment at the face of the column: $M_f = 2R_f(0.4) = 960$ kN•m.

$d = 900 - 150 - 30 = 720$ mm

depth of compression stress block $a = 33$ mm

tension reinforcement required based on the sectional method is thus: 4014 mm^2.

This reinforcement is significantly less than calculated by the S&T method
The magnitude of under reinforcement is ~ 25%, see explanation under 9.5.2.3.3.

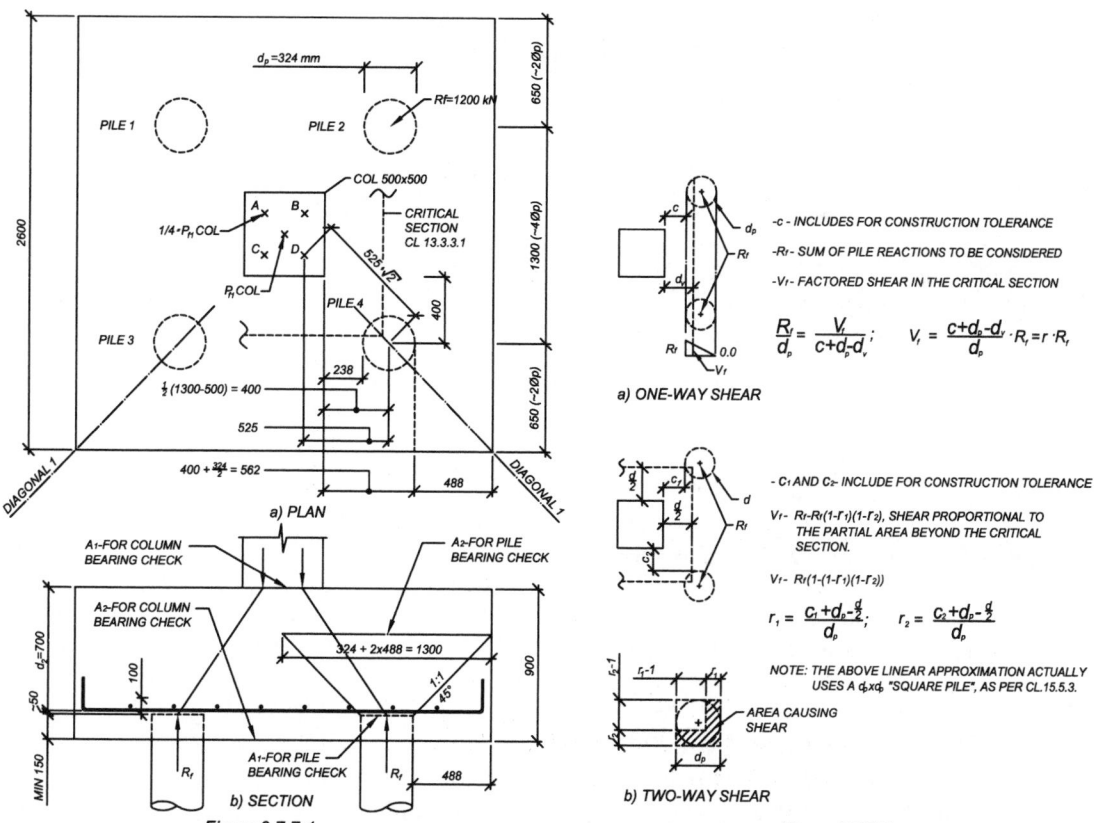

Figure 9.7.7-1

Figure 9.7.7-2

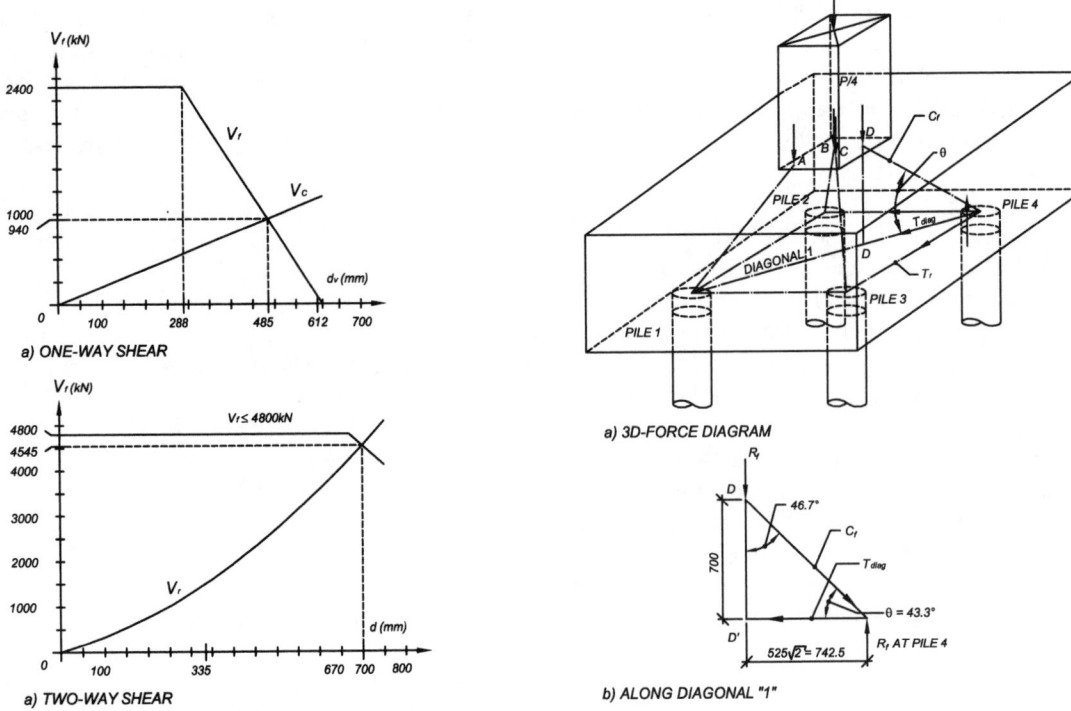

a) ONE-WAY SHEAR

a) TWO-WAY SHEAR

Figure 9.7.7-3

a) 3D-FORCE DIAGRAM

b) ALONG DIAGONAL "1"

Figure 9.7.7-4

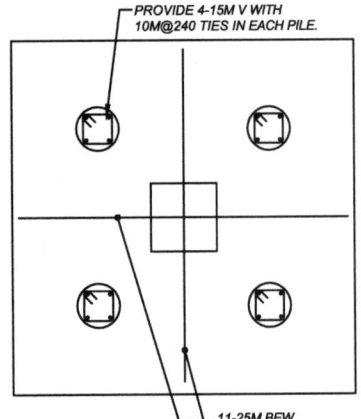

Figure 9.7.7-5 - REINFORCEMENT

Example 9.7.8 Rectangular Pile Cap Design

Determine pile cap dimensions and reinforcement for the given column load and piles. Due to construction and geometrical constraints the pile cap has to be rectangular.

Factored column load: $P_f = 4400$ kN (No moment acts at the base of column.).
Column size: 400 x 500 mm; $f_c' = 35$ MPa.

Factored pipe pile capacity (by the geotechnical consultant) is $P_r = 600$ kN.
Pipe pile suggested by the geotechnical consultant is: DN200; Ø219.1 x 8.18, spaced at 4 pile diameters.

Pile cap concrete strength at 28 days: $f_c' = 30$ MPa.

Pile location tolerance is 50 mm in any direction.

1. Number of piles required:

    $n = 4400/600 = 7.33$ thus use 8 piles

    Factored pile reaction is: $R_f = 4400/8 = 550$ kN

2. Preliminary depth is based on sectional method as discussed in Example 9.7.7.
    See Figure 9.7.8-1 for plan geometry.

2.1 One-way shear

    Based on Figure 9.7.7-2.a, and assuming that the critical section is beyond piles, 3-7 and 2-6
    respectively; and equating $V_c = V_f$ by using Clauses 11.3.4 and 11.3.6.2:

    $$0.65(1)(0.21)\sqrt{30}\,(1.6)d_v = 2(0.55)\,\frac{0.89 + 0.22 - d_v}{0.22}$$

    where the distance to the edge of the outer piles is:

    $150 + 800 - 110 + 50$(tolerance) $= 890$ mm.

    Solving for d_v, yields $d_v = 0.90$ m thus almost the full pile is beyond the critical section,
    and $V_f = 0 < 1.07$ MN < 1.1 OK.

2.2 Two-way shear

    The location of indicated section (at $d/2$) is based on the assumption that piles 1, 4, 5 and 8
    are fully outside of the critical section and that a portion of pile reactions of piles 2, 3, 6 and 7
    will contribute to the factored shear. Equating V_c with V_f (Clause 13.3.4.1.c and using Figure
    9.7.7.-2.b):

    $$0.38(1)(0.65)\sqrt{30}\,(2)\left((0.4+d)+(0.5+d)\right)d =$$

    $$= 4(0.55) + 4(0.55)\left\{1 - \left(1 - \frac{0.09 + 0.22 - d/2}{0.22}\right)\left(1 - \frac{0.14 + 0.22 - d/2}{0.22}\right)\right\};$$

    Where:

    $2((0.4 + d) + (0.5 + d))d$ is the shear surface area

    0.55 MN – pile reaction

    $c_1 = 0.09$ m; $c_1 = 150 - 110 + 50$ (tolerance) $= 90$ mm

    $c_2 = 0.14$ m; $c_2 = 200 - 110 + 50 = 140$ mm

    The solution yields $d = 568$ mm with $V_f = 3.13$ MN $< 8(0.55) = 4.4$ MN

    Note: Clause 13.3.4.4 is therefore not applicable.

    Based on one and two-way shear checks the largest value $d_v = 0.9$ m, thus $d = 1.0$ m will be
    used for the strut-and-tie check.

    Pile cap total depth is $h = 1000 + 30$ (bar diameter) $+ 150 = 1200$ mm. This pile cap is
    classified as a deep pile cap based on Clause 11.3.6.2 (b).

3. Strut-and-tie method

    The bearing resistance, based on previous example is:

    $$f_b = 11.7 + 21.36\,\alpha\,\beta$$

    At column:

    $$\sqrt{\frac{A_2}{A_1}} = \sqrt{\frac{1.6(3.2)}{0.4(0.5)}} = 5.06 > 4 \text{ thus } \alpha = 0.33(4.0 - 1) = 1.0$$

9

Foundations

$$h_{eff} = \sqrt{0.4(0.5)} \cong 0.5 \ m \quad \beta = 0.33\left(\frac{2(1.0)}{0.5} - 1\right) = 1.0$$

f_b = 11.7 + 21.36(1)(1.0) = 33.1 MPa

Factored bearing stress under the column: f_{bf} = 4.4/(0.4 (0.5)) = 22 MPa < 33.1 MPa o.k.

At pile:

$$\sqrt{\frac{A_2}{A_1}} = \sqrt{\frac{0.4^2}{0.11^2}} = 3.63 \ \text{thus} \ \alpha = 0.33(3.63 - 1) = 0.87$$

$$\beta = 0.33\left(\frac{1.0}{0.22} - 1\right) = 1.17 > 1 \ \text{thus} \ \beta = 1.0$$

f_b = 11.7 + 21.36(0.87)(1.0) = 30.3 MPa

Factored bearing stress over the pile top: $f_{bf} = \dfrac{0.55}{0.11^2 \pi} = 14.5 \ MPa < 30.3$ MPa O.K.

4.   Internal forces and reinforcement
      See Figure 9.7.8.2 for arrangement of reinforcement.

4.1   Tie forces and reinforcement: See Figure 9.7.8-1b:

Pile No.	θ	α	β	T_d – kN	T_s – kN	T_L – kN
1, 5, 4, 8	41.9	15.6	74.4	613	165	590
2, 3, 6, 7	67.9	47.5	42.5	224	165	151

Ties	Factored tension kN	$A_{s, required}$ mm^2	$A_{s, provided}$ mm^2
1-5; 4-8	165	485	1-25M
2-6; 3-7	165	485	1-25M
1-2; 5-6; 3-4; 7-8	590	1735	4-25M
2-3; 6-7	590 +151 = 741	2179	5-25M

4.2   Minimum reinforcement
      $A_{s,min}$ = 0.002A_g = 0.002(1200)(1000) = 2400 mm^2/m. In short direction, $A_{s,min}$ = 3.2(2400) = 7680 mm^2, which is more than the total tie reinforcement of 4(500) = 2000 mm^2; thus use 16-25M BUL uniformly spaced. In long direction, $A_{s,min}$ = 1.6(2400) = 3840 mm^2 , which is less than the total reinforcement of 2(5)(500) = 5000 mm^2 . Since the difference between the minimum and the required tension tie reinforcement is relatively small use 10-25M BLL uniformly spaced.

4.3   Dowels from Piles into the Pile cap:
      See explanation in example 9.7.7.
      A_{dowel} = 0.005(220/2)$^2 \pi$ = 190 mm^2
      Since the area is very small use 2-15M vertical for each pile without ties.

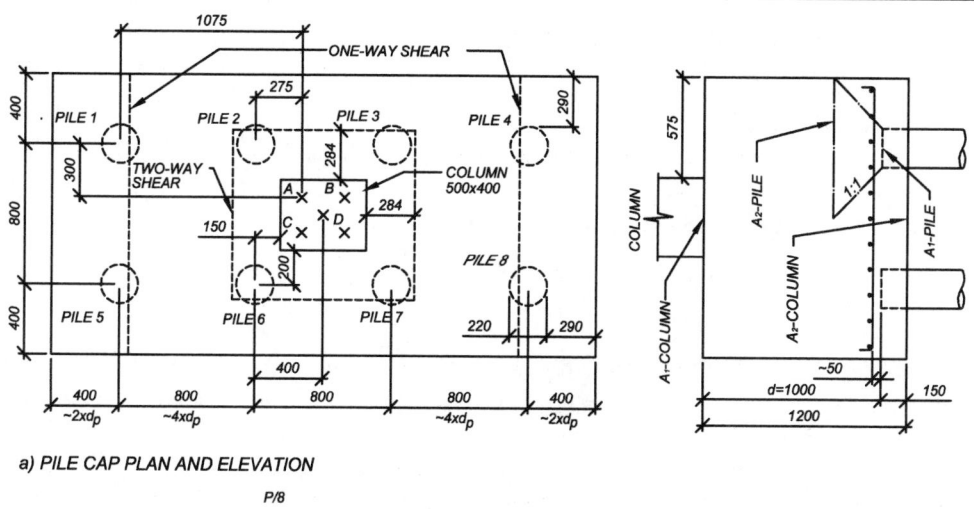

a) PILE CAP PLAN AND ELEVATION

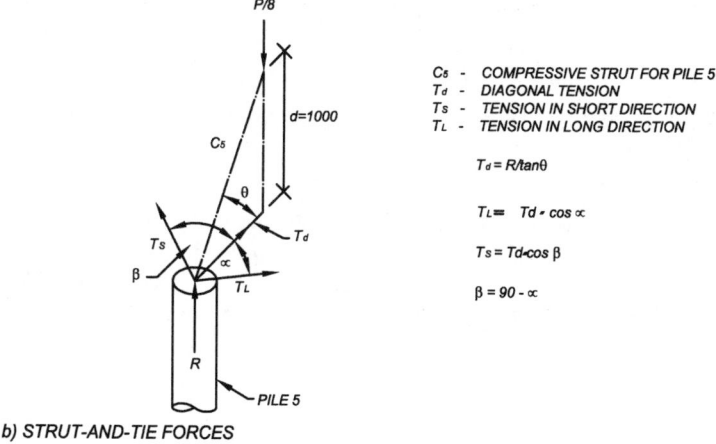

C_5 - COMPRESSIVE STRUT FOR PILE 5
T_d - DIAGONAL TENSION
T_s - TENSION IN SHORT DIRECTION
T_L - TENSION IN LONG DIRECTION

$T_d = R/\tan\theta$

$T_L = T_d \cdot \cos \alpha$

$T_s = T_d \cdot \cos \beta$

$\beta = 90 - \alpha$

b) STRUT-AND-TIE FORCES

Figure 9.7.8-1

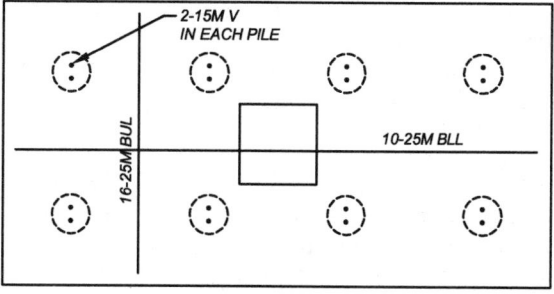

Figure 9.7.8-2

Example 9.7.9 Design of a Drilled Pile

Determine the reinforcement required for the uncased drilled pile with the following parameters:

Pile shaft diameter: 1219 mm (auger size)

Pile length: 12 m

Concrete: $f'_c = 30$ MPa

Factored loads calculated at the top of the drilled pile:

$P_f = 9800$ kN compression

$V_f = 700$ kN shear

Construction tolerance: $e = 75$ mm

Geotechnical parameters:

Rock end bearing: $q_{sf} = 9.0$ MPa

Side friction: $v_s = 0.4$ MPa, in the lower 2 metres.

Linear spring constant in upper 10 m: $k_1 = 20$ MN/m^3

Linear spring constant in lower 2 m: $k_2 = 750$ MN/m^3

1. Establish structural model – see Figure 9.7.9-1a-b:

    Use reduced pile shaft diameter based on Clause 15.8.2.2, thus $d_p = 1169$ mm. Use this diameter for establishing all geometrical properties, bearing and side friction capacities and shaft resistance.

    Spring constants: Spring support spacing of 1.0 m c/c was used. The spacing is arbitrary, but a closer spacing will provide better results. In general terms the spring constant can be established as

    K_1(MN/m) = k_1 (MN/m^3) A (m^2); where A = 1.0(spring spacing) x reduced d_p (pile diameter), represents the shaft's bearing area concentric to the selected spring support. Thus:

    K_1= 20(1.169)(1.0) = 23.8 MN/m,

    K_2= 750(1.169)(1.0) = 876.7 MN/m – see Figure 9.7.9-1a and b.

    The spring support reactions must be checked against the soil bearing capacity (not checked in this example) to ensure that the soil is capable of supporting the horizontal loads. In case the soil bearing capacity is exceeded, the geotechnical consultant may adjust the spring constants or a different pile diameter or length used to converge to equilibrium.

2. Bearing capacity check:

    Pile area: $A = 1.07$ m^2

    Pile perimeter: $C = 3.67$ m

    Bearing capacity check (compression): B_r = 9(1.07) + 2(3.67)(0.4) = 12.6 MN > 9.8 MN thus the size of the drilled pile is acceptable.

3. Cross sectional forces

    See Figure 9.7.9-1c-f for the cross sectional forces. The cross sectional forces were established using SAP 2000 software.

4. Design of cross section:

    Based on Clause 15.8.2.3 an additional 0.9 reduction factor must be applied to the factored resistances defined in Clauses 10 and 11.

    Shear design:

    V_c: Based on Clause 11.3.4, Clause 11.2.10.3 ($b_w = d$), Clause 11.3.6.3 (a) ($\beta = 0.18$) and Clause 15.8.2.3:

    $d = 1169 - 75 - 15 - 35/2 = 1062$ mm; where 15M ties, 75 mm cover and 35M verticals are assumed. $d_v = 0.9d = 955$ mm,

    $V_c = 0.9(0.65)(1)(0.18) \sqrt{30}$ (1.062)(0.955) = 0.58 MN < $V_f = 0.7$ MN.

    Required V_s: $V_s = V_f - V_c$, thus $V_{s,min} = 0.7 - 0.58 = 0.12$ MN.

    Minimum area of shear reinforcement based on Equation (11-1):

$$A_{s,min} = 0.06\sqrt{30}\,\frac{1.062(0.35)}{400}\,10^6 = 305\ mm^2\ /\ 350\ mm$$

Note: 15M @350 mm stirrup spacing was used to increase the cage stiffness.
Calculating V_s: Using $\theta = 35°$ (Clause 11.3.6.3) and Clause 11.3.5.1 using 15M @350 stirrups.

$$V_s = 0.9\phi_s A_v f_y d_v\ cot\ \theta\ /\ s + 0.9(0.65)400^{-6}(400)(0.955\ cot\ 35\,)\,/\,0.35 = 0.36\ MN$$

Calculation of V_r:
$V_r = V_c + V_s = 0.58 + 0.36 = 0.94$ MN $> V_f = 0.7$ MN. Thus use 15M @350 ties.

Flexure: Use 12-30M V.

Note: In this example the interface between the pile cap and the pile shaft has not been addressed.

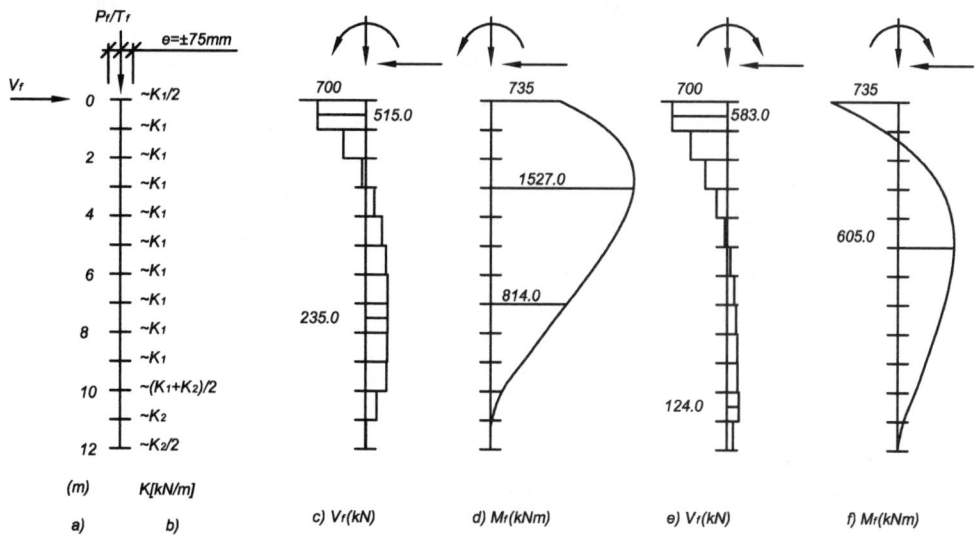

Figure 9.7.9-1

9.8   Design Tables

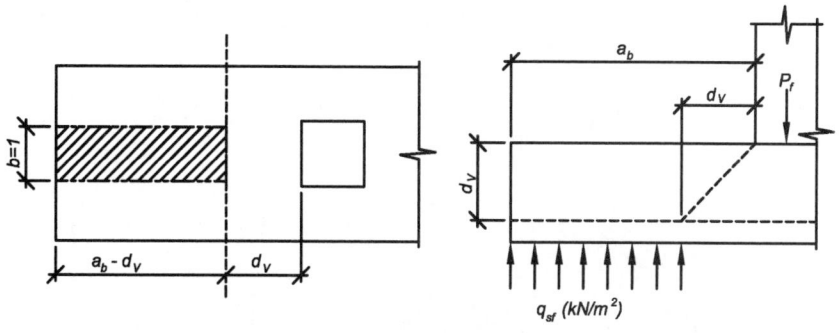

PLAN   ELEVATION
EFFECTIVE DEPTH d_v REQUIRED BY ONE-WAY SHEAR ACTION FOR SPREAD FOOTINGS

Figure 9.8-1

Table 9.1   One-way Shear Action $f'_c = 20$ MPa $\Phi_c = 0.65$

q_{sf} (kN/m²)	Values of d_v (mm) — a_b (m)														
	0.2	0.4	0.6	0.8	1.0	1.2	1.4	1.6	1.8	2.0	2.2	2.4	2.6	2.8	3.0
100	150	150	150	150	150	169	197	225	291	332	375	421	468	518	571
150	150	150	150	158	197	237	320	378	439	505	574	648	726	808	895
200	150	150	150	197	247	344	417	494	577	665	733	800	867	933	1000
250	150	150	174	232	333	400	467	533	600	667	733	800	867	933	1000
300	150	150	198	267	333	400	467	533	600	667	733	800	867	933	1000
350	150	150	219	292	364	437	510	583	656	729	802	875	947	1020	1093
400	150	158	238	317	396	475	554	633	713	792	871	950	1029	1108	1188
450	150	170	255	339	424	509	594	679	764	849	934	1018	1103	1188	1273
500	150	180	270	360	450	540	630	720	810	901	991	1081	1171	1261	1351
550	150	190	284	379	474	569	664	758	853	948	1043	1137	1232	1327	1422
600	150	198	297	397	496	595	694	793	892	991	1091	1190	1289	1388	1487
650	150	206	309	413	516	619	722	825	928	1031	1135	1238	1341	1444	1547
700	150	214	321	427	534	641	748	855	962	1068	1175	1282	1389	1496	1603
750	150	221	331	441	551	662	772	882	992	1103	1213	1323	1433	1544	1654
800	150	227	340	454	567	681	794	908	1021	1134	1248	1361	1475	1588	1702
850	150	233	349	466	582	698	815	931	1048	1164	1280	1397	1513	1630	1746
900	150	238	358	477	596	715	834	953	1073	1192	1311	1430	1549	1668	1788
950	150	244	365	487	609	731	852	974	1096	1218	1339	1461	1583	1705	1826
1000	150	248	373	497	621	745	869	994	1118	1242	1366	1490	1614	1739	1863
1100	150	257	386	514	643	772	900	1029	1158	1286	1415	1543	1672	1801	1929
1200	150	265	398	530	663	795	928	1061	1193	1326	1458	1591	1723	1856	1988
1300	150	272	408	544	680	817	953	1089	1225	1361	1497	1633	1769	1905	2041
1400	150	279	418	557	696	836	975	1114	1253	1393	1532	1671	1811	1950	2089
1500	150	284	426	569	711	853	995	1137	1279	1422	1564	1706	1848	1990	2132

Table 9.2 **One-way Shear Action** $f'_c = 25$ MPa $\Phi c = 0.65$

Values of d_v (mm)

q_{sf} (kN/m²)	a_b (m)														
	0.2	0.4	0.6	0.8	1.0	1.2	1.4	1.6	1.8	2.0	2.2	2.4	2.6	2.8	3.0
100	150	150	150	150	150	153	179	204	230	295	333	372	413	457	502
150	150	150	150	150	180	216	287	339	393	451	512	577	645	718	794
200	150	150	150	181	227	312	377	446	521	599	683	772	866	933	1000
250	150	150	161	214	304	379	459	533	600	667	733	800	867	933	1000
300	150	150	183	244	333	400	467	533	600	667	733	800	867	933	1000
350	150	150	203	271	339	407	475	542	610	678	746	814	881	949	1017
400	150	150	222	296	370	443	517	591	665	739	813	887	961	1035	1109
450	150	159	238	318	397	477	556	636	715	795	874	954	1033	1113	1192
500	150	169	254	338	423	507	592	677	761	846	930	1015	1099	1184	1268
550	150	178	268	357	446	535	625	714	803	892	982	1071	1160	1249	1339
600	150	187	281	374	468	561	655	749	842	936	1029	1123	1216	1310	1404
650	150	195	293	390	488	585	683	780	878	976	1073	1171	1268	1366	1463
700	150	203	304	405	506	608	709	810	911	1013	1114	1215	1316	1418	1519
750	150	209	314	419	524	628	733	838	942	1047	1152	1257	1361	1466	1571
800	150	216	324	432	540	648	755	863	971	1079	1187	1295	1403	1511	1619
850	150	222	333	444	555	666	777	887	998	1109	1220	1331	1442	1553	1664
900	150	227	341	455	569	682	796	910	1024	1137	1251	1365	1479	1592	1706
950	150	233	349	466	582	698	815	931	1047	1164	1280	1397	1513	1629	1746
1000	150	238	357	475	594	713	832	951	1070	1189	1308	1426	1545	1664	1783
1100	150	247	370	494	617	741	864	987	1111	1234	1358	1481	1604	1728	1851
1200	150	255	382	510	637	765	892	1020	1147	1275	1402	1530	1657	1785	1912
1300	150	262	393	525	656	787	918	1049	1180	1311	1443	1574	1705	1836	1967
1400	150	269	403	538	672	807	941	1076	1210	1345	1479	1613	1748	1882	2017
1500	150	275	412	550	687	825	962	1100	1237	1375	1512	1649	1787	1924	2062

Table 9.3 **One-way Shear Action** $f'_c = 30$ MPa $\Phi_c = 0.65$

Values of d_v (mm)

q_{sf} (kN/m²)	a_b (m)														
	0.2	0.4	0.6	0.8	1.0	1.2	1.4	1.6	1.8	2.0	2.2	2.4	2.6	2.8	3.0
100	150	150	150	150	150	150	165	189	212	236	302	337	373	412	452
150	150	150	150	150	167	201	234	310	359	411	466	524	585	650	718
200	150	150	150	169	211	287	346	410	477	549	625	706	791	882	977
250	150	150	150	200	251	350	424	503	588	667	733	800	867	933	1000
300	150	150	172	229	327	400	467	533	600	667	733	800	867	933	1000
350	150	150	191	267	333	400	467	533	600	667	733	800	867	933	1000
400	150	150	209	279	349	418	488	558	627	697	767	836	906	976	1046
450	150	150	225	301	376	451	526	601	676	751	827	902	977	1052	1127
500	150	160	240	321	401	481	561	641	721	802	882	962	1042	1122	1202
550	150	170	254	339	424	509	593	678	763	848	932	1017	1102	1187	1272
600	150	178	267	356	445	534	623	712	801	890	979	1069	1158	1247	1336
650	150	186	279	372	465	558	651	744	837	930	1023	1116	1209	1302	1395
700	150	193	290	387	484	580	677	774	870	967	1064	1161	1257	1354	1451
750	150	200	300	401	501	601	701	801	901	1002	1102	1202	1302	1402	1502
800	150	207	310	414	517	620	724	827	930	1034	1137	1241	1344	1447	1551
850	150	213	319	426	532	638	745	851	958	1064	1170	1277	1383	1490	1596
900	150	218	328	437	546	655	765	874	983	1092	1202	1311	1420	1529	1639
950	150	224	336	448	560	672	783	895	1007	1119	1231	1343	1455	1567	1679
1000	150	229	343	458	572	687	801	916	1030	1144	1259	1373	1488	1602	1717
1100	150	238	357	476	595	714	833	953	1072	1191	1310	1429	1548	1667	1786
1200	150	246	370	493	616	739	863	986	1109	1232	1355	1479	1602	1725	1848
1300	150	254	381	508	635	762	889	1016	1143	1270	1397	1524	1651	1778	1905
1400	150	261	391	522	652	782	913	1043	1173	1304	1434	1565	1695	1825	1956
1500	150	267	400	534	667	801	934	1068	1201	1335	1468	1602	1735	1869	2002

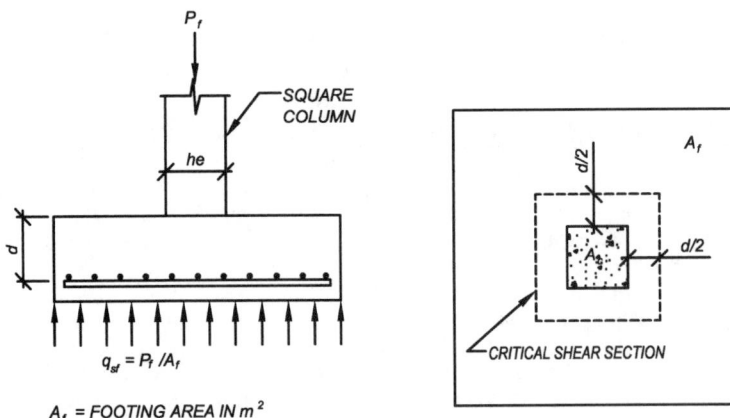

A_f = FOOTING AREA IN m^2
A_c = COLMN AREA IN m^2
FOR CIRCULAR, POLGONAL, OR RECTANGULAR COLUMNS WITH
SPECT RATIOS NOT EXCEEDING 2.0, USE h$_e$=$\sqrt{A_c}$

EFFECTIVE DEPTH dv REQUIRED BY TWO-WAY SHEAR ACTION FOR SPREAD FOOTINGS
SUPPORTING COLUMNS WITH ASPECT RATIONS NOT EXCEEDING 2.0

Figure 9.8-2

Table 9.4   **Two-way Shear Action** f'_c = 20 MPa Φ_c = 0.65

q_{sf}	Footing to column area ratios, A_f/A_c															
	d/h_e															
(kN/m^2)	0.5	0.6	0.7	0.8	0.9	1.0	1.1	1.2	1.3	1.4	1.5	1.6	1.7	1.8	1.9	2.0
100	35.4	45.0	55.5	66.9	79.2	92.4	106.5	121.6	137.4	154.2	172.0	190.5	210.1	230.4	251.9	274.0
150	24.4	30.8	38.0	45.7	54.0	62.9	72.5	82.6	93.4	104.8	116.8	129.3	142.6	156.4	170.8	185.8
200	18.8	23.8	29.2	35.1	41.4	48.2	55.5	63.2	71.4	80.0	89.2	98.7	108.8	119.3	130.2	141.6
250	15.5	19.5	23.9	28.7	33.8	39.4	45.2	51.5	58.1	65.2	72.5	80.3	88.4	96.9	105.8	115.1
300	13.3	16.7	20.4	24.5	28.8	33.5	38.4	43.7	49.3	55.3	61.5	68.0	74.9	82.1	89.6	97.4
350	11.7	14.7	17.9	21.4	25.2	29.3	33.6	38.2	43.1	48.2	53.6	59.3	65.3	71.5	78.0	84.8
400	10.5	13.2	16.0	19.2	22.5	26.1	29.9	34.0	38.3	42.9	47.7	52.7	58.0	63.5	69.3	75.3
450	9.6	12.0	14.6	17.4	20.4	23.6	27.1	30.8	34.7	38.8	43.1	47.6	52.4	57.3	62.5	67.9
500	8.9	11.1	13.4	16.0	18.7	21.7	24.8	28.2	31.7	35.5	39.4	43.5	47.9	52.4	57.1	62.0
550	8.3	10.3	12.5	14.8	17.4	20.1	23.0	26.1	29.3	32.8	36.4	40.2	44.2	48.3	52.7	57.2
600	7.8	9.6	11.7	13.9	16.2	18.7	21.4	24.3	27.3	30.5	33.9	37.4	41.1	45.0	49.0	53.2
650	7.4	9.1	11.0	13.0	15.2	17.6	20.1	22.8	25.6	28.6	31.8	35.1	38.5	42.1	45.9	49.8
700	7.0	8.6	10.4	12.3	14.4	16.6	19.0	21.5	24.2	27.0	29.9	33.0	36.3	39.7	43.2	46.9
750	6.7	8.2	9.9	11.7	13.7	15.8	18.0	20.4	22.9	25.6	28.4	31.3	34.3	37.6	40.9	44.4
800	6.4	7.9	9.5	11.2	13.1	15.1	17.2	19.4	21.8	24.3	27.0	29.7	32.7	35.7	38.9	42.2
850	6.2	7.6	9.1	10.7	12.5	14.4	16.4	18.6	20.8	23.2	25.8	28.4	31.2	34.1	37.1	40.2
900	5.9	7.3	8.7	10.3	12.0	13.8	15.8	17.8	20.0	22.3	24.7	27.2	29.8	32.6	35.5	38.5
950	5.7	7.0	8.4	9.9	11.6	13.3	15.2	17.1	19.2	21.4	23.7	26.1	28.6	31.3	34.0	36.9
1000	5.6	6.8	8.1	9.6	11.2	12.8	14.6	16.5	18.5	20.6	22.8	25.1	27.6	30.1	32.8	35.5
1100	5.3	6.4	7.7	9.0	10.5	12.0	13.7	15.5	17.3	19.3	21.3	23.5	25.8	28.1	30.6	33.1
1200	5.0	6.1	7.3	8.5	9.9	11.4	12.9	14.6	16.3	18.1	20.1	22.1	24.2	26.4	28.7	31.1
1300	4.8	5.8	6.9	8.1	9.4	10.8	12.3	13.8	15.5	17.2	19.0	20.9	22.9	25.0	27.2	29.4
1400	4.6	5.6	6.6	7.8	9.0	10.3	11.7	13.2	14.7	16.4	18.1	19.9	21.8	23.8	25.8	27.9
1500	4.5	5.4	6.4	7.5	8.7	9.9	11.2	12.6	14.1	15.7	17.3	19.0	20.8	22.7	24.7	26.7

See page 48 for the note to tables 9.4 to 9.6.

Table 9.5   **Two-way Shear Action** $f'_c = 25$ MPa $\Phi_c = 0.65$

Footing to column area ratios, A_f/A_c

q_{sf} (kN/m²)	d/h_e															
	0.5	0.6	0.7	0.8	0.9	1.0	1.1	1.2	1.3	1.4	1.5	1.6	1.7	1.8	1.9	2.0
100	39.3	50.0	61.7	74.5	88.1	102.9	118.6	135.3	153.0	171.8	191.4	212.3	233.9	256.9	280.6	305.3
150	27.0	34.2	42.1	50.7	59.9	69.9	80.5	91.8	103.8	116.5	129.8	143.8	158.5	173.9	189.9	206.7
200	20.8	26.3	32.3	38.8	45.9	53.4	61.5	70.1	79.2	88.8	98.9	109.6	120.7	132.4	144.6	157.3
250	17.1	21.5	26.4	31.7	37.4	43.5	50.1	57.0	64.4	72.2	80.4	89.0	98.0	107.5	117.3	127.6
300	14.6	18.4	22.5	27.0	31.8	36.9	42.5	48.3	54.5	61.1	68.0	75.3	82.9	90.8	99.2	107.8
350	12.8	16.1	19.7	23.6	27.8	32.2	37.0	42.1	47.5	53.2	59.2	65.5	72.1	79.0	86.2	93.7
400	11.5	14.4	17.6	21.0	24.7	28.7	32.9	37.5	42.2	47.3	52.6	58.2	64.0	70.1	76.5	83.1
450	10.5	13.1	16.0	19.1	22.4	26.0	29.8	33.8	38.1	42.7	47.4	52.4	57.7	63.2	68.9	74.9
500	9.7	12.1	14.7	17.5	20.5	23.8	27.2	30.9	34.8	39.0	43.3	47.9	52.6	57.6	62.9	68.3
550	9.0	11.2	13.6	16.2	19.0	22.0	25.2	28.6	32.2	36.0	40.0	44.1	48.5	53.1	57.9	62.9
600	8.4	10.5	12.7	15.1	17.7	20.5	23.4	26.6	29.9	33.5	37.2	41.0	45.1	49.4	53.8	58.5
650	8.0	9.9	11.9	14.2	16.6	19.2	22.0	24.9	28.0	31.3	34.8	38.4	42.2	46.2	50.3	54.6
700	7.5	9.3	11.3	13.4	15.7	18.1	20.7	23.5	26.4	29.5	32.7	36.1	39.7	43.4	47.3	51.4
750	7.2	8.9	10.7	12.7	14.9	17.2	19.6	22.2	25.0	27.9	31.0	34.2	37.5	41.1	44.7	48.5
800	6.9	8.5	10.2	12.1	14.2	16.4	18.7	21.2	23.8	26.5	29.4	32.5	35.6	39.0	42.5	46.1
850	6.6	8.1	9.8	11.6	13.6	15.6	17.8	20.2	22.7	25.3	28.1	30.9	34.0	37.1	40.4	43.9
900	6.4	7.8	9.4	11.1	13.0	15.0	17.1	19.3	21.7	24.2	26.8	29.6	32.5	35.5	38.7	41.9
950	6.2	7.6	9.1	10.7	12.5	14.4	16.4	18.6	20.8	23.2	25.8	28.4	31.2	34.1	37.1	40.2
1000	6.0	7.3	8.8	10.4	12.1	13.9	15.8	17.9	20.1	22.4	24.8	27.3	30.0	32.7	35.6	38.7
1100	5.6	6.9	8.2	9.7	11.3	13.0	14.8	16.7	18.7	20.9	23.1	25.5	27.9	30.5	33.2	36.0
1200	5.3	6.5	7.8	9.2	10.7	12.2	13.9	15.7	17.6	19.6	21.7	23.9	26.2	28.6	31.1	33.7
1300	5.1	6.2	7.4	8.7	10.1	11.6	13.2	14.9	16.7	18.5	20.5	22.6	24.7	27.0	29.4	31.8
1400	4.9	5.9	7.1	8.3	9.6	11.1	12.6	14.2	15.8	17.6	19.5	21.4	23.5	25.6	27.9	30.2
1500	4.7	5.7	6.8	8.0	9.2	10.6	12.0	13.5	15.1	16.8	18.6	20.5	22.4	24.4	26.6	28.8

Table 9.6   **Two-way Shear Action** $f'_c = 30$ MPa $\Phi_c = 0.65$

Footing to column area ratios, A_f/A_c

q_{sf} (kN/m²)	d/h_e															
	0.5	0.6	0.7	0.8	0.9	1.0	1.1	1.2	1.3	1.4	1.5	1.6	1.7	1.8	1.9	2.0
100	42.9	54.6	67.3	81.2	96.2	112.2	129.4	147.7	167.1	187.5	209.2	231.8	255.7	280.6	306.5	333.7
150	29.3	37.2	45.8	55.2	65.3	76.2	87.8	100.1	113.2	127.0	141.6	156.9	173.0	189.7	207.3	225.6
200	22.6	28.6	35.1	42.2	49.9	58.2	67.0	76.3	86.3	96.7	107.8	119.4	131.6	144.3	157.6	171.5
250	18.5	23.3	28.7	34.4	40.6	47.3	54.4	62.0	70.0	78.5	87.4	96.8	106.7	117.0	127.7	138.9
300	15.8	19.9	24.4	29.3	34.5	40.1	46.1	52.5	59.2	66.4	73.9	81.8	90.1	98.8	107.8	117.3
350	13.9	17.4	21.3	25.5	30.1	34.9	40.2	45.7	51.6	57.7	64.3	71.1	78.3	85.8	93.7	101.8
400	12.4	15.6	19.0	22.7	26.8	31.1	35.7	40.6	45.8	51.2	57.0	63.1	69.4	76.0	83.0	90.2
450	11.3	14.1	17.2	20.6	24.2	28.1	32.2	36.6	41.3	46.2	51.4	56.8	62.5	68.5	74.7	81.2
500	10.4	13.0	15.8	18.9	22.2	25.7	29.4	33.4	37.7	42.1	46.8	51.8	57.0	62.4	68.1	74.0
550	9.6	12.0	14.6	17.4	20.5	23.7	27.2	30.9	34.7	38.9	43.2	47.7	52.5	57.4	62.6	68.0
600	9.0	11.2	13.6	16.2	19.0	22.1	25.3	28.7	32.3	36.1	40.1	44.3	48.7	53.3	58.2	63.2
650	8.5	10.6	12.8	15.2	17.9	20.7	23.7	26.8	30.2	33.8	37.5	41.4	45.5	49.8	54.3	59.0
700	8.1	10.0	12.1	14.4	16.8	19.5	22.3	25.3	28.4	31.8	35.3	38.9	42.8	46.8	51.0	55.4
750	7.7	9.5	11.5	13.6	16.0	18.4	21.1	23.9	26.9	30.0	33.3	36.8	40.4	44.2	48.2	52.3
800	7.3	9.1	10.9	13.0	15.2	17.5	20.0	22.7	25.5	28.5	31.6	34.9	38.4	42.0	45.7	49.6
850	7.0	8.7	10.5	12.4	14.5	16.7	19.1	21.7	24.3	27.2	30.1	33.3	36.5	39.9	43.5	47.2
900	6.8	8.3	10.0	11.9	13.9	16.0	18.3	20.7	23.3	26.0	28.8	31.8	34.9	38.2	41.6	45.1
950	6.5	8.0	9.7	11.4	13.4	15.4	17.6	19.9	22.3	24.9	27.6	30.5	33.4	36.6	39.8	43.2
1000	6.3	7.8	9.3	11.0	12.9	14.8	16.9	19.1	21.5	23.9	26.6	29.3	32.1	35.1	38.2	41.5
1100	5.9	7.3	8.8	10.3	12.0	13.9	15.8	17.8	20.0	22.3	24.7	27.3	29.9	32.7	35.5	38.5
1200	5.6	6.9	8.3	9.7	11.3	13.0	14.8	16.8	18.8	20.9	23.2	25.5	28.0	30.6	33.3	36.1
1300	5.4	6.6	7.8	9.2	10.7	12.3	14.0	15.8	17.7	19.8	21.9	24.1	26.4	28.8	31.4	34.0
1400	5.2	6.3	7.5	8.8	10.2	11.7	13.3	15.1	16.9	18.8	20.8	22.9	25.0	27.3	29.7	32.2
1500	5.0	6.0	7.2	8.4	9.8	11.2	12.7	14.4	16.1	17.9	19.8	21.8	23.9	26.0	28.3	30.7

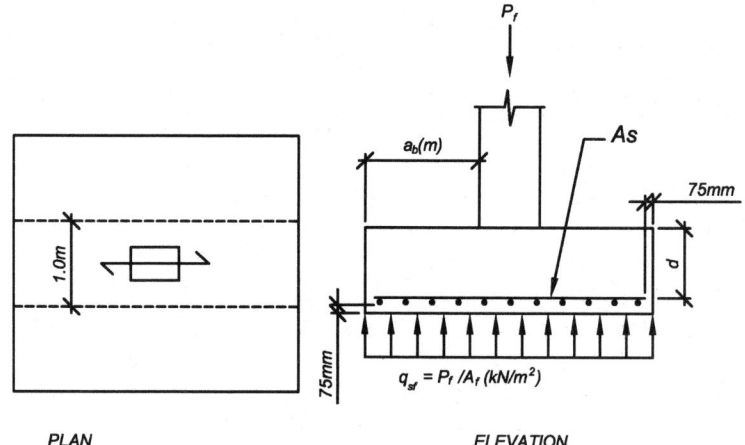

PLAN   ELEVATION

STEEL AREAS PER 1.0m WIDTH FOR SPREAD FOOTINGS. fy=400 MPa

Figure 9.8-3

Table 9.7a   **Values of A_s required for a 1 m width** $f'_c = 20$ MPa $\Phi_c = 0.65$

$q_{sf}\,a_b^2$	d (mm)															
(kN)	150	175	200	225	250	275	300	325	350	375	400	425	450	475	500	525
50	519	550	600	650	700	750	800	850	900	950	1000	1050	1100	1150	1200	1250
60	630	550	600	650	700	750	800	850	900	950	1000	1050	1100	1150	1200	1250
70	745	624	600	650	700	750	800	850	900	950	1000	1050	1100	1150	1200	1250
80	864	719	619	650	700	750	800	850	900	950	1000	1050	1100	1150	1200	1250
90	986	817	701	650	700	750	800	850	900	950	1000	1050	1100	1150	1200	1250
100	1112	917	784	687	700	750	800	850	900	950	1000	1050	1100	1150	1200	1250
120	1378	1123	955	834	741	750	800	850	900	950	1000	1050	1100	1150	1200	1250
140	1669	1340	1131	984	872	784	800	850	900	950	1000	1050	1100	1150	1200	1250
160	1989	1569	1314	1137	1006	903	820	850	900	950	1000	1050	1100	1150	1200	1250
180	2354	1812	1504	1295	1142	1023	928	850	900	950	1000	1050	1100	1150	1200	1250
200		2072	1701	1458	1281	1146	1038	949	900	950	1000	1050	1100	1150	1200	1250
250		2831	2237	1886	1643	1461	1318	1202	1106	1025	1000	1050	1100	1150	1200	1250
300			2857	2353	2027	1790	1608	1462	1343	1242	1156	1082	1100	1150	1200	1250
350			3616	2872	2438	2136	1910	1731	1585	1464	1361	1272	1194	1150	1200	1250
400				3466	2883	2502	2224	2008	1834	1690	1569	1465	1374	1295	1224	1250
450					3373	2891	2552	2295	2090	1922	1781	1661	1556	1465	1385	1313
500					3923	3309	2897	2592	2353	2159	1997	1860	1741	1638	1547	1466
600						4262	3649	3225	2906	2652	2444	2269	2120	1991	1877	1777
700							4515	3922	3499	3173	2911	2695	2511	2353	2215	2094
800								4707	4144	3728	3403	3138	2916	2726	2562	2419
900								5625	4856	4325	3922	3601	3335	3111	2919	2751
1000									5663	4973	4475	4087	3772	3509	3285	3091
1200										6506	5713	5146	4707	4351	4053	3800
1400											7233	6364	5745	5265	4876	4551
1600													6931	6276	5766	5352
1800														7422	6745	6216
2000															7846	7159
2200															9128	8210

Table 9.7b — Values of A_s required for a 1 m width — $f'_c = 20$ MPa — $\Phi_c = 0.65$

$q_{sf}\,a_b^2$ (kN)	550	575	600	625	650	675	700	725	750	775	800	825	850	900	950	1000
400	1300	1350	1400	1450	1500	1550	1600	1650	1700	1750	1800	1850	1900	2000	2100	2200
500	1393	1350	1400	1450	1500	1550	1600	1650	1700	1750	1800	1850	1900	2000	2100	2200
600	1687	1606	1533	1467	1500	1550	1600	1650	1700	1750	1800	1850	1900	2000	2100	2200
700	1986	1889	1802	1723	1651	1584	1600	1650	1700	1750	1800	1850	1900	2000	2100	2200
800	2291	2178	2075	1983	1898	1821	1750	1685	1700	1750	1800	1850	1900	2000	2100	2200
900	2603	2471	2353	2246	2150	2061	1980	1905	1836	1772	1800	1850	1900	2000	2100	2200
1000	2921	2770	2636	2514	2404	2304	2212	2128	2050	1978	1911	1850	1900	2000	2100	2200
1200	3580	3387	3216	3063	2925	2800	2685	2581	2484	2395	2312	2236	2164	2034	2100	2200
1400	4273	4031	3819	3630	3461	3309	3170	3044	2927	2820	2721	2629	2544	2389	2252	2200
1600	5004	4706	4447	4219	4016	3833	3668	3518	3380	3254	3137	3029	2929	2748	2589	2449
1800	5782	5418	5104	4831	4589	4373	4179	4004	3844	3697	3562	3437	3321	3113	2931	2769
2000	6617	6171	5794	5469	5184	4932	4706	4503	4318	4149	3995	3852	3720	3483	3276	3094
2200	7524	6976	6523	6138	5804	5510	5250	5016	4805	4612	4436	4275	4126	3859	3626	3422
2400	8524	7845	7298	6841	6451	6111	5811	5544	5304	5086	4888	4706	4539	4240	3981	3754
2600	9655	8795	8129	7586	7129	6737	6393	6090	5818	5573	5350	5147	4960	4628	4341	4090
2800		9854	9030	8380	7845	7391	6998	6653	6347	6072	5823	5597	5389	5022	4706	4431
3000			10023	9235	8603	8077	7628	7237	6892	6585	6308	6057	5827	5423	5077	4775
3500					10758	9977	9341	8805	8343	7938	7579	7257	6966	6458	6028	5657
4000						12274	11326	10572	9947	9414	8950	8540	8174	7545	7019	6571
4500								12645	11768	11053	10448	9926	9467	8692	8055	7519
5000										12925	12119	11444	10866	9910	9143	8507
5500											14040	13143	12401	11216	10292	9539
6000												15106	14123	12631	11513	10623
6500														14188	12822	11767
7000														15940	14240	12982
7500															15801	14283

Table 9.8a   Values of A_s required for a 1 m width f'_c = 25 MPa Φ_c = 0.65

$q_{sf}a^2$ (kN)	150	175	200	225	250	275	300	325	350	375	400	425	450	475	500	525
50	513	550	600	650	700	750	800	850	900	950	1000	1050	1100	1150	1200	1250
60	621	550	600	650	700	750	800	850	900	950	1000	1050	1100	1150	1200	1250
70	732	616	600	650	700	750	800	850	900	950	1000	1050	1100	1150	1200	1250
80	846	709	612	650	700	750	800	850	900	950	1000	1050	1100	1150	1200	1250
90	962	804	693	650	700	750	800	850	900	950	1000	1050	1100	1150	1200	1250
100	1081	900	774	680	700	750	800	850	900	950	1000	1050	1100	1150	1200	1250
120	1328	1097	939	823	734	750	800	850	900	950	1000	1050	1100	1150	1200	1250
140	1589	1301	1109	969	862	777	800	850	900	950	1000	1050	1100	1150	1200	1250
160	1868	1513	1282	1117	992	893	813	850	900	950	1000	1050	1100	1150	1200	1250
180	2168	1734	1461	1269	1124	1010	919	850	900	950	1000	1050	1100	1150	1200	1250
200	2495	1965	1645	1423	1258	1129	1026	940	900	950	1000	1050	1100	1150	1200	1250
250		2597	2130	1824	1603	1433	1298	1187	1094	1016	1000	1050	1100	1150	1200	1250
300		3344	2662	2251	1963	1747	1577	1440	1325	1228	1145	1073	1100	1150	1200	1250
350			3256	2707	2341	2073	1865	1698	1560	1444	1345	1259	1184	1150	1200	1250
400			3941	3201	2739	2411	2161	1963	1800	1664	1548	1448	1360	1283	1214	1250
450				3743	3162	2764	2467	2234	2045	1887	1753	1638	1538	1450	1372	1302
500				4352	3614	3134	2784	2513	2295	2114	1962	1832	1718	1619	1531	1452
600					4637	3933	3453	3094	2812	2582	2390	2226	2085	1962	1853	1756
700						4840	4182	3714	3355	3068	2832	2632	2461	2312	2181	2065
800						5918	4990	4380	3929	3576	3289	3050	2846	2670	2516	2380
900							5912	5105	4540	4109	3765	3481	3242	3036	2857	2700
1000								5907	5194	4671	4261	3928	3649	3411	3206	3026
1200									6687	5902	5324	4871	4501	4191	3926	3696
1400										7340	6512	5898	5414	5017	4682	4395
1600											7882	7036	6401	5896	5479	5126
1800												8331	7486	6842	6324	5894
2000													8703	7872	7228	6705
2200														9013	8204	7567
2400														10314	9273	8491
2600															10470	9493
2800																10597

Table 9.8b   **Values of A_s required for a 1 m width** $f'_c = 25$ **MPa** $\Phi_c = 0.65$

$q_{sf}a_b^2$ (kN)	550	575	600	625	650	675	700	725	750	775	800	825	850	900	950	1000
							d (mm)									
400	1300	1350	1400	1450	1500	1550	1600	1650	1700	1750	1800	1850	1900	2000	2100	2200
500	1382	1350	1400	1450	1500	1550	1600	1650	1700	1750	1800	1850	1900	2000	2100	2200
600	1670	1591	1520	1455	1500	1550	1600	1650	1700	1750	1800	1850	1900	2000	2100	2200
700	1962	1868	1784	1707	1637	1572	1600	1650	1700	1750	1800	1850	1900	2000	2100	2200
800	2258	2149	2051	1962	1880	1805	1736	1672	1700	1750	1800	1850	1900	2000	2100	2200
900	2560	2435	2322	2219	2126	2040	1962	1889	1822	1759	1800	1850	1900	2000	2100	2200
1000	2866	2724	2596	2480	2374	2278	2189	2107	2032	1961	1896	1850	1900	2000	2100	2200
1200	3494	3315	3155	3010	2879	2760	2650	2550	2457	2370	2290	2216	2146	2019	2100	2200
1400	4146	3926	3730	3554	3396	3252	3120	3000	2888	2785	2690	2601	2518	2368	2235	2200
1600	4823	4557	4323	4113	3925	3755	3600	3458	3327	3207	3095	2992	2895	2720	2566	2429
1800	5528	5212	4934	4688	4468	4269	4089	3925	3774	3635	3507	3388	3277	3077	2900	2744
2000	6267	5893	5567	5280	5025	4796	4589	4401	4229	4070	3924	3789	3664	3437	3238	3062
2200	7044	6603	6223	5892	5598	5336	5100	4887	4692	4513	4348	4196	4055	3802	3579	3383
2400	7865	7347	6906	6524	6188	5891	5624	5383	5164	4963	4779	4610	4453	4170	3924	3706
2600	8740	8130	7618	7180	6798	6461	6160	5890	5645	5422	5218	5029	4855	4544	4272	4033
2800	9680	8958	8364	7861	7428	7048	6711	6409	6137	5889	5663	5456	5264	4922	4624	4363
3000	10703	9841	9149	8573	8081	7653	7276	6941	6639	6366	6117	5889	5679	5305	4980	4696
3500		12388	11336	10512	9834	9261	8767	8332	7947	7601	7289	7005	6744	6284	5888	5543
4000				12773	11815	11039	10388	9830	9341	8909	8522	8173	7855	7298	6823	6412
4500					14144	13055	12185	11460	10841	10302	9826	9401	9017	8351	7788	7305
5000							14228	13269	12476	11802	11216	10699	10238	9447	8786	8224
5500								15330	14290	13435	12710	12082	11529	10592	9821	9171
6000									16359	15248	14338	13568	12902	11794	10897	10150
6500										17315	16142	15185	14377	13062	12020	11163
7000												16975	15978	14408	13196	12215
7500													17746	15848	14433	13311
8000														17407	15743	14455
8500														19118	17139	15656
9000															18642	16923
9500															20280	18267
10000																19706
10500																21262

Table 9.9a   Values of A_s required for a 1 m width $f'_c = 30$ MPa $\Phi_c = 0.65$

$q_{sf}a_b^2$ (kN)	\multicolumn{16}{c}{d (mm)}

$q_{sf}a_b^2$ (kN)	150	175	200	225	250	275	300	325	350	375	400	425	450	475	500	525
50	509	550	600	650	700	750	800	850	900	950	1000	1050	1100	1150	1200	1250
60	616	550	600	650	700	750	800	850	900	950	1000	1050	1100	1150	1200	1250
70	724	611	600	650	700	750	800	850	900	950	1000	1050	1100	1150	1200	1250
80	835	703	608	650	700	750	800	850	900	950	1000	1050	1100	1150	1200	1250
90	947	795	687	650	700	750	800	850	900	950	1000	1050	1100	1150	1200	1250
100	1062	889	767	676	700	750	800	850	900	950	1000	1050	1100	1150	1200	1250
120	1298	1081	929	816	729	750	800	850	900	950	1000	1050	1100	1150	1200	1250
140	1545	1277	1094	959	855	772	800	850	900	950	1000	1050	1100	1150	1200	1250
160	1803	1480	1263	1104	983	887	808	850	900	950	1000	1050	1100	1150	1200	1250
180	2076	1689	1435	1252	1112	1002	912	850	900	950	1000	1050	1100	1150	1200	1250
200	2364	1905	1611	1402	1243	1119	1018	934	900	950	1000	1050	1100	1150	1200	1250
250	3182	2482	2070	1788	1579	1416	1285	1177	1087	1010	1000	1050	1100	1150	1200	1250
300		3126	2561	2192	1925	1721	1558	1425	1314	1219	1138	1067	1100	1150	1200	1250
350		3866	3091	2617	2285	2035	1838	1677	1544	1432	1335	1251	1177	1150	1200	1250
400			3671	3067	2659	2358	2124	1935	1779	1647	1534	1437	1351	1275	1208	1250
450			4319	3547	3050	2692	2417	2197	2017	1865	1736	1624	1527	1440	1364	1295
500			5066	4062	3460	3037	2718	2465	2259	2087	1940	1814	1704	1607	1521	1444
600				5246	4349	3768	3345	3019	2756	2539	2356	2199	2063	1944	1838	1743
700					5364	4563	4013	3599	3273	3006	2783	2594	2430	2286	2160	2047
800						5446	4729	4211	3811	3489	3222	2997	2804	2635	2487	2355
900						6452	5506	4859	4373	3989	3674	3411	3185	2990	2819	2668
1000							6364	5552	4964	4509	4141	3835	3576	3352	3157	2985
1200								7118	6251	5617	5122	4720	4384	4098	3851	3634
1400									7732	6842	6182	5661	5235	4877	4570	4304
1600										8231	7342	6670	6134	5692	5319	4997
1800											8638	7765	7093	6551	6100	5716
2000											10133	8971	8124	7461	6919	6464
2200												10333	9248	8432	7782	7245
2400													10493	9479	8697	8064
2600														10622	9674	8927
2800														11894	10728	9841
3000															11881	10817

Table 9.9b   **Values of A_s required for a 1 m width** $f'_c = 30$ MPa $\Phi_c = 0.65$

$q_{sf}a_b^2$ (kN)	550	575	600	625	650	675	700	725	750	775	800	825	850	900	950	1000
400	1300	1350	1400	1450	1500	1550	1600	1650	1700	1750	1800	1850	1900	2000	2100	2200
500	1374	1350	1400	1450	1500	1550	1600	1650	1700	1750	1800	1850	1900	2000	2100	2200
600	1658	1582	1512	1450	1500	1550	1600	1650	1700	1750	1800	1850	1900	2000	2100	2200
700	1946	1855	1772	1697	1628	1564	1600	1650	1700	1750	1800	1850	1900	2000	2100	2200
800	2238	2132	2036	1948	1868	1795	1727	1664	1700	1750	1800	1850	1900	2000	2100	2200
900	2533	2411	2301	2202	2110	2027	1950	1878	1812	1751	1800	1850	1900	2000	2100	2200
1000	2832	2694	2570	2458	2355	2261	2174	2094	2020	1951	1886	1850	1900	2000	2100	2200
1200	3442	3271	3116	2977	2850	2734	2628	2530	2439	2355	2276	2203	2134	2009	2100	2200
1400	4069	3861	3675	3507	3355	3216	3089	2972	2863	2763	2670	2583	2502	2354	2224	2200
1600	4716	4468	4247	4049	3869	3706	3557	3420	3294	3177	3069	2968	2873	2702	2551	2416
1800	5384	5092	4833	4602	4394	4205	4033	3875	3730	3596	3472	3356	3249	3053	2881	2728
2000	6074	5734	5435	5169	4930	4714	4517	4338	4173	4021	3880	3750	3628	3408	3214	3041
2200	6790	6397	6054	5749	5477	5232	5010	4808	4622	4451	4294	4147	4011	3765	3549	3357
2400	7535	7083	6690	6345	6037	5761	5512	5285	5078	4888	4712	4550	4399	4126	3887	3676
2600	8312	7794	7347	6956	6610	6302	6024	5771	5541	5331	5137	4957	4791	4491	4229	3997
2800	9127	8532	8025	7585	7198	6854	6545	6266	6012	5780	5567	5370	5187	4859	4573	4320
3000	9984	9302	8728	8233	7801	7419	7077	6770	6491	6236	6002	5787	5588	5231	4920	4645
3500	12372	11398	10611	9951	9387	8895	8460	8073	7724	7408	7120	6856	6612	6178	5802	5471
4000		13835	12728	11841	11104	10475	9928	9447	9017	8631	8281	7962	7670	7151	6704	6314
4500			15199	13970	12994	12187	11500	10904	10379	9912	9492	9111	8764	8153	7630	7175
5000					15122	14069	13200	12462	11822	11259	10758	10307	9899	9185	8579	8056
5500						16186	15067	14145	13363	12685	12089	11557	11080	10252	9555	8957
6000							17162	15989	15024	14205	13495	12869	12312	11356	10559	9881
6500								18053	16840	15840	14991	14253	13603	12502	11594	10829
7000									18864	17622	16596	15723	14963	13695	12664	11803
7500										19599	18340	17296	16404	14941	13772	12805
8000											20265	18998	17943	16249	14922	13839
8500												20868	19601	17628	16120	14906
9000													21413	19092	17372	16012
9500														20658	18687	17159
10000														22351	20073	18354
11000															23123	20913

Table 9.10   Tension Development length, ℓ_d (mm) for deformed reinforcing bars with f_y = 400 MPa, for normal density concrete according to Clause 12.2.3.

$$\ell_d = 0.45k_1k_2k_3k_4 \frac{f_y}{\sqrt{f_c'}} d_b$$

f_c'	Bar Size							
MPa	10M	15M	20M	25M	30M	35M	45M	55M
20	320	480	640	1010	1210	1410	1810	2210
25	290	430	580	900	1080	1260	1620	1980
30	260	390	530	820	990	1150	1480	1810
35	240	370	490	760	910	1060	1370	1670
40	230	340	460	710	850	1000	1280	1570
45	210	320	430	670	800	940	1210	1480
50	200	310	410	640	760	890	1150	1400
55	190	290	390	610	730	850	1090	1330
60	190	280	370	580	700	810	1050	1280
≥ 64	180	270	360	560	680	790	1010	1240

Notes:

1. The modification factor for bar size (k_4) has been included in Table value. See Clause 12.2.4 for other modification factors.
2. After application of all modification factors, the development length must not be less than 300 mm.

Table 9.11   Compression development lengths, ℓ_d, for deformed reinforcing bars with f_y = 400 MPa, for normal density concrete according to Clause 12.3.

f_c'	Bar Size							
MPa	10M	15M	20M	25M	30M	35M	45M	55M
20	210	320	430	540	640	750	970	1180
25	190	290	380	480	580	670	860	1060
≥ 30	180	260	350	440	530	620	790	970

Note:
The modification factors given by Clause 12.3.3 must be considered individually by the designer.

Note to Tables 9.4 to 9.6: Tables 9.4 to 9.6 are worked out as described in paragraph 9.4.3.2 of the Handbook. Thus to a given q_{sf} and A_f/A_c initial design parameters a d/h_e is calculated based on Equation (13-7). Clause 13.3.4.4 however would give a different/larger d/h_e value for the same q_{sf} and A_f/A_c initial design parameters, for cases when $3d<a_b$. When $3d<a_b$ the smallest d value shall be used calculated based on Clause 13.3.4.4 and $a_b/3$.
Clause 13.3.4.4 (thus Clause 13.3.4.3) in combination with Equation (13-7) results in a cubic equation (refer to Equation 9.4 in the Handbook):

$$(1.3/(1+d))0.38\lambda\phi_c\sqrt{f_c'} = (A_fq_{sf} - q_{sf}h_e^2 - 2q_{sf}h_ed - q_{sf}d^2)/(4h_ed + 4d^2)$$

where: q_{sf} (MPa), v_c (MPa), h_e (m), A_f (m^2).

9.9   References

1.   National Building Code of Canada, 2005, National Research Council.

2.   James G. MacGregor and F. Michael Bartlett, Reinforced Concrete Mechanics and Design, Prentice Hall Canada Inc., 2000.

3.   Park R. and Paulay T.: Reinforced Concrete Structures, Wiley-Interscience Publication, John Wiley and Sons, Toronto, 1975.

4.   Joseph E. Bowles, Foundation Analysis and Design, 5th Edition, The McGraw-Hill Companies Inc., 1997.

5.   Edward J. Ulrich, Design and Performance of Mat Foundations – State of the Art Review, ACI-SP152, 1995.

6.   Suggested Analysis and Design Procedures for Combined Footings and Mats, ACI Manual of Concrete Practice 2003, ACI 336.2R-88 (Reapproved 2002).

7.   Design and Construction of Drilled Piles, ACI Manual of Concrete Practice 2003, ACI 336.3R-93 (Reapproved 1998).

8.   Canadian Foundation Engineering Manual

9.   Michael P. Collins and Denis Mitchell: Prestressed Concrete Structures, Response Publications, Canada, 1997.

10.   Adebar, P., Kuchma, D., and Collins, M.P., "Strut-and-Tie Models for the Design of Pile Caps: An Experimental Study," *ACI Structural Journal*, Vol. 87, No. 1, Jan.-Feb. 1990, pp. 81–92.

11.   Adebar, P., and Zhou, Z., "Bearing Strength of Compressive Struts Confined by Plain Concrete," *ACI Structural Journal*, Vol. 90, No. 5, Sept.-Oct. 1993, pp. 534–541.

12.   Adebar, P., and Zhou, Z, Design of Deep Pile Caps by Strut-and-Tie Models *ACI Structural Journal*, Vol. 93, No. 4, July-Aug. 1996, pp. 437–448.

13.   Adebar, P., "One-way shear strength of large footings," *Canadian Journal of Civil Engineering*, 27(3), June 2000, pp. 553–562.

14.   Concrete Design Handbook, Footings, Canadian Portland Cement Association, 1995.

15.   Concrete Reinforcing Steel Institute (CRSI), Design Handbook, 1996

16.   State of Ohio Department of Highways: Investigation of the strength of the connection between a concrete cap and the embedment end of a steel H-pile, 1947.

17.   Adebar, P., An evaluation of pile cap design methods in accordance with the Canadian design standard," *Canadian Journal of Civil Engineering*, Vol. 31, pp. 1123–1126.

9

Foundations

10

By Wayne Kassian
Walter Dilger

Prestressed Concrete

10.1   Notation

a = depth of equivalent rectangular compression block

A = area of that part of cross section between flexural tension face and centroid of gross section

A_c = area of concrete cross section

A_{cr} = area of cracked section

A_s = area of tension reinforcement

A_{sb} = minimum area of bottom reinforcement crossing one face of the periphery of a column and connecting the slab to the column or support to provide structural integrity

A'_s = area of compression reinforcement

A_p = area of prestressing tendons in tension zone

A_{tr} = area of uncracked transformed section

A_v = area of shear reinforcement perpendicular to the axis of the member

b = width of compression face of member

b_o = perimeter of critical section for slabs

b_v = effective web width

b_w = width of web

c = neutral axis depth

C_r = factored axial load capacity of concrete stress block

C_t = creep coefficient

c_y = neutral axis depth assuming $f_{pr} = f_{py}$

d = effective depth (see Eq. 10.5.13)

d_p = effective depth for prestressing steel

d_s = effective depth for reinforcing steel

d' = distance to centroid of compression steel from extreme compression fibre

d_v = effective shear depth

e = eccentricity of tendon

e_{cr} = eccentricity of tendons in cracked transformed section

e_{tr} = eccentricity of tendons in uncracked transformed section

E_c = modulus of elasticity of concrete

E_p = modulus of elasticity of prestressing tendons

E_s = modulus of elasticity of reinforcement

f_c = concrete stress at level considered

f'_c = specified concrete cylinder strength

f'_{ci} = concrete strength at prestress transfer

f_{cp} = effective prestress at the centroid of the section (see notation in Clause 2.3 of CSA A23.3)

f_{ns} = steel stress in non-prestressed reinforcement as defined in Eq. 10.5.18

f_{pe} = effective stress in prestressing tendons (after losses)

f_{po} = stress in prestressing tendons when the stress in the surrounding concrete is zero

f_{pr} = stress in prestressing tendons at factored resistance

f_{pi} = initial stress in tendon after stressing

f_{pu} = tensile strength of prestressing tendon

f_{py} = yield strength of prestressing tendon

f_{re} = intrinsic relaxation loss in prestressing tendons

f_r = modulus of rupture

f_s = difference in steel stress in the non-prestressed reinforcement as defined by Eq. 10.5.1 or Eq. 10.5.4 or stress in the non-prestressed tension reinforcement at factored resistance

f'_s = stress in compression reinforcement at factored resistance

f_y = specified yield strength of tension reinforcement

f_{yv} = specified yield strength of headed shear reinforcement

f'_y = specified yield strength of compression reinforcement

h = overall depth of member

h_f = depth of compression flange

I_c = moment of inertia of concrete section

I_{cr} = moment of inertia of the cracked section

I_e = effective moment of inertia

I_g = moment of inertia of gross concrete section

I_{tr} = moment of inertia of uncracked transformed section

k = c/d

k_p = factor for type of prestressing steel

k_1 = coefficient (Eq. 10.4.6)

k_y = coefficient for distance of centroid from compression fibre

K_u = coefficient = $M_r / f'_c b d_p^2$

ℓ = length of span

ℓ_d = development length

ℓ_o = effective length of tendon as described in Section 10.6.6

ℓ_n = length of clear span (two-way slabs)

ℓ_2 = length of span transverse to ℓ_n

M_{cr} = cracking moment

M_D = moment due to specified dead load

M_{dc} = decompression moment

M_f = moment due to factored loads

M_g = moment due to girder weight

M_L = moment due to specified live load

M_{net} = moment due to net load

M_p = total moment due to prestressing

M'_p = primary moment due to prestressing

M''_p = secondary moment due to prestressing

M_r = factored moment resistance

M_s = moment due to specified loads

M_{sust} = sustained load moment

n = modular ratio

n_p = E_p/E_c

n_s = E_s/E_c

N = total number of post-tensioning tendons

p = coefficient (Eq. 10.5.14)

P = decompression force

$P_{(i)}$ = prestressing force before transfer

P_i = prestressing force after transfer

P_o = jacking force

P_r = axial load resistance

P_x = prestress force at distance x from jacking end

P_e = effective prestress force after all losses

P_s = force in nonprestressed reinforcement due to time-dependent effects

P_{ro} = factored axial load resistance of column with zero eccentricity

P_{rmax} = maximum factored load resistance (= 0.8 P_{ro})

r = radius of gyration

10

Prestressed Concrete

s	=	sag of prestressing tendons or, spacing of shear reinforcement
s_1	=	length of critical section (Eq. 10.8.6)
S	=	section modulus for tension fibre
T	=	factored tensile force in a group of bars
t	=	time since prestressing (Eq. 10.4.6)
v_c	=	shear stress resisted by concrete
v_f	=	factored shear stress
v_r	=	shear stress resistance
V_c	=	shear force resisted by concrete
V_{cr}	=	cracking shear resistance
V_f	=	factored shear force
V_p	=	shear resisted by prestressing
V_r	=	factored shear resistance
V_{se}	=	shear due to specified loads
w_{bal}	=	portion of load balanced by prestressing
w_{net}	=	portion of specified load not balanced by prestressing
w_s	=	specified load
x	=	distance from jacking end (m)
x_a	=	length of cable affected by anchorage slip
y_{cr}	=	distance to tension fibre being considered from centroid of cracked section
y_{tr}	=	distance to extreme tension fibre from centroid of uncracked transformed section
z	=	quantity limiting distribution of flexural tension reinforcement
α	=	M_s/bd^2 (see Eq. 10.5.17) or, angular change of prestressing tendon between jacking end and point x (radians)
α_b	=	b_w/b
α_c	=	creep reduction coefficient determined from Fig.10.4
α_D	=	load factor on dead load
α_f	=	h_f/d
α_L	=	load factor on live load
α_p	=	load factor on prestressing force
α_r	=	relaxation reduction coefficient from Fig. 10.3
α_1	=	ratio of average stress in rectangular compression block to the specified concrete strength
β	=	$f_{pi}/f_{pu},$ or factor accounting for shear resistance of cracked concrete
β_1	=	ratio of depth of equivalent rectangular compression block to depth to neutral axis = a/c
Δf_c	=	change in concrete stress
Δf_p	=	change in prestress due to creep, shrinkage and relaxation
Δf_s	=	change in stress in reinforcement due to creep and shrinkage
Δ_i	=	initial deflection
ΔL	=	anchor set
Δ_t	=	time-dependent deflection
Δ_i^{su}	=	initial deflection due to sustained load
Δ_t^{su}	=	time dependent deflection due to sustained load
Δ_i^{p}	=	initial deflection due to prestressing
Δ_t^{p}	=	time dependent deflection due to prestressing
ΔP	=	change in prestressing force (loss)
ΔP_{el}	=	change in prestressing force due to elastic loss
ΔP_{elt}	=	total change in prestressing force due to elastic loss in a post-tensioned member
ΔP_p	=	force in prestressed reinforcement corresponding to f_c due to dead load and effective prestress
ΔP_s	=	force in non-prestressed reinforcement corresponding to f_c due to dead load and effective prestress

ε_{ce} = strain in concrete corresponding to a stress of f_{pe} in the steel and zero applied load
ε_p = strain at level of prestressed reinforcement
ε_s = strain in non-prestressed tension reinforcement
ε_{pe} = strain in prestressing steel corresponding to f_{pe}
ε_{sh} = shrinkage strain
ε_{total} = total strain
ε'_s = strain in compression reinforcement
ε_x = longitudinal strain at mid-depth of the member due to factored loads
ε'_y = yield strain of compression reinforcement
θ = angle of inclination of diagonal compressive stresses to the longitudinal axis of member
μ = coefficient of curvature friction
κ = wobble friction coefficient
λ = factor to account for low density concrete
ρ = reinforcement area ratio
ρ_p = A_p / A_c
ρ_s = A_s / A_c
ϕ_c = resistance factor for concrete
ϕ_s = resistance factor for reinforcing bars
ϕ_p = resistance factor for prestressing tendons
ω_{pu} = reinforcement index
Ω = $\Delta f_s / f_{pi}$

10

Prestressed Concrete

10.2   Introduction

This chapter of the Handbook provides a summary of the procedures for the design of fully and partially prestressed concrete members in accordance with CSA Standard A23.3, Clause 18.

The design examples that are presented have been selected to provide a broad spectrum of practical cases. Due to the general nature of the examples, it is anticipated that the designer will find them to be useful when clarification of the text is required.

A list of useful references can be found at the conclusion of this chapter. Further information may be obtained from the current edition of the Design Manual for Precast and Prestressed Concrete published by the Canadian Precast Prestressed Concrete Institute, Ottawa, Canada.

Sign Convention

Throughout this Chapter a positive stress in concrete is tensile and a negative stress is compressive.

10.3   Permissible Concrete Stresses in Flexural Members

10.3.1   General

The limits on permissible stresses in concrete given in Clause 18.3 provide for adequate serviceability but do not ensure adequate strength. Stresses are calculated using specified (unfactored) loads and compared with the given limits.

10.3.2   Permissible Concrete Stresses at Transfer

Clause 18.3.1 provides the limits of tensile and compressive concrete stresses immediately after transfer of the prestress force.

Whereas the tensile stresses may be exceeded, provided bonded reinforcement is added to resist the total tensile force (and developed in accordance with Clause 12), the extreme fibre stress in compression should not exceed $0.6\,f_c'$ unless tests or analyses show that performance will not be impaired. Beyond this limit creep increases non-linearly and the camber becomes unpredictable. In computing the prestress force immediately after transfer allowance should be made for losses due elastic shortening, shrinkage, relaxation of the tendons, temperature change and the anchorage seating. If the member is post-tensioned additional losses due to friction should be included.

10.3.3   Permissible Concrete Stresses due to Prestress and Specified Loads

Clause 18.3.2 provides the limits for tensile and compressive concrete stresses due to prestress and specified loads when cracking in the precompressed tensile zone is to be avoided. When cracking of the precompressed tensile zone is acceptable, the stress limit given in 18.3.2(c) can be exceeded, resulting in a partially prestressed member, that is subject to the additional requirements of Clause 18.3.3. The permissible extreme fibre stress in compression due to total load is $0.6\,f_c'$ while that due to sustained loads is $0.45\,f_c'$. Exceeding the permissible stresses due to sustained loads will cause excessive creep of the concrete and result in undesirably high deflections.

The prestress force should be reduced from the initial force, to allow for all prestress losses, when computing concrete stresses due to prestress and specified loads. Losses from the time of transfer are influenced by relaxation, creep, shrinkage, non-prestressed reinforcement, composite action and sustained loads, and may be calculated as discussed in Section 10.4. The calculation of permissible stresses is illustrated in Example 10.5.

10.3.4   Section Properties

The section properties (area, moment of inertia, section moduli and location of the section centroid) are calculated using traditional formulae. In addition, consideration must be given to the effect of openings at a particular cross section.

In general, the section properties should be calculated by taking into account the effects of the prestressed and non-prestressed reinforcement. However, in most practical cases the effects of reinforcement are small enough to be negligible. If a substantial quantity of non-prestressed reinforcement is required for a partially prestressed member, all reinforcement should be included when calculating the section properties.

For partially prestressed members (that are assumed to be cracked under application of specified loads), it is recommended that the designer use bilinear moment-deflection relationships to investigate instantaneous deflections. Alternatively, the effective moment of inertia can be calculated in accordance with Clause 9.8.2.3 and the deflection can then be calculated by substituting I_e for I_g in the deflection calculation.

10.3.5   Critical Section for Pretensioned Members

For concrete stresses immediately after transfer, the critical section is usually near the end of the element, although in elements with depressed or draped tendons, the stresses at midspan or at the depressed points may also be critical and should be checked. The critical end stress in pre-tensioned elements occurs at the point where the prestressing force has been completely transferred to the concrete, usually assumed to be about 50 strand diameters from the end. For convenience, it is normal practice to calculate the stress at the end assuming full transfer and, only if necessary, check the stress at the transfer point.

Under uniform specified loads, the critical section in flexure is at mid-span for elements with straight tendons and near 40% of the span for elements with tendons depressed at the mid-point. For other combinations of specified load and tendon profile, the critical section can be found by analysis.

10.4   Prestress Losses and Deflection

10.4.1   General

The loss of prestress is defined as the difference between the initial prestress and the effective prestress. While the loss of prestress does not significantly affect the strength of a member it affects the serviceability, namely camber and deflection, the magnitude of the concrete stresses, and the extent of cracking in partially prestressed members. The prestress losses may be divided into instantaneous losses, that occur at the time of application of the prestressing force, and time-dependent losses, that develop after the prestressing force has been applied. In post-tensioned structures the instantaneous losses occur during the post-tensioning operation, as a result of curvature friction and wobble friction, anchor set, and elastic losses caused by sequential stressing of the tendons. In pre-tensioned members the instantaneous losses are due to the elastic shortening of the concrete only. The loss of prestress due to relaxation of the prestressing steel occurring before prestress transfer needs to be considered when calculating the prestress force being transferred to the concrete.

The time-dependent losses in post-tensioned and pretensioned concrete are due to creep and shrinkage of the concrete, and relaxation of the prestressing steel.

10.4.2   Instantaneous Losses

Elastic losses

In pretensioned members the elastic loss corresponds to the elastic strain at the level of the tendon due to the combined effects of prestressing force and the girder weight applied at transfer. The change of force $\Delta P_{e\ell}$ in the prestressing steel is accurately determined by the relation

$$\Delta P_{e\ell} = \left[\frac{P_{(i)}}{A_{tr}} + \frac{\left(P_{(i)} e_{tr} + M_g \right)}{I_{tr}} e_{tr} \right] \frac{E_p}{E_c} A_p \qquad (10.4.1)$$

where

$P_{(i)}$ = prestressing force before transfer (after deducting relaxation losses occurring prior to transfer)

A_{tr} = area of uncracked transformed section (including transformed areas of prestressed and nonprestressed reinforcement)

I_{tr} = moment of inertia of uncracked transformed section

e_{tr} = eccentricity of tendons in uncracked transformed section

M_g = moment due to girder weight

E_p = modulus of elasticity of prestressing tendons

E_c = modulus of elasticity of concrete

A_p = area of prestressing tendons in tension zone

10

Prestressed Concrete

It should be noted that the prestressing force acting on the concrete is compressive and therefore is assumed to be negative in Eq. 10.4.1. In addition, eccentricities below the centroid of the section are taken as positive.

In post-tensioned members the overall elastic loss, ΔP_{ett} is due to sequential stressing of the tendons and is given by

$$\Delta P_{ett} = \frac{N-1}{2N} \Delta P_{e\ell}$$ (10.4.2)

where N is the total number of post-tensioning tendons.

Friction losses

The friction loss depends on the type of tendon and the type of duct used for a particular post-tensioning system.

Values of curvature friction μ, associated with the intentional curvature of a tendon, and of wobble friction, κ, associated with unintentional curvature of the duct, should be obtained from the manufacturers of the tendons. The range of values given in the table below serve as a guide to values that might be expected.

Type of tendon and sheath	Wobble Coefficient, κ per metre length x10^{-3}	Curvature Coefficient, μ
Tendons in flexible metal sheathing		
Wire tendons	3.3 – 5.0	0.15 – 0.25
7 wire strand	1.6 – 6.5	0.15 – 0.25
high strength bars	0.3 – 2.0	0.08 – 0.30
Tendons in rigid metal sheath		
7 wire strand	0.70	0.15 – 0.25
Pre-greased tendons		
Wire tendons and 7 wire strand	1.0 – 6.5	0.05 – 0.15
Mastic coated tendons		
Wire tendons and 7 wire strand	3.3 – 6.6	0.05 – 0.15

The curvature friction coefficient is a proper friction coefficient, that is a dimensionless quantity, while the wobble friction coefficient is given per metre length.

The force at distance x from the jacking end of the tendon is

$$P_x = P_o \, e^{-(\mu\alpha + \kappa x)}$$ (10.4.3)

where

P_x = prestress force at distance x from jacking end
P_o = jacking force
μ = coefficient of curvature friction
α = total change in angle between jacking end and point x (in radians)
κ = wobble friction coefficient (m^{-1})
x = distance from jacking end to point where loss is desired (in metres).

Anchor set

Anchor set develops at the anchorage when the prestressing force is transferred to the anchorage due to the slip necessary to set the anchor. This results in a decrease of prestress over a certain distance from the anchor. Average values for the anchor set are 8 mm to 12 mm slip for 13 mm diameter and 15 mm diameter strands, respectively. The value of the anchor set for a particular prestressing system can be provided by the post-tensioning contractor.

The length, x_a, over which the stress in the tendon is affected is

$$x_a = \left[\frac{E_p A_p x_1}{\Delta P_{x_1}} \Delta L \right]^{1/2}$$
(10.4.4)

and the reduction in prestress at the anchor is

$$\Delta P = 2 \Delta P_{x_1} \frac{x_a}{x_1}$$
(10.4.5)

In Eqns. 10.4.4 and 10.4.5:

ΔP_{x_1} = prestress loss at distance x_1 from jacking end

x_1 = arbitrary distance from jacking end; for best results x_1 should be about equal to x_a

ΔL = anchor set

Care should be taken to ensure that compatible units are used in these equations.

10.4.3   Time-dependent Losses

The time-dependent loss of prestress depends on the magnitude of creep and shrinkage of the concrete, the intrinsic relaxation of the prestressing steel, the concrete stress at the level of the tendon and the section parameters. The intrinsic relaxation is the relaxation obtained from tests under constant strain.

The creep and shrinkage can be predicted with the information provided in Chapter 1, Section 1.2.3 and Table 1.2.

In lieu of detailed information from the manufacturer the intrinsic relaxation of prestressing tendons may be predicted as

$$f_{re}(t) = \frac{\log t}{k_1} (\frac{f_{pi}}{f_{py}} - 0.55) f_{pi}$$
(10.4.6)

In this equation

$f_{re}(t)$ = intrinsic relaxation at time t (under constant strain)

f_{pi} = initial stress in tendon after stressing

f_{py} = 0.85 f_{pu} for stress relieved wires and strands

= 0.90 f_{pu} for low relaxation strands

f_{pu} = tensile strength of prestressing tendon

t = time since prestressing (hours)

k_1 = 10 to 12 for stress relieved steel

= 45 for low relaxation steel

Assuming 50 years as the lifetime of the structure the final value for the intrinsic relaxation of stress-relieved steel (with $k_1 = 12$) is:

$$f_{re} = 0.470 (\frac{f_{pi}}{f_{py}} - 0.55) f_{pi}$$
(10.4.7)

and for low relaxation steel (with $k_1 = 45$)

$$f_{re} = 0.125 (\frac{f_{pi}}{f_{py}} - 0.55) f_{pi}$$
(10.4.8)

10

Prestressed Concrete

These equations are valid for temperatures up to 20°C. At higher temperatures the relaxation increases (see Fig. 10.2).

The loss of prestress, Δf_p, for a member with one layer of tendons and non-prestressed steel at about the same level can be estimated from the relation (Ref. 10.1)

$$\Delta f_p = \frac{n f_c C_t + \varepsilon_{sh} n E_c + f_{re}}{1 + n(\rho_p + \rho_s)(1 + e^2/r^2)(1 + 0.8 C_t)} \qquad (10.4.9)$$

where

n	=	average modular ratio
f_c	=	concrete stress at level of tendon due to sustained load and initial prestressing force P_i
C_t	=	creep coefficient
ε_{sh}	=	shrinkage strain
ρ_p	=	A_p/A_c
ρ_s	=	A_s/A_c
A_c	=	area of concrete cross section
e	=	eccentricity of tendon
r^2	=	I_c/A_c
I_c	=	moment of inertia of concrete section

The factor 0.8 in the denominator is the value of the so-called aging coefficient (Ref. 10.2 and 10.3) assumed for practical creep calculations. Since the relaxation loss is considerably reduced by the creep and shrinkage of the concrete, the intrinsic loss f_{re} may be replaced by a reduced value $\alpha_r f_{re}$. The coefficient α_r is determined from Fig. 10.3 using the parameters $\beta = f_{pi}/f_{pu}$ and $\Omega = \Delta f_s/f_{pi}$. The stress f_{pi} is the initial stress applied to the tendon, f_{pu} is the tensile strength of the tendon, and Δf_s is the loss of prestress due to creep and shrinkage only.

$$\Delta f_s = \frac{n f_c C_t + \varepsilon_{sh} n E_c}{1 + n(\rho_p + \rho_s)(1 + \frac{e^2}{r^2})(1 + 0.8 C_t)} \qquad (10.4.10)$$

The value Δf_s is also the time-dependent stress in the non-prestressed steel, the centroid of which is assumed to coincide with that of the prestressing steel. The total reduction in the compression acting on the concrete is

$$\Delta P = \Delta f_p A_p + \Delta f_s A_s \qquad (10.4.11)$$

Since the stress at the level of the tendon, f_c, is normally compressive, and ε_{sh} and Δf_{re} are always negative, both Δf_p and Δf_s are always negative, resulting in a reduction of the tension in the tendon and an increased compression in the non-prestressed steel (see Examples 10.5 and 10.6.).

If the non-prestressed steel is uniformly distributed throughout the section the term ρ_s in the denominator of eq. 10.4.9 is omitted, and the creep and shrinkage coefficients are multiplied by the creep reduction coefficient α_c depicted in Fig. 10.4 as a function of ρn and the creep coefficient C_t. Thus:

$$\Delta f_p = \frac{n f_c \alpha_c C_t + \varepsilon_{sh} \alpha_c n E_c + f_{re}}{1 + n \rho_p (1 + e^2/r^2)(1 + 0.8 \alpha_c C_t)} \qquad (10.4.12)$$

For detailed treatment of the general case with multiple layers of steel see References 10.1 and 10.2.

10.4.4   Deflections

Two different cases are encountered when computing the deflection of prestressed concrete members namely, uncracked and cracked members.   These two cases will be discussed separately.

Uncracked members

The elastic deflections at the time of prestressing are calculated by conventional methods of analysis.   The downward deflection due to gravity load is reduced by the upward deflection (camber) due to prestressing.   Expressions for computing the camber for the most common tendon profiles are given in Fig. 10.5.   Expressions for deflections due to other types of loading are given in Table 1.14.

The initial deflection due to prestressing force is calculated using the initial prestressing force, P_i.

The time-dependent deflections Δ_t^{su} due to sustained loads are obtained by multiplying the initial deflections Δ_i^{su} by the creep coefficient C_t giving

$$\Delta_t^{su} = \Delta_i^{su} C_t \tag{10.4.13}$$

The time-dependent deflections due to prestressing are obtained from the following equation

$$\Delta_t^p = \Delta_i^p [C_t - \frac{\Delta P}{P_i}(1+0.8\,C_t)] \tag{10.4.14}$$

The term $\Delta_i^p\, C_t$ is the time-dependent deflection assuming that the prestressing force is constant and equal to P_i. The second term in the square bracket is due to the prestress loss ΔP as defined by Eq. 10.4.11. Equation 10.4.14 includes the effect of shrinkage on deflection. The general case with multiple layers of steel is discussed in References 10.1 and 10 2.

The calculation of the deflection due to prestress by using the effective prestress leads to less accurate results, which may, however, still be acceptable considering the uncertainty of the values of creep and shrinkage.

Cracked members

Partially prestressed members are designed so that cracking may be expected under full specified loads. The deflection may be calculated using an effective moment of inertia of the cracked section or a bilinear moment curvature diagram. Such a diagram may be established using the information given in Section 10.5, using Fig. 10.7 for rectangular sections and using Figs. 10.8.1 to 10.8.16 for T-beams, or in Table 10.2.

The effective moment of inertia for a cracked prestressed concrete beam is expressed by the relation:

$$I_e = I_{cr} + (I_{tr} - I_{cr})(\frac{M_{cr}}{M_s - M_{dc}})^3 \le I_g \tag{10.4.15}$$

where

$$M_{cr} = f_r I_{tr}/y_{cr} \tag{10.4.16}$$

$$M_{dc} = f_{pd} I_{tr}/y_{tr} \tag{10.4.17}$$

In these equations
I_{cr} =   moment of inertia of cracked section
I_{tr} =   moment of inertia of the uncracked transformed section, or less accurately of the gross section

10

Prestressed Concrete

y_{tr} = distance to extreme tension fibre from centroid of uncracked transformed section
f_{pd} = concrete stress due to effective prestress at the extreme fibre where tensile stresses are caused by applied loads (negative value)
M_s = maximum moment due to specified loads

In continuous structures the average value of I_e has to be established. This is discussed in Chapter 6.

Further details about the calculation of deflections of partially prestressed members are found in Ref. 10.4.

10.5   Partially Prestressed Members

In many prestressed concrete structures it is not likely that the full specified load will be applied during the lifetime of the structure. It is therefore possible to design the structural members so that some cracking will occur under full specified load if it should be applied. Under the dead load, however, cracking should normally not occur.

The advantages of partial prestressing are:

- a reduction of camber
- a reduction in prestress force that may allow an increase of the tendon eccentricity
- reduction of cracking in the end zones of post-tensioned structures
- a reduction in relaxation loss where partial prestressing is achieved by a lower stress in the tendon

Partial prestressing may be achieved in different ways:

(1) By providing non-prestressed steel in addition to the prestressing tendons. This would normally occur in post-tensioned construction

(2) By reducing the effective prestress below the maximum allowable stress and relying on the increase in tendon stress after decompression and cracking to resist the increase in moment. This is a useful option in pretensioned construction because of difficulties in placing non-prestressed steel.

In order to assure that the cracks developing in a partially prestressed member are within acceptable limits, crack width criteria similar to those for reinforced concrete have to be satisfied.

For the calculation of the quantity z the same equation (Eq. 10-6 in the Code) as for reinforced concrete members has been adopted. In this equation, the steel stress f_s is the increase in stress in the reinforcing or (bonded) prestressing steel beyond the state of decompression.

The steel stress increase f_s may be calculated as the stress corresponding to the difference between the moment due to specified loads M_s and the decompression moment M_{dc} according to:

$$f_s = \frac{M_s - M_{dc}}{(A_p + A_s)d} \qquad (10.5.1)$$

The decompression moment M_{dc} is the moment that reduces the compressive stress on the tensile face of a prestressed member to zero. It should be emphasized that the decompression moment does not correspond to the state of decompression of the whole section. Complete decompression requires the removal of the bending moment due to applied loads and the application of the fictitious decompression force, P, as discussed below.

Equation 10.5.1 gives reasonable results for most members, but for members with a small value of ρ it is normally conservative. For this reason a more detailed method of calculating f_s is presented here (see Ref 10.5).

The rigorous calculation of f_s for a given moment M_s is complicated since it is undertaken for a cracked section subjected to an axial force and a bending moment, and because creep and shrinkage of the concrete put the non-prestressed steel in compression and thus reduce the compression in the precompressed tension fibres. The reference point for the determination of f_s is zero stress in the concrete section. The following fictitious decompression force would create zero stress throughout the concrete section:

$$P = P_e + \Delta P_p + P_s + \Delta P_s \qquad (10.5.2)$$

where

P_e = effective prestress (after all losses)

$\Delta P_p = \dfrac{-f_c}{E_c} E_p A_p$

= force in tendons corresponding to the concrete stress f_c at the level of the tendon under dead load and effective prestress

P_s = force in the non-prestressed steel due to time-dependent strain in the non-prestressed steel

$\Delta P_s = \dfrac{-f_c}{E_c} E_s A_s$

= force in non-prestressed steel corresponding to the concrete stress f_c at the level of the non-prestressed steel under dead load and effective prestress.

The concrete stress f_c is negative when compressive, and the forces ΔP_p and ΔP_s are normally small and may be neglected.

The effective prestress $P_e = A_p(f_{pi} - \Delta f_p)$ where f_{pi} is the initial prestress and Δf_p is calculated according to Eq.10.4.9.

The time-dependent force in the non–prestressed steel

$$P_s = A_s \Delta f_s \qquad (10.5.3)$$

where Δf_s is defined by Eq. 10.4.10.

With the decompression force P, known, the steel stress under specified load is equal to n times the concrete stress at the level of the steel:

$$f_s = \left(\frac{P}{A_{cr}} + \frac{P e_{cr} + M_s}{I_{cr}} y_{cr} \right) n \qquad (10.5.4)$$

In this equation the terms with subscript "cr" refer to the cracked sections. The parameter y_{cr} is the distance of the steel considered from the centroid of the cracked section, and n is the modular ratio for the steel considered (i.e. n_s or n_p).

Cracked section properties

The cracked section properties for a given section are dependent on the decompression force P and the moment M_s due to specified loads.

The calculation of the cracked section properties involves the determination of the neutral axis depth, c, the centroidal depth of the section, y_{cr}, the area, A_{cr}, and the moment of inertia, I_{cr}. With the notation and the forces of Fig. 10.6 we have to solve the following cubic equation in c for the general case of T-section (Ref. 10.5)

10

Prestressed Concrete

$$\frac{1}{3}Pc^3 - \frac{1}{2}\left[M_s - P(d_p - c)\right]bc^2 + \left[\begin{array}{l} n_s A_s(d_s - c)^2 \\ + n_p A_p(d_p - c)^2 \end{array}\right]P + \left[n_s A_s(d_s - c) + n_p A_p(d_p - c)\right]$$

$$\times\left[M_s - P(d_p - c)\right] - \frac{1}{3}P(b - b_w)(c - h_f)^3 + \frac{1}{2}(b - b_w)(c - h_f)^2\left[M_s - P(d_p - c)\right] = 0 \qquad (10.5.5)$$

The centroidal depth, area and the moment of inertia of the cracked section are, respectively:

$$y_{cr} = \frac{\frac{1}{2}(b - b_w)h_f^2 + \frac{1}{2}b_w c^2 + n_s A_s d_s + n_p A_p d_p}{(b - b_w)h_f + b_w c + n_s A_s + n_p A_p} \qquad (10.5.6)$$

$$A_{cr} = b_w c + (b - b_w)h_f + n_s A_s + n_p A_p \qquad (10.5.7)$$

$$I_{cr} = \frac{1}{12}[h_f^3(b - b_w) + b_w c^3] + \left[(y_{cr} - \frac{h_f}{2})^2(b - b_w)h_f\right] + (y_{cr} - \frac{c}{2})^2 b_w c$$

$$+ (d_s - y_{cr})^2 n_s A_s + (d_p - y_{cr})^2 n_p A_p \qquad (10.5.8)$$

For rectangular sections $b = b_w$, so that Eqns. 10.5.5 to 10 5.8 simplify to:

$$\frac{1}{3}Pc^3 - \frac{1}{2}[M_s - P(d_p - c)]bc^2 + [n_s A_s(d_s - c)^2 + n_p A_p(d_p - c)^2]P$$

$$+ [n_s A_s(d_s - c) + n_p A_p(d_p - c)][M_s - P(d_p - c)] = 0 \qquad (10.5.9)$$

$$y_{cr} = \frac{\frac{1}{2}bc^2 + n_s A_s d_s + n_p A_p d_p}{bc + n_s A_s + n_p A_p} \qquad (10.5.10)$$

$$A_{cr} = bc + n_s A_s + n_p A_p \qquad (10.5.11)$$

$$I_{cr} = \frac{1}{12}bc^3 + (y_{cr} - \frac{c}{2})^2 bc + (d_s - y_{cr})^2 n_s A_s + (d_p - y_{cr})^2 n_p A_p \qquad (10.5.12)$$

Assuming $(A_s + A_p)$ to be located at

$$d = \frac{A_s E_s d_s + A_p E_p d_p}{A_s E_s + A_p E_p} \qquad (10.5.13)$$

and introducing the parameters

$$k = c/d \qquad \alpha_b = b_w / b \qquad p = Pd_p / M_s \qquad \alpha_f = h_f / d \quad \text{and}$$

$$n\frac{A_s E_s + A_p E_p}{E_c bd} \qquad (10.5.14)$$

the neutral axis depth coefficients for T-Sections and rectangular sections, respectively, can be expressed by

$$k^3 p - 3k^2(p-1) - 6n\rho(1-k) - (1-\alpha_b)(k-\alpha_f)(kp + 2p\alpha_1 - 3p + 3) = 0 \qquad (10.5.15)$$

$$k^3 p - 3k^2(p-1) - 6n\rho(1-k) = 0 \qquad (10.5.16)$$

Knowing k, the section properties can be determined and the steel stress f_s, calculated using Eq. 10.5.4. To facilitate determination of f_s, Figs. 10.7 and 10.8.1 to 10.8.15 have been established expressing f_s in the non-dimensional form $f_s/(n\alpha)$ as a function of $n\rho$ for different values of p. The term n is the modular ratio and

$$\alpha = \frac{M_s}{bd^2} \qquad (10.5.17)$$

If the two steels are not located at the same level, the stress in the non-prestressed steel is:

$$f_{ns} = f_s \frac{d_s - kd}{d(1-k)} \qquad (10.5.18)$$

The use of the design charts is demonstrated in Example 10.6.

10.6 Factored Flexural Resistance

10.6.1 Introduction

The factored flexural resistance of an element must be greater than the moment due to factored load.

$$M_r \geq M_f$$

The factored flexural resistance can be determined for any section using procedures that take into account equilibrium and strain compatibility. For many sections a satisfactory approximate solution can be obtained using the Equations (18-1) and (18-2) to determine the stress in the tendons at factored resistance. Equation (18-2) differs slightly from the previous CSA Standard A23.3-M 94.

Figure 10.1 provides typical stress-strain curves for 1860 MPa strand commonly used in Canada. Grade 1720 MPa strand is not commonly used and is provided for historical reference only. Tables 1.3 and 1.4 provide sizes and properties for strand, wire and deformed prestressing bars.

Typical concrete strengths for prestressed concrete members range from 30 to 50 MPa. Release strengths f'_{ci} will generally be in the range from 20 to 30 MPa.

10

Prestressed Concrete

10.6.2 Analysis of Section Reinforced with Bonded Tendons and Nonprestressed Steel

Provided $f_{pe} > 0.6\, f_{py}$ and c/d_p is not greater than 0.5, the stress in the prestressing tendons at factored resistance, f_{pr}, may be found from the approximate equation given in Clause 18.6 :

$$f_{pr} = f_{pu}\, [1 - k_p\,(c/d_p\,)] \qquad (18-1)$$

where

$$k_p = 2\,(1.04 - f_{py}\,/\,f_{pu}\,)$$

The term k_p accounts for the different shapes of the stress-strain curves for the different types of prestressing steel and values of f_{py}/f_{pu} for typical prestressing steels are given in Clause 18.4 of A23.3. The term c/d_p in Eq. 18-1 may be found from a consideration of the conditions in a section at factored resistance. Fig. 10.6.2 shows the strain distribution and related stress block for a T-section containing prestressed and non-prestressed tensile reinforcement, as well as non-prestressed compression reinforcement. Equilibrium of forces in the section requires

$$\phi_s A'_s f'_s + \alpha_1 \phi_c f'_c h_f (b - b_w) + \alpha_1 \phi_c f'_c a b_w = \phi_p A_p f_{pr} + \phi_s A_s f_s$$

Substituting for f_{pr} from Eq. 18-1, setting $a = \beta_1 c$ and rearranging gives

$$\frac{c}{d_p} = \frac{\phi_p A_p f_{pr} + \phi_s A_s f_s - \phi_s A'_s f'_s - \alpha_1 \phi_c f'_c h_f (b - b_w)}{\alpha_1 \phi_c f'_c \beta_1 b_w d_p + \phi_p k_p A_p f_{pu}}$$

The depth of the equivalent rectangular stress block may be found from the above figure in a similar manner and is given by:

$$a = \frac{\phi_p A_p f_{pr} + \phi_s A_s f_s - \phi_s A'_s f'_s - \alpha_1 \phi_c f'_c h_f (b - b_w)}{\alpha_1 \phi_c f'_c b_w}$$

and the factored resistance is

$$M_r = \phi_p A_p f_{pr} (d_p - a/2) + \phi_s A_s f_s (d_s - a/2) - \phi_s A'_s f'_s (d' - a/2)$$
$$- \alpha_1 \phi_c f'_c h_f (b - b_w)(\frac{h_f}{2} - \frac{a}{2})$$

The stresses f_s and f'_s will generally be equal to f_y and f'_y respectively. If the strain at the level of the reinforcing steel is less than the yield strain a strain compatibility analysis will be needed to establish these stresses.

The above is the most general formulation. All of the simpler cases can be determined by eliminating the redundant terms. If $a < h_f$ the section should be treated as a rectangular section with $b_w = b$.

A step-by-step analysis of a section using both the code equation and strain compatibility to determine f_{pr} is illustrated in Example 10.1. In this example the stress-strain curve for Grade 1860 low-relaxation strand of Fig 10.1 is used.

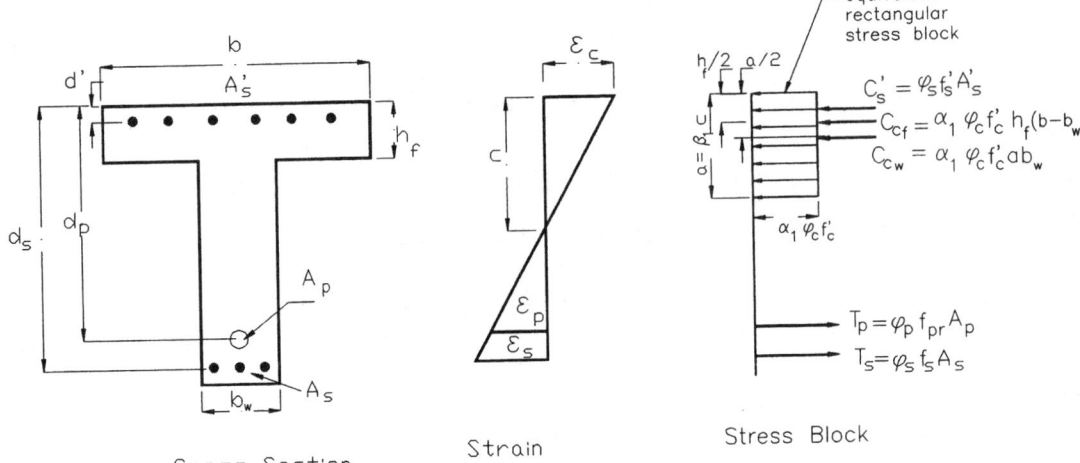

Cross Section   Strain   Stress Block

10.6.3   Minimum Factored Flexural Resistance

Based on Clause 18.7 flexural members (except 2-way slabs) must be designed so that

$$M_r > 1.2 M_{cr}$$

unless

$$M_r > 1.33 M_f$$

The cracking moment M_{cr} is given by:

$$M_{cr} = -P_e (e + S/A_c) + f_r S$$

where

P_e = effective prestress force after losses

e = eccentricity of tendon

A_c = area of concrete cross section

f_r = modulus of rupture = $0.6\lambda\phi_c\phi_c\sqrt{f_c'}$ MPa

S = section modulus for tension fibre

It should be noted that P_e is a compressive force on the concrete and should be taken as negative in calculating M_{cr}

10.6.4   Design Tables

Tables 10.1(a) and (b) provide a simple way of quickly estimating the capacity of a given section or establishing the required size of a design section. The tables include the values of k_p for common prestressing steels, as well as α_1 and β_1 for concrete strengths ranging from 30 to 80 MPa.

It should be noted that $\phi_c = 0.65$ has been assumed in Table 10.1 (a). However, Clause 16.1.3 permits a value of $\phi_c = 0.70$ to be used for precast elements manufactured in certified plants, so $\phi_c = 0.70$ has been assumed in Table 10.1 (b).

The use of Table 10.1 (b) is illustrated in Example 10.4.

10.6.5   Over-Reinforced Sections with Bonded Tendons

It is generally not economical to design over-reinforced beams. These will occur only in rare instances when for some reason more reinforcement than desired must be used.

In over-reinforced sections c/d_p will generally be greater than 0.5 and the approximate equation for f_{pr} cannot be used. However, the approximate equation can still be used to provide a starting point for an iterative strain-compatibility and equilibrium analysis.

10.6.6   Analysis of Section with Unbonded Tendons

Equation (18-2) differs from that used in CSA Standard A23.3-94 in that the term $\sum_{n}\left(d_p - c_y\right)$ now clarifies how to apply this equation to continuous beams where d_p may vary between positive and negative moment regions.

The approximate equation prescribed by Clause 18.6.2(b) of the standard is the following:

$$f_{pr} = f_{pe} + \frac{8000}{\ell_0}\sum_{n}(d_p - c_y) \leq f_{py} \tag{18-2}$$

where $\sum_{n}\left(d_p - c_y\right)$ is the sum of the distance $\left(d_p - c_y\right)$ for each of the plastic hinges in the span under consideration.

$$c_y = \frac{\phi_p A_p f_{py} + \phi_s A_s f_s - \phi_s A_s' f_s' - \alpha_1 \phi_c f_c' h_f (b - b_w)}{\alpha_1 \phi_c \beta_1 f_c' b}$$

10

Prestressed Concrete

and ℓ_0 = overall length of tendon between anchors. The definition of ℓ_0 is illustrated in Fig. N 18.6 of the Explanatory Notes.

This equation emphasizes the importance of making a realistic assessment of the number of plastic hinges that would have to develop before the particular span under consideration would collapse.   The analysis of a section with unbonded tendons is illustrated in Example 10.2 and 10.9.

10.6.7   Prestressed Members Subjected to Flexure and Axial Loads

The design of these members is usually carried out by choosing a section and the reinforcing, and then calculating a sufficient number of points on an interaction diagram to establish whether the design is adequate.

The procedure can most easily be illustrated by a sample calculation as indicated in Example 10.3. The easiest approach is to assume a series of neutral axis locations with the strain of 0.0035 at the extreme compression fibre and to then determine the corresponding values of P_r and M_r.

10.7   Factored Shear Resistance

As discussed in Chapter 4, the shear resistance attributed to the concrete is calculated using Eq. (11-6). The value of β can be determined using the new simplified method, the general method, or taken as 0.21 for special member types in accordance with Clause 11.3.6.2.   When using the simplified method, the maximum yield strength limit of 400 MPa in Clause 11.3.6.3 is intended for non prestressed reinforcement only. For prestressed members, this yield strength limitation does not apply.

The application of the methods for shear design of reinforced concrete members is explained in detail in Chapter 4. For this reason only the differences between non-prestressed and prestressed concrete members with regard to shear design are discussed here.

First, the shear force due to prestressing, V_p, may be included in the shear resisted by concrete, Eq. (11-4). Second, due to prestressing the longitudinal strain, ε_x at mid-depth of the member is affected by the prestressing force $A_p f_{po}$ in the numerator of Eq. (11-13) and by the term $E_p A_p$ in the same equation. The stress f_{po} represents the stress in the prestressing tendons at decompression, that is defined as the tendon stress when the strain in the surrounding concrete is zero. In lieu of detailed calculations, f_{po} may be taken as 0.7 f_{pu} for bonded tendons outside the transfer length and f_{pe} for unbonded tendons.

As for reinforced concrete the longitudinal strain at mid-depth ε_x shall not be taken greater than 0.003 (Clause 11.3.6.4 (f)) and if ε_x is negative, it shall not be taken less than - 0.002, (Clause 11.3.6.4 (c)).

10.8   Prestressed Concrete Slabs

10.8.1   General

In Chapter 5 the analysis and design of reinforced concrete slabs is discussed in detail. In this section only those aspects of the design of prestressed slabs that are different from reinforced slabs will be discussed. Only unbonded slabs are considered here.

While the design of reinforced concrete slabs is done only for factored loads, prestressed slabs, as all other prestressed members, also have to satisfy the permissible stress criteria of Clause 18.3.2 or in the case of partially prestressed members have to satisfy crack control criteria under specified loads (Clause 18.3.3).

10.8.2   One-Way Slabs

The design of one-way prestressed slabs is essentially a wide beam design. The only difference is the amount of transverse nonprestressed steel required that is normally governed by the minimum requirements of Clause 7.8.   The thickness of continuous one-way slabs prestressed slabs may be taken as $\ell/40$ to $\ell/50$.

The analysis of one-way slabs subjected to uniform loading is efficiently done by the load balancing method whereby a certain fraction of the dead load is balanced by the upward load caused by prestressing. For normal live loads about 75 to 85 percent of the dead load needs to be balanced if no cracks are allowed (i.e. satisfying Clause 18.3.2c). For partially prestressed slabs only about 60 percent of the dead load needs to be balanced.

For a parabolic tendon profile, the load balanced by the effective prestress

$$w_{bal} = \frac{8 P_e s}{\ell^2}$$ (10.8.1)

where

P_e = effective prestress after all losses (normally per metre width)

s = sag of tendon

ℓ = length of span measured centre-to-centre of supports

The balanced load and prestressing result in zero flexural stress so that only an axial stress P_e/A_c, is present, where A_c is the cross sectional area of the slab per metre width. Bending moments are caused only by the net load

$$w_{net} = w_s - w_{bal}$$ (10.8.2)

where w_s = specified load (dead load plus live load).

The moments due to w_{net} are determined by established methods of structural analysis.

If the flexural tensile stresses exceed the value permitted in Clause 18.3.2(c), the criteria of Clause 18.3.3 have to be satisfied. The moment due to factored loads is calculated in accordance with Eq. 10.8.3.

10.8.3   Two-Way Slabs

Slab Thickness

Prestressed slabs can be considerably more slender than non-prestressed slabs. The thickness h may range between $\ell/40$ to $\ell/50$ with $\ell/45$ being a frequently used value. Because of the smaller thickness, punching shear becomes more critical, particularly at exterior columns. Drop panels or shear reinforcement may be provided to increase the shear resistance locally if it is not desirable to increase the overall slab thickness or to provide an edge beam.

Analysis

One of the major differences between the design of reinforced and prestressed two-way slabs is that only the procedures of Clause 13.8, or more detailed methods of analysis, can be used for the design.   The approach outlined in Clause 13.8.2 was formally called "Equivalent Frame Method" and involves non-prismatic modelling of member stiffnesses.   The Prismatic Modelling Method described in Clause 13.8.3 is simpler as it uses a simple equation for the reduced column stiffness. Examples 10.9 and 10.10, respectively, illustrate the design of a fully prestressed slab and a partially prestressed slab. The load balancing concept, together with the

10

Prestressed Concrete

Prismatic Modelling Method is used to analyze two-way prestressed slabs. For slabs without stiff beams, 75 to 90 percent of the dead load is balanced by the effective prestress (in each direction). These percentages apply to slabs in which no cracks are expected to develop under full specified load. For partially prestressed slabs it is normally adequate to balance 60 to 70 percent of the slab dead load.

Calculation of Flexural Stress

The flexural stresses are calculated for the moments due to the net (unbalanced) loads. The positive and negative moments determined according to the methods of Clause 13.8 for the full width of the slab strip (width ℓ_2) shall be assigned to column strip according to Clause 18.12.2.1. This clause specifies that 75% of the interior negative moment, 100% of the exterior negative moment and 60% of the positive moment shall be taken by the column strip, unless a more detailed analysis is made. This requirement will assure that the moments due to the load not balanced by prestressing are assessed realistically and that the calculated flexural stresses are realistic values.

The axial stress, however, is more or less uniformly distributed across the width of the panel, particularly at the interior supports (see Clause 18.12.2.2).

If the flexural stress exceeds the value permitted in Clause 18.3.2(c), cracking is expected to occur and the crack control criteria of Clause 18.8.3 have to be satisfied.

Factored Moment

In continuous structural systems prestressing introduces secondary moments. These secondary moments are added to the moments due to factored loads such that

$$M_f = \alpha_D M_D + \alpha_L M_L + \alpha_p M_p''$$ (10.8.3)

In this equation: α_D and α_L are the load factors for dead load and live load respectively, M_D and M_L are the moments due to specified dead and live loads, M_p'' is the secondary moment due to prestressing and α_p is the load factor for moments due to reactions introduced by prestressing (secondary moments). According to Clause 18.10, $\alpha_p = 1.0$.

The moments due to factored loads may be determined at the face of the column. The flexural resistance of the cross section is calculated according to Clause 18.6.

Minimum Reinforcement

In prestressed two-way slabs, minimum bonded reinforcement has to be provided in accordance with Clause 18.12.5 and Table 18-1.

Shear

The shear strength of reinforced concrete slabs is discussed in detail in Chapter 5. In prestressed concrete the beneficial effect of the axial stress $f_{cp} = P_e/A_c$ and the vertical component of the prestressing force at the critical section, V_p, increase the shear resistance of the concrete, V_c, considerably. According to Clause 18.12.3.3 the shear stress resistance of the concrete is given by Eq. 18-5 as:

$$v_c = \beta_p \lambda \phi_c \sqrt{f_c'} \sqrt{1 + \frac{\phi_p f_{cp}}{0.33 \lambda \phi_c \sqrt{f_c'}}} + \frac{V_p}{b_o d}$$ (10.8.4)

where

β_p = the smaller of 0.33 or $(\alpha_s d/b_o + 0.15)$

α_s = 4 for interior columns, 3 for edge columns and 2 for corner columns

b_o = perimeter of the critical section specified in Clause 13.3.3

f_{cp} = the average value of f_{cp} in the two directions not to exceed 3.5 MPa

V_p = factored vertical component of all prestressing forces crossing the critical section

However, the beneficial effect of prestressing can only be counted on if (a) no portion of the column cross section is closer to a discontinuous edge than 4 times the slab thickness, h_s, (b) the strength of the slab concrete is not taken greater than 35 MPa and (c) f_{cp} in Eq.10.8.4 shall not exceed 3.5 MPa.

Shear reinforcement consisting of stirrups or headed shear reinforcement may be used to increase the shear resistance. The design of shear reinforcement consisting of headed studs with anchor plates, referred to in Clause 13.3.8 is discussed in some detail in the following section. The design of this reinforcement is described in detail in References 10.6 and 10.7. The design of stirrup reinforcement is specified in Clause 13.3.9.

Headed Shear Reinforcement

When headed shear reinforcement is used as shear reinforcement anchor plates having an area of at least 10 times the cross sectional area of the rods have to be provided.

The design of the headed shear reinforcement (studs) is based on the assumption that the shear resisted by concrete is (Clause 13.3.8.3)

$$v_c = 0.28 \lambda \phi_c \sqrt{f'_c} \tag{10.8.5}$$

The required area of headed shear reinforcement of one headed vertical bar along the critical section

$$A_v = \frac{(v_f - v_c)s_1 s}{\phi_s f_{yv}} \tag{10.8.6}$$

where

s = spacing between rows of rods measured perpendicular to the column face.

s_1 = length of critical section considered divided by rows of headed bars.

f_{yv} = specified yield strength of headed shear reinforcement.

The shear reinforcement shall extend to a distance away from the column face so that the shear stress v_f at a distance $d/2$ from the outermost row of shear reinforcement does not exceed v_c of Eq. 10.8.7. The spacing requirements for the headed shear reinforcement are specified in Clause 13.3.8.6. The upper limit on the shear stress resistance of slabs with headed studs is $0.75\lambda\phi_c\sqrt{f'_c}$, (Clause 13.3.8.2).

Normal closed stirrups are only allowed if the slab thickness is at least 300 mm (Clause 13.3.9.1) and the design of the shear reinforcement is based on a shear stress resistance of the concrete of (Clause 13.3.9.3):

$$v_c = 0.19\lambda\phi_c\sqrt{f'_c} \tag{10.8.7}$$

The design equation for A_v is given by Eq. 10.8.6 and the extension of the shear reinforcement is the same as for headed shear reinforcement. The upper limit for the shear stress resistance of slabs with stirrups is $v_c = 0.55\lambda\phi_c\sqrt{f'_c}$, (Clause 13.3.9.2).

10

Prestressed Concrete

Structural Integrity

Progressive collapse may develop as a result of a local slab failure caused by punching if there is no mechanism provided to suspend the slab at the point of punching failure. According to Ref. 10.8 an effective mechanism to prevent progressive collapse is the membrane type action provided by draped tendons passing through the columns or reaction areas. In general two tendons in each direction over the column will be sufficient to satisfy the provisions of CSA Standard A23.3 (Clauses 18.12.6.3 and 13.10.6). These requirements are expressed by the following equation (c.f. Eq. 13-26 of the Standard).

$$\Sigma A_{sb} \geq \frac{2V_{se}}{f_{py}} \tag{10.8.8}$$

where

A_{sb} = area of prestressing steel and non-prestressed reinforcement crossing through one face of the periphery of a column

V_{se} = shear force transmitted to column or column capital, defined by Eq.10.8.9

f_{py} = yield strength of tendon (see Table N 18-4) and

$$V_{se} = w_s[\ell_{1a}\ell_{2a} - c_1c_2] \tag{10.8.9}$$

In Eq. 10.8.9

w_s = total specified load but not less than twice the self-weight of the slab

ℓ_{1a} = average length for spans adjacent to a column

ℓ_{2a} = length of span transverse to ℓ_1

c_1 = size of rectangular or equivalent rectangular, support area of slab

c_2 = size of rectangular or equivalent rectangular support area transverse to c_1

Partial Prestressing

For partially prestressed beams, one-way slabs and two-way slabs on stiff supports, the determination of the parameters needed for the calculation of the stress f_s in Eq. 10-6 of CSA Standard A23.3 is straightforward. For flat slabs, these parameters need some discussion.

To determine the necessary parameters it is best to consider a one metre wide strip of the column strip. For this strip the following terms are defined:

M_s: the moment due to specified load is 75% of the total negative moment, at the face of the column, divided by the width of the column strip.

P_e : the effective prestressing force is the total force in the panel (in one direction) divided by the width of the panel, ℓ_2.

A_s: total area of the non-prestressed steel (in one direction) divided by the width of the column strip.

A_p: total area of the prestressing steel divided by the width of the panel, ℓ_2. If the tendons are unbonded, A_p should not be considered in Eqs. 10.5.13 and 10.5.14.

For flat slabs with unbonded tendons, Eq. 10.5.1 simplifies to

$$f_s = \frac{M_{net} - P_e(h_s/6 + e)}{A_s d} \tag{10.8.10}$$

where

M_{net} = 75% of the total panel moment due to net load, at face of support, divided by the width of the column strip.

P_e, A_s = as defined above
h_s =   slab thickness
d =   effective slab depth.
e =   tendon eccentricity

See Example 10.10. Note: M_{net}, P_e and e are positive in Eq.10.8.10.

10.9   Composite Flexural Members

The general requirements for composite flexural members are provided in Clause 17 and it is implicit in this clause that both the strength and serviceability limit states have to be satisfied.

It is generally considered more economical to place the topping without additional shoring. Hence, the mass of the cast-in-place concrete must be carried by the precast member alone and the strength of the system must be evaluated for both the non-composite and composite sections.

Besides an analysis of the deflections at the various loading stages, serviceability checks should also be carried out considering the time-dependent prestress losses (relaxation, creep and shrinkage) from the time of transfer. As previously discussed, the losses will not significantly affect strength but should be investigated to obtain an assessment of immediate and long-term camber or deflection.

10.10   References

10

10.1   Neville, A M., Dilger, W.H. and Brooks, J.J., "Creep of Plain and Structural Concrete", *Longman* 1983, 392 pp.

10.2   Dilger, W.H., "Creep Analysis of Prestressed Concrete Members Using Creep-Transformed Section Properties", *PCI Journal*, Vol. 27, No. 1, Jan.-Feb.1982, pp. 98 -118.

10.3   Bazant, Z., "Prediction of Concrete Creep Using Age-Adjusted Effective Modulus Method", *ACI Journal* 69, 1972, pp. 212-17.

10.4   Branson, D.E. and Trost, H., "Application of the Effective Method in Calculating Deflections of Partially Prestressed Members", *PCI Journal*, Vol. 27, No.5, Sept.-Oct., 1982, pp. 62 -77.

10.5   Dilger, W.H. and Suri, K.M., "Steel stresses in Partially Prestressed Concrete Flexural Members", *PCI Journal*, Vol. 31, No. 3, May-June 1986, pp. 88 -113.

10.6   Dilger, W.H. and Ghali, A., "Shear Reinforcement for Concrete Slabs", *ASCE Journal*, Vol. 107, No. ST12, Dec. 1981, pp. 2903 -2920.

10.7   Ghali, A. and Elgabry, A., M.K., "Design of Stud-Shear Reinforcement for Slabs", *ACI Structural Journal*, Vol. 87, No. 3, May-June 1990.

10.8   Mitchell, D. and Cook, W.D., "Preventing Progressive Collapse of Slab Structures", *ASCE Journal*, Vol. 110, No. 7, July 1984, pp. 1513 -1532.

Prestressed Concrete

Example 10.1

Flexural Resistance with Bonded Prestressed Steel

Concrete: $f'_c = 40$ MPa, $E_c = 4500\sqrt{40} = 28\,460$ MPa

Steel: See sketch below

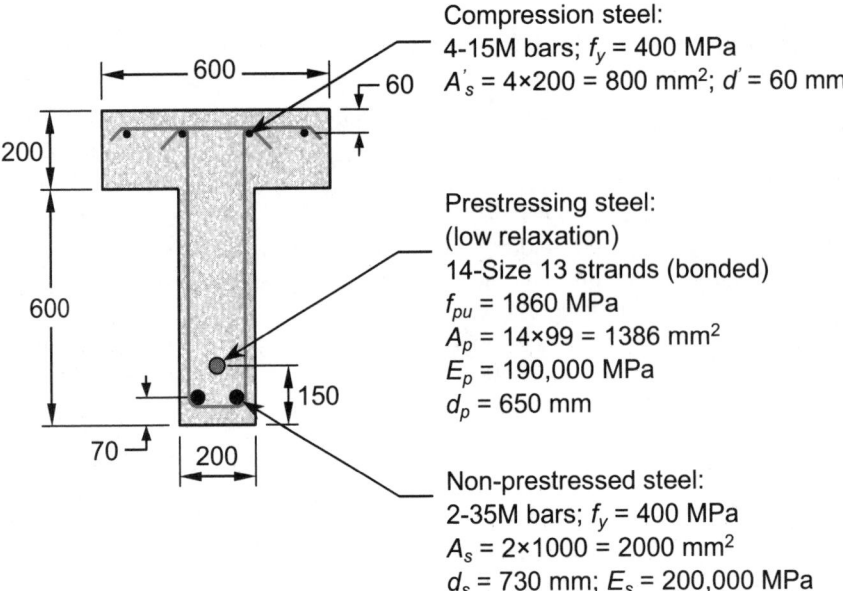

Compression steel:
4-15M bars; $f_y = 400$ MPa
$A'_s = 4\times200 = 800$ mm²; $d' = 60$ mm

Prestressing steel:
(low relaxation)
14-Size 13 strands (bonded)
$f_{pu} = 1860$ MPa
$A_p = 14\times99 = 1386$ mm²
$E_p = 190,000$ MPa
$d_p = 650$ mm

Non-prestressed steel:
2-35M bars; $f_y = 400$ MPa
$A_s = 2\times1000 = 2000$ mm²
$d_s = 730$ mm; $E_s = 200,000$ MPa

Fig. 10.1.1

Section Properties:

$A_c = 0.2(0.6) + 0.6(0.2) = 0.240$ m²

$$y_b = \frac{0.12 \cdot 0.3 + 0.12 \cdot 0.7}{0.24} = 0.500 \text{ m}$$

$e = 0.350$ m

$$I_c = \frac{0.20(0.60)^3}{12} + \frac{(0.20)^3 0.60}{12} + 0.12(0.20)^2 + 0.12(0.20)^2 = 0.0136 \text{ m}^4$$

$\alpha_1 = 0.85 - 0.0015 f'_c = 0.79 > 0.67$

$\beta_1 = 0.97 - 0.0025 f'_c = 0.87 > 0.67$

$k_p = 2(1.04 - 0.90) = 0.28$

$\alpha_1 \phi_c f'_c = 0.79(0.65)40 = 20.54$ MPa

$$c/d_p = \frac{\phi_p A_p f_{pu} + \phi_s A_s f_y - \phi_s A'_s f'_y - \alpha_1 \phi_c f'_c h_f (b - b_w)}{\alpha_1 \phi_c f'_c \beta_1 b_w d_p + \phi_p k_p A_p f_{pu}}$$

$\phi_p A_p f_{pu} = 0.9(1386)1860\left(10^{-6}\right) = 2.320$ MN

$\phi_s A_s f_y = 0.85(2000)400\left(10^{-6}\right) = 0.68$ MN

$\phi_s A'_s f'_y = 0.85(800)400\left(10^{-6}\right) = 0.272$ MN

$\alpha_1 \phi_c f'_c h_f (b - b_w) = 20.54 (0.20)0.40 = 1.643$ MN

$$c/d_p = \frac{2.320 + 0.680 - 0.272 - 1.643}{20.54\,(0.87)0.2\,(0.65) + 0.28\,(2.320)} = 0.365$$

as $c/d_p \le 0.50$ Eq. (18-1) may be used giving

$$f_{pr} = f_{pu}\,(1 - k_p\,c/d_p\,) = 1860\,[1 - 0.28\,(0.365)] = 1670\ \text{MPa}$$

Although the code equation may be used in this case to compute f_{pr}, the strain compatibility approach in computing f_{pr} is presented for completeness.

Use code equation for the first iteration

$$\phi_p\,A_p\,f_{pr} = 0.9 \cdot 1386\,(10^{-6})1670 = 2.083\ \text{MN}$$

$$c = \frac{\phi_p\,A_p\,f_{pr} + \phi_s\,A_s\,f_s - \phi_s\,A'_s\,f'_s - \alpha_1\,\phi_c\,f'_c\,h_f\,(b - b_w)}{\alpha_1\,\phi_c\,f'_c\,\beta_1\,b_w} = \frac{2.083 - 1.235}{3.574} = 0.237\ \text{m}$$

$$\varepsilon'_s = -0.0035\,(-237 + 60)/(-237) = -0.00261$$

$$\varepsilon'_y = -400\,/\,200\,000 = -0.00200$$

compression steel yields since strain exceeds yield strain.

$$\varepsilon_s = -0.0035\,(730 - 237)/(-237) = 0.00728$$

tension steel yields since strain exceeds yield strain.

$$\varepsilon_p = -0.0035\,(650 - 237)/(-0.237) = 0.00610$$

The prestressing steel has an additional prestrain corresponding to the elastic strain in the steel when the concrete stress is zero at the level of the tendon.

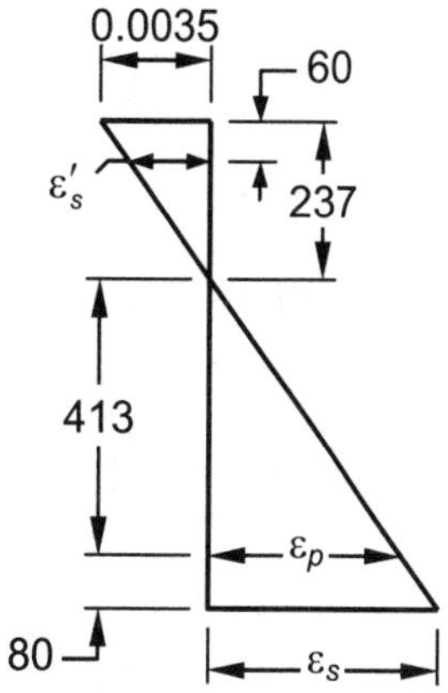

Assume $f_{pe} = 0.6\,f_{pu} = 1116\ \text{MPa}$

Fig. 10.1.2

$$f_{ce} = P_e\left(\frac{1}{A_c} + \frac{e^2}{I_c}\right) + \frac{M_D}{I_c}e = -1386\,(10^{-6})1116\left(\frac{1}{0.240} + \frac{0.350^2}{0.0136}\right) + \frac{500(10^{-6})0.350}{0.0136}$$

$$= -7.5\ \text{MPa}$$

Note that a dead load moment of 500 kN·m has been assumed in computing f_{ce}

$$\varepsilon_{ce} = -7.5\,/\,28\,460 = -0.00026$$

$$\varepsilon_{pe} = \frac{f_{pe}}{E_p} - \varepsilon_{ce} = \frac{1116}{190\,000} - (-0.00026) = 0.00613$$

Total strain in prestressing steel $= 0.00613 + 0.00610 = 0.01223$

From the stress-strain curve in Fig. 10.1 $f_{pr} = 1760\ \text{MPa}$

This is higher than the initial estimate of 1670 MPa. The correct value of f_{pr} is bracketed by these values

i.e $1670 < f_{pr} < 1760\ \text{MPa}$

Try $f_{pr} = (1670 + 1760)/2 = 1715$ MPa

$$c = \frac{2.083(1715/1670) - 1.235}{3.574} = 0.253 \text{ m}$$

$$\varepsilon_p = -0.0035(650 - 253)/(-253) = 0.00549$$

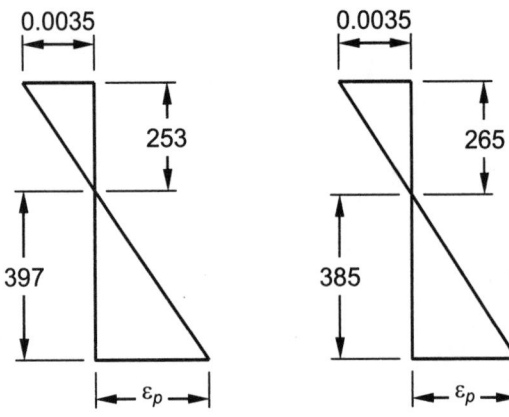

Fig. 10.1.3

Total strain $= 0.00613 + 0.00549 = 0.0116$ and from Fig. 10.1 $f_{pr} = 1750$ MPa

Try $f_{pr} = 1750$ MPa

$$c = \frac{2.083(1750/1670) - 1.235}{3.574} = 0.265 \text{ m}$$

Total strain $= 0.00613 + 0.00508 = 0.0112$ and from Fig. 10.1 $f_{pr} = 1750$ MPa (approx).

This matches the trial value so that this is the correct solution. Note that the strain compatibility approach gives a higher value of f_{pr} than the code equation.

By inspection it is clear that the strains in the non-prestressed tension and compression steels exceed the yield strains

$$M_r = \phi_p A_p f_{pr}(d_p - \frac{a}{2}) + \phi_s A_s f_y(d - \frac{a}{2}) - \phi_s A'_s f'_y(d' - \frac{a}{2}) - \alpha_1 \phi_c f'_c h_f(b - b_w)(\frac{h_f}{2} - \frac{a}{2})$$

$a = \beta_1 c = 0.87(265) = 230$ mm, $a/2 = 115$ mm

$\phi_p A_p f_{pr} = 0.9(1386 \times 10^{-6})1750 = 2.183$ MN

$M_r = 2.183(650 - 115) + 0.68(730 - 115) - 0.272(60 - 115) - 1.643(100 - 115) = 1626$ kN·m

Example 10.2

Flexural Resistance with Unbonded Prestressed Steel

Assume: 10 m span with 400 mm overhangs on each end

$f'_c = 40$ MPa, $\alpha_1 = 0.79, \beta_1 = 0.87$ 4 - Size 13 low-relaxation strands:

$A_p = 396 \text{ mm}^2, f_{pu} = 1860 \text{ MPa}$

$d_p = 700 \text{ mm}$

Assume $f_{pe} = 1100 \text{ MPa}$

$f_{py} = 0.9(1860) = 1674 \text{ MPa}$

The centroid of the section is 500 mm from bottom.

The concrete area below the centroid: $A = 100{,}000 \text{ mm}^2$.

The minimum area of bonded reinforcing (Clause 18.8.1) is $0.004A = 400 \text{ mm}^2$. Use 2- 15M bars.

Assuming that the depth of the stress block is less than 200 mm and that the non-prestressed reinforcement is Grade 400.

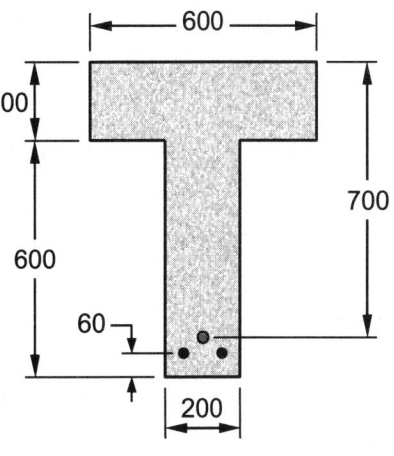

Fig. 10.2.1

$$c_y = \frac{\phi_p A_p f_{py} + \phi_s A_s f_y}{\alpha_1 \phi_c f_c' \beta_1 b} = \frac{0.9 \cdot 396 \cdot 1674 + 0.85 \cdot 400 \cdot 400}{0.79 \cdot 0.65 \cdot 40 \cdot 0.87 \cdot 600} = 68 \text{ mm}$$

For one plastic hinge and anchors each end of the beam

$\ell_o = 10\,800 \text{ mm}$

Eq. (18-2):

$$f_{pr} = f_{pe} + \frac{8000}{10800}(700 - 68) = 1100 + 468 = 1568 \text{ MPa}$$

$$M_r = \phi_p A_p f_{pr}(d_p - a/2) + \phi_s A_s f_y(d - a/2)$$

$$a = \frac{\phi_p A_p f_{pr} + \phi_s A_s f_y}{\alpha_1 \phi_c f_c' b} = \frac{0.9 \cdot 396 \cdot 1568 + 0.85 \cdot 400 \cdot 400}{0.79 \cdot 0.65 \cdot 40 \cdot 600} = 56 \text{ mm} < 200 \text{ mm}$$

$$M_r = 0.559(700 - 56/2) + 0.136(740 - 56/2) = 376 + 97 = 473 \text{ kN} \cdot \text{m}$$

Example   10.3

Analysis of Pretensioned Short Column

$f_c' = 50 \text{ MPa}, \gamma_c = 2400 \text{ kg/m}^3 \quad \phi_c = 0.65$

$$E_c = (3\,300\sqrt{f_c'} + 6\,900)\left(\frac{\gamma_c}{2300}\right)^{1.5} = 32\,230 \text{ MPa}$$

$\alpha_1 = 0.775, \quad \beta_1 = 0.845, \quad \alpha_1 \phi_c f_c' = 25.19 \text{ MPa}$

$A_p = 99 \text{ mm}^2/\text{strand}$

$E_p = 190\,000 \text{ MPa}, \ f_{pe} = 1100 \text{ MPa}$

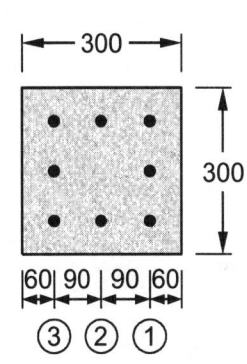

Fig. 10.3.1

10

Prestressed Concrete

Determine prestrain with zero concrete stress

$\varepsilon_{pe} = 1100/190\,000 = 0.00579$

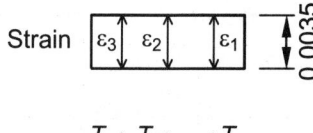

$f_c = P / A = \dfrac{-1100(99)8}{300^2} = -9.68 \text{ MPa}$

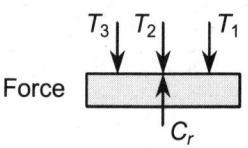

$\varepsilon_{ce} = -9.68/32\,230 = -0.00030$

$\varepsilon_{pe} - \varepsilon_{ce} = 0.00579 - (-0.00030) = 0.00609$

Fig. 10.3.2

Axial load with zero eccentricity

$\varepsilon_c = -0.0035$

$\varepsilon_{total} = 000609 - 0.0035 = 0.00579$

$f_{pr} - 0.00259 \cdot 190\,000 = 492 \text{ MPa} \quad \text{tension}$

$C_r = \alpha_1 \phi_c f_c' \, bc = 25.19(0.3)^2 = 2.267 \text{ MN compression}$

$T_1 + T_2 + T_3 = \phi_p A_p f_{pr} = 0.9 \cdot 8 \cdot 99(10^{-6})\,492 = 0.351 \text{MN tension}$

$P_{ro} = 2.267 - 0.351 = 1.916 \text{ MN compression}$

$P_{r(max)} = 0.8 \times 1.916 = 1.533 \text{ MN compression}$

Consider $c = 300$ mm, $a = 253$ mm (Fig. 10.3.3)							
Section	**Area** mm^2	ε_p	ε_{total}	f_{pr} **MPa**	P_r **MN**	**Moment Arm, mm**	M_r **kN·m**
Concrete					+1.915	+23.25	+44.4
1	297	-0.00280	0.00329	625	-0.167	+90	-15.0
2	198	-0.00175	0.00434	825	-0.147	0	0
3	297	-0.00070	0.00539	1024	-0.274	-90	+24.7
					1.327		54.1

$P_r = 1.327 \text{ MN compression}$

$M_r = 54.1 \text{ kN} \cdot \text{m}$

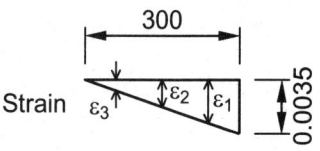

Note: $\varepsilon_{total} = 0.00609 + \varepsilon_p$

$P_r = \alpha_1 \phi_c \, f_c' \, ba - \Sigma \left(\phi_p A_p f_{pr} \right)$

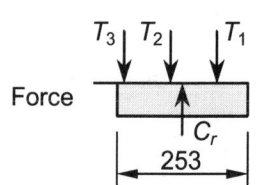

$M_r = \alpha_1 \phi_c \, f_c' \, ba(h/2 - a/2) - \Sigma \left(\phi_p A_p f_{pr} \, y \right)$

where y = distance from plastic centroid to the force.

Fig. 10.3.3

Consider $c = 250$ mm, $a = 211$ mm (Fig. 10.3.4)							
Section	Area	ε_p	ε_{total}	f_{pr}	P_r	Moment arm	M_r
Concrete	63375				+1.596	+44.37	+70.84
1	297	-0.00266	0.00343	652	-0.174	+90	-15.68
2	198	-0.00140	0.00469	891	-0.159	0	0
3	297	-0.00014	0.00595	1130	-0.302	-90	+27.20
					0.961		82.36
$P_r = 0.961$ MN, $M_r = 82.36$ kN·m							

Fig. 10.3.4

Fig. 10.3.5

Consider $c = 200$ mm, $a = 169$ mm (Fig. 10.3.5)							
Section	Area	ε_p	ε_{total}	f_{pr}	P_r	Moment Arm	M_r
Concrete	50700				+1.277	+65.5	+83.64
1	297	-0.00245	0.00364	692	-0.185	+90	-16.64
2	198	-0.00087	0.00522	991	-0.177	0	0
3	297	0.00070	0.00679	1290	-0.345	-90	+31.03
					0.570		98.03
$P_r = 0.570$ MN, $M_r = 98.03$ kN·m							

10

Prestressed Concrete

Consider $c = 160$ mm, $a = 135$ mm (Fig. 10.3.6)							
Section	Area	ε_p	ε_{total}	f_{pr}	P_r	Moment Arm	M_r
Concrete	40560				+1.022	+82.4	+84.18
1	297	-0.00219	+0.00390	741	-0.198	+90	-17.84
2	198	-0.00022	+0.00587	1115	-0.199	0	0
3	297	+0.00175	+0.00784	1490	-0.398	-90	35.84
					0.227		102.18
$P_r = 0.227$ MN, $M_r = 102.2$ kN·m							

Fig. 10.3.6   Fig. 10.3.7

Consider $c = 144$ mm, $a = 122$ mm (Fig. 10.3.7)							
Section	Area	ε_p	ε_{total}	f_{pr}	P_r	Moment Arm	M_r
Concrete	36504				+0.920	+89.1	+81.98
1	297	-0.00204	0.00405	769	-0.206	+90	-18.50
2	198	0.00015	0.00624	1185	-0.211	0	0
3	297	+0.00233	0.00842	1600	-0.428	-90	+38.50
					+0.075		101.98
$P_r = 0.075$ MN; $M_r = 102.0$ kN·m							

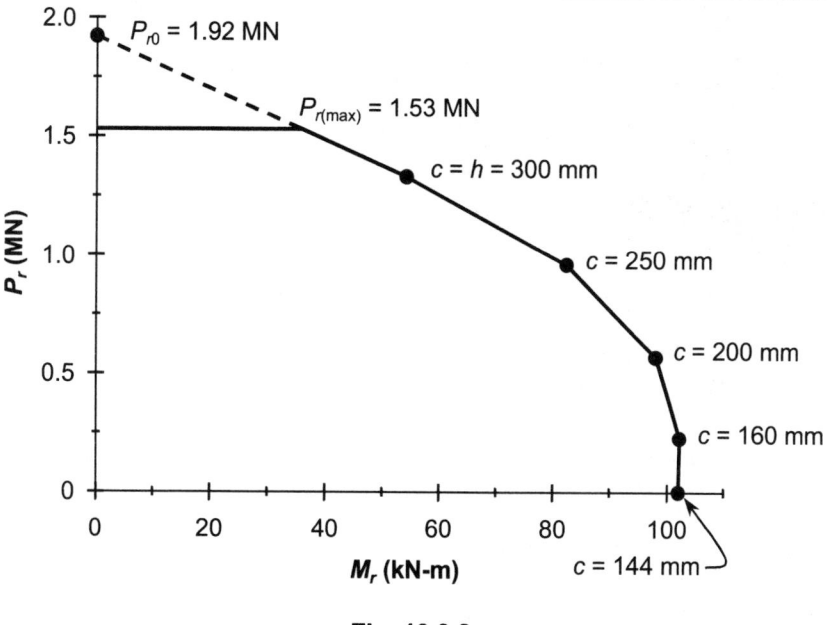

Fig. 10.3.8

Example   10.4

Calculation of A_p and A_s to Resist Factored Loads

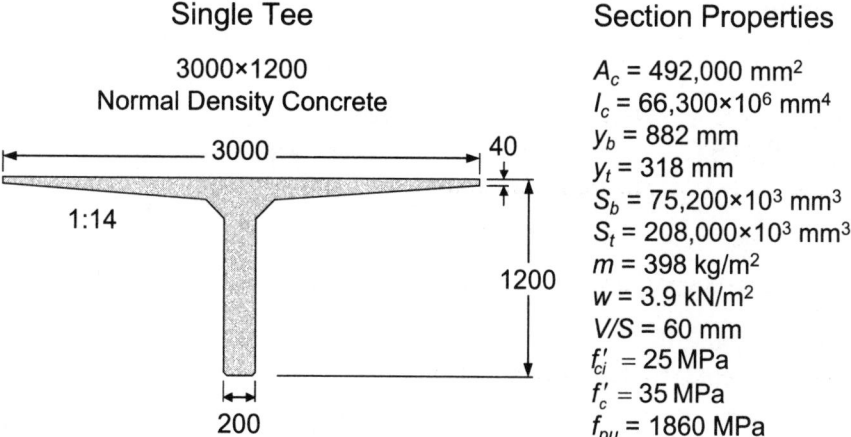

Fig. 10.4.1

Given:

Prestressed reinforcement:
All strands to be Grade 1860 low-relaxation and bonded.

A_p = 99 mm²/strand (Size 13 strand)

d_p = 1050 mm

e_c = 1050 − 318 = 732 mm

Non-prestressed reinforcement:

$f_y = 400$ MPa

$A_s = 500$ mm^2/bar (25M)

$d_s = 1100$ mm

Specified loads:

Dead load $= 3.9$ kN/m^2

Superimposed dead load $= 1.5$ kN/m^2

Live load $= 2.0$ kN/m^2

Span $= 27\,000$ mm

Solution:

$w_f = 3.0\left[1.25(3.9) + 1.25(1.5) + 1.5(2.0)\right] = 29.25$ kN/m

$$M_f = \frac{w_f l^2}{8} = \frac{29.25(27.0)^2}{8} = 2665 \text{ kN} \cdot \text{m}$$

$f_{pr} = f_{pu}\left(1 - k_p\, c/d_p\right)$

where $k_p = 2(1.04 - f_{py}/f_{pu}) = 0.28$

Assume $a < h_f$ and treat as a rectangular section with A_s and A_p giving

$$c/d_p = \frac{\phi_p A_p f_{pu} + \phi_s A_s f_y}{\alpha_1 \phi_c \beta_1 f_c' b\, d_p + \phi_p k_p A_p f_{pu}}$$

$$a = \frac{\phi_p A_p f_{pr} + \phi_s A_s f_y}{\alpha_1 \phi_c f_c' b}$$

and $\quad M_r = \phi_p A_p f_{pr}(d_p - a/2) + \phi_s A_s f_y(d - a/2)$

The above equations are valid provided:

$c/d_p \leq 0.5$

$f_{pe} \geq 0.6 f_{py}$

Now select values of A_s and A_p, and compute f_{pr} and M_r using $\alpha_1 = 0.797$ and $\beta_1 = 0.882$.

The following results were obtained assuming $\phi = 0.70$ according to Clause 16.1.3 for elements produced in a certified precast manufacturing plant.

A_s mm^2	No. of strands	A_p mm^2	c/d_p	f_{pr} MPa	a mm	M_r kN·m	$1.2\, M_{cr}$ kN·m
0	16	1584	0.0482	1835	45	2688	2197
0	18	1782	0.0541	1832	50	3011	2432
1000	14	1386	0.0484	1835	45	2718	1963
1000	16	1584	0.0543	1832	50	3042	2197
2000	12	1188	0.0486	1835	45	2748	1728
2000	14	1386	0.0546	1832	51	3072	1963
3000	12	1188	0.0548	1831	51	3102	1728

Although the effective depth of the compression block, a, is greater than the thickness of the flange at the tip, the precise calculation causes insignificant adjustments to the results.

The results satisfy the basic equations and are all valid solutions with respect to factored flexural resistance since $M_r > M_f$ in each case.

Clause 18.7 requires that $M_r \geq 1.2\ M_{cr}$, where M_{cr} is the cracking moment based on the modulus of rupture, f_r. At this stage of the design, it is sufficient to make a realistic assessment of the final prestress force, after all losses have occurred. In this example it is assumed that the initial stress in the tendons is 0.75 f_{pu} with losses of 20%.

$$\therefore f_{pe} = 0.8(0.75)1860 = 1116\ \text{MPa}$$

and M_{cr} can be calculated from,

$$M_{cr} = (-\frac{P}{A} - \frac{P \cdot e}{S_b} + f_r)\,S_b$$

where $\ f_r = 0.6\lambda\sqrt{f_c'}\qquad$ Eq. $(8\text{-}3)$

Note that P is a compressive force on concrete and should be taken as negative.

Although this design example is concerned with the factored flexural strength of the member, it is customary to design partially prestressed members such that the moment due to sustained loads does not exceed the cracking moment.

The maximum specified moment due to dead load plus superimposed dead load is 1476 kN·m which is less than M_{cr} for all combinations of A_p and A_s except for the two cases where $A_p = 1188$ mm^2 for which $M_{cr} = 1440$ kN·m.

Table 10.1(b) can also be used to determine A_p for a precast member with bonded prestressed reinforcement only.

With $\ K_u = \dfrac{M_f}{f_c'\,bd_p^2} = \dfrac{2665(10^6)}{35\,(3000)1050^2} = 0.0230$

from Table 10.1(b) with $k_p = 0.28$ and $\ f_c' = 35\ \text{MPa}$

$\omega_{pu} = 0.0264$

$A_p = \omega_{pu}f_c'bd_p/f_{pu} = 0.0264 \cdot 35 \cdot 3000 \cdot 1050/1860 = 1565\ \text{mm}^2$

Provide 16 - Size 13 strands, $A_p = 1584$ mm^2

Examples 10.5 and 10.6 investigate the permissible stress requirements of Clauses 18.3.1 and 18.3.2

Example 10.5

Calculation of Critical Concrete Stresses to Comply with Clauses 18.3.1 and 18.3.2 (fully prestressed member)

Given:

The data and notation from Example 10.4

$E_c = 26.600$ MPa

Solution:

For an initial estimate of A_p, find A_p required at midspan due to action of all specified loads and assume 20% prestress losses.

Moment due to specified loads

$$M_s = 3.0\,(3.9 + 1.5 + 2.0)\,27^2/8 = 2023\ \text{kN}\cdot\text{m}$$

In accordance with Clause 18.3.2.(c), maximum permissible extreme fibre stress in tension in the precompressed tensile zone (for fully-prestressed member) is $0.5\lambda\sqrt{f_c'}$ which is 2.96 MPa.

$$\therefore \frac{-P_e}{A_c} + \frac{-P_e\,e}{S_b} + \frac{M_s}{S_b} \le 2.96\ \text{MPa}$$

where $A_c = 492\,000\ \text{mm}^2$, $e = e_c = 732\ \text{mm}$ and $S_b = 75\,200\,(10^3)\ \text{mm}^3$

from which, the minimum final prestress force, $P_e = 2055\ \text{kN}$

$\therefore$ Initial prestress force, $P_i = 2055/0.8 = 2569\ \text{kN}$

Initial prestress force/strand $= 0.75\,(1860)\,99\,(10^{-3}) = 138.1\ \text{kN}$

$\therefore$ Minimum number of Size 13 strands required to satisfy Clause 18.3.2(c) is:

$2569/138.1 = 18.6$ strands

Hence, initial estimate of minimum number of strands for symmetrical pattern is 20, giving $A_p = 1980\ \text{mm}^2$.

Instantaneous prestress losses:

$$\Delta P_{e\ell} = \left[\frac{P_{(i)}}{A_{tr}} + \frac{(P_{(i)}\,e_{tr} + M_g)\,e_{tr}}{I_{tr}}\right]\frac{E_p}{E_c}\,A_p \quad \text{(Eq. 10.4.1)}$$

In this example, using low-relaxation steel, $P_{(i)} \approx P_o$ and, because ρ_p is small, the properties of the gross concrete section can be used

$$P_o = 0.75 \cdot 20 \cdot 99 \cdot 1860\,(10^{-3}) = 2762\ \text{kN}$$

$$\Delta P_{e\ell} = \left[\frac{-2762 \cdot 10^3}{492\,000} + \frac{(-2762 \cdot 10^3 \cdot 732 + 1066 \cdot 10^6)\,732}{66\,300 \cdot 10^6}\right]\frac{190{,}000}{26\,600} \cdot 1980\big(10^{-3}\big)$$

$$= -228\ \text{kN}\quad (= 8\%\ \text{of } P_o)$$

Time-dependent prestress losses:

According to Eqs. (1.9) and (1.10), respectively:

Creep Coefficient $C_t = \dfrac{t^{0.6}}{10 + t^{0.6}}\,C_u\,Q_{cr}\,0$

Shrinkage $\varepsilon_{sh} = \dfrac{t}{C_s + t}\,\varepsilon_{shu}\,P_{sh}\,0$

According to Table 1.2: $Q_{cr} = Q_a\,Q_h\,Q_f\,Q_r\,Q_s\,Q_v$

and $P_{sh} = P_c\,P_h\,P_f\,P_r\,P_s\,P_v$

The coefficients Q and P are determined for the following assumptions:

	Q	P
Age at loading - 1 day, steam cured	1.00	–
Cement content - 300 kg/m^3	–	0.93
Relative Humidity - 60%	0.87	0.80
Ratio of fine to total aggregate - 0.40	0.98	0.86
Volume to surface ratio - 60 mm	0.89	0.89
Slump - 50 mm	0.95	0.97
Air content - 7%	1.09	1.00

With C_u = 2.35 and ε_{shu} = 780 (10^{-6}), (see Section 1.2.3) we get at time t_∞ :

C_∞ = 2.35 x 1.00 x 0.87 x 0.98 x 0.89 x 0.95 x 1.09 = 1.84

$\varepsilon_{sh\infty}$ = 780 x 10^{-6} x 0.93 x 0.80 x 0.86 x 0.89 x 0.97 x 1.00 = 430 x 10^{-6}

Intrinsic relaxation at 20°C after 50 years (Eq. 10.4.7), f_{re} = 50 MPa.

Concrete stress at level of tendons due to sustained load and initial prestress

$P_i = 2762 - 228 = 2534$ kN

$$f_c = \frac{P_i}{A_c} + \frac{(M_{sust} + P_i e)\, e}{I_c}$$

$$f_c = \frac{-2534 \cdot 10^3}{492{,}000} + \frac{((1066 + 410)10^6 - 2534 \cdot 10^3 \cdot 732)\, 732}{66\,300 \cdot 10^6} = -9.33 \text{ MPa}$$

We first determine the loss of prestress due to creep and shrinkage alone to be able to determine the relaxation reduction coefficient α_r according to Fig. 10.3.

$\rho_p = A_p / A_c = 1980/(492\,000) = 0.00402$

$n_p = 190\,000/26\,600 = 7.14$

$r = (I/A)^{1/2} = [66.3 \cdot 10^9 / 492\,000]^{1/2} = 367$ mm

From Eq. (10.4.9)

$$\Delta f_s = \frac{7.14(-9.33)1.84 - 430\left(10^{-6}\right)190\,000}{1 + 7.14 \cdot 0.00402\left\{1 + \left(\dfrac{732}{367}\right)^2 [1 + 0.8(1.84)]\right\}} = -\frac{204.3}{1.31} = -156 \text{ MPa}$$

$\beta = \dfrac{f_{pi}}{f_{pu}} = 0.75$

$\Omega = \dfrac{\Delta f_s}{f_{pi}} = \dfrac{156}{0.75 \cdot 1860} = 0.112$, and from Fig. 10.3 $\alpha_r = 0.72$

Prestress loss, including reduced relaxation,

$$\Delta f_{pr} = -156 - \frac{50 \cdot 0.72}{1.31} = -183 \text{ MPa}$$

This corresponds to a 13 percent loss of the initial prestress.

Hence, total prestress loss = 8% + 13% = 21%.

Prestress Force:

$$P_i = 0.92 \cdot 2762 = 2541 \, \text{kN}$$
$$P_e = 0.79 \cdot 2762 = 2182 \, \text{kN}$$

Check if deflected strands are required at transfer by determining the maximum eccentricity of prestress force at ends of member, e_e, assuming no additional top reinforcement.

For top tension

$$\max e_e = \left(0.5 \sqrt{f'_{ci}} + \frac{P_i}{A_c}\right) \frac{S_t}{P_i} = (2.50 + 5.16)\frac{208 \cdot 10^6}{2541 \cdot 10^3} = 627 \, \text{mm}$$

For bottom compression

$$\max e_e = \left(0.6 f'_{ci} - \frac{P_i}{A_c}\right) \frac{S_b}{P_i} = (15.00 - 5.16)\frac{75.2 \cdot 10^6}{2541 \cdot 10^3} = 291 \, \text{mm} \; \text{(governs)}$$

Stresses at transfer and at final condition for various sections are given in the following table,

where, f_b = concrete stress in bottom fibre and f_t = concrete stress in top fibre

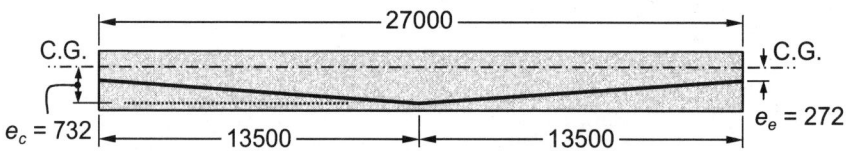

Centroid of Prestressing Force

Fig. 10.5.1

Load	End at Transfer Prestress = P_i		Midspan at Transfer Prestress = P_i		0.4ℓ at Final Condition Prestress = P_e	
	f_b	f_t	f_b	f_t	f_b	f_t
P_i/A_c or P_e/A_c $P_i e/S$ or $P_e e/S$ M_g/S M_{sd}/S $M\ell/S$	-5.16 -9.19	-5.16 +3.32	-5.16 -24.73 +14.18	-5.16 +8.94 -5.13	-4.53 -18.57 +13.62 +5.24 (+6.98)	-4.53 +6.71 -4.92 -1.89 (-2.52)
Stresses	-14.35	-1.84	-15.71	-1.35	-4.24 (+2.74)	-4.63 (-7.15)
Allowable	$-0.6 f'_{ci}$	$-0.6 f'_{ci}$	$-0.6 f'_{ci}$	$-0.6 f'_{ci}$	$+0.5 \sqrt{f'_{ci}}$	$-0.45 f'_c$ $(-0.6 f'_c)$
	-15.00	-15.00	-15.00	-15.00	+2.96	-15.75 (-21.00)
	OK	OK	NG	OK	OK	OK

$e_e = 272$ mm $e_c = 732$ mm $e_{(0.4\,\ell)} = 640$ mm

Note that Clause 18.3.2 specifies a permissible compressive stress of $0.45 f_c'$ under sustained loads and $0.6 f_c'$ under total load. In the above table stress under total load is shown in parenthesis.

Therefore, to satisfy the requirements of Clauses 18.3.1 and 18.3.2, provide 20-Size 13 strands with profile shown, but increase f_{ci}' to 27 MPa in order to accommodate the compressive stress of 15.71 MPa that occurs in the bottom at the mid-span of the member at transfer.

Referring to the results of Example 10.4, the value of A_p to satisfy permissible stresses is greater than that required for factored flexural resistance. This is often the case with prestressed members designed in accordance with Clause 18.3.2(c).

Example 10.6

Calculation of Critical Stresses and Crack Widths to Comply with Clause 18.3.3 (partially prestressed member)

Given: The data from Example 10.4 with

$$A_p = 1188 \text{ mm}^2$$

$$A_s = 2000 \text{ mm}^2$$

Solution:

From the results of Example 10.5, it is apparent that if A_p is reduced from 1980 mm² to 1188 mm², the member does not comply with Clause 18.3.2(c) and the member is partially prestressed.

Transformed Section Properties:

$$A_{tr} = (492{,}000 - 1188 - 2000) + \left(1188 \cdot \frac{190{,}000}{26{,}600}\right) + 2000 \cdot \frac{200{,}000}{26{,}600} = 512300 \text{ mm}^2$$

$$y_{tr} = \frac{(492000 \cdot 882) + (13026 \cdot 100) + (7290 \cdot 150)}{512300} = 852 \text{ mm}$$

$$e_{tr} = 852 - (1200 - 1050) = 702 \text{ mm}$$

$$I_{tr} = 77.7 \cdot 10^9 \text{mm}^4$$

Instantaneous prestress losses:

$$\Delta P_{e\ell} = \left[\frac{P_{(i)}}{A_{tr}} + \frac{(P_{(i)}\,e_{tr} + M_g)\,e_{tr}}{I_{tr}}\right]\frac{E_p}{E_c}\,A_p$$

$$P_{(i)} = 0.75 \cdot 1188 \cdot 1860 \times 10^{-3} = 1657 \text{ kN}$$

$$\Delta P_{e\ell} = \left[\frac{-1657 \times 10^3}{512{,}300} + \frac{(-1657 \times 10^3 \cdot 702 + 1066 \times 10^6)\,702}{77.7 \times 10^9}\right]\frac{190{,}000}{26{,}620} \cdot 1188 \times 10^{-3}$$

$$= -34.8 \text{ kN } (2\%)$$

Time-dependent losses:

The following data were established in Example 10.5 for the time-dependent material properties:

Creep Coefficient $C_\infty = 1.84$

Shrinkage $\varepsilon_{sh\infty} = 430 \times 10^{-6}$

Intrinsic Relaxation $f_{re} = 50$ MPa

Concrete stress at the tendon level under sustained load (= dead load)

$$f_c = \frac{-1657\times10^3}{512\,300} + \left[\frac{(1066+410)-1657\cdot0.732}{77.7\times10^9}\right]732\times10^6 = -3.23 + 2.48 = -0.75 \text{ MPa}$$

Since both layers of steel have a common centroid the loss of prestress without relaxation is equal to the compressive stress in the nonprestressed steel.
With

$$\rho_p n_p = \frac{1188}{492,000} \times \frac{190,000}{26620} = 0.0172 \text{ and}$$

$$\rho_s n_s = \frac{2000}{492,000} \times \frac{200,000}{26\,600} = 0.0305$$

$$\Delta f_s = \frac{7.3(-0.75)1.84 - (430\times10^{-6}\cdot190,000)}{1+(0.0172+0.0305)\left[\left(1+\dfrac{732}{367}\right)^2(1+0.8\cdot1.84)\right]} = \frac{-91.8}{1.587} = -57.8 \text{ MPa}$$

Relaxation reduction coefficient:

With $\beta = 0.75$, $\Omega = \dfrac{57.8}{0.75\cdot1860} = 0.041$

we obtain from Fig. 10.3: $\alpha_r = 0.95$

so that the loss, including relaxation is:

$$\Delta f_{pr} = -57.8 - \frac{50\cdot0.95}{1.587} = -87.7 \text{ MPa (5\%)}$$

The total reduction of the compression on the concrete is

$$\Delta P = (87.8\cdot1188 + 57.8\cdot2000)10^{-3} = 219 \text{ kN}$$

This corresponds to a reduction in compressive stress at the bottom fibre of:

$$\Delta f_c = \frac{219(10^3)}{492(10^3)} + \frac{219(10^3)732}{66.3(10^9)}\cdot882 = 2.58 \text{ MPa}$$

Total prestress loss = 2% + 5% = 7%

Prestress force:

P_i = 0.98 (1657) = 1624 kN

P_e = 0.93 (1657) = 1541 kN

With deflected strands such that e_e = 540 mm and e_c = 705 mm, the following concrete stresses are calculated at transfer.

Load	End at Transfer		Midspan at Transfer	
	f_b	f_t	f_b	f_t
$P_{(i)}/A_{tr}$ $P_{(i)}e_{tr}/S_{tr}$ M_g/S_{tr}	-3.17 -9.08	-3.17 +3.71	-3.17 -12.02 +11.69	-3.17 +4.91 -4.77
Stresses	-12.26	+0.54	-3.50	-3.03
Allowable	$-0.6\,f'_{ci}$	$+0.5\,\sqrt{f'_{ci}}$	$-0.6\,f'_{ci}$	$-0.6\,f'_{ci}$
	-15.00	+2.50	-15.00	-15.00
	OK	OK	OK	OK

In this table f_b and f_t are concrete stresses in bottom and top fibre, respectively.

Hence, concrete stresses at transfer are within permissible limits of Clause 18.3.1.

Crack Control:

Components of the decompression force P are:

$P_e = 1541$ kN

$P_s = \Delta f_s A_s = -57.8 \cdot 2000 \text{x} 10^{-3} = -116$ kN

$\Delta P_p = \dfrac{-f_c}{E_c} E_p A_p = \dfrac{0.75}{26\,600} 190 \text{x} 10^3 \cdot 1188 \text{x} 10^{-3} = 6.4$ kN

$\Delta P_s = \dfrac{-f_c}{E_c} E_s A_s = \dfrac{0.75}{26\,600} 200 \text{x} 10^3 \cdot 2000 \text{x} 10^{-3} = 11.3$ kN

It is obvious that the terms ΔP_p and ΔP_s are small and could be neglected.

The following parameters are needed to determine $f_s/(n\alpha)$ from Figure 10.8:

$d = \dfrac{A_s E_s d_s + A_p E_p d_p}{A_s E_s + A_p E_p} = \dfrac{2000 \cdot 200 \cdot 1100 + 1188 \cdot 190 \cdot 1050}{2000 \cdot 200 + 1188 \cdot 190} \text{x} \dfrac{10^3}{10^3} = 1082$ mm

$n\rho = \dfrac{A_p E_p + A_s E_s}{E_c bd} = \dfrac{(1188 \cdot 190 + 2000 \cdot 200)10^3}{26\,600 \cdot 3000 \cdot 1082} = 0.00714$

10

Prestressed Concrete

$$p = \frac{Pd_p}{M_s} = \frac{1408 \cdot 1050\left(10^3\right)}{\left(1066 + 410 + 547\right)10^6} = 0.749$$

$$\alpha_b = \frac{b_w}{b} = \frac{200}{3000} = 0.0667$$

$$\alpha_f = \frac{h_f}{d} = \frac{90}{1082} = 0.0832$$

With these values were find by interpolation $f_s/n\alpha = 43$

Steel stress at the level of the centroid of the steel:

$$f_s = 43 \frac{nM_s}{bd^2} = 43\left[\frac{7.5\left(2023\right)10^6}{3000\left(1082\right)^2}\right] = 186 \text{ MPa}$$

Disregarding the bundled prestressing steel for the calculation of A, we find

$$A = \frac{200(2)100}{4} = 10\,000 \text{ mm}^2$$

Thus

$$z = f_s \sqrt[3]{d_c\,A} = 181\left(50 \cdot 10\,000\right)^{1/3}\left(10^{-3}\right) = 14.8$$

For interior exposure (assumed), $z \leq 20$ (Clause 18.8.3)

Hence, 12-Size 13 strands plus 4-25M bars satisfy concrete stresses at transfer and crack control under specified loads.

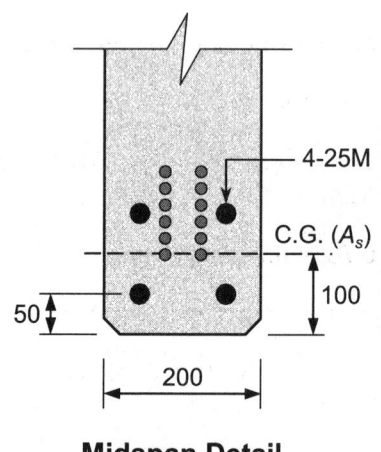

Midspan Detail

Fig. 10.6.1

Example 10.7

Shear Design of a Prestressed Concrete Member – Simplified Method

When using the Simplified Method, the maximum yield strength limit of 400 MPa in Clause 11.3.6 is intended for non-prestressed reinforcement only. For prestressed members, this yield strength limit does not apply.

The beam of Example 10.4 is designed for shear.

Data given:
h = 1200 mm	b_w = 200 mm	A_p = 20 mm
a_g = 20 mm	w_f = 29.25 kN/m	f_{pu} = 1860 MPa
f_c' = 35 MPa	f_y = 400 MPa for A_v	

The member has been produced in a manufacturing plant certified in accordance with Clause 16.1.3 so $\phi_c = 0.70$

Effective prestress P_e = 2210 kN (assuming initial prestress of 75% f_{pu} and 20% losses)

Slope of the tendons (732 - 272)/13500 = 0.03407

V_p = 0.9(2210)0.03407 = 68 kN

Shear force at distance d_v = 0.72h = 0.72(1200) = 864 mm from face of support:

V_f = 29.25 [27/2 - (0.10 + 0.864)] = 367 kN

Since h = 1200 mm > 750 mm, the new Clause 11.2.8.1(b) specifies that minimum shear reinforcement be provided over the full length of the beam.

Minimum shear reinforcement (Clause 11.2.8.2):

$$(\frac{A_v}{s}) min = 0.06 \sqrt{f_c'} \frac{b_w}{f_y} = 0.06\sqrt{35}(\frac{200}{400}) = 0.177 \text{ mm}^2/\text{mm}$$

For 10M stirrups the spacing is

s = 2(100)/ 0.177 = 1130 mm

The maximum spacing of transverse reinforcement is limited to $0.7d_v$ or 600 mm (Clause11.3.8.1):

$0.7d_v$ = 0.7(864) = 605 mm.

Hence for minimum shear reinforcement, provide 10M stirrups at 600 mm.

Using the Simplified Method Clause 11.3.6.3 with θ = 35⁰ the shear resistance provided by these stirrups:

$$V_s = \frac{\phi_s A_v f_y d_v \cot \theta}{s} = 0.85(2 \cdot 100) \cdot 400 \cdot \frac{864}{600} \cdot cot(35)10^{-3} = 140 \text{ kN} \quad \text{Eq. (11-7)}$$

Calculation of V_c :

$$V_c = \phi_c \lambda \beta \sqrt{f_c'} b_w d_v \quad \text{Eq. (11- 6)}$$

If a section contains at least the minimum transverse reinforcement, $\beta = 0.18$, thus:

$$V_c = 0.7(1.0)0.18\sqrt{35}(200)864(10^{-3}) = 129 \text{ kN}$$

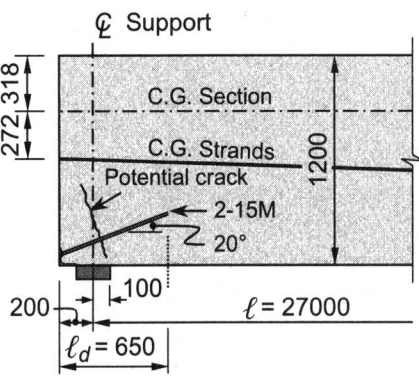

Fig. 10.7.1 Beam end zone

Transfer length = 50 (13) = 650 mm (Clause 11.2.11)

The solution to this example will be determined by constructing the V_c and V_f diagrams.

The shear force due to prestressing, V_p, is zero at the end of the member and increases linearly to reach its maximum value at 650 mm from the end. At the face of the support, 300 mm from the beam end:

$V_r = V_c + V_s + V_p = 129 + 140 + 68(300)/650 = 300$ kN

In the end region $V_f = 367$ kN. At the face of the support V_f exceeds 300 kN so additional shear reinforcement will be required, see shaded area in Fig. 10.7.2. With $V_c = 129$kN, $V_p = 31$ kN and using 10M stirrups:

$$s = \frac{\phi_s\, A_v f_y d_v\, \cot\theta}{V_f - V_c - V_p} = 0.85(400)2(100)\frac{864}{367 - 129 - 31} \cdot \cot(35)10^{-3} = 405 \text{ mm}$$

The shear resistance diagram of Fig. 10.7.2 indicates that the point where the factored shear force V_f exceeds $V_r = V_c + V_{smin} + V_p$ = 129 + 140 + 68 = 337 kN is 1.88 m from the face of the support. Provide 10M at 405 mm over this length.

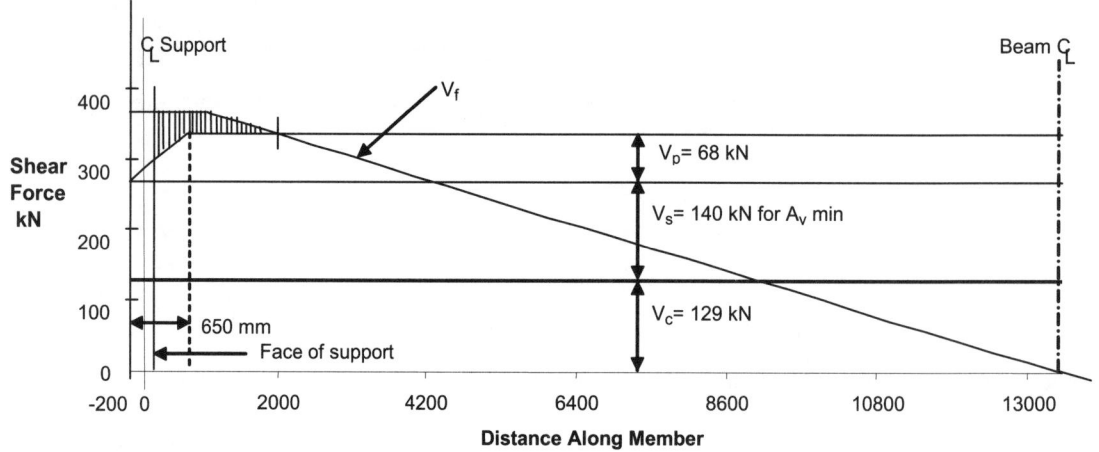

Fig. 10.7.2 Shear design diagram

In order to complete the shear design of Example 10.7, the additional tension and anchorage requirements of longitudinal reinforcement, (Clauses 11.3.9.1 and 11.3.9.5) and the capacity of the inclined shear friction plane must be examined. This is illustrated in Example 10.8 (5) and 10.8 (6) respectively.

Example 10.8

Shear Design of Prestressed Concrete Member - General Method

The beam of Example 10.4 is designed for shear.

Data given: h = 1200 mm b_w = 200 mm A_p = 1980 mm^2

                a_g = 20 mm w_f = 29.25 kN/m f_{pu} = 1860 MPa

                f_c' = 35 MPa f_y = 400 MPa

The member has been produced in a manufacturing plant certified in accordance with Clause 16.1.3 so $\phi_c = 0.70$

Effective prestress P_e = 2210 kN (assuming initial prestress of 75% f_{pu} and 20% losses)

Slope of the tendons (732 - 272)/13 500 = 0.03407

V_p = 0.9(2210) 0.03407 = 68 kN

1. Factored Shear Force and Moment:

According to Clause 11.3.2, the critical section may be taken at a distance d_v from the face of the support where d_v is the larger of 0.9d or 0.72h (Clause 2.3). Due to the draped strand, d_v = 0.72 (1200) = 864 mm (= 0.864 m). Shear force and moment due to factored load at (864 + 100) = 964 mm (= 0.964 m) from the centreline of the support are (see Fig. 10.7.1):

V_f = 29.25 (13.50 - 0.964) = 367 kN.

M_f = 0.5(29.25) 0.964(27.00 - 0.964) = 367 k·Nm

and check Clause 11.3.6.4(a) that M_f is not less than $(V_f - V_p)d_v$ = (367 – 67.8) 0.864 = 258 kN·m.

2. Determination of ε_x

According to Eq. 11-13 with N_f = 0, A_s = 0, f_{po} = 0.7f_{pu} and $A_p f_{po}$ = 2578 kN

$$\varepsilon_x = \frac{367/0.864 + 367 - 67.8 - 2578}{2(190\,000)1980\left(10^{-3}\right)} = -0.002464$$

Since the value of ε_x is negative, it shall be taken either as zero, or the value shall be calculated with the denominator of Eq. (11–13) replaced by $2(E_s A_s + E_p A_p + E_c A_{ct})$, Clause 11.3.6.4(c). In Example 10.8 ε_x is assumed to be zero.

10

Prestressed Concrete

3. Determination of β

Assuming no transverse reinforcement, Eq. (11–10) applies. The prestressing strands are fanned out at the member end. With 20 strands in two rows, the average spacing would be approximately (1200 – 2(50)/9 = 122 mm, say 125 mm. The exact spacing would have to be established according the end block geometry at the manufacturing plant. Each layer satisfies the criterion $A_s > 0.003\,b_w s_z$ specified in Clause 11.3.6.3(c): 198 mm^2 > 0.003(200)125 = 75 mm^2. With $s_z = 125$ mm:

$$s_{ze} = \frac{35 s_z}{(15 + a_g)} = \frac{35(125)}{(15 + 20)} = 125 \geq 0.85 s_z = 0.85(125) = 106 \text{ mm}$$

using $\varepsilon_x = 0$ and $s_{ze} = 125$ in Eq. (11-11):

$$\beta = \frac{0.4}{1 + 1500(0)} \cdot \frac{1300}{(1000 + 125)} = 0.462$$

$$V_c = 0.7\,(1.0)0.462\,\sqrt{35}\,(200)0.864 = 330 \text{ kN} \quad \text{Eq.(11-6)}$$

$$V_c + V_p = 330 + 68 = 398 \text{ kN}$$

According to these calculations, stirrups would not be required. However, since $h > 750$ mm minimum shear reinforcement is required, see Example 10.7.

Including the fanned strands in the shear calculations is not possible if the strands no longer reach the mid-height of the beam i.e. beyond about 8.0 m from the support.

4. Determination of θ

$$\theta = 29 + 7000\,\varepsilon_x = 29^0 \quad \text{Eq. (11-12)}$$

5. Check of tension reinforcement near support, (Clauses 11.3.9.1 and 11.3.9.5)

At the inside edge of the bearing area, V_f = 29.25(13.5-0.1) = 392 kN, M_f = 0.5(29.25)0.1(27.0 - 0.1) = 39.3 kN·m and V_p = 68(300/650) = 31.3 kN.

In addition, a horizontal force, H_f, has to be considered at the support. This force depends on the friction developed at the interface between the bearing and the girder. For a sliding bearing (e.g. teflon), friction is very small so that the horizontal force may be neglected. On the other hand, the friction coefficient between concrete surfaces may be as high as 0.8. Assume (arbitrarily) a friction coefficient of 0.3. Thus, the reaction due to factored load, R_f = (29.25) 27.0/2 = 395 kN, produces H_f = 0.3(395) = 118 kN

Transposing this horizontal force (that is applied at the bottom of the member) to the mid-height of the beam yields a normal force $N_f = H_f$ and a moment $M_f = N_f(h/2) = 118(1.20)/2 = 70.8$ kN·m, that is to be added to the above moment; thus: M_f = 39.3 + 70 8 = 110 kN·m. According to Eq. (11-14) with $V_s = 0$:

$$F_{lt} = \frac{M_f}{d_v} + 0.5 N_f + \left(V_f - V_p\right)\cot\theta = 110/0.864 + 0.5(118) + (392 - 31.3)\cot\left(29^\circ\right) = 837 \text{ kN}$$

According to Clause 11.3.9.5 this tension force shall be developed at the point, where a line inclined at angle θ to the longitudinal axis and extending from the inside edge of the bearing area intersects the reinforcement. As shown in Fig. 10.8.1, only the two (straight) bottom strands do not develop the full prestressing force as they cross the inclined plane at angle θ. The full effective prestressing force P_e= 2210 kN far exceeds the force F_{lt} so that there is no need to calculate the exact value of the force in the bottom strands at the inclined crack.

6. Shear friction

In addition to the above check, the interface shear between a wedge sheared off at an angle from the inside edge of the bearing to the end face of the beam (see Fig. 10.8.1) needs to be investigated.

For the shear stress resistance the following code equation is used.

$$v_r = \lambda \phi_c k \sqrt{\sigma f_c'} + \phi_s \rho_v f_y \cos \alpha_f \quad \text{Eq. (11-25)}$$

For monolithically placed concrete $k = 0.6$. σ and ρ_v are defined in the Standard as:

$$\sigma = \rho_v f_y \sin \alpha_f + N / A_g \quad \text{Eq. (11-26)}$$

$$\rho_v = A_{vf} / A_{cv} \quad \text{Eq. (11-27)}$$

N is the unfactored permanent (dead) load perpendicular to the shear plane.

With w_D = 3(3.9+1.5) = 16.2 kN/m, R_D = 16.2(27.0/2) = 219 kN. The corresponding unfactored horizontal force H_D = 0.3(219) = 65.6 kN. The resulting force acting perpendicular to the shear plane is N.

Assuming that the strands contribute to the shear stress resistance at the inclined shear friction plane, the most critical conditions exist at the steepest plane that is intersected only by the pair of straight strands at the bottom of the beam, see Fig. 10.8.1. For the geometry shown in the figure, $\alpha_f = 37.8°$. The area of the inclined shear friction plane $A_{cv} = 75\,970$ mm^2 and $\rho_v = 2(99)/75\,970$ = 0.00261. The embedment length of the two strands beyond the shear friction plane is 236 mm yielding an effective stress at the shear plane of 1116(236/650) = 404 MPa. With the normal stress due to unfactored vertical reaction N = 219 kN and concurrent horizontal force H = 65.6 kN, $\sigma = 1.75$ MPa and $\lambda = 1.0$, $\phi_c = 0.70$, $f_c' = 35$ MPa, the shear stress resistance according to Clause 11.5.3 is

$$v_r = 1.0(0.7)0.6\sqrt{35}\left[(404)0.00261\left(\sin 38°\right)+1.75\right]+0.9(404)0.00261\left(\cos 38°\right)= 4.59 \text{ MPa}$$
$$> v_f = 4.41 \text{ MPa} \quad \text{OK.}$$

No additional steel required.

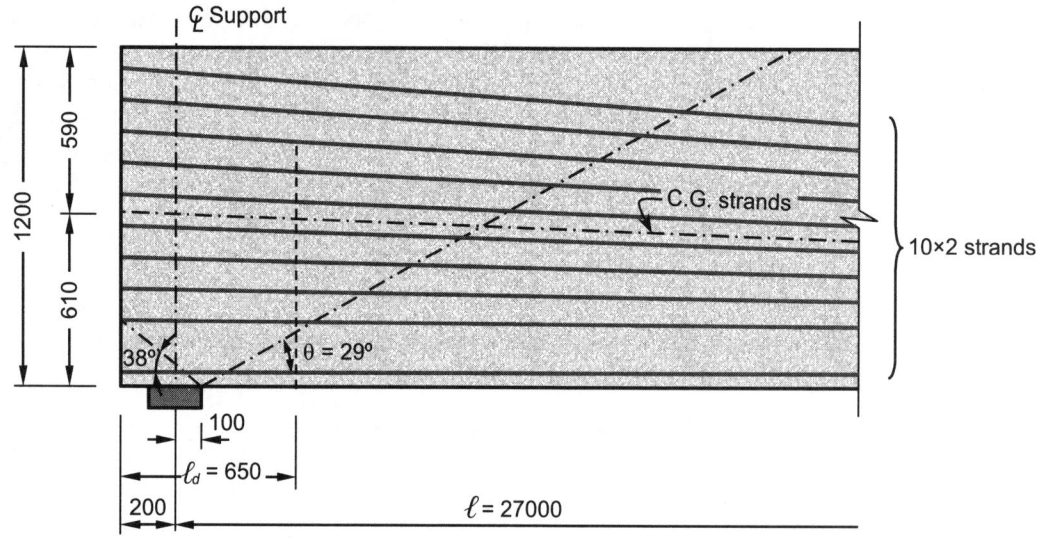

Example   10.9

Design of Fully Prestressed Concrete Slab

1.   Geometry - (See Fig. 10.9.1)

2.   Materials

Concrete Strength:
Slab: f'_c = 30 MPa, f'_{ci} = 25 MPa, α_1 = 0.805, β_1 = 0. 895
Column: f'_c = 40 MPa
Prestressing Steel:
Low-relaxation strand, 15 mm diameter
              f_{pu} = 1860 MPa, f'_{py} = 1670 MPa, A_p = 140 mm^2
Non-prestressed Steel: f_y = 400 MPa

3.   Slab Thickness

h = ℓ/45 = 7500/45 = 167 mm, select 170 mm

4.   Loads

Specified Loads
Dead Load:
170 mm slab (170/1000) 2.4 (9.81)   =   4.00 kN/m^2
Partitions: =   1.30 kN/m^2

	w_D =	5.30 kN/m^2

Live Load: w_L =   2.40 kN/m^2

$w_s = w_D + w_L$ =	7.70 kN/m^2	

w_L < (3/4) w_D - Use full live loads on all spans (Clause 13.8.4.2)

Factored Loads:
w_{Df} = 1.25 (5.30)   =   6.63 kN/m^2
w_{Lf} = 1.50 (2.40   =   3.60 kN/m^2

	w_f =	10.23 kN/m^2

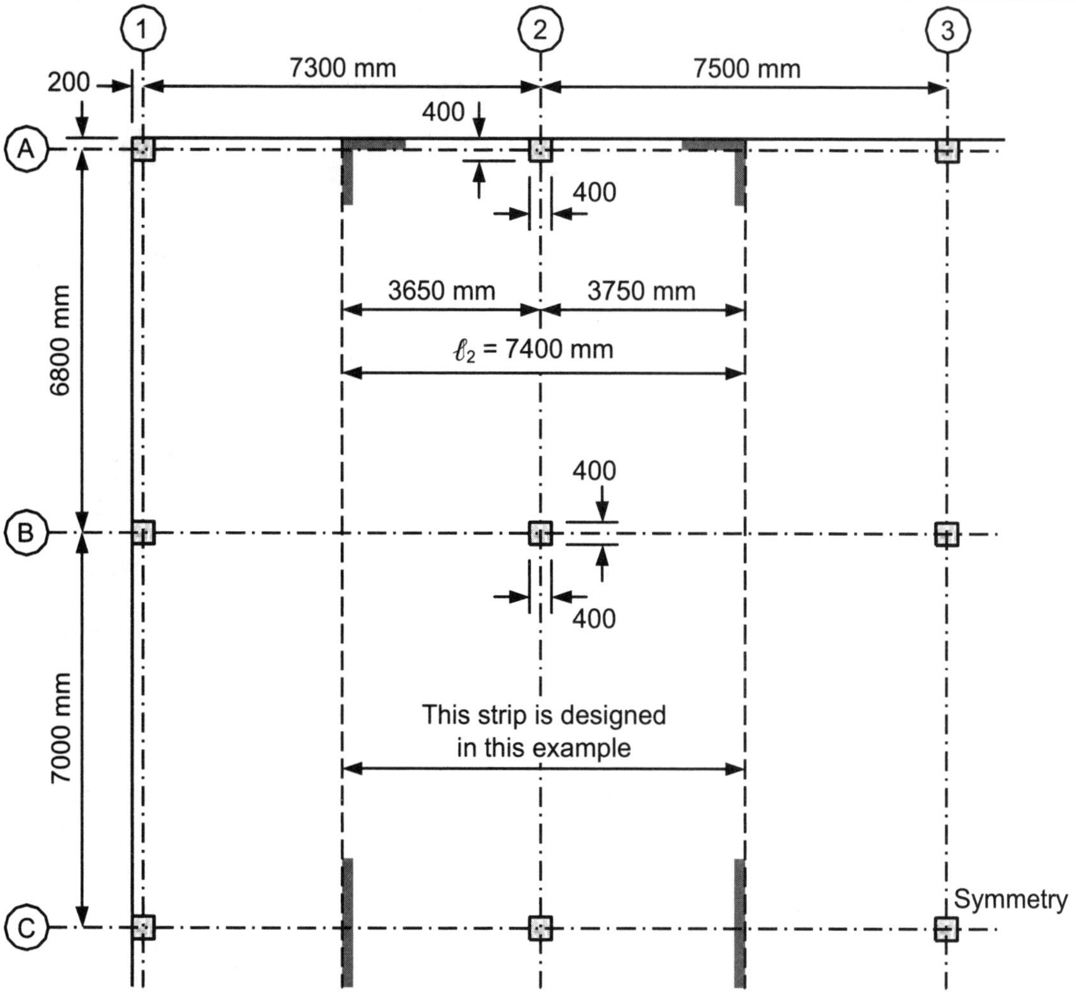

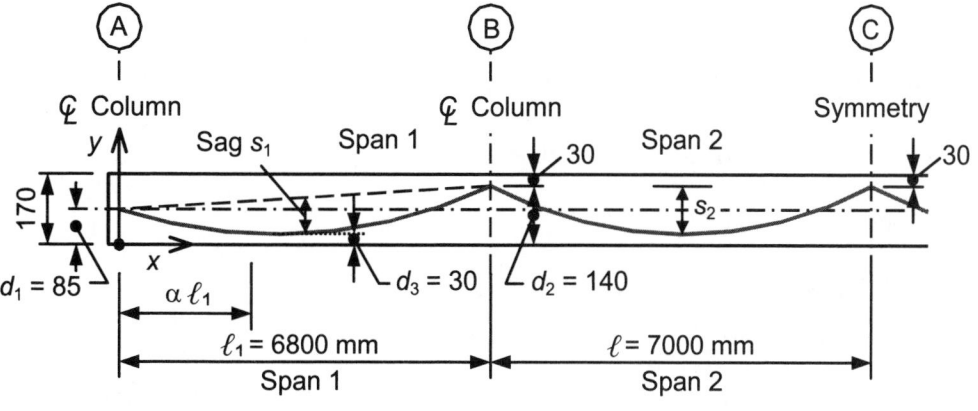

Fig. 10.9.1 – Slab geometry

Fig. 10.9.5 – Tendon profile

5. Cable Profile

Point of maximum eccentricity in span 1 is at $x = \alpha\ell_1$ (see Fig. 10.9.5):

$$\alpha = 1/[1 + (\frac{d_2 - d_3}{d_1 - d_2})^{1/2}] = 1/[1 + (\frac{140 - 30}{85 - 30})^{1/2}] = 0.4142$$

Equation of parabola of span 1 (y from bottom of slab in mm, x in m)

$$y = \frac{d_1 - d_3}{(\alpha\ell_1)^2} x^2 + 2\frac{d_1 - d_3}{\alpha\ell_1} x + d_1$$

$$y = 6.93 \cdot 10^{-6} x^2 - 0.03905x + 85$$

At $x = \ell_1/2 = 3400$ mm: $y = 32$ mm

Sag in span 1:

$$s_1 = 85 - 32 + \frac{1}{2}(85 - 30) = 80\text{mm} = 0.080 \text{ m}$$

An approximate value of s_1 = 82 mm is obtained by assuming that the maximum eccentricity occurs at mid span.

6. Load Balancing

Assume that approximately 80 percent of the dead load is balanced by the effective prestressing force

$W_{bal} = 0.80 \times 5.30 = 4.24$ kN/m^2

Span 1
Required effective prestressing force (per metre)

$$P_e = \frac{W_{bal}\,\ell_1^2}{8s_1} = \frac{4.24 \times 6.80^2}{8 \times 0.080} = 306 \text{ kN}$$

For full width of panel

$P_e = 306(7.40) = 2267$ kN
Assuming the effective prestress to be $0.6\,f_{pu}$, we have per tendon

$$P_e = 0.60 f_{pu} A_p = 0.6(1860)140(10^{-3}) = 156 \text{ kN}$$

Number of tendons required

$N = 2.267/156 = 14.5$. Select 15 tendons providing $15(156) = 2340$ kN.

Actual balanced load in span 1:

$$W_{bal} = \frac{8P_e s_1}{\ell_1^2} = \frac{8 \cdot 2340 \cdot 0.080}{6.80^2} = 32.4 \text{ kN/m}$$

Per metre width

w_{bal} = 32.4 /7.40 = 4.38 kN/m^2

Unbalanced Load

w_{net} = w_s - w_{bal} = 7.70 - 4.38 = 3.32 kN/m^2

Span 2
Utilizing the maximum possible cable sag s_2 = 140 - 30 = 110 mm results in a balanced load (neglecting friction), per metre width

$$w_{bal} = \frac{8P_e s_2}{\ell_1 \ell_2^2} = \frac{8 \cdot 2340 \cdot 0.110}{7.40 \cdot 7.00^2} = 5.68 \text{ kN/m}^2$$

This is too high since it exceeds the dead load. A balanced load w_{bal} = 4.70 kN/m^2 is chosen. The sag corresponding to this balanced load is

$$s_2 = \frac{4.70 \cdot 7.4 \cdot 7.00^2}{8 \cdot 2340} = 0.091 \text{m} \ (91\text{mm})$$

Unbalanced load in span 2

w_{net} = 7.70 - 4.70 = 3.00 kN/m^2

7. Analysis according to Clause 13.8.3 - Prismatic modelling of members

7.1 Section Properties
Slab - Beam:

I_s = (1/12) $\ell_{2a} h_s^3$ = (1/12) 7400 (170)^3 = 3.03 x 10^9 mm^4

Column:

I_c = (1/12) 400 (400)^3 = 2.13 x 10^9 mm^4

Effective moment of inertia of column (Clause 13.8.3.3)

I_{ec} = ψI_c

From Eq. (13-22) for ℓ_2/ℓ_1 > 1.0:

$$\psi = 0.6(\ell_2 / \ell_1 - 0.5) + (1.3 - 0.6 \ell_2 / \ell_1)\alpha_1 \ell_2 / \ell_1$$

For both spans $\alpha_1 \ell / \ell_1$ = 0.

Column A: ℓ_2/ℓ_1 = 7400/6800 = 1.088
ψ = 0.6 (1.088 – 0.5) = 0.353

Column B: ℓ_2/ℓ_1 = 7400/6900 = 1.072;
ψ = 0.6 (1.072-0.5) = 0.343

10

Prestressed Concrete

Column C: $\ell_2/\ell_1 = 7400/7000 = 1.057$
$\psi = 0.6\,(1.057 - 0.5) = 0.334$

Thus: $I_{ec1} = 0.353\,(\,2.13\,)\,10^9 = 0.752\,(10^9)\ \text{mm}^4$
       $I_{ec2} = 0.343\,(\,2.13\,)\,10^9 = 0.731\,(10^9)\ \text{mm}^4$
       $I_{ec3} = 0.334\,(\,2.13\,)\,10^9 = 0.711\,(10^9)\ \text{mm}^4$

7.2 Frame Geometry
The dimensions and the moment of inertia used in the frame analysis are shown in Fig. 10.9.7.2.

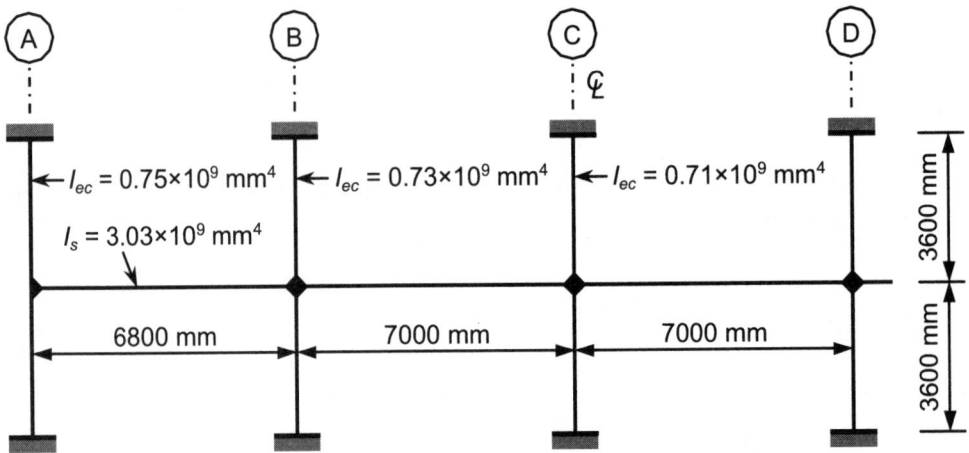

Fig. 10.9.7.2 – Frame geometry

7.3 Results of Frame Analysis
The results for the unbalanced (net) loads are shown in Fig. 10.9.7.3 (1).

7.4 Check of Flexural Stresses

Maximum Stress at Face of Column B
Moment at face of column (calculated for slab width $\ell_2 = 7.4\ m$) due to unbalanced loads is 92.0 kN·m. (See Fig. 10.9.7.3(1)) In the column strip 75 percent of the total moment is resisted (Clause. 18.12.2.1). The moment per metre in the column strip at the face of the column is obtained with a width of the column strip $0.5(7.00 + 6.80)/2 = 3.45$ m:

$$M_B = -\frac{92.0\,(0.75)}{3.45} = -20.0\ \text{kN} \cdot \text{m}$$

Fig. 10.9.7.3 Moment and shear force diagrams

Concrete stress in top fibre

$$f_c = \frac{P_e}{A_c} - \frac{M}{S} = \frac{-2340 \times 10^3}{7400 \times 170} - \frac{(-20.0)10^6}{170^2 \times 1000/6} = -1.86 + 4.16 = 2.30\ \text{MPa}$$

Permissible $f_c = 0.50\sqrt{30} = 2.74\ \text{MPa}$ OK.

Note: The axial stress is calculated as the average stress over the full width of the slab (Clause. 18.12.2.2).

Concrete stress in bottom fibre

$f_c = -1.86 - 4.16 = -6.02$ MPa $< Permissible \ f_c = 0.60 \ f_c' = 18.0$ MPa

(Compression)   OK.

(1) Moments due to specified loads and prestressing (= unbalanced loads)

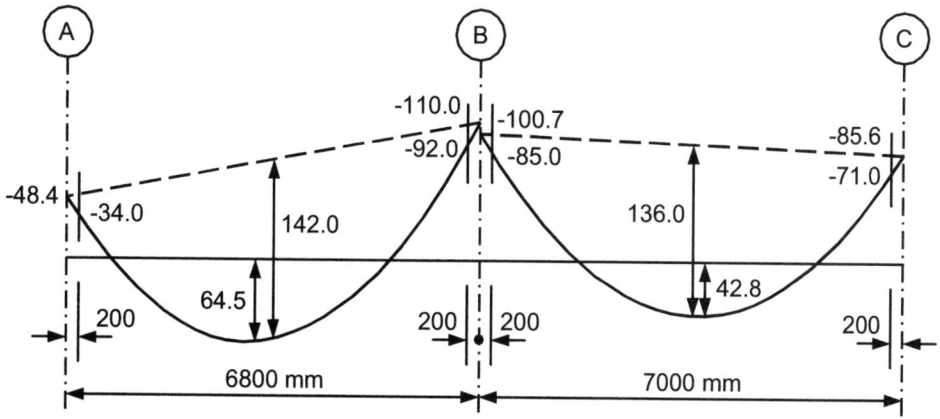

(2) Moments due to factored loads (with and without secondary moments)

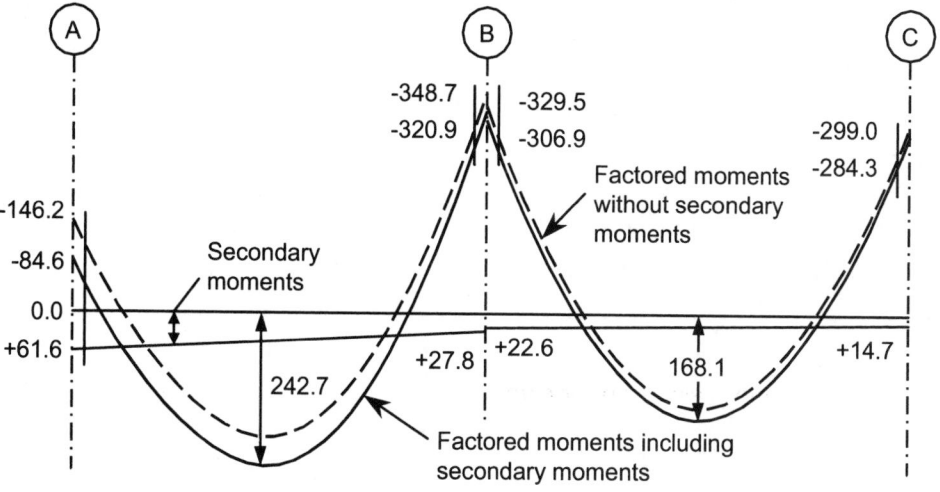

(3) Shear force due to factored loads and secondary moments

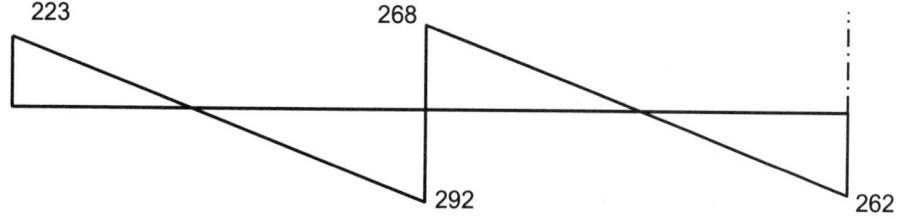

Fig. 10.9.7.3 – Moment and shear force diagrams

Mid Span:

Maximum moment in Span 1 from Fig. 10.9.7.3(1). The positive moment in the column strip is equal to 60% of the total positive moment. Moment per metre (width 3.45 m)

$$M_1 = \frac{64.5 \cdot 0.60}{3.45} = 11.2 \text{ kN} \cdot \text{m/m}$$

Bottom fibre stress

$$f_c = -1.86 + \frac{11.2 \cdot 10^6}{170^2 \cdot 1000/6} = -1.86 + 2.33 = 0.47 \text{ MPa}$$

< permissible $f_c = 0.50\sqrt{30} = 2.74$ MPa

Non-prestressed steel not required because $f_c \leq 0.2\sqrt{f_c'} = 1.09$ MPa , (Table 18-1).

8. Factored Flexural Resistance

The factored flexural resistance, M_f, must be at least equal to the bending moment due to factored load, plus the secondary moment due to prestressing:

$$M_f = \alpha_D M_D + \alpha_L M_L + \alpha_p M_p''$$

According to CSA Standard A 23.3 Clause 18.10 $\alpha_p = 1.0$ and Annex C, Table C1: $\alpha_D = 1.25$, $\alpha_L = 1.50$.

8.1 Factored Moments

The factored moments due to $w_f = 10.23$ kN/m² = 75.7 kN/m are plotted in Fig. 10.9.7.3(2), together with the secondary moments, M_p'', and the moments at the column faces, and in the spans. These moments are summarized in the following table:

Support		A	B_{left}	B_{right}	C
$\alpha_D M_D + \alpha_L M_L$	kN·m	- 146.2	- 348.7	- 329.5	- 299.0
$\alpha_p M_p''$ [1]	kN·m	+ 61.6	+ 27.8	+ 22.6	+ 14.7
M_f	kN·m	- 84.6	- 320.9	- 306.9	- 284.3
V_f	kN	222.6	292.2	268.2	261.7
M_f at column face [2]	kN·m	40.7 [1]	- 268.0	- 259.0	- 238.0
M_f - span	kN·m	242.0		164.0	

[1] The secondary moments are obtained from $M_p'' = M_{unbal} - M_s - M_p'$ where $M_p' = P_e \, e$.

[2] At column face $M_f = -84.6 + 222.6 \times 0.20 - \frac{1}{2}(0.2)^2 \, 75.7 = -41.6$ kN·m

8.2 Factored Flexural Resistance

8.2.1 At interior columns

According to Clause 18.8.1 (Table 18-1):

$$\min A_s = 0.0006 h_s / \ell_n = 0.0006 \cdot 170 \cdot 6600 = 673 \text{ mm}^2$$

Provide 7- 10M bars = 700 mm^2. These bars shall be placed within a zone $c_2 + 3h = 400 + 3 \times 170 = 910$ mm at the column (Clause. 18.12.5.2).

Stress in unbonded tendon at flexural failure (Eq. 18-2)

$$f_{pr} = f_{pe} + \frac{8000}{\ell_o} \sum_n (d_p - c_y) \le f_{py}$$

Total length of tendon between anchors: $\ell_o = 2\,(200 + 6800 + 7000) = 28\,000$ mm.
Three hinges are necessary to form a mechanism in this frame. In negative moment zones: $d_p = 140$ mm, $A_p = 15\,(140) = 2100$ mm^2, $f_{py} = 1670$ MPa, $f_y = 400$ MPa

$$c_y = \frac{0.9(2100)1670 + 0.85(700)400}{0.805(0.895)0.65(30)7400} = 33 \text{mm}$$

In positive moment zone no non-prestressed reinforcement is provided, thus:

$$c_y = \frac{0.9(2100)1670}{0.805(0.895)0.65(30)7400} = 30 \text{ mm}$$

$$f_{pr} = 0.6(1860) + \frac{8000}{28000}\left[(85 - 33) + (140 - 33) + (140 - 30)\right] = 1193 \text{MPa} < 1670 \text{ MPa}$$

$$a = \frac{\phi_p A_p f_{pr} + \phi_s A_s f_y}{\alpha_1 \phi_c f_c' \ell_2} = \frac{0.9(2100)1193 + 0.85(700)400}{0.805(0.65)30(7400)} = 22 \text{ mm}$$

$$M_f = 0.9 \cdot 2100 \cdot 1193\,(140 - 11) + 0.85 \cdot 700 \cdot 400\,(140 - 11) = 322 \cdot 10^6 \text{ Nmm}$$
$$= 322 \text{kN} \cdot \text{m} > 268 \text{ kN} \cdot \text{m}$$

9. Shear Design

9.1 At Exterior Column

9.1.1 Shear Force

Shear due to factored loads on slab and M_p'':		= 222.6 kN
Facade: Brick + glass, 2.4 kN/m:	1.25 (2.4) 7.4	= 22.2 kN
	Total Shear: V_f	= 244.8 kN

The beneficial effect of prestressing on shear resistance can not be considered (Clause. 18.12.3.3). At exterior columns a portion of the unbalanced moment is transferred to the column by eccentricity of shear.

10

Prestressed Concrete

9.1.2 Section Properties of Critical Section

With d = 130 mm, $d/2$ = 65 mm (see sketch)

$A_1 = d(2b_1 + b_2) = 130 \, (\, 2 \times 465 + 530) = 190 \times 10^3 \ mm^2$

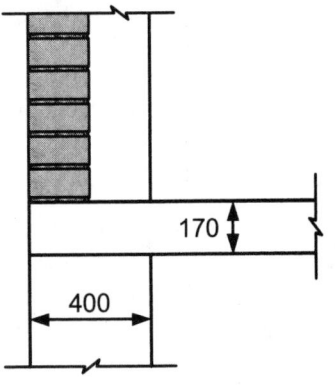

$$e_1 = \frac{b_1^2}{2b_1 + b_2} = \frac{465^2}{2 \cdot 465 + 530} = 148 \ mm$$

$e_3 = (b_1 / 2) - e_1 = 530/2 - 148 = 117 \ mm$

$$J = \frac{1}{6}(b_1 d^3 + b_1^3 d) + b_2 d e_1^2 + 2db_1(\frac{1}{2}b_1 + e_1)^2$$

$$= \frac{1}{6}(465 \cdot 130^3 + 465^3 \cdot 130) + 530 \cdot 130 \cdot 148^2 +$$

$$2 \cdot 130 \cdot 465(\frac{1}{2}465 + 148)^2 = 4.72 \cdot 10^9 \ mm^4$$

9.1.3 Moment Transfer by Eccentricity of Shear

The moment to be transferred from the slab to the column, M_f, is the unbalanced moment due to factored load to be taken at the centroid of the critical section, i.e., the moment obtained at the column axis, minus the shear times the eccentricity e_3.

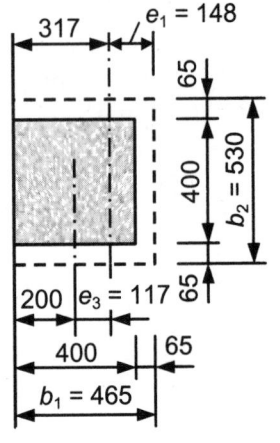

M_f = - 84.6 + 222.6 x 0.117 = - 58.6 kN·m

Fig. 10.9.9.1.2

$$\gamma_v = 1 - \frac{1}{1 + \frac{2}{3}\left(\frac{b_1}{b_2}\right)^{1/2}} = 1 - \frac{1}{1 + \frac{2}{3}\left(\frac{465}{530}\right)^{1/2}} = 0.384 \text{ , (Clause. 13.3.5.3)}$$

Maximum shear stress under factored loads:

$$v_f = \frac{V_f}{A} + \frac{\gamma_v M_f e_1}{J} = \frac{244.8 \cdot 10^3}{190 \cdot 10^3} + \frac{0.384 \cdot 58.7 \cdot 10^6 \cdot 148}{4.72 \cdot 10^9} = 1.29 + 0.70 = 1.99 \ MPa$$

The shear stress resistance of concrete (Clause 13.3.4) is controlled by Eq.13–7.

$$v_r = v_c = 0.38\lambda\phi_c\sqrt{f_c'} = 0.38 \cdot 1.0 \cdot 0.65\sqrt{30} = 1.35 \ MPa < 1.99 \ MPa$$

Shear reinforcement is required.

9.1.4 Design of Shear Reinforcement
The shear stress v_f =1.99 MPa is at the upper limit of the allowable value for stirrups $v_c = 0.55\lambda\phi_c\sqrt{f_c'} = 1.99 \, MPa$ (c.f. Clause 13.3.9.2), but less than the maximum allowable value for headed shear reinforcement $v_c = 0.75\lambda\phi_c\sqrt{f_c'} = 2.63 \, MPa$ (Clause 13.3.8.2). However normal stirrups are not allowed for this slab since $h < 300$ mm (Clause 13.3.9.1).

Headed Shear Reinforcement

Using shear reinforcement (f_{vy} = 400 MPa), which is mechanically anchored at top and bottom (Clause. 13.3.8) the shear stress resistance of concrete

$$v_c = 0.28\lambda\,\phi_c\sqrt{f_c'} = 0.28 \cdot 1.0 \cdot 0.65\sqrt{30} = 1.00 \text{ MPa}.$$

Using two rows of headed bars along the strip of width b_2 = 530 mm, the area of shear reinforcement per unit length of each row is:

$$\frac{A_v}{s} = \frac{(v_f - v_c)b_2/2}{\phi_s f_{yv}} = \frac{(1.99 - 1.00)\,530/2}{0.85 \cdot 400} = 0.78\,\frac{\text{mm}^2}{\text{mm}}$$

Selecting 9.5 mm diameter headed stirrups (A_v = 71 mm^2) requires

$$s \le \frac{71}{078} = 91 \text{ mm}$$

According to Clause 13.3.8.6, max $s = 0.75d = 0.75\,(130) = 98$ mm for a shear stress $v_f \le 0.56\lambda\,\phi_c\sqrt{f_c'} = 2.00$ MPa. Select $s = 90$ mm. The first stirrup is to be located at 0.4d = 52 mm, say 50 mm, from column face.

The selected bars with area A_v = 71 mm^2 must have an anchor plate area of at least 10 x 71 = 710 mm^2, corresponding to a head diameter of 30 mm.

The headed shear reinforcement has to extend to a zone where $v_f = v_c = 0.19\,\lambda\,\phi_c\sqrt{f_c'} = 0.68$ MPa The arrangement of the headed shear reinforcement is shown on Fig. 10.9.9.1.4.
At distance 565 mm from the faces of the column (see Fig. 10.9.9.1.4)

$$A = (3 \cdot 400 + 2 \cdot 565\sqrt{2})130 = 364 \cdot 10^3 \text{mm}^2$$

$$e_1 = \frac{2 \cdot 400(565 + 400/2) + 2\sqrt{2} \cdot 565\,(565/2)}{3 \cdot 400 + 2 \cdot 565\sqrt{2}} = 380 \text{ mm}$$

$$e_3 = 965 - 380 - 400/2 = 385 \text{ mm}$$

$$J = d\sum\frac{\ell_i}{3}(y_i^2 + y_i y_j + y_j^2)$$

where y_i and y_j are the coordinates of the end points of the strait segments of length ℓ_i along the critical section with respect to its centroidal axis.

$$J = \frac{130}{3}\left\{\begin{array}{l}400\left[(-585)^2 + (-585)(-185) + (-185)^2\right]2 + \\ 799\left[(-185)^2 + (-185)380 + 380^2\right]2 + 400(3)380^2\end{array}\right\} = 31.8\left(10^9\right)\text{mm}^4$$

Factored moment at e_3 = 0.385 m from center line of column

$$M_f = -84.6 + 222.6 \cdot 0.385 - 10.23 \cdot 7.40\,(0.385)^2/2 = -4.5 \text{ kN} \cdot \text{m}$$

10

Prestressed Concrete

$$V_f = 244.8 - (1.530 \cdot 0.965 - 0.565^2)10.23 = 233 \text{ kN}$$

For the critical section outside the shear reinforced zone $b_1 = 965$ mm, $b_2 = 1530$ mm, thus

$$\gamma_v = \cfrac{1}{1 + \cfrac{2}{3}\left(\cfrac{965}{1530}\right)^{1/2}} 0.346$$

$$V_f = \frac{233 \cdot 10^3}{364 \cdot 10^3} + \frac{0.346 \cdot 4.5 \cdot 10^6}{31.8 \cdot 10^9}(380) = 0.64 + 0.02 = 0.66\text{MPa} < v_c = 0.68 \text{ MPa} \quad \text{O.K.}$$

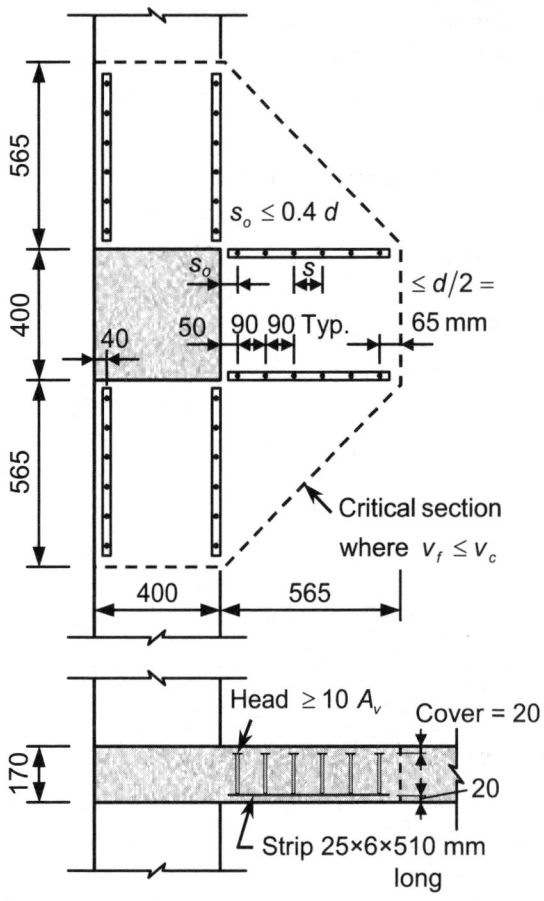

Fig. 10.9.9.1.4 – Arrangement of headed reinforcement

9.2 At Interior Column B
Shear force (see table in Section 8.1)

$$V_f = 292.2 + 268.2 - 10.23\,(0.53^2) = 557 \text{ kN}$$

Unbalanced moment

$$M_f = 348.7 - 329.5 = 19.2 \text{ kN·m}$$

Properties of the critical section (see sketch)

$$A = 4(130)530 = 275\left(10^3\right) \text{mm}^2$$

$$J = \frac{1}{6}\left[530\left(130^3\right) + 130\left(530^3\right)\right] + \frac{1}{2}130\left(530^3\right) = 13.10\left(10^9\right)\text{mm}^4$$

$$\gamma_v = 1 - \frac{1}{1 + \frac{2}{3}\left(\frac{530}{530}\right)^{0.5}} = 0.40$$

$$v_f = \frac{557\left(10^3\right)}{275\left(10^3\right)} + \frac{0.40\,(19.2)10^6\,(530/2)}{13.10\left(10^9\right)} = 2.02 + 0.15 = 2.17 \text{ MPa}$$

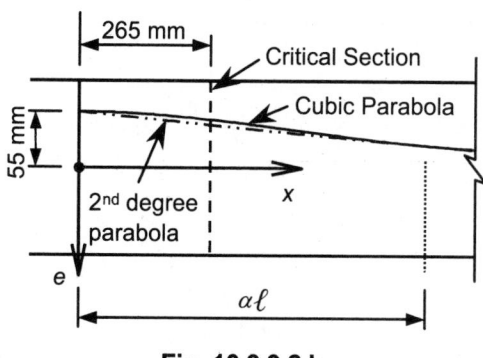

Critical Section

$b_1 = 530$

$b_2 = 530$

Fig. 10.9.9.2

Assuming that 2 tendons cross the critical section in one direction and 4 (bundled) tendons in the other direction, the vertical component of the prestressing force is:

$$V_p = 2(2+4)\,P_e\,\sin\beta$$

where P_e = effective prestressing force per strand and β = slope of strand at the critical section. It is assumed that the cable profile over the columns is a cubic parabola over length $\alpha\ell$.

Equation of the cubic parabola for $0 \leq x \leq \alpha\ell$

$$e(x) = -\frac{s}{\alpha^2\ell^3}(4-\delta)x^3 - \frac{2}{\alpha\ell^2}[4\alpha - 2(4-\delta)]x^2 + e_A$$

where

s = sag

$$\delta = \frac{e_A - e_B}{s}$$

The other symbols are defined in the sketch.

265 mm

Critical Section

55 mm

Cubic Parabola

2nd degree parabola

x

e

$\alpha\ell$

Fig. 10.9.9.2.b

Considering Span 2, $e_A = e_B = -55$ mm, $s = 91$ mm, $\delta = 0$, and assuming $\alpha\ell = 700$ mm, i.e., $\alpha = 0.1$;

$$e(x) = -\frac{91}{0.1^2 \cdot 7000^3}(4-0)x^3 - \frac{91}{0.1 \cdot 7000^2}[4 \cdot 0.1 - 2(4-0)]x^2 - 55$$

$$= -0.106 \cdot 10^{-6}x^3 + 141 \cdot 10^{-6}x^2 - 55$$

Slope $\beta = de(x)/dx$:

$$\beta(x) = -0.318\left(10^{-6}\right)x^2 + 282\left(10^{-6}\right)x$$

10

Prestressed Concrete

At critical section ($x = 265$ mm) $\beta = 0.0524$

Assuming the same slope to apply for all cables we find with $P_e = 156$ kN per strand:

$V_p = 2(2+4)\ 156 \times 0.0524 = 98$ kN

Shear resisted by concrete (CSA Standard A23.3 Eq.18-5): With $f_{cp} = 1.86$ MPa

$$v_c = 0.33 \cdot 1.0 \cdot 0.65\sqrt{30}\left[1 + \frac{0.9 \cdot 1.86}{0.33 \cdot 1.0 \cdot 0.65\sqrt{30}}\right]^{0.5} + 0.9\frac{98 \cdot 10^3}{275 \cdot 10^3} = 2.15 \text{ MPa}$$

$\approx v_f = 2.17$ MPa   O.K.

The limitations for applications of Eq. 18-5 are satisfied (Clause 18.12.3.3).

10. Structural Integrity
CSA Standard A 23.3, Eq. (13-26) has to be satisfied (Clause 13.10.6)

$$\sum A_{sb} = \frac{2V_{se}}{f_y} = \frac{2(2)4.00\left(10^{-3}\right)7400\,(6900)}{0.9\,(1860)} = 488\,\text{mm}^2 < 8\,(140) = 1120\ \text{mm}^2$$

(2 strands in each direction).

11. Cable Layout
The cable layout is shown in Fig. 10.9.11.

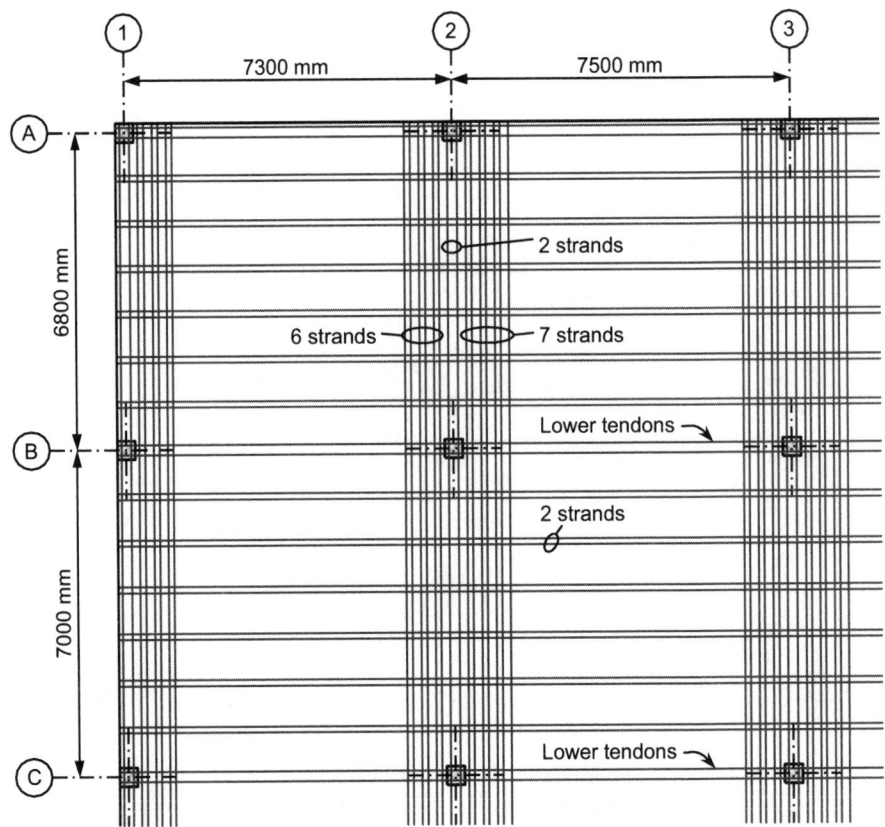

Strand layout: the strands are banded in one direction and in the other direction
they are placed in pairs at equal spacing.

Fig. 10.9.11 – Cable layout

Example 10.10

Design of Partially Prestressed Concrete Slab

Example 10.9 is redesigned as a partially prestressed slab

1. Load Balancing

Assuming that about 60% of the dead load is balanced by prestressing

$w_{bal} = 0.6 \times 5.30 = 3.18 \text{ kN/m}^2$

Span 1:

$P_e = \dfrac{3.18 \times 6.80^2}{8 \times 0.080} = 230 \text{ kN/m}$

For full width of panel

$P_e = 230 \times 7.40 = 1702 \text{ kN}$

Number of tendons $N = 702/156 = 10.9$. Select 11 tendons. Load balanced by 11 tendons with $P_e = 11(156) = 1716 \text{ kN}$:

$w_{bal} = 8 \times 1716 \times 0.080 / (6.80^2) = 23.7 \text{ kN/m}$

Per m width: $w_{bal} = 23.7 / 7.40 = 3.20 \text{ kN/m}^2$
Net Load: $w_{net} = 7.70 - 3.20 = 4.50 \text{ kN/m}^2$

Span 2:
Making use of maximum possible sag $s = 170 - 2\,(30) = 110 \text{ mm}$.

$w_{bal} = 8 \times 1716 / (7.00)^2 = 30.8 \text{ kN/m}$

Per m width: $w_{bal} = 30.8 / 7.40 = 4.16 \text{ kN/m}^2$
Net Load: $w_{net} = 7.70 - 4.16 = 3.54 \text{ kN/m}^2$

2. Moments and Stresses

From frame analysis (see Fig. 10.9.7.2)

$M_{AB} = -66.3 \text{ kN·m}$
$M_{BA} = -144.4 \text{ kN·m}$
$M_{BD} = -126.2 \text{ kN·m}$
$M_{DB} = -97.3 \text{ kN·m}$
$M_1 = 89.1 \text{ kN·m}$
$M_2 = 49.0 \text{ kN·m}$

Moment at face of column B:

$M_{BA} = -120.2 \text{ kN·m}$

10

Prestressed Concrete

Column Strip:

Negative moment per metre width (Clause 18.12.2.1)

$$M = \frac{-120.2 \times 0.75}{3.45} = -26.1 \text{ kNm}$$

$$f_c = \frac{(-1716)10^3}{170\,(7400)} + \frac{26.1\,(10^6)}{170^2\,(1000)/6} = -1.36 + 5.42 = +4.06 \text{ MPa} > 0.5\sqrt{f_c'} = 2.73 \text{ MPa}$$

Slab will crack in the vicinity of the column under full service load.
The average compressive stress criterion of Clause 18.12.2.3 is satisfied, i.e.

$f_{cp} = 1.36$ MPa > 0.8 MPa

Minimum non-prestressed steel required (Table 18-1)

$A_s = 0.00075 \times 170 \times 6600 = 842$ mm^2

It is anticipated that more non-prestressed steel will be required to provide the necessary factored flexural resistance (see 10.4).
Positive moment per meter width of column strip

$M = 89.4 \times 0.6 / 3.45 = 15.5$ kN·m/m

Stress in bottom fibre:

$$f_c = -1.36 + \frac{15.5 \times 10^6}{170^2 \times 1000/6} = -1.36 + 3.22 = 1.86 \text{ MPa} < 2.73 \text{ MPa} > 0.2\sqrt{f_c'} = 1.10 \text{ MPa}$$

Slab will not crack in positive moments zone of the column strip.
For steel provided see strength requirements

Middle Strip:
Moment per metre width in middle strip at face of column

$$M = \frac{-120.2\,(0.25)}{7.40 - 3.45} = -7.60 \text{ kNm/m}$$

Top fibre stress

$$f_c = -1.36 - \frac{-7.60\,(10^6)}{170^2\,(1000)/6} = 0.22 \text{ MPa} < 2.73 \text{ MPa.   O.K.}$$

Positive moment per metre width of middle strip

$M = 89.1(\,0.40) / 3.95 = 9.02$ kN·m/m

Bottom fibre stress

$$f_c = -1.36 + \frac{9.02 \times 10^6}{170^2 \times 1000/6} = 0.52 \text{ MPa} < 1.10 \text{ MPa.   O.K.}$$

No additional steel required.

3. Moments due to Factored Loads

The moments due to the factored load $w_f = 10.23$ kN/m^2 are the same as for example 10.9 but the secondary moments, M_p'' are different. The values are listed below:

Support		A	B_{left}	B_{right}	C
$\alpha_D M_D + \alpha_L M_L$	kN·m	- 144.8	- 349.1	- 329.8	- 298.7
$\alpha_p M_p''$	kN·m	+ 42.1	+ 24.0	+ 27.6	+ 33.2
M_f	kN·m	- 101.7	- 325.1	- 302.2	- 265.5
V_f	kN	224.6	290.2	262.6	252.1
M_f at column face	kN·m	- 58.6	- 268.6	- 251.2	- 216.6
M_f - span	kN·m	231.0		153.3	

4. Factored Flexural Resistance

4.1 At Edge Column

Factored moments at face of column $M_f = -58.6$ kN·m

Assuming 4 tendons to be anchored within a width $b_b = (c_2 + 3h_s) = 910$ mm (Clause 13.10.2)

$A_p = 4 \times 140 = 560$ mm^2

$f_{pr} = 1193$ MPa - see Example 10.9.

Non-prestressed steel: Table 18-1.

$A_s = 0.00075 \times 170 (6800 - 400) = 816$ mm^2

Provide: 3 - 15M + 4 - 10M bars with $A_s = 1000$ mm^2

$$a = \frac{0.9(1193)560 + 0.85(400)1000}{0.805(0.65)30(910)} = 66 \text{ mm}$$

$M_r = 0.9 (1193) 560(85-66/2) + 0.85(1000)400(140-66/2) = 67.6 \times 10^6$ Nmm

     $= 67.6$ kN·m > 58.6 kN·m   OK.

Note: The 3.- 15M bars are bent into column.

4.2 At Interior Column

Factored moment at face of column: $M_f = -268.6$ kN·m

Factored moment resistance provided by 11-15mm strands $(A_p = 1540$ mm$^2)$ assuming $f_{pr} = 1200$ MPa:

$$M_{pr} = 0.9(1200)1540(140 - 10) = 216(10^6) \text{ Nmm} = 216 \text{ kN} \cdot \text{m}$$

Estimate of the non-prestressed steel required:

$$A_s = \frac{M_f - M_{pr}}{\phi_s f_y (d - a/2)} = \frac{(268.6 - 216.0)10^6}{0.85(400)(140 - 10)} = 1190 \text{ mm}^2$$

Provide 12 - 10M bars with A_s = 1200 mm^2.
Check:
In negative moment region:

$$c_y = \frac{0.9(1670)1540 + 0.85(400)1200}{0.805(0.895)0.65(30)7400} = 26 \text{ mm}$$

In positive moment region:

$$c_y = \frac{0.9(1670)1540}{0.805(0.895)0.65(30)7400} = 22 \text{ mm}$$

$$f_{pr} = 0.6(1860) + \frac{8000}{28000}\left[(85-26)+(140-22)+(140-26)\right] = 1200 \text{ MPa}$$

$$a = \frac{0.9(1200)1540 + 0.85(400)1200}{0.805(0.65)30(7400)} = 18 \text{ mm}$$

$$M_r = \left[0.9(1200)1540(140 - 18/2) + 0.85(400)1200(140 - 18/2)\right]10^{-6}$$
$$= 271.3 \text{ kNm} > 268.6 \text{ kNm} \quad \text{O.K.}$$

Provide 12 - 10M bars @ 300 mm in column strip.

4.3 Span 1
Positive moment due to factored loads for full width of panel M_f = 231 kN·m. Factored moment resistance provided by tendons M_{pr} = 217.9 kN·m. Non-prestressed steel required for strength:

$$A_s = \frac{(230.0 - 217.9)10^6}{(0.85)400(140 - 9)} = 300 \text{ mm}^2$$

Provide 4 – 10M bars in column strip.

5. Crack Control
According to Eq. 10.8.10 with 10M bars @ 300 mm at face of column B and a prestressing force P_e =1716 / 7.40 = 232 kN/m:

$$f_s = \frac{M_{net} - P_e(h/6+e)}{A_s d} = \frac{26.1(10^3)(170/6 + 55)}{(100/0.30)140} = 145 \text{ MPa}$$

$z = f_s (d_c A)^{1/3}$ = 145 [(30) 2 (30) 300]$^{1/3}$ = 11800 N/mm
= 11.8 kN/mm < 20 kN/mm . OK.(Clause. 18.8.3).

Table 10.1a Flexural Resistance Coefficients, k_u, for Rectangular Elements with Bonded Prestressing Steel Only

(Assuming $\phi_c = 0.65$ and $\phi_p = 0.90$)

	$k_p = 0.28$						$k_p = 0.38$						$k_p = 0.48$					
f'_c	30	40	50	60	70	80	30	40	50	60	70	80	30	40	50	60	70	80
α_1	0.805	0.790	0.775	0.760	0.745	0.730	0.805	0.790	0.775	0.760	0.745	0.730	0.805	0.790	0.775	0.760	0.745	0.730
β_1	0.895	0.870	0.845	0.820	0.795	0.770	0.895	0.870	0.845	0.820	0.795	0.770	0.895	0.870	0.845	0.820	0.795	0.770
w_{pu}	k_u						k_u						k_u					
0.005	0.0045	0.0045	0.0045	0.0045	0.0045	0.0045	0.0045	0.0045	0.0045	0.0045	0.0045	0.0045	0.0045	0.0045	0.0045	0.0045	0.0045	0.0045
0.010	0.0089	0.0089	0.0089	0.0089	0.0089	0.0089	0.0089	0.0089	0.0088	0.0088	0.0088	0.0088	0.0088	0.0088	0.0088	0.0088	0.0088	0.0088
0.015	0.0132	0.0132	0.0132	0.0132	0.0132	0.0132	0.0132	0.0132	0.0132	0.0132	0.0131	0.0131	0.0131	0.0131	0.0131	0.0131	0.0131	0.0131
0.020	0.0175	0.0175	0.0175	0.0175	0.0174	0.0174	0.0174	0.0174	0.0174	0.0174	0.0174	0.0173	0.0174	0.0174	0.0173	0.0173	0.0173	0.0173
0.025	0.0217	0.0217	0.0217	0.0217	0.0216	0.0216	0.0216	0.0216	0.0216	0.0215	0.0215	0.0215	0.0215	0.0215	0.0215	0.0214	0.0214	0.0214
0.030	0.0259	0.0259	0.0258	0.0258	0.0258	0.0257	0.0258	0.0257	0.0257	0.0256	0.0256	0.0255	0.0256	0.0256	0.0255	0.0255	0.0254	0.0254
0.035	0.0300	0.0300	0.0299	0.0299	0.0298	0.0298	0.0298	0.0298	0.0297	0.0296	0.0296	0.0295	0.0296	0.0296	0.0295	0.0294	0.0294	0.0293
0.040	0.0341	0.0340	0.0339	0.0339	0.0338	0.0337	0.0338	0.0337	0.0337	0.0336	0.0335	0.0334	0.0336	0.0335	0.0334	0.0333	0.0332	0.0331
0.045	0.0380	0.0380	0.0379	0.0378	0.0377	0.0377	0.0377	0.0377	0.0376	0.0375	0.0374	0.0373	0.0374	0.0373	0.0372	0.0371	0.0370	0.0369
0.050	0.0420	0.0419	0.0418	0.0417	0.0416	0.0415	0.0416	0.0415	0.0414	0.0413	0.0412	0.0410	0.0412	0.0411	0.0410	0.0409	0.0407	0.0406
0.055	0.0459	0.0458	0.0457	0.0455	0.0454	0.0453	0.0454	0.0453	0.0452	0.0450	0.0449	0.0447	0.0450	0.0448	0.0447	0.0445	0.0444	0.0442
0.060	0.0497	0.0496	0.0494	0.0493	0.0492	0.0490	0.0492	0.0490	0.0489	0.0487	0.0486	0.0484	0.0487	0.0485	0.0483	0.0481	0.0480	0.0477
0.065	0.0535	0.0533	0.0532	0.0530	0.0529	0.0527	0.0529	0.0527	0.0525	0.0523	0.0521	0.0519	0.0523	0.0521	0.0519	0.0517	0.0515	0.0512
0.070	0.0572	0.0570	0.0569	0.0567	0.0565	0.0563	0.0565	0.0563	0.0561	0.0559	0.0557	0.0554	0.0558	0.0556	0.0554	0.0551	0.0549	0.0546
0.075	0.0609	0.0607	0.0605	0.0603	0.0601	0.0598	0.0601	0.0599	0.0596	0.0594	0.0591	0.0589	0.0593	0.0591	0.0588	0.0585	0.0583	0.0580
0.080	0.0645	0.0643	0.0641	0.0638	0.0636	0.0633	0.0636	0.0634	0.0631	0.0628	0.0626	0.0623	0.0628	0.0625	0.0622	0.0619	0.0616	0.0612
0.085	0.0680	0.0678	0.0676	0.0673	0.0670	0.0668	0.0671	0.0668	0.0665	0.0662	0.0659	0.0656	0.0661	0.0658	0.0655	0.0652	0.0648	0.0644
0.090	0.0716	0.0713	0.0710	0.0708	0.0705	0.0701	0.0705	0.0702	0.0699	0.0695	0.0692	0.0688	0.0694	0.0691	0.0688	0.0684	0.0680	0.0676
0.095	0.0750	0.0747	0.0744	0.0741	0.0738	0.0735	0.0738	0.0735	0.0732	0.0728	0.0724	0.0720	0.0727	0.0723	0.0719	0.0715	0.0711	0.0706
0.100	0.0784	0.0781	0.0778	0.0775	0.0771	0.0767	0.0772	0.0768	0.0764	0.0760	0.0756	0.0752	0.0759	0.0755	0.0751	0.0746	0.0742	0.0737
0.105	0.0818	0.0815	0.0811	0.0807	0.0803	0.0799	0.0804	0.0800	0.0796	0.0792	0.0787	0.0782	0.0791	0.0786	0.0782	0.0777	0.0772	0.0766
0.110	0.0851	0.0848	0.0844	0.0840	0.0835	0.0831	0.0836	0.0832	0.0827	0.0823	0.0818	0.0813	0.0822	0.0817	0.0812	0.0807	0.0801	0.0795
0.115	0.0884	0.0880	0.0876	0.0871	0.0867	0.0862	0.0868	0.0863	0.0858	0.0853	0.0848	0.0842	0.0852	0.0847	0.0842	0.0836	0.0830	0.0824
0.120	0.0916	0.0912	0.0907	0.0903	0.0898	0.0893	0.0899	0.0894	0.0889	0.0883	0.0878	0.0872	0.0882	0.0877	0.0871	0.0865	0.0858	0.0852
0.125	0.0948	0.0943	0.0939	0.0934	0.0928	0.0923	0.0929	0.0924	0.0919	0.0913	0.0907	0.0900	0.0911	0.0906	0.0899	0.0893	0.0886	0.0879
0.130	0.0979	0.0974	0.0969	0.0964	0.0958	0.0952	0.0959	0.0954	0.0948	0.0942	0.0935	0.0928	0.0940	0.0934	0.0928	0.0921	0.0913	0.0906
0.135	0.1010	0.1005	0.0999	0.0994	0.0988	0.0981	0.0989	0.0983	0.0977	0.0970	0.0963	0.0956	0.0969	0.0962	0.0955	0.0948	0.0940	0.0932
0.140	0.1041	0.1035	0.1029	0.1023	0.1017	0.1010	0.1018	0.1012	0.1005	0.0998	0.0991	0.0983	0.0997	0.0990	0.0982	0.0975	0.0966	0.0958
0.145	0.1071	0.1065	0.1058	0.1052	0.1045	0.1038	0.1047	0.1040	0.1033	0.1026	0.1018	0.1010	0.1024	0.1017	0.1009	0.1001	0.0992	0.0983
0.150	0.1100	0.1094	0.1087	0.1080	0.1073	0.1066	0.1075	0.1068	0.1061	0.1053	0.1045	0.1036	0.1052	0.1044	0.1035	0.1027	0.1018	0.1008
0.155	0.1129	0.1123	0.1116	0.1108	0.1101	0.1093	0.1103	0.1096	0.1088	0.1080	0.1071	0.1062	0.1078	0.1070	0.1061	0.1052	0.1043	0.1032
0.160	0.1158	0.1151	0.1144	0.1136	0.1128	0.1120	0.1130	0.1123	0.1114	0.1106	0.1097	0.1087	0.1104	0.1096	0.1087	0.1077	0.1067	0.1056
0.165	0.1186	0.1179	0.1171	0.1163	0.1155	0.1146	0.1157	0.1149	0.1141	0.1131	0.1122	0.1112	0.1130	0.1121	0.1111	0.1101	0.1091	0.1080
0.170	0.1214	0.1206	0.1198	0.1190	0.1181	0.1172	0.1184	0.1175	0.1166	0.1157	0.1147	0.1136	0.1155	0.1146	0.1136	0.1125	0.1114	0.1103
0.175	0.1241	0.1233	0.1225	0.1216	0.1207	0.1197	0.1210	0.1201	0.1192	0.1182	0.1171	0.1160	0.1180	0.1170	0.1160	0.1149	0.1138	0.1126
0.180	0.1269	0.1260	0.1251	0.1242	0.1232	0.1222	0.1236	0.1226	0.1216	0.1206	0.1195	0.1184	0.1205	0.1194	0.1184	0.1172	0.1160	0.1148
0.185	0.1295	0.1286	0.1277	0.1267	0.1257	0.1247	0.1261	0.1251	0.1241	0.1230	0.1219	0.1207	0.1229	0.1218	0.1207	0.1195	0.1182	0.1169
0.190	0.1321	0.1312	0.1303	0.1293	0.1282	0.1271	0.1286	0.1276	0.1265	0.1254	0.1242	0.1230	0.1253	0.1241	0.1230	0.1217	0.1204	0.1191
0.195	0.1347	0.1338	0.1328	0.1317	0.1306	0.1295	0.1311	0.1300	0.1289	0.1277	0.1265	0.1252	0.1276	0.1264	0.1252	0.1239	0.1226	0.1212
0.200	0.1373	0.1363	0.1352	0.1341	0.1330	0.1318	0.1335	0.1324	0.1312	0.1300	0.1287	0.1274	0.1299	0.1287	0.1274	0.1261	0.1247	0.1232

$$K_u = \frac{M_f}{f'_c\, b\, d_p^{\,2}}$$

$$A_p = \frac{w_{pu}\, f'_c\, b\, d_p}{f_{pu}}$$

Table 10.1b   Flexural Resistance Coefficients, k_u, for Rectangular Elements with Bonded Prestressing Steel Only

(Assuming $\phi_c = 0.70$ and $\phi_p = 0.90$)

f'_c	$k_p = 0.28$						$k_p = 0.38$						$k_p = 0.48$					
	30	40	50	60	70	80	30	40	50	60	70	80	30	40	50	60	70	80
α_1	0.805	0.790	0.775	0.760	0.745	0.730	0.805	0.790	0.775	0.760	0.745	0.730	0.805	0.790	0.775	0.760	0.745	0.730
β_1	0.895	0.870	0.845	0.820	0.795	0.770	0.895	0.870	0.845	0.820	0.795	0.770	0.895	0.870	0.845	0.820	0.795	0.770
w_{pu}	k_u						k_u						k_u					
0.005	0.0045	0.0045	0.0045	0.0045	0.0045	0.0045	0.0045	0.0045	0.0045	0.0045	0.0045	0.0045	0.0045	0.0045	0.0045	0.0045	0.0045	0.0045
0.010	0.0089	0.0089	0.0089	0.0089	0.0089	0.0089	0.0089	0.0089	0.0089	0.0089	0.0088	0.0088	0.0089	0.0088	0.0088	0.0088	0.0088	0.0088
0.015	0.0132	0.0132	0.0132	0.0132	0.0132	0.0132	0.0132	0.0132	0.0132	0.0132	0.0132	0.0132	0.0132	0.0132	0.0131	0.0131	0.0131	0.0131
0.020	0.0175	0.0175	0.0175	0.0175	0.0175	0.0175	0.0175	0.0175	0.0174	0.0174	0.0174	0.0174	0.0174	0.0174	0.0174	0.0174	0.0173	0.0173
0.025	0.0218	0.0218	0.0217	0.0217	0.0217	0.0217	0.0217	0.0217	0.0216	0.0216	0.0216	0.0215	0.0216	0.0216	0.0215	0.0215	0.0215	0.0214
0.030	0.0260	0.0259	0.0259	0.0259	0.0258	0.0258	0.0258	0.0258	0.0258	0.0257	0.0257	0.0256	0.0257	0.0257	0.0256	0.0256	0.0255	0.0255
0.035	0.0301	0.0301	0.0300	0.0300	0.0299	0.0299	0.0299	0.0299	0.0298	0.0298	0.0297	0.0297	0.0298	0.0297	0.0296	0.0296	0.0295	0.0294
0.040	0.0342	0.0341	0.0341	0.0340	0.0340	0.0339	0.0340	0.0339	0.0338	0.0338	0.0337	0.0336	0.0337	0.0337	0.0336	0.0335	0.0334	0.0333
0.045	0.0382	0.0382	0.0381	0.0380	0.0379	0.0378	0.0379	0.0379	0.0378	0.0377	0.0376	0.0375	0.0376	0.0376	0.0375	0.0374	0.0373	0.0371
0.050	0.0422	0.0421	0.0420	0.0419	0.0418	0.0417	0.0418	0.0417	0.0416	0.0415	0.0414	0.0413	0.0415	0.0414	0.0413	0.0411	0.0410	0.0409
0.055	0.0461	0.0460	0.0459	0.0458	0.0457	0.0456	0.0457	0.0456	0.0455	0.0453	0.0452	0.0451	0.0453	0.0452	0.0450	0.0449	0.0447	0.0445
0.060	0.0500	0.0499	0.0498	0.0496	0.0495	0.0494	0.0495	0.0494	0.0492	0.0491	0.0489	0.0487	0.0490	0.0489	0.0487	0.0485	0.0483	0.0482
0.065	0.0538	0.0537	0.0535	0.0534	0.0532	0.0531	0.0532	0.0531	0.0529	0.0528	0.0526	0.0524	0.0527	0.0525	0.0523	0.0521	0.0519	0.0517
0.070	0.0576	0.0574	0.0573	0.0571	0.0569	0.0567	0.0569	0.0568	0.0566	0.0564	0.0562	0.0559	0.0563	0.0561	0.0559	0.0557	0.0554	0.0552
0.075	0.0613	0.0611	0.0610	0.0608	0.0606	0.0603	0.0606	0.0604	0.0602	0.0599	0.0597	0.0594	0.0599	0.0596	0.0594	0.0591	0.0588	0.0586
0.080	0.0650	0.0648	0.0646	0.0644	0.0641	0.0639	0.0642	0.0639	0.0637	0.0634	0.0632	0.0629	0.0634	0.0631	0.0628	0.0625	0.0622	0.0619
0.085	0.0686	0.0684	0.0682	0.0679	0.0677	0.0674	0.0677	0.0674	0.0672	0.0669	0.0666	0.0663	0.0668	0.0665	0.0662	0.0659	0.0655	0.0652
0.090	0.0722	0.0719	0.0717	0.0714	0.0711	0.0708	0.0712	0.0709	0.0706	0.0703	0.0700	0.0696	0.0702	0.0699	0.0695	0.0692	0.0688	0.0684
0.095	0.0757	0.0754	0.0752	0.0749	0.0746	0.0742	0.0746	0.0743	0.0740	0.0736	0.0733	0.0729	0.0735	0.0732	0.0728	0.0724	0.0720	0.0716
0.100	0.0792	0.0789	0.0786	0.0783	0.0779	0.0776	0.0780	0.0776	0.0773	0.0769	0.0765	0.0761	0.0768	0.0764	0.0760	0.0756	0.0751	0.0747
0.105	0.0826	0.0823	0.0820	0.0816	0.0813	0.0809	0.0813	0.0809	0.0806	0.0801	0.0797	0.0793	0.0800	0.0796	0.0792	0.0787	0.0782	0.0777
0.110	0.0860	0.0857	0.0853	0.0849	0.0845	0.0841	0.0846	0.0842	0.0838	0.0833	0.0829	0.0824	0.0832	0.0828	0.0823	0.0818	0.0813	0.0807
0.115	0.0894	0.0890	0.0886	0.0882	0.0878	0.0873	0.0878	0.0874	0.0869	0.0865	0.0860	0.0854	0.0863	0.0859	0.0853	0.0848	0.0842	0.0836
0.120	0.0927	0.0923	0.0919	0.0914	0.0909	0.0905	0.0910	0.0906	0.0901	0.0896	0.0890	0.0884	0.0894	0.0889	0.0884	0.0878	0.0872	0.0865
0.125	0.0959	0.0955	0.0951	0.0946	0.0941	0.0935	0.0942	0.0937	0.0931	0.0926	0.0920	0.0914	0.0925	0.0919	0.0913	0.0907	0.0900	0.0893
0.130	0.0992	0.0987	0.0982	0.0977	0.0972	0.0966	0.0973	0.0967	0.0962	0.0956	0.0950	0.0943	0.0954	0.0948	0.0942	0.0936	0.0929	0.0921
0.135	0.1023	0.1018	0.1013	0.1008	0.1002	0.0996	0.1003	0.0997	0.0992	0.0985	0.0979	0.0972	0.0984	0.0977	0.0971	0.0964	0.0956	0.0949
0.140	0.1055	0.1049	0.1044	0.1038	0.1032	0.1025	0.1033	0.1027	0.1021	0.1014	0.1007	0.1000	0.1013	0.1006	0.0999	0.0991	0.0984	0.0975
0.145	0.1085	0.1080	0.1074	0.1068	0.1061	0.1055	0.1063	0.1057	0.1050	0.1043	0.1035	0.1028	0.1041	0.1034	0.1027	0.1019	0.1010	0.1002
0.150	0.1116	0.1110	0.1104	0.1097	0.1090	0.1083	0.1092	0.1085	0.1078	0.1071	0.1063	0.1055	0.1069	0.1062	0.1054	0.1046	0.1037	0.1028
0.155	0.1146	0.1140	0.1133	0.1126	0.1119	0.1111	0.1121	0.1114	0.1106	0.1098	0.1090	0.1081	0.1097	0.1089	0.1081	0.1072	0.1063	0.1053
0.160	0.1176	0.1169	0.1162	0.1155	0.1147	0.1139	0.1149	0.1142	0.1134	0.1126	0.1117	0.1108	0.1124	0.1116	0.1107	0.1098	0.1088	0.1078
0.165	0.1205	0.1198	0.1191	0.1183	0.1175	0.1167	0.1177	0.1169	0.1161	0.1152	0.1143	0.1134	0.1151	0.1142	0.1133	0.1123	0.1113	0.1103
0.170	0.1234	0.1226	0.1219	0.1211	0.1202	0.1193	0.1205	0.1197	0.1188	0.1179	0.1169	0.1159	0.1177	0.1168	0.1158	0.1148	0.1138	0.1127
0.175	0.1262	0.1255	0.1247	0.1238	0.1229	0.1220	0.1232	0.1223	0.1214	0.1205	0.1195	0.1184	0.1203	0.1194	0.1184	0.1173	0.1162	0.1150
0.180	0.1290	0.1282	0.1274	0.1265	0.1256	0.1246	0.1259	0.1250	0.1240	0.1230	0.1220	0.1209	0.1229	0.1219	0.1208	0.1197	0.1186	0.1174
0.185	0.1318	0.1310	0.1301	0.1292	0.1282	0.1272	0.1285	0.1276	0.1266	0.1255	0.1244	0.1233	0.1254	0.1243	0.1233	0.1221	0.1209	0.1197
0.190	0.1345	0.1337	0.1327	0.1318	0.1308	0.1297	0.1311	0.1301	0.1291	0.1280	0.1269	0.1257	0.1279	0.1268	0.1256	0.1245	0.1232	0.1219
0.195	0.1372	0.1363	0.1354	0.1343	0.1333	0.1322	0.1337	0.1327	0.1316	0.1304	0.1293	0.1280	0.1303	0.1292	0.1280	0.1268	0.1255	0.1241
0.200	0.1399	0.1389	0.1379	0.1369	0.1358	0.1346	0.1362	0.1351	0.1340	0.1328	0.1316	0.1303	0.1327	0.1315	0.1303	0.1290	0.1277	0.1263

$$K_u = \frac{M_f}{f'_c \, b \, d_p{}^2}$$

$$A_p = \frac{w_{pu} \, f'_c \, b \, d_p}{f_{pu}}$$

Table 10.2   Moment of Inertia of Rectangular Transformed Section

ρ_p	$I_{cr}/bd^3 = k^3/3 + n\rho_p(1-k)^2$ $k = \sqrt{(n\rho_p)^2 + 2(n\rho_p)} - n\rho_p$ $\rho_p = A_p/bd \quad n = E_s/E_c$						
	20	30	40	50	60	70	80
Normal Density Concrete **(2400kg/m³)** 0.0005	0.0038	0.0033	0.0030	0.0028	0.0026	0.0025	0.0023
0.001	0.0073	0.0064	0.0058	0.0054	0.0050	0.0047	0.0045
0.0015	0.0105	0.0092	0.0084	0.0078	0.0073	0.0069	0.0066
0.002	0.0136	0.0120	0.0109	0.0101	0.0095	0.0090	0.0085
0.0025	0.0165	0.0146	0.0133	0.0123	0.0116	0.0109	0.0104
0.003	0.0193	0.0171	0.0156	0.0145	0.0136	0.0129	0.0123
0.0035	0.0220	0.0195	0.0178	0.0165	0.0155	0.0147	0.0141
0.004	0.0246	0.0218	0.0200	0.0186	0.0175	0.0166	0.0158
0.0045	0.0271	0.0241	0.0220	0.0205	0.0193	0.0183	0.0175
0.005	0.0296	0.0263	0.0241	0.0224	0.0211	0.0201	0.0192
0.0055	0.0319	0.0285	0.0261	0.0243	0.0229	0.0217	0.0208
0.006	0.0343	0.0305	0.0280	0.0261	0.0246	0.0234	0.0224
0.0065	0.0365	0.0326	0.0299	0.0279	0.0263	0.0250	0.0239
0.007	0.0387	0.0346	0.0318	0.0296	0.0280	0.0266	0.0254
0.0075	0.0408	0.0365	0.0336	0.0313	0.0296	0.0281	0.0269
0.008	0.0429	0.0384	0.0353	0.0330	0.0312	0.0297	0.0284
0.0085	0.0450	0.0403	0.0371	0.0347	0.0327	0.0312	0.0298
0.009	0.0470	0.0421	0.0388	0.0363	0.0343	0.0326	0.0313
0.0095	0.0489	0.0439	0.0405	0.0378	0.0358	0.0341	0.0326
0.01	0.0508	0.0457	0.0421	0.0394	0.0373	0.0355	0.0340
Semi-Low Density Concrete **(2000kg/m³)** 0.0005	0.0049	0.0043	0.0039	0.0036	0.0034	0.0032	0.0030
0.001	0.0093	0.0082	0.0075	0.0069	0.0065	0.0061	0.0058
0.0015	0.0134	0.0118	0.0108	0.0100	0.0093	0.0088	0.0084
0.002	0.0172	0.0152	0.0139	0.0129	0.0121	0.0114	0.0109
0.0025	0.0209	0.0185	0.0169	0.0157	0.0147	0.0139	0.0133
0.003	0.0243	0.0216	0.0197	0.0183	0.0172	0.0164	0.0156
0.0035	0.0276	0.0245	0.0225	0.0209	0.0197	0.0187	0.0178
0.004	0.0308	0.0274	0.0251	0.0234	0.0220	0.0209	0.0200
0.0045	0.0339	0.0302	0.0277	0.0258	0.0243	0.0231	0.0221
0.005	0.0368	0.0329	0.0302	0.0282	0.0266	0.0252	0.0241
0.0055	0.0397	0.0355	0.0326	0.0304	0.0287	0.0273	0.0261
0.006	0.0425	0.0380	0.0349	0.0326	0.0308	0.0293	0.0281
0.0065	0.0451	0.0405	0.0372	0.0348	0.0329	0.0313	0.0300
0.007	0.0478	0.0428	0.0395	0.0369	0.0349	0.0332	0.0318
0.0075	0.0503	0.0452	0.0416	0.0390	0.0368	0.0351	0.0336
0.008	0.0528	0.0474	0.0438	0.0410	0.0388	0.0369	0.0354
0.0085	0.0552	0.0497	0.0458	0.0429	0.0406	0.0388	0.0371
0.009	0.0575	0.0518	0.0479	0.0449	0.0425	0.0405	0.0389
0.0095	0.0598	0.0539	0.0498	0.0468	0.0443	0.0423	0.0405
0.01	0.0621	0.0560	0.0518	0.0486	0.0461	0.0440	0.0422

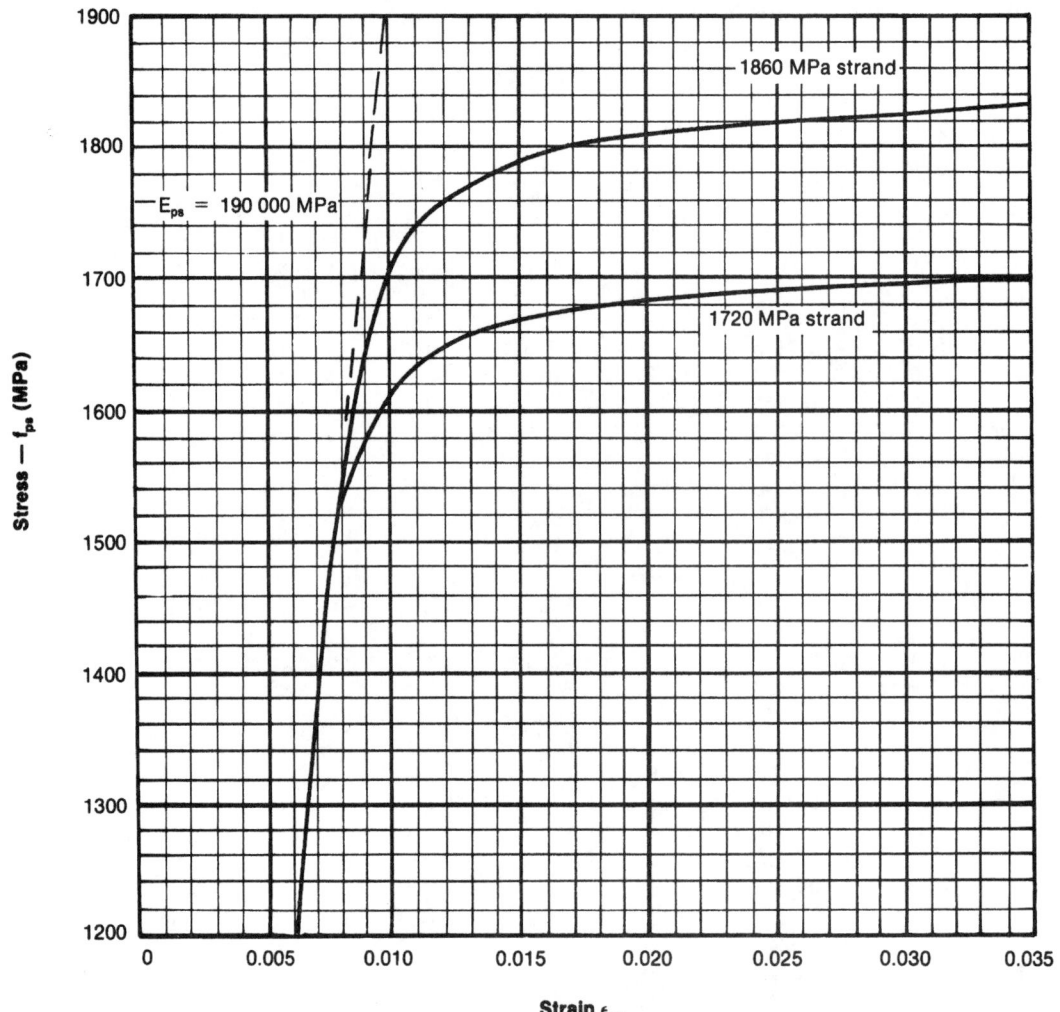

These curves are based on the following equations

For $\epsilon_{ps} \leq 0.008$, $f_{ps} = 190\,000\,\epsilon_{ps}$ (MPa)

Grade 1720 — For $\epsilon_{ps} > 0.008$, $f_{ps} = 1710 - \dfrac{0.400}{\epsilon_{ps} - 0.006} < 0.98\,f_{pu}$ (MPa)

Grade 1860 — For $\epsilon_{ps} > 0.008$, $f_{ps} = 1848 - \dfrac{0.517}{\epsilon_{ps} - 0.0065} < 0.98\,f_{pu}$ (MPa)

The above curves exceed the minimum requirements of CSA
Standard G279. The designer should check that the properties of the steel used correspond to the assumed values.

Fig. 10.1   Typical stress-strain curve, 7-wire stress-relieved and low-relaxation prestressing strand

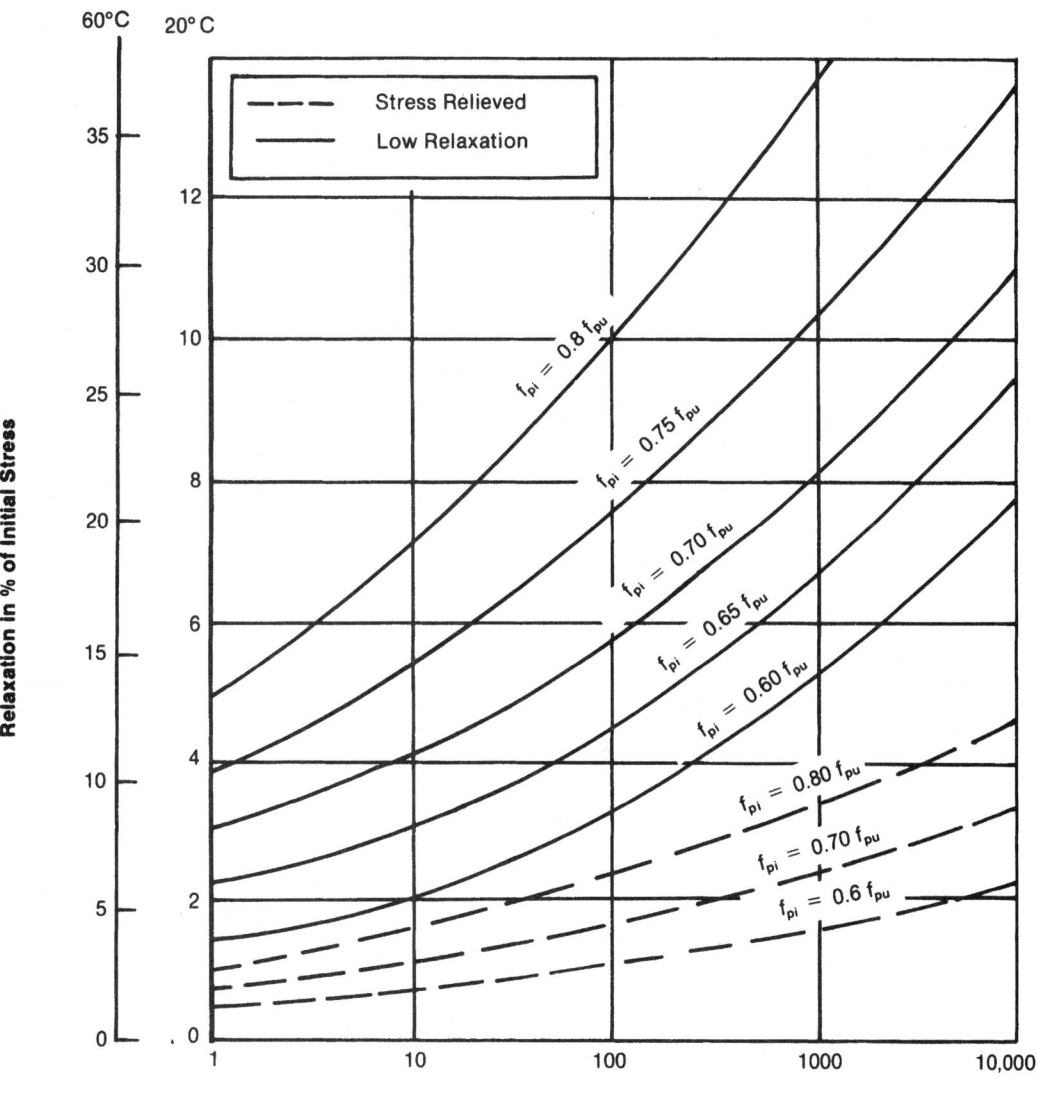

Time, days

Fig. 10.2   Intrinsic relaxation of stress relieved and low relaxation strand for different levels of initial stress f_{psi} at 20° C and 60° C.

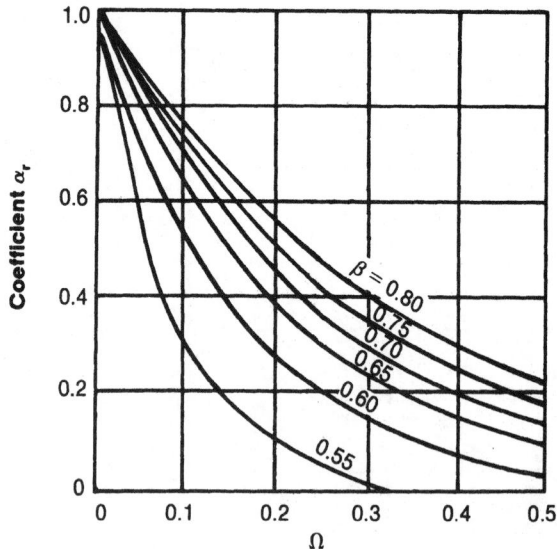

Fig. 10.3   Relaxation reduction coefficient α_r as a function of $\Omega = \dfrac{\Delta f_s}{f_{pi}}$ for different values of $\beta = \dfrac{f_{pi}}{f_{pu}}$

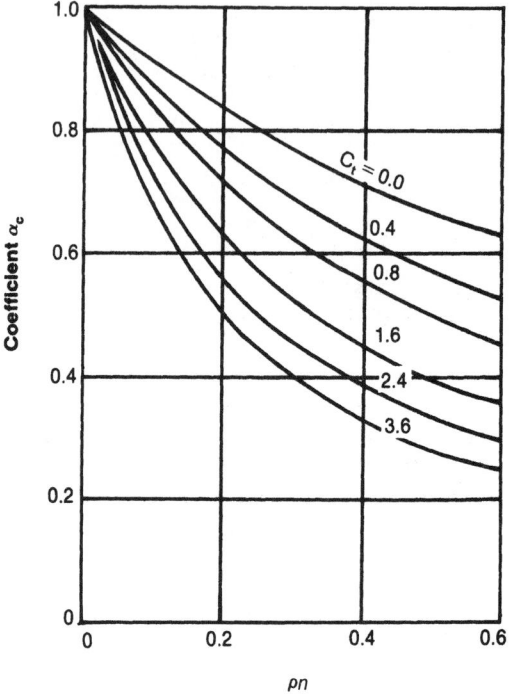

Fig. 10.4   Coefficient α_c as a function of ρn and C_t

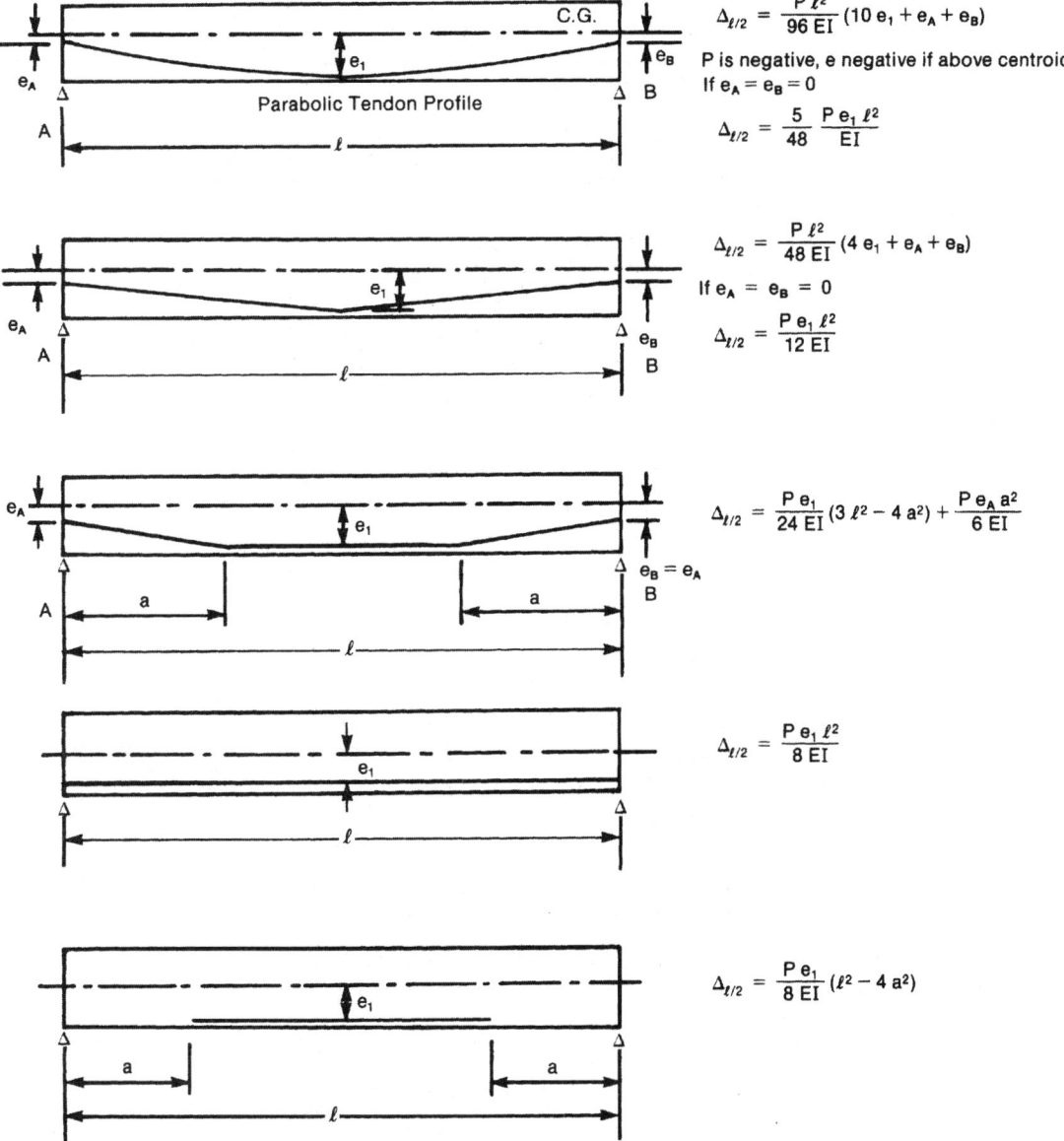

$$\Delta_{\ell/2} = \frac{P\,\ell^2}{96\,EI}\,(10\,e_1 + e_A + e_B)$$

P is negative, e negative if above centroid.
If $e_A = e_B = 0$

$$\Delta_{\ell/2} = \frac{5}{48}\,\frac{P\,e_1\,\ell^2}{EI}$$

$$\Delta_{\ell/2} = \frac{P\,\ell^2}{48\,EI}\,(4\,e_1 + e_A + e_B)$$

If $e_A = e_B = 0$

$$\Delta_{\ell/2} = \frac{P\,e_1\,\ell^2}{12\,EI}$$

$$\Delta_{\ell/2} = \frac{P\,e_1}{24\,EI}\,(3\,\ell^2 - 4\,a^2) + \frac{P\,e_A\,a^2}{6\,EI}$$

$$\Delta_{\ell/2} = \frac{P\,e_1\,\ell^2}{8\,EI}$$

$$\Delta_{\ell/2} = \frac{P\,e_1}{8\,EI}\,(\ell^2 - 4\,a^2)$$

Fig. 10.5   Deflection formulas for prestressed concrete beams with different tendon profiles.

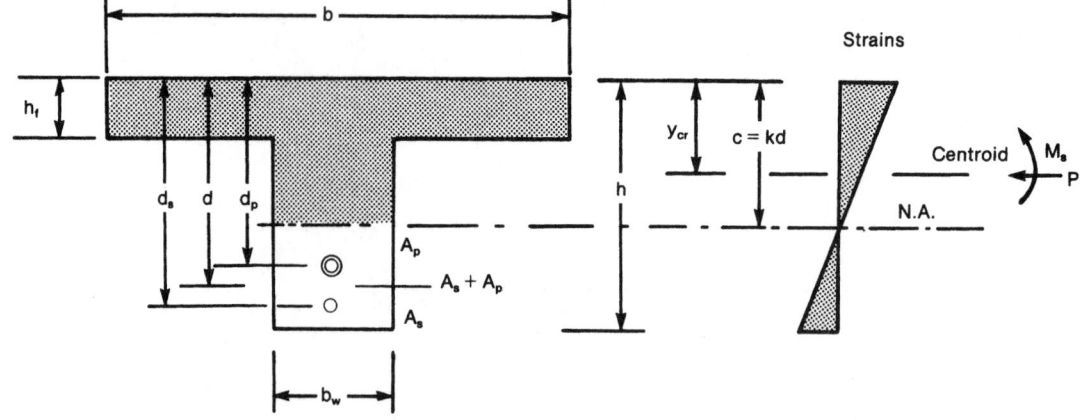

Fig. 10.6   T-Section subjected to M_s and decompression force P

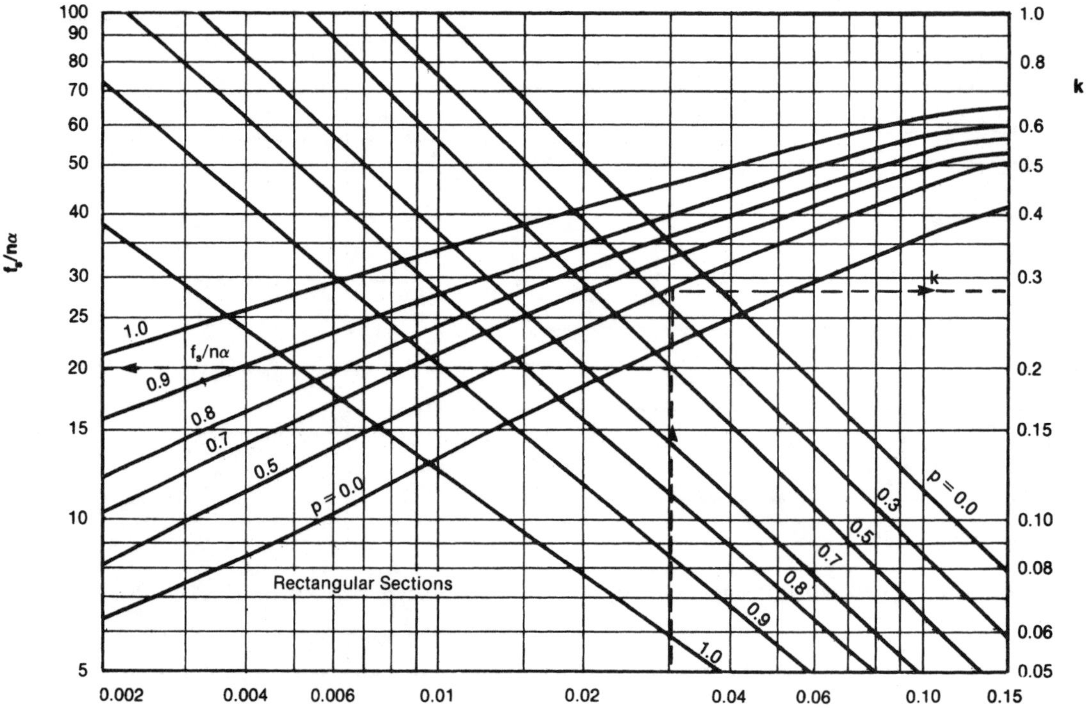

Fig. 10.7 $f_s/n\alpha$ and k versus nρ for rectangular sections.

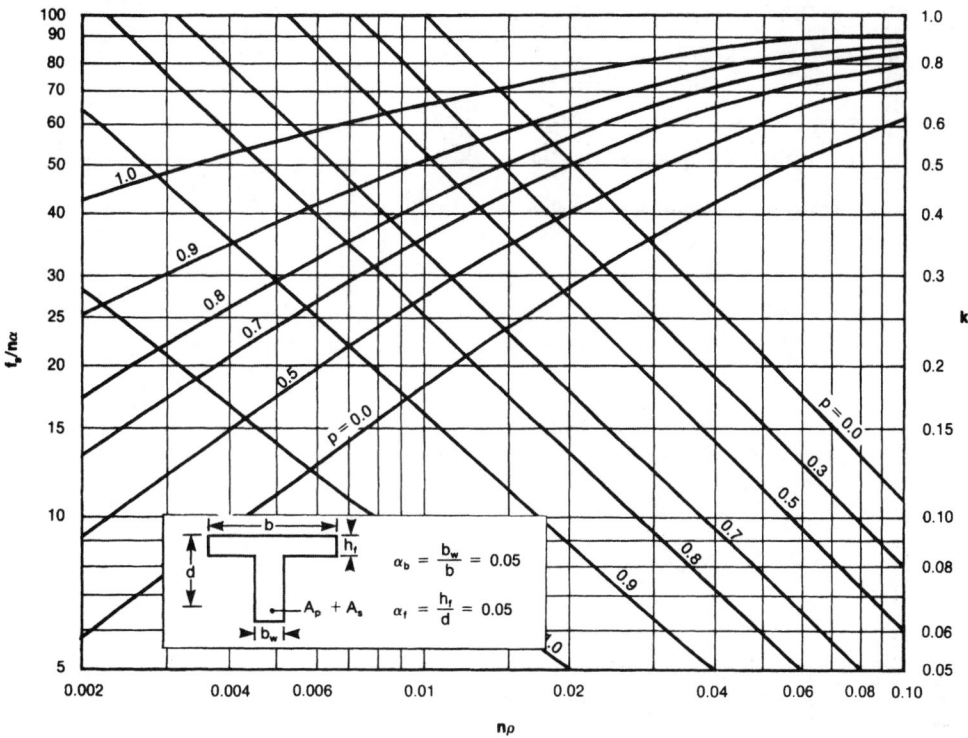

Fig. 10.8.1 $f_s/n\alpha$ and k versus nρ for T-beams with $\alpha_b = 0.05$ and $\alpha_f = 0.05$.

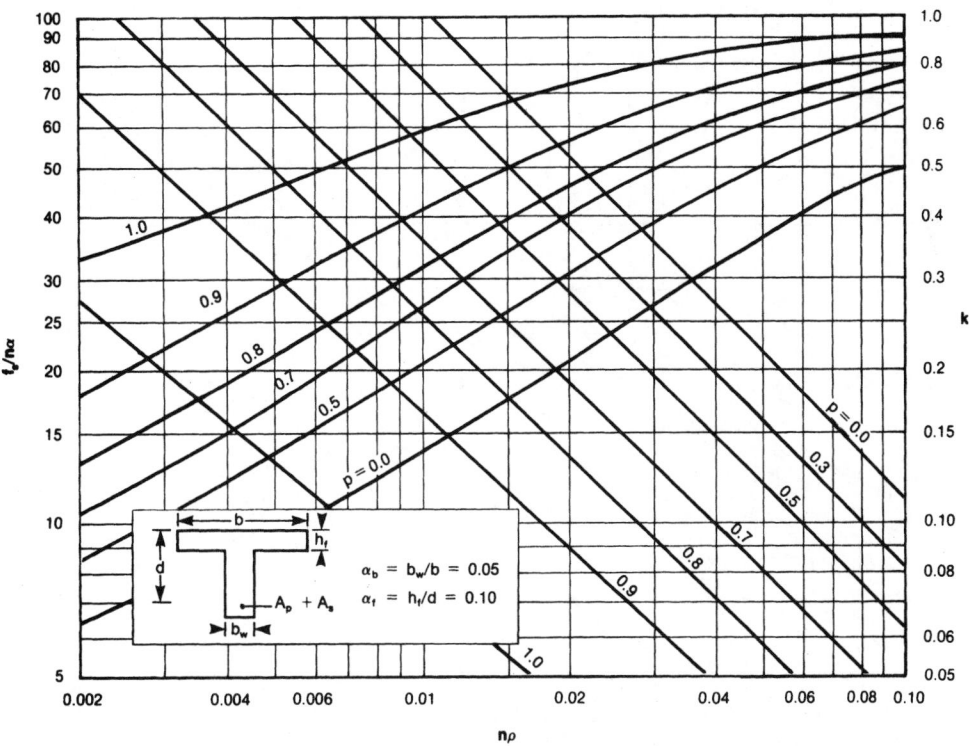

Fig. 10.8.2 $f_s/n\alpha$ and k versus nρ for T-beams with $\alpha_b = 0.05$ and $\alpha_f = 0.10$.

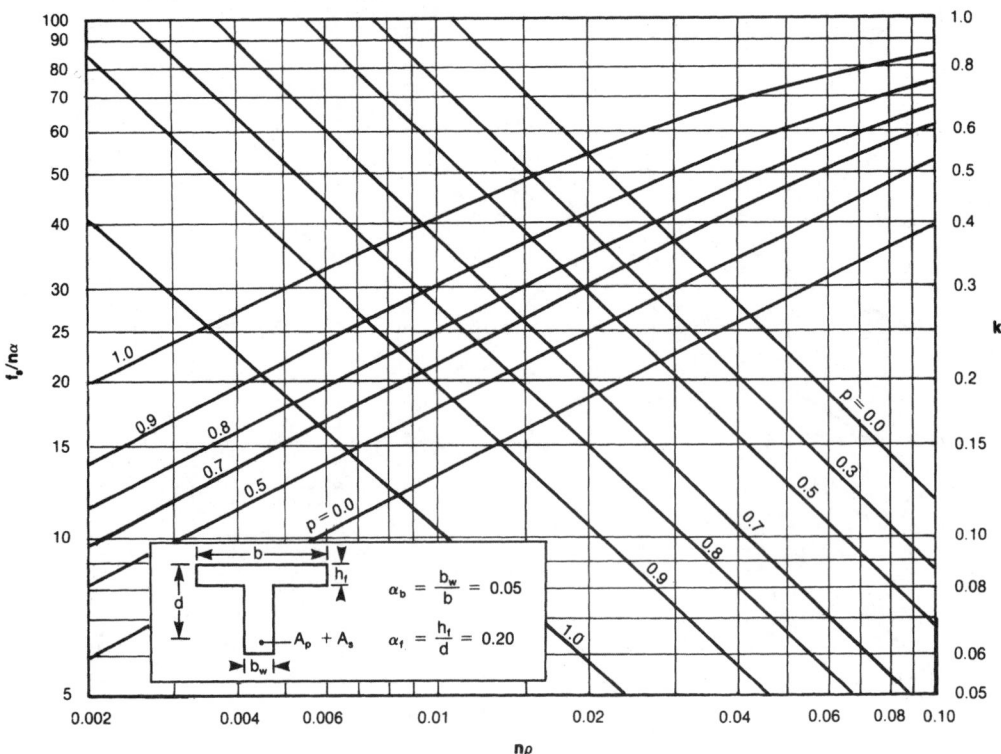

Fig. 10.8.3 $f_s/n\alpha$ and k versus $n\rho$ for T-beams with $\alpha_b = 0.05$ and $\alpha_f = 0.20$.

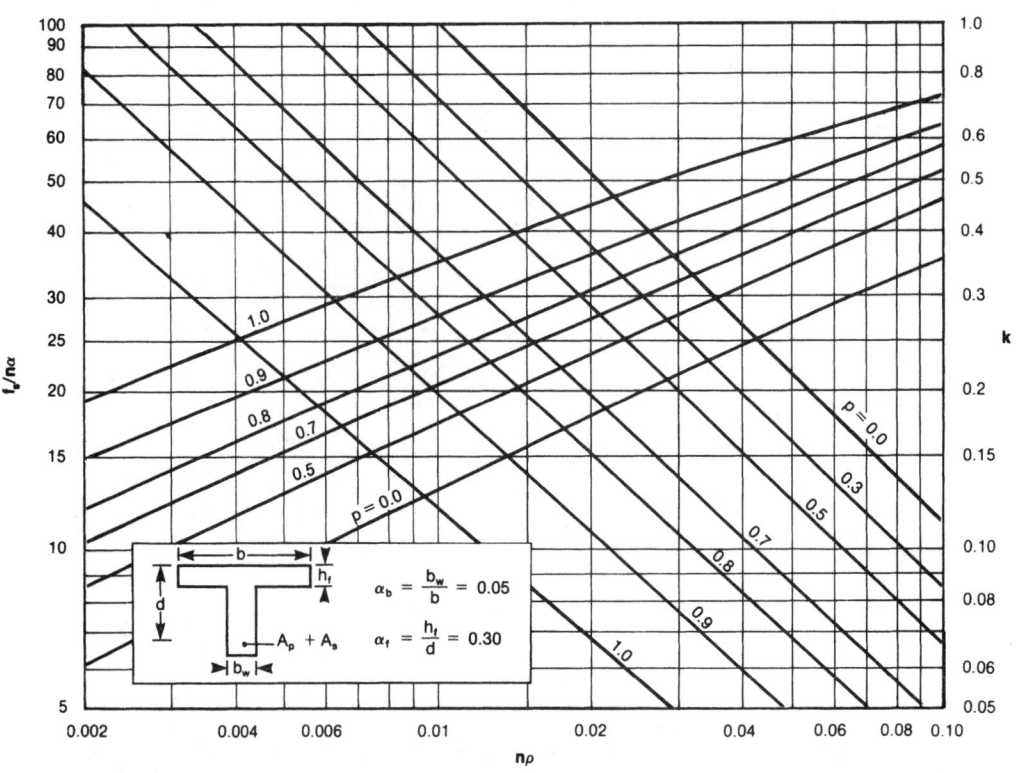

Fig. 10.8.4 $f_s/n\alpha$ and k versus $n\rho$ for T-beams with $\alpha_b = 0.05$ and $\alpha_f = 0.30$.

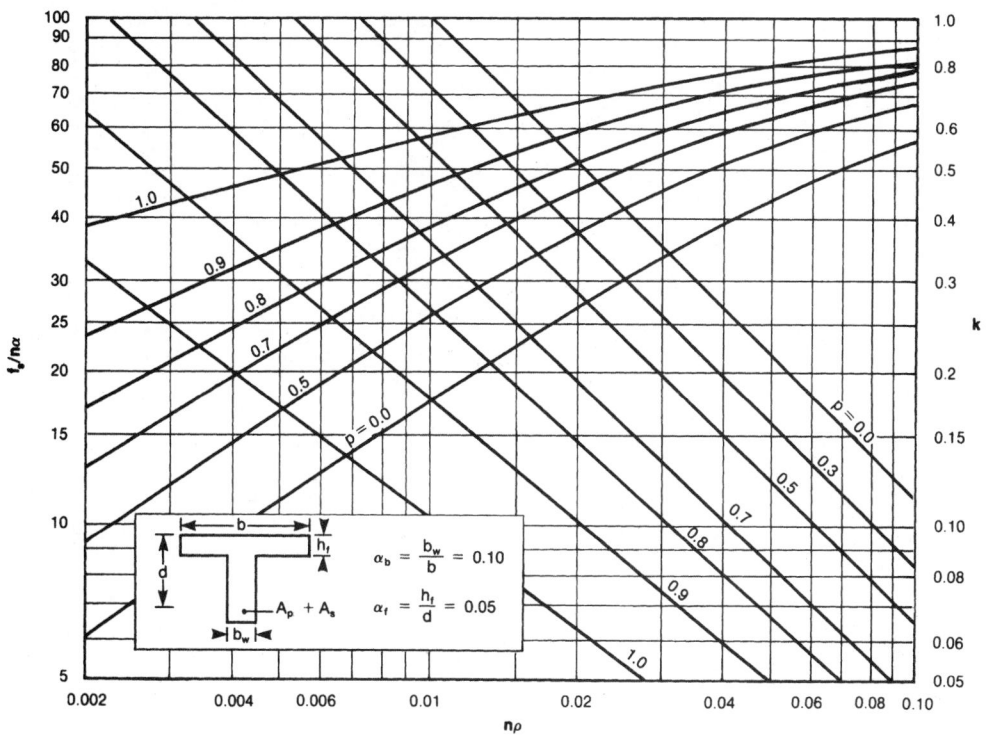

Fig. 10.8.5 $f_s/n\alpha$ and k versus $n\rho$ for T-beams with $\alpha_b = 0.10$ and $\alpha_f = 0.05$.

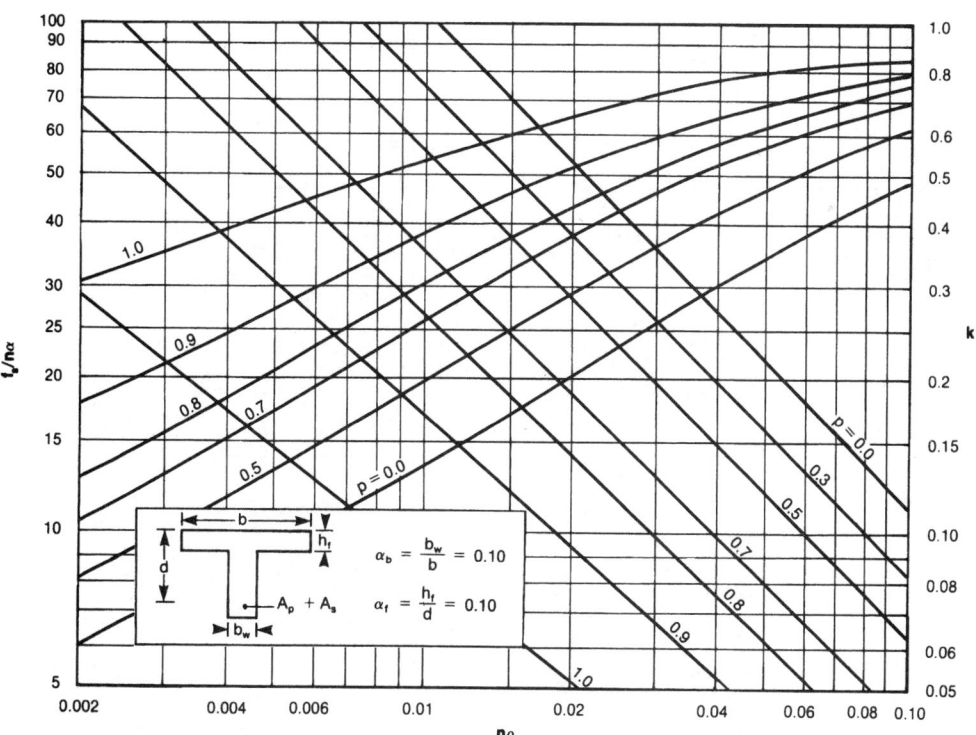

Fig. 10.8.6 $f_s/n\alpha$ and k versus $n\rho$ for T-beams with $\alpha_b = 0.10$ and $\alpha_f = 0.10$.

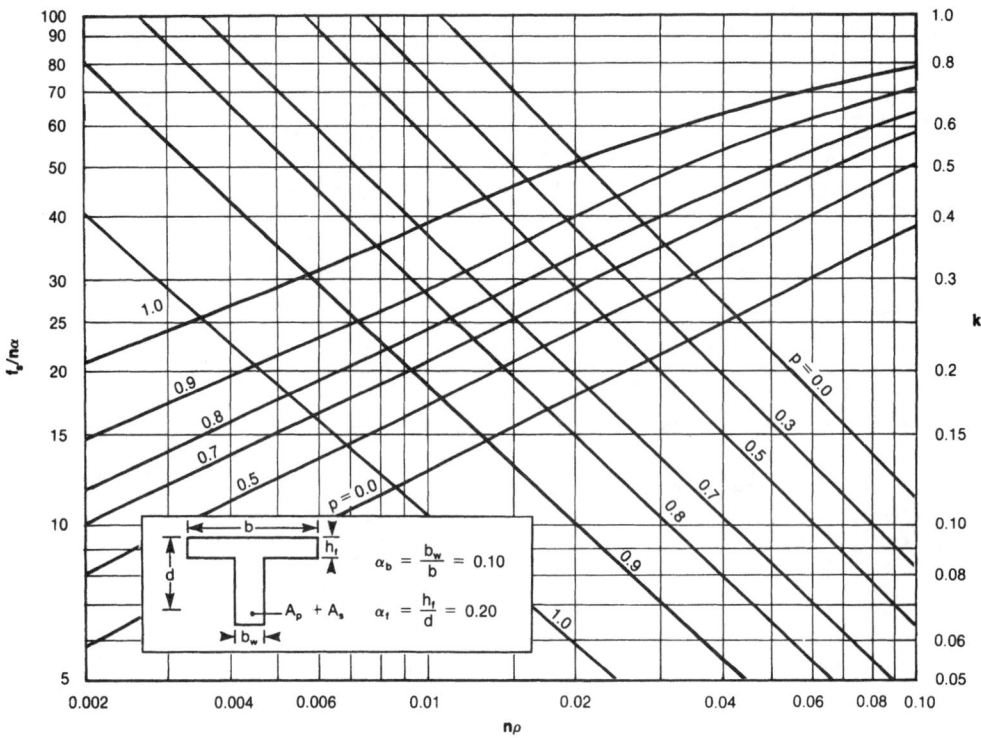

Fig. 10.8.7 $f_s/n\alpha$ and k versus $n\rho$ for T-beams with $\alpha_b = 0.10$ and $\alpha_f = 0.20$.

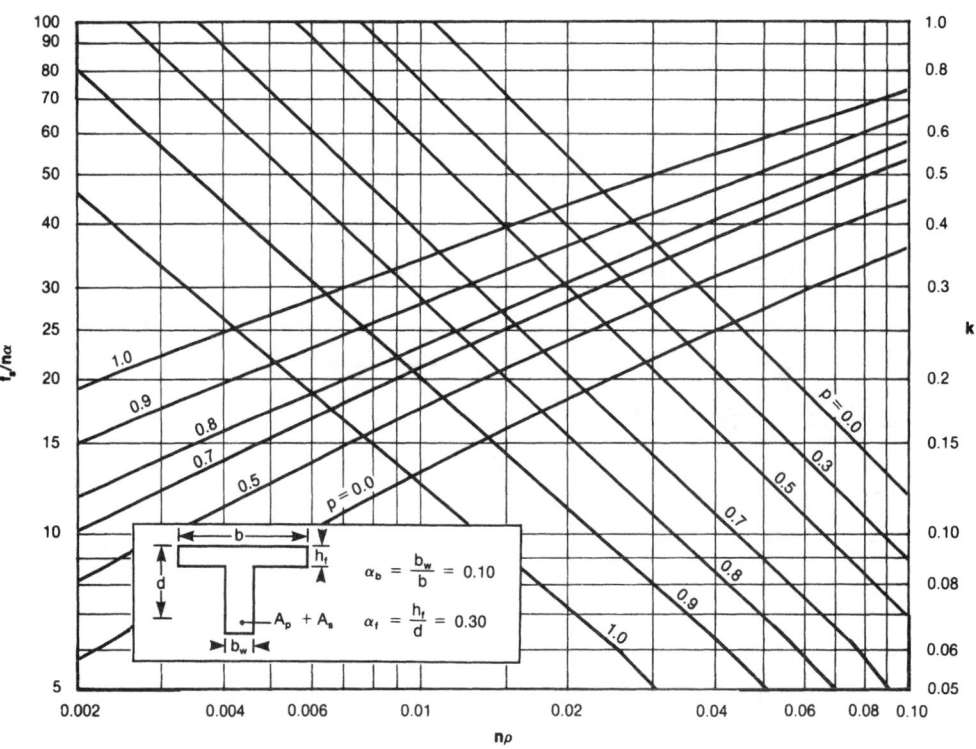

Fig. 10.8.8 $f_s/n\alpha$ and k versus $n\rho$ for T-beams with $\alpha_b = 0.10$ and $\alpha_f = 0.30$.

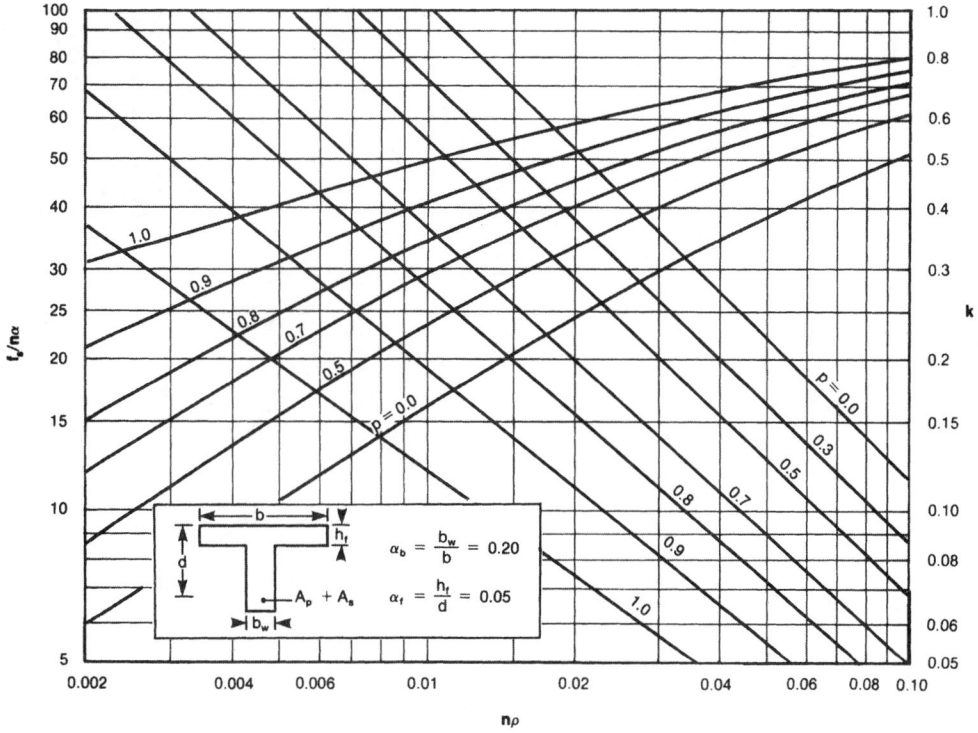

Fig. 10.8.9 $f_s/n\alpha$ and k versus $n\rho$ for T-beams with $\alpha_b = 0.20$ and $\alpha_f = 0.05$.

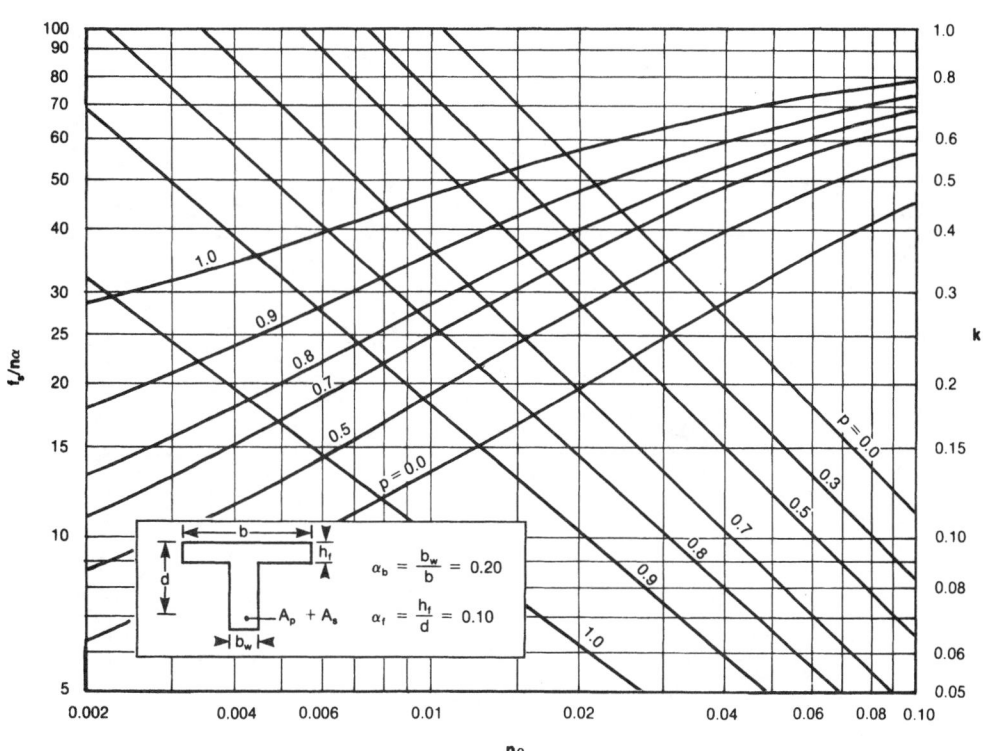

Fig. 10.8.10 $f_s/n\alpha$ and k versus $n\rho$ for T-beams with $\alpha_b = 0.20$ and $\alpha_f = 0.10$.

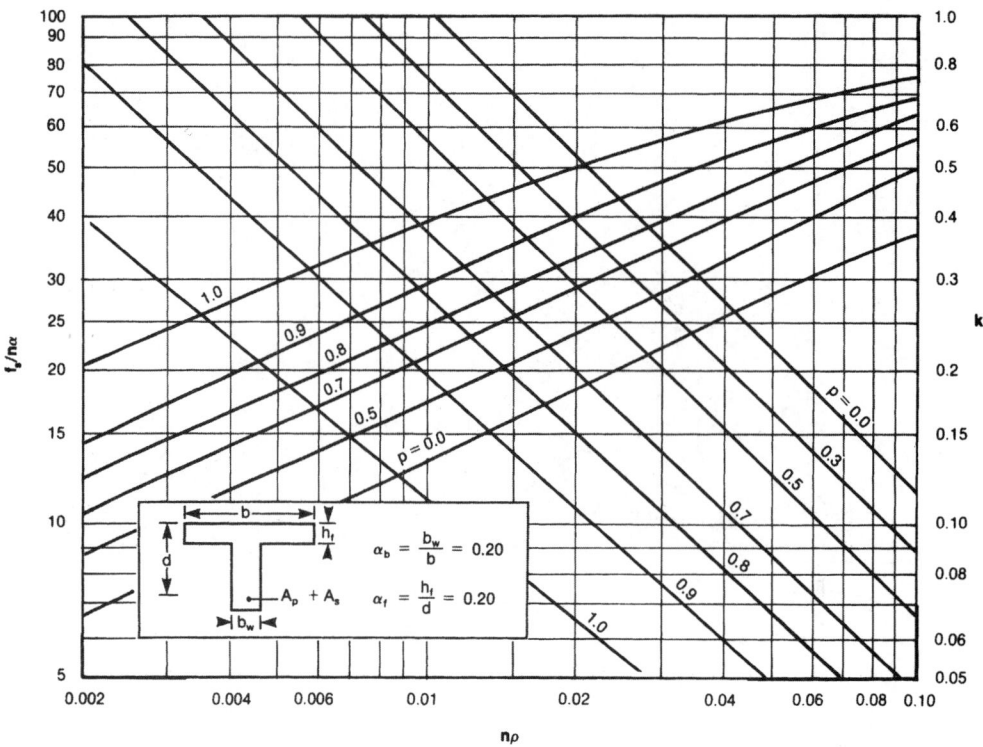

Fig. 10.8.11 $f_s/n\alpha$ and k versus nρ for T-beams with α_b = 0.20 and α_f = 0.20.

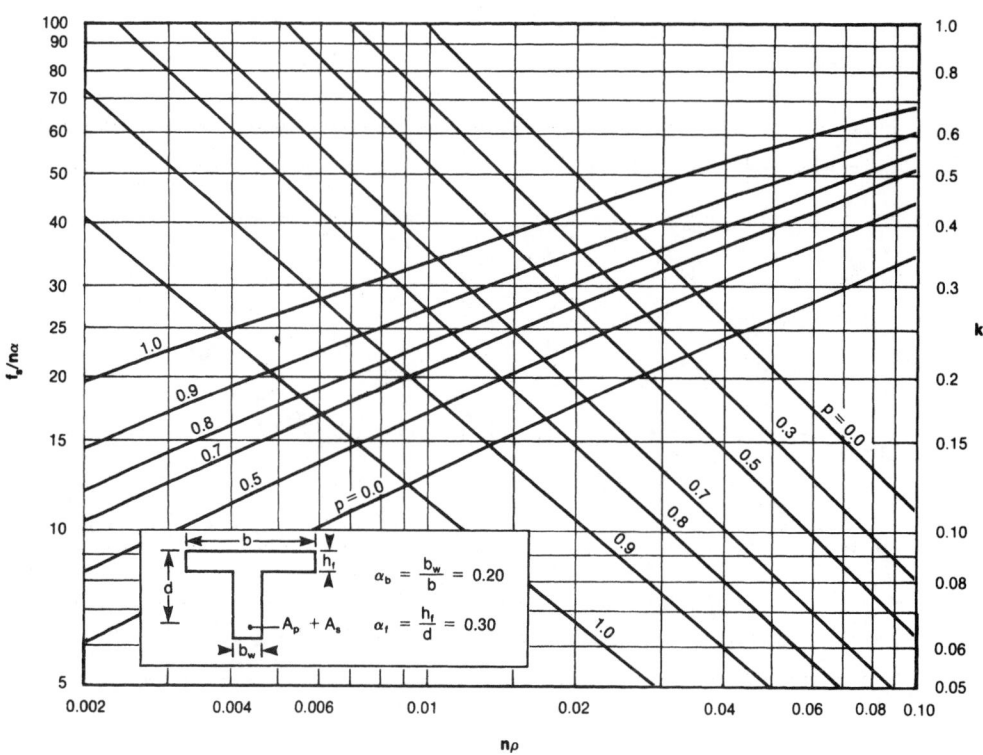

Fig. 10.8.12 $f_s/n\alpha$ and k versus nρ for T-beams with α_b = 0.20 and α_f = 0.30.

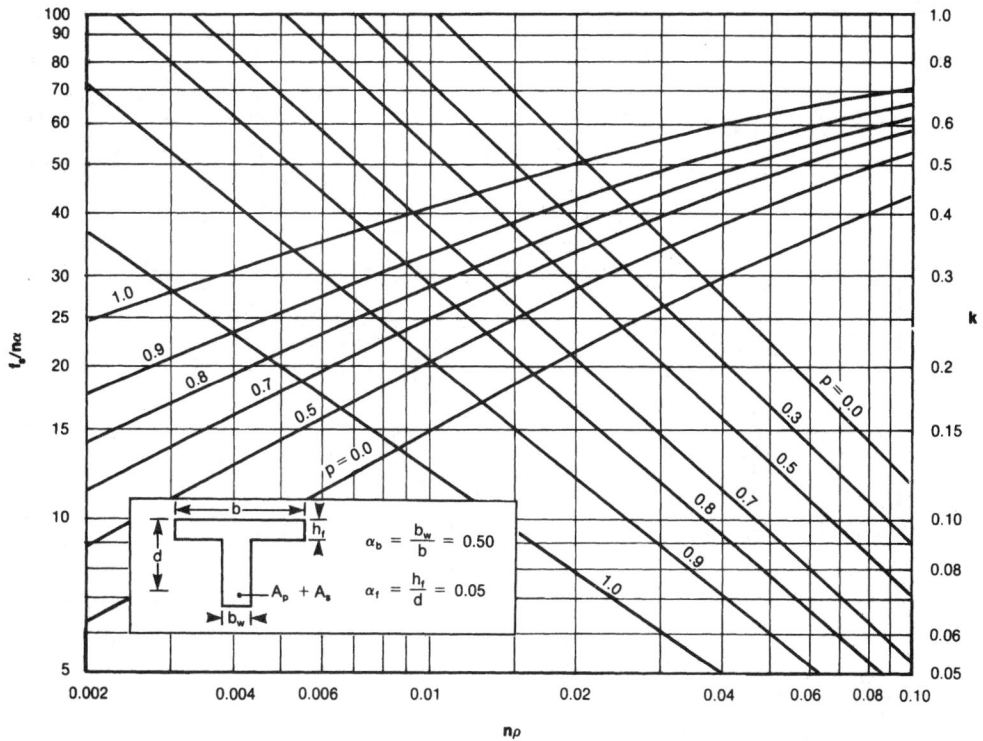

Fig. 10.8.13 $f_s/n\alpha$ and k versus $n\rho$ for T-beams with $\alpha_b = 0.50$ and $\alpha_f = 0.05$.

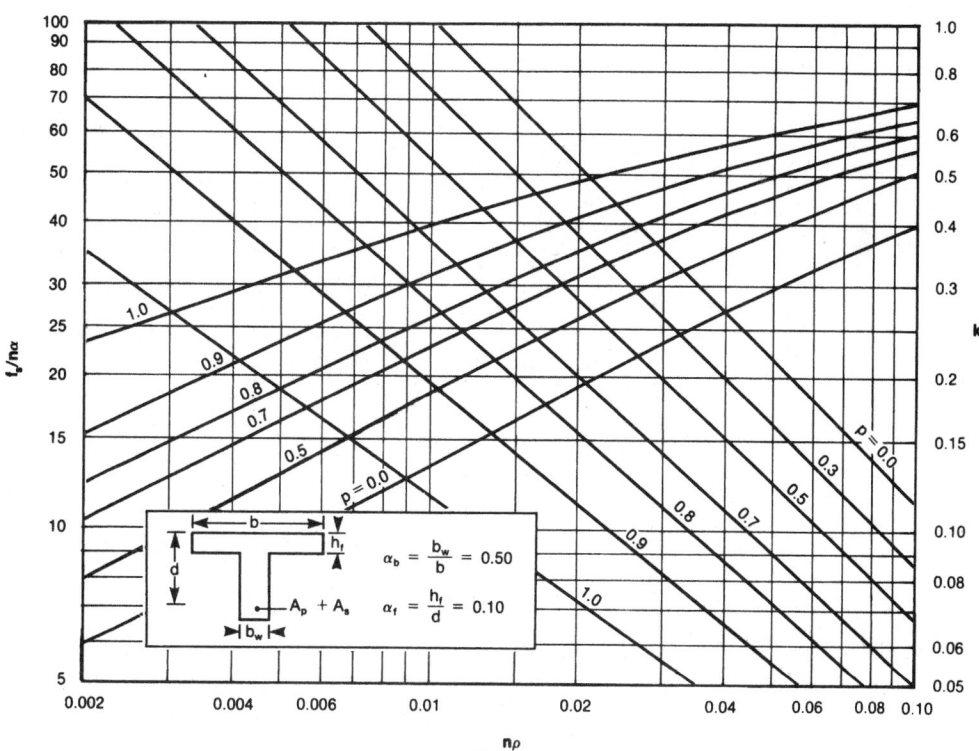

Fig. 10.8.14 $f_s/n\alpha$ and k versus $n\rho$ for T-beams with $\alpha_b = 0.50$ and $\alpha_f = 0.10$.

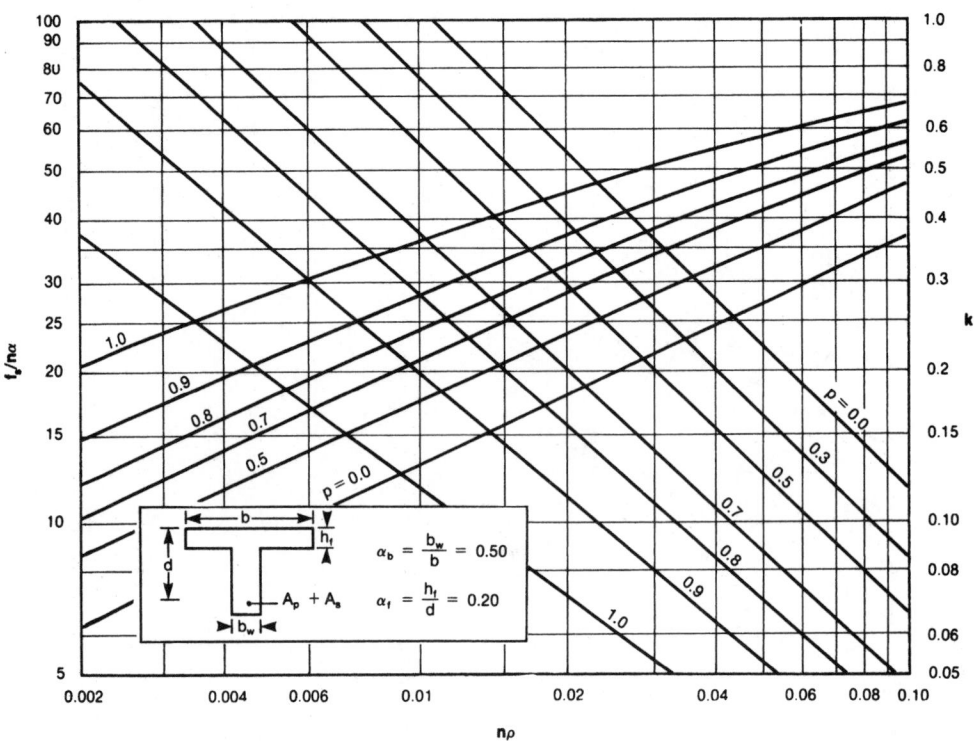

Fig. 10.8.15 $f_s/n\alpha$ and k versus $n\rho$ for T-beams with $\alpha_b = 0.50$ and $\alpha_f = 0.20$.

11

**By Denis Mitchell
and Patrick Paultre**

Seismic Design

11.1   Introduction

The 2005 National Building Code of Canada (NBCC) gives the minimum lateral earthquake force for the equivalent static force procedure as:

$$V = \frac{S(T_a)M_v I_E W}{R_d R_o} \geq \frac{S(2.0)M_v I_E W}{R_d R_o}$$

and for a Seismic Force Resisting System (SFRS) with an R_d equal to or greater than 1.5 , V need not be taken greater than $\dfrac{2}{3}\dfrac{S(0.2)I_E W}{R_d R_o}$

where:

$S(T_a)$	=	design spectral response acceleration, expressed as a ratio to gravitational acceleration for a period of T_a
M_v	=	factor to account for higher mode effect on base shear
I_E	=	earthquake importance factor for the structure
T_a	=	fundamental period of vibration of the building in seconds in the direction under consideration
W	=	dead load, plus 25% of the design snow load, plus 60% of storage load and the full contents of any tanks. Minimum partition load need not exceed 0.5 kPa
R_d	=	ductility-related force modification factor that reflects the capability of a structure to dissipate energy through inelastic behaviour
R_o	=	overstrength-related force modification factor that accounts for the dependable portion of reserve strength in a structure.

The designer chooses the type of SFRS, with the corresponding force modification factors, R_d and R_o. The values of R_d and R_o are a function of the type of lateral load resisting system and the manner in which the structural members are designed and detailed. Table 11.1 provides a guide for the required design and detailing provisions of CSA Standard A23.3 associated with the corresponding factors, R_d and R_o.

11

Seismic Design

Table 11.1 Design and Detailing Provisions Required for Different Reinforced Concrete Structural Systems and Corresponding R_d and R_o Factors

Type of SFRS	R_d	R_o	Summary of design and detailing requirements in CSA A23.3-04
Ductile moment resisting frames	4.0	1.7	Beams capable of flexural hinging with shear failure and bar buckling avoided. Beams and columns must satisfy ductile detailing requirements. Columns properly confined and stronger than beams. Joints properly confined and stronger than beams.
Moderately ductile moment resisting frames	2.5	1.4	Beams and columns must satisfy detailing requirements for moderate ductility. Beams and columns to have minimum shear strengths. Joints must satisfy moderate ductility detailing requirements and must be capable of transmitting shears from beam hinging.
Ductile coupled walls	4.0	1.7	At least 66% of base overturning moment resisted by wall system must be carried by axial tension and compression in coupled walls. Coupling beams to have ductile detailing and be capable of flexural hinging or resist loads with diagonal reinforcement (shear failure and bar buckling avoided). Walls must have minimum resistance to permit attainment of nominal strength in coupling beams and minimum ductility level.
Ductile partially coupled walls	3.5	1.7	Coupling beams to have ductile detailing and be capable of flexural hinging or resist loads with diagonal reinforcement (shear failure and bar buckling avoided). Walls must have minimum resistance to permit attainment of nominal strength in coupling beams and minimum ductility level.
Ductile shearwalls	3.5	1.6	Walls must be capable of flexural yielding without local instability, shear failure or bar buckling. Walls must satisfy ductile detailing and ductility requirements.
Moderately ductile shearwalls	2.0	1.4	Walls must satisfy detailing and ductility requirements for moderate ductility. Walls must have minimum shear strength.
Conventional construction: Moment resisting frames	1.5	1.3	Beams and columns must have factored resistances greater than or equal to factored loads. Columns and beams must satisfy minimum detailing requirements for conventional construction. Closely spaced hoops required in columns unless factored resistance of columns greater than factored resistance of beams or if $R_d R_o = 1.0$.
Conventional construction: Shearwalls	1.5	1.3	Walls must have factored resistances greater than or equal to factored loads. Factored shear resistance must exceed shear corresponding to factored flexural resistance or shear corresponding to $R_d R_o = 1.0$. Walls must satisfy minimum detailing requirements for conventional construction.
Other SFRS(s)	1.0	1.0	

11.2 Seismic Design Considerations

Seismic design is concerned not only with providing the required strength but also with providing minimum levels of ductility and choosing appropriate structural systems. These goals may be achieved by:

(i) choosing structural systems which are as symmetrical as possible in plan and as uniform as possible in elevation (minimizing structural irregularities);

(ii) designing the primary lateral load resisting structural components so that desirable energy dissipating systems will form (e.g., "weak-beam strong-column");

(iii) detailing the energy dissipating regions of the primary lateral load resisting components to ensure that substantial inelastic deformations can be achieved without significant loss of strength, and

(iv) ensuring that secondary members which are not part of the lateral load resisting system can maintain their gravity load carrying capacity as they undergo the required lateral deformations.

In the design of ductile members it is necessary to determine the hierarchy of strengths of different members. To ensure that certain hierarchy of strengths are achieved the CSA Standard defines "probable", "nominal" and "factored" resistances. Table 11.2 summarizes the various types of flexural resistances used in the CSA Standard and suggests approximate relationships between these resistances.

Table 11.2 Factored, Nominal and Probable Moment Resistances

Type of flexural resistance	Calculated using	Where used	Approximate relationships for flexure
M_r = factored resistance	$\phi_c = 0.65$ $\phi_s = 0.85$	All members must satisfy $M_r \geq M_f$	
M_n = nominal resistance	$\phi_c = 1.0$ $\phi_s = 1.0$	To ensure columns stronger than beams	$M_n \approx 1.2 M_r$
M_p = probable resistance	$\phi_c = 1.0$ $\phi_s = 1.0$ $f_s = 1.25 f_y$		$M_p \approx 1.47 M_r$

Note: the relationship between M_n and M_r for the case of flexure and axial load depends on the level of axial load

11

Seismic Design

11.3 Loading Cases

For loading combinations including earthquake, the factored load combinations shall include:

Principal loads:
$1.0D + 1.0E$

and either of the following combinations of principal and companion loads:

1) For storage occupancies, equipment areas and service rooms:
$1.0D + 1.0E + 1.0L + 0.25S$

2) For other occupancies:
$1.0D + 1.0E + 0.5L + 0.25S$

11.4   Design of a Six-Storey Ductile Moment-Resisting Frame Building

11.4.1   Description of Building and Loads

The six-storey reinforced concrete frame building shown in Fig. 11.1 is located in Vancouver and is to be designed as a ductile moment resisting frame structure. The six-storey reinforced concrete office building has 7 - 6 m bays in the N-S direction and 3 bays in the E-W direction which consist of 2 - 9 m office bays and a central 6 m corridor bay.

The interior columns are all 500 x 500 mm while the exterior columns are 450 x 450 mm. The one-way slab floor system consists of a slab 110 mm thick spanning in the E-W direction supported by beams in the N-S direction. The secondary beams supporting the slab are 300 mm wide x 350 mm deep (from top of slab to bottom of beam). The beams of both the N-S and E-W frames are 400 mm wide x 600 mm deep for the first three storeys and 400 x 550 mm for the top three storeys.

Material Properties
Concrete: normal density concrete with $f'_c = 30$ MPa
Reinforcement: $f_y = 400$ MPa

Live loads
Floor live loads:
2.4 kN/m^2 on typical office floors
4.8 kN/m^2 on 6 m wide corridor bay

Roof load
2.2 kN/m^2 snow load, accounting for parapets and equipment projections
1.6 kN/m^2 mechanical services loading in 6 m wide strip over corridor bay

Dead loads
self-weight of reinforced concrete members calculated as 24 kN/m^3
1.0 kN/m^2 partition loading on all floors
0.5 kN/m^2 mechanical services loading on all floors
0.5 kN/m^2 roofing

Wind loading
1.84 kN/m^2 net lateral pressure for top 4 storeys
1.75 kN/m^2 net lateral pressure for bottom 2 storeys

The fire-resistance rating of the building is assumed to be 1 hour.

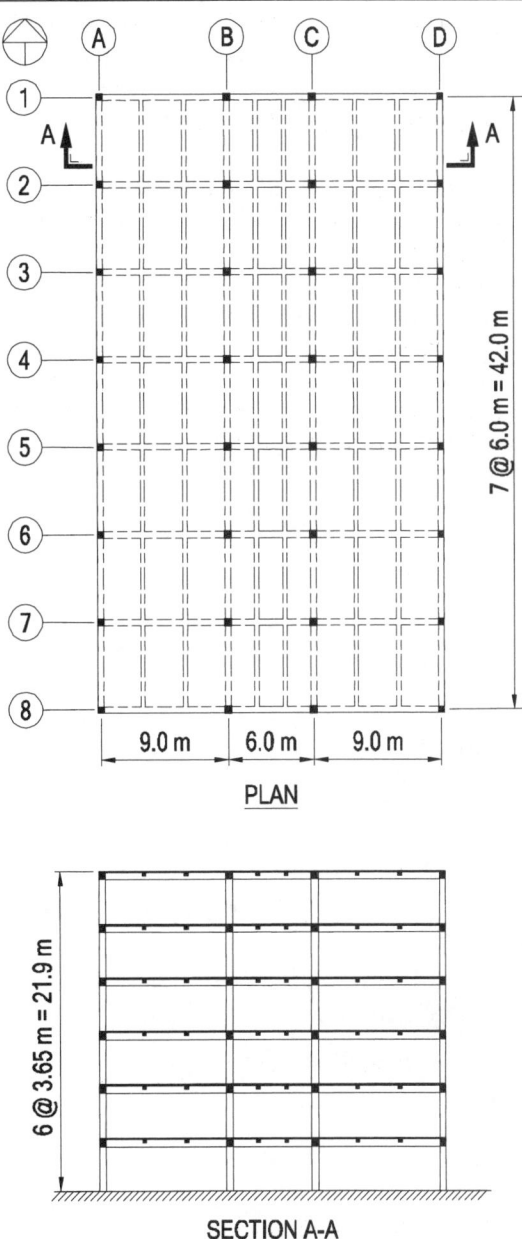

PLAN

SECTION A-A

Fig. 11.1 Six-storey structure located in Vancouver

11.4.2 Determination of Design Forces

11.4.2.1 Gravity Loading

To determine the member forces, the structure was analyzed using ETABS. To make allowances for cracking, member stiffnesses were assumed to be 0.4 of the gross I for all beams as required by CSA A23.3. To account for the influence of the axial load level on the column stiffnesses, average estimated cracked moments of inertia of 0.6 and 0.7 of I_g were used for the columns in the top three storeys and bottom three storeys, respectively (Clause 21.2.5.2). The analysis models and the gravity loading are illustrated in Fig. 11.2.

To illustrate the requirements for the design of a ductile moment-resisting frame, components of a typical interior E-W frame will be designed in the following examples.

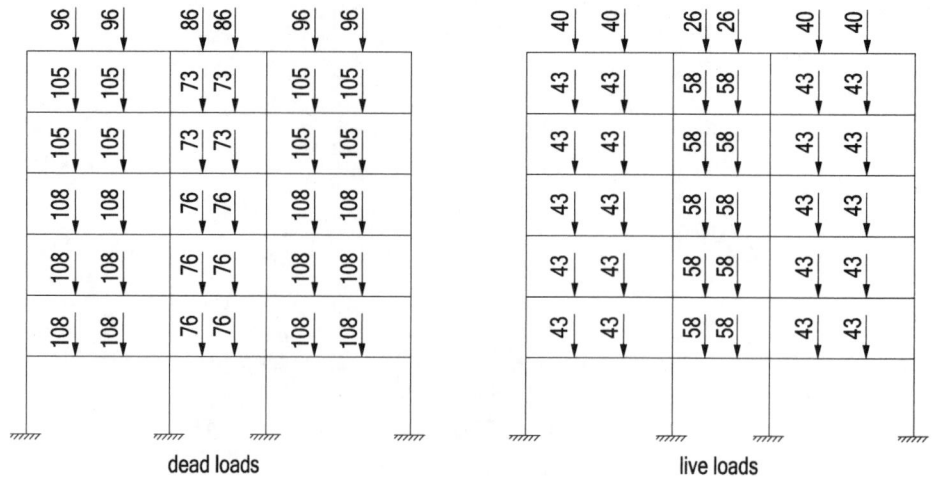

Units in kN

Fig. 11.2 Unfactored loading cases considered in design of typical interior frame

11.4.2.2 Seismic Loading

Minimum Lateral Earthquake Force

The structure is located in Vancouver and is founded on very dense soil and soft rock. Therefore the site classification is "C" and the acceleration-based and velocity-based site coefficients are $F_a = 1.0$ and $F_v = 1.0$, respectively.

The seismic response factor, S, is dependent on the fundamental period, T, of the structure. The 5% damped spectral response accelerations, $S_a(0.2)$, $S_a(0.5)$, $S_a(1.0)$ and $S_a(2.0)$ are 0.94, 0.64, 0.33 and 0.17, respectively. The design spectral response accelerations are given by the product of the site coefficients and S_a as shown in Fig. 11.3.

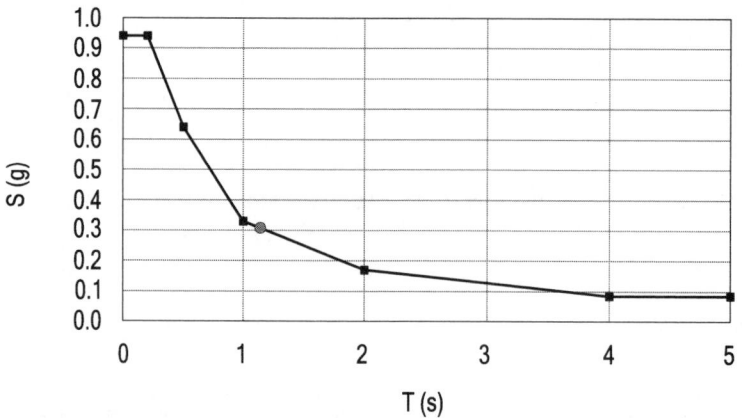

Figure 11.3 Design spectral response acceleration

The empirical fundamental lateral period, T_a, for concrete moment frames is given by:

$$T_a = 0.075h_n^{3/4} = 0.075 \times 21.9^{3/4} = 0.759\,\text{s}$$

The calculated period for this structure, using the computer program ETABS is 1.35 s. The value of the fundamental lateral period cannot be taken greater than $1.5 \times 0.759 = 1.139$, and hence use $T_a = 1.14$ s. The corresponding value of $S(T_a)$ is 0.308 (see Fig. 11.3).

For this office building, the earthquake importance factor, $I_E = 1.0$. The values of M_v and J depend on the ratio of $S_a(0.2)/S_a(2.0) = 0.94/0.17 = 5.53$ and the value of T_a. For this case $M_v = 1.0$ and $J = 1.0$.

For this ductile moment resisting frame structure $R_d = 4.0$ and $R_o = 1.7$. Hence the seismic base shear, V, is:

$$V = \frac{S(T_a)M_v I_E W}{R_d R_o} = \frac{0.308 \times 1.0 \times 1.0 \times W}{4.0 \times 1.7} = 0.0453W$$

$$V_{min} = \frac{S(2.0)M_v I_E W}{R_d R_o} = \frac{0.17 \times 1.0 \times 1.0 \times W}{4.0 \times 1.7} = 0.025W$$

$$V_{max} = \frac{2}{3}\frac{S(0.2)I_E W}{R_d R_o} = \frac{2}{3}\frac{0.94 \times 1.0 \times W}{4.0 \times 1.7} = 0.092W$$

For this structure, $W = 44{,}765$ kN.

Hence, $V = 0.0453W = 0.0453 \times 44{,}765 = 2026$ kN.

The portion of V concentrated at the top of the building is $F_t = 0.07 T_a V = 0.07 \times 1.139 \times 2026.1 = 161.5$ kN, but need not be taken greater than $0.25V = 0.25 \times 2026.1 = 506.5$ kN.

The calculations of the seismic lateral forces at each floor level are summarized in Table 11.3.

Table 11.3 Lateral Load Calculations for Each Floor Level

Floor	h_x, m	W_x, kN	$h_x W_x$, kN·m	F_x, kN	V_x, kN	T_x, kN·m
6 roof	21.90	7457	163,308	696	0	2953
5	18.25	7365	134,411	440	696	1866
4	14.60	7365	107,529	352	1,135	1493
3	10.95	7526	82,410	270	1,487	1144
2	7.30	7526	54,940	180	1,757	763
1	3.65	7526	27,470	90	1,936	381
0	0.00	-	-	0	2,026	
Total	-	44,765	570,068	2,026	-	8601

Accidental Torsion

The 3-D model shown in Fig. 11.4 was used to calculate accidental torsional effects by applying the lateral forces F_x (see Table 11.3) at an accidental eccentricity of $\pm 0.1 D_{nx}$, where D_{nx} is the plan dimension of the building at level x, perpendicular to the direction of seismic loading. This gives an accidental torsional eccentricity of 4.245 m, from the centre of mass (same as centre of rigidity) for loading in the E-W direction. The resulting floor torques, T_x, are given in Table 11.3.

11

Seismic Design

Dynamic Analysis

This symmetrical structure has no structural irregularities in the vertical or horizontal directions and in addition is not sensitive to torsion (see Section 11.4.3). Therefore, In accordance with NBCC a dynamic analysis is not required. However, a dynamic analysis was carried to determine the lateral period of vibration (see above). This dynamic analysis was also used to determine the design forces for the members and to estimate the lateral displacements. The purpose of carrying out a dynamic analysis in this example is to illustrate the approach required and to obtain a more realistic design force distribution.

The first step is to determine V_e from a linear dynamic analysis. The design base shear V_d is obtained from:

$$V_d = \frac{V_e}{R_d R_o} I_E$$

However for this regular structure, V_d shall not be taken less than $0.8V$.

All forces and deflections obtained from the linear dynamic analysis are scaled by the factor V_d / V_e to obtain the design values. However, in order to obtain realistic values of anticipated deflections and drifts, the design values need to be multiplied by $R_d R_o / I_E$.

Fig. 11.4 shows the 3-D model for the dynamic analysis, using ETABS. In the analysis, rigid end offsets were used to simulate the dimensions of the joints and rigid diaphragms were assumed. The total mass for each floor was concentrated at the centre of mass (coincident with the centre of rigidity for this structure). To account for sway effects (P-Delta) the ETABS program option, accounting for second order effects by the addition of the so-called geometric stiffness, which is a function of the compression forces in the columns from gravity loads, was used. These compressive forces were obtained from the consistent loading case of $1.0D + 0.5L + 0.25S$, with live load reduction factors.

The first three lateral modes in the E-W direction are shown in Fig. 11.5, together with the associated periods of vibration and the modal participating mass ratios. Note that the sum of these ratios is 96.9% of the total mass and hence exceeds the minimum required ratio of 90% of the total mass (NBCC). Spectral modal superposition, using SRSS for the first three modes in the E-W direction was used to determine all forces and deformations.

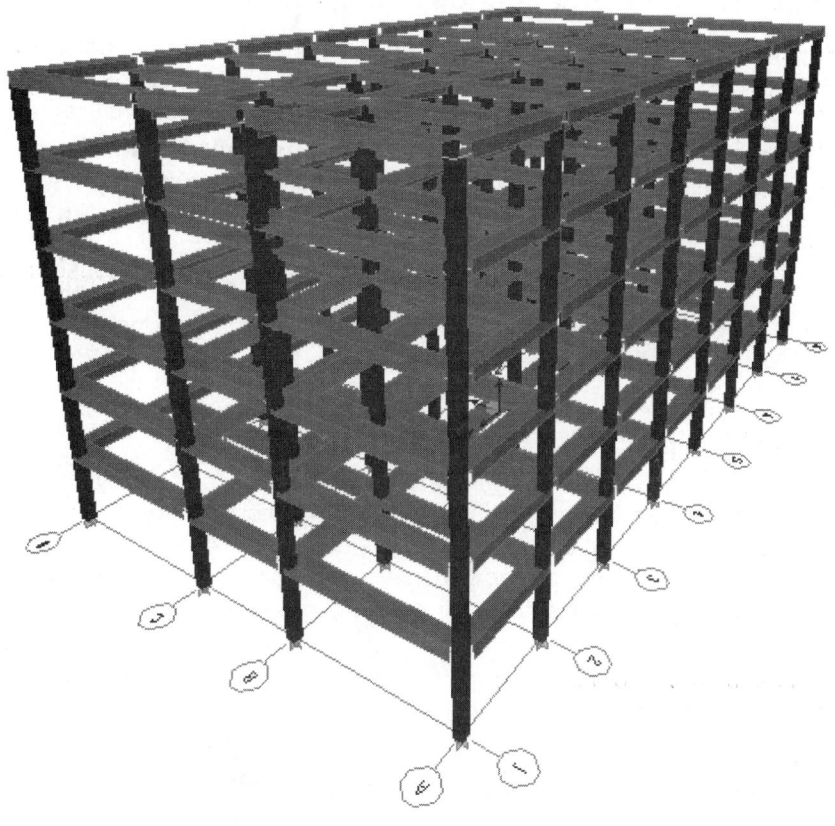

Figure 11.4 3-D Model used for dynamic analysis

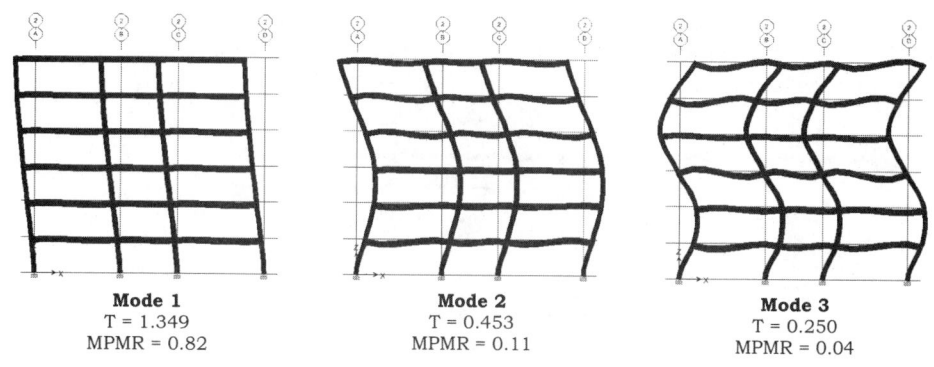

Mode 1	Mode 2	Mode 3
T = 1.349	T = 0.453	T = 0.250
MPMR = 0.82	MPMR = 0.11	MPMR = 0.04

Figure 11.5 Mode shapes, corresponding lateral periods of vibration and modal participating mass ratios

The base shear determined by dynamic analysis is $V_e = 10690$ kN.

Therefore:

$$V_d = \frac{10690}{4.0 \times 1.7} 1.0 = 1572 \text{ kN}$$

However for this regular building V_d shall not be taken less than $0.8V = 0.8 \times 2026.1 = 1620.9$ kN. Hence, all forces and deflections obtained from the dynamic analysis shall be multiplied by $V_d / V_e = 1620.9 / 10690 = 0.152$.

11.4.3   Deflections, Drift Ratios and Torsional Sensitivity

The deflections obtained from the dynamic analysis need to be multiplied by the factor 0.152 to account for the total anticipated displacements, including the inelastic effects. It is necessary to multiply these deflections by the factor $R_d R_o / I_E$ to obtain the design values. Note that the deflections obtained from dynamic analysis include P-Delta effects. The deflections arising from accidental torsional eccentricity shall be added to the deflections from the dynamic analysis.

To determine if the structure is sensitive to torsion, the value of B_x is determined from the maximum and average displacements of the structure at level x in the E-W and N-S directions. The maximum value, B, of the B_x values is at the first floor level for loading in the E-W direction (an average displacement of 5.1 mm and a maximum displacement of 6.8 mm), giving:

$$B = \frac{\delta_{max}}{\delta_{ave}} = \frac{6.8}{5.1} = 1.35$$

Because B is less than 1.7, the structure is not sensitive to torsion.

The maximum interstorey drift ratio occurs in Frames 1 and 8 in the second storey for the E-W direction of loading. From the dynamic analysis the maximum interstorey drift ratio is 0.0015 and the interstorey drift ratio from accidental torsion at this level is 0.0007, for a maximum interstorey drift ratio of 0.0022. Therefore the anticipated interstorey drift ratio, including inelastic effects is $0.0022 \times 4.0 \times 1.7 / 1.0 = 0.0146$. This anticipated maximum interstorey drift ratio is less than the NBCC limit of 0.025.

11.4.4   Design of Ductile Beam

To illustrate the procedures involved in designing a beam in a ductile moment-resisting frame, a typical first storey interior beam will be designed below. For illustration purposes frame 2 will be designed. This frame, although it has a smaller torsional shear than frame 1, will require more reinforcement than frame 1 because it carries larger dead and live loads. The details of the beam and column framing are given in Fig. 11.6.

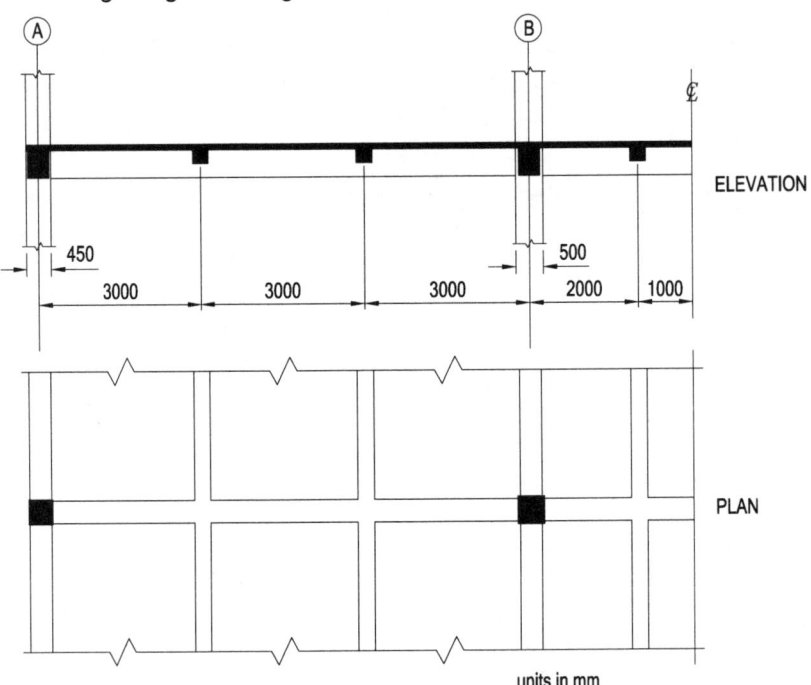

units in mm

Fig. 11.6 Typical beam and column framing

11.4.4.1 Determination of Design Moments

The moments in the beams resulting from dead load, D, live load, L, and earthquake loading, E, as determined from frame analyses, are in Fig. 11.7. Note that the moments are given at the face of the columns. Since most of the gravity loading in beams AB, BC and CD is introduced at the locations of the secondary beams, the small uniformly distributed loading has been approximated by additional concentrated loads at the secondary beam locations.

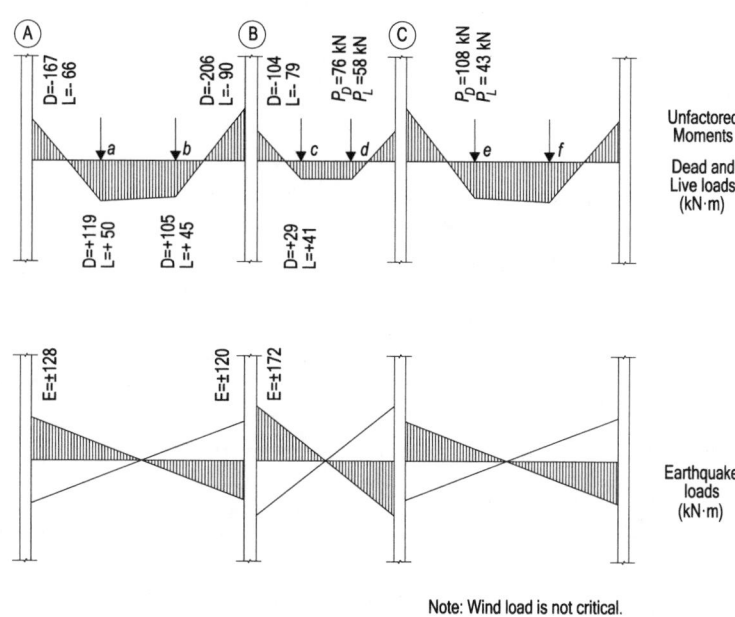

Note: Wind load is not critical.

Fig. 11.7 Loading cases on typical interior beam at second floor level

Table 11.4 gives the unfactored moments at critical locations and also gives the factored moment combinations which need to be considered.

11.4.4.2 Moment Redistribution and Moment Envelopes

Instead of designing each of the critical sections for the maximum factored moments given in Table 11.4, moment redistribution will be used to reduce some of the maximum design moments. Since the beams in a ductile moment-resisting frame structure are designed and detailed to exhibit considerable ductility the maximum redistribution of 20%, permitted by Clause 9.2.4, will be used.

While it is possible to redistribute the earthquake moments, care must be exercised to ensure that the total column shears in any one storey remain unchanged after redistribution. A simpler approach is to redistribute only the dead load and live load moments.

In order to reduce the magnitude of the negative moments at location BA, the dead and live load support moments are reduced at this location by the maximum permitted amount (20%). The positive moments in span AB are increased by the appropriate amounts. The resulting moments are summarized in Table 11.5.

Table 11.4 Moments at Critical Locations (kN·m) Before Redistribution

	AB	a	b	BA	BC	c
D	-167	+119	+105	-206	-104	+29
L	-66	+50	+45	-90	-79	+41
Accidental Torsion	± 30	± 11	± 9	± 28	± 41	± 15
E without accidental torsion	± 98	± 36	± 30	± 92	± 131	± 48
E with accidental torsion	± 128	± 47	± 39	± 120	± 172	± 63
1.25D+1.5L	-308	**+224**	**+199**	**-393**	-249	+98
1.0D+1.0E	-39	+166	+144	-86	+68	+92
1.0D-1.0E	-295	+72	+66	-326	-276	-34
1.0D+0.5L+1.0E	-72	+191	+167	-131	+29	**+112**
1.0D+0.5L-1.0E	**-328**	+97	+88	-371	**-316**	-13

Note: controlling load combinations shown in bold

Table 11.5 Moments at Critical Locations (kN·m) after Redistribution

	AB	a	b	BA	BC	c
D	-167	+132	+133	-165	-104	+29
L	-66	+56	+57	-72	-79	+41
Accidental Torsion	± 30	± 11	± 9	± 28	± 41	± 15
E without accidental torsion	± 98	± 36	± 30	± 92	± 131	± 48
E with accidental torsion	± 128	± 47	± 39	± 120	± 172	± 63
1.25D+1.5L	-308	**+249**	**+252**	-314	-249	+98
1.0D+1.0E	-39	+180	+172	-45	+68	+92
1.0D-1.0E	-295	+85	+94	-284	-276	-34
1.0D+0.5L+1.0E	-72	+208	+201	-81	+29	**+112**
1.0D+0.5L-1.0E	**-328**	+113	+122	**-320**	**-316**	-13

Note: controlling load combinations shown in bold

It is noted that, after redistribution, earthquake loading governs at all negative moment sections at the second floor level.

11.4.4.3 Design of Flexural Reinforcement at Critical Sections

Top bars at column faces

In deciding on the appropriate top reinforcement, note that Clause 21.5.5.6 limits the diameter, d_b, passing through the joint to $\ell_j / 24$ for this normal density concrete structure and uncoated bars. Thus for this case the maximum diameter of beam bars passing through the interior columns is $500 / 24 = 21$ mm. Hence the maximum beam bar size is 20M.

At column A, a factored moment resistance of at least 328 kN·m is required. Assuming a flexural lever arm of $0.75h = 0.75 \times 0.600 = 0.450$ m, the required area of top bars would be $328 \times 1000 / (0.450 \times 0.85 \times 400) = 2144$ mm^2. If it is assumed that slab reinforcement within a distance of $3h_f$ from the sides of the beam is effective, then 4–10M bars in the slab are effective.

It is assumed that these 10M bars in the flange are effective under reversed cyclic loading even though there is no anti-buckling reinforcement for these bars. Note that larger bars may not be effective. The additional reinforcement required is then 1744 mm^2. Note that it is unwise to be too conservative when designing the top reinforcement since beam shears, joint shears, column moments and column shears are all increased if the flexural capacity at the end of the beam is increased.

Let us try an arrangement of 6–20M bars as shown in Fig. 11.8. Keeping in mind that the positive moment resistance of the beam needs to be at least one-half of the negative moment resistance, try using 4–20M bars on the bottom of the beam.

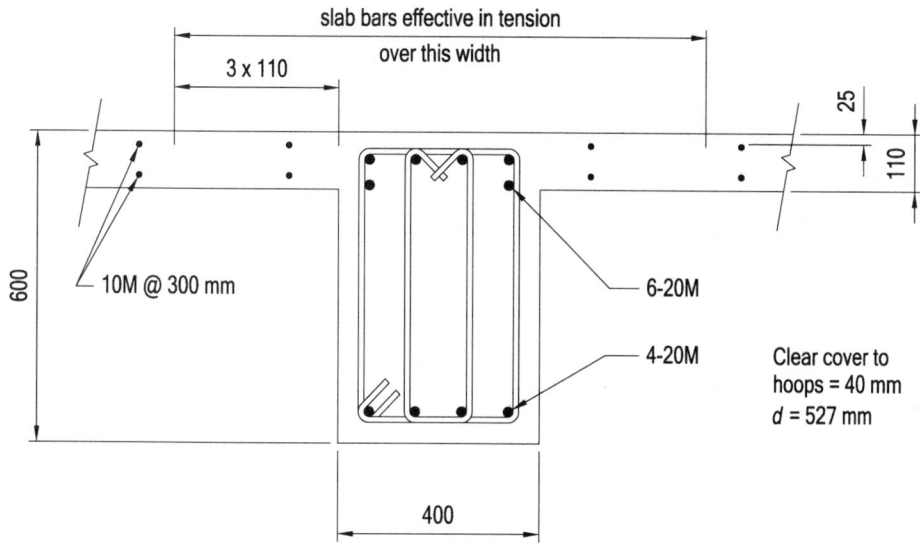

Fig. 11.8 Beam cross section near column face

Accounting for the presence of the compression reinforcement, the depth of compression, c, is found to be 92 mm and the factored negative moment resistance is 359 kN·m. Hence the moment capacity is satisfactory.

The required minimum top and bottom reinforcement, $A_{s,min}$, from Clause 21.3.2.1 is:

$$A_{s,min} = 1.4 b_w d / f_y = 1.4 \times 400 \times 527 / 400 = 738 \text{ mm}^2 \leq 1200 \text{ mm}^2 \quad \text{O.K.}$$

The maximum reinforcement permitted is:

$$0.025 b_w d = 0.025 \times 400 \times 527 = 5270 \text{ mm}^2 \geq 2200 \text{ mm}^2 \quad \text{O.K.}$$

Note that in choosing the arrangement of the beam bars at column faces the following factors must be considered:

(a) the need to restrain the longitudinal bars from buckling by providing lateral restraint in the form of hoops and ties.

(b) the need to pass the beam bars through the column cage, and

(c) the need to provide adequate space between top bars to permit placement and vibration of concrete.

Since the magnitudes of the negative moment resistances required at column faces AB, BA and BC are all about the same, we will use the same reinforcing arrangement at these three locations.

11

Seismic Design

Bottom bars for positive moment regions

Span BC:

For span BC, the effective compressive flange width is 1600 mm (see Clause 10.3.3). For 4–20M bars ($A_s = 1200$ mm²), M_r at the column face, accounting for the large amount of top reinforcement, is 229 kN·m which is larger than one half of 359 kN·m (i.e., M_r at column face where $A_s = 2200$ mm²).

As 4–20M bottom bars are provided at column faces AB, BA and BC, use 4–20M bars in span BC. The positive moment resistance M_r is 229 kN·m in the midspan regions of span BC. As 229 kN·m exceeds 112 kN·m (Table 11.5), 4-20M bars will be satisfactory.

Span AB:

For span AB, the effective compressive flange width is 2200 mm (see Clause 10.3.3). For $M_r \geq 252$ kN·m (Table 11.5) try 6- 20M bottom bars. Neglecting the top reinforcement, the depth of the equivalent rectangular stress block is 18 mm and $M_r = 315$ kN·m (see Fig. 11.9). Accounting for the large amount of top reinforcement, the positive moment M_r at the column face is 246 kN·m.

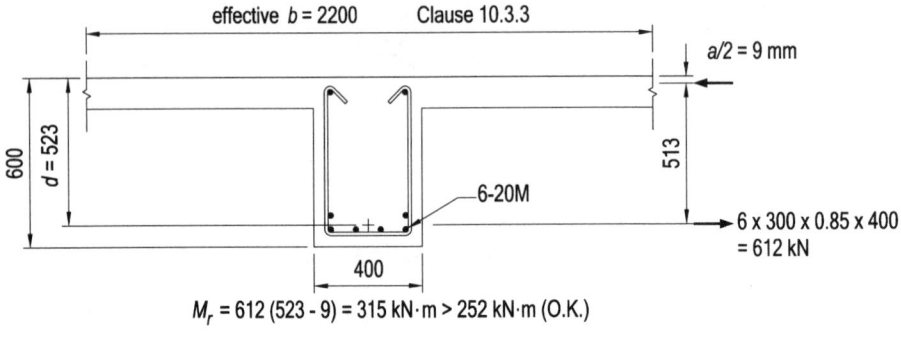

$M_r = 612 (523 - 9) = 315$ kN·m > 252 kN·m (O.K.)

Bottom bars for positive moment regions in span A-B

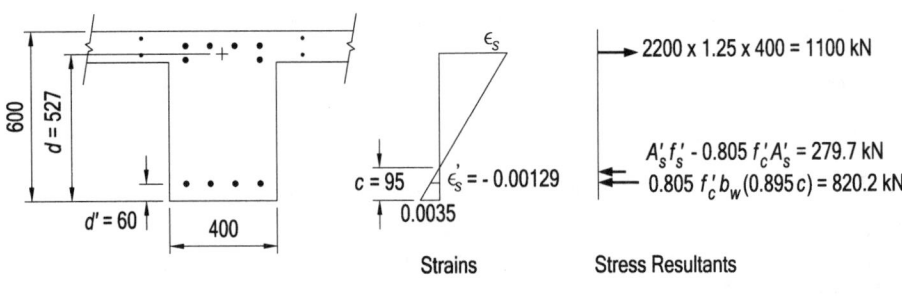

$M_{pr}^- = 820.2(527 - 85/2) + 279.7 (527 - 60) = 528$ kN·m

Probable negative moment resistance M_{pr}^-

Fig. 11.9 Positive and negative moment capacities of beam

11.4.4.4   Design of Transverse Reinforcement in Beams

Shear requirements

Determine the shears corresponding to the development of flexural hinging at both ends of the beam. For the chosen reinforcement at the beam ends the probable moment resistances are:

(i)   Probable negative moment resistance, M_{pr}^-

Using a strain compatibility approach to calculate M_{pr}^- results in a depth of compression, $c = 95$ mm, a stress block depth of 85 mm and $M_{pr}^- = 528$ kN·m (see Fig. 11.9). Note that the probable moment resistance of the beams can be estimated by multiplying M_r by the ratio $1.25 / 0.85 = 1.47$. In this case M'pr would be $359 \times 1.47 = 528$ kN·m. This simple approach is sufficiently accurate for design purposes.

(ii)   Probable positive moment resistance, M_{pr}^+

The factored moment resistance at the ends in span BC is 229 kN·m and hence we can estimate the probable moment resistance as $M_{pr}^+ = 1.47 \times 229 = 337$ kN·m. Similarly, the probable moment resistance at the ends of span AB is $1.47 \times 246 = 362$ kN·m.

(iii) Determine factored shears

The shear diagrams shown in Fig. 11.10 are drawn for lateral forces acting in the west direction. For lateral forces acting in the east direction the shear diagrams will be "mirror images" of those shown (e.g., the shear at B would be 234 kN).

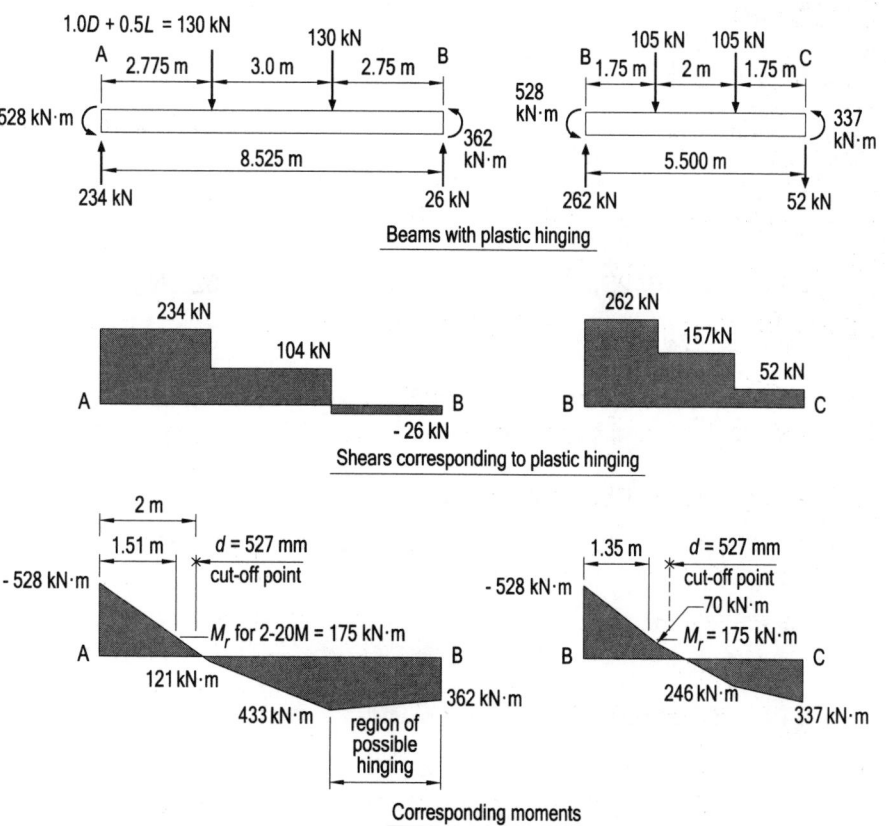

Fig. 11.10 Determinaton of shears corresponding to flexural hinging

Using $\theta = 45°$ and $\beta = 0$ gives (Clause 21.3.4.2):

$$V_r = \phi_s A_v f_y d_v / s$$

At the column faces the transverse reinforcement consists of 4–10M legs, hence $A_v = 400$ mm^2.

At the ends A and B the required spacing for shear is:

$$s = \frac{0.85 \times 400 \times 400 \times 0.9 \times 527}{234 \times 1000} = 276 \ \text{mm}$$

At the ends B and C the required spacing for shear is:

$$s = \frac{234}{262} \times 276 = 247 \ \text{mm}.$$

If 2-legged 10M stirrups are used as transverse reinforcement ($A_v = 200$ mm^2) the required spacings in the middle regions of beams AB and BC are 344 mm and 228 mm, respectively.

Other shear design requirements:

(i)   Maximum shear (Clause 11.3.3)

$$V_{r,max} = 0.25\phi_c f_c' b_w d_v = 0.25 \times 0.65 \times 30 \times 400 \times 0.9 \times 527 = 925 \ \text{kN}$$

(ii)   Minimum amount of stirrups (Clause 11.2.8.2):

for 4 stirrup legs:

$$s \leq \frac{A_v f_y}{0.06 \sqrt{f_c'} \, b_w} = \frac{400 \times 400}{0.06 \sqrt{30} \times 400} = 1217 \ \text{mm}$$

for 2 stirrup legs:

$$s \leq 608 \ \text{mm}$$

(iii)   Spacing limits (Clause 11.3.8.3):

Since $V_f < 0.125 \, \phi_c \, f_c' \, b_w \, d_v = 0.125 \times 0.65 \times 30 \times 400 \times 0.9 \times 527 = 462 \ \text{kN}$

Then $s_{max} = 600$ mm or $0.7 d_v = 0.7 \times 0.9 \times 527 = 332$ mm.

Note that near the ends of the beams the stirrup spacing required for shear cannot exceed 276 and 247 mm for spans AB and BC, respectively.

"Anti-buckling" requirements (Clause 21.3.3.2)

Hoops to prevent buckling of longitudinal bars are required over a length of 2d from the face of the columns. The spacing of the hoops shall not exceed:

(i) $d/4 = 527/4 = 132$ mm

(ii) $8d_{bl} = 8 \times 20 = 160$ mm

(iii) $24d_{bh} = 24 \times 10 = 240$ mm

(iv)   300 mm

Note that the 4-legged arrangement of transverse reinforcement satisfies Clause 21.3.3.3. Hence use a spacing of 130 mm for 4-legged hoops over a length of at least $2d = 2 \times 527 = 1054$ mm.

11.4.4.5   Checking Extent of Plastic Hinging

The moment diagrams corresponding to plastic hinging at both ends of beams AB and BC are shown in Fig. 11.10. Hinging can spread over a distance of about 3.43 m from the face of column B in beam AB. Since the earthquake loading can reverse, provide 4-legged hoop reinforcement spaced at 130 mm as shown in Fig. 11.11. The bottom 4-20M bars can only be spliced near midspan of the beam (Clause 21.3.2.3). Therefore, to satisfy the maximum spacing requirements of Clause 21.3.2.3 for regions of lap splices, provide 2-legged hoops spaced at 100 mm in the middle region of beam AB (see Fig. 11.11). For span BC, provide 4-legged hoops at a spacing of 130 mm over a distance of $2d$ (1054 mm) from the column faces. Outside of these regions, the provision of 2-legged hoops at a spacing of 100 mm satisfies both the shear requirements and the confinement requirements for lap splices (see Fig. 11.11).

11.4.4.6   Bar Cut-offs

The locations of bar cut-offs are determined from the moment diagrams corresponding to the formation of plastic hinges at the ends of the beams. The theoretical cut-off location is located at a distance of 1.51 m from the face of the column (see Fig. 11.10). From Clause 12.10.4 it is required to provide an embedment length beyond the theoretical cut-off point of at least d or $12d_b$. Hence the minimum length required is $1510 + d = 1510 + 527 = 2037$ mm. Continue the 6–20M top bars a distance of 3 m from the column face such that the bars are terminated in a region of lower shear. For span BC, extend the 6-20M top bars a distance of 2.0 m from the face of the column.

11.4.4.7   Splice Details

Flexural reinforcement cannot be spliced within a distance of 2d from the column face nor within a distance d from of a potential plastic hinge location (Clause 21.3.2.3). In evaluating cut-off locations, d was taken as 527 mm.

In determining locations of bar cut-offs and splices we will consider the moment diagram corresponding to the formation of hinges at the ends of the beams (see Fig. 11.10). The splices for the top bars will be located in a region of the beam where the bars are predicted to remain in compression. However, as it is required to have a minimum negative and positive moment resistance at the face of the joint (Clause 21.3.2.2) the splice length will be calculated as for a tension splice.

(a)   Splicing of the 2–20M "continuous" top bars

The required minimum moment capacity along the length of the beam (Clause 21.3.2.2) is $0.25 \times 359 = 90$ kN·m. M_r for 2-20M top bars is 175 kN·m. Hence for the classification of tension lap splices in accordance with Clause 12.15.2 (A_s provided)/ A_s required) is $175 / 90 = 1.94$. Hence Class B splices are required. The development length ℓ_d for these top bars from Table 12-1 is:

$$\ell_d = 0.45k_1k_2k_3k_4 \frac{f_y}{\sqrt{f'_c}} d_b = 0.45 \times 1.3 \times 1 \times 1 \times 0.8 \times \frac{400}{\sqrt{30}} \times 20 = 684 \text{ mm}$$

Thus the splice length is $1.3 \times 684 = 890$ mm.

(b)   Splicing of the 4–20M "continuous" bars

The development length for these bottom bars is:

$$\ell_d = 0.45k_1k_2k_3k_4 \frac{f_y}{\sqrt{f'_c}} d_b = 0.45 \times 1 \times 1 \times 1 \times 0.8 \times \frac{400}{\sqrt{30}} \times 20 = 526 \text{ mm}$$

Thus the splice length is $1.3 \times 526 = 684$ mm.

The details of the reinforcement in the beam are illustrated in Fig. 11.11.

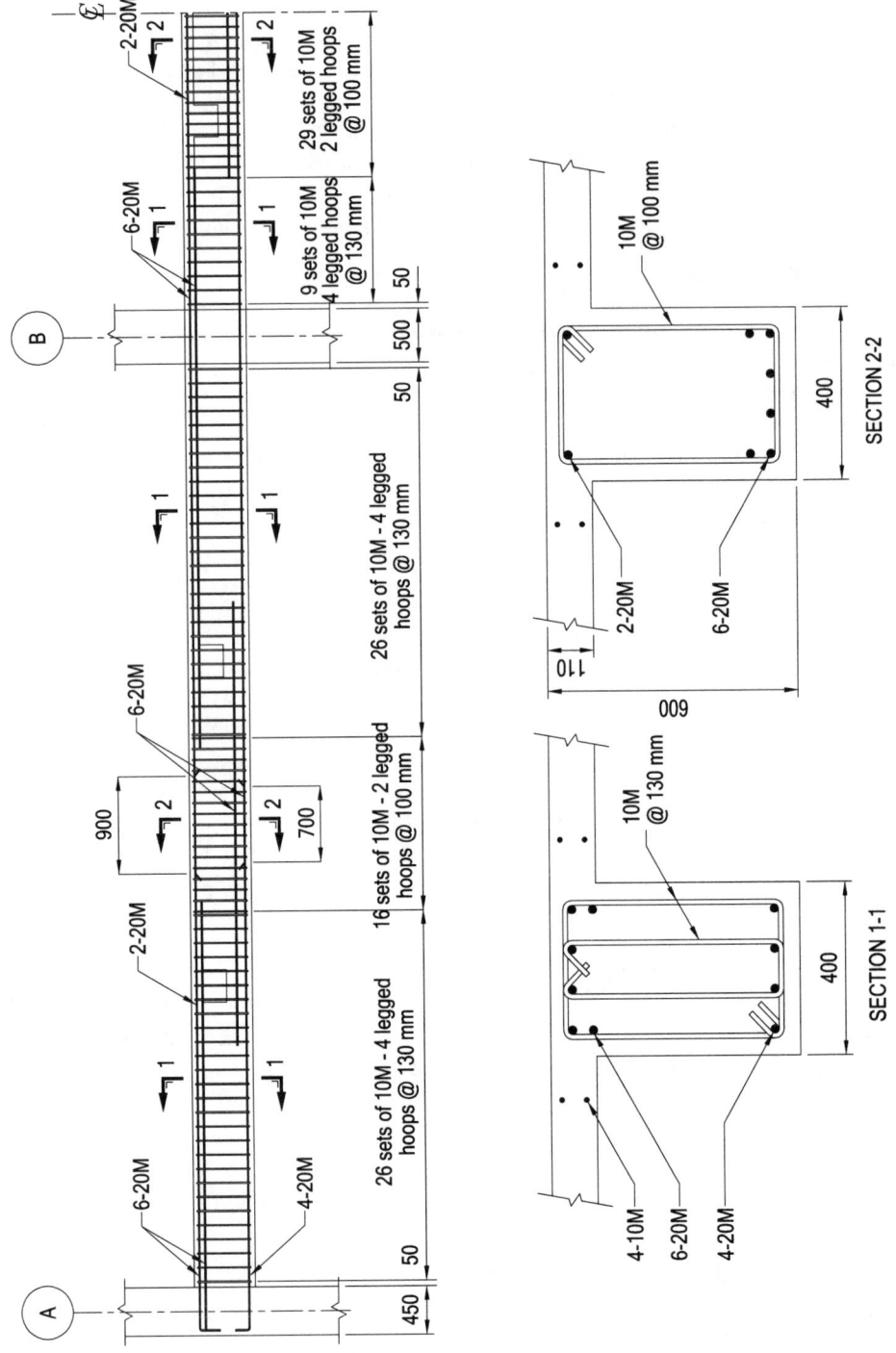

Fig. 11.11 Reinforcement details in beams

11.4.5   Design of Interior Ductile Column

To illustrate the procedures involved in designing a column in a ductile moment resisting frame a typical first storey interior column in Frame 2 or 7 of the building described in Section 11.4 will be designed. The column that will be designed is shown in Fig. 11.12.

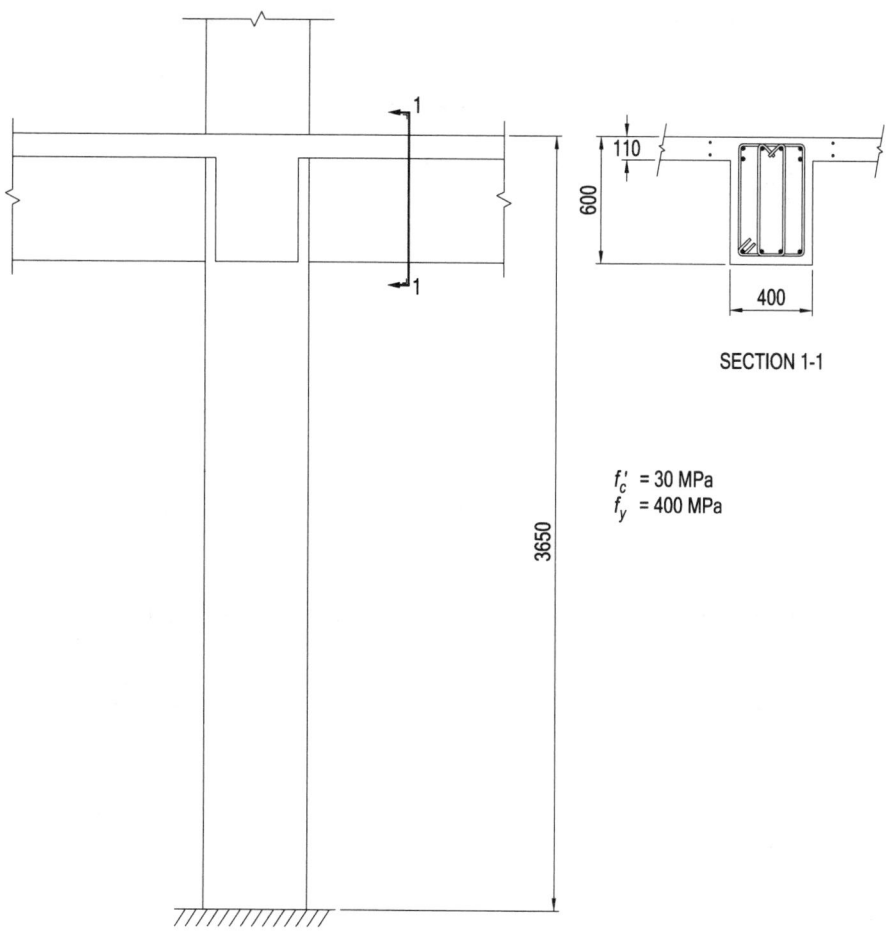

Fig. 11.12 Beam-column framing

11.4.5.1   Column End-Actions from Analysis

The column end actions obtained from analysis are summarized in Table 11.6. The earthquake forces given are those for lateral seismic forces acting in the E-W direction. For the live load values, pattern loading and live load reduction values were considered.

Table 11.6 Column End Actions

	P_D kN	P_L kN	P_E kN	M_D kN·m	M_L kN·m	M_E kN·m	V_D kN	V_L kN	V_E kN
2nd floor bottom of column	1598	486	±106	+41	+28	±147	+20	+13	±92
1st floor top of column	1704	556	±137	-53	-37	±112	+28	+19	±94
1st floor bottom of column	1704	556	±137	+32	+22	±183	+28	+19	±94

11.4.5.2 Factored Axial Loads and Moments

The column must be designed to resist the appropriate combinations of axial load and moment. From Table 11.6, it is evident that the factored moments at the base of the column will be larger than that at the top.

For the base of the column at the ground floor level the factored axial load and moment combinations are given in Table 11.7.

Table 11.7 Factored Axial Load and Moments at Column Bases

	Case 1 1.25D +1.5L	Case 2 1.0D +1.0E	Case 3 1.0D -1.0E	Case 4 1.0D+0.5L +1.0E	Case 5 1.0D+0.5L -1.0E
P_f kN	-2964	-1841	-1567	-2119	-1845
M_f kN·m	+73	+216	-151	+226	-140

Note that for this member $A_g f_c' / 10 = (500 \times 500) \times 30 / 10 = 750$ kN. As P_f exceeds this value, the requirements of Clause 21.4 apply (Clause 21.4.1.1).

11.4.5.3 Preliminary Selection of Column Reinforcement

In selecting the column bars, recall that the diameter of these bars must satisfy the requirements that $d_b \leq \ell_j / 24 = 600 / 24 = 25$ mm (Clause 21.5.5.6) for this normal density concrete and for uncoated bars. Hence the maximum bar size is 25M. Try using 8-25M bars as shown in Fig. 11.13.

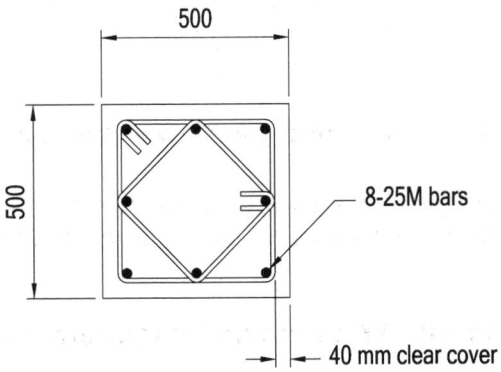

500

500

8-25M bars

40 mm clear cover

Fig. 11.13 Column reinforcement details

For this arrangement of reinforcement $A_{st} = 8 \times 500 = 4000$ mm^2. From Clause 21.4.3.1 the minimum area of longitudinal steel is $0.01 \times 500 \times 500 = 2500$ mm^2 and the maximum area of longitudinal steel outside of lap splice regions (assuming lap splicing with an equal area of steel) is $0.03 \times 500 \times 500 = 7500$ mm^2. Hence this steel arrangement satisfies these requirements.

Checking Column Capacity

The axial load-moment interaction diagram for the chosen column section is shown in Fig. 11.14. It can be seen that the column has adequate capacity to resist the various combinations of P_f and M_f which occur at the base of the column.

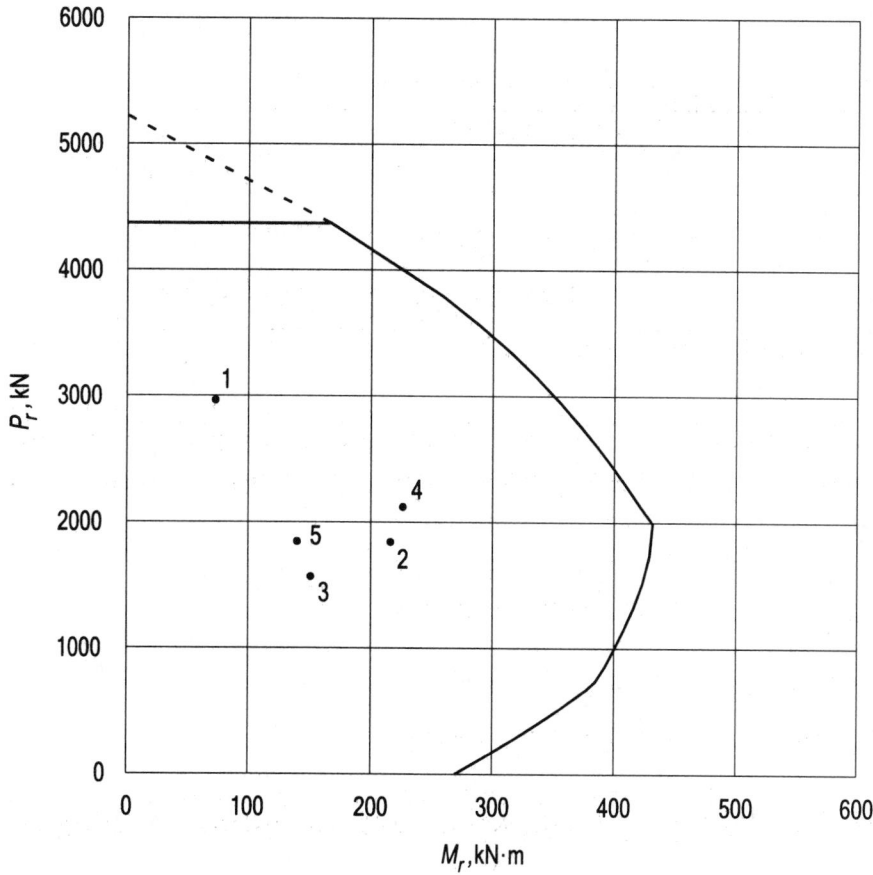

Fig. 11.14 P_r - M_r **interaction diagram for column section**

Although there is a considerable excess of moment capacity in the column, this additional capacity is needed at the top of the column in order to ensure that the columns are stronger than the beams (see below).

11.4.5.4 "Strong Column - Weak Beam" Requirement

The flexural capacity of the columns must exceed the flexural capacity of the beams so that

$$\sum M_{nc} \geq \sum M_{pb}$$

Hence it is necessary to first determine the probable resistances of the beams framing into the column.

(a)   Probable negative moment resistance, M_{pb}^-

Note that the probable resistance, M_{pb}^-, can be approximated as $1.47 M_r = 1.47 \times 359 = 528$ kN·m. This simple approach is sufficiently accurate for design purposes as can be seen from Fig. 11.9.

(b)   Nominal positive moment resistance, M_{pb}^+

$M_{pb}^+ = 1.47 \times 246 = 362$ kN·m.

(c)   Determination of $\sum M_{nc}$

To determine $\sum M_{nc}$ for a particular loading case we need to calculate the nominal moment resistance of the column above and below the beam-column joint. The lowest flexural resistance will occur at either the highest or lowest axial load, that is, load cases 3 and 4 need to be investigated (load case 1 does not involve lateral load). The axial load corresponding to cases 3 and 4 are given in Fig. 11.15 along with the column nominal moment resistances corresponding to these axial loads (from the P-M interaction diagram).

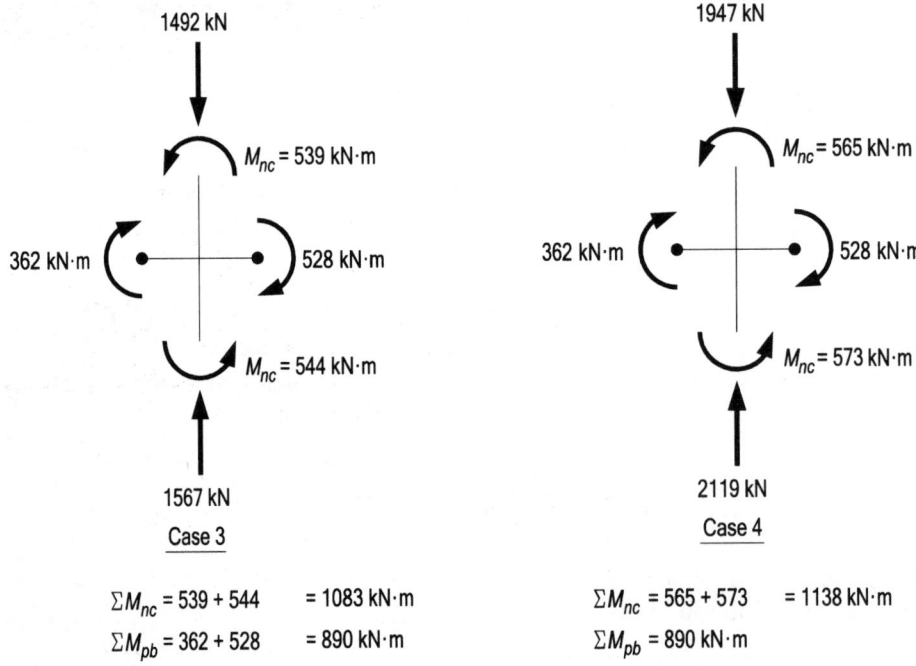

$\sum M_{nc} = 539 + 544$ = 1083 kN·m	$\sum M_{nc} = 565 + 573$ = 1138 kN·m
$\sum M_{pb} = 362 + 528$ = 890 kN·m	$\sum M_{pb} = 890$ kN·m

Fig. 11.15 Capacity design of columns and factored loads on column

Thus the requirement that $\sum M_{nc} \geq \sum M_{pb}$ is satisfied. Note that for simplicity the above calculations have neglected the influence of the beam and column shears acting at the joint faces.

11.4.5.5   Design of Transverse Reinforcement in Column

Shear requirements

The column must have a factored shear resistance, V_r, which exceeds the column shear corresponding to the probable moment resistance in the beams and which exceeds the shear forces due to factored loads (Clause 21.4.5.1). From Table 11.6, load case 4 $(1.0D + 0.5L + 1.0E)$ gives the maximum factored shear of 132 kN.

The moment at the top of the column corresponding to the development of the probable moment resistances of the beams may be estimated from:

$$M_c = \left(M_{pr}^+ + M_{pr}^-\right) \times \frac{K_c}{\sum K_c} = (362 + 528) \times \frac{1/3.05}{2 \times 1/3.05} = 445 \text{ kN·m}$$

However since we are designing a ground storey column a different approach is required at the base of this column. It is assumed that the column frames into a substructure that is considerably stronger and stiffer than the column and hence the possibility of hinging at the column base must be accounted for. To ensure adequate column shear capacity, it is necessary to determine the maximum probable moment resistance corresponding to all axial loads. Because the axial loads for all the seismic load cases are close to the balanced axial load level, the moment at the base of the column will be taken as the probable moment resistance corresponding to the balanced loading conditions (i.e., the highest probable moment resistance possible). The calculations involved in determining this moment resistance are summarized in Fig. 11.16.

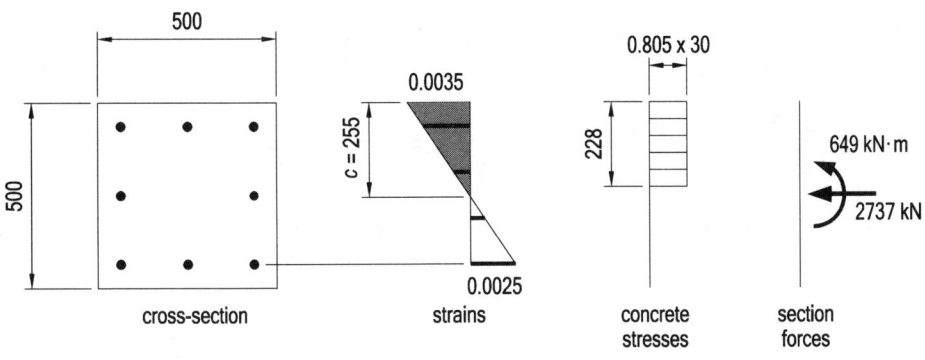

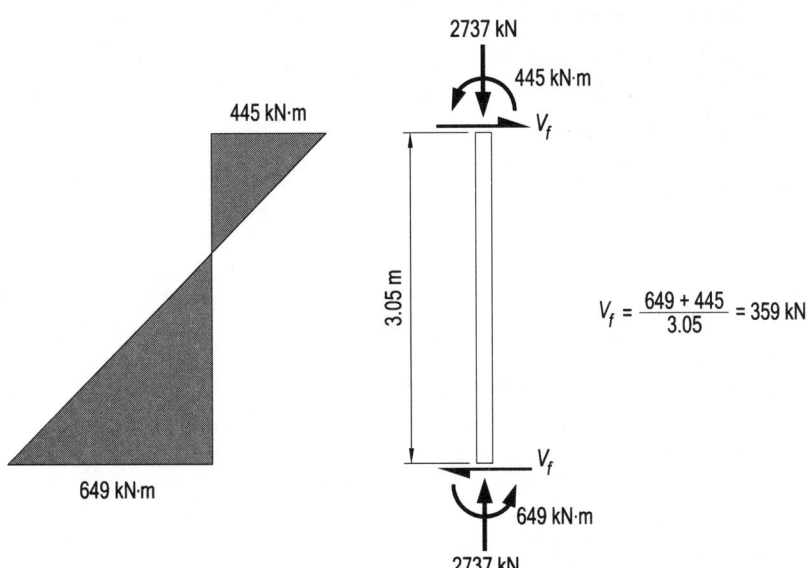

Fig. 11.16 Determination of factored shear strength in ground storey column

The column actions which will correspond to the formation of hinges in the beams at the top of the column and the formation of a hinge at the base of the column are shown in Fig. 11.16.

From Clause 21.4.5.2 the shear carried by the concrete is determined with values of β and θ taken from Clause 11 but limited to a maximum of 0.10 and a minimum of 45°, respectively. For this column containing greater than minimum amounts of transverse reinforcement and subjected to axial compression, Clause 11.3.6.3 applies, but the limits for β and θ given above control. The shear resistance attributed to the concrete, assuming that $d_v = 0.72h$, is:

$$V_c = \phi_c \lambda \beta \sqrt{f_c'} b_w d_v = 0.65 \times 0.10 \times \sqrt{30} \times 500 \times 0.72 \times 500 = 64.1 \text{ kN}$$

The required V_s is equal to $359 - 64.1 = 294.9$ kN. Using the transverse reinforcement arrangement shown in Fig. 11.13 with square and diamond shaped hoops, the effective area of shear reinforcement is $A_v = (2 + 2\cos 45°) \times 100 = 3.41 \times 100 = 341$ mm^2. Hence, the required stirrup spacing can be found from Equation (11-7) as:

$$s = \frac{\phi_s A_v f_y d_v \cot \theta}{V_s} = \frac{0.85 \times 341 \times 400 \times 0.72 \times 500 \times \cot 45°}{294.9 \times 1000} = 142 \text{ mm}$$

Since V_f of 359 kN is less than $0.125 \lambda \phi_c f_c' b_w d_v = 439$ kN, then from Clause 11.3.8.1, the maximum spacing of the shear reinforcement is the smaller of $0.7 \times 0.72 \times 500 = 252$ mm or 600 mm.

In order to satisfy the minimum shear reinforcement requirements of Clause 11.2.8.2, the maximum spacing of the 10M stirrups is:

$$s = \frac{A_v f_y}{0.06 \sqrt{f_c'} b_w} = \frac{341 \times 400}{0.06 \times \sqrt{30} \times 500} = 830 \text{ mm}$$

Therefore for shear a spacing of 142 mm controls.

(b) Confinement requirements

Since the column under consideration is at the base of the structure confinement reinforcement must be provided over the full height of the column (Clause 21.4.4.6).

From Clause 21.4.4.2, the total cross-sectional area of rectangular hoop reinforcement depends on the following factors:

$$k_n = \frac{n_\ell}{n_\ell - 2} = \frac{8}{8 - 2} = 1.33$$

$$P_o = \alpha_1 f_c' (A_g - A_{st}) + f_y A_{st} = 0.805 \times 30 (500^2 - 4000) + 400 \times 4000 = 7541 \text{ kN}$$

$$k_p = P_f / P_o = 2119 / 7541 = 0.281$$

Hence, the total area of confinement reinforcement is:

$$A_{sh} = 0.2 k_n k_p \frac{A_g}{A_{ch}} \frac{f_c'}{f_{yh}} sh_c = 0.2 \times 1.33 \times 0.281 \times \frac{500^2}{420^2} \times \frac{30}{400} \times 420s = 3.34s$$

but not less than:

$$A_{sh} = 0.09 sh_c \frac{f_c'}{f_{yh}} = 0.09 \times 420 \times \frac{30}{400} s = 2.84s$$

For $A_{sh} = 341 \text{mm}^2$, $s = 341 / 3.34 = 102$ mm.

From Clause 21.4.4.3 the spacing of the hoops shall not exceed:

(i) $h/4 = 500/4 = 125$ mm

(ii) $6d_b = 6 \times 25 = 150$ mm

(iii) $s_x = 100 + (350 - h_x)/3 = 100 + (350 - 187.5)/3 = 154$ mm

Hence use 10M hoops at 100 mm centres as shown in Fig. 11.17. The chosen arrangement of hoops and longitudinal reinforcement also satisfies Clauses 21.4.4.4 and 7.6.5. The details of the first-storey column reinforcement are given in Fig. 11.17.

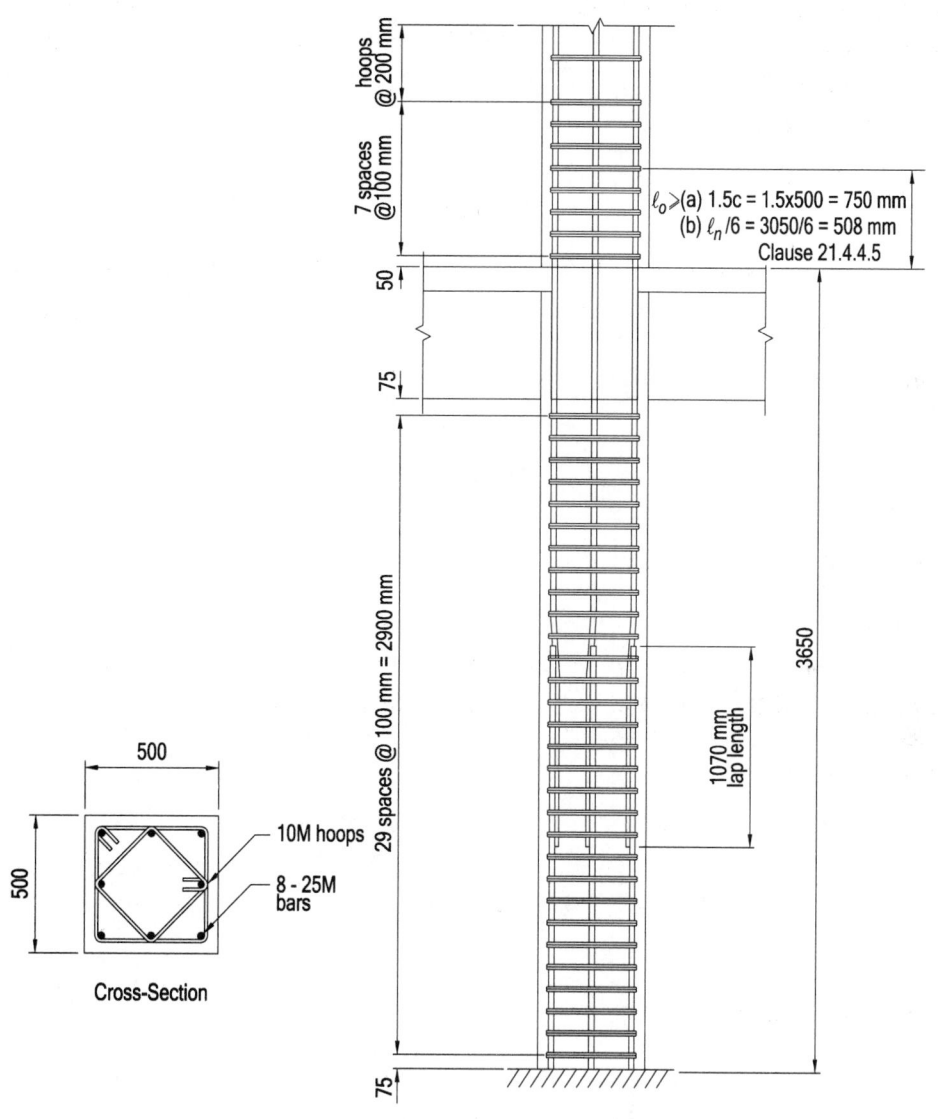

Fig. 11.17 Details of reinforcement in first-storey column

11.4.5.6 Splice Details

We will splice the column bars at mid-height of the column with tension lap splices in accordance with Clause 21.4.3.2. The development length, ℓ_d, can be found from Table 12-1 as:

$$\ell_d = 0.45k_1k_2k_3k_4\frac{f_y}{\sqrt{f_c'}}d_b = 0.45 \times 1 \times 1 \times 1 \times 1 \times \frac{400}{\sqrt{30}} \times 25 = 822 \text{ mm}$$

Provide a lap length of $1.3\ell_d = 1.3 \times 822 = 1068$ mm (see Fig. 11.17).

11.4.6   Design of Interior Beam-Column Joint

To illustrate the procedures involved in designing a beam-column joint in a ductile moment-resisting frame, an interior joint in the structure described in Section 11.4 will be designed. A description of the joint details is given in Fig. 11.18.

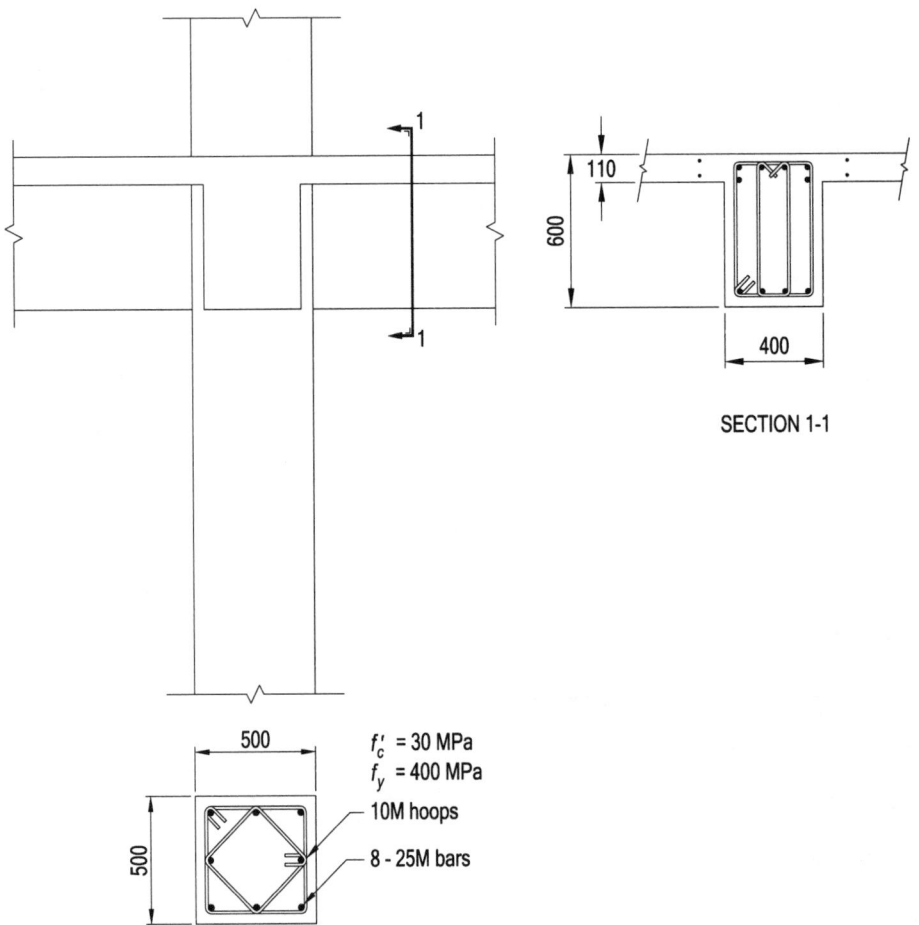

$f_c' = 30$ MPa
$f_y = 400$ MPa
— 10M hoops
— 8 - 25M bars

Fig. 11.18 Geometry of interior beam-column joint

11.4.6.1 Determination of Factored Forces in Joint

In accordance with Clause 21.5.1.2, assume that the tensile force in the beam reinforcement is $1.25A_sf_y$.

To estimate the corresponding shear, V_{col}, in the column above the joint, assume that flexural hinging occurs in the beams at the first and second storey levels. The calculations are summarized in Fig. 11.19.

(a)

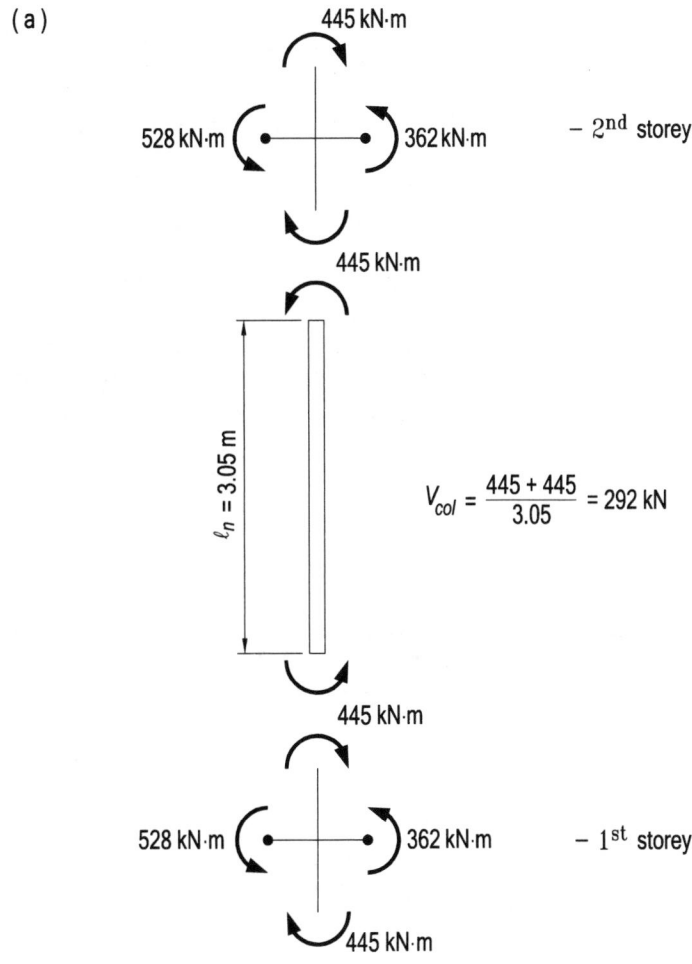

$$V_{col} = \frac{445 + 445}{3.05} = 292 \text{ kN}$$

(b)

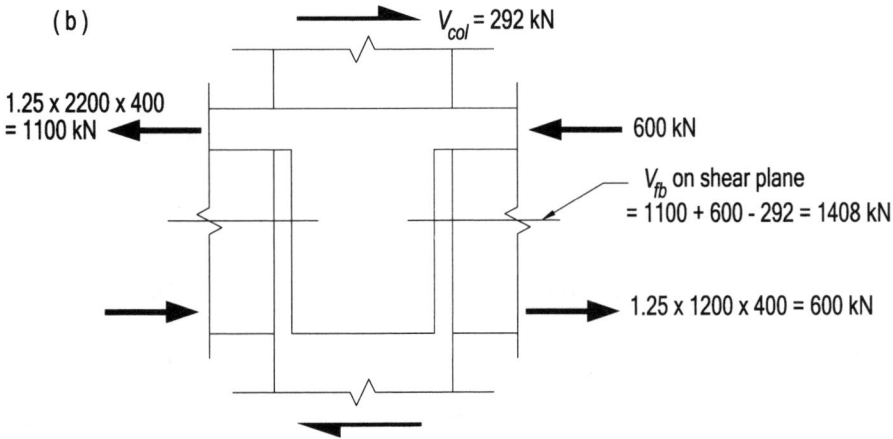

Fig. 11.19 Determination of factored shear resistance in joint

11

Seismic Design

11.4.6.2 Check Factored Shear Resistance of Joint

Since four equal depth beams frame into the joint and each covers more than 3/4 of each face of the joint, the joint is considered to be externally confined (Clause 21.5.4.1). Hence the factored shear resistance of the joint is taken as:

$$V_r = 2.2\lambda\phi_c \sqrt{f'_c}\, A_j = 2.2 \times 0.65\sqrt{30} \times 500 \times 500 = 1958 \text{ kN}$$

As the design shear in the joint of 1408 kN is less than 1958 kN, the shear resistance of the joint is adequate.

11.4.6.3 Transverse Reinforcement Required in Joint

As the joint is framed by four equal depth beams which provide confinement, only one-half of the confinement steel required for the column is required through the joint (Clause 21.5.2.2). The spacing required for confinement in the joint is therefore 200 mm. However the spacing limits of Clause 21.4.4.3 control ($s_{max} = h/4 = 125$ mm). Hence provide 3 sets of 10M hoops between the flexural bars in the beams as shown in Fig. 11.20.

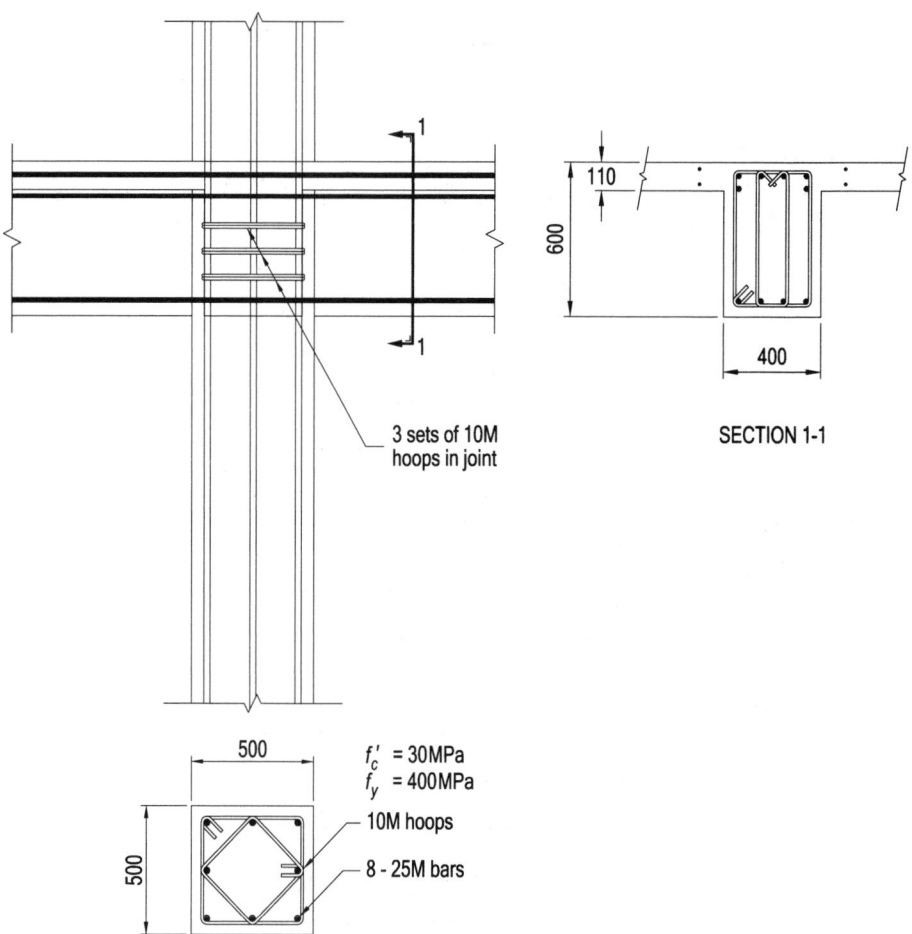

3 sets of 10M
hoops in joint

110

600

400

SECTION 1-1

500

500

$f'_c = 30$MPa
$f_y = 400$MPa

10M hoops

8 - 25M bars

Fig. 11.20 Details of joint reinforcement

11.4.6.4   Bond of beam Bars

As the beam bars pass through the joint their bond characteristics are checked by the requirement in Clause 21.5.5.6 that the bar diameters be not greater than $\ell_j / 24 = 500 / 24 = 21$ mm (normal density concrete and uncoated bars). Since this exceeds the actual bar diameter of 20 mm this requirement is met.

11.5   Analysis of a Ductile Core-Wall Structure

11.5.1   Description of Building and Loads

The twelve-storey reinforced concrete building shown in Fig. 11.21 is located in Montreal and is founded on stiff soil.

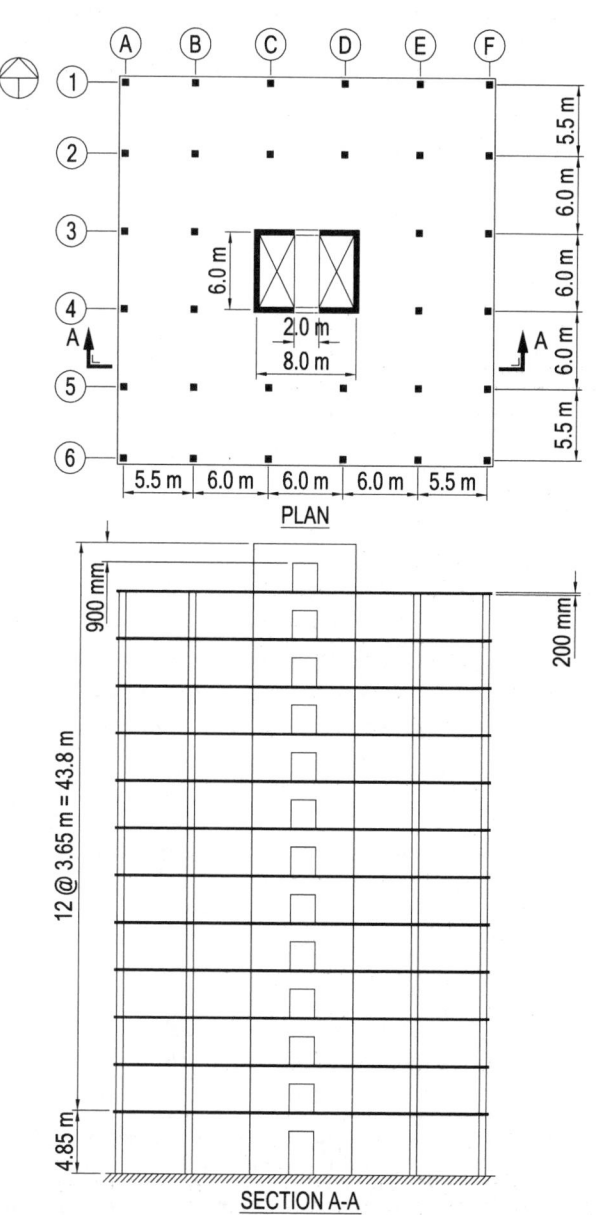

11

Seismic Design

Fig. 11.21 Plan and elevation of twelve-storey office building

The twelve-storey reinforced concrete office building has a centrally located elevator core. Each floor consists of a 200 mm thick flat plate with 6 m interior spans and 5.5 m end spans. The columns are all 550 x 550 mm and the thickness of the core wall components 400 mm. The 400 mm thick wall thickness was initially chosen such that it exceeds $\ell_u / 14 = 4650 / 14 = 332$ mm (Clause 21.6.3). This value is checked in Section 11.5.6.5. The core wall measures 6.4 m by 8.4 m, outside to outside of the walls. Two 400 mm wide x 900 mm deep coupling beams connect the two C-shaped walls at the ceiling level of each floor. The core walls extend one storey above the roof at the 12th floor level forming an elevator penthouse at the 13th floor level. The slab has a 100 mm overhang.

Material Properties

Concrete: normal density concrete with $f_c' = 30$ MPa

Reinforcement: $f_y = 400$ MPa

Gravity and Wind Loadings

Floor live load: 2.4 kN/m^2 on typical office floors
                     4.8 kN/m^2 on 12 m by 12 m corridor area around core

Roof load: 2.2 kN/m^2 full snow load
                     1.6 kN/m^2 mechanical services loading in 6 m wide strip over corridor bay

Dead loads: self-weight of members calculated at 24 kN/m^3
                     1.0 kN/m^2 partition loading on all floors
                     0.5 kN/m^2 ceiling and mechanical services loading on all floors
                     0.5 kN/m^2 roofing

Wind loading: varies from 1.1 to 1.37 kN/m^2 net lateral pressure over the height of the building

The building is to be designed with a fire-resistance rating of 2 hours.

11.5.2   Analysis Assumptions

To determine the forces in the walls and the coupling beams and the periods of vibration, the three-dimensional core wall system was analyzed using ETABS. To make allowances for cracking, member stiffnesses were based on effective properties equal to $0.25I_g$ for the moment of inertia and $0.45A_g$ for the shear area for all diagonally reinforced coupling beams as required by Clause 21.2.5.2.1. The walls were modeled with an effective flexural stiffness of $0.7EI_g$ and an effective axial stiffness of $0.7EA_g$, determined as a function of the axial loading at the base of the walls (see Clause 21.2.5.2.1).

11.5.3   Seismic loading

For the force modification factors, R_d and R_o, we will assume that the core-wall system will take 100% of the lateral loads as allowed by the NBCC. In the N-S direction we will design and detail the walls as ductile shear walls and hence $R_d = 3.5$ and $R_o = 1.6$. In the E-W direction we will design and detail the coupling beams and walls as a ductile coupled wall system and hence $R_d = 4.0$ and $R_o = 1.7$. In order for the E-W direction to qualify as a ductile coupled wall system we must check the degree of coupling as determined by analysis of the structure.

11.5.3.1   Minimum Lateral Earthquake Force

The structure is located in Montreal and is founded on stiff soil. Therefore the site classification is "D". The acceleration-based site coefficient $F_a = 1.124$ and the velocity-based site coefficient $F_v = 1.360$. The seismic response factor, $S(T_a)$, is dependent on the fundamental period, T_a, of the structure. The 5% damped spectral response accelerations, $S_a(T)$, for Montreal are given in Table 11.8. Table 11.8 also gives the design spectral response accelerations, $S(T)$, obtained from the product of the site coefficients and S_a as shown in Fig. 11.22.

Table 11.8 Spectral response accelerations and design spectral response accelerations

	$T \leq 0.2$	$T = 0.5$	$T = 1.0$	$T = 2.0$	$T \geq 4.0$
$S_a(T)$	0.69	0.34	0.14	0.048	0.024
$S(T)$	0.776	0.462	0.190	0.065	0.033

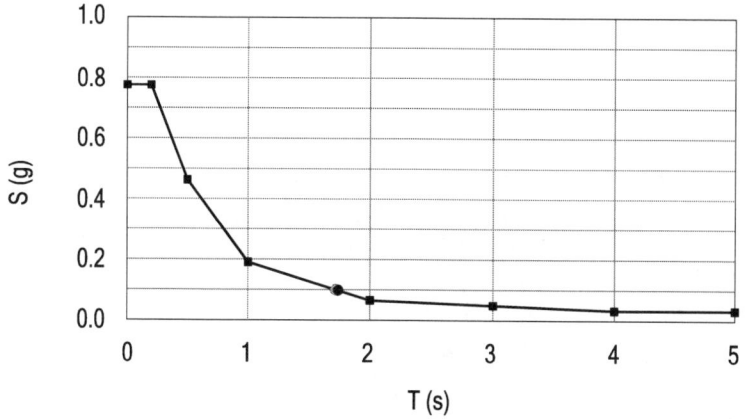

Figure 11.22 Design spectral response acceleration

The empirical fundamental lateral period, T_a, for this shear wall structure in the N-S and E-W directions, is given by:

$$T_a = 0.05h_n^{3/4} = 0.05 \times 45.0^{3/4} = 0.869 \text{ s}$$

N-S Direction

The calculated period for this structure in the N-S direction, using the computer program ETABS, is 1.83 s. Note that a 3-D model including the walls, the slabs and the columns was also analysed and resulted in a period of 1.75 s. Because this period is within 15% of the periods of the walls alone, then a period of 1.83 s was used.

The value of the fundamental lateral period cannot be taken greater than $2 \times 0.869 = 1.74$ and hence use $T_a = 1.74$ s. From linear interpolation, $S(T_a) = 0.0981$ (see Fig. 11.22).

The values of M_v and J depend on the ratio of $S_a(0.2)/S_a(2.0) = 0.69/0.048 = 14.4$ and the value of T_a. It is necessary to interpolate the value of $S(T_a)M_v$ and the value of J between periods of 1.0 and 2.0 s and 0.5 and 2.0 s, respectively. This interpolation results in $S(T_a)M_v = 0.170$, $M_v = 1.736$ and $J = 0.505$.

This office building has an earthquake importance factor, $I_E = 1.0$. For this ductile shear wall $R_d = 3.5$ and $R_o = 1.6$.

Hence the seismic base shear, V, is:

$$V = \frac{S(T_a)M_v I_E W}{R_d R_o} = \frac{0.0981 \times 1.736 \times 1.0 \times W}{3.5 \times 1.6} = 0.0304W$$

$$V_{min} = \frac{S(2.0)M_v I_E W}{R_d R_o} = \frac{0.0653 \times 2.5 \times 1.0 \times W}{3.5 \times 1.6} = 0.0291W$$

$$V_{max} = \frac{2}{3}\frac{S(0.2)I_E W}{R_d R_o} = \frac{2}{3}\frac{0.7756 \times 1.0 \times W}{3.5 \times 1.6} = 0.0923W$$

For this structure, $W = 90590$ kN.

Hence $V = 0.0304W = 0.0304 \times 90590 = 2756$ kN.

The portion of V concentrated at the top of the building is $F_t = 0.07T_a V = 0.07 \times 1.737 \times 2755.6 = 335$ kN, but need not be taken greater than $0.25V = 0.25 \times 2755.6 = 688.9$ kN.

The calculations of the seismic lateral forces at each floor level are summarized in Table 11.9.

E-W Direction

The calculated period for this structure in the E-W direction, using the computer program ETABS is 1.72 s. It is noted that this period may be used because the period for the full 3-D structure (walls, slabs and columns) is within 15% of this value. The value of the fundamental lateral period cannot be taken greater than $2 \times 0.869 = 1.74$ and hence use $T_a = 1.72$ s. From linear interpolation, $S(T_a) = 0.101$ (see Fig. 11.22).

It is necessary to interpolate the value of $S(T_a)M_v$ and the value of J between periods of 1.0 and 2.0 s and 0.5 and 2.0 s, respectively. This interpolation results in $S(T_a)M_v = 0.110$, $M_v = 1.093$ and $J = 0.757$.

For the ductile coupled wall system in the E-W direction $R_d = 4.0$ and $R_o = 1.7$.

Hence the seismic base shear, V, is:

$$V = \frac{S(T_a)M_v I_E W}{R_d R_o} = \frac{0.101 \times 1.093 \times 1.0 \times W}{4.0 \times 1.7} = 0.0162W$$

$$V_{min} = \frac{S(2.0)M_v I_E W}{R_d R_o} = \frac{0.065 \times 1.2 \times 1.0 \times W}{4.0 \times 1.7} = 0.0115W$$

$$V_{max} = \frac{2}{3}\frac{S(0.2)I_E W}{R_d R_o} = \frac{2}{3}\frac{0.776 \times 1.0 \times W}{4.0 \times 1.7} = 0.0760W$$

For this structure $W = 90590$ kN.

Hence $V = 0.0162W = 0.0162 \times 90590 = 1466$ kN.

The portion of V concentrated at the top of the building is $F_t = 0.07T_a V = 0.07 \times 1.72 \times 1466 = 176.2$ kN, but need not be taken greater than $0.25V = 0.25 \times 1466 = 366.5$ kN.

The calculations of the seismic lateral forces at each floor level using the equivalent static force procedure are summarized in Table 11.9. The weight of the penthouse has been included at the roof level.

Table 11.9 Lateral Load Calculations for Each Floor Level

Floor	h_i, m	W_i, kN	$h_i W_i$, kN·m	N-S		E-W	
				F_x	T_x	F_x	T_x
12	45.00	8154	366930	727.1	2163	385.1	1146
11	41.35	7467	308761	329.8	981	175.8	523
10	37.70	7467	281506	300.7	895	160.3	477
9	34.05	7467	254251	271.6	808	144.7	431
8	30.40	7467	226997	242.5	721	129.2	384
7	26.75	7467	199742	213.4	635	113.7	338
6	23.10	7467	172488	184.3	548	98.2	292
5	19.45	7467	145233	155.2	462	82.7	246
4	15.80	7467	117979	126.0	375	67.2	200
3	12.15	7467	90724	96.9	288	51.7	154
2	8.50	7467	63470	67.8	202	36.1	108
1	4.85	7766	37665	40.2	120	21.4	64
0							
Total		90590	2265745	2756	8198	1466	4362

11

Seismic Design

11.5.3.2 Accidental Torsion

The 3-D model shown in Fig. 11.23 was used to calculate accidental torsional effects by applying the lateral forces F_x (see Table 11.9) at an accidental eccentricity of $\pm 0.1 D_{nx}$, where D_{nx} is the plan dimension of the building at level x, perpendicular to the direction of seismic loading. This gives an accidental torsional eccentricity of 2.975 m, from the centre of mass (same as centre of rigidity) for loading in the N-S and E-W directions. The values of T_x are given in Table 11.9.

The structure was analysed with a 3-D model of the core-wall structure for both wind and seismic loading, with and without eccentricity. In these analyses the participation of the flat plate and columns was neglected.

11.5.3.3 Degree of Coupling

In the calculations of the base shear it was assumed that there was sufficient coupling of the walls in the E-W direction to qualify this wall system as a ductile coupled wall system rather than a partially coupled wall system. To check the degree of coupling by the wall system in the E-W direction, the base overturning moment resisted by axial tension and compression forces in the walls (resulting from shear in the coupling beams), divided by the total base overturning moment is determined. Although the design forces were obtained from dynamic analysis, it is not appropriate to use these values to determine the degree of coupling because the values obtained from modal combination (e.g., SRSS or CQC) does not satisfy static equilibrium. The degree of coupling was determined using static analysis with the F_x forces from the equivalent static force procedure, giving:

$$\frac{T\ell}{M_1 + M_2 + T\ell} = \frac{5513 \times 6.5}{2 \times 6400 + 5513 \times 6.5} = 0.74$$

where

T = axial tension and compression acting at centroid of coupled walls
ℓ = distance between centroids of coupled walls, equal to 6.5 m for this example

The degree of coupling is 74%, which is exceeds the minimum limit for ductile coupled walls of 66%. Hence $R_d = 4.0$ and $R_o = 1.7$, as assumed above.

11.5.3.4 Check on Structural Irregularity

To determine if the structure is sensitive to torsion, the values of B need to be determined at all levels from the maximum and average displacements of the structure at in the E-W and N-S directions. The maximum value, B (determined at the extreme points of the structure), in the N-S direction occurs in the first storey, with a displacement due to accidental torsion of 1.04 mm and a displacement due to F_x of 1.30 mm. Hence:

$$B = \frac{\delta_{max}}{\delta_{ave}} = \frac{1.04 + 1.30}{1.30} = 1.80$$

Because B is greater than 1.7, the structure is sensitive to torsion and hence is designated as irregular. The maximum value of B in the E-W direction occurs in the first storey and is 1.66.

Note that a 3-D analysis of the structure, including the columns and slabs as well as the actual mass distributions indicates that the first and fourth modes of vibration are torsional with periods of 1.89 and 0.54 s, respectively. This confirms that the structure is indeed torsionally sensitive.

This design example illustrates the steps necessary to design this common type of structure, that is torsionally sensitive.

11.5.3.5 Dynamic Analysis

The NBCC requires that the Dynamic Analysis Procedure be used except that the Equivalent Static Force Procedure may be used for structures that meet any one of the three conditions in parts (a), (b) and (c) of Clause 4.1.8.7. For this building, the term $I_E F_a S_a (0.2)$ is greater than 0.35 and hence the condition in part (a) is not satisfied. The presence of the structural irregularity due to torsion sensitivity means that the Equivalent Static Force Procedure cannot be used (part (b) of 4.1.8.7). Part (c) of 4.1.8.7 is also not satisfied. Accordingly, the Equivalent Static Force Procedure is not permitted as an alternative to the Dynamic Analysis Procedure for this example building. The first step is to determine V_e from a linear dynamic analysis. The design base shear V_d is obtained from:

$$V_d = \frac{V_e}{R_d R_o} I_E$$

Because this is an irregular structure, that requires dynamic analysis (NBCC 4.1.8.7), V_d shall not be taken less than $1.0V$ rather than $0.8V$, permitted for a regular structure.

All forces and deflections obtained from the linear dynamic analysis are scaled by the factor V_d/V_e to obtain the design values. However, in order to obtain realistic values of anticipated deflections and drifts, the design values need to be multiplied by $R_d R_o / I_E$.

Fig. 11.23 shows the 3-D ETABS model that considers only the core wall system (SFRS) and is used for the dynamic analysis. The second model used is the entire structure including the frame members not considered part of the SFRS (columns and the slabs) to check the ductility and strength of these members subjected to seismically induced deformations. The total mass for each floor was concentrated at the centre of mass (same as centre of rigidity for this example) and rigid diaphragms were assumed at each floor level. Sway effects (P-Delta) were included using the ETABS program option. For this analysis, compressive loads on the walls were obtained from the consistent loading case of $1.0D + 0.5L + 0.25S$, with live load reduction factors.

The first three lateral modes in the N-S and E-W directions are shown in Fig. 11.24, together with the associated periods of vibration and the modal participating mass ratios. Note that the sum of these ratios is 94.9% and 93.8% of the total mass in the N-S and E-W directions, respectively. These ratios exceed the minimum required ratio of 90% of the total mass (NBCC). Spectral modal superposition, using SRSS for the first three modes in the both directions was used to determine all forces and deformations.

The base shear in the N-S direction determined by dynamic analysis is $V_e = 14159$ kN. Therefore:

$$V_d = 14159 \times \frac{1.0}{3.5 \times 1.6} = 2528 \text{ kN}$$

11

However for this irregular building V_d shall not be taken less than $V = 2755.6$ kN. Hence, all forces and deflections obtained from the dynamic analysis shall be multiplied by $V_d/V_e = 2755.6/14159 = 0.195$ in the N-S direction.

The base shear in the E-W direction determined by dynamic analysis is $V_e = 11021$ kN. Therefore:

$$V_d = 11021 \times \frac{1.0}{4.0 \times 1.7} = 1621 \text{ kN}$$

However for this irregular building V_d shall not be taken less than $V = 1466.1$ kN. Hence, all forces and deflections obtained from the dynamic analysis shall be multiplied by $V_d/V_e = 1621/11021 = 0.147$ in the E-W direction.

Seismic Design

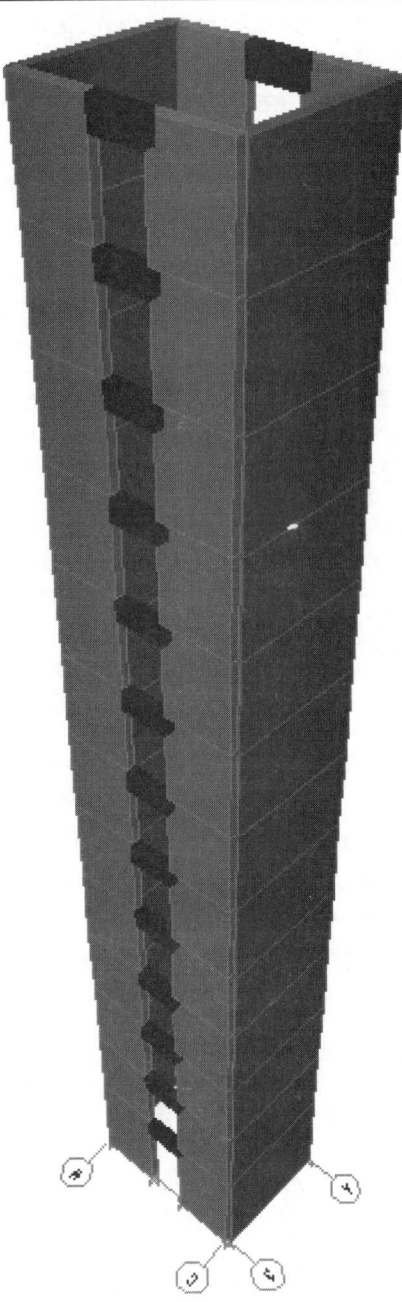

Figure 11.23 3-D Model used for dynamic analysis

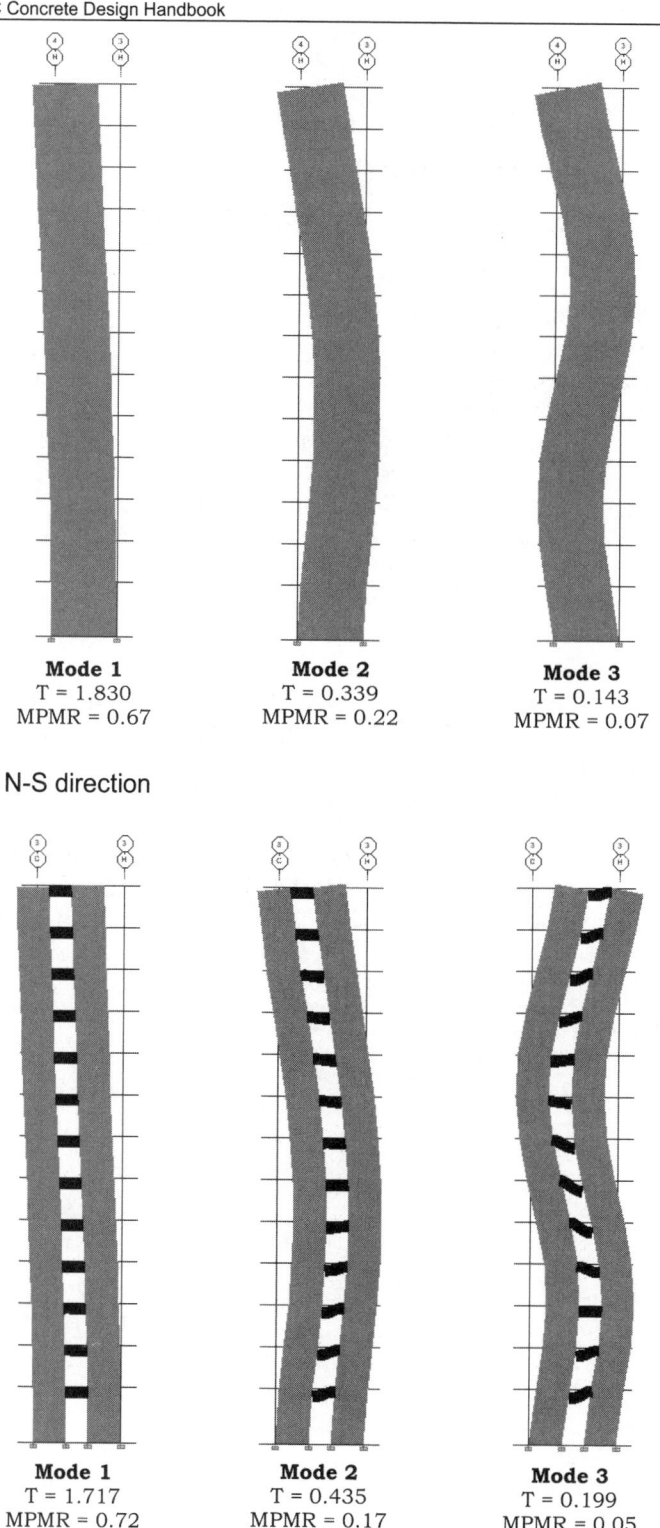

Mode 1
T = 1.830
MPMR = 0.67

Mode 2
T = 0.339
MPMR = 0.22

Mode 3
T = 0.143
MPMR = 0.07

(a) N-S direction

11

Seismic Design

Mode 1
T = 1.717
MPMR = 0.72

Mode 2
T = 0.435
MPMR = 0.17

Mode 3
T = 0.199
MPMR = 0.05

(b) E-W direction

Figure 11.24 Mode shapes, corresponding lateral periods of vibration and modal participating mass ratios in the N-S and E-W directions

11.5.3.6 Deflections and Drift Ratios

The deflections obtained from the dynamic analysis are multiplied by the factor 0.195 in the N-S direction and 0.147 in the E-W direction. To account for the total anticipated displacements, including the inelastic effects it is necessary to multiply these deflections by the factor $R_d R_o / I_E$ to obtain the design values. Note that the factor $\dfrac{V_d}{V_e} \dfrac{R_d R_o}{I_E}$ is equal to 1.0 unless V_d is controlled by the value of V, as in the N-S direction in this example (see 11.5.3.5). The deflections obtained from dynamic analysis include P-Delta effects. The deflections arising from accidental torsional eccentricity are added to the deflections from the dynamic analysis.

The maximum total interstorey drift in the N-S direction occurs in the eighth storey. From the dynamic analysis the interstorey drift in this storey is 0.00060 and the interstorey drift from accidental torsion at this level is 0.00041, for a maximum interstorey drift of 0.0010. Therefore the anticipated interstorey drift, including inelastic effects, is $0.0010 \times 3.5 \times 1.6 / 1.0 = 0.0056$. Similarly the maximum anticipated interstorey drift in the E-W direction is 0.0047. These anticipated maximum interstorey drift ratios are less than the NBCC limit of 0.025.

11.5.4   Design Forces

The results from the 3-D analyses for both seismic and wind loading are summarized in Tables 11.10, 11.11, 11.12 and 11.13. It is noted that for wind loading, the case with eccentric wind loading does not govern. Table 11.10 gives the forces from seismic loading analysis in the N-S direction, without and with accidental torsion effects.

Table 11.11 gives the forces from seismic loading analysis in the E-W direction, without accidental torsion effects.

Table 11.12 gives the forces from accidental torsion due to seismic loading analysis in the E-W direction. It is noted that accidental torsion is resisted by shear flow around the components of the C-shaped walls and by shear in the coupling beams. The accidental torsion does not create any global moments, axial loads or shears in the C-shaped walls, but results in local moments, axial loads and shears in the component parts, AB, BC and CD (see Fig. 11.27).

Table 11.10   Results of Seismic Loading Analyses (1.0E) in N-S direction for one wall, including accidental torsion

Storey	Wall moment without torsion, kN·m	Wall moment with torsion, kN·m	Wall shear without torsion, kN	Wall shear with torsion, kN
13 top	0	492	0	114
13 bot	0	907	0	114
12 top	0	1503	406	509
12 bot	1484	2611	406	509
11 top	1484	3297	605	787
11 bot	3689	4839	605	787
10 top	3689	5623	647	898
10 bot	6022	7040	647	898
9 top	6022	7922	589	902
9 bot	8037	8797	589	902
8 top	8037	9767	518	886
8 bot	9504	9890	518	886
7 top	9504	10931	515	934
7 bot	10391	10494	515	934
6 top	10391	11375	596	1062
6 bot	10831	11548	596	1062
5 top	10831	11212	738	1249
5 bot	11097	12582	738	1249
4 top	11097	11514	923	1478
4 bot	11647	14090	923	1478
3 top	11647	13107	1119	1719
3 bot	13033	16685	1119	1719
2 top	13033	15859	1283	1943
2 bot	15567	20803	1283	1943
1 top	15567	20210	1378	2057
1 bot	20396	28332	1378	2057

11

Seismic Design

Table 11.11   Results of Seismic Loading Analyses (1.0E) in E-W direction (Coupled Wall) for one wall

Storey	Wall moment, kN·m	Wall axial load, kN	Wall shear, kN	Coupling beam shear without torsion, kN	Coupling beam shear with torsion, kN
13 top	452	139	0	69.6	113.0
13 bot	452	139	0		
12 top	1078	332	252	96.3	149.0
12 bot	309	332	252		
11 top	1086	596	390	132.2	192.8
11 bot	618	596	390		
10 top	945	913	441	159.5	228.9
10 bot	1135	913	441		
9 top	1019	1251	438	173.6	251.6
9 bot	1515	1251	438		
8 top	1280	1583	430	179.3	265.1
8 bot	1720	1583	430		
7 top	1527	1895	440	184.6	276.7
7 bot	1815	1895	440		
6 top	1708	2188	466	194.6	290.7
6 bot	1859	2188	466		
5 top	1826	2469	508	210.2	307.4
5 bot	1860	2469	508		
4 top	1820	2753	581	228.9	323.3
4 bot	1889	2753	581		
3 top	1597	3047	678	242.9	329.8
3 bot	2205	3047	678		
2 top	1303	3341	764	237.3	310.4
2 bot	3090	3341	764		
1 top	1957	3588	810	191.8	244.3
1 bot	5577	3588	810		

Table 11.12 Local forces due to accidental torsion (1.0E) in E-W direction (Coupled Wall Direction) in different components of C-shaped wall

Storey	Wall component AB or CD ($\pm$) 3.2 m long segments			Wall component BC ($\pm$) 6.4 m long segment		
	Moment, kN·m	Axial load, kN	Shear, kN	Moment, kN·m	Axial load, kN	Shear, kN
13 top	90.4	-58.0	-36.9	-81.1	0.0	58.2
13 bot	-44.4	-58.0	-36.9	131.3	0.0	58.2
12 top	115.0	-94.9	-55.3	232.9	0.0	-55.6
12 bot	-86.8	-94.9	-55.3	30.2	0.0	-55.6
11 top	142.0	-106.4	-70.0	330.6	0.0	-97.9
11 bot	-113.5	-106.4	-70.0	-26.6	0.0	-97.9
10 top	168.2	-105.9	-84.5	398.0	0.0	-134.7
10 bot	-140.2	-105.9	-84.5	-93.7	0.0	-134.7
9 top	191.0	-95.3	-97.8	442.9	0.0	-167.7
9 bot	-165.9	-95.3	-97.8	-169.1	0.0	-167.7
8 top	209.9	-75.6	-109.4	468.1	0.0	-197.3
8 bot	-189.6	-75.6	-109.4	-252.1	0.0	-197.3
7 top	224.2	-47.1	-119.1	475.1	0.0	-224.4
7 bot	-210.6	-47.1	-119.1	-343.8	0.0	-224.4
6 top	233.2	-9.0	-126.5	464.1	0.0	-249.4
6 bot	-228.4	-9.0	-126.5	-446.1	0.0	-249.4
5 top	235.9	40.1	-131.0	433.9	0.0	-273.0
5 bot	-242.4	40.1	-131.0	-562.7	0.0	-273.0
4 top	231.0	102.9	-132.3	382.1	0.0	-296.3
4 bot	-251.8	102.9	-132.3	-699.3	0.0	-296.3
3 top	217.2	183.4	-129.8	304.9	0.0	-319.7
3 bot	-256.7	183.4	-129.8	-861.8	0.0	-319.7
2 top	189.4	286.1	-118.7	190.8	0.0	-350.8
2 bot	-243.9	286.1	-118.7	-1089.6	0.0	-350.8
1 top	221.8	457.3	-120.2	248.5	0.0	-359.1
1 bot	-361.0	457.3	-120.2	-1493.1	0.0	-359.1

11

Seismic Design

Table 11.13 Results of Wind Loading Analyses (1.4W)

Storey	N-S Direction	E-W Direction (Coupled Wall Direction)		
	Wall moment, kN·m	Wall moment, kN·m	Wall axial load, kN	Coupling beam shear, kN
13 top	0	159	49	24.5
13 bot	0	159	49	
12 top	-74	444	119	38.9
12 bot	122	178	119	
11 top	47	633	241	64.4
11 bot	577	72	241	
10 top	503	735	426	95.7
10 bot	1287	-84	426	
9 top	1212	800	679	128.8
9 bot	2263	-281	679	
8 top	2190	827	1001	162.5
8 bot	3498	-508	1001	
7 top	3427	819	1391	195.5
7 bot	4990	-767	1391	
6 top	4923	770	1845	227.0
6 bot	6734	-1060	1845	
5 top	6672	665	2358	255.5
5 bot	8726	-1402	2358	
4 top	8670	473	2918	278.3
4 bot	10962	-1823	2918	
3 top	10915	130	3504	290.5
3 bot	13433	-2385	3504	
2 top	13396	-496	4073	281.5
2 bot	16161	-3233	4073	
1 top	16136	-1669	4546	233.3
1 bot	20087	-5599	4546	

The design forces for both seismic and wind loading are given in Fig. 11.25. The distribution of wall moments for wind loading is typical for a coupled wall system. The distribution of wall moments for seismic loading was obtained from modal combinations (SRSS) and therefore the moments obtained are absolute values.

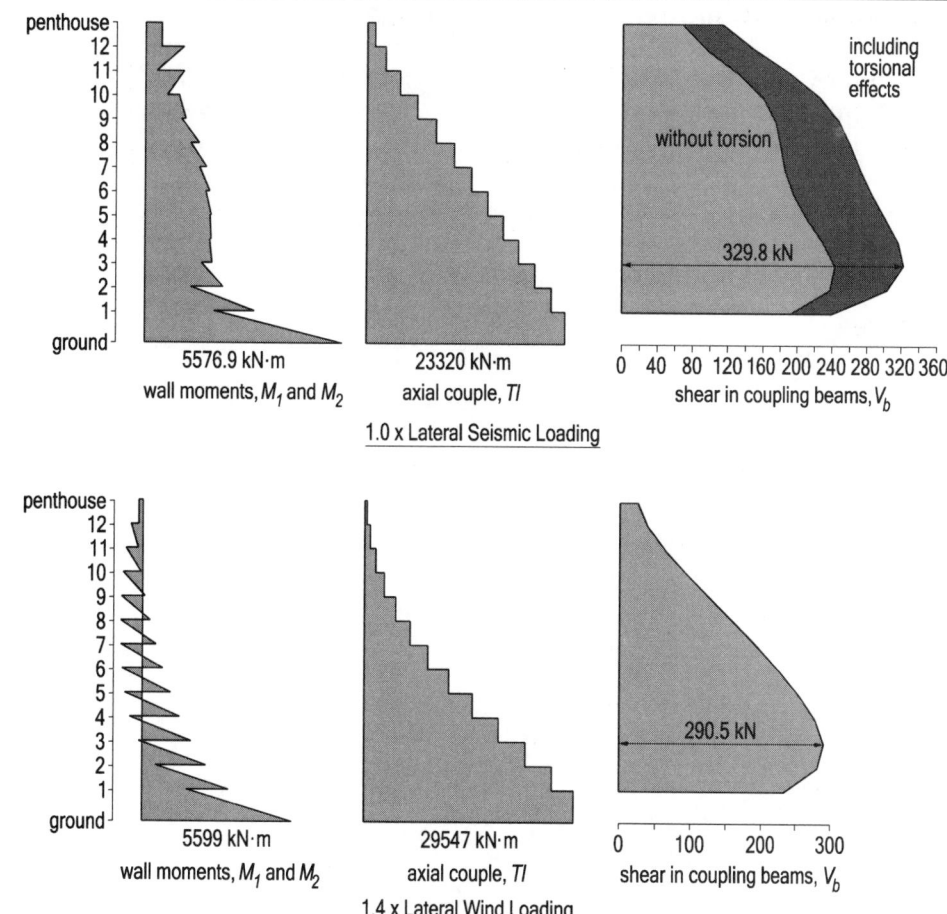

Fig. 11.25 Results of analyses for seismic and wind loading

11.5.5   Design of Coupling Beams

11.5.5.1   Design Forces for Coupling Beams

The maximum coupling beam shear due to factored wind loading is 290.5 kN and due to earthquake effects (including accidental torsion) is 329.8 kN. Hence the seismic loading case governs the design of the coupling beams. These maximum shears occur in the coupling beams in the third storey (see Tables 11.11 and 11.13).

In designing the coupling beams we can account for redistribution of moments between the beams and hence the factored shear resistance required for earthquake loading would be the sum of the shears in the coupling beams divided by the number of coupling beams. This would require a factored shear resistance of 3283 / 13 = 252.5 kN for seismic loading.

The coupling beams have a depth of 900 mm and a clear span of 2000 mm and hence satisfy the dimensional limitation that the depth must not be greater than twice the clear span (Clause 21.6.8.5). The ductile coupling beams must be designed with diagonal reinforcement, rather than longitudinal bars and vertical hoops, because the clear span of each beam is not equal to or greater than four times the effective depth (see Clauses 21.6.8.6 and 21.3.1.1).

Since the design torsions arise only from accidental torsional eccentricity, which can act in either direction, the same coupling design forces and beam details will be used on the north and south sides of the core wall.

11.5.5.2 Design and detailing of coupling beams

Fig. 11.26 shows the details of the diagonal reinforcement in a coupling beam. From the geometry of the reinforcement, the angle α between the centroidal axis of one set of diagonal bars and the horizontal is 19.4°.

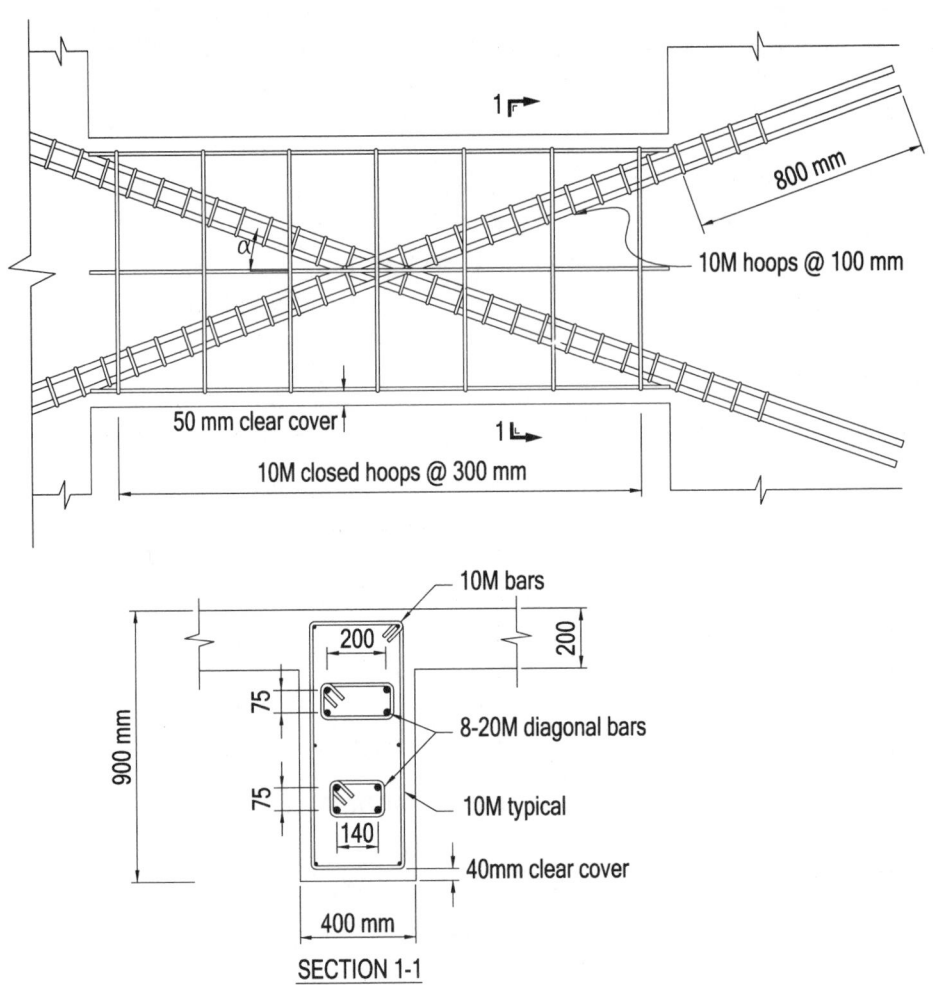

Fig. 11.26 Coupling beam reinforcing details

If 4-20M bars are provided in each set of diagonal bars then the factored shear resistance is:

$$V_r = 2\phi_s A_s f_y \sin\alpha = 2 \times 0.85 \times 4 \times 300 \times 400 \times \sin 19.4 = 271.0 \text{ kN}$$

If this reinforcement is placed in the lower storeys, then a moment redistribution of 17.8% would be required in the coupling beam with maximum moment due to seismic loading and 6.7% redistribution would be required for wind loading. Clause 9.2.4 permits a moment redistribution up to 20%.

The diagonal reinforcement must have closely spaced hoops as required in Clause 21.6.8.7 with a maximum spacing given by the smaller of:

(a) $6d_{b\ell} = 6 \times 20 = 120$ mm

(b) $24d_{bh} = 24 \times 10 = 240$ mm

(c)   100 mm

Hence use 10M hoops spaced at 100 mm.

The diagonal reinforcement must extend into the wall at each end a minimum distance of $1.5\ell_d = 1.5 \times 526 = 789$ mm. Hence use an embedment length of 800 mm. In addition to the diagonal reinforcement, provide minimum transverse and longitudinal reinforcement, as shown in Fig. 11.26, but only in the clear span of the beam.

Although a designer might choose to use the same coupling beams details, with 4-20M diagonal bars, over the full height of this building, reducing the amount of reinforcement in the coupling beams near the top of the structure is advantageous whenever possible. This approach is illustrated below.

If the reinforcement in the coupling beams is reduced to 4-15M near the top of the structure, then the factored resistance per beam is:

$$V_r = 2\phi_s A_s f_y \sin\alpha = 2 \times 0.85 \times 4 \times 200 \times 400 \times \sin 19.4 = 180.7 \text{ kN}.$$

The beams with 4-15M bars would require a hoop spacing of 90 mm.

Provide coupling beams with 4-20M bars for storeys 1 to 11 and beams with 4-15M bars for the top two coupling beams. This arrangement gives a total shear capacity of the 13 beams of:

$$\sum V_r = 11 \times 271.0 + 2 \times 180.7 = 3342 \text{ kN}$$

This shear resistance of the thirteen coupling beams exceeds the required shear resistance of 3283 kN.

Hence provide diagonally reinforced coupling beams with 4-20M for the first 11 storeys and beams with 4-15M diagonal bars for the top two coupling beams.

11.5.5.3   Ductility of coupling beams

The inelastic rotational capacity of the coupling beams must be greater than the rotational demand. The rotational demand is given by (Clause 21.6.8.4):

$$\theta_{id} = \left(\frac{\Delta_f R_d R_o}{h_w}\right)\frac{\ell_{cg}}{\ell_u} = \left(\frac{0.019 \times 4.0 \times 1.7}{45.0}\right)\frac{6.5}{2.0} = 0.0093$$

The rotational capacity of diagonally reinforced coupling beams (Clause 21.6.8.4) is 0.04. Hence the coupling beams have sufficient ductility.

11.5.6   Design of Ductile Walls

11.5.6.1   Design Forces in E-W Direction

The design forces in the walls are determined from a capacity design approach. It is desired that the walls be strong enough such that flexural hinging occurs in the coupling beams, which are the primary energy dissipators of the structural system. In order to determine the design forces in the walls we will consider a "push-over" type of loading on the coupled wall system. For this analysis it is required that the factored resistance of the walls be at least equal to the moment corresponding to the development of flexural hinging in the beams.

The "push-over" approach used for this twelve-storey coupled wall structure provides a conservative design approach to the requirements of Clause 21.6.8.12. For taller coupled wall structures the provisions of Clause 21.6.8.12 should be used.

The nominal shear resistance, V_n, for the coupling beam containing 4-20M diagonal reinforcing bars is:

$$V_n = 2\phi_s A_s f_y \times \sin\alpha = 2 \times 1.0 \times 1200 \times 400 \times \sin 19.4 = 318.9 \text{ kN}$$

Similarly the nominal resistance for the beams containing the 4-15M bars is 212.6 kN.

11

Seismic Design

In order to satisfy the capacity design requirement, the factored wall moments will be increased at each level x by the factor γ_{bx}, determined as:

$$\gamma_{bx} = \frac{\sum V_n}{\sum V_f}$$

where:

$\sum V_n$ = sum of the shears corresponding to the nominal flexural resistance of coupling beams above level x

$\sum V_f$ = sum of factored shears above level x

The beam overstrength factors, cumulative dead and live loads and the factored axial loads and factored moments in each wall multiplied by γ_{bx} are shown on Table 11.14. The values of $\sum V_f$ are taken as the wall axial loads given in Table 11.14, since the axial load wall is the sum of the shears in the coupling beams.

Table 11.14 Coupling Beam Overstrength Factors and Dead and Live Loads per Wall

Storey	V_n, kN	V_f, kN	γ_{bx}	P_D, kN	P_L, kN	P_n, kN	$\gamma_{bx}M_1$, kN·m
13 top	212.6	113.0	1.88	-945	0	± 425	851
13 bot				-945	0	± 425	851
12 top	212.6	149.0	1.62	-1701	-196	± 850	1750
12 bot				-1701	-196	± 850	501
11 top	318.9	192.8	1.64	-2457	-394	± 1488	1777
11 bot				-2457	-394	± 1488	1012
10 top	318.9	228.9	1.55	-3213	-513	± 2126	1469
10 bot				-3213	-513	± 2126	1765
9 top	318.9	251.6	1.48	-3969	-621	± 2764	1506
9 bot				-3969	-621	± 2764	2239
8 top	318.9	265.1	1.42	-4725	-725	± 3402	1814
8 bot				-4725	-725	± 3402	2438
7 top	318.9	276.7	1.37	-5481	-825	± 4039	2088
7 bot				-5481	-825	± 4039	2483
6 top	318.9	290.7	1.32	-6237	-924	± 4677	2259
6 bot				-6237	-924	± 4677	2459
5 top	318.9	307.4	1.28	-6993	-1020	± 5315	2338
5 bot				-6993	-1020	± 5315	2382
4 top	318.9	323.3	1.24	7749	1115	± 5953	2259
4 bot				7749	1115	± 5953	2344
3 top	318.9	329.8	1.21	8506	1208	± 6591	1929
3 bot				8506	1208	± 6591	2664
2 top	318.9	310.4	1.19	9262	1301	± 7228	1550
2 bot				9262	1301	± 7228	3676
1 top	318.9	244.3	1.20	9797	1393	± 7866	2345
1 bot				9797	1393	± 7866	6682

The required moment capacity at the base of each wall, given in Table 11.14, is 6682 kN·m for seismic loading without accidental torsion. It is noted that the required moment at the base of each wall due to wind (see Table 11.13) is 5599 kN·m. Hence the seismic capacity design requirements control the design.

From Table 11.14, the minimum axial force at the base of the "tension wall" corresponding to development of flexural hinges in the coupling beams is:

$P_s + P_n = -9797 + 7866 = -1931$ kN, that is a compressive load.

The maximum axial force at the base of the "compression wall" corresponding to development of flexural hinges in the coupling beams is:

$P_s + P_n = -9797 - 0.5 \times 1393 - 7866 = -18360$ kN.

To account for the local forces (see Table 11.12) from accidental torsion a simplified approach will be taken. Although the axial loads and moments on parts AB and CD have opposite signs it will be assumed that the C-shaped wall is subjected to an additional axial load of twice the axial tension or compression acting on segments AB or CD and an additional moment of twice the moment acting in these segments. For example, at the base of the structure the additional axial load for design is $2 \times \pm 457 = \pm 914$ kN and the additional moment is $2 \times \pm 361 = \pm 722$ kN·m.

11.5.6.2   Design Forces in N-S Direction

From Tables 11.10 and 11.13, the base moment in each wall due to lateral seismic loading is 28332 kN·m (including accidental torsion) and the base moment due to factored wind loading is 20087 kN·m, respectively. Hence, for flexural design in the N-S direction, the earthquake loading controls. The corresponding axial load for the two walls is $2(P_D + 0.5P_L) = 2(-9797 - 0.5 \times 1393) = 2 \times -10494 = -20988$ kN.

11.5.6.3   Design of base of wall for flexure and axial load

Preliminary choice of vertical reinforcement

(a)   Minimum area of concentrated reinforcement (Clause 21.6.6.4)

In the 3.2 m long walls in the E-W direction:

$A_s = 0.0015 b_w \ell_w = 0.0015 \times 400 \times 3200 = 1920$ mm^2

Therefore try 4–25M bars ($A_s = 2000$ mm^2) as concentrated reinforcement at one end of the 3.2 m long wall (segments AB and CD).

In the 6.4 m long wall (segment BC) in the N-S direction

$A_s = 0.0015 b_w \ell_w = 0.0015 \times 400 \times 6400 = 3840$ mm^2

For the case of flanged walls, concentrated reinforcement at the ends of the effective flanges may supply up to one half of the required minimum wall web concentrated reinforcement (Clause 21.6.6.5). Hence the required concentrated reinforcement at the web-flange intersection is $0.5 \times 3840 = 1920$ mm^2. Hence try 4-25M at the intersection of the two walls.

Outside the plastic hinge regions, only two-thirds of this area of the concentrated reinforcement is required.

Provide a clear cover for the hoops of 40 mm, resulting in a clear cover of 50 mm for the main vertical reinforcement in the wall, as required for a two-hour fire-resistance rating.

In regions of plastic hinging, the uniformly distributed horizontal reinforcement must be anchored within the region of concentrated reinforcement to develop $1.25f_y$ (Clause 21.6.5.5).

11

Seismic Design

The development length required for the 10M bars, using the simplified equation in Clause 12.2.3 is:

$$\ell_d = 0.45k_1k_2k_3k_4\frac{1.25f_y}{\sqrt{f_c'}}d_b = 0.45 \times 1 \times 1 \times 1 \times 0.8\frac{500}{\sqrt{30}} \times 10 = 329 \ \text{mm}$$

The length provided in the region of concentrated reinforcement (see Fig. 11.27) is 320 mm. With the significant cover provided on the bars and the additional confinement provided in this region of concentrated reinforcement, the development length can be shown to be less than 320 mm using Eq. 12-1 in Clause 12.2.2. Hence, the hoop configuration shown in Fig. 11.27 is adequate.

(b)   Maximum area of concentrated reinforcement (Clause 21.6.4.3)

Clause 21.6.4.3 limits the reinforcement ratio, including regions with lap splices, to 0.06. With the layout of the 4-25M bars at the ends of the flanges and at the web-flange junctions, as shown in Fig. 11.27, the percentage of steel equals $(4 \times 500)/(400 \times 400) = 0.0125$. This arrangement allows for lap splicing of the reinforcement without exceeding the limit of 0.06.

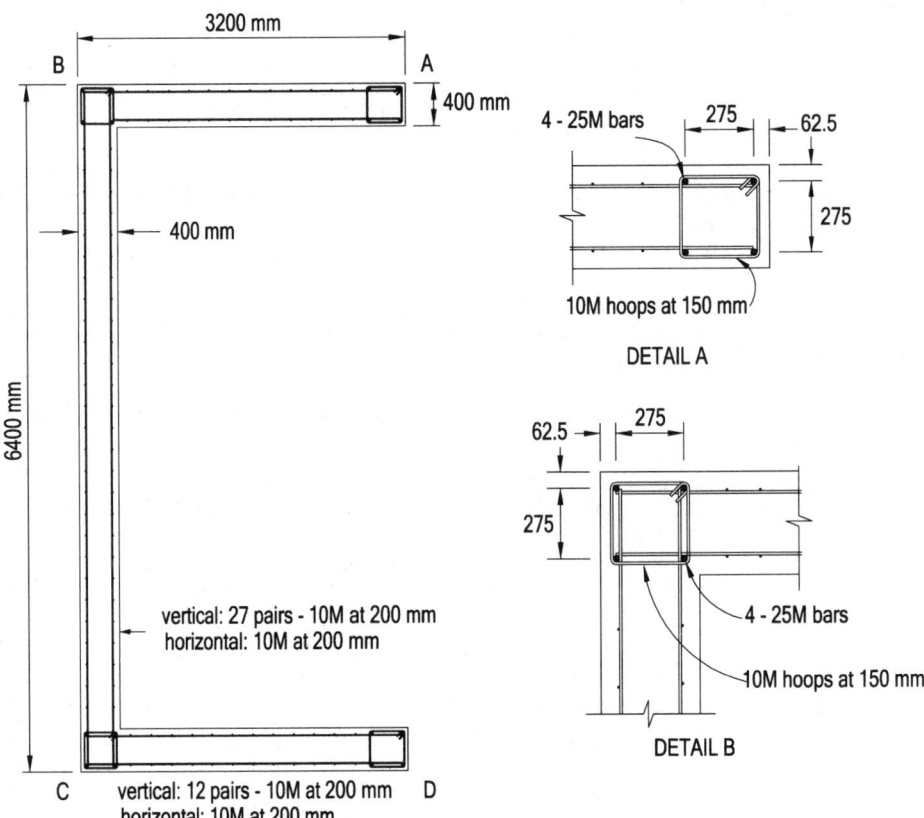

Fig. 11.27 Details of reinforcement in walls.

At the base of the walls the spacing of the horizontal distributed reinforcement must be decreased to 120 mm in component BC and to 150 mm in components AB and CD (see Section 11.5.6.7).

(c)   Maximum bar diameters (Clause 21.6.4.4)

In the 400 mm thick walls, the maximum diameter of reinforcement is $400/10 = 40$ mm.

(d)   Distributed reinforcement (Clauses 21.6.5)

In the plastic hinge region, the spacing of the distributed reinforcement must not exceed 300 mm in each direction. Outside of this region, the maximum spacing is 450 mm. The distributed reinforcement ratio must be greater than 0.0025 in each direction.

In the 400 mm thick wall elements, the maximum spacing, assuming two curtains of 10M reinforcing bars is $(2 \times 100)/(0.0025 \times 400) = 200$ mm. Hence, at the base of the walls, use 2 curtains of 10M bars at 200 mm spacing in the horizontal and vertical directions.

In the regions of plastic hinging, two curtains of reinforcement must be provided in the N-S direction if the design shear in one wall exceeds (Clause 21.6.5.3):

$$0.18 \lambda \phi_c \sqrt{f_c'} A_{cv} = 0.18 \times 0.65 \times \sqrt{30} \times 400 \times 6400 = 1641 \text{ kN}.$$

Two curtains of reinforcement must be provided in the E-W direction if the design shear in one wall exceeds:

$$0.18 \lambda \phi_c \sqrt{f_c'} A_{cv} = 0.18 \times 0.65 \times \sqrt{30} \times 800 \times 3200 = 1641 \text{ kN}.$$

Calculation of M_r at base of walls

The factored moment resistances for different loading cases were determined using the stress block factors of Clause 10.1.7, strain compatibility and a maximum concrete compressive strain of 0.0035. Table 11.15 summarizes the results.

Table 11.15 Predicted Factored Moment Resistances and Depths of Compression per Wall at the base (Global wall forces)

	Load Case	N_f kN	M_f kN·m	N_r kN	M_r kN·m	c mm
E-W (1 "C-shaped" wall)						
"tension" wall	$1.0D + 1.0E$	-1931	6682	-1931	15058	493
"compression" wall	$1.0D + 1.0E$	-17663	6682	-17663	21773	226
	$1.0D + 0.5L + 1.0E$	-18360	6682	-18360	22280	233
N-S (per wall)						
	$1.0D + 1.0E$	-9797	28332	-9797	49058	290
	$1.0D + 0.5L + 1.0E$	-10494	28332	-10494	51097	303

The required moment capacity in the E-W direction from analysis is 6682 kN·m per wall. As can be seen from Table 11.15, the "tension" wall has a factored moment resistance of 15058 kN·m, while the compression wall has a factored moment resistance of 22280 kN·m. Hence the factored flexural resistance exceeds the required factored moment. Figure 11.28 illustrates the moment resistances for the walls in the E-W direction.

It is noted that the total forces in the E-W tension wall, including global (Table 11.15) and local (Table 11.12) forces at its base is:

$N_f = -1931 + 914 = -1017$ kN and $M_f = 6682 + 722 = 7405$ kN·m.

For this level of axial load the factored moment resistance is 13385 kN·m. Hence the wall strength is adequate for both global and local forces. It can be shown, in a similar way, that the factored resistance of the compression wall is adequate for global and local forces.

Clause 21.6.8.8 requires that the walls at each end of a coupling beam be designed so that the factored moment resistance of the wall about its centroid, calculated using axial loads $P_s + P_n$,

11

Seismic Design

exceeds the moment corresponding to the nominal resistance of the coupling beam. This requirement will be satisfied at all the different levels of the structure because the "push-over" analysis summarized in Table 11.14 already considers the attainment of the nominal resistances of the coupling beams over the entire height of the structure. Hence all of the design moments and axial forces correspond to these conditions.

In the N-S direction, the factored moment resistance for both load cases significantly exceeds the required moment (see Table 11.15 and Fig. 11.29).

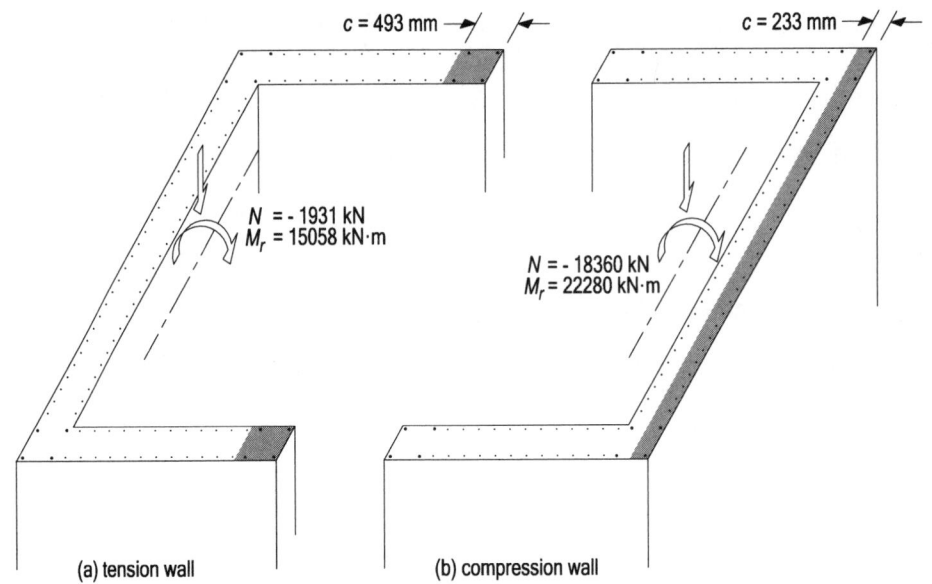

Fig. 11.28 Factored moment resistances of ductile coupled walls (E-W direction)

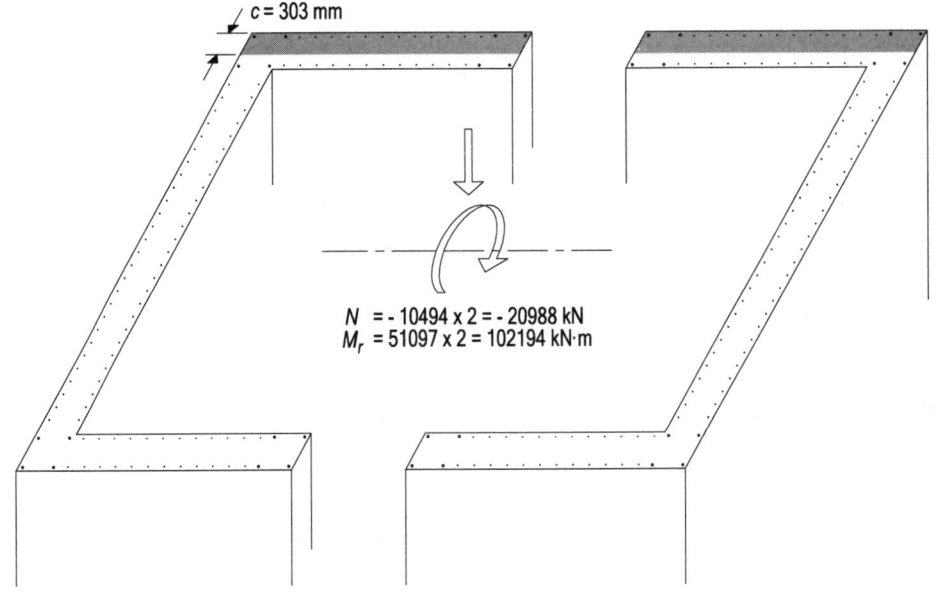

Fig. 11.29 Factored moment resistance of ductile shear walls (N-S direction)

11.5.6.4   Ductility of walls

E-W Direction - Ductile Coupled Walls (Clause 21.6.8)

For ductile coupled walls, the inelastic rotational demand θ_{id} is taken as:

$$\theta_{id} = \frac{\Delta_f R_o R_d}{h_w} = \frac{0.019 \times 1.7 \times 4.0}{45.0} = 0.0029 \geq 0.004$$

The inelastic rotational capacity θ_{ic}, taking ℓ_w as the length of the coupled wall system (Clause 21.6.8.3) and assuming $\varepsilon_{cu} = 0.0035$ is:

$$\theta_{ic} = \left(\frac{\varepsilon_{cu} \ell_w}{2c} - 0.002\right) = \left(\frac{0.0035 \times 8.4}{2 \times 0.493} - 0.002\right) = 0.0278 \leq 0.025$$

Because the rotational capacity of 0.025 exceeds the rotational demand of 0.004, sufficient ductility is provided.

N-S Direction - Ductile Shear Walls (Clause 21.6.7)

For ductile shear walls, the ratio of the nominal flexural resistance to the factored flexural resistance, M_f, at the base is 1.95 and hence the inelastic rotational demand θ_{id} is taken as:

$$\theta_{id} = \frac{\left(\Delta_f R_o R_d - \Delta_f \gamma_w\right)}{\left(h_w - \frac{\ell_w}{2}\right)} = \frac{\left(0.028 \times 1.6 \times 3.5 - 0.028 \times 1.95\right)}{\left(45.0 - \frac{6.4}{2}\right)} = 0.0024 \geq 0.004$$

The inelastic rotational capacity θ_{ic}, assuming $\varepsilon_{cu} = 0.0035$ is:

$$\theta_{ic} = \left(\frac{\varepsilon_{cu} \ell_w}{2c} - 0.002\right) = \left(\frac{0.0035 \times 6.4}{2 \times 0.303} - 0.002\right) = 0.0350 \leq 0.025$$

Because the rotational capacity of 0.025 exceeds the rotational demand of 0.004, sufficient ductility is provided.

Confinement of concentrated reinforcement (Clause 21.6.7.3)

Because the inelastic rotational capacities of the walls in the E-W and N-S directions were determined using $\varepsilon_{cu} = 0.0035$, it is not necessary to check the confinement requirements of Clause 21.6.7.4 for the concentrated reinforcement in the walls.

11.5.6.5   Checking wall thickness for stability (Clause 21.6.3)

Clause 21.6.3 requires a wall thickness of $\ell_u / 10$ in those parts of a wall that, under factored vertical and lateral loads, are more than half way from the neutral axis to the compression face of the wall section.

The 3200 mm long portions of the E-W "tension wall" may be considered as simple rectangular wall elements as shown in Fig. 11.28 with a neutral axis depth of 493 mm. Since the neutral axis depth is less than $4b_w = 4 \times 400 = 1600$ mm and is less than $0.3\ell_w = 0.3 \times 3200 = 960$ mm, the $\ell_u / 10$ limit need not apply (see Clause 21.6.3.4). According to Clause 21.6.3.2 the wall thickness in the plastic hinge region must not be less than $\ell_u / 14 = 4650 / 14 = 332$ mm. Hence the wall thickness of 400 mm is adequate.

11

Seismic Design

For the 6400 mm long portion of the E-W "compression wall", it is noted that $c/2 = 233/2 = 117$ mm, which is less than the wall thickness, and furthermore, the wall is laterally supported at its ends by the 3200 mm wall portions. Hence, this portion of the wall need not have a thickness of $\ell_u/10$ (see Clause 21.6.3.5).

For stability considerations for the wall loaded in the N-S direction, the value of $c/2 = 303/2 = 152$ mm is smaller than the 400 mm thickness of the flanges. Therefore the 400 mm wall dimension is adequate and the width of the flange of 3200 mm, greatly exceeds $\ell_u/5$ (see Clause 21.6.3.5).

Therefore all of the stability requirements are satisfied.

11.5.6.6 "Buckling prevention" ties for concentrated reinforcement (Clause 21.6.6.9)

The concentrated reinforcement should have buckling prevention ties in accordance with Clause 7.6 and the ties must be detailed as hoops (Clause 21.6.6.9). In plastic hinge regions, the hoop spacing shall not exceed:

(i) $6d_{b\ell} = 6 \times 25 = 150$ mm

(ii) $24d_{bh} = 24 \times 10 = 240$ mm

(iii) one-half the wall thickness $= 400/2 = 200$ mm.

Hence provide 10M hoops at a spacing of 150 mm as shown in Fig. 11.27.

11.5.6.7 Design for shear at base of walls (Clause 21.6.9)

The walls must be designed to resist the shear corresponding to the formation of plastic hinges at their bases (Clause 21.6.9.1).

Determine probable moment resistances of walls

In order to determine the probable moment resistances of the walls, axial load-moment calculations were carried out with $\phi_c = \phi_s = 1.0$ and using an equivalent "yield" strength of steel of $1.25f_y$. In the E-W direction, we only need to determine the probable moment resistance of the "compression wall" subjected to an axial load corresponding to $1.0E + 1.0D + 0.5L$, since it results in the larger resistance. From calculations, the probable moment resistance of the wall, M_{pw}, is 26235 kN·m in the E-W direction and 60679 kN·m per wall in the N-S direction.

It is assumed that earthquake loading causes plastic hinging at the base of the walls. Assuming that the ratio of the shear to moment at the base of a wall remains constant as the moment increases to the probable resistance, the shear at the base as the wall develops a plastic hinge will be:

$$V = \frac{M_{pw}}{M_f} \times V_f$$

N-S direction:

$$V = \frac{M_{pw}}{M_f} \times V_f = \frac{60679}{28332} \times 2057 = 4406 \text{ kN}$$

In calculating the shear capacity of the wall, the effective shear depth d_v is taken as $0.9d = 0.9 \times 6200 = 5580$ mm, but need not be taken less than $0.8\ell_w = 0.8 \times 6400 = 5120$ mm (Clause 21.6.9.3).

In the region of expected plastic hinging, at the base of the wall, the inelastic rotational demand θ_{id} is less than 0.005 and hence the factored shear demand cannot exceed:

$$0.15\phi_c f'_c b_w d_v = 0.15 \times 0.65 \times 30 \times 400 \times 5120 = 5990 \text{ kN}$$

The factored shear demand of 4406 kN is less than this upper limit.

Because the inelastic rotational demand θ_{id} is less than 0.005, the factored shear resistance is calculated using $\beta = 0.18$. The axial load on the "tension" wall is -10494 kN (compression). This axial load is less than: $0.1f'_c A_g = 0.1 \times 30 \times (3200 \times 800 + 5600 \times 400) = 14400$ kN.

Hence θ is taken as 45° (Clause 21.6.9.6). The factored shear resistance (Clauses 11.3.4 and 11.3.5), assuming pairs of 10M bars at 120 mm spacing is:

$$V_r = \phi_c \beta \sqrt{f'_c} b_w d_v + \frac{\phi_s A_v f_y d_v \cot\theta}{s}$$

$$= 0.65 \times 0.18\sqrt{30} \times 400 \times 5580 + \frac{0.85 \times 200 \times 400 \times 5580 \, cot 45°}{120}$$

$$= 1430 + 3162 = 4592 \text{ kN}$$

Hence the shear resistance is adequate with pairs of 10M horizontal bars spaced at 120 mm.

It is noted that the accidental torsion causes shear in segments AB and CD. This shear, due to accidental torsion, must be considered in design, accounting for the fact that the critical flange will be in tension and have large flexural cracks due to the attainment of plastic hinging for loading in the N-S direction. A method to check the shear resistance of these segments, accounting for large cracks and possible redistribution of shear resisting torsion, is described in the calculations below for loading in the E-W direction.

11

E-W direction:

In the E-W direction it is necessary to first determine the shear from seismic loading and include accidental torsion effects. The shear at the base without accidental torsion is $810/2 = 405$ kN in segment AB. The analysis including accidental torsion indicates a shear force of 120 kN on wall segments AB and CD (see Table 11.12). In accordance with Clause 21.6.8.13 it may be necessary to redistribute the shear force of 359 kN in the segment BC because under plastic hinging this wall segment will experience large tensile strains and cracks. If the torsion arising from this 359 kN force is redistributed to wall segments AB and CD, then an additional shear force will be necessary. This additional shear force is:

$$\Delta V_{AB} = V_{BC} \times \frac{8.0}{6.0} = 359 \times \frac{8.0}{6.0} = 479 \text{ kN in two segments}$$

Hence the total shear in segment AB is $405 + 120 + 479/2 = 765$ kN.

In lieu of redistributing the torsional shear from wall segment BC, a more detailed analysis will be conducted (Clause 21.6.8.13). Wall component BC is lightly loaded in shear but must resist the shear with large cracks in this tension wall. In order to determine the shear resistance under these conditions the "dowel action" resistance will be determined, considering the resistance of the reinforcement only. From Paulay and Priestley (1992) the dowel resistance can be taken as:

$$V_r = 0.25\phi_s A_v f_y = 0.25 \times 0.85 \times 27 \times 200 \times 400 = 459 \text{ kN}.$$

Because this resistance exceeds the shear force of 359 kN, redistribution of the shear from the tension wall BC to wall AB is not necessary. Hence the total shear in segment AB is $405 + 120 = 525$ kN.

The design shear for segment AB, including torsional effects is:

$$V = \frac{M_{pw}}{M_f} \times V_f = \frac{26235}{6682 + 722} \times 525 = 1860 \text{ kN}$$

For segment CD, the shear from accidental torsion acts in the opposite direction from that in segment AB. Hence the total shear for segment CD is $405 - 120 = 285$ kN. This results in a design shear for this segment of:

$$V = \frac{M_{pw}}{M_f} \times V_f = \frac{26235}{6682 + 722} \times 285 = 1010 \text{ kN}.$$

Segments AB and CD must both be designed for the larger shear of 1860 kN because the accidental torsion can reverse.

In calculating the shear capacity of the wall, in accordance with Clause 21.6.9.3, we will assume an effective shear depth, $d_v = 0.8\ell_w = 0.8 \times 3200 = 2560$ mm.

In the region of expected plastic hinging, at the base of the wall, the inelastic rotational demand θ_{id} is less than 0.005 and hence the factored shear demand in one segment cannot exceed:

$$0.15\phi_c f'_c b_w d_v = 0.15 \times 0.65 \times 30 \times 400 \times 2560 = 2995 \text{ kN}$$

The factored shear demand of 1860 kN is less than this upper limit.

Because the inelastic rotational demand θ_{id} is less than 0.005, the factored shear resistance is calculated using $\beta = 0.18$. The axial load on the tension wall is -1017 kN. This axial load is less than: $0.1 f'_c A_g = 0.1 \times 30 \times (3200 \times 800 + 5600 \times 400) = 14400$ kN.

Hence θ is taken as 45° (Clause 21.6.9.6). The factored shear resistance (Clauses 11.3.4 and 11.3.5) for wall segment AB at the base with pairs of 10M bars at a spacing of 150 mm is:

$$V_r = \phi_c \beta \sqrt{f'_c} b_w d_v + \frac{\phi_s A_v f_y d_v \cot \theta}{s}$$

$$= 0.65 \times 0.18\sqrt{30} \times 400 \times 2560 + \frac{0.85 \times 200 \times 400 \times 2560 \cot 45°}{150}$$

$$= 656 + 1161 = 1817 \text{ kN}$$

Segment AB is overstressed by only 2%, while segment BC is very lightly loaded and hence a portion can be redistributed to this segment. Hence the shear strength in the E-W direction is adequate with 2-10M bars at 150 mm spacing.

Extend the 10M horizontal reinforcement into the confined core of the region of concentrated reinforcement as close to the outside surface of the walls as cover will permit (see Fig 11.27 and Section 11.5.6.3).

11.5.6.8 Checking sliding shear resistance at construction joints (Clause 21.6.9.4)

In accordance with Clause 21.6.9.4, we must check the sliding shear resistance of the construction joints. Since the vertical uniformly distributed reinforcement is constant over the height of the walls, the most critical situation is at the base of the walls.

N-S direction:

In the N-S direction, the required shear strength is 4406 kN per wall. If the construction joint is intentionally roughened, the factored shear stress resistance from Clauses 11.5.1 and 11.5.2 is:

$$v_r = \phi_c \left(c + \mu \left(\rho_v f_y + \frac{N}{A_g} \right) \right)$$

$$= 0.65 \left(0.50 + 1.0 \left(0.0025 \times 400 + \frac{9797 \times 1000}{800 \times 3200 + 400 \times 5600} \right) \right)$$

$$= 2.302 \, \text{MPa}$$

Hence, the sliding shear resistance is: $2.302 \times A_{cv} = 2.302 \times 400 \times 6400 = 5893$ kN

Since the sliding shear resistance exceeds the shear corresponding to plastic hinging, sliding shear will be prevented.

E-W direction:

In the E-W direction, the required shear strength of segment AB is 1860 kN. It will be assumed that the net compressive axial load is acting on the segments AB and CD (the segment BC is in tension). If the construction joint is intentionally roughened, the factored shear stress resistance from Clause 11.5 is:

$$v_r = \phi_c \left(c + \mu \left(\rho_v f_y + \frac{N}{A_g} \right) \right)$$

$$= 0.65 \left(0.50 + 1.0 \left(0.0025 \times 400 + \frac{1931 \times 1000}{800 \times 3200} \right) \right)$$

$$= 1.465 \, \text{MPa}$$

Hence, the sliding shear resistance of segment AB is:

$$1.465 \times A_{cv} = 1.465 \times 400 \times 3200 = 1875 \text{ kN}.$$

The sliding shear resistance is adequate.

11.5.6.9 Determination of plastic hinge region (Clause 21.6.2)

As the wall cross sectional dimensions remain constant over the 48.65 m height of the wall and provided that the main flexural reinforcement is appropriately curtailed, only one plastic hinge region will form, near the base of the walls. The height over which plastic hinging could take place from the base of the wall is governed by the longer, N-S, wall (Clause 21.6.2.2) and is taken as $1.5 \times 6.4 = 9.6$ m. Therefore detail the first three storeys as plastic hinge regions.

11.5.6.10 Changes in horizontal distributed reinforcement over the height of the walls (Clause 21.6.5)

The maximum spacing of the 2–10M horizontal bars, outside of the plastic hinge region is 200 mm, since the minimum reinforcement ratio of 0.0025 must be satisfied. Therefore use 2 - 10M bars at 200 mm spacing above the plastic hinge region.

11

Seismic Design

11.5.6.11 Changes in Vertical distributed reinforcement over the height of the walls (Clause 21.6.5)

Once again, the minimum reinforcement ratio of 0.0025 governs the selection of vertical distributed reinforcement. Hence use 2-10M bars at 200 mm spacing over the entire height of the wall.

11.5.6.12 Changes in concentrated vertical reinforcement over the height of the walls (Clause 21.6.6)

The minimum area of concentrated reinforcement which can be used outside the plastic hinge region is $0.001b_w\ell_w$ (Clause 21.6.6.3). At one end of the 3200 mm long wall, the minimum amount of concentrated reinforcement is $0.001\times400\times3200 = 1280$ mm^2. Similarly, the minimum amount of concentrated reinforcement required at the intersection of the wall components is $2560 - 1280 = 1280$ mm^2 (Clause 21.6.6.5).

Note that in deciding on the changes to the concentrated reinforcement over the height of the structure, it is necessary to ensure that the factored moment resistance at each floor level is sufficient to develop the plastic hinging at the base of the structure. This check should be made with due consideration for the effect of lap splices in the reinforcement. An example of the calculations necessary to ensure adequate flexural strength is given in Reference 1.

11.5.7 Frame Members Not Considered Part of the SFRS

Clause 21.12 provides design requirements for members that are not considered part of the seismic force resisting system. The shear walls and coupled wall system were designed to take 100% of the seismic loading effects. The slabs and the columns must be checked to determine if the levels of ductility and strength of these important vertical load carrying members are sufficient.

11.5.7.1 Slab-column connections (Clause 21.12.3)

The reduction factor, R_E, on two-way slab shear stress is a function of the interstorey drift. The maximum drifts at the extremities of the structure including torsional effects is 0.00565 (8th storey) in the N-S direction and 0.0047 (8th storey) in the E-W direction. Hence the reduction factor is:

$$R_E = \left(\frac{0.005}{\delta_i}\right)^{0.85} = \left(\frac{0.005}{0.00565}\right)^{0.85} = 0.901$$

Interior slab-column connection:

For an interior slab-column connection, the gravity load two-way shear stress (excluding shear from unbalanced loading and determined using the seismic load combinations $(1.0D + 0.5L)$ can be determined for a first interior columns location as follows:

$$V_f = [1.0(4.8+1.5)+0.5(2.4)]\times(5.75\times6.0-0.71^2) = 255 \text{ kN}$$

A clear cover of 25 mm and 15M top bars are assumed for the slab.

The corresponding shear stress is:

$$v_f = \frac{V_f}{b_o d} = \frac{255\times1000}{4\times(550+160)\times160} = 0.561 \text{ MPa}$$

The limiting shear stress obtained by multiplying R_E by the two-way shear stress for this square column from Clause 13.3.4.1 is:

$$v_c = 0.38\phi_c \sqrt{f'_c} R_E = 0.38 \times 0.65\sqrt{30} \times 0.901 = 1.219 \text{ MPa}$$

Hence, no shear reinforcement is required.

Corner slab-column connection:

Applying the same principles to a corner slab-column connection gives a factored shear of:

$$V_f = [1.0(4.8 + 1.5) + 0.5(2.4)] \times (3.125^2 - 0.73^2) = 69.2 \text{ kN}$$

$$v_f = \frac{V_f}{b_o d} = \frac{69.2 \times 1000}{2 \times (100 + 550 + 160/2) \times 160} = 0.296 \text{ MPa}$$

The limiting shear stress obtained by multiplying R_E by the one-way shear stress for this corner column from Clause 13.3.6 and 11.3.6.2 is:

$$v_c = 0.21\phi_c \sqrt{f'_c} R_E = 0.21 \times 0.65\sqrt{30} \times 0.901 = 0.674 \text{ MPa}$$

Hence, no shear reinforcement is required.

11.5.7.2   Check on design and detailing of columns (Clause 21.12)

Clauses 21.12.1 to 21.12.2 provide detailed requirements for the columns which are not considered part of the seismic force resisting system. Minimum design and detailing requirements must be applied or the columns must be analyzed to determine if the factored moments in the columns exceed their nominal resistances when the structure is deformed laterally to the design displacements.

11.5.8   Comparisons with the Design Using the 1994 CSA Standard

The structure designed in this chapter is the same structure designed in Reference 2, except that the structure designed in this chapter was for a foundation on soil of site Class D (stiff soil), whereas the structure in Reference 2 was for the same structure founded on rock. In addition, 900 mm deep diagonally reinforced coupling beams were used, instead of 600 mm deep coupling beams with conventional reinforcement. It is noted that, for this structure, the design force levels using the 2005 NBCC are somewhat lower than those using the 1995 NBCC.

11.5.9   References

1.   Mitchell, D. and Collins, M.P., "Chapter 11 - Seismic Design", Concrete Design Handbook, Canadian Portland Cement Association, Ottawa, 1985, pp. 11-1 – 11-31.

2.   Mitchell, D., Paultre, P. and Collins, M.P., "Chapter 11 - Seismic Design", Concrete Design Handbook, Cement Association of Canada, Ottawa, 1995, pp. 11-1 – 11-33.

3.   Paulay, T., Priestley, M.J.N., "Seismic Design of Reinforced Concrete and Masonry Buildings", John Wiley and Sons, NY, 1992, 744p.

11

Seismic Design

12

By Richard J. McGrath
Ahmed Abdel-Akher

Anchorage

12.1   Introduction

CSA A23.3-04[12-1] Annex "D" is included as an "informatory", (non-mandatory) part of the A23.3 Standard, and provides design requirements for anchorage to concrete. Anchorage design requirements were first introduced in the 1984 A23.3 Standard as Appendix "H", and were later carried forward unchanged as Appendix "D" in the 1994 edition. The anchorage requirements were based on the 45° cone model which was developed in the mid 1970's and documented by researchers such as Cannon, Godfrey, and Moreadith[12-2]. The requirements were only applicable for cast-in-place headed anchors.

Following the development of the 45° cone model, a comprehensive series of anchorage tests were performed at the University of Stuttgart in the 1980's. A variety of anchor types were tested with various embedment depths, edge distances, and group configurations. Tests were conducted using both cracked and uncracked concrete. The Kappa (K) method[12-3, 12-4] that emerged from the work at Stuttgart, was further refined in the 1990's at the University of Texas in Austin. The design procedures resulting from the work in Texas comprise what is now known as the Concrete Capacity Design (CCD) method[12-5, 12-6].

In the CSA A23.3-04 Standard, the CCD method for anchorage design has now replaced the 45° cone method. The specifications are again contained in a non-mandatory Annex "D" of the Standard. The CCD requirements are similar to those found in the ACI 318-05 Code[12-7] with the exception that they have been adapted for use with the Limit States Design provisions of the CSA A23.3-04 Standard and the load factors required by the National Building Code of Canada 2005 (NBCC)[12-8]. The resistance levels provided by CSA A23.3 Annex "D" have been calibrated to support the same service load levels as provided by the ACI 318-05 Code.

12.2   General Principles

When designing anchors, consideration must be given to the capacity of both the steel anchor and the embedded portion of the anchor. The nuances of the CCD method vs the 45° cone method deal primarily with the embedded portion of the anchor.

As the name suggests, the 45° cone method utilizes a 45° conical failure surface in the determination of the concrete breakout capacity. This results in design expressions that are based on the square of the embedment depth, (h_{ef}^{2}). The CCD method however considers fracture mechanics (size effect) in utilizing a 35° projected failure surface for the embedded portion of the anchor. This results in expressions with the embedment depth raised to the power of 1.5, $(h_{ef}^{1.5})$. In the CCD method, the capacity expressions have been calibrated to the extensive database of experimental tests that have been conducted over the last 20 years. The equation coefficients have been selected to predict the 5% fractile failure level from these tests. This implies, with a 90% confidence level, that 95 times out of 100 the actual strength of the anchor will exceed the nominal strength. Addressing a greater variety of anchor types, and design conditions, the CCD method provides a more consistent level of safety for a wider variety of anchorage failure modes in both cracked and uncracked concrete and represents a significant advancement in anchorage design.

12.3   Design Provisions

12.3.1   General Requirements

Section D.4 of Annex "D" refers the designer to Clause 8 of the Standard for the applicable load factors and load combinations to be use in the design of anchors.

12.3.2   Plastic vs Elastic Analysis

The analysis method used to distribute forces to individual anchors in a group anchor arrangement will depend on a number of variables, including the rigidity of the attached base plate, the embedment of the anchors and the nature of the loading.

Sufficiently stiff base plates may be capable of distributing a concentric tension load equally to all anchors in a group, simplifying the design. A more flexible base plate on the other hand may yield, allowing prying action to take place in some of the anchors in the group and thus necessitating a more detailed analysis of the resulting forces on individual anchors in the group.[12-9, 12-10]

Unless sufficient ductility is provided by the anchors to allow for a redistribution of the forces to the individual anchors in a group, an elastic analysis approach should be used. Where sufficient ductility exists, a plastic design approach may be more appropriate. The plastic approach will assume that the resulting tension force is equally distributed to all tension anchors in the group. The plastic design approach requires that the anchors be provided with sufficient embedment to preclude a brittle concrete breakout failure prior to a ductile steel failure. For group anchors resisting moment, the plastic analysis is similar to the case of multiple layers of reinforcement in a concrete beam. Anchors at a sufficient distance from the neutral axis are considered to have yielded. In group anchors where concrete breakout is the critical failure mode, little if any redistribution of forces will take place between individual anchors and an elastic analysis approach is required.

The exact location of the compressive resultant in a group anchor subjected to moment cannot currently be established regardless of the analysis method used. Since plane sections do not remain plane, traditional beam theory will not provide a definitive solution to this problem. At present, this aspect of the anchorage design is an evolving science, and the following conservative approach to this problem as illustrated in Fig. 12.1 is suggested. To conservatively estimate the load on the anchors, locate the compressive resultant at the leading edge of the compression element of the attached member. This will ensure that the minimum lever arm is assumed in the moment of resistance provided by the anchor group. To conservatively design the base plate stiffness, take the compression resultant as acting at the leading edge of the base plate. A more detailed discussion on this topic can be found in references 12.9 and 12.10.

12

Anchorage

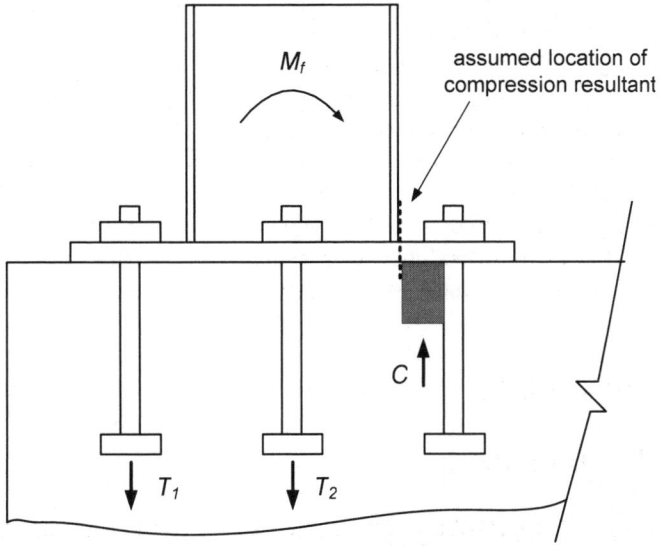

Fig. 12.1 Location of Compression Resultant

12.3.3   Seismic Design Considerations

When load combinations include seismic effects under the condition $I_E F_a S_a(0.2) \geq 0.35$, an additional 25% reduction is applied to the calculated anchor capacity. Annex "D" prohibits the location of anchors in plastic hinge zones of concrete structures as cracking in these regions is expected to exceed the 0.3 mm crack widths used in the tests on which the specifications are based.

12.3.4   Concrete Density and Strength

All concrete capacity expressions contained in Annex "D" assume normal density concrete. As specified in D.4.4 when low-density concrete is used all values of $\sqrt{f_c'}$ should be multiplied by λ as defined in Clause 8.6.5 of CSA A23.3-04. For calculation purposes, the value of f_c' is limited to 70 MPa for cast-in anchors and 55 MPa for post-installed anchors. These limits represent the scope of the database of tests on which the CCD method is based. Designers are required to verify by tests the capacity of post-installed anchors in concrete stronger than 55 MPa.

12.4   General Requirements for Resistance of Structural Anchors

The resistance of an anchor is determined on the basis of seven possible failure modes as described in D.5.1.1.
Tension capacity is taken as the lesser of:
$N_r \leq$ Steel strength of anchor in tension, or
      Concrete breakout resistance in tension, or
      Pullout resistance of anchor in tension, or
      Concrete side face blowout resistance in tension

Shear capacity is taken as the lesser of:
$V_r \leq$ Steel strength of anchor in shear, or
      Concrete breakout resistance of anchor in shear, or
      Concrete pryout resistance of anchor in shear

The critical values of N_r and V_r determined from the failure modes listed above are then taken as the factored resistance of the anchor in tension and shear.
In all instances the factored resistance must to equal or exceed the factored load effect:

$N_r \geq N_f$
$V_r \geq V_f$

Where seismic loads are included, Clause D.4.3 requires that the factored resistance values listed above be reduced by an additional 25%.
Clause D.5.2.1 of Annex "D" provides the designer with the option of using alternative design procedures provided they result in predicted capacities in agreement with the results of tests. The nominal resistance must be based on the 5% fractile of the basic individual anchor resistance.
The provisions of Annex "D" are based on tests conducted on anchors ≤ 50 mm in diameter with embedment depths ≤ 625 mm.
The force modification factor "R" defined in clause D.5.4 is applied to the tension and shear capacity expressions in Annex "D" to ensure proper calibration of the Limit States Design (LSD) resistance levels in A23.3-04 with the ultimate strength design (USD) provisions of the ACI 318-05 Code.

In Clause D.5.4(c) R factors are listed for concrete related shear and tension failures associated with two conditions, A and B. Condition A applies where supplemental reinforcement[12.11, 12.12] is provided to restrain the concrete failure prism. Further information on supplemental reinforcement is given if Sections 12.5.5 for restraint of tension breakout sections and Section 12.6.4 for shear breakout sections. Condition B applies where such reinforcement is not present.

Condition "A" should not be assumed in cases of pullout or pryout failure as the effective anchorage of the breakout section is not considered possible in these cases. Likewise in the case of post-installed anchors it would be difficult to ensure that the required reinforcement was located so as to effectively restrain the breakout section. As a result Condition "B" should always be assumed for post-installed anchors. Reference 12-13 provides a more detailed discussion on the detailing of supplemental reinforcement to prevent breakout failure.

Tables 12.5 and 12.6 provide anchor tension and shear capacities for a variety of anchor sizes, embedment depths and concrete strengths. Condition ""B" is assumed for all concrete breakout capacity calculations. The anchor bolt data used to generate Tables 12.5 and 12.6 is given in Table 12.4. Note that the A_{se} values used for the tension anchors are calculated values and are slightly larger than the conservative $0.7A_g$ estimate permitted by Annex "D".

12.5   Design Requirements for Tensile Loading

12.5.1   Steel Anchor Tensile Resistance

The capacity of the steel anchor is determined using the effective cross sectional area of the anchor and the specified tensile strength of the steel f_{ut}. Typical embedment steels exhibit significant variation in actual yield strength above specified minimums, and have widely differing ratios of yield to tensile strength. Therefore in keeping with the LSD approach of the A23.3-04 Standard, $\phi_s f_{ut}$ rather than $\phi_s f_y$ is used. Clause D.6.1.2 limits f_{ut} of the steel anchor to $1.9f_y$ to ensure that the anchor does not yield under service loads. This limit is derived by dividing the average load factor using a live to dead load ratio of 1.0, by the product of the steel material resistance factor ϕ_s and the largest R value applicable to ductile steel anchors in tension. The R values listed in Clause D.5.4 are rounded down from the exact calibrated values. The upper limit on f_{ut} of 860 MPa represents the scope of the tests used in developing the requirements of the CCD method. This limit will probably be approached only with stainless steel anchors.

The term A_{se} in Clause D.6.1.2 is to be taken as the net tensile area of a steel anchor. Where threaded rods are used A_{se} would be the net tensile area in the threaded region of the anchor. If welded steel studs are used, A_{se} would be the gross area A_g of the stud, In lieu of more detailed calculations Annex "D" permits the net tensile area for threaded anchor bolts to be taken as 70% of the gross area. CSA Standard S16-01 Limit States Design of Steel Structures, provides the following expressions to calculate the net area of threaded bolts for tension only.

$$A_{se} = \frac{\pi}{4}(d - 0.938P)^2 \text{ for metric rods, where } P = \text{the pitch of the thread, or}$$

$$A_{se} = \frac{\pi}{4}\left(d - \frac{0.974}{n}\right)^2 \text{ for imperial rods, where } n = \text{the number of threads per inch.}$$

In Canada, anchor rod material for most applications is produced to CSA G40.21 Grade 300W (f_y = 300 MPa) or ASTM A36 with f_y = 248 MPa. However, the ASTM A36 round stock is more readily available. Anchor rods may be threaded at one or both ends to receive a washer and nut, or may be bent at the other end to form a hook. The term "anchor rod" is used to differentiate it from the ASTM A325 and A490 bolt material specifications. The term "standard anchor bolt" when used in this Chapter means a bolt with dimensions conforming to those for Square Headed

12

Anchorage

Bolts listed in CSA Standard B18.2.1-1961, Hexagonal Headed Bolts listed in CSA Standard B33.1-1961 or ASTM A307 Bolts. Table 12.1 in Section 12 presents a list of ASTM steel types for cast-in-place headed anchor bolts. ASTM bolt and nut dimensions (in inches) are listed in Table 12.2 in Section 12. Table 12.3 lists the bearing area A_{bh} for ASTM square and hexagonal nuts. More information on Canadian fasteners can be obtained from the Canadian Fasteners Institute at www.cfi-fasteners.org.

12.5.2   Concrete Breakout for Tensile Resistance

The concrete breakout cone depicted in Figure D.2(c) and D.4(a) of Annex "D" is assumed in the derivation of equations (D-4) and (D-5) for single and group anchors as shown below.

$$N_{cbr} = \frac{A_N}{A_{No}} \psi_{ed,N} \, \psi_{c,N} \, \psi_{cp,N} \, N_{br} \tag{D-4}$$

$$N_{cbgr} = \frac{A_N}{A_{No}} \psi_{ec,N} \, \psi_{ed,N} \, \psi_{c,N} \, \psi_{cp,N} \, N_{br} \tag{D-5}$$

The individual terms are reviewed below. N_{cbr} capacity values are listed in Table 12.5.

N_{br} is the factored concrete breakout resistance of a single anchor in tension in cracked concrete unaffected by free edges or overlapping stress cones, and is derived as follows:

$$N_{br} = k_1 \sqrt{f_c'} \cdot k_2 {h_{ef}}^2 \cdot k_3 {h_{ef}}^{-0.5}$$

where k_1, k_2, k_3 are calibration factors. The product of these calibration factors is the resulting k coefficient that appears in the concrete breakout capacity expressions in Annex "D".

$$k = k_1 k_2 k_3$$

The ${h_{ef}}^{1.5}$ term accounts for a size effect. The consideration of fracture mechanics accounts for the higher tensile stresses that exist at the embedded head of the anchor as illustrated in Figure 12-2 below.

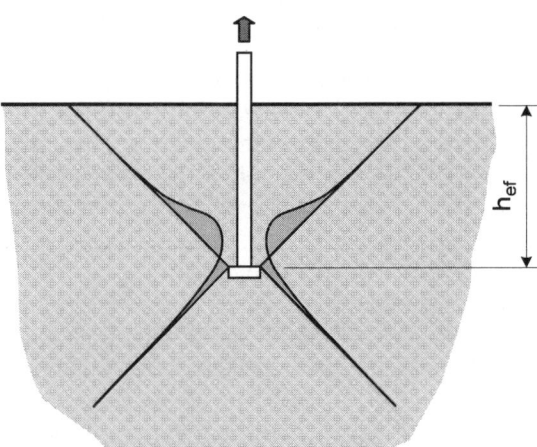

Figure 12-2 Stress Distribution Around an Anchor

The resulting nominal capacity expression for N_{br} is given by:

$$N_{br} = k_c \sqrt{f_c'} \, h_{ef}^{1.5}$$

In Annex "D" the LSD concrete material resistance factor ϕ_c is applied along with the resistance modification factor "R" to yield the expression:

$$N_{br} = k \phi_c \sqrt{f_c'} \, {h_{ef}}^{1.5} R \tag{D.6.2.2}$$

The constant k is calibrated to the 5% fractile of test results on headed anchors in concrete with crack widths up to 0.3 mm. Where crack widths are expected to exceed this value, crack control reinforcement should be provided to ensure this limit is not exceeded.

When calculating the concrete breakout capacity, Clause D.6.2.8 allows the designer to modify the effective depth of embedment through the use of a washer or plate at the head of the anchor. The failure surface is then calculated as projecting outward from the effective perimeter of the plate or washer, providing the modified effective depth "h_{ef} modified" as illustrated in Figure 12.3 below.

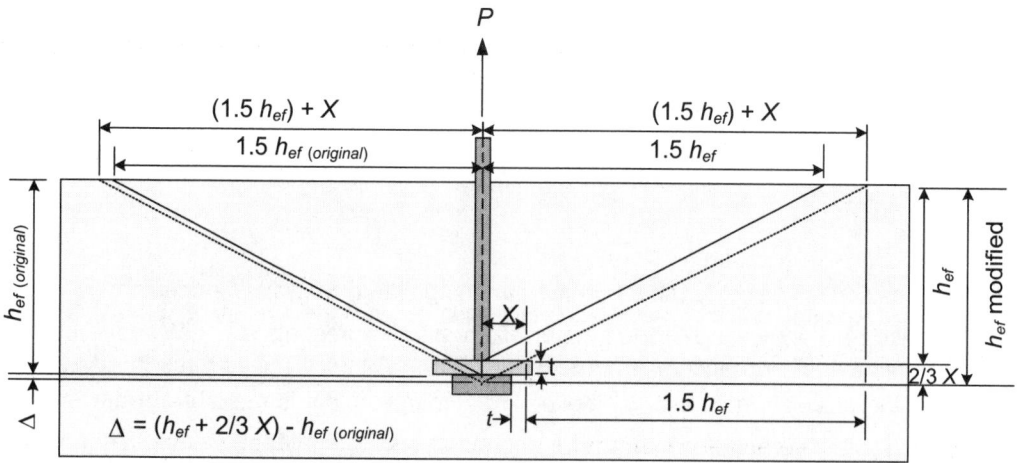

Figure 12.3 Increasing h_{ef} Using a Washer or Plate

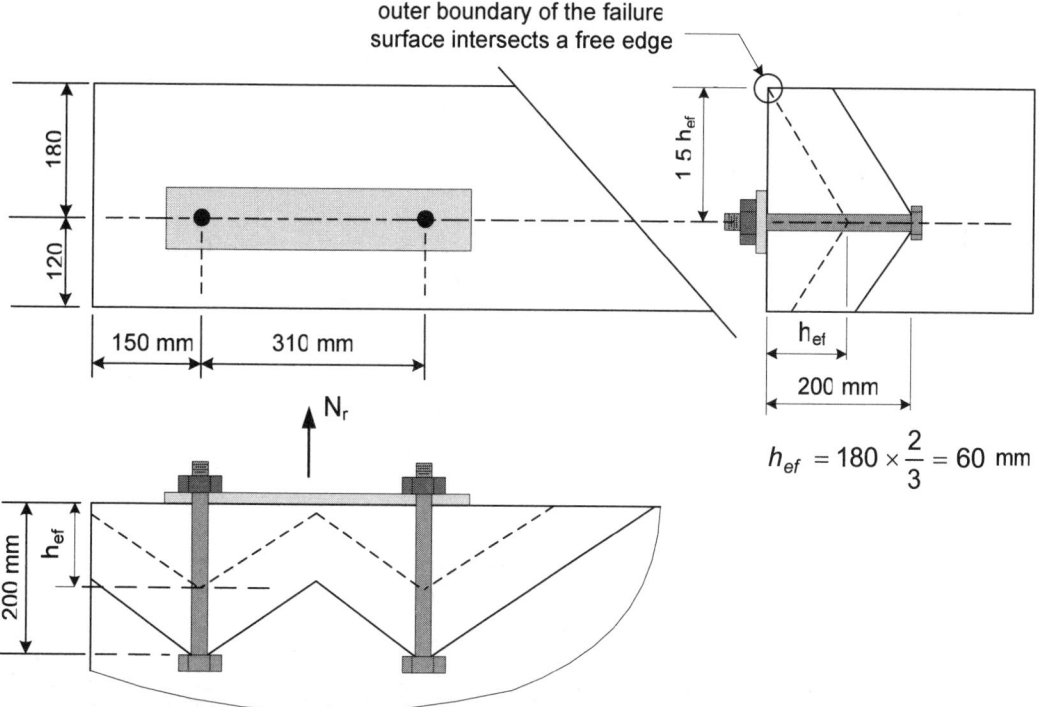

$$h_{ef} = 180 \times \frac{2}{3} = 60 \text{ mm}$$

Figure 12.4 Modified h_{ef} in Narrow Member

12

Anchorage

The term A_N/A_{No} accounts for the presence of adjacent anchors and or free edges. A_{No} is the projected area of a 35° failure plane of a single anchor measured relative to the surface of the concrete as depicted in Annex "D" Figure D.5. A_N is a similarly projected area limited by edges and adjacent anchors. For single anchors located distant from free edges the A_N/A_{No} term equals 1.0.

Clause D.6.2.3 requires that the designer use a modified h_{ef} value in calculating the breakout capacity when three or more edges are within $1.5h_{ef}$ of the anchor. This determination of this modified effective embedment depth h'_{ef} is illustrated in Figure 12.4.

The term $\psi_{ec,N}$ is used to reflect the reduced capacity of group anchors loaded eccentrically and is calculated using equation D-9 as shown below:

$$\psi_{ec,N} = \frac{1}{\left(1 + \dfrac{2e'_N}{3h_{ef}}\right)} \qquad \text{where } e'_N \le \frac{s_o}{2} \tag{D-9}$$

The expression for $\psi_{ec,N}$ is based on the punching shear analysis of eccentrically loaded flat slabs[12-14]. These tests indicate that the chosen expression represents a conservative estimate of the effects of eccentricity on anchor groups. Figure D.8 in Annex "D" illustrates the determination of e'_N used in the calculation of $\psi_{ec,N}$ above. The dimension e'_N is measured from the point of load application to the centre of gravity of the anchors resisting the tensile force. When an anchor group is loaded in such a way that only some of the anchors are in tension, only those anchors in tension are used in determining e'_N. The dimension "s_o" used to define the limit of application of equation D-27, can be taken as the center to center spacing of the outermost anchors in tension as illustrated in Figure 12.5.

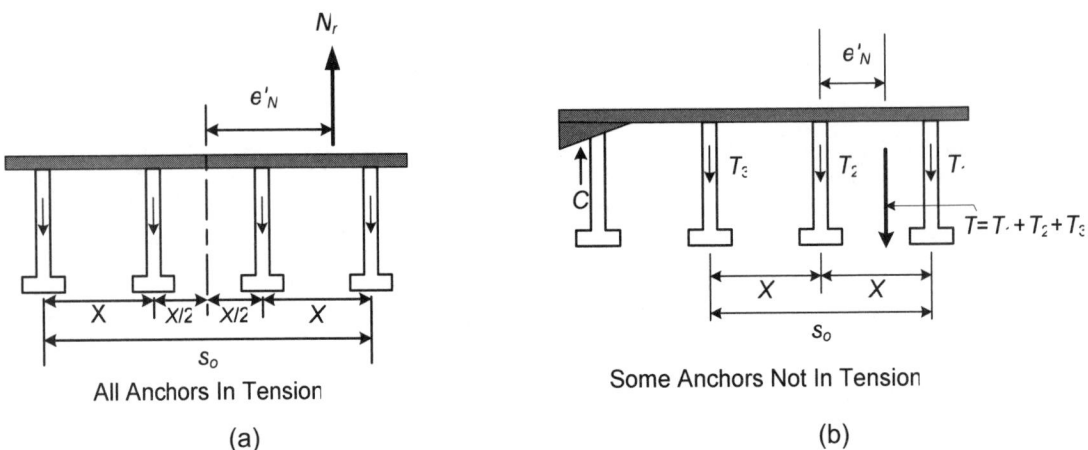

All Anchors In Tension

(a)

Some Anchors Not In Tension

(b)

Figure 12.5 Determination of e'_N

The term $\psi_{ed,N}$ is a modification factor for edge effects. Free edges influence the capacity of cast in place headed anchors where the edge distance is $< 1.5h_{ef}$. This dimension can be greater for post-installed anchors. The presence of a free edge distorts the distribution of concrete stresses around an anchor similar to the presence of cracks in the concrete, reducing the capacity of the embedment. In such cases $\psi_{ed,N}$ is used to capture this effect by further reducing the calculated capacity of the embedment beyond that provided by A_N / A_{No}; $\psi_{ed,N}$ is given by equations D-11 and D-12 in Annex "D" as shown below:

$$\psi_{ed,N} = 1.0 \qquad\qquad \text{if } c_{min} \geq 1.5\,h_{ef}$$

$$\psi_{ed,N} = 0.7 + 0.3\frac{c_{min}}{1.5\,h_{ef}} \qquad \text{if } c_{min} < 1.5\,h_{ef} \qquad\qquad\qquad \text{(D.6.2.5)}$$

The distortion in the anchor stress distribution due to edge effects is similar to that caused by the presence of cracks at an anchor location. Tests indicate that the concrete breakout loads in cracked concrete is approximately 70% of the values obtained in uncracked concrete. As a result, a lower limit of $\psi_{ed,N} = 0.7$ has been established for the limiting case of edge distance $c_1 = 0.0$, where the maximum disruption of the symmetric stress distribution occurs[12-14].

$\psi_{c,N}$ accounts for the influence of cracks on the anchor capacity. When cracks are present $\psi_{c,N}$ is taken as 1.0 for both cast-in headed anchors and post installed anchors. All post-installed anchors used in cracked concrete must be qualified by ACI 355.2 for use in cracked concrete. Where cracking is not present a 25% increase is applied to cast-in headed anchor capacities and a 40% premium is applied to post-installed anchor designs.

$\psi_{cp,N}$ is an additional factor applicable to post-installed anchors used in uncracked concrete without supplemental reinforcement to control cracking. Clause D.6 assumes that anchors will develop their basic breakout strength if the shortest edge distance is at least $1.5h_{ef}$. While this is true for cast-in headed anchors, it is not necessarily true for post-installed anchors. Expansion or torque controlled post-installed anchors, and some undercut anchors, impose tensile stresses on the surrounding concrete during installation. These stresses are additive to the tensile stresses that are imposed on the concrete when the anchor is loaded. The result is that the required minimum edge distance required to achieve the basic breakout section may well exceed $1.5h_{ef}$. In such cases Annex "D" provides the additional reduction factor $\psi_{cp,N}$ which in turn is dependent on the critical edge distance c_{ac}, for that particular type of anchor being used. $\psi_{cp,N}$ is calculated as follows:

$$\psi_{cp,N} = 1.0 \qquad\qquad \text{if } c_{a,min} \geq c_{ac}$$

$$= \frac{c_{a,min}}{c_{ac}} \geq \frac{1.5h_{ef}}{c_{ac}} \qquad \text{if } c_{a,min} < c_{ac} \qquad\qquad\qquad \text{(D.6.2.7)}$$

In calculating $\psi_{cp,N}$ the critical edge distance c_{ac} is obtained from Clause D.9.7 or alternatively from tests in accordance with ACI 355.2/355.2R.

12.5.3 Pullout

The pullout provisions of Annex "D" apply to cast-in headed and hooked bolts only.[12-5, 12-6] Equations D-15 to D-17 are used to determine cast-in anchor pullout capacity. The effective bearing area "A_{bh}" of a bolt head is the gross area of the bolt head minus the area of the anchor shaft. Pullout capacity can be increased by using washers or plates to increase the bearing area A_{bh}. When this is done the perimeter limits defined in Clause D.6.2.8 should be observed. Equation D-16 predicts the onset of local crushing at the anchor head and not the actual pullout of the anchor[12-5]. Pullout tests using very lightweight concrete with weak aggregates have demonstrated a significantly reduced pullout capacity as a result of local crushing at the bearing surface of the anchor head. This reduction in strength may not be adequately captured by the application of the lightweight concrete factor λ to the design expression.

12

Anchorage

Hooked bolts will fail through bearing at the inside of the hook[12-9]. The minimum hook length e_h for L and J bolts is measured from the inner surface of the anchor shaft to the outside tip of the L or J bolt as illustrated in Figure 12.6.

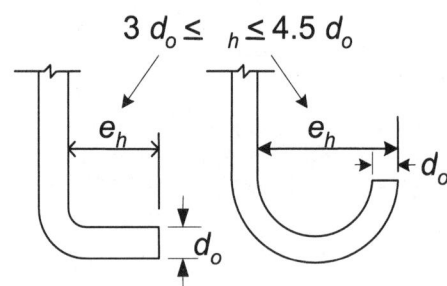

Fig. 12.6 Dimension e_h for L and J Bolts

Through the use of the $\psi_{c,P}$ factor in Equation D-15, Annex "D" allows a 40% increase in the pullout capacity of a cast-in anchor in uncracked concrete over that provided in cracked concrete. The Resistance Modification Factor "R" in equations D-16 and D-17 will always be 1.0 as the application of Condition "A" to the pullout failure mode is not permitted by Annex "D".

The additional variables associated with post-installed anchors make it impossible to predict the pullout capacity of these anchors with a general expression. As a result, Annex "D" requires that the pullout capacity of post-installed anchors be verified by tests in conformance with ACI 355.2.

Pullout capacity values are listed in Table 12.5

12.5.4   Side Face Blowout

Side face blowout occurs when the lateral pressure which develops at the embedded head of cast-in anchors under load exceeds the confining strength of the surrounding concrete. Equations D-18 and D-19 in Annex "D" predict side face blowout capacities for single and group anchors within a distance $0.4h_{ef}$ of a free edge. Edge distances greater than this preclude blowout failures for cast-in-headed anchors. These equations are not applicable to J or L bolt anchors for which there are currently no side face blowout expressions. L bolts located in close proximity to a free edge with the hook oriented parallel to the free edge will exhibit a blowout type failure. With no expression provided for this L bolt failure, designers are encouraged to use headed anchors in close proximity to free edges. Side face blowout capacities are listed in Table 12.5.

Where a second orthogonal free edge c_2 is within $3c$ of the anchor, (a corner for example), Clause D.6.4 further reduces the side face blowout strength by up to 50% as dimension c_2 reduces from a value of $3c$ to c. This reduction factor is given by the expression $(1 + c_2/c)/4$ where $1 \leq c_2/c \leq 3$.

The provisions of Clause D.6.4 are based on reference 12-15. The equations are calibrated for use with cast-in headed anchors and are not meant to be used with L or J bolts. Post-installed anchors in proximity to a free edge tend to develop splitting failures that are not characteristic of the side-face blowout failures covered by Clause D.6.4. As a result these provisions are not applicable to post-installed anchors. The splitting failure of post-installed anchors is evaluated by tests in accordance with ACI 355.2[12-16].

In Equation D-19 of Annex "D" the term s_o is taken as the spacing between the individual outer anchors parallel to a free edge as illustrated in Figure 12.7.

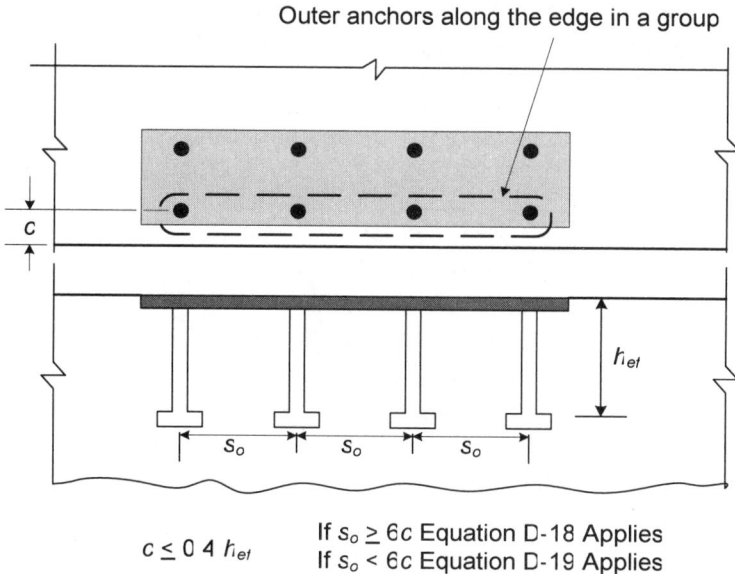

Outer anchors along the edge in a group

$$c \leq 0\ 4\ h_{ef}$$

If $s_o \geq 6c$ Equation D-18 Applies
If $s_o < 6c$ Equation D-19 Applies

Fig 12.7 Dimension s_o for use in Clause D.6.4.2

12.5.5 Supplemental Reinforcement for Tension

Clause D.5.4(c) permits a 15% increase in capacity for tension embedment sections that are restrained from breakout by supplemental reinforcement. To utilize this 15% increase in capacity however the designer must ensure that the supplemental reinforcement is designed to restrain the full breakout force required for the anchor. In looking at the concrete tensile stress distribution around an embedded anchor in Figure 12.8, it is obvious that the reinforcement will be most effective when placed in the region of greatest tensile stress, i.e. close to the anchor. Tests have shown that only reinforcement running parallel to the applied load and in close proximity to the anchor is effective in restraining the concrete breakout section[12-11, 12-12]. This is often achieved using hairpin reinforcement or hooked bars. The basic concept is illustrated in Fig 12.8.

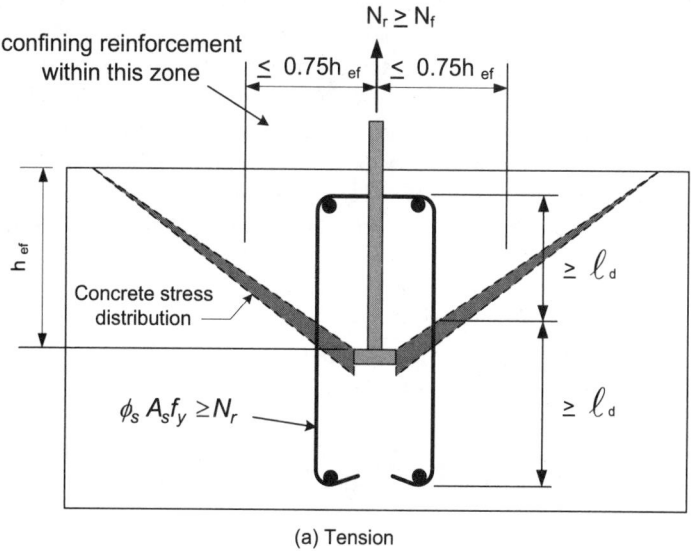

(a) Tension

Fig 12.8 Supplemental Reinforcement for Tension

When detailing supplemental reinforcement it should be oriented in the same direction as the applied load and it should not be placed any farther than $0.75h_{ef}$ from the anchor. Reinforcement more distant from the anchor than this will not be able to restrain the large tensile stresses that surround the immediate area around the anchor. Reinforcement placed perpendicular to the anchor and close to the surface of the concrete will have virtually no effect on restraining the concrete breakout section. The reinforcement must also be properly detailed to develop its yield strength across the failure plane of the concrete as illustrated in figure 12.8. Usually this can only be achieve with the use of hairpin reinforcing bars and well anchored bars with hooks. The hook should engage a horizontal bar to improve the anchorage.

12.6   Design Requirements for Shear Loading

In the design for shear, the designer must check three possible failure modes:
- a) shear failure of the steel anchor,
- b) concrete breakout of the embedment, and
- c) concrete pryout failure.

12.6.1   Steel Anchor Shear Resistance

As in the case of tension capacity, Clause D.7.1.2 limits f_{ut} of the steel anchor to $1.9f_y$ to ensure that the anchor does not yield under service loads. The derivation of this limit is discussed in Section 12.5.1. The f_{ut} strength of steel is used instead of the yield strength because anchor materials do not exhibit a well-defined yield point. The upper limit on f_{ut} of 860 MPa represents the scope of the tests used in developing the requirements of Annex "D".

The shear resistance of the cast-in headed stud anchors is given by equation D-20.

$$V_{sr} = \phi_s n A_{se} f_{ut} R \qquad\qquad \text{Eq.(D-20)}$$

Tests[12-17] show that cast-in headed stud anchors welded to a base plate do not exhibit the 40% reduction in shear strength characteristic of headed and hooked bolts. As a result, the 0.6 reduction is not applied to these anchors in shear.

A_{se} in equations D-20 and D-21 represents the net cross-sectional area of the steel anchor while "n" is the number of anchors in a group. While not explicitly stated in Clause D.7.1.2 if threads in the steel anchor intercept the shear plane the effective area of the anchor should be taken as being $0.70 A_g$. For shear calculations, CSA Standard S16-01 Limit States Design of Steel Structures requires that 70% of the gross area be taken as the effective net area A_{se} for threaded bolts. V_{sr} capacity values for threaded anchor bolts are given in Table 12.6.

Many post-installed anchors with expansion mechanisms have reduced cross-sectional areas. In such cases the manufacturer should always supply the effective cross-sectional area data.

In some cases with post-installed anchors, the sleeve may act independently from the shaft of the anchor in resisting shear. In recognition of this, the area of the sleeve is excluded from equation D-21. However, Clause D.7.1.2(c) has been included to recognize the beneficial effect that anchor sleeves may have on the shear resistance of the steel anchor when supported by tests conducted in accordance with ACI 355.2.

The 20% reduction in shear capacity required by Clause D.7.1.3 reflects the effect of flexural stresses that develop in the anchor if the supporting grout pad fractures under the application of the shear load.

12.6.2   Concrete Breakout

Equations D-22 and D-23 give the shear breakout capacity for single and group anchors respectively when loaded in shear perpendicular to a free edge.

In cases where shear acts parallel to a free edge, Clause D.7.2.1(c) limits the shear force to no greater than twice the capacity determined for shear forces acting perpendicular to the edge. This is illustrated in Figure D-11(a) in Annex "D".

When an anchor is located near a corner, the designer is required to evaluate the shear capacity in both orthogonal directions and limit the shear load to the lesser of the two.

The determination of shear concrete breakout resistance is given by Equation D-23 of Annex "D" shown below:

$$V_{cbgr} = \frac{A_V}{A_{Vo}} \psi_{ec,V} \, \psi_{ed,V} \, \psi_{c,V} \, V_{br}$$ Eq.(D-23)

As in the case for tension, a 35° breakout prism angle is assumed. The shear breakout capacity is determined by first evaluating the basic concrete breakout resistance for an anchor in shear V_{br}, and then by applying the additional factors accounting for group effects, eccentricity of loading, edge conditions, and cracking in the concrete. These contributing factors are discussed below.

A_V/A_{Vo} represents the ratio of the shear breakout area of a group anchor arrangement "A_V" vs the full shear breakout area of a single anchor "A_{Vo}" unaffected by edge distance, spacing or section depth. Figure D.9 in Annex "D" illustrates the area A_{Vo} while Figure D.10(a), (b) and (c) illustrate the area A_V applicable for conditions involving limited section depth, edge constraints and anchor spacing.

For anchor groups loaded in shear towards a free edge the two conditions illustrated in Figure D.10(d) and (e) should be investigated. If the anchors are spaced sufficiently far enough apart such that their failure surfaces do not intersect, $\geq 1.5c_1$, then two possible failure conditions should be investigated. If the two anchors are not rigidly connected then the front anchor, which possesses a smaller failure surface, would present the critical design condition. Where the two anchors are rigidly connected, the shear capacity will be determined by the back anchor[12-12]. In this case when the front anchor begins to break out, the entire shear load is transferred to the back anchor. The lone back anchor will then carry the entire load and the break out section associated with that anchor will become the critical failure surface.

The factored concrete breakout resistance of an anchor is affected by the anchor stiffness and diameter[12-4, 12-5, 12-18] and is given by equation D-25 in Annex "D" as shown below.

$$V_{br} = 0.58 \left(\frac{\ell}{d_o}\right)^{0.2} \sqrt{d_o} \, \phi_c \sqrt{f'_c} \, c_1^{1.5} R$$ Eq.(D-25)

For anchors welded to a steel attachment in accordance with Clause D.7.2.3, equation D-26 shown below is used to calculate the shear capacity.

$$V_{br} = 0.66 \left(\frac{\ell}{d_o}\right)^{0.2} \sqrt{d_o} \, \phi_c \sqrt{f'_c} \, c_1^{1.5} R$$ Eq.(D-26)

The ℓ/d_o ratio is limited to 8.0 when used in equations D-25 and D-26 of Annex "D". The constants in these equations were calibrated from test results[12-5, 12-19]. They represent the 5% fractile values calibrated for cracked concrete.

Clause D.7.2.3(c) requires the use of supplemental reinforcement. More information on the use of supplemental reinforcement is given in references 12-18, 12-13, and 12-20.

12

Anchorage

Clause D.7.2.4 requires that where shear anchors are located in narrow or thin sections, and the anchor is influenced by three or more edges, the value of c_1 used in the shear capacity equations in Annex "D" should be modified as illustrated in Figure D.7 of Annex D, and Fig. 12.9. As can be seen in Fig. 12.9, if more than one c_2 edge distance is less than c1, then the larger c_2 value should be used to calculate c1. It should be noted that there is a third criteria that is not currently listed in Clause D.7.2.4. While it is not explicitly stated in D.7.2.4, c_1 need not be taken less than $s/3$ where "s" is the centre to centre spacing of the anchors in the group. Taking c_1 less than this value would produce a failure surface less than that which would actually develop.

$\psi_{ec,V}$ is a factor that accounts for eccentric shear load application on an anchor group. The shear load is assumed oriented towards a free edge. The determination of e_v' is illustrated in Figure D.12 in Annex "D". The dimension s_o is determined on the basis of the centre-to-centre distance between the outermost anchors loaded in shear in the same direction as the applied shear. This is illustrated in Figure D-12 of Annex "D".

Clause D.7.2.7 requires that $\psi_{c,V}$ be taken as *1.0* if a cracking analysis has not been conducted and no supplemental reinforcement has been provided to control cracking. Where it has been determined that the concrete will remain uncracked at service load levels, then a 40% increase in the shear capacity of the anchor is permitted. However, In order to take advantage of this increased capacity, the analysis must include temperature and shrinkage effects in addition to structural load effects. Values for $\psi_{c,V}$ vary from 1.0 and 1.4 provided reinforcement in accordance with Clause D.7.2.7 is provided. These requirements are based on a limited number of anchor tests which may not represent the behaviour of all anchor types and sizes. These provisions should not be used with anchors in excess of 25 mm in diameter. A maximum crack width of 0.3 mm is assumed with $\psi_{c,V} = 1.0$. If higher values of $\psi_{c,V}$ are used, designers are encouraged to evaluate the anchorage case in question utilizing the reinforcement provided to ensure that the crack widths will be less than 0.3 mm. More information on supplemental reinforcement can be found in references 12-11, 12-12, and 12-21.

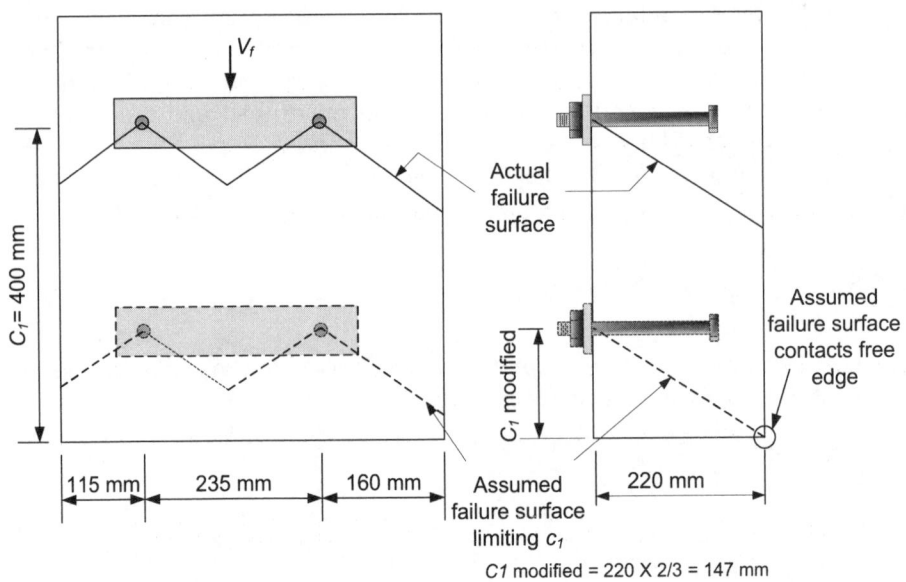

Figure 12.9 Modified Free Edge Distance c_1 in Shallow Members

Table 12.6 lists V_{cbr} values for a variety of anchor sizes and embedment conditions.

12.6.3   Concrete Pryout Resistance

The pryout resistance of cast-in anchors has been found to be equal to the tensile concrete breakout capacity for embedment depths less than 65 mm and twice that value for embedment depths greater than 65 mm[12-5]. Pryout resistance values are listed in Table 12.6.

12.6.4   Supplemental Reinforcement for Shear

Supplemental reinforcement restraining a shear breakout section is depicted in Figure 12.10 below. As in the case of tension breakout the reinforcement should be aligned with the force on the anchor and be located in close proximity to the anchor. The hairpin reinforcement shown in Fig. 12.10 has proven in tests to be very efficient in restraining the anchor but will not prevent the concrete section from breaking out. Hairpin reinforcement will prove more efficient when placed in direct contact with the anchor and angled down from the surface of the concrete as shown. Reference 12.3 provided more detailed information on supplemental reinforcement.

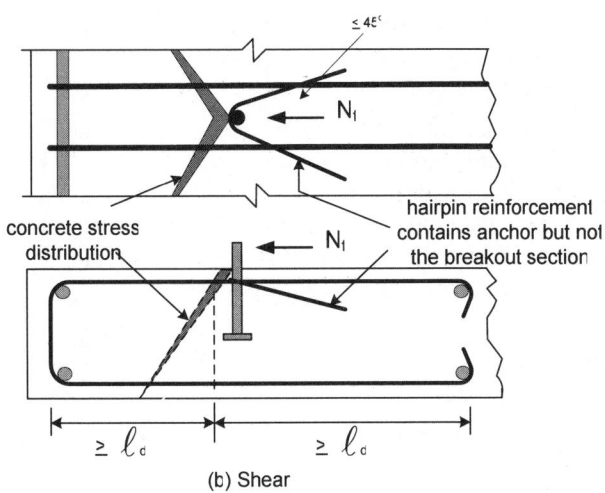

(b) Shear

Fig 12.10 Supplemental Reinforcement for Shear

12.7   Interaction of Tensile and Shear Forces

The trilinear provision of Clause D.8 is a simplification of the expression:

$$\left(\frac{N_r}{N_f}\right)^\zeta + \left(\frac{V_r}{V_f}\right)^\zeta \le 1.0$$

where ζ varies from 1.0 to 2.0. The provisions of Clause D.8, assume $\zeta = 5/3$. Tests indicate that a 20% tolerance can be accommodated before interaction effects need be considered for cases involving both tension and shear effects. Clause D.5.3 allows alternative interaction expressions provided they agree with test results.

12.8   Edge Distances, Spacing, and Thickness to Preclude Splitting Failure

Splitting failures, as illustrated in Figure D.2(e), occur where anchors are a) located in close proximity to an edge, b) spaced too closely together, or c) anchored in a thin section of concrete. Splitting failure is dictated to a large extent by the type of anchor being used. Anchors which do not exert additional lateral stress on the concrete can tolerate shorter edge distances and closer spacing than anchors that rely on lateral pressure to develop their resistance. As a result, anchors that will be torqued prior to the application of load are more sensitive to splitting failure and require larger edge distances.

Post-installed anchors are required to have a minimum spacing of $6d_o$ vs $4d_o$ for untorqued cast-in anchors. Minimum edge distances for post-installed anchors range from $6d_o$ to $10d_o$, while the minimum edge distance for untorqued cast-in anchors is governed only by the minimum cover requirements of Clause 7.9.

Tests have indicated that assumed concrete breakout capacities are not met when $c_{a,min} = 1.5h_{ef}$ for many post-installed anchors. This effect is recognized with the application of $\psi_{cp,n}$ in equations D-4 and D-5. Clause D.9.7 provides default values for the critical edge distance c_{ac} to be used in the determination of $\psi_{cp,n}$ in Clause D.6.2.7. These values are applicable to post-installed anchors only. Alternatively the designer may use values for c_{ac} based on ACI 355.2 qualification reports for the particular post-installed anchor being used.

12.9   Installation

Certain types of post-installed anchors can be sensitive to installation variables such as hole-diameter and condition, angle of inclination, cracking, degree of installation torque, etc. Post-installed anchors should always be installed in accordance with the manufacturer's specifications, as these specifications are the basis for the ACI 355.2 product evaluation testing. During the evaluation, post-installed anchors are classified into one of three categories depending on their degree of sensitivity to the installation variables. Different values of the Resistance Modification Factor "R" are applied to the three different category classifications.

12.10 References:

12-1) "CSA A23.3-04 Design of Concrete Structures," Canadian Standards Association. Mississauga Ontario, Canada.

12-2) Cannon, R.W., Godfrey D.A., and Moreadith, F.L., "Guide to the Design of Anchor Bolts and Other Steel Embedments," Concrete International, V. 3, No. 7, July 1981, pp. 28-41.

12-3) Eligehausen, R., Fuchs, W., and Mayer, B., "Load Bearing Behavior of Anchor Fastenings in Tension," Betonwerk und Fertigteil-technik, 12/1987. pp. 29-35.

12-4) Eligehausen, R., Fuchs, W., "Loadbearing Behavior of Anchor Fastenings Under Shear, Combined Tension and Shear or Flexural Loadings," Betonwerk und Fertigteil-technik, No. 2,1988, pp. 48-56.

12-5) Fuchs, W., Eligehausen, R., and Breen J.E., "Concrete Capacity Design (CCD) Approach for Fastening to Concrete," ACI Structural Journal, V. 92, No. 1, January-February, 1995, pp. 73-94.

12-6) Eligehausen, R., and Balogh, T., "Behavior of Fasteners Loaded in Tension in Cracked Reinforced Concrete," ACI Structural Journal, V. 92, No. 3, May-June 1995, pp. 365-379.

12-7) "Building Code Requirements for Structural Concrete (ACI 318-05) and Commentary (ACI 318-05)," American Concrete Institute, Farmington Hills, MI.

12-8) "National Building Code of Canada 2005," National Research Council of Canada, Ottawa, Ontario, Canada.

12-9) Cook, R.A. and Klingner, R.E., "Ductile Multiple-Anchor Steel-to-Concrete Connections," Journal of Structural Engineering, ASCE, V.118, No. 6, June 1992, pp. 1645-1665.

12-10) Lotze, D. and Klingner, R.E., "Behavior of Multiple-Anchor Connections to Concrete from the Perspective of Plastic Theory," Report PMFSEL 96-4, Ferguson Structural Engineering Laboratory, The University of Texas at Austin, March 1997.

12-11) Rodriguez, M., Lotze, D., Gross, J.H., Zhang, Y., Klingner, R.E. and Graves, III, H. L., "Dynamic Behavior of Tensile Anchors to Concrete," Structures Journal, American Concrete Institute, Farmington Hills, Michigan, V. 98, No. 4, July-August 2001, pp. 511-524.

12-12) Gross, J.H., Klingner, R.E., and Graves, III, H. L., "Dynamic Behavior of Single and Double Near-Edge Anchors Loaded in Shear," Structures Journal, American Concrete Institute, Farmington Hills, Michigan, V. 98, No. 5, September-October 2001, pp. 665-676.

12-13) "Design of Fastenings in Concrete – Design Guide," Comité Euro-International du Béton (CEB) Thomas Telford Services Ltd., London, Jan 1997.

12-14) Eligehausen, R., Mallée, R., and Silva, J. F., "Anchorage in Concrete and Masonry Construction," Whiley-VCH, Berlin, 2005.

12-15) Furche, J. and Eligehausen, R., "Lateral Blow-out Failure of Headed Studs near a Free Edge," Anchors in Concrete-Design and Behavior, SP130, ACI Detroit, 1991, pp. 235-252.

12-16) "Qualification of Post-Installed Mechanical Anchors in Concrete (ACI 355.2-04) and Commentary (ACI 355.2R-04)," American Concrete Institute.

12-17) Anderson, N.S. and Meinheit, D. F., "Design Criteria for Headed Stud Groups in Shear: Part 1 – Steel Capacity and Back Edge Effects," PCI Journal, V. 45, No. 5, September/October 2000, pp. 46-75.

12-18) "Fastenings to Concrete and Masonry Structures, State of the Art Report," Comité Euro-International du Béton, (CEB), Bulletin No. 216, Thomas Telford Services Ltd., London, 1994.

12-19) Shaikh, A. F., and Yi, W., "In-Place Strength of Welded Headed Studs," PCI Journal, V. 30, No.2, March/April 1985, pp. 56- 81.

12-20) Klingner, R.E., Mendonca, J.A., and Malik, J.B., "Effect of Reinforcing Details on the Shear Resistance of Anchor Bolts under Reversed Cyclic Loading," ACI Journal Proceedings V. 79, No. 1, January-February 1982, pp. 3-12.

12-21) Zhang, Y.-G., Klingner, R. E. and Graves, III, H. L., "Seismic Response of Multiple-Anchor Connections to Concrete," Structures Journal, American Concrete Institute, Farmington Hills, Michigan, V. 98, No. 6, November-December 2001, pp. 811-822.

12

Anchorage

12.11 Design Examples

Example 12.1 Tension Capacity with No Edge Effects

What is the maximum factored tensile capacity of the single AWS D1.1 welded stud anchor shown. Assume the stud is distant from any edges, the concrete is cracked at service loads, and no supplemental reinforcement is used.

Welded Stud: shank diameter d_o = 15.7 mm, head diameter d_{head} = 25.4 mm, fy = 344 MPa, f_{ut} = 414 MPa. Assume ductile steel.

f_c' = 30 MPa ϕ_c = 0.65 ϕ_s = 0.85 h_{ef} = 125 mm

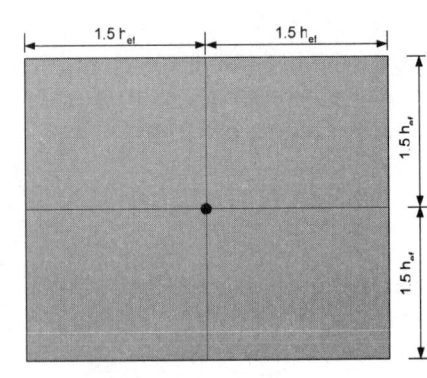

Determine the tensile capacity of the steel stud

($A_{se} = A_g$ for an unthreaded steel stud)

f_{ut} / f_y = 414/344 = 1.2 < 1.9   (D.6.1.2)

$$A_{se} = \frac{\pi d^2}{4} = \frac{\pi 15.7^2}{4} = 193 \text{ mm}^2$$

$N_{sr} = \phi_s n A_{se} f_{ut} R$ Eq.(D-3)

$R = 0.8$ (ductile steel loaded in tension)   (D.5.4(a))

N_{sr} = 0.85×1×193×414×0.8 = 54,333 N

N_{sr} = 54.3 kN

Determine the tensile concrete breakout capacity

$N_{br} = k\phi_c \sqrt{f_c'} h_{ef}^{1.5} R$ where R = 1.0 (D.5.4(c) Condition "B" tension)   Eq.(D-7)

R = 1.0 (condition "B" tension load)   (D.5.4(c))

$N_{br} = 10 \times 0.65 \times \sqrt{30} \times 125^{1.5} \times 1.0$ kN

$N_{br} = 49.7$ kN

$N_{cbr} = \dfrac{A_N}{A_{No}} \left(\psi_{ed,N} \times \psi_{c,N} \times \psi_{cp,N} \right) \times N_{br}$ Eq. (D-4)

$A_{No} = 9\, h_{ef}^2$ Eq. (D-6)

$A_N = A_{No} = 9\, h_{ef}^2$ (the anchor is distant from all edges)

$\psi_{ed,N}$ = 1.0 (anchor is distant from all edges) (D.6.2.5)

$\psi_{c,N}$ = 1.0 (cracked concrete)   (D.6.2.6)

$\psi_{cp,N}$ is applicable to post-installed anchors only. Taken as 1.0 for cast-in anchors

$$N_{cbr} = \frac{9h_{ef}^2}{9h_{ef}^2}(1.0\,x1.0x1.0)x49.7$$

$$= 1.0x(1.0x1.0x1.0)x49.7$$

$$= 49.7kN$$

Check Pullout Capacity

$$N_{pr} = A_{bh}8\phi_c f_c' R \qquad\qquad\qquad\qquad\qquad\qquad\qquad\qquad\text{(D.6.3.4)}$$

The bearing area A_{bh} of the head of the steel stud =

$$A_{bh} = \frac{\pi(d_{head}^2 - d_o^2)}{4} = \frac{\pi(25.4^2 - 15.7^2)}{4} = 313.1 \text{ mm}^2$$

$R = 1.0$ (condition "B" always assumed for pullout failure)   (D.5.4(c)) Note

$$N_{pr} = 313.1x\,8\,x\,0.65\,x\,30\,x1.0 = 48{,}843 \text{ N} = 48.8 \text{ kN}$$

$$N_{cpr} = \psi_{c,p}Npr = 1.0 \times 48{,}843 = 48.8 \text{ kN}$$

For cracked concrete $\psi_{c,p} = 1.0$

$$N_{cpr} = 1.0 \times 48{,}843 = 48.843 \text{ kN}$$

Side Face Blowout – not applicable as edge distance > $0.4h_{ef}$ (D.6.4.1)

Summary:
N_{sr} = 54.3 kN
N_{cbr} = 49.7 kN
N_{cpr} = 48.8 kN → Governs

The tensile strength of the anchor is governed by the anchor pullout capacity.
N_r = 48.8 kN.

Example 12.2 Shear Capacity With No Edge Effects

Determine the factored shear capacity of the 19 mm (3/4") threaded Grade A ASTM A307 anchor shown. Assume uncracked 30 MPa concrete, f_y = 250 MPa, f_{ut} = 414 MPa.

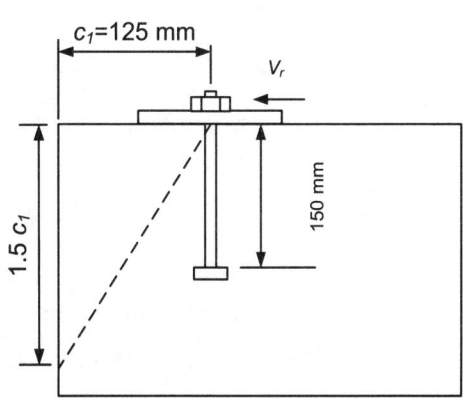

$f_{ut} / f_y = 1.65 < 1.9$ OK   (D.7.1.2)

Calculate the Shear Capacity of the A307 Bolt

$$V_{sr} = \phi_s n A_{se} 0.6 f_{ut} R \qquad\qquad \text{Eq.(D-21)}$$

(A_{se} can be assumed to be $0.70A_g$ for a threaded anchor bolt in tension)   (D.6.1.2)

Calculate A_{se} of the 19mm anchor.

$$A_{se} = 0.7\frac{\pi d^2}{4} = 0.7\frac{\pi 19^2}{4} = 198 \text{ mm}^2$$

$R = 0.75$ (ductile steel anchor loaded in shear)   (D.5.4(a))

$V_{sr} = 0.85 x 1.0 x 198 x 0.6 x 414 x 0.75 = 31,354$ N

V_{sr} = 31.3 kN   (Table 12.6 gives a value of 33.0 kN for this bolt but uses the effective area values listed in Table 12.4 rather than the approximate value above.

Determine the shear concrete breakout capacity

$$V_{cbr} = \frac{A_V}{A_{Vo}}\left(\psi_{ed,V} \; x \psi_{c,V} \right) x V_{br}$$ (D.7.2.1)

$A_V = 4.5 c_1^2$ (no edge or thickness constraints)

$A_{Vo} = 4.5 c_1^2$ Eq.(D-24)

$\psi_{ed,V} = 1.0$ (no edge effects considered)

$\psi_{c,V} = 1.4$ (assume concrete is uncracked at service load levels)

$$V_{br} = 0.58\left(\frac{\ell}{d_o}\right)^{0.2} \sqrt{d_o} \; \phi_c \; \sqrt{f'_c} \; c_1^{1.5} R$$ (D-25)

$R = 1.0$ (condition "B", shear load on a headed bolt)   (D.5.4(c))

$\frac{\ell}{d_o} = \left(\frac{150}{19}\right) = 7.89 < 8$ therefore use 7.89

$V_{br} = 0.58(7.89)^{0.2} \sqrt{19} \; x 0.65 \; x \sqrt{30} \; x 125^{1.5} \; x 1.0 = 19,012$ N

V_{br} = 19.0 kN

$$V_{cbr} = \frac{4.5 c_1^2}{4.5 c_1^2}(1.0 \; x 1.4) x 19.0 = 26.6 \text{ kN}$$

Check the Pryout Capacity

$V_{cpr} = k_{cp} N_{cbr}$ (D.7.3)

$k_{cp} = 2.0$ Pryout capacity taken as twice the tensile breakout capacity for $h_{ef} \geq 65$ mm

Calculate N_{cbr} to complete the pryout capacity determination.

$$N_{cbr} = \frac{A_n}{A_{no}}\left(\psi_{ed,N} \; x \psi_{c,N} x \psi_{cp,N} \right) x N_{br}$$ (D.6.2.1)

$A_N = (125 + 1.5 x \; h_{ef}) x (3 h_{ef})$

$A_N = (125 + (1.5 x 150)) \; x \; (3 x 150)$

$A_N = 157,500$ mm^2

$A_{No} = 9 h_{ef}^2 = 9 \; x \; 150^2 = 202,500$ mm^2

$\psi_{ed,N} = 0.7 + 0.3\dfrac{c_{min}}{1.5 \; h_{ef}}$ if $c_{min} < 1.5 \; h_{ef}$ (D.6.2.5)

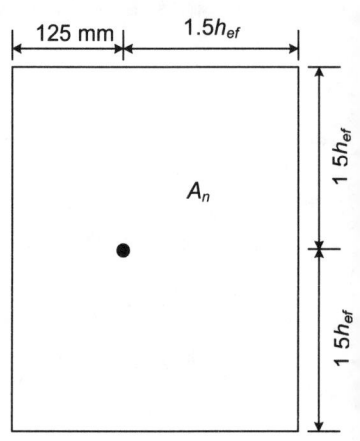

$$\psi_{ed,N} = 0.7 + 0.3 \frac{125}{1.5(150)} = 0.867$$

$\psi_{c,N} = 1.25$ (assume uncracked concrete)

Calculate N_{br}

$$N_{br} = k\phi_c \sqrt{f_c'} h_{ef}^{1.5} R \quad \text{where } R = 1.0 \qquad\qquad \text{Eq. (D-7)}$$

$$N_{br} = 10 \times 0.65 \times \sqrt{30} \times 150^{1.5} \times 1.0 = 65,404 \text{ N}$$

$N_{br} = 65.4$ kN

$$N_{cbr} = \frac{157,500}{202,500}(0.867 \times 1.25 \times 1.0) \times 65.4 = 55.1 \text{kN}$$

$$V_{cpr} = 2.0 N_{cbr}$$

$$V_{cpr} = 2.0 \times 55.1 = 110.2 \text{ kN}$$

Summary

$V_{sr} = 31.3$ kN
$V_{cbr} = 26.6$ kN   → Governs
$V_{cpr} = 110.2$ kN

The maximum factored shear capacity of the anchor $V_r = 26.6$ kN

12

Anchorage

Example 12.3 Shear With the Influence of Thin Section and Edge Effects

Determine the concrete breakout capacity in shear for the 13 mm diameter threaded anchor embedded in the 200 mm deep uncracked concrete section shown.

Assume uncracked concrete with $f_c' = 40$ MPa, $\phi_c = 0.65$

$d_o = 13$ mm, $h_{ef} = 130$ mm, $c_1 = 150$ mm, $c_{2min} = 120$ mm, $h = 200$ mm

Calculate breakout capacity in Shear V_{cbr}

$$V_{cbr} = \frac{A_V}{A_{Vo}}\left(\psi_{ed,V} \times \psi_{c,V}\right) \times V_{br} \qquad\qquad \text{Eq.(D-22)}$$

$$\psi_{ed,V} = 0.7 + 0.3 \frac{120}{1.5(150)} = 0.86 \qquad\qquad \text{Eq.(D-30)}$$

$\psi_{c,V} = 1.4$ (assume uncracked concrete)   (D.7.2.7)

$\psi_{cp,V} = 1.0$ (cast- in anchor)

$$A_{Vo} = 4.5 \ c_1^2 = 4.5 \times 150^2 = 101,250 \text{ mm}^2$$

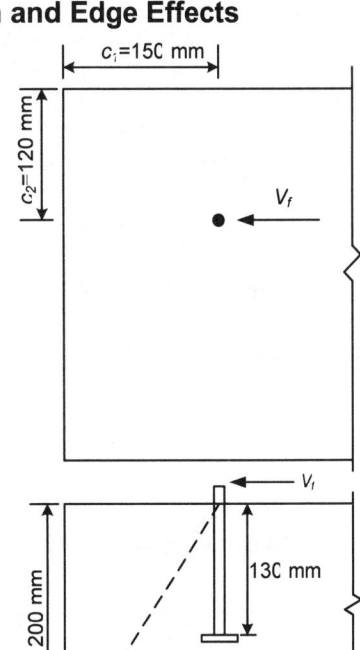

Determine A_V. Thin section will not allow the full depth of the concrete breakout section to develop. Calculate A_V accordingly.

$1.5 \times c_1 = 225 > 200$ mm $\therefore$ use 200 mm in calculating A_v below.

$A_V = (120+1.5c_1) \times 200$

$A_V = (120+(1.5(150)) \times 200$

$A_V = 69{,}000$ mm^2

Now calculate V_{br}

$$V_{br} = 0.58\left(\frac{\ell}{d_o}\right)^{0.2}\sqrt{d_o}\,\phi_c\,\sqrt{f'_c}\,c_1^{1.5}R$$

Eq.(D-25)

(use $R = 1.0$, shear with Condition "B")

(D.5.4(c))

$\ell/d_o = 130/13 = 10.0 > 8.0$ therefore use 8.0

(D.3)

$V_{br} = 0.58(8)^{0.2}\sqrt{13} \times 0.65 \times \sqrt{40} \times 150^{1.5} \times 1.0 = 23{,}938$ N

$V_{br} = 23.9$ kN

$$V_{cbr} = \frac{69{,}000}{101{,}250}(0.86 \times 1.4) \times 23.9 = 19.6 \text{ kN}$$

The concrete breakout capacity V_{cbr} for the anchor assembly in the direction of the applied load is 19.6 kN.

Note that Clause D.7.2.1 requires that breakout capacity of anchors near a corner be evaluated in both orthogonal directions towards the free edges, see Fig. D.11 in Annex "D". The breakout strength of the single anchor shown in Example 12.3 would have to be evaluated again taking $c_1 = 120$ mm and an edge distance of 150 mm as shown. The lesser of these two capacities would then be taken as the critical breakout capacity of the embedment in shear.

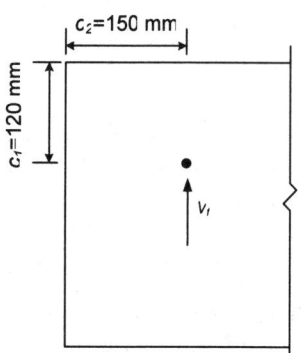

Example 12.4 Group of Headed Studs in Tension Near an Edge

This example problem has been adapted from Example problems 34.2 and 34.3 of the "Notes on ACI 318-05", published by the Portland Cement Association.

Design a group of four AWS D1.1 Type B welded headed studs spaced 150 mm c/c each way and eccentrically loaded with a factored load $N_f = 45$ kN.

Assume: $f'_c = 30$ MPa $\phi_c = 0.65$ $\phi_s = 0.85$ ductile Steel, $f_{ut} = 414$ MPa, $f_{ut}/f_y < 1.9$,

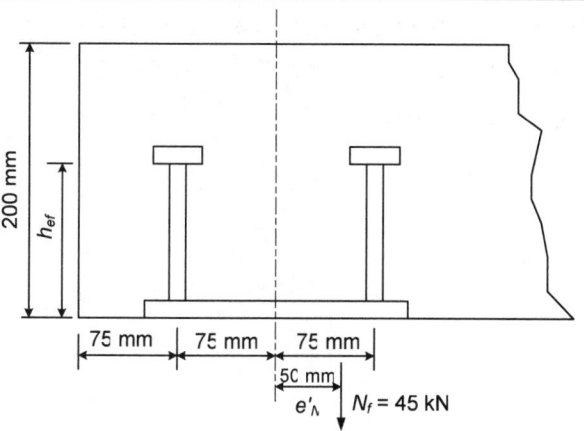

Calculate the required anchor diameter

Due to the eccentric application of the load, the two interior studs will receive a load of

45 kN x (75+50) / (75+75) = 37.5 kN

Each of the two interior studs will support 37.5 / 2 = 18.7 kN.

Calculate the required area of steel for the studs

$N_{sr} = nA_{se}\phi_s f_{ut}R$ where R for steel tension = 0.8 for a ductile element   Eq.(D-3)

Rearranging gives $A_{se} = \dfrac{N_{sr}}{n\phi_s f_{ut}R} = \dfrac{18,700}{1 \times 0.85 \times 414 \times 0.8} = 66.4 \text{ mm}^2$

12

From Table 12.3 select a ½" diameter stud which will provide A_{se} = 126 mm² (0.195 in²)   OK

The anchor should be selected with consideration given to the pullout resistance as well. The selected anchor has a head diameter of 25.4mm.

N_{sr} provided = 4 x 126 x 0.85 x 414 x 0.8 = 141,886 N = 141.9 kN > N_f = 45 kN   OK

Determine the required h_{ef} based on the concrete breakout capacity in tension
Assume Condition "B" applies (no supplementary reinforcement)

$N_{cbr} = \dfrac{An}{Ano}\left(\psi_{ec,N} \times \psi_{ed,N} \times \psi_{c,N} \times \psi_{cp,N}\right) \times N_{br}$ Eq.(D-5)

$\psi_{cp,N}$ is taken as 1.0 for a cast-in anchor.

Welded studs are manufactured in discrete lengths. The ½" diameter anchor selected is 102 mm long and will provide 115 mm of embedment depth when welded to a 13 mm thick base plate.

Evaluate the terms in Equation (D-5) using h_{ef} = 115 mm.

A_N = (75+150+ (1.5x h_{ef}))((1.5x h_{ef})+150+(1.5x h_{ef}))

A_N = (75+150+172)(172+150+172) = 196,118 mm²

A_{No} = 9 h_{ef}^2 = 9 (115)² = 119,025 mm² (failure surface without edge effects) (D.6.2.1)

Check for Group Effect $A_N < A_{No}$ (D.6.2.1)

196,118 mm^2 < 4 (119,025) = 476,820 mm^2 OK (group effect)

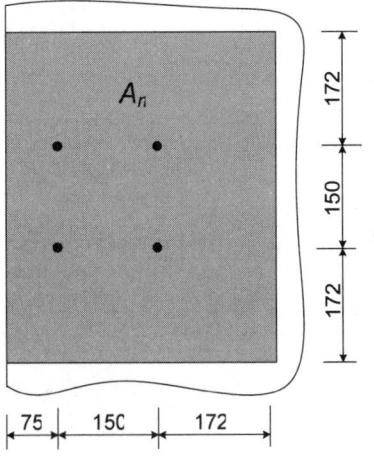

Calculate eccentricity coefficient $\psi_{ec.N}$ with the applied load acting at a distance of 50 mm from the centroid of the anchors

s_o = 150 mm e'_N= 50 mm < s_o / 2 = 75 mm OK

$$\psi_{ec,N} = \frac{1}{\left(1+\dfrac{2e'_N}{3h_{ef}}\right)} = \frac{1}{\left(1+\dfrac{2(50)}{3(115)}\right)} = 0.775$$

Calculate edge effect coefficient $\psi_{ed.N}$

$$\psi_{ed,N} = 0.7 + 0.3\frac{c_{min}}{1.5(h_{ef})}$$ (D.6.2.5)

$$\psi_{ed,N} = 0.7 + 0.3\frac{75}{1.5(115)} = 0.83$$

$\psi_{c,N}$= 1.0 (cracked concrete)   (D.6.2.6)

$\psi_{cp,N}$ = 1.0 for cast-in anchors

Determine N_{br} for a single stud unaffected by edges

$N_{br} = k\phi_c \sqrt{f'_c} h_{ef}^{1.5} R$ where R = 1.0 (D.5.4(c) Condition "B" tension)   Eq.(D-7)

$N_{br} = 10x0.65x\sqrt{30}x115^{1.5}x1.0 = 43.9$ kN

Now calculate N_{cbgr} as

$$N_{cbrg} = \frac{A_n}{A_{no}}\left(\psi_{ec,N}x\,\psi_{ed,N}\,x\psi_{c,N}x\psi_{cp,N}\right)x\,N_{br}$$

$$N_{cbrg} = \frac{196,118}{119,025}(0.818x\,0.83\,x1.0x1.0)x\,43.9 = 49.1\text{ kN}\ > N_f = 45\text{ kN}\quad \text{OK}$$

Check the pullout capacity N_{pr} for the two most heavily loaded studs

The ½" - diameter studs are manufactured with a 1" diameter head. The provided bearing area A_{bh} = 380 mm^2.

$N_{pr} = 8A_{bh}\phi_c f'_c R$ (D.6.3.4)

$N_{pr} = 8x380x0.65x30x1.0 = 59,280$ N

N_{pr} = 59.3 kN > 18.7 kN   (the maximum load on each interior anchor)   OK

Check minimum edge distance requirements.

Welded headed anchor studs are not torqued so the minimum cover requirements of Annex "A" of CSA A23.3 apply. The required cover for reinforcement with exposure class N concrete is 30 mm. The provided cover of 75 – (25.4) / 2 = 62.3 mm > 30 mm.   OK

SUMMARY

N_f = 45.0 kN

Nsr = 141.9 kN

N_{cbrg} = 49.1 kN → Governs

N_{pr} = 59.2 kN

The four ½" diameter studs selected with f_{ut} = 414 in the arrangement illustrated will provide sufficient anchorage for the eccentric factored load of 45 kN.

12.12 Design Aids

TABLE 12.1 Mechanical Properties of ASTM Fastening Materials-
Source – Strength Design of Anchors, By R. Cook, Portland Cement Association, publication code EB080.01.

Material Specification[1]	Grade or Type	Diameter (in)	Tensile Strength min (MPa)	Yield Strength, min		Elongation min		Reduction of area min, (%)
				MPa	method	%	length	
AWS D.1.1[1]	B	½ – 1	414	344	0.2%	20	2"	50
ASTM A307[2]	A	≤ 4	414	...	...	18	2"	...
	C	≤ 4	400- 414	248	...	23	2"	...
ASTM A354[3]	BC	≤ 4	860	751	0.2%	16	2"	50
	BD	≤ 4	1034	896	0.2%	14	2"	40
ASTM A449[4]	1	≤ 1	828	634	0.2%	14	4D	35
		1 – 1 ½	724	558	0.2%	14	4D	35
		> 1 ½	620	400	0.2%	14	4D	35
ASTM A687[5]		5/8 - 3	...	724	...	15	2"	45
ASTM A1554[6]	36	≤ 2	400-551	248	0.2%	23	2"	40
	55	≤ 2	517-655	379	0.2%	21	2"	30
	105	≤ 2	860-1034	724	0.2%	15	2"	45

1) *Structural Welding Code* – Steel – This specification covers welded headed studs or welded hooked studs (unthreaded).
2) *Standard Specification for Carbon Steel Bolts and Studs*, 414 MPa Tensile Strength – This material is commonly used for concrete fastening applications. Grade C is equivalent to ASTM A36 steel.
3) *Standard Specification for Quenched and Tempered Alloy Steel Bolts*, Studs and Other Externally threaded Fasteners – The strength of Grade BD is equivalent to ASTM A490.
4) *Standard Specification for Quenched and Tempered Steel Bolts and Studs* – This specification is referenced by ASTM A325 for "equivalent" anchor bolts.
5) *Standard Specification for Anchor Bolts* – This specification covers high-strength fasteners for anchorage application with enhanced Charpy V-notch properties. The material does not have a minimum specified tensile strength (maximum is given as 1034 MPa.
6) *Standard Specification for Anchor Bolts* – This specification covers straight and bent, headed and headless, anchor bolts in three strength grades. Anchors are available in diameters ≤ 100 mm but reduction in area requirements vary for anchors < 50 mm.

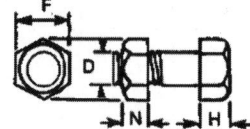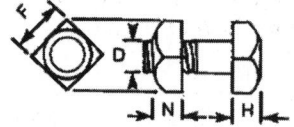

Table 12.2 ASTM Bolt and Nut Dimensions in inches

Nominal Diameter of bolt	Square Bolts		Hex Bolts		Minimum Thread Lengths		Square Nuts		Hex Nuts	
	Width Across Flats Basic F	Head Height Basic H	Width Across Flats Basic F	Head Height Basic H	Length Under Head		Width Across Flats Basic F	Thickness Basic H	Width Across Flats Basic F	Thickness Basic H
					6 inches and under	Over 6 inches				
Inches	Inches	Inches	Inches	Inches	Inches	Inches	Inches	Inches	Inches	Inches
1/4	3/8	11/64	7/16	5/32	3/4	1	7/16	7/32	7/16	7/32
3/8	9/16	1/4	9/16	15/64	1	1 1/4	5/8	21/64	9/16	21/64
1/2	3/4	21/64	3/4	5/16	1 1/4	1 1/2	13/16	7/16	3/4	7/16
5/8	15/16	27/64	15/16	25/64	1 1/2	1 3/4	1	35/64	15/16	35/64
3/4	1 1/8	1/2	1 1/8	15/32	1 3/4	2	1 1/8	21/32	1 1/8	41/64
7/8	1 5/16	19/32	1 5/16	35/64	2	2 1/4	1 5/16	49/64	1 5/16	3/4
1	1 1/2	21/32	1 1/2	39/64	2 1/4	2 1/2	1 1/2	7/8	1 1/2	55/64
1 1/8	1 11/16	3/4	1 1/16	11/16	2 1/2	2 3/4	1 11/16	1	1 11/16	31/32
1 1/4	1 7/8	27/32	1 7/8	25/32	2 3/4	3	1 7/8	1 3/32	1 7/8	1 1/16

Table 12.3 Bearing Areas Abh for Square and Hexagonal Nuts
(source - Notes on ACI 318-05, published by the Portland Cement Association)

Anchor Diameter d_o mm (in)	Anchor Diameter d_o mm	Gross Area of Anchor A_g mm^2	Effective Area of Anchor A_{se} mm^2	Bearing Area of Heads and Nuts A_{bh} mm^2			
				Square	Heavy Square	Hex	Heavy Hex
0.250	6.350	32	21	92	130	75	108
0.375	9.525	71	50	181	234	106	193
0.500	12.700	127	92	299	367	188	301
0.625	15.875	198	146	412	530	293	433
0.750	19.050	285	215	532	723	422	588
0.875	22.225	388	298	723	945	575	766
1.000	25.400	507	391	945	1196	750	968
1.125	28.575	641	492	1196	1478	950	1194
1.250	31.750	792	625	1476	1789	1172	1443
1.375	34.935	959	748	1785	2129	1219	1715
1.500	38.100	1140	910	2126	2499	1688	2012
1.750	44.450	1552	1226	--	--	--	2674
2.000	50.800	2027	1613	--	--	--	3430

Table 12.4 ASTM Anchor Data Used In Developing Tables 12.5 and 12.6

Anchor Diameter d_o	Gross Area of Anchor	Effective Area of Anchor A_{se}	Bearing Area A_{brg} of Hex Nut
in	in^2	in^2	in^2
0.250	0.049	0.032	0.117
0.375	0.110	0.078	0.164
0.500	0.196	0.142	0.291
0.625	0.307	0.226	0.454
0.750	0.442	0.334	0.654
0.875	0.601	0.462	0.891
1.000	0.785	0.606	1.163
1.125	0.994	0.763	1.472
1.250	1.227	0.969	1.817
1.375	1.485	1.160	2.199
1.500	1.767	1.410	2.617
1.750	2.405	1.900	4.144
2.000	3.142	2.500	5.316

Notes For Tension Tables 12.5 A, B and C

NP – Not practical. Resulting edge distance, c_1, yields less than 20 mm cover.

1. Design strengths in table are for single cast-in anchors near one edge only. The values do not apply where the distance between adjacent anchors is less than $3h_{ef}$, or where the perpendicular distance, c_2, to the edge distance being considered, c_1, is less than $1.5h_{ef}$.

2. In seismic regions where ($I_e F_a S_a(0.2) \geq 0.35$), the design strengths in the table must be reduced   by 25%. In addition, the anchor must be designed so strength is governed by a ductile steel element, unless D.4.3.6 is satisfied. Therefore, the design strengths based on the three concrete failure modes, N_{br}, N_{pr} and N_{sbr}, must exceed the design strength of the steel in tension, N_{sr}. This requirement effectively precludes the use of hooked anchor bolts in the seismic zones noted above.

3. For design purposes the tensile strength of the anchor steel, f_{ut}, must not exceed $1.9f_y$ or 860 MPa.

4. Design strengths in the table are based on resistance modification factor "R", of Section D.5.4. Factored tensile load N_f must be computed from the load combinations referenced in Clause 8.3.2. Design strengths for concrete breakout, N_{br}, pullout, N_{pr}, and sideface blowout, N_{sbr}, are based on Condition B. Where supplementary reinforcement is provided to satisfy Condition A, design strengths for N_{br} and N_{sbr} may be increased by the ratio of $R_{(condition\ A)}$ / $R_{(condition\ B)}$. This increase does not apply to pullout strength, N_{pr}.

5. Design strengths for concrete breakout in tension, N_{br}, are based on N_{br} determined in accordance with Eq. (D-7) and apply to headed and hooked anchors. To determine the design strength of headed bolts with embedment depth, h_{ef}, greater than 275 mm in accordance with Eq. (D-8), multiply the table value by $[3.9(h_{ef}^{5/3})]/[10(h_{ef}^{1.5})]$.

6. Where analysis indicates that there will be no cracking at service load levels ($f_t < f_r$) in the region of the anchor, the design strengths for concrete breakout in tension, N_{br}, may be increased 25%.

7. The design strengths for pullout in tension, N_{pr}, for headed bolts with diameter, d_o, less than 45 mm are based on bolts with regular hex heads. The design strengths for 45 mm and 2-in. bolts are based on heavy hex heads. For bolts with d_o less that 45 mm having heads with a larger bearing area, A_{bh}, than assumed, the design strengths may be increased by multiplying by the bearing area of the larger head and dividing by the bearing area of the regular hex head.

8. The design strengths for pullout in tension, N_{pr}, for hooked bolts with hook-length, e_h, between 3 and 4.5 times diameter, d_o, may be determined by interpolation.

9. Where analysis indicates there will be no cracking at service load levels ($f_t < f_r$) in the region of the anchor, the design strengths for pullout in tension, N_{pr}, may be increased 40%.

10. The design strengths for side-face blowout in tension, N_{sbr}, are applicable to headed bolts only and where edge distance, c_1, is less than $0.4h_{ef}$. The values for $0.4h_{ef}$ are shown for interpolation purposes only. The design strengths for bolts with diameter, d_o, less than 45 mm are based on bolts with regular hex heads. The design strengths for 45 mm and 50 mm bolts are based on bolts with heavy hex heads. For bolts with d_o less than 45 mm having heads with a larger bearing area, A_{bh}, than assumed, the design strengths may be increased by multiplying by the square root of the quotient resulting from dividing the bearing area of the larger head by the bearing area of the regular hex head ($\sqrt{A_{bh(larger)} / A_{bh(smaller)}}$).

Notes For Shear Tables 12.6 A, B and C

NP – Not practical. Resulting edge distance, c_1, yields less than 20 mm cover.

1. Design strengths in table are for single cast-in anchors near one edge only. The values do not apply where the distance to an edge, measured perpendicular to c_1, is less than $1.5c_1$. See Note 9.

   The values do not apply where the distance between adjacent anchors is less than $3c_1$, where c_1 is the distance from the center of the anchor to the edge in the direction of shear application.

2. In seismic regions where ($I_e F_a S_a(0.2) \geq 0.35$), the design strengths in the table must be reduced by 25%. In addition, the anchor must be designed so failure is initiated by a ductile steel element, unless D.4.3.6 is satisfied. This means that all the design strengths based on the two concrete failure modes, V_{br} and V_{pr}, must equal or exceed the design strength of the steel in shear, V_{sr}.

3. Concrete pryout strength, V_{pr}, is to be taken equal to tension breakout strength, N_{cbr}, where h_{ef} is less than 65 mm, and to be taken as twice N_{cbr}, where h_{ef} is equal to or greater than 65 mm Condition B (see D.4.4) must be assumed even where supplementary reinforcement qualifying for Condition A is present (i.e., strength reduction factor, must be taken equal to 0.70).

4. For design purposes the tensile strength of the anchor steel, f_{ut}, must not exceed $1.9f_y$ or 860 MPa.

5. Design strengths in table are based on strength reduction factor "R" of Section D.4.4 Factored shear load V_f must be computed from the load combinations referenced in Clause 8.3.2. Design strengths for concrete breakout, V_{cbr}, are based on Condition B. Where supplementary reinforcement is provided to satisfy Condition A, this design strength may be increased by the ratio of $R_{(condition\ A)} / R_{(condition\ B)}$. This does not apply to pryout capacities, for which condition "B" is always assumed.

6. Where analysis indicates that there will be no cracking at service load levels ($f_t < f_r$) in the region of the anchor, the design strengths for concrete breakout in shear, V_{cbr}, may be increased 40%.

7. In regions of members where analysis indicates cracking at service level loads, the strengths in the table for concrete breakout, V_{cbr}, may be increased in accordance with the factors in D.7.2.7 if edge reinforcement is provided in accordance with that section.

8. The design strengths for concrete breakout, V_{br}, are based on the shear load being applied perpendicular to the edge. If the load is applied parallel to the edge, the strengths may be increased 100%.

9. Where the anchor is located near a corner with an edge distance perpendicular to direction of shear, c_2, less than $1.5c_1$, design strengths for concrete breakout, V_{br}, shall be reduced by multiplying by modification factor, $\psi_{ed,v}$, determined from Eq. (D-30). The calculated values in the table do not apply where two edge distances perpendicular to direction of shear, c_2, are less than $1.5c_1$. See D.7.2.4.

10. This value of thickness, h, is not practical since the head or hook would project below the bottom surface of the concrete. It was chosen to facilitate mental calculation of the actual edge distance, c_1, since the variable used in the calculation c_1 is a function of embedment depth, h_{ef}.

11. Linear interpolation for intermediate values of edge distance, c_1 is permissible. Linear interpolation for intermediate values of embedment depth, h_{ef}, is unconservative.

12. For 20 mm cover and for $c_1 = 0.25h_{ef}$ and $0.50h_{ef}$, see portion of table for $h = h_{ef}$.

13. For 20 mm cover and for $c_1 = 0.25h_{ef}$ and $0.50h_{ef}$, see portion of table for $h = h_{ef}$. For $c_1 = h_{ef}$, see portion of table for $h = 1.5h_{ef}$.

Table 12.5(A) Factored resistance for Single Cast-In Anchors Subject to Tensile Loads (f'c = 20 MPa)[1,2,4]

do mm (in)	h_{ef} mm	N_{sr} - Tension Strength of Anchor (kN) f_{ut} - for design purpose[3] - (MPa)							N_{cbr} - Tension Breakout[4,5,6] (kN) c_1 - edge distance					N_{cpr} - Pullout[9] (kN)			N_{sbr} - Sideface Blowout[4,10] (kN) c_1 - edge distance		
		400	414	517	620	724	827	860	38 mm cover	$0.25h_{ef}$	$0.5h_{ef}$	h_{ef}	$\geq1.5h_{ef}$	head[7]	"J" or "L" hook[8] $e_h = 3do$	$e_h = 4.5do$	38 mm cover	$0.25h_{ef}$	$0.4h_{ef}$
6.35 (0.25)	50	5.6	5.8	7.3	8.7	10.2	11.6	12.1	6.6	NP	NP	7.7	10.3	7.9	1.4	2.1	12.8	NP	NP
	75	5.6	5.8	7.3	8.7	10.2	11.6	12.1	10.1	NP	NP	14.2	18.9	7.9	1.4	2.1	12.8	NP	NP
	100	5.6	5.8	7.3	8.7	10.2	11.6	12.1	14.1	NP	15.5	21.8	29.1	7.9	1.4	2.1	12.8	NP	13.4
	125	5.6	5.8	7.3	8.7	10.2	11.6	12.1	18.6	NP	21.7	30.5	40.6	7.9	1.4	2.1	12.8	NP	16.8
	150	5.6	5.8	7.3	8.7	10.2	11.6	12.1	23.4	NP	28.5	40.1	53.4	7.9	1.4	2.1	12.8	NP	20.2
9.525 (0.375)	50	13.7	14.2	17.7	21.2	24.8	28.3	29.4	6.6	NP	NP	7.7	10.3	11.0	3.2	4.8	15.1	NP	NP
	75	13.7	14.2	17.7	21.2	24.8	28.3	29.4	10.1	NP	NP	14.2	18.9	11.0	3.2	4.8	15.1	NP	NP
	100	13.7	14.2	17.7	21.2	24.8	28.3	29.4	14.1	NP	15.5	21.8	29.1	11.0	3.2	4.8	15.1	NP	15.9
	125	13.7	14.2	17.7	21.2	24.8	28.3	29.4	18.6	NP	21.7	30.5	40.6	11.0	3.2	4.8	15.1	NP	19.9
	150	13.7	14.2	17.7	21.2	24.8	28.3	29.4	23.4	NP	28.5	40.1	53.4	11.0	3.2	4.8	15.1	NP	23.9
12.7 (0.5)	50	24.9	25.8	32.2	38.6	45.1	51.5	53.6	6.6	NP	NP	7.7	10.3	19.5	5.7	8.5	20.1	NP	NP
	75	24.9	25.8	32.2	38.6	45.1	51.5	53.6	10.1	NP	NP	14.2	18.9	19.5	5.7	8.5	20.1	NP	21.2
	100	24.9	25.8	32.2	38.6	45.1	51.5	53.6	14.1	NP	15.5	21.8	29.1	19.5	5.7	8.5	20.1	NP	26.5
	125	24.9	25.8	32.2	38.6	45.1	51.5	53.6	18.6	NP	21.7	30.5	40.6	19.5	5.7	8.5	20.1	NP	31.8
	150	24.9	25.8	32.2	38.6	45.1	51.5	53.6	23.4	NP	28.5	40.1	53.4	19.5	5.7	8.5	20.1	NP	37.1
	175	24.9	25.8	32.2	38.6	45.1	51.5	53.6	28.6	29.4	35.9	50.5	67.3	19.5	5.7	8.5	20.1	23.2	42.4
	200	24.9	25.8	32.2	38.6	45.1	51.5	53.6	34.2	36.0	43.9	61.7	82.2	19.5	5.7	8.5	20.1	26.5	42.4
15.875 (0.625)	75	39.7	41.0	51.3	61.5	71.8	82.0	85.3	10.1	NP	NP	14.2	18.9	30.5	8.8	13.3	25.1	NP	NP
	100	39.7	41.0	51.3	61.5	71.8	82.0	85.3	14.1	NP	15.5	21.8	29.1	30.5	8.8	13.3	25.1	NP	26.5
	125	39.7	41.0	51.3	61.5	71.8	82.0	85.3	18.6	NP	21.7	30.5	40.6	30.5	8.8	13.3	25.1	NP	33.1
	150	39.7	41.0	51.3	61.5	71.8	82.0	85.3	23.4	NP	28.5	40.1	53.4	30.5	8.8	13.3	25.1	NP	39.7
	175	39.7	41.0	51.3	61.5	71.8	82.0	85.3	28.6	29.4	35.9	50.5	67.3	30.5	8.8	13.3	25.1	28.9	46.3
	200	39.7	41.0	51.3	61.5	71.8	82.0	85.3	34.2	36.0	43.9	61.7	82.2	30.5	8.8	13.3	25.1	33.1	52.9
	225	39.7	41.0	51.3	61.5	71.8	82.0	85.3	40.0	42.9	52.3	73.6	98.1	30.5	8.8	13.3	25.1	37.2	59.6
	250	39.7	41.0	51.3	61.5	71.8	82.0	85.3	46.2	50.3	61.3	86.2	114.9	30.5	8.8	13.3	25.1	41.4	66.2
19.05 (0.75)	100	58.6	60.7	75.8	90.8	106.1	121.2	126.0	14.1	NP	15.5	21.8	29.1	43.9	12.7	19.1	30.2	NP	31.8
	125	58.6	60.7	75.8	90.8	106.1	121.2	126.0	18.6	NP	21.7	30.5	40.6	43.9	12.7	19.1	30.2	NP	39.7
	150	58.6	60.7	75.8	90.8	106.1	121.2	126.0	23.4	NP	28.5	40.1	53.4	43.9	12.7	19.1	30.2	NP	47.6
	175	58.6	60.7	75.8	90.8	106.1	121.2	126.0	28.6	29.4	35.9	50.5	67.3	43.9	12.7	19.1	30.2	34.7	55.6
	200	58.6	60.7	75.8	90.8	106.1	121.2	126.0	34.2	36.0	43.9	61.7	82.2	43.9	12.7	19.1	30.2	39.7	63.5
	225	58.6	60.7	75.8	90.8	106.1	121.2	126.0	40.0	42.9	52.3	73.6	98.1	43.9	12.7	19.1	30.2	44.7	71.5
	250	58.6	60.7	75.8	90.8	106.1	121.2	126.0	46.2	50.3	61.3	86.2	114.9	43.9	12.7	19.1	30.2	49.6	79.4
	300	58.6	60.7	75.8	90.8	106.1	121.2	126.0	59.4	66.1	80.6	113.3	151.0	43.9	12.7	19.1	30.2	59.6	95.3
22.225 (0.875)	100	81.1	83.9	104.8	125.7	146.7	167.6	174.3	14.1	NP	15.5	21.8	29.1	59.8	17.3	26.0	35.2	NP	37.1
	150	81.1	83.9	104.8	125.7	146.7	167.6	174.3	23.4	NP	28.5	40.1	53.4	59.8	17.3	26.0	35.2	NP	55.6
	200	81.1	83.9	104.8	125.7	146.7	167.6	174.3	34.2	36.0	43.9	61.7	82.2	59.8	17.3	26.0	35.2	46.3	74.2
	300	81.1	83.9	104.8	125.7	146.7	167.6	174.3	59.4	66.1	80.6	113.3	151.0	59.8	17.3	26.0	35.2	69.5	111.2
	375	81.1	83.9	104.8	125.7	146.7	167.6	174.3	81.2	92.4	112.6	158.3	211.1	59.8	17.3	26.0	35.2	86.9	139.0
	450	81.1	83.9	104.8	125.7	146.7	167.6	174.3	105.1	121.4	148.0	208.1	277.5	59.8	17.3	26.0	35.2	104.3	166.8
	625	81.1	83.9	104.8	125.7	146.7	167.6	174.3	168.3	198.7	242.2	340.7	454.2	59.8	17.3	26.0	35.2	144.8	231.7

25.4 (1.0)	150	106.3	110.1	137.4	164.8	192.5	219.9	228.6	23.4	NP	28.5	40.1	53.4	78.0	22.6	34.0	40.2	NP	63.5
	225	106.3	110.1	137.4	164.8	192.5	219.9	228.6	40.0	42.9	52.3	73.6	98.1	78.0	22.6	34.0	40.2	59.6	95.3
	300	106.3	110.1	137.4	164.8	192.5	219.9	228.6	59.4	66.1	80.6	113.3	151.0	78.0	22.6	34.0	40.2	79.4	127.1
	375	106.3	110.1	137.4	164.8	192.5	219.9	228.6	81.2	92.4	112.6	158.3	211.1	78.0	22.6	34.0	40.2	99.3	158.9
	450	106.3	110.1	137.4	164.8	192.5	219.9	228.6	105.1	121.4	148.0	208.1	277.5	78.0	22.6	34.0	40.2	119.1	190.6
	525	106.3	110.1	137.4	164.8	192.5	219.9	228.6	130.9	153.0	186.5	262.3	349.7	78.0	22.6	34.0	40.2	139.0	222.4
	625	106.3	110.1	137.4	164.8	192.5	219.9	228.6	168.3	198.7	242.2	340.7	454.2	78.0	22.6	34.0	40.2	165.5	264.8
29 (1.125)	150	133.9	138.6	173.1	207.5	242.3	276.8	287.9	23.4	NP	28.5	40.1	53.4	98.8	28.7	43.0	45.3	NP	71.5
	225	133.9	138.6	173.1	207.5	242.3	276.8	287.9	40.0	42.9	52.3	73.6	98.1	98.8	28.7	43.0	45.3	67.0	107.2
	300	133.9	138.6	173.1	207.5	242.3	276.8	287.9	59.4	66.1	80.6	113.3	151.0	98.8	28.7	43.0	45.3	89.4	143.0
	375	133.9	138.6	173.1	207.5	242.3	276.8	287.9	81.2	92.4	112.6	158.3	211.1	98.8	28.7	43.0	45.3	111.7	178.7
	450	133.9	138.6	173.1	207.5	242.3	276.8	287.9	105.1	121.4	148.0	208.1	277.5	98.8	28.7	43.0	45.3	134.0	214.5
	525	133.9	138.6	173.1	207.5	242.3	276.8	287.9	130.9	153.0	186.5	262.3	349.7	98.8	28.7	43.0	45.3	156.4	250.2
	625	133.9	138.6	173.1	207.5	242.3	276.8	287.9	168.3	198.7	242.2	340.7	454.2	98.8	28.7	43.0	45.3	186.2	297.9
31.75 (1.25)	150	170.0	176.0	219.8	263.6	307.8	351.6	365.6	23.4	NP	28.5	40.1	53.4	121.9	35.4	53.1	50.3	NP	79.4
	225	170.0	176.0	219.8	263.6	307.8	351.6	365.6	40.0	42.9	52.3	73.6	98.1	121.9	35.4	53.1	50.3	74.5	119.1
	300	170.0	176.0	219.8	263.6	307.8	351.6	365.6	59.4	66.1	80.6	113.3	151.0	121.9	35.4	53.1	50.3	99.3	158.8
	375	170.0	176.0	219.8	263.6	307.8	351.6	365.6	81.2	92.4	112.6	158.3	211.1	121.9	35.4	53.1	50.3	124.1	198.6
	450	170.0	176.0	219.8	263.6	307.8	351.6	365.6	105.1	121.4	148.0	208.1	277.5	121.9	35.4	53.1	50.3	148.9	238.3
	525	170.0	176.0	219.8	263.6	307.8	351.6	365.6	130.9	153.0	186.5	262.3	349.7	121.9	35.4	53.1	50.3	173.7	278.0
	625	170.0	176.0	219.8	263.6	307.8	351.6	365.6	168.3	198.7	242.2	340.7	454.2	121.9	35.4	53.1	50.3	206.8	330.9
34.925 (1.375)	150	203.6	210.7	263.1	315.5	368.4	420.9	437.7	23.4	NP	28.5	40.1	53.4	147.5	42.8	64.2	55.3	NP	87.4
	225	203.6	210.7	263.1	315.5	368.4	420.9	437.7	40.0	42.9	52.3	73.6	98.1	147.5	42.8	64.2	55.3	81.9	131.1
	300	203.6	210.7	263.1	315.5	368.4	420.9	437.7	59.4	66.1	80.6	113.3	151.0	147.5	42.8	64.2	55.3	109.2	174.7
	375	203.6	210.7	263.1	315.5	368.4	420.9	437.7	81.2	92.4	112.6	158.3	211.1	147.5	42.8	64.2	55.3	136.5	218.4
	450	203.6	210.7	263.1	315.5	368.4	420.9	437.7	105.1	121.4	148.0	208.1	277.5	147.5	42.8	64.2	55.3	163.8	262.1
	525	203.6	210.7	263.1	315.5	368.4	420.9	437.7	130.9	153.0	186.5	262.3	349.7	147.5	42.8	64.2	55.3	191.1	305.8
	625	203.6	210.7	263.1	315.5	368.4	420.9	437.7	168.3	198.7	242.2	340.7	454.2	147.5	42.8	64.2	55.3	227.5	364.1
38.1 (1.5)	300	247.4	256.1	319.8	383.5	447.9	511.6	532.0	59.4	66.1	80.6	113.3	151.0	175.6	51.0	76.4	60.4	119.1	190.6
	375	247.4	256.1	319.8	383.5	447.9	511.6	532.0	81.2	92.4	112.6	158.3	211.1	175.6	51.0	76.4	60.4	148.9	238.3
	450	247.4	256.1	319.8	383.5	447.9	511.6	532.0	105.1	121.4	148.0	208.1	277.5	175.6	51.0	76.4	60.4	178.7	285.9
	525	247.4	256.1	319.8	383.5	447.9	511.6	532.0	130.9	153.0	186.5	262.3	349.7	175.6	51.0	76.4	60.4	208.5	333.6
	625	247.4	256.1	319.8	383.5	447.9	511.6	532.0	168.3	198.7	242.2	340.7	454.2	175.6	51.0	76.4	60.4	248.2	397.2
44.45 (1.75)	300	333.4	345.1	430.9	516.8	603.5	689.3	716.9	59.4	66.1	80.6	113.3	151.0	278.0	69.4	104.0	76.0	149.9	239.9
	375	333.4	345.1	430.9	516.8	603.5	689.3	716.9	81.2	92.4	112.6	158.3	211.1	278.0	69.4	104.0	76.0	187.4	299.9
	450	333.4	345.1	430.9	516.8	603.5	689.3	716.9	105.1	121.4	148.0	208.1	277.5	278.0	69.4	104.0	76.0	224.9	359.8
	525	333.4	345.1	430.9	516.8	603.5	689.3	716.9	130.9	153.0	186.5	262.3	349.7	278.0	69.4	104.0	76.0	262.4	419.8
	625	333.4	345.1	430.9	516.8	603.5	689.3	716.9	168.3	198.7	242.2	340.7	454.2	278.0	69.4	104.0	76.0	312.4	499.8
50.8 (2.0)	300	438.7	454.1	567.0	680.0	794.1	907.0	943.2	59.4	66.1	80.6	113.3	151.0	356.7	90.6	135.9	86.0	169.8	271.7
	375	438.7	454.1	567.0	680.0	794.1	907.0	943.2	81.2	92.4	112.6	158.3	211.1	356.7	90.6	135.9	86.0	212.3	339.6
	450	438.7	454.1	567.0	680.0	794.1	907.0	943.2	105.1	121.4	148.0	208.1	277.5	356.7	90.6	135.9	86.0	254.7	407.5
	525	438.7	454.1	567.0	680.0	794.1	907.0	943.2	130.9	153.0	186.5	262.3	349.7	356.7	90.6	135.9	86.0	297.2	475.5
	625	438.7	454.1	567.0	680.0	794.1	907.0	943.2	168.3	198.7	242.2	340.7	454.2	356.7	90.6	135.9	86.0	353.8	566.0

Table 12.5(B) Factored resistance for Single Cast-In Anchors Subject to Tensile Loads (f'c = 30 MPa)

d_o mm (in)	h_{ef} mm	N_{sr} - Tension Strength of Anchor (kN) f_{ut} - for design purpose[3] - (MPa)							N_{cbr} - Tension Breakout[4,5,6] (kN)					N_{cpr} - Pullout[9] (kN)			N_{sbr} - Sideface Blowout[4,10] (kN)		
									38 mm cover	c_1 - edge distance				head[7]	"J" or "L" hook[8]		38 mm cover	c_1 - edge distance	
		400	414	517	620	724	827	860		$0.25h_{ef}$	$0.5h_{ef}$	h_{ef}	$\geq1.5h_{ef}$		$\theta_h = 3d_o$	$\theta_h = 4.5d_o$		$0.25h_{ef}$	$0.4h_{ef}$
6.35 (0.25)	50	5.6	5.8	7.3	8.7	10.2	11.6	12.1	8.1	NP	NP	9.4	12.6	11.8	2.1	3.2	15.6	NP	NP
	75	5.6	5.8	7.3	8.7	10.2	11.6	12.1	12.4	NP	NP	17.3	23.1	11.8	2.1	3.2	15.6	NP	NP
	100	5.6	5.8	7.3	8.7	10.2	11.6	12.1	17.3	NP	19.0	26.7	35.6	11.8	2.1	3.2	15.6	NP	16.5
	125	5.6	5.8	7.3	8.7	10.2	11.6	12.1	22.8	NP	26.5	37.3	49.8	11.8	2.1	3.2	15.6	NP	20.6
	150	5.6	5.8	7.3	8.7	10.2	11.6	12.1	28.7	NP	34.9	49.1	65.4	11.8	2.1	3.2	15.6	NP	24.7
9.525 (0.375)	50	13.7	14.2	17.7	21.2	24.8	28.3	29.4	8.1	NP	NP	9.4	12.6	16.5	4.8	7.2	18.5	NP	NP
	75	13.7	14.2	17.7	21.2	24.8	28.3	29.4	12.4	NP	NP	17.3	23.1	16.5	4.8	7.2	18.5	NP	19.5
	100	13.7	14.2	17.7	21.2	24.8	28.3	29.4	17.3	NP	19.0	26.7	35.6	16.5	4.8	7.2	18.5	NP	24.4
	125	13.7	14.2	17.7	21.2	24.8	28.3	29.4	22.8	NP	26.5	37.3	49.8	16.5	4.8	7.2	18.5	NP	29.2
	150	13.7	14.2	17.7	21.2	24.8	28.3	29.4	28.7	NP	34.9	49.1	65.4	16.5	4.8	7.2	18.5	NP	
12.7 (0.5)	50	24.9	25.8	32.2	38.6	45.1	51.5	53.6	8.1	NP	NP	9.4	12.6	29.3	8.5	12.7	24.7	NP	NP
	75	24.9	25.8	32.2	38.6	45.1	51.5	53.6	12.4	NP	NP	17.3	23.1	29.3	8.5	12.7	24.7	NP	26.0
	100	24.9	25.8	32.2	38.6	45.1	51.5	53.6	17.3	NP	19.0	26.7	35.6	29.3	8.5	12.7	24.7	NP	32.4
	125	24.9	25.8	32.2	38.6	45.1	51.5	53.6	22.8	NP	26.5	37.3	49.8	29.3	8.5	12.7	24.7	NP	38.9
	150	24.9	25.8	32.2	38.6	45.1	51.5	53.6	28.7	NP	34.9	49.1	65.4	29.3	8.5	12.7	24.7	NP	45.4
	175	24.9	25.8	32.2	38.6	45.1	51.5	53.6	35.1	36.1	44.0	61.8	82.4	29.3	8.5	12.7	24.7	28.4	51.9
	200	24.9	25.8	32.2	38.6	45.1	51.5	53.6	41.9	44.1	53.7	75.5	100.7	29.3	8.5	12.7	24.7	32.4	
15.875 (0.625)	75	39.7	41.0	51.3	61.5	71.8	82.0	85.3	17.3	NP	NP	17.3	23.1	45.7	13.3	19.9	30.8	NP	NP
	100	39.7	41.0	51.3	61.5	71.8	82.0	85.3	22.8	NP	19.0	26.7	35.6	45.7	13.3	19.9	30.8	NP	32.4
	125	39.7	41.0	51.3	61.5	71.8	82.0	85.3	28.7	NP	26.5	37.3	49.8	45.7	13.3	19.9	30.8	NP	40.5
	150	39.7	41.0	51.3	61.5	71.8	82.0	85.3	35.1	36.1	34.9	49.1	65.4	45.7	13.3	19.9	30.8	NP	48.6
	175	39.7	41.0	51.3	61.5	71.8	82.0	85.3	41.9	44.1	44.0	61.8	82.4	45.7	13.3	19.9	30.8	35.5	56.7
	200	39.7	41.0	51.3	61.5	71.8	82.0	85.3	49.0	52.6	53.7	75.5	100.7	45.7	13.3	19.9	30.8	40.5	64.8
	225	39.7	41.0	51.3	61.5	71.8	82.0	85.3	56.6	61.6	64.1	90.1	120.2	45.7	13.3	19.9	30.8	45.6	72.9
	250	39.7	41.0	51.3	61.5	71.8	82.0	85.3	72.8	80.9	75.1	105.5	140.7	45.7	13.3	19.9	30.8	50.6	81.0
19.05 (0.75)	100	58.6	60.7	75.8	90.8	106.1	121.2	126.0	17.3	NP	19.0	26.7	35.6	65.8	19.1	28.7	37.0	NP	38.9
	125	58.6	60.7	75.8	90.8	106.1	121.2	126.0	22.8	NP	26.5	37.3	49.8	65.8	19.1	28.7	37.0	NP	48.6
	150	58.6	60.7	75.8	90.8	106.1	121.2	126.0	28.7	NP	34.9	49.1	65.4	65.8	19.1	28.7	37.0	NP	58.4
	175	58.6	60.7	75.8	90.8	106.1	121.2	126.0	35.1	36.1	44.0	61.8	82.4	65.8	19.1	28.7	37.0	42.6	68.1
	200	58.6	60.7	75.8	90.8	106.1	121.2	126.0	41.9	44.1	53.7	75.5	100.7	65.8	19.1	28.7	37.0	48.6	77.8
	225	58.6	60.7	75.8	90.8	106.1	121.2	126.0	49.0	52.6	64.1	90.1	120.2	65.8	19.1	28.7	37.0	54.7	87.5
	250	58.6	60.7	75.8	90.8	106.1	121.2	126.0	56.6	61.6	75.1	105.5	140.7	65.8	19.1	28.7	37.0	60.8	97.3
	300	58.6	60.7	75.8	90.8	106.1	121.2	126.0	72.8	80.9	98.7	138.7	185.0	65.8	19.1	28.7	37.0	72.9	116.7
22.225 (0.875)	100	81.1	83.9	104.8	125.7	146.7	167.6	174.3	17.3	NP	19.0	26.7	35.6	89.7	26.0	39.0	43.1	NP	45.4
	150	81.1	83.9	104.8	125.7	146.7	167.6	174.3	28.7	NP	34.9	49.1	65.4	89.7	26.0	39.0	43.1	NP	68.1
	200	81.1	83.9	104.8	125.7	146.7	167.6	174.3	41.9	44.1	53.7	75.5	100.7	89.7	26.0	39.0	43.1	56.8	90.8
	300	81.1	83.9	104.8	125.7	146.7	167.6	174.3	72.8	80.9	98.7	138.7	185.0	89.7	26.0	39.0	43.1	85.1	136.2
	375	81.1	83.9	104.8	125.7	146.7	167.6	174.3	99.4	113.1	137.9	193.9	258.5	89.7	26.0	39.0	43.1	106.4	170.3
	450	81.1	83.9	104.8	125.7	146.7	167.6	174.3	128.7	148.7	181.3	254.0	339.9	89.7	26.0	39.0	43.1	127.7	204.3
	625	81.1	83.9	104.8	125.7	146.7	167.6	174.3	206.1	243.4	296.7	417.2	556.3	89.7	26.0	39.0	43.1	177.4	283.8

25.4 (1.0)	150	106.3	110.1	137.4	164.8	192.5	219.9	228.6	28.7	NP	34.9	49.1	65.4	117.1	34.0	51.0	49.3	NP	77.8
	225	106.3	110.1	137.4	164.8	192.5	219.9	228.6	49.0	52.6	64.1	90.1	120.2	117.1	34.0	51.0	49.3	73.0	116.7
	300	106.3	110.1	137.4	164.8	192.5	219.9	228.6	72.8	80.9	98.7	138.7	185.0	117.1	34.0	51.0	49.3	97.3	155.6
	375	106.3	110.1	137.4	164.8	192.5	219.9	228.6	99.4	113.1	137.9	193.9	258.5	117.1	34.0	51.0	49.3	121.6	194.6
	450	106.3	110.1	137.4	164.8	192.5	219.9	228.6	128.7	148.7	181.3	254.9	339.9	117.1	34.0	51.0	49.3	145.9	233.5
	525	106.3	110.1	137.4	164.8	192.5	219.9	228.6	160.4	187.4	228.4	321.2	428.3	117.1	34.0	51.0	49.3	170.2	272.4
	625	106.3	110.1	137.4	164.8	192.5	219.9	228.6	206.1	243.4	296.7	417.2	556.3	117.1	34.0	51.0	49.3	202.7	324.3
29 (1.125)	150	133.9	138.6	173.1	207.5	242.3	276.8	287.9	28.7	NP	34.9	49.1	65.4	148.1	43.0	64.5	55.4	NP	87.6
	225	133.9	138.6	173.1	207.5	242.3	276.8	287.9	49.0	52.6	64.1	90.1	120.2	148.1	43.0	64.5	55.4	82.1	131.3
	300	133.9	138.6	173.1	207.5	242.3	276.8	287.9	72.8	80.9	98.7	138.7	185.0	148.1	43.0	64.5	55.4	109.4	175.1
	375	133.9	138.6	173.1	207.5	242.3	276.8	287.9	99.4	113.1	137.9	193.9	258.5	148.1	43.0	64.5	55.4	136.8	218.9
	450	133.9	138.6	173.1	207.5	242.3	276.8	287.9	128.7	148.7	181.3	254.9	339.9	148.1	43.0	64.5	55.4	164.2	262.7
	525	133.9	138.6	173.1	207.5	242.3	276.8	287.9	160.4	187.4	228.4	321.2	428.3	148.1	43.0	64.5	55.4	191.5	306.4
	625	133.9	138.6	173.1	207.5	242.3	276.8	287.9	206.1	243.4	296.7	417.2	556.3	148.1	43.0	64.5	55.4	228.0	364.8
31.75 (1.25)	150	170.0	176.0	219.8	263.6	307.8	351.6	365.6	28.7	NP	34.9	49.1	65.4	182.9	53.1	79.6	61.6	NP	97.3
	225	170.0	176.0	219.8	263.6	307.8	351.6	365.6	49.0	52.6	64.1	90.1	120.2	182.9	53.1	79.6	61.6	91.2	145.9
	300	170.0	176.0	219.8	263.6	307.8	351.6	365.6	72.8	80.9	98.7	138.7	185.0	182.9	53.1	79.6	61.6	121.6	194.5
	375	170.0	176.0	219.8	263.6	307.8	351.6	365.6	99.4	113.1	137.9	193.9	258.5	182.9	53.1	79.6	61.6	152.0	243.2
	450	170.0	176.0	219.8	263.6	307.8	351.6	365.6	128.7	148.7	181.3	254.9	339.9	182.9	53.1	79.6	61.6	182.4	291.8
	525	170.0	176.0	219.8	263.6	307.8	351.6	365.6	160.4	187.4	228.4	321.2	428.3	182.9	53.1	79.6	61.6	212.8	340.5
	625	170.0	176.0	219.8	263.6	307.8	351.6	365.6	206.1	243.4	296.7	417.2	556.3	182.9	53.1	79.6	61.6	253.3	405.3
34.925 (1.375)	150	203.6	210.7	263.1	315.5	368.4	420.9	437.7	28.7	NP	34.9	49.1	65.4	221.3	64.2	96.3	67.8	NP	107.0
	225	203.6	210.7	263.1	315.5	368.4	420.9	437.7	49.0	52.6	64.1	90.1	120.2	221.3	64.2	96.3	67.8	100.3	160.5
	300	203.6	210.7	263.1	315.5	368.4	420.9	437.7	72.8	80.9	98.7	138.7	185.0	221.3	64.2	96.3	67.8	133.8	214.0
	375	203.6	210.7	263.1	315.5	368.4	420.9	437.7	99.4	113.1	137.9	193.9	258.5	221.3	64.2	96.3	67.8	167.2	267.5
	450	203.6	210.7	263.1	315.5	368.4	420.9	437.7	128.7	148.7	181.3	254.9	339.9	221.3	64.2	96.3	67.8	200.6	321.0
	525	203.6	210.7	263.1	315.5	368.4	420.9	437.7	160.4	187.4	228.4	321.2	428.3	221.3	64.2	96.3	67.8	234.1	374.5
	625	203.6	210.7	263.1	315.5	368.4	420.9	437.7	206.1	243.4	296.7	417.2	556.3	221.3	64.2	96.3	67.8	278.7	445.9
38.1 (1.5)	300	247.4	256.1	319.8	383.5	447.9	511.6	532.0	72.8	80.9	98.7	138.7	185.0	263.4	76.4	114.6	73.9	145.9	233.5
	375	247.4	256.1	319.8	383.5	447.9	511.6	532.0	99.4	113.1	137.9	193.9	258.5	263.4	76.4	114.6	73.9	182.4	291.8
	450	247.4	256.1	319.8	383.5	447.9	511.6	532.0	128.7	148.7	181.3	254.9	339.9	263.4	76.4	114.6	73.9	218.9	350.2
	525	247.4	256.1	319.8	383.5	447.9	511.6	532.0	160.4	187.4	228.4	321.2	428.3	263.4	76.4	114.6	73.9	255.4	408.6
	625	247.4	256.1	319.8	383.5	447.9	511.6	532.0	206.1	243.4	296.7	417.2	556.3	263.4	76.4	114.6	73.9	304.0	486.4
44.45 (1.75)	300	333.4	345.1	430.9	516.8	603.5	689.3	716.9	72.8	80.9	98.7	138.7	185.0	417.1	104.0	156.0	93.0	183.6	293.8
	375	333.4	345.1	430.9	516.8	603.5	689.3	716.9	99.4	113.1	137.9	193.9	258.5	417.1	104.0	156.0	93.0	229.5	367.2
	450	333.4	345.1	430.9	516.8	603.5	689.3	716.9	128.7	148.7	181.3	254.9	339.9	417.1	104.0	156.0	93.0	275.4	440.7
	525	333.4	345.1	430.9	516.8	603.5	689.3	716.9	160.4	187.4	228.4	321.2	428.3	417.1	104.0	156.0	93.0	321.3	514.1
	625	333.4	345.1	430.9	516.8	603.5	689.3	716.9	206.1	243.4	296.7	417.2	556.3	417.1	104.0	156.0	93.0	382.6	612.1
50.8 (2.0)	300	438.7	454.1	567.0	680.0	794.1	907.0	943.2	72.8	80.9	98.7	138.7	185.0	535.0	135.9	203.8	105.4	208.0	332.8
	375	438.7	454.1	567.0	680.0	794.1	907.0	943.2	99.4	113.1	137.9	193.9	258.5	535.0	135.9	203.8	105.4	260.0	416.0
	450	438.7	454.1	567.0	680.0	794.1	907.0	943.2	128.7	148.7	181.3	254.9	339.9	535.0	135.9	203.8	105.4	312.0	499.1
	525	438.7	454.1	567.0	680.0	794.1	907.0	943.2	160.4	187.4	228.4	321.2	428.3	535.0	135.9	203.8	105.4	364.0	582.3
	625	438.7	454.1	567.0	680.0	794.1	907.0	943.2	206.1	243.4	296.7	417.2	556.3	535.0	135.9	203.8	105.4	433.3	693.3

Table 12.5(C) Factored resistance for Single Cast-In Anchors Subject to Tensile Loads (f'c = 40 MPa)

do mm (in)	h_{ef} mm	N_{sr} - Tension Strength of Anchor (kN), f_{ut} - for design purpose[3] - (MPa)							N_{cbr} - Tension Breakout[4,5,6] (kN), c_1 - edge distance					N_{cpr} - Pullout[9] (kN)			N_{sbr} - Sideface Blowout[4,10] (kN), c_1 - edge distance		
		400	414	517	620	724	827	860	38 mm cover	$0.25h_{ef}$	$0.5h_{ef}$	h_{ef}	$\geq 1.5h_{ef}$	head[7]	"J" or "L" hook[9] $e_h=$ 3do	$e_h=$ 4.5do	38 mm cover	$0.25h_{ef}$	$0.4h_{ef}$
6.35 (0.25)	50	5.6	5.8	7.3	8.7	10.2	11.6	12.1	9.3	NP	NP	10.9	14.5	15.7	2.8	4.2	18.1	NP	NP
	75	5.6	5.8	7.3	8.7	10.2	11.6	12.1	14.3	NP	NP	20.0	26.7	15.7	2.8	4.2	18.1	NP	NP
	100	5.6	5.8	7.3	8.7	10.2	11.6	12.1	20.0	NP	21.9	30.8	41.1	15.7	2.8	4.2	18.1	NP	19.0
	125	5.6	5.8	7.3	8.7	10.2	11.6	12.1	26.3	NP	30.6	43.1	57.5	15.7	2.8	4.2	18.1	NP	23.8
	150	5.6	5.8	7.3	8.7	10.2	11.6	12.1	33.1	NP	40.3	56.6	75.5	15.7	2.8	4.2	18.1	NP	28.5
9.525 (0.375)	50	13.7	14.2	17.7	21.2	24.8	28.3	29.4	9.3	NP	NP	10.9	14.5	22.0	6.4	9.6	21.4	NP	NP
	75	13.7	14.2	17.7	21.2	24.8	28.3	29.4	14.3	NP	NP	20.0	26.7	22.0	6.4	9.6	21.4	NP	22.5
	100	13.7	14.2	17.7	21.2	24.8	28.3	29.4	20.0	NP	21.9	30.8	41.1	22.0	6.4	9.6	21.4	NP	28.1
	125	13.7	14.2	17.7	21.2	24.8	28.3	29.4	26.3	NP	30.6	43.1	57.5	22.0	6.4	9.6	21.4	NP	33.7
	150	13.7	14.2	17.7	21.2	24.8	28.3	29.4	33.1	NP	40.3	56.6	75.5	22.0	6.4	9.6	21.4	NP	—
12.7 (0.5)	50	24.9	25.8	32.2	38.6	45.1	51.5	53.6	9.3	NP	NP	10.9	14.5	39.1	11.3	17.0	28.5	NP	NP
	75	24.9	25.8	32.2	38.6	45.1	51.5	53.6	14.3	NP	NP	20.0	26.7	39.1	11.3	17.0	28.5	NP	NP
	100	24.9	25.8	32.2	38.6	45.1	51.5	53.6	20.0	NP	21.9	30.8	41.1	39.1	11.3	17.0	28.5	NP	30.0
	125	24.9	25.8	32.2	38.6	45.1	51.5	53.6	26.3	NP	30.6	43.1	57.5	39.1	11.3	17.0	28.5	NP	37.5
	150	24.9	25.8	32.2	38.6	45.1	51.5	53.6	33.1	NP	40.3	56.6	75.5	39.1	11.3	17.0	28.5	NP	44.9
	175	24.9	25.8	32.2	38.6	45.1	51.5	53.6	40.5	41.6	50.8	71.4	95.2	39.1	11.3	17.0	28.5	32.8	52.4
	200	24.9	25.8	32.2	38.6	45.1	51.5	53.6	48.3	50.9	62.0	87.2	116.3	39.1	11.3	17.0	28.5	37.5	59.9
15.875 (0.625)	75	39.7	41.0	51.3	61.5	71.8	82.0	85.3	14.3	NP	NP	20.0	26.7	60.9	17.7	26.5	35.6	NP	NP
	100	39.7	41.0	51.3	61.5	71.8	82.0	85.3	20.0	NP	21.9	30.8	41.1	60.9	17.7	26.5	35.6	NP	37.4
	125	39.7	41.0	51.3	61.5	71.8	82.0	85.3	26.3	NP	30.6	43.1	57.5	60.9	17.7	26.5	35.6	NP	46.8
	150	39.7	41.0	51.3	61.5	71.8	82.0	85.3	33.1	NP	40.3	56.6	75.5	60.9	17.7	26.5	35.6	NP	56.1
	175	39.7	41.0	51.3	61.5	71.8	82.0	85.3	40.5	41.6	50.8	71.4	95.2	60.9	17.7	26.5	35.6	40.9	65.5
	200	39.7	41.0	51.3	61.5	71.8	82.0	85.3	48.3	50.9	62.0	87.2	116.3	60.9	17.7	26.5	35.6	46.8	74.9
	225	39.7	41.0	51.3	61.5	71.8	82.0	85.3	56.6	60.7	74.0	104.1	138.7	60.9	17.7	26.5	35.6	52.6	84.2
	250	39.7	41.0	51.3	61.5	71.8	82.0	85.3	65.4	71.1	86.7	121.9	162.5	60.9	17.7	26.5	35.6	58.5	93.6
19.05 (0.75)	100	58.6	60.7	75.8	90.8	106.1	121.2	126.0	20.0	NP	21.9	30.8	41.1	87.8	25.5	38.2	42.7	NP	44.9
	125	58.6	60.7	75.8	90.8	106.1	121.2	126.0	26.3	NP	30.6	43.1	57.5	87.8	25.5	38.2	42.7	NP	56.2
	150	58.6	60.7	75.8	90.8	106.1	121.2	126.0	33.1	NP	40.3	56.6	75.5	87.8	25.5	38.2	42.7	NP	67.4
	175	58.6	60.7	75.8	90.8	106.1	121.2	126.0	40.5	41.6	50.8	71.4	95.2	87.8	25.5	38.2	42.7	49.1	78.6
	200	58.6	60.7	75.8	90.8	106.1	121.2	126.0	48.3	50.9	62.0	87.2	116.3	87.8	25.5	38.2	42.7	56.2	89.8
	225	58.6	60.7	75.8	90.8	106.1	121.2	126.0	56.6	60.7	74.0	104.1	138.7	87.8	25.5	38.2	42.7	63.2	101.1
	250	58.6	60.7	75.8	90.8	106.1	121.2	126.0	65.4	71.1	86.7	121.9	162.5	87.8	25.5	38.2	42.7	70.2	112.3
	300	58.6	60.7	75.8	90.8	106.1	121.2	126.0	84.0	93.5	113.9	160.2	213.6	87.8	25.5	38.2	42.7	84.2	134.8
22.225 (0.875)	100	81.1	83.9	104.8	125.7	146.7	167.6	174.3	20.0	NP	21.9	30.8	41.1	119.6	34.7	52.0	49.8	NP	52.4
	150	81.1	83.9	104.8	125.7	146.7	167.6	174.3	33.1	NP	40.3	56.6	75.5	119.6	34.7	52.0	49.8	NP	78.7
	200	81.1	83.9	104.8	125.7	146.7	167.6	174.3	48.3	50.9	62.0	87.2	116.3	119.6	34.7	52.0	49.8	65.5	104.9
	300	81.1	83.9	104.8	125.7	146.7	167.6	174.3	84.0	93.5	113.9	160.2	213.6	119.6	34.7	52.0	49.8	98.3	157.3
	375	81.1	83.9	104.8	125.7	146.7	167.6	174.3	114.8	130.6	159.2	223.9	298.5	119.6	34.7	52.0	49.8	122.9	196.6
	450	81.1	83.9	104.8	125.7	146.7	167.6	174.3	148.6	171.7	209.3	294.3	392.4	119.6	34.7	52.0	49.8	147.5	236.0
	625	81.1	83.9	104.8	125.7	146.7	167.6	174.3	238.0	281.0	342.6	481.8	642.3	119.6	34.7	52.0	49.8	204.8	327.7

Size		C1	C2	C3	C4	C5	C6	C7	C8	C9	C10	C11	C12	C13	C14	C15	C16	C17	C18
25.4 (1.0)	150	106.3	110.1	137.4	164.8	192.5	219.9	228.6	33.1	NP	40.3	56.6	75.5	156.1	45.3	67.9	56.9	NP	89.9
	225	106.3	110.1	137.4	164.8	192.5	219.9	228.6	56.6	60.7	74.0	104.1	138.7	156.1	45.3	67.9	56.9	84.2	134.8
	300	106.3	110.1	137.4	164.8	192.5	219.9	228.6	84.0	93.5	113.9	160.2	213.6	156.1	45.3	67.9	56.9	112.3	179.7
	375	106.3	110.1	137.4	164.8	192.5	219.9	228.6	114.8	130.6	159.2	223.9	298.5	156.1	45.3	67.9	56.9	140.4	224.7
	450	106.3	110.1	137.4	164.8	192.5	219.9	228.6	148.6	171.7	209.3	294.3	392.4	156.1	45.3	67.9	56.9	168.5	269.6
	525	106.3	110.1	137.4	164.8	192.5	219.9	228.6	185.2	216.4	263.7	370.9	494.5	156.1	45.3	67.9	56.9	196.6	314.5
	625	106.3	110.1	137.4	164.8	192.5	219.9	228.6	238.0	281.0	342.6	481.8	642.3	156.1	45.3	67.9	56.9	234.0	374.4
29 (1.125)	150	133.9	138.6	173.1	207.5	242.3	276.8	287.9	33.1	NP	40.3	56.6	75.5	197.5	57.3	86.0	64.0	NP	101.1
	225	133.9	138.6	173.1	207.5	242.3	276.8	287.9	56.6	60.7	74.0	104.1	138.7	197.5	57.3	86.0	64.0	94.8	151.6
	300	133.9	138.6	173.1	207.5	242.3	276.8	287.9	84.0	93.5	113.9	160.2	213.6	197.5	57.3	86.0	64.0	126.4	202.2
	375	133.9	138.6	173.1	207.5	242.3	276.8	287.9	114.8	130.6	159.2	223.9	298.5	197.5	57.3	86.0	64.0	158.0	252.7
	450	133.9	138.6	173.1	207.5	242.3	276.8	287.9	148.6	171.7	209.3	294.3	392.4	197.5	57.3	86.0	64.0	189.6	303.3
	525	133.9	138.6	173.1	207.5	242.3	276.8	287.9	185.2	216.4	263.7	370.9	494.5	197.5	57.3	86.0	64.0	221.1	353.8
	625	133.9	138.6	173.1	207.5	242.3	276.8	287.9	238.0	281.0	342.6	481.8	642.3	197.5	57.3	86.0	64.0	263.3	421.2
31.75 (1.25)	150	170.0	176.0	219.8	263.6	307.8	351.6	365.6	33.1	NP	40.3	56.6	75.5	243.8	70.8	106.1	71.1	NP	112.3
	225	170.0	176.0	219.8	263.6	307.8	351.6	365.6	56.6	60.7	74.0	104.1	138.7	243.8	70.8	106.1	71.1	105.3	168.5
	300	170.0	176.0	219.8	263.6	307.8	351.6	365.6	84.0	93.5	113.9	160.2	213.6	243.8	70.8	106.1	71.1	140.4	224.6
	375	170.0	176.0	219.8	263.6	307.8	351.6	365.6	114.8	130.6	159.2	223.9	298.5	243.8	70.8	106.1	71.1	175.5	280.8
	450	170.0	176.0	219.8	263.6	307.8	351.6	365.6	148.6	171.7	209.3	294.3	392.4	243.8	70.8	106.1	71.1	210.6	337.0
	525	170.0	176.0	219.8	263.6	307.8	351.6	365.6	185.2	216.4	263.7	370.9	494.5	243.8	70.8	106.1	71.1	245.7	393.1
	625	170.0	176.0	219.8	263.6	307.8	351.6	365.6	238.0	281.0	342.6	481.8	642.3	243.8	70.8	106.1	71.1	292.5	468.0
34.925 (1.375)	150	203.6	210.7	263.1	315.5	368.4	420.9	437.7	33.1	NP	40.3	56.6	75.5	295.1	85.6	128.4	78.3	NP	123.6
	225	203.6	210.7	263.1	315.5	368.4	420.9	437.7	56.6	60.7	74.0	104.1	138.7	295.1	85.6	128.4	78.3	115.8	185.3
	300	203.6	210.7	263.1	315.5	368.4	420.9	437.7	84.0	93.5	113.9	160.2	213.6	295.1	85.6	128.4	78.3	154.5	247.1
	375	203.6	210.7	263.1	315.5	368.4	420.9	437.7	114.8	130.6	159.2	223.9	298.5	295.1	85.6	128.4	78.3	193.1	308.9
	450	203.6	210.7	263.1	315.5	368.4	420.9	437.7	148.6	171.7	209.3	294.3	392.4	295.1	85.6	128.4	78.3	231.7	370.7
	525	203.6	210.7	263.1	315.5	368.4	420.9	437.7	185.2	216.4	263.7	370.9	494.5	295.1	85.6	128.4	78.3	270.3	432.5
	625	203.6	210.7	263.1	315.5	368.4	420.9	437.7	238.0	281.0	342.6	481.8	642.3	295.1	85.6	128.4	78.3	321.8	514.9
38.1 (1.5)	300	247.4	256.1	319.8	383.5	447.9	511.6	532.0	84.0	93.5	113.9	160.2	213.6	351.2	101.9	152.9	85.4	168.5	269.6
	375	247.4	256.1	319.8	383.5	447.9	511.6	532.0	114.8	130.6	159.2	223.9	298.5	351.2	101.9	152.9	85.4	210.6	337.0
	450	247.4	256.1	319.8	383.5	447.9	511.6	532.0	148.6	171.7	209.3	294.3	392.4	351.2	101.9	152.9	85.4	252.7	404.4
	525	247.4	256.1	319.8	383.5	447.9	511.6	532.0	185.2	216.4	263.7	370.9	494.5	351.2	101.9	152.9	85.4	294.9	471.8
	625	247.4	256.1	319.8	383.5	447.9	511.6	532.0	238.0	281.0	342.6	481.8	642.3	351.2	101.9	152.9	85.4	351.0	561.7
44.45 (1.75)	300	333.4	345.1	430.9	516.8	603.5	689.3	716.9	84.0	93.5	113.9	160.2	213.6	556.1	138.7	208.1	107.4	212.0	339.2
	375	333.4	345.1	430.9	516.8	603.5	689.3	716.9	114.8	130.6	159.2	223.9	298.5	556.1	138.7	208.1	107.4	265.0	424.1
	450	333.4	345.1	430.9	516.8	603.5	689.3	716.9	148.6	171.7	209.3	294.3	392.4	556.1	138.7	208.1	107.4	318.0	508.9
	525	333.4	345.1	430.9	516.8	603.5	689.3	716.9	185.2	216.4	263.7	370.9	494.5	556.1	138.7	208.1	107.4	371.1	593.7
	625	333.4	345.1	430.9	516.8	603.5	689.3	716.9	238.0	281.0	342.6	481.8	642.3	556.1	138.7	208.1	107.4	441.7	706.8
50.8 (2.0)	300	438.7	454.1	567.0	680.0	794.1	907.0	943.2	84.0	93.5	113.9	160.2	213.6	713.4	181.2	271.7	121.7	240.1	384.2
	375	438.7	454.1	567.0	680.0	794.1	907.0	943.2	114.8	130.6	159.2	223.9	298.5	713.4	181.2	271.7	121.7	300.2	480.3
	450	438.7	454.1	567.0	680.0	794.1	907.0	943.2	148.6	171.7	209.3	294.3	392.4	713.4	181.2	271.7	121.7	360.2	576.4
	525	438.7	454.1	567.0	680.0	794.1	907.0	943.2	185.2	216.4	263.7	370.9	494.5	713.4	181.2	271.7	121.7	420.3	672.4
	625	438.7	454.1	567.0	680.0	794.1	907.0	943.2	238.0	281.0	342.6	481.8	642.3	713.4	181.2	271.7	121.7	500.3	800.5

Table 12.6(A) Factored resistance for Single Cast-In Anchors Subject to Shear Loads (f'c = 20 MPa)[1,2,3,5]

Column groups:
- V_{sr} – Shear Strength of Anchor (kN); f_{ut} – for design purpose[4] (MPa): columns 400, 414, 517, 620, 724, 827, 860
- V_{cbr} – Shear Breakout (kN)[5,6,7,8,9]
  - $h = h_{ef}$[10], $c_1 =$[11]: columns 0.25h_{ef}, 0.5h_{ef}, h_{ef}, 1.5h_{ef}, 3h_{ef}
  - $h = 1.5h_{ef}$, $c_1 =$[11,12]: columns h_{ef}, 1.5h_{ef}, 3h_{ef}
  - $h = 2.25h_{ef}$, $c_1 =$[11,12]: columns h_{ef}, 1.5h_{ef}, 3h_{ef}

d_o mm (in)	h_{ef} mm	400	414	517	620	724	827	860	38 mm cover	0.25h_{ef}	0.5h_{ef}	h_{ef}	1.5h_{ef}	3h_{ef}	h_{ef}	1.5h_{ef}	3h_{ef}	h_{ef}	1.5h_{ef}	3h_{ef}
6.35 (0.25)	50	3.4	3.5	4.4	5.2	6.1	7.0	7.3	1.3	NP	NP	1.5	1.9	2.6	2.3	2.8	3.9	4.2	4.8	5.9
	75	3.4	3.5	4.4	5.2	6.1	7.0	7.3	1.5	NP	NP	2.8	3.4	4.8	4.2	5.1	7.2	7.7	8.9	10.9
	100	3.4	3.5	4.4	5.2	6.1	7.0	7.3	1.5	NP	2.3	4.3	5.3	7.4	6.4	7.9	11.2	11.8	13.7	16.7
	125	3.4	3.5	4.4	5.2	6.1	7.0	7.3	1.5	NP	3.2	6.0	7.3	10.4	9.0	11.0	15.6	16.5	19.1	23.4
	150	3.4	3.5	4.4	5.2	6.1	7.0	7.3	1.5	NP	4.2	7.9	9.7	13.7	11.8	14.5	20.5	21.7	25.1	30.7
9.525 (0.375)	50	7.6	7.9	9.8	11.8	13.8	15.7	16.3	1.5	NP	NP	1.7	2.1	3.0	2.6	3.1	4.4	4.7	5.4	6.7
	75	7.6	7.9	9.8	11.8	13.8	15.7	16.3	1.8	NP	NP	3.4	4.2	5.9	5.1	6.3	8.8	9.4	10.8	13.3
	100	7.6	7.9	9.8	11.8	13.8	15.7	16.3	1.8	NP	2.8	5.3	6.4	9.1	7.9	9.7	13.7	14.5	16.7	20.5
	125	7.6	7.9	9.8	11.8	13.8	15.7	16.3	1.8	NP	3.9	7.3	9.0	12.7	11.0	13.5	19.1	20.2	23.4	28.6
	150	7.6	7.9	9.8	11.8	13.8	15.7	16.3	1.8	NP	5.1	9.7	11.8	16.7	14.5	17.7	25.1	26.6	30.7	37.6
12.7 (0.5)	50	13.5	14.0	17.5	21.0	24.5	28.0	29.1	1.6	NP	NP	1.9	2.3	3.2	2.8	3.4	4.8	5.1	5.9	7.3
	75	13.5	14.0	17.5	21.0	24.5	28.0	29.1	2.0	NP	NP	3.7	4.5	6.4	5.6	6.8	9.6	10.2	11.8	14.5
	100	13.5	14.0	17.5	21.0	24.5	28.0	29.1	2.1	NP	3.2	6.1	7.4	10.5	9.1	11.1	15.7	16.7	19.3	23.6
	125	13.5	14.0	17.5	21.0	24.5	28.0	29.1	2.1	NP	4.5	8.5	10.4	14.7	12.7	15.6	22.0	23.4	27.0	33.1
	150	13.5	14.0	17.5	21.0	24.5	28.0	29.1	2.1	NP	5.9	11.2	13.7	19.3	16.7	20.5	29.0	30.7	35.5	43.5
	175	13.5	14.0	17.5	21.0	24.5	28.0	29.1	2.1	2.6	7.5	14.1	17.2	24.3	21.1	25.8	36.5	38.7	44.7	54.8
	200	13.5	14.0	17.5	21.0	24.5	28.0	29.1	2.1	3.2	9.1	17.2	21.0	29.7	25.8	31.5	44.6	47.3	54.6	66.9
15.875 (0.625)	75	21.2	22.0	27.4	32.9	38.4	43.9	45.6	2.1	NP	NP	4.0	4.9	6.9	6.0	7.3	10.3	10.9	12.6	15.5
	100	21.2	22.0	27.4	32.9	38.4	43.9	45.6	2.3	NP	3.4	6.5	7.9	11.2	9.7	11.9	16.8	17.8	20.6	25.2
	125	21.2	22.0	27.4	32.9	38.4	43.9	45.6	2.4	NP	5.0	9.5	11.6	16.4	14.2	17.4	24.6	26.1	30.1	36.9
	150	21.2	22.0	27.4	32.9	38.4	43.9	45.6	2.4	NP	6.6	12.5	15.3	21.6	18.7	22.9	32.4	34.4	39.7	48.6
	175	21.2	22.0	27.4	32.9	38.4	43.9	45.6	2.4	2.9	8.3	15.7	19.2	27.2	23.6	28.9	40.8	43.3	50.0	61.2
	200	21.2	22.0	27.4	32.9	38.4	43.9	45.6	2.4	3.6	10.2	19.2	23.5	33.3	28.8	35.3	49.9	52.9	61.1	74.8
	225	21.2	22.0	27.4	32.9	38.4	43.9	45.6	2.4	4.3	12.1	22.9	28.1	39.7	34.4	42.1	59.5	63.1	72.9	89.3
	250	21.2	22.0	27.4	32.9	38.4	43.9	45.6	2.4	5.0	14.2	26.8	32.9	46.5	40.2	49.3	69.7	73.9	85.4	104.6
19.05 (0.75)	100	30.5	31.6	39.5	47.3	55.3	63.1	65.7	2.4	NP	3.6	6.8	8.4	11.8	10.3	12.6	17.8	18.8	21.7	26.6
	125	30.5	31.6	39.5	47.3	55.3	63.1	65.7	2.5	NP	5.3	10.0	12.2	17.3	15.0	18.3	25.9	27.5	31.8	38.9
	150	30.5	31.6	39.5	47.3	55.3	63.1	65.7	2.6	NP	7.2	13.6	16.7	23.6	20.4	25.0	35.4	37.5	43.3	53.1
	175	30.5	31.6	39.5	47.3	55.3	63.1	65.7	2.6	3.2	9.1	17.2	21.1	29.8	25.8	31.6	44.7	47.4	54.8	67.1
	200	30.5	31.6	39.5	47.3	55.3	63.1	65.7	2.6	3.9	11.2	21.0	25.8	36.4	31.5	38.6	54.6	58.0	66.9	82.0
	225	30.5	31.6	39.5	47.3	55.3	63.1	65.7	2.6	4.7	13.3	25.1	30.7	43.5	37.6	46.1	65.2	69.2	79.9	97.8
	250	30.5	31.6	39.5	47.3	55.3	63.1	65.7	2.6	5.5	15.6	29.4	36.0	50.9	44.1	54.0	76.4	81.0	93.5	114.5
	300	30.5	31.6	39.5	47.3	55.3	63.1	65.7	2.6	7.2	20.5	38.6	47.3	66.9	58.0	71.0	100.4	106.5	122.9	150.6
22.225 (0.875)	100	41.5	43.0	53.7	64.4	75.2	85.9	89.3	2.5	NP	3.8	7.2	8.8	12.4	10.7	13.2	18.6	19.7	22.8	27.9
	150	41.5	43.0	53.7	64.4	75.2	85.9	89.3	2.7	NP	7.6	14.3	17.5	24.7	21.4	26.2	37.1	39.3	45.4	55.6
	200	41.5	43.0	53.7	64.4	75.2	85.9	89.3	2.8	4.3	12.0	22.7	27.8	39.3	34.1	41.7	59.0	62.6	72.3	88.5
	300	41.5	43.0	53.7	64.4	75.2	85.9	89.3	2.8	7.8	22.1	41.7	51.1	72.3	62.6	76.7	108.4	115.0	132.8	162.6
	375	41.5	43.0	53.7	64.4	75.2	85.9	89.3	2.8	10.9	30.9	58.3	71.4	101.0	87.5	107.1	151.5	160.7	185.6	227.3
	450	41.5	43.0	53.7	64.4	75.2	85.9	89.3	2.8	14.4	40.7	76.7	93.9	132.8	115.0	140.9	199.2	211.3	244.0	298.8
	625	41.5	43.0	53.7	64.4	75.2	85.9	89.3	2.8	23.5	66.6	125.5	153.7	217.4	188.2	230.5	326.0	345.8	399.3	489.1

Group	Size																			
25.4 (1.0)	150	57.9	47.2	40.9	38.6	27.3	22.3	25.7	18.2	14.8	7.9	NP	2.8	116.6	112.1	98.2	84.1	70.1	56.1	54.2
	225	112.9	92.2	79.9	75.3	53.2	43.5	50.2	35.5	29.0	15.4	5.4	3.0	116.6	112.1	98.2	84.1	70.1	56.1	54.2
	300	173.9	142.0	122.9	115.9	82.0	66.9	77.3	54.6	44.6	23.7	8.4	3.0	116.6	112.1	98.2	84.1	70.1	56.1	54.2
	375	243.0	198.4	171.8	162.0	114.5	93.5	108.0	76.4	62.4	33.1	11.7	3.0	116.6	112.1	98.2	84.1	70.1	56.1	54.2
	450	319.4	260.8	225.9	212.9	150.6	122.9	142.0	100.4	82.0	43.5	15.4	3.0	116.6	112.1	98.2	84.1	70.1	56.1	54.2
	525	402.5	328.7	284.6	268.3	189.7	154.9	178.9	126.5	103.3	54.8	19.4	3.0	116.6	112.1	98.2	84.1	70.1	56.1	54.2
	625	522.8	426.9	369.7	348.6	246.5	201.2	232.4	164.3	134.2	71.1	25.2	3.0	116.6	112.1	98.2	84.1	70.1	56.1	54.2
29 (1.125)	150	59.9	48.9	42.4	40.0	28.3	23.1	26.6	18.8	15.4	8.2	NP	2.9	147.7	142.0	124.3	106.5	88.8	71.1	68.7
	225	119.4	97.5	84.4	79.6	56.3	46.0	53.1	37.5	30.6	16.2	5.7	3.2	147.7	142.0	124.3	106.5	88.8	71.1	68.7
	300	184.4	150.6	130.4	122.9	86.9	71.0	82.0	58.0	47.3	25.1	8.9	3.2	147.7	142.0	124.3	106.5	88.8	71.1	68.7
	375	257.7	210.4	182.2	171.8	121.5	99.2	114.5	81.0	66.1	35.1	12.4	3.2	147.7	142.0	124.3	106.5	88.8	71.1	68.7
	450	338.8	276.6	239.6	225.9	159.7	130.4	150.6	106.5	86.9	46.1	16.3	3.2	147.7	142.0	124.3	106.5	88.8	71.1	68.7
	525	426.9	348.6	301.9	284.6	201.3	164.3	189.7	134.2	109.6	58.1	20.5	3.2	147.7	142.0	124.3	106.5	88.8	71.1	68.7
	625	554.5	452.8	392.1	369.7	261.4	213.4	246.5	174.3	142.3	75.5	26.7	3.2	147.7	142.0	124.3	106.5	88.8	71.1	68.7
31.75 (1.25)	150	61.9	50.5	43.7	41.2	29.2	23.8	27.5	19.4	15.9	8.4	NP	3.0	182.3	175.3	153.5	131.4	109.6	87.7	84.8
	225	123.2	100.6	87.1	82.2	58.1	47.4	54.8	38.7	31.6	16.8	5.9	3.3	182.3	175.3	153.5	131.4	109.6	87.7	84.8
	300	194.4	158.7	137.5	129.6	91.6	74.8	86.4	61.1	49.9	26.5	9.4	3.4	182.3	175.3	153.5	131.4	109.6	87.7	84.8
	375	271.7	221.8	192.1	181.1	128.1	104.6	120.7	85.4	69.7	37.0	13.1	3.4	182.3	175.3	153.5	131.4	109.6	87.7	84.8
	450	357.1	291.6	252.5	238.1	168.3	137.5	158.7	112.2	91.6	48.6	17.2	3.4	182.3	175.3	153.5	131.4	109.6	87.7	84.8
	525	450.0	367.4	318.2	300.0	212.1	173.2	200.0	141.4	115.5	61.2	21.7	3.4	182.3	175.3	153.5	131.4	109.6	87.7	84.8
	625	584.5	477.3	413.3	389.7	275.6	225.0	259.8	183.7	150.0	79.5	28.1	3.4	182.3	175.3	153.5	131.4	109.6	87.7	84.8
34.925 (1.375)	150	63.7	52.0	45.0	42.4	30.0	24.5	28.3	20.0	16.3	8.7	NP	3.1	220.6	212.1	185.7	159.0	132.6	106.2	102.6
	225	126.8	103.5	89.7	84.5	59.8	48.8	56.4	39.9	32.5	17.3	6.1	3.4	220.6	212.1	185.7	159.0	132.6	106.2	102.6
	300	203.9	166.5	144.2	135.9	96.1	78.5	90.6	64.1	52.3	27.7	9.8	3.5	220.6	212.1	185.7	159.0	132.6	106.2	102.6
	375	284.9	232.6	201.5	190.0	134.3	109.7	126.6	89.5	73.1	38.8	13.7	3.5	220.6	212.1	185.7	159.0	132.6	106.2	102.6
	450	374.6	305.8	264.8	249.7	176.6	144.2	166.5	117.7	96.1	51.0	18.0	3.5	220.6	212.1	185.7	159.0	132.6	106.2	102.6
	525	472.0	385.4	333.7	314.7	222.5	181.7	209.8	148.3	121.1	64.2	22.7	3.5	220.6	212.1	185.7	159.0	132.6	106.2	102.6
	625	613.1	500.6	433.5	408.7	289.0	236.0	272.5	192.7	157.3	83.4	29.5	3.5	220.6	212.1	185.7	159.0	132.6	106.2	102.6
38.1 (1.5)	300	212.3	173.3	150.1	141.5	100.1	81.7	94.3	66.7	54.5	28.9	10.2	3.7	262.5	252.4	221.0	189.2	157.8	126.4	122.1
	375	297.6	243.0	210.4	198.4	140.3	114.5	132.3	93.5	76.4	40.5	14.3	3.7	262.5	252.4	221.0	189.2	157.8	126.4	122.1
	450	391.2	319.4	276.6	260.8	184.4	150.6	173.9	122.9	100.4	53.2	18.8	3.7	262.5	252.4	221.0	189.2	157.8	126.4	122.1
	525	493.0	402.5	348.6	328.7	232.4	189.7	219.1	154.9	126.5	67.1	23.7	3.7	262.5	252.4	221.0	189.2	157.8	126.4	122.1
	625	640.3	522.8	452.8	426.9	301.9	246.5	284.6	201.2	164.3	87.1	30.8	3.7	262.5	252.4	221.0	189.2	157.8	126.4	122.1
44.45 (1.75)	300	222.3	181.5	157.2	148.2	104.8	85.6	98.8	69.9	57.0	30.3	10.7	3.9	357.3	343.6	300.8	257.6	214.8	172.0	166.2
	375	321.4	262.5	227.3	214.3	151.5	123.7	142.9	101.0	82.5	43.7	15.5	4.0	357.3	343.6	300.8	257.6	214.8	172.0	166.2
	450	422.6	345.0	298.8	281.7	199.2	162.6	187.8	132.8	108.4	57.5	20.3	4.0	357.3	343.6	300.8	257.6	214.8	172.0	166.2
	525	532.5	434.8	376.5	355.0	251.0	205.0	236.7	167.3	136.6	72.5	25.6	4.0	357.3	343.6	300.8	257.6	214.8	172.0	166.2
	625	691.6	564.7	489.1	461.1	326.0	266.2	307.4	217.4	177.5	94.1	33.3	4.0	357.3	343.6	300.8	257.6	214.8	172.0	166.2
50.8 (2.0)	300	231.4	188.9	163.6	154.3	109.1	89.1	102.8	72.7	59.4	31.5	11.1	4.0	466.8	448.9	393.0	336.5	280.6	224.7	217.1
	375	338.2	276.1	239.1	225.4	159.4	130.2	150.3	106.3	86.8	46.0	16.3	4.2	466.8	448.9	393.0	336.5	280.6	224.7	217.1
	450	451.7	368.8	319.4	301.2	212.9	173.9	200.8	142.0	115.9	61.5	21.7	4.3	466.8	448.9	393.0	336.5	280.6	224.7	217.1
	525	569.2	464.8	402.5	379.5	268.3	219.1	253.0	178.9	146.1	77.5	27.4	4.3	466.8	448.9	393.0	336.5	280.6	224.7	217.1
	625	739.4	603.7	522.8	492.9	348.6	284.6	328.6	232.4	189.7	100.6	35.6	4.3	466.8	448.9	393.0	336.5	280.6	224.7	217.1

Table 12.6(B) Factored resistance for Single Cast-In Anchors Subject to Shear Loads (f'c = 30 MPa)[1,2,3,5]

| | | V_{sr} - Shear Strength of Anchor (kN) f_{ut} - for design purpose[4] (MPa) | | | | | | | | V_{cbr} - Shear Breakout (kN)[5,6,7,8,9] | | | | | | | | | | |
| | | | | | | | | | 38 mm cover | $h = h_{ef}$[10] | | $c_1 = 11$ | | | $h = 1.5\,h_{ef}$, $c_1 = 11,12$ | | | $h = 2.25\,h_{ef}$, $c_1 = 11,12$ | | |
d_o mm (in)	h_{ef} mm	400	414	517	620	724	827	860		$0.25h_{ef}$	$0.5h_{ef}$	h_{ef}	$1.5h_{ef}$	$3h_{ef}$	h_{ef}	$1.5h_{ef}$	$3h_{ef}$	h_{ef}	$1.5h_{ef}$	$3h_{ef}$
6.35 (0.25)	50	3.4	3.5	4.4	5.2	6.1	7.0	7.3	1.6	NP	NP	1.9	2.3	3.2	2.8	3.4	4.8	5.1	5.9	7.2
	75	3.4	3.5	4.4	5.2	6.1	7.0	7.3	1.8	NP	NP	3.4	4.2	5.9	5.1	6.3	8.9	9.4	10.9	13.3
	100	3.4	3.5	4.4	5.2	6.1	7.0	7.3	1.8	NP	2.8	5.3	6.4	9.1	7.9	9.7	13.7	14.5	16.7	20.5
	125	3.4	3.5	4.4	5.2	6.1	7.0	7.3	1.8	NP	3.9	7.3	9.0	12.7	11.0	13.5	19.1	20.2	23.4	28.6
	150	3.4	3.5	4.4	5.2	6.1	7.0	7.3	1.8	NP	5.1	9.7	11.8	16.7	14.5	17.7	25.1	26.6	30.7	37.6
9.525 (0.375)	50	7.6	7.9	9.8	11.8	13.8	15.7	16.3	1.8	NP	NP	2.1	2.6	3.6	3.1	3.8	5.4	5.8	6.7	8.2
	75	7.6	7.9	9.8	11.8	13.8	15.7	16.3	2.3	NP	NP	4.2	5.1	7.2	6.3	7.7	10.8	11.5	13.3	16.2
	100	7.6	7.9	9.8	11.8	13.8	15.7	16.3	2.3	NP	3.4	6.4	7.9	11.2	9.7	11.8	16.7	17.7	20.5	25.1
	125	7.6	7.9	9.8	11.8	13.8	15.7	16.3	2.3	NP	4.8	9.0	11.0	15.6	13.5	16.5	23.4	24.8	28.6	35.1
	150	7.6	7.9	9.8	11.8	13.8	15.7	16.3	2.3	NP	6.3	11.8	14.5	20.5	17.7	21.7	30.7	32.6	37.6	46.1
12.7 (0.5)	50	13.5	14.0	17.5	21.0	24.5	28.0	29.1	2.0	NP	NP	2.3	2.8	4.0	3.4	4.2	5.9	6.3	7.3	8.9
	75	13.5	14.0	17.5	21.0	24.5	28.0	29.1	2.5	NP	NP	4.5	5.6	7.9	6.8	8.4	11.8	12.5	14.5	17.7
	100	13.5	14.0	17.5	21.0	24.5	28.0	29.1	2.6	NP	3.9	7.4	9.1	12.8	11.1	13.6	19.3	20.4	23.6	28.9
	125	13.5	14.0	17.5	21.0	24.5	28.0	29.1	2.6	NP	5.5	10.4	12.7	18.0	15.6	19.1	27.0	28.6	33.1	40.5
	150	13.5	14.0	17.5	21.0	24.5	28.0	29.1	2.6	NP	7.2	13.7	16.7	23.7	20.5	25.1	35.5	37.6	43.5	53.2
	175	13.5	14.0	17.5	21.0	24.5	28.0	29.1	2.6	3.2	9.1	17.2	21.1	29.8	25.8	31.6	44.7	47.4	54.8	67.1
	200	13.5	14.0	17.5	21.0	24.5	28.0	29.1	2.6	3.9	11.2	21.0	25.8	36.4	31.5	38.6	54.6	58.0	66.9	82.0
15.875 (0.625)	75	21.2	22.0	27.4	32.9	38.4	43.9	45.6	2.6	NP	NP	4.9	6.0	8.4	7.3	8.9	12.6	13.4	15.5	18.9
	100	21.2	22.0	27.4	32.9	38.4	43.9	45.6	2.8	NP	4.2	7.9	9.7	13.7	11.9	14.6	20.6	21.8	25.2	30.9
	125	21.2	22.0	27.4	32.9	38.4	43.9	45.6	2.9	NP	6.1	11.6	14.2	20.1	17.4	21.3	30.1	31.9	36.9	45.1
	150	21.2	22.0	27.4	32.9	38.4	43.9	45.6	2.9	NP	8.1	15.3	18.7	26.5	22.9	28.1	39.7	42.1	48.6	59.5
	175	21.2	22.0	27.4	32.9	38.4	43.9	45.6	2.9	3.6	10.2	19.2	23.6	33.3	28.9	35.4	50.0	53.0	61.2	75.0
	200	21.2	22.0	27.4	32.9	38.4	43.9	45.6	2.9	4.4	12.5	23.5	28.8	40.7	35.3	43.2	61.1	64.8	74.8	91.6
	225	21.2	22.0	27.4	32.9	38.4	43.9	45.6	2.9	5.3	14.9	28.1	34.4	48.6	42.1	51.5	72.9	77.3	89.3	109.3
	250	21.2	22.0	27.4	32.9	38.4	43.9	45.6	2.9	6.2	17.4	32.9	40.2	56.9	49.3	60.4	85.4	90.6	104.6	128.1
19.05 (0.75)	100	30.5	31.6	39.5	47.3	55.3	63.1	65.7	2.9	NP	4.4	8.4	10.3	14.5	12.6	15.4	21.7	23.1	26.6	32.6
	125	30.5	31.6	39.5	47.3	55.3	63.1	65.7	3.1	NP	6.5	12.2	15.0	21.2	18.3	22.5	31.8	33.7	38.9	47.7
	150	30.5	31.6	39.5	47.3	55.3	63.1	65.7	3.2	NP	8.8	16.7	20.4	28.9	25.0	30.6	43.3	46.0	53.1	65.0
	175	30.5	31.6	39.5	47.3	55.3	63.1	65.7	3.2	4.0	11.2	21.1	25.8	36.5	31.6	38.7	54.8	58.1	67.1	82.2
	200	30.5	31.6	39.5	47.3	55.3	63.1	65.7	3.2	4.8	13.7	25.8	31.5	44.6	38.6	47.3	66.9	71.0	82.0	100.4
	225	30.5	31.6	39.5	47.3	55.3	63.1	65.7	3.2	5.8	16.3	30.7	37.6	53.2	46.1	56.5	79.9	84.7	97.8	119.8
	250	30.5	31.6	39.5	47.3	55.3	63.1	65.7	3.2	6.7	19.1	36.0	44.1	62.4	54.0	66.1	93.5	99.2	114.5	140.3
	300	30.5	31.6	39.5	47.3	55.3	63.1	65.7	3.2	8.9	25.1	47.3	58.0	82.0	71.0	86.9	122.9	130.4	150.6	184.4
22.225 (0.875)	100	41.5	43.0	53.7	64.4	75.2	85.9	89.3	3.1	NP	4.6	8.8	10.7	15.2	13.2	16.1	22.8	24.2	27.9	34.2
	150	41.5	43.0	53.7	64.4	75.2	85.9	89.3	3.3	NP	9.3	17.5	21.4	30.3	26.2	32.1	45.4	48.1	55.6	68.1
	200	41.5	43.0	53.7	64.4	75.2	85.9	89.3	3.5	5.2	14.8	27.8	34.1	48.2	41.7	51.1	72.3	76.7	88.5	108.4
	300	41.5	43.0	53.7	64.4	75.2	85.9	89.3	3.5	9.6	27.1	51.1	62.6	88.5	76.7	93.9	132.8	140.9	162.6	199.2
	375	41.5	43.0	53.7	64.4	75.2	85.9	89.3	3.5	13.4	37.9	71.4	87.5	123.7	107.1	131.2	185.6	196.8	227.3	278.4
	450	41.5	43.0	53.7	64.4	75.2	85.9	89.3	3.5	17.6	49.8	93.9	115.0	162.6	140.9	172.5	244.0	258.8	298.8	365.9
	625	41.5	43.0	53.7	64.4	75.2	85.9	89.3	3.5	28.8	81.5	153.7	188.2	266.2	230.5	282.4	399.3	423.5	489.1	599.0

		70.9	57.9	50.1	47.2	33.4	27.3	31.5	22.3	18.2	9.6	NP	3.5	116.6	112.1	98.2	84.1	70.1	56.1	54.2
25.4 (1.0)	150	70.9	57.9	50.1	47.2	33.4	27.3	31.5	22.3	18.2	9.6	NP	3.5	116.6	112.1	98.2	84.1	70.1	56.1	54.2
	225	138.3	112.9	97.8	92.2	65.2	53.2	61.5	43.5	35.5	18.8	6.7	3.7	116.6	112.1	98.2	84.1	70.1	56.1	54.2
	300	212.9	173.9	150.6	142.0	100.4	82.0	94.6	66.9	54.6	29.0	10.2	3.7	116.6	112.1	98.2	84.1	70.1	56.1	54.2
	375	297.6	243.0	210.4	198.4	140.3	114.5	132.3	93.5	76.4	40.5	14.3	3.7	116.6	112.1	98.2	84.1	70.1	56.1	54.2
	450	391.2	319.4	276.6	260.8	184.4	150.6	173.9	122.9	100.4	53.2	18.8	3.7	116.6	112.1	98.2	84.1	70.1	56.1	54.2
	525	493.0	402.5	348.6	328.7	232.4	189.7	219.1	154.9	126.5	67.1	23.7	3.7	116.6	112.1	98.2	84.1	70.1	56.1	54.2
	625	640.3	522.8	452.8	426.9	301.9	246.5	284.6	201.2	164.3	87.1	30.8	3.7	116.6	112.1	98.2	84.1	70.1	56.1	54.2
29 (1.125)	150	73.4	59.9	51.9	48.9	34.6	28.3	32.6	23.1	18.8	10.0	NP	3.6	147.7	142.0	124.3	106.5	88.8	71.1	68.7
	225	146.2	119.4	103.4	97.5	68.9	56.3	65.0	46.0	37.5	19.9	7.0	3.9	147.7	142.0	124.3	106.5	88.8	71.1	68.7
	300	225.9	184.4	159.7	150.6	106.5	86.9	100.4	71.0	58.0	30.7	10.9	3.9	147.7	142.0	124.3	106.5	88.8	71.1	68.7
	375	315.7	257.7	223.2	210.4	148.8	121.5	140.3	99.2	81.0	43.0	15.2	3.9	147.7	142.0	124.3	106.5	88.8	71.1	68.7
	450	414.9	338.8	293.4	276.6	195.6	159.7	184.4	130.4	106.5	56.5	20.0	3.9	147.7	142.0	124.3	106.5	88.8	71.1	68.7
	525	522.9	426.9	369.7	348.6	246.5	201.3	232.4	164.3	134.2	71.2	25.2	3.9	147.7	142.0	124.3	106.5	88.8	71.1	68.7
	625	679.2	554.5	480.3	452.8	320.2	261.4	301.9	213.4	174.3	92.4	32.7	3.9	147.7	142.0	124.3	106.5	88.8	71.1	68.7
31.75 (1.25)	150	75.8	61.9	53.6	50.5	35.7	29.2	33.7	23.8	19.4	10.3	NP	3.7	182.3	175.3	153.5	131.4	109.6	87.7	84.8
	225	150.9	123.2	106.7	100.8	71.2	58.1	67.1	47.4	38.7	20.5	7.3	4.0	182.3	175.3	153.5	131.4	109.6	87.7	84.8
	300	238.1	194.4	168.3	158.7	112.2	91.6	105.8	74.8	61.1	32.4	11.5	4.1	182.3	175.3	153.5	131.4	109.6	87.7	84.8
	375	332.7	271.7	235.3	221.8	156.8	128.1	147.9	104.6	85.4	45.3	16.0	4.1	182.3	175.3	153.5	131.4	109.6	87.7	84.8
	450	437.4	357.1	309.3	291.6	206.2	168.3	194.4	137.5	112.2	59.5	21.0	4.1	182.3	175.3	153.5	131.4	109.6	87.7	84.8
	525	551.2	450.0	389.7	367.4	259.8	212.1	245.0	173.2	141.4	75.0	26.5	4.1	182.3	175.3	153.5	131.4	109.6	87.7	84.8
	625	715.9	584.5	506.2	477.3	337.5	275.6	318.2	225.0	183.7	97.4	34.4	4.1	182.3	175.3	153.5	131.4	109.6	87.7	84.8
34.925 (1.375)	150	78.0	63.7	55.1	52.0	36.7	30.0	34.6	24.5	20.0	10.6	NP	3.8	220.6	212.1	185.7	159.0	132.6	106.2	102.6
	225	155.3	126.8	109.8	103.5	73.2	59.8	69.0	48.8	39.9	21.1	7.5	4.1	220.6	212.1	185.7	159.0	132.6	106.2	102.6
	300	249.7	203.9	176.6	166.5	117.7	96.1	111.0	78.5	64.1	34.0	12.0	4.3	220.6	212.1	185.7	159.0	132.6	106.2	102.6
	375	349.0	284.9	246.8	232.6	164.5	134.3	155.1	109.7	89.5	47.5	16.8	4.3	220.6	212.1	185.7	159.0	132.6	106.2	102.6
	450	458.7	374.6	324.4	305.8	216.2	176.6	203.9	144.2	117.7	62.4	22.1	4.3	220.6	212.1	185.7	159.0	132.6	106.2	102.6
	525	578.1	472.0	408.8	385.4	272.5	222.5	256.9	181.7	148.3	78.7	27.8	4.3	220.6	212.1	185.7	159.0	132.6	106.2	102.6
	625	750.9	613.1	530.9	500.6	354.0	289.0	333.7	236.0	192.7	102.2	36.1	4.3	220.6	212.1	185.7	159.0	132.6	106.2	102.6
38.1 (1.5)	300	260.0	212.3	183.8	173.3	122.6	100.1	115.5	81.7	66.7	35.4	12.5	4.5	262.5	252.4	221.0	189.2	157.8	126.4	122.1
	375	364.5	297.6	257.7	243.0	171.8	140.3	162.0	114.5	93.5	49.6	17.5	4.5	262.5	252.4	221.0	189.2	157.8	126.4	122.1
	450	479.1	391.2	338.8	319.4	225.9	184.4	212.9	150.6	122.9	65.2	23.1	4.5	262.5	252.4	221.0	189.2	157.8	126.4	122.1
	525	603.8	493.0	426.9	402.5	284.6	232.4	268.3	189.7	154.9	82.2	29.0	4.5	262.5	252.4	221.0	189.2	157.8	126.4	122.1
	625	784.2	640.3	554.5	522.8	369.7	301.9	348.6	246.5	201.2	106.7	37.7	4.5	262.5	252.4	221.0	189.2	157.8	126.4	122.1
44.45 (1.75)	300	272.3	222.3	192.5	181.5	128.4	104.8	121.0	85.6	69.9	37.1	13.1	4.7	357.3	343.6	300.8	257.6	214.8	172.0	166.2
	375	393.7	321.4	278.4	262.5	185.6	151.5	175.0	123.7	101.0	53.6	18.9	4.9	357.3	343.6	300.8	257.6	214.8	172.0	166.2
	450	517.5	422.6	365.9	345.0	244.0	199.2	230.0	162.6	132.8	70.4	24.9	4.9	357.3	343.6	300.8	257.6	214.8	172.0	166.2
	525	652.1	532.5	461.1	434.8	307.4	251.0	289.8	205.0	167.3	88.7	31.4	4.9	357.3	343.6	300.8	257.6	214.8	172.0	166.2
	625	847.1	691.6	599.0	564.7	399.3	326.0	376.5	266.2	217.4	115.3	40.8	4.9	357.3	343.6	300.8	257.6	214.8	172.0	166.2
50.8 (2.0)	300	283.4	231.4	200.4	188.9	133.6	109.1	126.0	89.1	72.7	38.6	13.6	4.9	466.8	448.9	393.0	336.5	280.6	224.7	217.1
	375	414.2	338.2	292.9	276.1	195.2	159.4	184.1	130.2	106.3	56.4	19.9	5.1	466.8	448.9	393.0	336.5	280.6	224.7	217.1
	450	553.3	451.7	391.2	368.8	260.8	212.9	245.9	173.9	142.0	75.3	26.6	5.2	466.8	448.9	393.0	336.5	280.6	224.7	217.1
	525	697.2	569.2	493.0	464.8	328.7	268.3	309.9	219.1	178.9	94.9	33.5	5.2	466.8	448.9	393.0	336.5	280.6	224.7	217.1
	625	905.6	739.4	640.3	603.7	426.9	348.6	402.5	284.6	232.4	123.2	43.6	5.2	466.8	448.9	393.0	336.5	280.6	224.7	217.1

Table 12.6(C) Factored resistance for Single Cast-In Anchors Subject to Shear Loads (f'c = 40 MPa)[1,2,3,5]

d_o mm (in)	h_{ef} mm	V_{sr} 400	414	517	620	724	827	860	38 mm cover	0.25h_{ef}	0.5h_{ef}	h_{ef}	1.5h_{ef}	3h_{ef}	h_{ef}	1.5h_{ef}	3h_{ef}	h_{ef}	1.5h_{ef}	3h_{ef}
		V_{sr} - Shear Strength of Anchor (kN), f_{ut} - for design purpose[4] (MPa)							V_{cbr} - Shear Breakout (kN)[5,6,7,8,9]	$h = h_{ef}$[10], $c_1 = 11$					$h = 1.5h_{ef}$, $c_1 = 11,12$			$h = 2.25h_{ef}$, $c_1 = 11,12$		
6.35 (0.25)	50	3.4	3.5	4.4	5.2	6.1	7.0	7.3	1.9	NP	NP	2.1	2.6	3.7	3.2	3.9	5.6	5.9	6.8	8.3
	75	3.4	3.5	4.4	5.2	6.1	7.0	7.3	2.1	NP	NP	3.9	4.8	6.8	5.9	7.2	10.2	10.9	12.5	15.4
	100	3.4	3.5	4.4	5.2	6.1	7.0	7.3	2.1	NP	3.2	6.1	7.4	10.5	9.1	11.2	15.8	16.7	19.3	23.7
	125	3.4	3.5	4.4	5.2	6.1	7.0	7.3	2.1	NP	4.5	8.5	10.4	14.7	12.7	15.6	22.0	23.4	27.0	33.1
	150	3.4	3.5	4.4	5.2	6.1	7.0	7.3	2.1	NP	5.9	11.2	13.7	19.3	16.7	20.5	29.0	30.7	35.5	43.5
9.525 (0.375)	50	7.6	7.9	9.8	11.8	13.8	15.7	16.3	2.1	NP	NP	2.4	3.0	4.2	3.6	4.4	6.3	6.7	7.7	9.4
	75	7.6	7.9	9.8	11.8	13.8	15.7	16.3	2.6	NP	NP	4.8	5.9	8.3	7.2	8.8	12.5	13.3	15.3	18.8
	100	7.6	7.9	9.8	11.8	13.8	15.7	16.3	2.6	NP	3.9	7.4	9.1	12.9	11.2	13.7	19.3	20.5	23.7	29.0
	125	7.6	7.9	9.8	11.8	13.8	15.7	16.3	2.6	NP	5.5	10.4	12.7	18.0	15.6	19.1	27.0	28.6	33.1	40.5
	150	7.6	7.9	9.8	11.8	13.8	15.7	16.3	2.6	NP	7.2	13.7	16.7	23.7	20.5	25.1	35.5	37.6	43.5	53.2
12.7 (0.5)	50	13.5	14.0	17.5	21.0	24.5	28.0	29.1	2.3	NP	NP	2.6	3.2	4.6	4.0	4.8	6.8	7.3	8.4	10.3
	75	13.5	14.0	17.5	21.0	24.5	28.0	29.1	2.8	NP	NP	5.2	6.4	9.1	7.9	9.6	13.6	14.5	16.7	20.5
	100	13.5	14.0	17.5	21.0	24.5	28.0	29.1	3.0	NP	4.5	8.6	10.5	14.8	12.8	15.7	22.2	23.6	27.2	33.4
	125	13.5	14.0	17.5	21.0	24.5	28.0	29.1	3.0	NP	6.4	12.0	14.7	20.8	18.0	22.0	31.2	33.1	38.2	46.8
	150	13.5	14.0	17.5	21.0	24.5	28.0	29.1	3.0	NP	8.4	15.8	19.3	27.3	23.7	29.0	41.0	43.5	50.2	61.5
	175	13.5	14.0	17.5	21.0	24.5	28.0	29.1	3.0	3.7	10.5	19.9	24.3	34.4	29.8	36.5	51.6	54.8	63.2	77.5
	200	13.5	14.0	17.5	21.0	24.5	28.0	29.1	3.0	4.6	12.9	24.3	29.7	42.1	36.4	44.6	63.1	66.9	77.3	94.6
15.875 (0.625)	75	21.2	22.0	27.4	32.9	38.4	43.9	45.6	3.0	NP	NP	5.6	6.9	9.7	8.4	10.3	14.6	15.5	17.9	21.9
	100	21.2	22.0	27.4	32.9	38.4	43.9	45.6	3.2	NP	4.9	9.2	11.2	15.9	13.7	16.8	23.8	25.2	29.1	35.7
	125	21.2	22.0	27.4	32.9	38.4	43.9	45.6	3.4	NP	7.1	13.4	16.4	23.2	20.1	24.6	34.7	36.9	42.6	52.1
	150	21.2	22.0	27.4	32.9	38.4	43.9	45.6	3.4	NP	9.4	17.6	21.6	30.5	26.5	32.4	45.8	48.6	56.1	68.7
	175	21.2	22.0	27.4	32.9	38.4	43.9	45.6	3.4	4.2	11.8	22.2	27.2	38.5	33.3	40.8	57.7	61.2	70.7	86.6
	200	21.2	22.0	27.4	32.9	38.4	43.9	45.6	3.4	5.1	14.4	27.2	33.3	47.0	40.7	49.9	70.5	74.8	86.4	105.8
	225	21.2	22.0	27.4	32.9	38.4	43.9	45.6	3.4	6.1	17.2	32.4	39.7	56.1	48.6	59.5	84.2	89.3	103.1	126.3
	250	21.2	22.0	27.4	32.9	38.4	43.9	45.6	3.4	7.1	20.1	37.9	46.5	65.7	56.9	69.7	98.6	104.6	120.7	147.9
19.05 (0.75)	100	30.5	31.6	39.5	47.3	55.3	63.1	65.7	3.4	NP	5.1	9.7	11.8	16.7	14.5	17.8	25.1	26.6	30.8	37.7
	125	30.5	31.6	39.5	47.3	55.3	63.1	65.7	3.6	NP	7.5	14.1	17.3	24.5	21.2	25.9	36.7	38.9	44.9	55.0
	150	30.5	31.6	39.5	47.3	55.3	63.1	65.7	3.7	NP	10.2	19.3	23.6	33.4	28.9	35.4	50.0	53.1	61.3	75.0
	175	30.5	31.6	39.5	47.3	55.3	63.1	65.7	3.7	4.6	12.9	24.3	29.8	42.2	36.5	44.7	63.2	67.1	77.5	94.9
	200	30.5	31.6	39.5	47.3	55.3	63.1	65.7	3.7	5.6	15.8	29.7	36.4	51.5	44.6	54.6	77.3	82.0	94.6	115.9
	225	30.5	31.6	39.5	47.3	55.3	63.1	65.7	3.7	6.7	18.8	35.5	43.5	61.5	53.2	65.2	92.2	97.8	112.9	138.3
	250	30.5	31.6	39.5	47.3	55.3	63.1	65.7	3.7	7.8	22.0	41.6	50.9	72.0	62.4	76.4	108.0	114.5	132.3	162.0
	300	30.5	31.6	39.5	47.3	55.3	63.1	65.7	3.7	10.2	29.0	54.6	66.9	94.6	82.0	100.4	142.0	150.6	173.9	212.9
22.225 (0.875)	100	41.5	43.0	53.7	64.4	75.2	85.9	89.3	3.6	NP	5.4	10.1	12.4	17.5	15.2	18.6	26.3	27.9	32.2	39.5
	150	41.5	43.0	53.7	64.4	75.2	85.9	89.3	3.9	NP	10.7	20.2	24.7	34.9	30.3	37.1	52.4	55.6	64.2	78.6
	200	41.5	43.0	53.7	64.4	75.2	85.9	89.3	4.0	6.0	17.0	32.1	39.3	55.6	48.2	59.0	83.5	88.5	102.2	125.2
	300	41.5	43.0	53.7	64.4	75.2	85.9	89.3	4.0	11.1	31.3	59.0	72.3	102.2	88.5	108.4	153.3	162.6	187.8	230.0
	375	41.5	43.0	53.7	64.4	75.2	85.9	89.3	4.0	15.5	43.7	82.5	101.0	142.9	123.7	151.5	214.3	227.3	262.5	321.4
	450	41.5	43.0	53.7	64.4	75.2	85.9	89.3	4.0	20.3	57.5	108.4	132.8	187.8	162.6	199.2	281.7	298.8	345.0	422.6
	625	41.5	43.0	53.7	64.4	75.2	85.9	89.3	4.0	33.3	94.1	177.5	217.4	307.4	266.2	326.0	461.1	489.1	564.7	691.6

Bar	Size																			
25.4 (1.0)	150	81.8	66.8	57.9	54.5	38.6	31.5	36.4	25.7	21.0	11.1	NP	4.0	116.6	112.1	98.2	84.1	70.1	56.1	54.2
	225	159.7	130.4	112.9	106.5	75.3	61.5	71.0	50.2	41.0	21.7	7.7	4.3	116.6	112.1	98.2	84.1	70.1	56.1	54.2
	300	245.9	200.8	173.9	163.9	115.9	94.6	109.3	77.3	63.1	33.5	11.8	4.3	116.6	112.1	98.2	84.1	70.1	56.1	54.2
	375	343.6	280.6	243.0	229.1	162.0	132.3	152.7	108.0	88.2	46.8	16.5	4.3	116.6	112.1	98.2	84.1	70.1	56.1	54.2
	450	451.7	368.8	319.4	301.2	212.9	173.9	200.8	142.0	115.9	61.5	21.7	4.3	116.6	112.1	98.2	84.1	70.1	56.1	54.2
	525	569.2	464.8	402.5	379.5	268.3	219.1	253.0	178.9	146.1	77.5	27.4	4.3	116.6	112.1	98.2	84.1	70.1	56.1	54.2
	625	739.4	603.7	522.8	492.9	348.6	284.6	328.6	232.4	189.7	100.6	35.6	4.3	116.6	112.1	98.2	84.1	70.1	56.1	54.2
29 (1.125)	150	84.8	69.2	59.9	56.5	40.0	32.6	37.7	26.6	21.7	11.5	NP	4.2	147.7	142.0	124.3	106.5	88.8	71.1	68.7
	225	168.9	137.9	119.4	112.6	79.6	65.0	75.0	53.1	43.3	23.0	8.1	4.5	147.7	142.0	124.3	106.5	88.8	71.1	68.7
	300	260.8	212.9	184.4	173.9	122.9	100.4	115.9	82.0	66.9	35.5	12.5	4.5	147.7	142.0	124.3	106.5	88.8	71.1	68.7
	375	364.5	297.6	257.7	243.0	171.8	140.3	162.0	114.5	93.5	49.6	17.5	4.5	147.7	142.0	124.3	106.5	88.8	71.1	68.7
	450	479.1	391.2	338.8	319.4	225.9	184.4	212.9	150.6	122.9	65.2	23.1	4.5	147.7	142.0	124.3	106.5	88.8	71.1	68.7
	525	603.8	493.0	426.9	402.5	284.6	232.4	268.3	189.7	154.9	82.2	29.0	4.5	147.7	142.0	124.3	106.5	88.8	71.1	68.7
	625	784.2	640.3	554.5	522.8	369.7	301.9	348.6	246.5	201.2	106.7	37.7	4.5	147.7	142.0	124.3	106.5	88.8	71.1	68.7
31.75 (1.25)	150	87.5	71.4	61.9	58.3	41.2	33.7	38.9	27.5	22.4	11.9	NP	4.3	182.3	175.3	153.5	131.4	109.6	87.7	84.8
	225	174.3	142.3	123.2	116.2	82.2	67.1	77.5	54.8	44.7	23.7	8.4	4.7	182.3	175.3	153.5	131.4	109.6	87.7	84.8
	300	274.9	224.5	194.4	183.3	129.6	105.8	122.2	86.4	70.5	37.4	13.2	4.8	182.3	175.3	153.5	131.4	109.6	87.7	84.8
	375	384.2	313.7	271.7	256.1	181.1	147.9	170.8	120.7	98.6	52.3	18.5	4.8	182.3	175.3	153.5	131.4	109.6	87.7	84.8
	450	505.0	412.4	357.1	336.7	238.1	194.4	224.5	158.7	129.6	68.7	24.3	4.8	182.3	175.3	153.5	131.4	109.6	87.7	84.8
	525	636.4	519.6	450.0	424.3	300.0	245.0	282.9	200.0	163.3	86.6	30.6	4.8	182.3	175.3	153.5	131.4	109.6	87.7	84.8
	625	826.7	675.0	584.5	551.1	389.7	318.2	367.4	259.8	212.1	112.5	39.8	4.8	182.3	175.3	153.5	131.4	109.6	87.7	84.8
34.925 (1.375)	150	90.0	73.5	63.7	60.0	42.4	34.6	40.0	28.3	23.1	12.2	NP	4.4	220.6	212.1	185.7	159.0	132.6	106.2	102.6
	225	179.3	146.4	126.8	119.6	84.5	69.0	79.7	56.4	46.0	24.4	8.6	4.8	220.6	212.1	185.7	159.0	132.6	106.2	102.6
	300	288.3	235.4	203.9	192.2	135.9	111.0	128.1	90.6	74.0	39.2	13.9	5.0	220.6	212.1	185.7	159.0	132.6	106.2	102.6
	375	403.0	329.0	284.9	268.6	190.0	155.1	179.1	126.6	103.4	54.8	19.4	5.0	220.6	212.1	185.7	159.0	132.6	106.2	102.6
	450	529.7	432.5	374.6	353.1	249.7	203.9	235.4	166.5	135.9	72.1	25.5	5.0	220.6	212.1	185.7	159.0	132.6	106.2	102.6
	525	667.5	545.0	472.0	445.0	314.7	256.9	296.7	209.8	171.3	90.8	32.1	5.0	220.6	212.1	185.7	159.0	132.6	106.2	102.6
	625	867.0	707.9	613.1	578.0	408.7	333.7	385.3	272.5	222.5	118.0	41.7	5.0	220.6	212.1	185.7	159.0	132.6	106.2	102.6
38.1 (1.5)	300	300.2	245.1	212.3	200.1	141.5	115.5	133.4	94.3	77.0	40.9	14.4	5.2	262.5	252.4	221.0	189.2	157.8	126.4	122.1
	375	420.9	343.6	297.6	280.6	198.4	162.0	187.1	132.3	108.0	57.3	20.2	5.2	262.5	252.4	221.0	189.2	157.8	126.4	122.1
	450	553.3	451.7	391.2	368.8	260.8	212.9	245.9	173.9	142.0	75.3	26.6	5.2	262.5	252.4	221.0	189.2	157.8	126.4	122.1
	525	697.2	569.2	493.0	464.8	328.7	268.3	309.9	219.1	178.9	94.9	33.5	5.2	262.5	252.4	221.0	189.2	157.8	126.4	122.1
	625	905.6	739.4	640.3	603.7	426.9	348.6	402.5	284.6	232.4	123.2	43.6	5.2	262.5	252.4	221.0	189.2	157.8	126.4	122.1
44.45 (1.75)	300	314.4	256.7	222.3	209.6	148.2	121.0	139.7	98.8	80.7	42.8	15.1	5.5	357.3	343.6	300.8	257.6	214.8	172.0	166.2
	375	454.6	371.2	321.4	303.1	214.3	175.0	202.0	142.9	116.6	61.9	21.9	5.6	357.3	343.6	300.8	257.6	214.8	172.0	166.2
	450	597.6	487.9	422.6	398.4	281.7	230.0	265.6	187.8	153.3	81.3	28.8	5.6	357.3	343.6	300.8	257.6	214.8	172.0	166.2
	525	753.0	614.9	532.5	502.0	355.0	289.8	334.7	236.7	193.2	102.5	36.2	5.6	357.3	343.6	300.8	257.6	214.8	172.0	166.2
	625	978.1	798.6	691.6	652.1	461.1	376.5	434.7	307.4	251.0	133.1	47.1	5.6	357.3	343.6	300.8	257.6	214.8	172.0	166.2
50.8 (2.0)	300	327.3	267.2	231.4	218.2	154.3	126.0	145.4	102.8	84.0	44.5	15.7	5.7	466.8	448.9	393.0	336.5	280.6	224.7	217.1
	375	478.2	390.5	338.2	318.8	225.4	184.1	212.5	150.3	122.7	65.1	23.0	5.9	466.8	448.9	393.0	336.5	280.6	224.7	217.1
	450	638.8	521.6	451.7	425.9	301.2	245.9	283.9	200.8	163.9	86.9	30.7	6.0	466.8	448.9	393.0	336.5	280.6	224.7	217.1
	525	805.0	657.3	569.2	536.7	379.5	309.9	357.8	253.0	206.6	109.6	38.7	6.0	466.8	448.9	393.0	336.5	280.6	224.7	217.1
	625	1045.7	853.8	739.4	697.1	492.9	402.5	464.7	328.6	268.3	142.3	50.3	6.0	466.8	448.9	393.0	336.5	280.6	224.7	217.1

13

By Gerry Weiler

Tilt-up Concrete Wall Panels

13

Tilt-up

13.1   Introduction

Tilt-up concrete buildings have been constructed in Canada for over 40 years and have developed into the material of choice for commercial and industrial structures in many areas. The Canadian codes first addressed tilt-up concrete wall panels in CSA A23.3–94 Design of Concrete Structures. The latest edition, CSA A23.3–04, includes minor modifications to the provisions for tilt-up in Chapter 23, and has added new requirements for seismic design in Chapter 21.

Changes in NBCC 2005, Part 4 will have a significant effect on buildings using tilt-up panels, particularly for buildings in high-risk seismic areas.

This guide provides comprehensive design recommendations for tilt-up panels with vertical loading, transverse out-of-plane loading and in-plane shear. It also provides recommendations for panel connections, construction details and tolerances. Further development of this design standard is required in areas including:
- Service load deflections
- Analysis and design for seismic requirements

13.2   Concrete Wall Panel Analysis Method

Tilt-up concrete wall panels are most often used as load bearing wall elements spanning vertically from the floor slab to the roof. Bending moments induced by out-of-plane transverse loads (wind or seismic) may be significantly greater than those caused by eccentric axial loads. The P–Δ effects due to axial loads will increase these moments. Limit states failure of a slender wall panel is defined as the point where the maximum factored bending moment at or near mid height exceeds the resisting moment of the concrete section.

The maximum bending moment can be separated into two components:
- Primary moment due to applied loadings.
- Secondary moment due to P–Δ deflections.

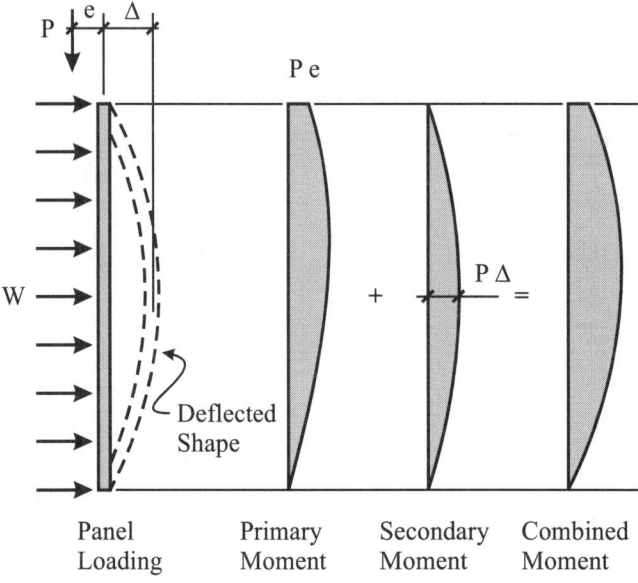

| Panel | Primary | Secondary | Combined |
| Loading | Moment | Moment | Moment |

Primary moments are determined from a conventional static analysis. In most cases, it is the moment at mid height that is of concern since this is where maximum bending moment and P–Δ deflections and eventual failure will normally occur.

Secondary moments are the result of an axial load, P, acting on a deflected shape, hence the term P–Δ moments. The deflection of a wall panel is dependent on its bending stiffness. For reinforced concrete, this bending stiffness can be difficult to evaluate since it varies with a number of parameters, including:

- Wall thickness
- Concrete compressive strength
- Concrete tensile strength
- Reinforcing steel quantities
- Location of reinforcing steel in the wall section
- Applied axial load
- Bending curvature

The bending properties of a concrete section behave in an elasto-plastic manner. Both strength and stiffness will vary with changes in axial compression and bending curvature. In most cases, however, the main concern is the failure condition due to factored loads, where the resisting moment and bending stiffness can be determined with reasonable accuracy by simple calculations.

13.2.1   Moment Magnifier for P–Δ Analysis

CSA A23.3, Chapter 23 has adopted the moment magnifier method of analysis for evaluation of the P–Δ effects in slender concrete walls subjected to the combined effects of axial and out-of-plane lateral loads. This method is poorly understood by most designers, primarily because of the complex way it has been employed in various codes for the design of slender columns in concrete, steel and wood. The following is a brief summary of the derivation for the moment magnifier equation.

Maximum bending moment at panel mid-height is given by:

$$M_{max} = M_0 + P\,\Delta_{max}$$

where

M_{max} =   maximum moment including P–Δ effects

M_0 =   maximum moment not including P–Δ effects

P =   applied axial load

Δ_{max} =   maximum panel deflection at mid height

The relation between maximum bending moment and deflection is:

$$\Delta_{max} = \frac{5}{48}\frac{\ell^2\,M_{max}}{EI} = \frac{M_{max}}{K_b}$$

$$K_b = \frac{M_{max}}{\Delta_{max}} = \frac{48\,EI}{5\ell^2}$$

where

K_b =   Bending stiffness, expressed as a bending moment per unit of deflection

ℓ =   clear vertical span of the member

E =   Elastic Modulus

I =   Moment of inertia

The maximum moment, M_{max}, can now be written in the following form:

$$M_{max} = M_o + \frac{P\,M_{max}}{K_b}$$

Rearranging the parameters:

$$M_{max} = M_o \left\{ \frac{1}{1 - P/K_b} \right\} = M_o\,\delta$$

where

$$\delta = \frac{1}{1 - P/K_b} = \text{moment magnification factor}$$

Alternately, the maximum bending moment including P–Δ effects may be obtained by iteration of deflection calculations with applied axial and lateral loadings. The results obtained by either the iterative method or moment magnifier method will be identical as long as the loading conditions, panel geometry and assumptions for material properties are consistent.

13.2.2   Panel Bending Stiffness

The parameter K_b is used to define bending stiffness of the wall panel:

$$K_b = \frac{48\,EI}{5\,\ell^2} \qquad \text{(kN-m/m)}$$

Bending stiffness represents the maximum bending moment in the panel divided by the maximum deflection:

$$K_b = \frac{M_{max}}{\Delta_{max}}$$

Where the member is simply supported, the maximum moment will occur at or near mid-span. It is worthwhile to note that K_b is approximately equivalent to the more familiar Euler critical buckling load:

$$P_{cr} = \frac{\pi^2\,EI}{\ell^2}$$

Critical buckling capacity is a by-product of the P–Δ analysis and represents the maximum axial load that can be sustained by a pin ended slender column (or wall) in the absence of any other applied loadings. The factor $\pi^2 = 9.87$ defines a sinusoidal single curvature deflected shape due to an axial load applied with a small initiating eccentricity. The deflected shape for a beam subjected to a uniformly distributed transverse load would be parabolic and the appropriate factor would be $48/5 = 9.6$. This is considered to be more representative for tilt-up panels. P_{cr} is expressed as a force (kN), and K_b is expressed as a bending moment per unit deflection (kN–m/m).

This method of analysis assumes that the bending properties of the cross section are elastic. However, reinforced concrete sections do not behave elastically throughout the full range of flexural bending. Testing (ref 2) has shown that the calculated properties of the cracked concrete section at failure load levels provide accurate but somewhat conservative results for design of slender concrete walls such as employed in tilt-up construction. This was originally adopted by the Uniform Building Code in the 1990's, and is now the basis for design of tilt-up wall panels in

ACI 318 and CSA A23.3. The main limitation to this method is that it is only applicable where axial compression loads are relatively small or less than about 0.1 $A_g f'_c$. Typically, the axial loads on wall panels for most tilt-up buildings are well below this threshold.

13.2.3   CSA A23.3 Chapter 23 Requirements

The basic design equations given in Chapter 23 are:

$$M_f \quad = \quad M_b \, \delta_b \qquad\qquad\qquad\qquad (23\text{–}2)$$

and $\quad M_r \quad \geq \quad M_f \qquad\qquad\qquad\qquad (23\text{–}3)$

where

$\quad M_f \quad = \quad$ factored moment including P–Δ effects
$\quad M_b \quad = \quad$ factored moment not including P–Δ effects
$\quad M_r \quad = \quad$ factored resisting moment
$\quad \delta_b \quad = \quad$ moment magnification factor

When combined axial and transverse loadings are applied to a wall panel, the maximum moment can be calculated as follows:

$\quad M_f \quad = \quad$ Primary Moment + Secondary Moment

$\quad\quad\quad\quad = \quad M_b + P_f \Delta$

$$M_b \quad = \quad \frac{w_f \ell^2}{8} + P_{tf} \, \frac{e}{2} + (P_{wf} + P_{tf})\Delta_o$$

$\quad P_f \quad = \quad P_{wf} + P_{tf} =$ factored axial load at mid height
$\quad P_{wf} \quad = \quad$ factored panel weight above mid height
$\quad P_{tf} \quad = \quad$ factored axial load at the top of panel
$\quad e \quad = \quad$ axial load eccentricity at the top of the panel
$\quad w_f \quad = \quad$ factored lateral load
$\quad \Delta_0 \quad = \quad$ initial deflection at panel mid height
$\quad \Delta \quad = \quad$ maximum total deflection at mid height $= M_f / K_b$

When there are other forces contributing to the primary moment such as transverse point loads, these should also be included when computing M_b.

Clause 23.3.1.2 specifies an upper limit for axial load on the mid-height cross section:

$$\frac{P_{wf} + P_{tf}}{A_g} \quad < \quad .09 \, \phi_c \, f'_c \qquad\qquad\qquad\qquad (23\text{–}1)$$

The factored moment M_f can now be written in the following form:

$$M_f \quad = \quad M_b + \frac{P_f M_f}{K_{bf}} \quad = \quad M_b \left\{ \frac{1}{1 - P_f / K_{bf}} \right\} = \quad M_b \delta_b$$

$$\delta_b \quad = \quad \frac{1}{1 - P_f / K_{bf}} \quad = \quad \text{Moment magnification factor} \; \geq \; 1.0$$

Bending stiffness, K_{bf} is given by:

$$K_{bf} \quad = \quad \frac{48 \, E_c \, I_{cr}}{5 \, \ell^2} \quad (kN - m/m)$$

13

Tilt-up

ℓ =   unsupported vertical span of wall panel   (m)

E_c =   4500 $\sqrt{f'_c}$ (MPa)

I_{cr} =   cracked section moment of inertia   (mm^4)

$$I_{cr} = \frac{b\,c^3}{3} + \frac{E_s\,A_s\,(d-c)^2}{E_c}$$

A_s =   reinforcing steel area (mm^2)

E_s =   200,000 (MPa)

d =   reinforcing depth (mm); b =   width of section (mm)

$$a = \frac{A_s\,\phi_s\,f_y}{\alpha_1\,\phi_c\,f'_c\,b} \quad \text{and} \quad c = \frac{a}{\beta_1} \quad \text{(mm)}$$

α_1 =   .85 − .0015 f'_c ≥ 0.67   (10–1)

     =   .805   for 30 MPa concrete

β_1 =   .97 − .0025 f'_c ≥ 0.67   (10–2)

     =   .895   for 30 MPa concrete

ϕ_c =   0.65   and ϕ_s = 0.85,   See Clauses 8.4.2 and 8.4.3

For design of panels in buildings, it is necessary to apply strength resistance factors to account for material variations and workmanship. The factors ϕ_c and ϕ_s are used to modify the calculated strength of concrete and the steel reinforcement in accordance with Chapter 10 provisions. The value of ϕ_c has been increased to 0.65 from the previous value of 0.6 in CSA A23.3-94.

In addition, the bending stiffness must also be modified using the member resistance factor, ϕ_m as required by Clause 10.15.3.1. This effectively increases P–Δ magnification:

$$\delta_b = \frac{1}{1 - \dfrac{P_f}{\phi_m\,K_{bf}}} \geq 1.0$$

where

ϕ_m =   0.75

The magnitude of ϕ_m has been increased from the previous value of 0.65, in order to be consistent with Chapter 10 provisions for slender columns. The primary reason for applying this factor is to take into account the effect of construction tolerance variations on the bending stiffness. For example, a 140 mm panel with 15M @ 300 mm o/c centered in the panel would have a cracked section moment of inertia, I_{cr} as follows:

Assume:

f'_c =   30 MPa f_y =   400 MPa E_c = 24,650 MPa E_s = 200,000 MPa

b =   300 mm h =   140 mm d = 70 mm A_s = 200 mm^2

$$a = \frac{200 \times .85 \times 400}{.805 \times 0.65 \times 30 \times 300} = 14.44 \text{ mm}$$

$$c = \frac{14.44}{.895} = 16.1 \text{ mm}$$

$$I_{cr} = \frac{300 \times 16.1^3}{3} + \frac{200,000 \times 200\,(70 - 16.1)^2}{24,650} = (.42 + 4.71)\,10^6 = 5.13 \times 10^6 \text{ mm}^4$$

A reduction in d from 70 mm to 60 mm would result in a decrease in I_{cr}

$$I_{cr} \quad = \quad 3.54 \times 10^6 \ \ mm^4$$

$$\text{Reduction} \ = \ \frac{3.54}{5.13} \ = 0.69 \quad (31\%)$$

The resisting moment M_r is calculated by conventional methods defined in Chapter 10.

$$M_r \quad = \quad \phi_s \, A_{se} \, f_y \, (d - a/2) \ \geq \ M_f \tag{23–3}$$

A modification in the area of reinforcement is used to partially account for the increased bending moment resistance due to applied axial loads. The axial load at the critical section or panel mid height is used.

$$A_{se} \quad = \quad \frac{\phi_s \, A_s \, f_y \, + \, P_f}{\phi_s \, f_y}$$

It is noted that axial loads on the concrete section will also increase the bending stiffness, resulting in a subsequent reduction in mid-height deflection. The ACI 318 code has recognized this for design of tilt-up panels where the modified area of reinforcement is used in the evaluation of bending stiffness. However, CSA A23.3 does not specifically permit this modification.

Clause 10.5.2 provides limits for tension reinforcement in flexural members:

$$\frac{c}{d} \quad \leq \quad \frac{700}{700 + f_y} \tag{10–5}$$

or

$$\frac{A_s}{bd} \quad \leq \quad \frac{\alpha_1 \beta_1 \phi_c \, f'_c}{\phi_s \, f_y} \left(\frac{700}{700 + f_y} \right)$$

This should be routinely checked, particularly for panels with large openings and narrow legs.

13.2.4   Panel Height to Thickness Limits

Clause 23. 2.3 provides a limitation to the maximum height to thickness ratios of tilt-up panels, depending on the reinforcement configuration used in the cross section:

	Maximum ℓ / t
• Single mat of reinforcement (centered in the panel cross section)	50
• 2 mats of reinforcement (25 mm clear of each face)	65

The strength design provisions in Chapter 23 are self-limiting, and arbitrary limits on panel structural thickness or maximum deflections due to factored loads are not necessarily required. These requirements do, however, serve as practical limits for slender concrete walls since reinforcement quantities become excessive beyond this, and thicker concrete sections will often be more economical. Panel height to thickness ratios may also be controlled by limitations on service load deflections. The limits indicated above should be divided by 2 for cantilever panels on a fixed base.

13.3   Deflection Limitations Due To Service Loads

Limitations on out-of-plane or lateral deflections for slender walls have long been a concern of building officials and code committees, not only because of the increased bending moments due to P–Δ effects, but also the potential for long-term warping of these elements.

13

Tilt-up

Experience with actual buildings, however, suggests that long-term deflections are not a serious problem. This is partially due to the fact that the lateral forces causing bending in panels are largely transient in nature, and the concrete section at service load conditions is much stiffer than at factored loads.

NBCC 2005 provides a reduction in service loads by the application of the Importance Factor $I_s = 0.9$ for snow loads and $I_w = 0.75$ for wind loads. No guidance is provided for the effect of companion loads when checking serviceability requirements. This can be important for lateral deflections on tilt-up panels where eccentric axial loads occur in combination with transverse loading due to wind, but the maximum effect of each will rarely coincide. It is left to the designer to make a judgement as to whether reductions in service companion loads are appropriate.

13.3.1   CSA A23.3 Requirements for Deflection Limitation

Clause 23.3.2 of CSA A23.3 provides a limit of $\ell/100$ for non-seismic transverse deflections of walls for service loads. The method for calculating the deflection Δ_s has been modified from the previous edition of this design guide as follows:

$$\Delta_s = \frac{5\,M_s\,\ell^2}{48\,E_c\,I_e} = \frac{M_s}{K_{bs}} \tag{23–5}$$

$$M_s = M_{bs}\,\delta_{bs}$$

$$M_{bs} = \frac{w_s\,\ell^2}{8} + P_{ts}\frac{e}{2} + (P_{ws} + P_{ts})\Delta_0$$

$$\delta_{bs} = \frac{1}{1 - \dfrac{P_s}{K_{bs}}} \geq 1.0$$

$$P_s = P_{ws} + P_{ts}$$

$$K_{bs} = \frac{48\,E_c\,I_e}{5\,\ell^2} \quad (kN\text{–}m/m)$$

I_e is the effective moment of inertia as defined in Clause 9.8.2.3:

$$I_e = I_{cr} + (I_g - I_{cr})\left(\frac{M_{cr}}{M_a}\right)^3 \leq I_g \tag{9–1}$$

and

$$M_{cr} = \frac{f_r\,I_g}{y_t} \tag{9–2}$$

$$f_r = 0.6\lambda\,\sqrt{f'_c} \quad (MPa) \tag{8–3}$$

I_{cr} should be based on a triangular stress distribution as follows:

$$I_{cr} = \frac{b\,(kd)^3}{3} + \frac{E_s\,A_s\,(kd - c)^2}{E_c}$$

Where $kd = \dfrac{-n\,A_s + \sqrt{(n\,A_s)^2 + 2\,b\,n\,A_s\,d}}{b}$; $n = \dfrac{E_s}{E_c}$

Alternatively, a rectangular stress distribution can be used, giving slightly less conservative results.

The prescribed deflection limit of $\ell/100$ will sometimes control the design of panels with large openings, or with reinforcement in the middle of the concrete cross-section. A thicker cross section may be necessary to meet the requirements. See Design Examples for deflection calculations.

The method of analysis adopted by CSA A23.3 and ACI 318 for service load deflections of concrete members due to flexure is currently under review since there are concerns that it may be non-conservative for thin concrete sections. The Uniform Building Code had recognized this, but only in their provisions for tilt-up wall panels.

13.3.2   Creep and Initial Deflections

Permanent out-of-plane panel deflections can occur as a result of initial deflections in combination with the effects of long-term creep in concrete under sustained loading. Initial out-of-straightness or warping of tilt-up panels may be the result of uneven casting beds, excessive bending caused by the tilting process, thermal gradients, or differential shrinkage. The advent of laser screeds for casting floor slabs on which panels are poured has lessened the problem in recent years. Clause 23.3.1.4 prescribes an initial deflection $\Delta_0 = \ell\,/\,400$ at mid height of the panel. This has generally been adequate for most applications.

Long-term creep deflections may be imparted due to sustained axial loading, particularly if these loads are applied with significant eccentricities relative to the centerline axis of the panel. These can be accounted for in design by increasing the initial deflection of the panel. Fortunately, this has not been a significant problem in the history of tilt-up panels, since applied axial loads are often relatively small.

13.4   Loading Conditions

13.4.1   Load Combinations

NBCC 2005 has introduced a new approach to load factors and load combinations that includes the concept of "Principal Loads" and "Companion Loads". This method is much more rational for design load evaluation and is particularly suited to the design of tilt-up panels. The following load combinations should be considered:

	Factored Resistance	Principal Load	Companion Load
1)	ϕR	1.4D	
2)	ϕR	1.25D + 1.5L	+ 0.5S or 0.4W
3)	ϕR	1.25D + 1.5S	+ 0.5L or 0.4W
4)	ϕR	1.25D + 1.4W	+ 0.5L or 0.5S
5)	ϕR + effect of 0.9D	1.4W or 1.5L or 1.5S	
6)	ϕR	1.0D + 1.0E	+ 0.5L or 0.25S
7)	ϕR + effect of 1.0D	1.0E	

A reduced load factor is used for companion loads when used in combination with a principal load. Where the companion live load is storage, the load factor must be increased from 0.5 to 1.0. A load factor of 1.0 is used for seismic loads since they are considered to be ultimate loads.

Combination (1) through (3) seldom apply to tilt-up design except for short panels with large eccentric axial loads. In most cases, combination (4) or (6) will control the design for out-of-plane bending. For the common load case of large bending moments due to lateral forces combined with small axial loads, the critical section for bending will occur near panel mid height. As axial load and top end eccentricity increase, this point will shift upwards.

Combinations (5) and (7) apply to in-plane shear forces on tilt-up panels causing overturning, uplift or sliding. NBCC does not specifically permit live loads or snow loads to be used to increase the resistance. This will affect calculations for sliding resistance and panel overturning.

13

Tilt-up

13.4.2   Lateral Wind Loads on Panel Elements

Wind pressures are applied to the wall panel as uniformly distributed lateral loads. For exterior walls, lateral load effects will often be the dominant factor in the design. NBCC 2005 Clause 4.1.7 specifies wind pressure as the algebraic difference between external and internal pressure or suction:

p = $I_w q C_e (C_p C_g + C_{pi} C_{gi})$

q =   1 in 50 reference velocity pressure.

I_w =   Importance factor. For normal importance buildings, this will be 1.0 for strength calculations (ULS) and 0.75 for serviceability (SLS)

$C_p C_g$ =   Combined exterior pressure/gust coefficient. Values in the order of $+1.3$ or -0.5 are often used for individual tilt-up panels.

C_{pi} =   Interior pressure coefficient. Values of $+0.3$ or -0.45 will be applicable for buildings with only a few small openings and ± 0.7 for a significant number of large openings.

C_{gi} =   Interior gust effect factor = 2.0 (a calculation is also permitted)

C_e =   Exposure factor. A value between 0.7 and 1.0 is applicable for most single storey buildings. Depends on the nature of surrounding terrain and building height.

Typical lateral wind load on a 10m high x 7m wide panel for a single storey warehouse in an urban environment:

Assume q = 0.5 kPa;   Panel area = 7 x 10 = 70 m^2

Exposure factor $C_e = 0.7 \left(\dfrac{h}{12} \right)^{0.3} \geq 0.7$

C_e = $0.7 \left(\dfrac{10}{12} \right)^{0.3} = 0.66 \rightarrow 0.7$ min

From Figure I-5 in the Commentaries:

External $C_p C_g = +1.3$ and -1.5

Internal pressure $C_{pi} = -0.45$ and $+0.30$ (Category 2); $C_{gi} = 2.0$

(positive denotes forces toward the surface and negative denotes away from the surface)

Importance factor: ULS $I_w = 1.0$ for normal importance;   SLS $I_w = 0.75$ for all categories

Strength (ULS):

Inward pressure p = $1.0 \times 0.5 \times 0.7 (1.3 + 0.45 \times 2.0) = 0.77$ kPa

Outward pressure p = $1.0 \times 0.5 \times 0.7 (-1.5 - 0.30 \times 2.0) = -0.735$ kPa

Deflection (SLS):

Inward pressure p = $0.75 \times 0.77 = 0.58$ kPa

Outward pressure p = $0.75 \times (-0.735) = -0.55$ kPa

13.4.3   Lateral Seismic Loads on Panel Elements

Seismic forces for the design of individual wall panels are obtained from NBC 2005 Clause 4.1.8.17 for Elements of Structures. The basic relation is:

V_p = $0.3 F_a S_a(0.2) I_E S_p W_p$

$S_a(0.2)$=   5% damped spectral response acceleration at 0.2 seconds. The value of this coefficient will depend on the building site location and is obtained from the published climatic data.

F_a =   Acceleration based site coefficient that is dependent on soil conditions and $S_a(0.2)$

$$S_p = \frac{C_p\,A_r\,A_x}{R_p} \quad \text{where } 0.7 \le S_p \le 4.0$$

$$A_x = \text{Height Factor} = 1 + 2\,\frac{h_x}{h_n}$$

h_x, h_n = height above the base level. For out-of-plane forces, h_x can be taken as the center of mass of the panel at each storey.

I_E = Importance Factor for Earthquakes = 1.0 for Normal Importance Buildings

W_p = Weight of element

Category 1 of NBCC Table 4.1.8.17 will apply to the design of tilt-up panel elements for out-of-plane bending:

C_p = Component risk factor. Usually taken as 1.0.

A_r = Dynamic amplification factor. For short period buildings with flexible walls, this is equal to 1.0.

If the natural frequency of the component is close to the fundamental period of the building, this factor could increase to as much as 2.5.

R_p = Response factor associated with the ductility of the component.

= 2.5 for most reinforced tilt-up wall panels.

Typical lateral seismic design forces for tilt-up wall panels in a single storey building in Vancouver with stiff soil conditions would be:

$$S_a(0.2) = 0.94$$
$$F_a = 1.1 \qquad \text{(Site Class D)}$$
$$h_x = 0.5\,h_n$$
$$A_x = 1 + 2 \times \frac{0.5\,h_n}{1.0\,h_n} = 2.0$$
$$S_p = \frac{1.0 \times 1.0 \times 2.0}{2.5} = 0.8$$
$$I_E = 1.0$$
$$V_p = 0.3 \times 1.1 \times 0.94 \times 1.0 \times 0.8\,W_p = .248\,W_p$$

This is a reduction from NBCC 1995. It should, however, be pointed out that the assumption of A_r = 1.0 may be non-conservative for many large warehouse structures where the fundamental period could be large due to the flexibility of the roof diaphragm. If the natural frequency of the wall panel component is close to this, A_r should be increased, resulting in larger values of V_p.

Seismic forces required for parts of a building such as the wall panels are usually greater than that required for the overall building, and will increase for components located above the first storey. Lateral seismic forces will sometimes exceed wind pressure, particularly for thicker panels in high seismic zones.

13.4.4 Axial Loads

Vertical loads from roof or floor joists can often be considered as uniformly distributed line loads for the purposes of wall panel design. These loads should be applied at an eccentricity to the centerline axis of the panel either intentionally or due to accidental bearing irregularities. A *minimum eccentricity* of one half the panel thickness is recommended, and should be in addition to the effect of lateral pressures.

Axial load eccentricities should not be used to reduce the bending moment caused by wind or seismic lateral loads. In addition, wind uplift on roof members should not be used to reduce axial load.

13

Tilt-up

Where large concentrated loads are supported directly on the panel, the effective width b_d of the design cross-section should be limited as indicated in the adjacent figure. Additional reinforcement, where required, should be located in this area of the panel. The maximum factored axial stress on the design width, b_d, is limited to $0.09 \, \phi_c \, f'_c$ for the purposes of using the methods in Chapter 23.

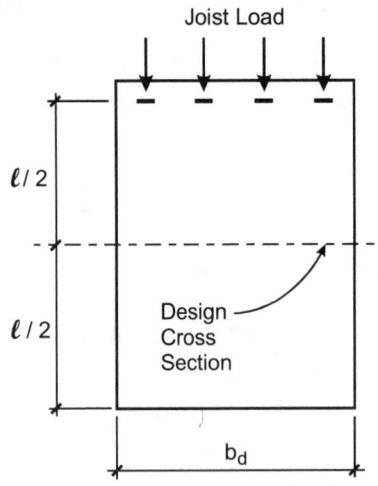

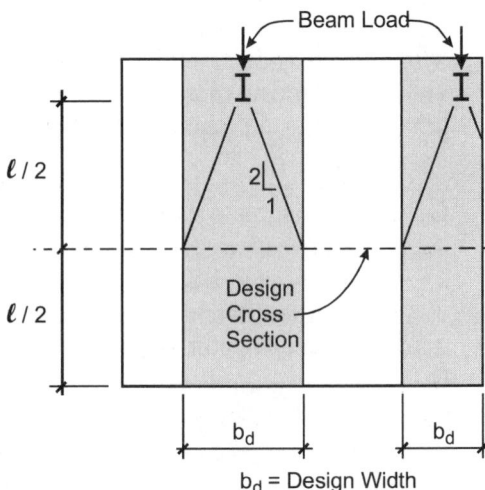

b_d = Design Width

13.4.5   Panel Self Weight

The effect of panel self-weight must be considered since it represents a significant contribution to P–Δ moments in slender walls. It is usually sufficient to assume that the weight of panel above the mid-height section acts as an additional concentrated axial load applied at the top with no eccentricity. This is illustrated by the following derivation:

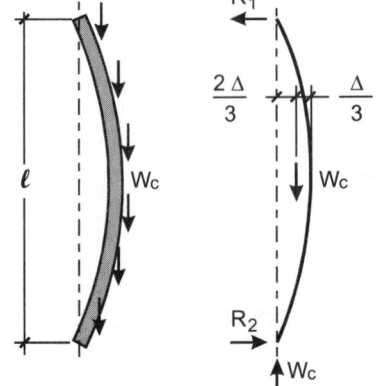

$$R_1 = R_2 = \frac{2 \, W_c \, \Delta}{3\ell}$$

The mid-height moment is:

$$M = \frac{R_1 \, \ell}{2} + \frac{W_c}{2} \, \frac{\Delta}{3} = \frac{W_c \, \Delta}{2}$$

W_c = self weight of concrete wall panel

Displacements at the top of the panel due to roof diaphragm flexibility have little or no effect on a pinned base panel. This is because full lateral support from the roof or floor assembly can almost always be assumed. The additional P–Δ effects due to the component of self-weight resulting from a 10 m high panel that is leaning 50 mm is negligible.

13.5   Continuity And End Fixity

Most tilt-up panels are designed as simply supported vertical slabs spanning between the footings and the roof structure. Where a panel is rigidly connected to the floor slab or the footing, some degree of end fixity can be considered. In other cases, a panel may be laterally supported by an intermediate floor, resulting in negative bending at the point of support and a reduction of positive bending between supports. It is difficult to analyze this condition and at best only approximate methods are practical.

Some of the analysis problems and limitations include the following:

- The bending moments are affected by lateral deflection at supports, particularly at flexible roof diaphragms.
- Effects of loading due to soil pressure below the floor slab may be significant.
- Lateral wind or seismic forces from intermediate floor or roof structures may add to the bending moments.
- Lateral restraint provided by footings or the connection to footings may be questionable such that full end fixity may not be fully realized.
- P–Δ calculations for statically indeterminate elements must be obtained by an iterative technique that is only practical with computer analysis.

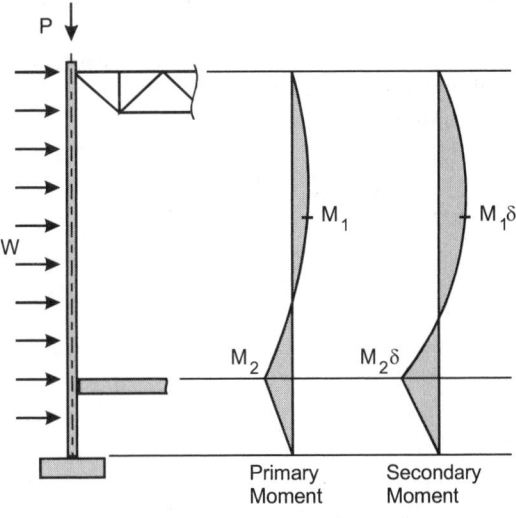

δ = Moment Magnifier

Because of these concerns, it is best to be somewhat conservative in the design approach. One technique involves the use of a reduced effective panel height coefficient, k. A value of k = 0.8 is suitable for an elastic column fixed at one end and pinned at the other. Since concrete section stiffness is not uniform and the ends are seldom completely fixed, k should not be taken as less than 0.9.

An alternative method of analysis is based on the assumption that the initial positive mid-height moment and negative support moment of the panel will increase proportionally by approximately the same amount when considering P–Δ magnifications. The primary moments are first calculated by conventional elastic methods. Both the positive and negative moments are then increased proportionally by the P–Δ moment magnifier.

Sometimes, designers try to reduce the effective panel height by connecting bottom chord extensions from the roof joists to the panel. In addition, they may assume that this also provides end fixity, thereby reducing the effective height even more. This technique could be dangerous since it could actually increase the panel bending moment due to joist rotation at the end support, and impart loads on the joist and connections that may not be fully accounted for by the joist designer. In general, it is not recommended.

The designer should also be aware that there might be a temporary condition during construction where lateral support at the intermediate floor slab is not present. This will increase the unsupported height of the panel and could become the controlling design condition. It is not sufficient to assume that this will be addressed by those responsible for tilt-up panel lifting and bracing.

13.6   Openings In Panels

The effect of openings for out-of-plane bending in tilt-up panels can be approximated by a simple one dimensional strip analysis that gives sufficient accuracy and economy for most designs.

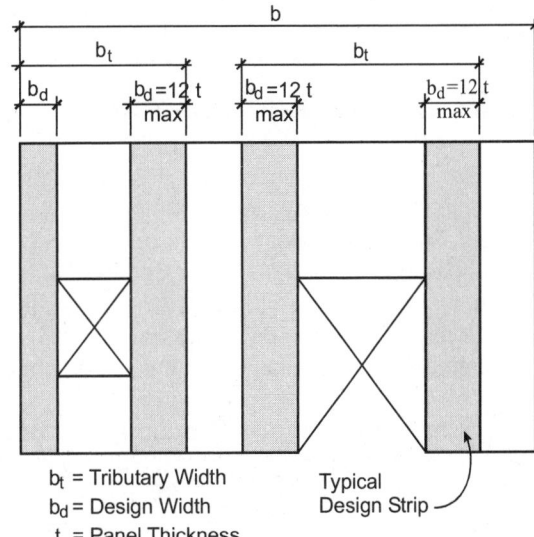

b_t = Tributary Width
b_d = Design Width
t = Panel Thickness

Typical Design Strip

Where openings occur, the entire lateral and axial load (including self weight) is distributed to supporting legs or design strips each side of the opening. The effective width of the strip should be limited to about 12 times the panel thickness in order to protect against localized stress concentrations at the edge of the opening. This limitation is intended primarily as a practical guideline. The tributary width for design can usually be taken as the leg width plus one half the width of adjacent openings.

For very wide openings, it may be necessary to provide an edge thickening or pilaster to carry the loads at each supporting leg. In addition, a horizontal header beam may also be required.

13.7   Isolated Footings and Pier Foundations

In many areas of Canada, soil conditions or frost depth requirements dictate the use of pier foundations. For convenience and economy, these piers are often located at the panel joints only. This has the effect of concentrating the vertical stresses at the edges of the panel.

Vertical support should effectively be grouped at either end as indicated in the adjacent figure. Where the clear panel height is greater than approximately 1½ times the clear distance between footings, the effect of isolated footings can usually be ignored.

Depending on the width of pier cap and effective bearing area at the bottom of the panel, additional hooked reinforcing or confining ties may be required to prevent localized shear or bearing failure. In many cases, there is continuous horizontal support provided at the top by the roof deck and at the bottom by ties to the floor slab. Where this occurs, lateral loads can be uniformly distributed across the width of panel.

Where panels contain multiple openings across the width, the exterior legs that are supported on the isolated footings should be designed to resist the axial load plus the tributary lateral load attributed to that portion of the panel. The intermediate legs may be designed to resist their tributary lateral loads only.

13.8   Stiffening Pilasters

Extra panel thickenings or pilasters are sometimes necessary to support heavy vertical loads. They may also be required at the edge of large openings as suggested in Section 13.6 of this Guide.

Some designers specify ties around all vertical reinforcing bars in a pilaster for the full height of the panel in accordance with the requirements in CSA A23.3 Chapter 10, for compression members. The axial stresses from roof or floor beams are usually concentrated at the point of bearing and quickly dissipate into the panel. The panel design is often

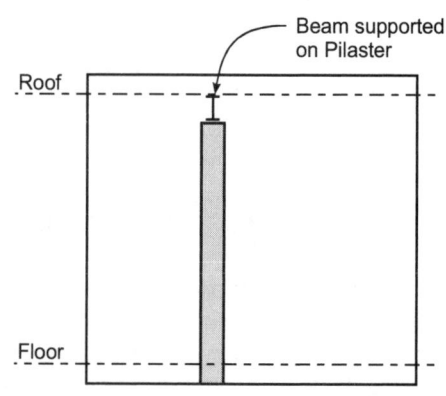

controlled by flexural tension of the vertical reinforcement and confining ties may not necessarily be required by code.

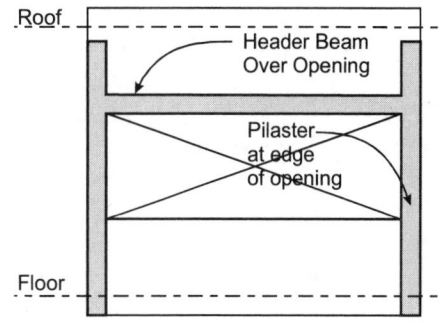

CSA A23.3 is unclear as to when a member is to be considered a column and subject to the requirements for ties. The definition for non-bearing walls in Chapter 2 is based on a vertical axial stress of less than 0.10 f'_c. Some of the provisions in Chapter 21 imply that a compression stress of 0.10 f'_c in a member can be used as the threshold below which it need not be considered as a column requiring confinement ties. As a minimum, ties should be specified in the vicinity of the point of bearing to ensure that the axial load is adequately distributed into the panel and that local bearing failure does not occur.

13.9   Concentrated Lateral Loads

Concentrated lateral loads can occur as a result of the following:

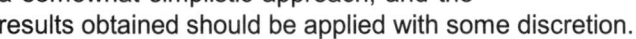
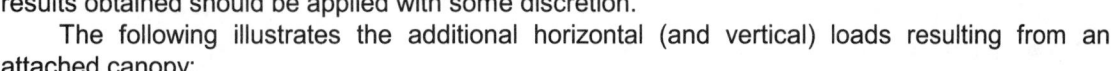

a. Suspended elements such as canopies

b. End reactions from header beams over wide panel openings

c. Lateral wind or seismic forces from intermediate floor or roof structures

d. Lateral loads from cranes or other equipment

The effect of these loads can be included in the analysis by adding the localized bending moment directly to the other primary bending moments. This is a somewhat simplistic approach, and the results obtained should be applied with some discretion.

The following illustrates the additional horizontal (and vertical) loads resulting from an attached canopy:

W   =   Weight of Canopy

$$R_1 = \text{End reaction} = \frac{W\,x}{2\ell} = R_2$$

$$H = \text{horiz. line load} = \frac{W\,x}{2\,b}$$

Where the horizontal reaction is a point load, the effective panel design width should be limited to about 12 times the panel thickness at the point of application. The load should be distributed evenly across this design width. Additional reinforcement may be required in this localized area.

13.10 Cantilever Panels

Tilt-up panels are sometimes required to function as vertical cantilevers. Typical examples include free-standing signs and screen walls, or parapets above the roof of a building. If the cantilever is high, P–Δ effects will increase the bending moments on the panel. A simple but conservative way to analyze a fixed end cantilever panel is to assume a simply supported panel with a height 2 times the cantilever height. The more correct method of analysis is the following:

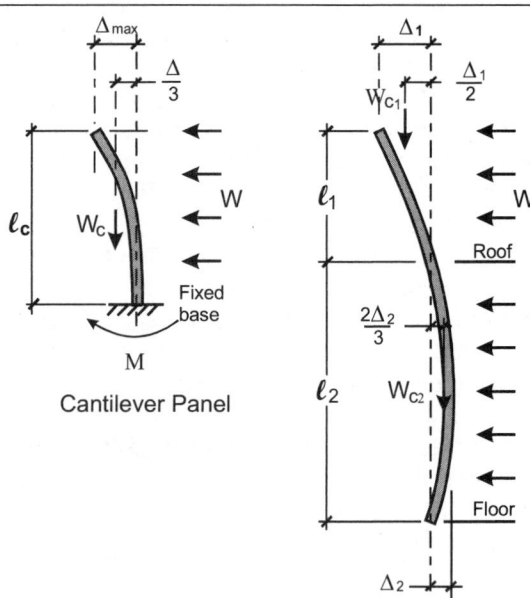

Cantilever Panel

Panel with Parapet

$$M_b = \frac{w_f \, \ell_c^2}{2}; \quad \ell_c = \text{cantilever height}$$

w_f = factored lateral load on cantilever (kN/m^2)

$$M_f = M_b + \frac{W_c \, \Delta}{3} = \frac{W_c}{3} \frac{M_f \, \ell_c^2}{4\,E\,I}$$

W_c = factored weight of concrete panel above the base

$$\Delta = \frac{M_f \, \ell_c^2}{4\,E\,I} = \frac{M_f}{K_{bc}}; \quad K_{bc} = \frac{4\,E\,I}{\ell_c^2}$$

$$M_f = M_b \, \delta_c \quad \text{where} \quad \delta_c = \frac{1}{1 - \dfrac{W_c}{3\,\phi_m\,K_{bc}}}$$

The dynamic effects of wind buffeting or seismic accelerations may temporarily increase the cantilever deflection since there may be very little structural damping. This should be taken into account when selecting design forces.

Where the cantilever is a high parapet, a more detailed analysis may be required. As can be seen by the adjacent diagram, rotation of the panel section at the roof connection can significantly increase the deflection and the associated P–Δ effects.

13.11 In–Plane Shear

Design procedures for in-plane shear forces are distinctly different from the methods used in design for out-of-plane bending. Forces from the roof or floor diaphragms acting parallel to the plane of the wall induce shear stresses and overturning moments in the panels. In seismic areas, the in-plane shear requirements may control the panel thickness and reinforcing design.

The following are design considerations for tilt-up panels subjected to in-plane forces:
- Resistance to sliding
- Resistance to panel overturning
- Concrete shear resistance
- Increased localized axial forces and out-of-plane P–Δ effects
- Load distribution to foundations
- Frame action in panels with openings
- Seismic ductility

13.11.1   Resistance to Panel Overturning

When roof and floor diaphragm forces are applied parallel to the plane of the wall panels, overturning moments and in-plane shears are induced. The overturning moments are usually taken about an outside corner of a panel. Resistance to overturning is obtained from a combination of panel weight, tributary roof or floor loads, panel edge connectors and tie down anchors to the foundations. The actual point of rotation will be close to the corner of the panel, at the center of the bearing area between the footing and the soil. In most cases, it is sufficient to assume that the width of bearing is zero and does not contribute to the overturning moment. This should be checked when R is large and soil bearing capacity is small.

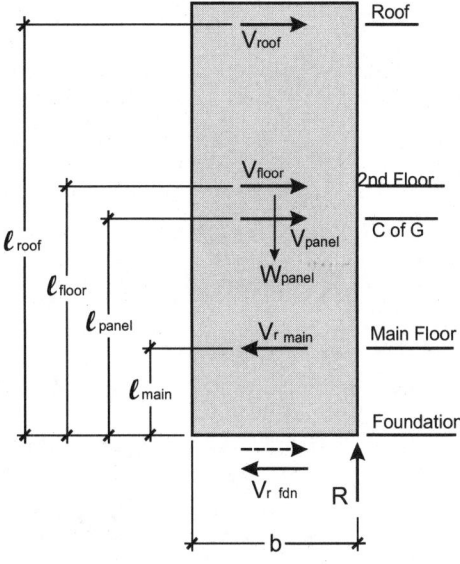

Panel Overturning Resistance

Factored Overturning Moment $M_{of} \leq$ Resisting Moment M_r

M_{of} = $V_{roof} \times \ell_{roof} + V_{floor} \times \ell_{floor} + V_{panel} \times \ell_{panel}$

V_{roof} = roof diaphragm shear force

ℓ_{roof} = distance from roof diaphragm to bottom of panel

V_{floor} = floor diaphragm shear force

ℓ_{floor} = distance from floor diaphragm to bottom of panel

V_{panel} = panel shear force (seismic only)

ℓ_{panel} = distance from panel center of gravity to bottom of panel

The resisting moment is given by:

M_r = $(W_{roof} + W_{floor} + W_{panel})\, b/2 + V_{r\ main}\, \ell_{main}$

W_{roof} = weight of tributary roof structure

W_{floor} = weight of tributary floor structure

W_{panel} = weight of panel

$V_{r\ main}$ = resisting shear force at main floor

ℓ_{main} = distance from main floor to bottom of panel

b = width of panel

In addition:

$V_{r\ fdn}$ = resisting shear force at the foundation of panel. This could be a negative number depending on the wall geometry and number of panel edge connectors used.

R = vertical reaction at footing

All applied shear forces contributing to overturning are factored. Forces and weights that resist overturning must be reduced in accordance with the load combination factors given in NBCC 4.1.3.2 and as outlined previously in Section 13.4.1 of this Design Guide. No additional safety factor need be applied. The unsupported edge of the panel must be checked to ensure that out-of-plane instability does not occur as a result of increased compression forces due to overturning. If this becomes a problem, additional reinforcement or edge thickenings can be used. Within some limits, all the panels can be connected together such that a panel edge in compression is stabilized by the adjacent panel edge in tension.

13

Tilt-up

Where the overturning capacity is insufficient, edge connections to an adjacent panel or tie down anchors to the foundation can be added until the overturning equation is satisfied:

Additional M_r = b x connector capacity

Capacity design principles may require the connections to be designed for the full weight of the adjacent panels. This additional uplift resistance may be limited to the weight of the foundation or adjacent panel(s). Foundations must also be checked to ensure that the structural capacity of the footing or the soil resisting pressure is not exceeded. The soil resisting pressure is a factored or ultimate value, and may be 1.5 to 2 times greater than the normal allowable soil bearing pressure. The geotechnical engineer should be consulted for assistance.

13.11.2 Resistance to Sliding

Resistance to sliding forces can be obtained by a combination of friction to the footing and connections to the floor slab or foundation. The coefficient of friction for factored sliding resistance between the bottom of the panel and the footing can usually be taken as 0.5. In some cases, friction may be all that is required. When friction resistance is insufficient, it can be supplemented by mechanical connections between the panel and footing or floor slab. A minimum of 2 connections per panel is recommended for all panels, but particularly when resisting seismic forces. These may be cast-in-place reinforcement dowels or welded embedded metal. Friction between the soil and footing or floor slab, or passive soil resistance must also be checked. The geotechnical engineer should be consulted for assistance.

13.11.3 Concrete Shear Resistance for In-Plane Forces

Requirements for concrete shear resistance for non-seismic conditions are covered in CSA A23.3 Chapter 11. Clause 11.3 requires:

$$V_r \quad \geq \quad V_f \tag{11–3}$$
$$\text{and} \quad V_r \quad = \quad V_c + V_s \ (+ V_p) \tag{11–4}$$

Concrete shear resistance is given by:

λ = 1.0 for normal weight concrete
ϕ_c = 0.65
β = 0.18 where minimum transverse reinforcement is used
b_w = thickness of concrete section = panel thickness t
d_v = effective shear depth = 0.9d or 0.72h   (See Clause 2.3, Symbols)

Chapter 11 does not specifically define the effective shear depth for walls subjected to in-plane shear. There is a reference under the seismic provisions in Chapter 21, Clause 21.6.9.3 that allows the effective shear depth to be taken as:

d_v = $0.8\,\ell_w$
ℓ_w = length of wall = panel width b

In using this reduction, it is assumed that the requirements of Clause 11.2.5 for anchorage of small diameter shear reinforcement are satisfied without the need for end hooks.

For 30 MPa concrete:

$$V_c \quad = \quad 0.65 \times 0.18 \sqrt{f'_c}\ \ 0.8\,b\,t = 0.51\,b\,t \text{ or } 0.51 A_g$$

The shear resistance of the transverse reinforcement is:

$$V_s \quad = \quad \frac{\phi_s\, A_v\, f_y\, d_v \cot\theta}{s} \tag{11–7}$$

For ϕ_s = .85, $\theta = 35^0$ and $f_y = 400$ MPa

$$V_s = \frac{.486\ A_v\ d_v}{s}$$

The minimum area of shear reinforcement is:

$$A_v = 0.06\ \sqrt{f'_c}\ \frac{b_w\ s}{f_y} \qquad\qquad (11\text{–}1)$$

where

s = spacing of transverse reinforcement
$\leq$ 0.7 d_v $\leq$ 600 mm   (See 11.3.8.1)

For f'_c = 30 MPa

$$A_v = 0.06\ \sqrt{30}\ \frac{t\,s}{400} = .00082\ A_g$$

t = thickness of wall

The minimum areas for distributed reinforcement specified for walls in Clauses14.1.8.5 and 14.1.8.6 will generally be greater than this:

Minimum vertical reinforcement   .0015 A_g
Minimum horizontal reinforcement   .0020 A_g

The upper limit for shear resistance is given by:

$$V_r \leq 0.25\ \phi_c\ f'_c\ b_w\ d_v \qquad\qquad (11\text{–}5)$$

For 30 MPa concrete and t = b_w, $d_v = 0.8b$

$$V_r \leq 0.25 \times .65 \times 30 \times t \times 0.8b = 3.90\ t\ b\ \text{ or } 3.90A_g$$

Clause 14.1.8.4 limits the spacing of distributed reinforcement to 3 times the wall thickness or 500 mm, whichever is less. Where the principal (vertical) reinforcement is placed in two layers, the horizontal distributed reinforcement can be placed on alternating faces with the spacing measured between alternate bars. See Section 13.13.3 of this Design Guide. The provisions of Chapter 21 for seismic design provide further requirements for shear resistance. This is discussed in the next section.

13

Tilt-up

13.11.4 Seismic Requirements for In-Plane Shear Forces

There are major changes to the seismic requirements in Clause 4.1.8 of NBCC 2005 and Chapter 21 of CSA A23.3-04. The focus has shifted from a strength design philosophy to capacity design and control of displacements. New limits on rotational demand for ductile shear walls and moment frames have now been introduced. The specified seismic loads in NBCC have been increased to reflect the greater return period for reoccurrence of a major earthquake.

A large number of tilt-up buildings are one or two storey structures with structural steel roof and floor framing systems. These buildings often rely on perimeter concrete walls to resist

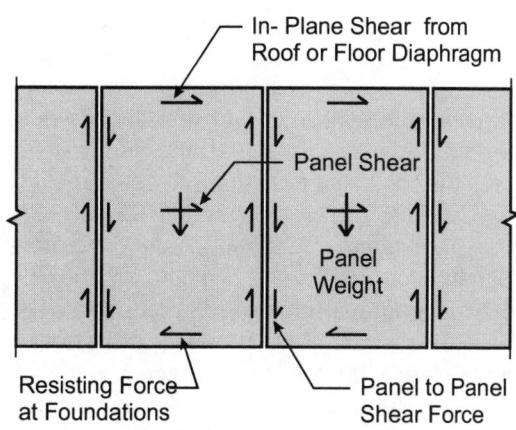

In-Plane Shear Forces

the seismic forces. The typical seismic load resisting system (SFRS) may be a complex mixture of load paths and components with widely varying properties. It is common to have a combination of flexible steel deck roof diaphragms, rigid concrete topped steel deck floor diaphragms, and stiff tilt-up panel shear walls. Many commercial and industrial structures will also employ supplementary steel bracing or moment frames as part of the SFRS. The tilt-up wall lines can be made up of a variety of panel shapes and sizes that are difficult to analyze with any degree of accuracy. It is not unusual to expect some portions of the building to behave differently compared to others. These factors, along with new building code requirements, will provide designers with a significant challenge.

The traditional methods for designing concrete tilt-up panel shear walls have focused on attaining sufficient strength to meet the prescribed seismic forces. Typically, we have tried to ensure that there was adequate overturning resistance and shear strength on the basis that ductility was automatically taken care of by the selection of the appropriate R-value. When there was any uncertainty, additional panel reinforcement or edge connectors would be added, on the assumption that more was better. There has been a general awareness on the need for continuity of the load path, capacity design of the components within the load path, and ensuring that the overall structure has been adequately tied together. Many designers have assumed that seismic ductility would be achieved through panel rocking, plastic yielding of the panel edge connections and, to some extent, deformation of the roof diaphragm. In most cases, the specified concrete shear stresses were relatively small and the risk of shear failure was low. Achieving ductility and energy dissipation within a solid concrete tilt-up panel was not usually a consideration.

One of the desirable features of using tilt-up panels in the SFRS is their ability to re-distribute seismic shear forces within a line of panel components. All panels can contribute to the seismic resistance, but some more than others. If the overturning resistance of a narrow panel is exceeded, the excess forces can be transferred to the wider panels by means of the connecting drag struts (steel edge angles). Similarly, excess shear force on panel edge connections do not necessarily mean that total failure will occur at this point. Deflection compatibility within the panel line ensures that the forces are re-distributed to the other panels. If the connections have reasonable ductility, it is possible to have most or all of the panels working together.

There is now a specific reference to tilt-up panels in Chapter 21 of CSA A23.3–04. Clause 21.7, Building Members Designed for Moderate Ductility:

21.7.1.2

Tilt-Up Wall Panels shall be designed to the requirements of Chapter 23 except that the requirements of Clause 21.7.2 shall apply to wall panels with openings when the maximum rotational demand on any part of the panel exceeds 0.02 radians. However, the inelastic rotational demand shall not exceed 0.04 radians. The requirements of Clause 21.7.4 shall apply to solid wall panels when the maximum in plane shear stress exceeds $0.1 \phi_c \sqrt{f'_c}$

Clause 21.7.2, *Moderately Ductile Moment-Resisting Frames*, could be applied to panels with openings acting as moment resisting frames, where plastic hinging is expected to occur at the interface between horizontal and vertical elements within the panel. There is a requirement to check the rotational demand at these panel joints.

Clauses 21.7.3, *Moderately Ductile Shear Walls*, and 21.7.4, *Squat Shear Walls*, were generally written for cast-in-place concrete walls where there is expected to be well-defined mechanisms for flexural yielding of the longitudinal (vertical) reinforcement. Limitations on rotational demand have been introduced. It is possible to provide tie down anchorage at the ends of each individual tilt-up panel in order to fit in with these requirements, but it is unlikely that the construction industry will embrace this concept. Alternatively, an independent SFRS could be employed, such as cast-in-place concrete ductile shear walls or interior steel bracing. The tilt-up panels may have to be seismically isolated and their contribution to the SFRS ignored. This has been employed in some buildings with 3 or more storeys, but would not be economically viable for most one or two storey buildings.

Clause 21.9.3, *Ductile Shear Walls Constructed Using Precast Concrete*, expects the precast concrete component to have a ductile vertical tie to the foundations. This has rarely been used in tilt-up buildings.

The most attractive design option could be to make use of the provisions in Clause 21.8, *Conventional Construction*. Solid shear walls would be designed under Clause 21.8.3 *Walls* for R_d = 1.5 and R_o = 1.3. There appears to be no specific requirement in this part of the code for checking rotational demand, or restrictions in using panel edge connectors to resist panel overturning forces. Increased design forces resulting form the reduction in the value of R_d are the primary consequence. It is important to note that NBCC Clause 4.1.8.10(2)(c) requires an SFRS with a R_d of 2.0 or greater for post-disaster buildings.

Wall lines in tilt-up buildings do not always consist of a series of solid panel elements. Below is an illustration of a typical wall line for a single storey tilt-up building. The shear forces from the roof will essentially be resisted by only a few solid panels. The narrow legs on the remaining panels will be very flexible compared to the solid panels, but will assist in the distribution of the base shear forces into the foundations and contribute to the overturning resistance of the system through panel edge connectors.

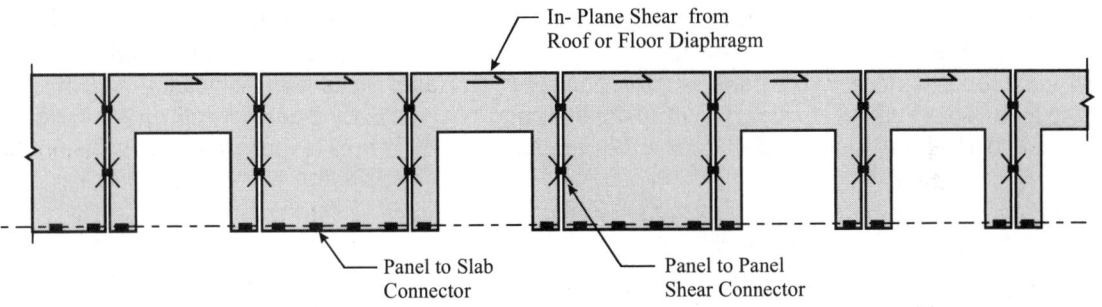

In- Plane Shear from Roof or Floor Diaphragm

Panel to Slab Connector

Panel to Panel Shear Connector

In-Plane Shear Forces

13

Tilt-up

The connections between the panels would ideally have sufficient ductility to allow for some re-distribution of forces through the various panel components, but strong enough to limit and control the overturning forces in the panels.

Unfortunately, there is no guidance provided by CSA A23.3 for designing tilt-up panel shear walls where seismic ductility is achieved only through panel overturning and edge connections. Clause 21.8 is a compromise solution but does not specifically address the requirement to control seismic deformations. Further, it will not necessarily provide the most desirable results since overloading and failure of other components in the load path, such as the steel roof diaphragm or non-ductile connections may occur prematurely. Further research in this area is needed.

13.11.5   Seismic Shear Walls Consisting of Solid Panels

Where the wall line consists of a series of panels that are mostly solid, the in-plane seismic resistance can be achieved by ensuring that panel overturning and concrete shear failure does not occur when the specified seismic forces are applied. The following design procedures are proposed:

- Design solid tilt-up concrete panel shear walls elements for low ductility requirements in accordance with Clause 21.8.3, *Conventional Construction*, for seismic force levels based on R_o = 1.3 and a maximum R_d = 1.5.

- Design the concrete cross section for a minimum shear capacity based on R_dR_o = 1.0 forces, using the procedures in Chapter 11 as previously outlined Section 13.11.3 of this Guide.

- Provide a minimum shear reinforcement ratio of .0015 in the vertical direction and .0020 in the horizontal direction in accordance with the recommendations of Chapter 14. Note that there is no requirement in Clause 21.8.3 to use an increased reinforcement ratio of .0025, as specified in other parts of Chapter 21.

- Compute panel overturning moments based on $R_d = 1.5$ and $R_o = 1.3$ forces. Where required, provide ductile edge connectors such as the EM5 to achieve the required overturning resistance. See Section 13.12 of this Guide. Check the compression edge of unconnected panels for out-of-plane stability as discussed in Section 13.11.1 of this Design Guide.

- Compute sliding forces for $R_d = 1.5$ and $R_o = 1.3$. These can be resisted by the connections in combination with friction between the panels and the foundations. Ductile connections, such as the EM5 or cast-in dowels can be used. Where non-ductile connections are employed, such as weld plates with studs, the design forces should be based on $R_d = 1.0$ and $R_o = 1.3$. Sometimes, the floor slab is poured through the openings at the base of a panel, effectively "locking in" the panel. This can significantly increase the resistance to sliding and decrease the number of mechanical connections. A minimum of 2 mechanical connections per panel is recommended.

There will be situations where the shear forces become so large that the overturning capacity in the panel line will be insufficient. Tie down anchorage to the foundations will then be required, and can be designed in accordance with Clause 21.7.4 with increased R–values. Increased foundation requirements, both for uplift resistance and for additional compression forces may be required. This is beyond the scope of the Design Guide.

13.11.6 Frame Panels Subjected to Seismic Shear

Panels with large openings that rely on frame action to resist in-plane seismic shear forces can be designed in accordance with Clause 21.7.2, *Moderately Ductile Moment Resisting Frames* using $R_d = 2.5$ and $R_o = 1.4$. Plastic hinging may occur in some of the panel joints and adequate resistance must be provided to ensure that concrete shear failure does not occur first. Clause 21.7.2.3 requires that the shear resistance should be greater than the sum of that required to develop the moment at the joint plus the effect of gravity loads, but need not exceed the shear force obtained using earthquake loads based on $R_d R_o = 1.0$.

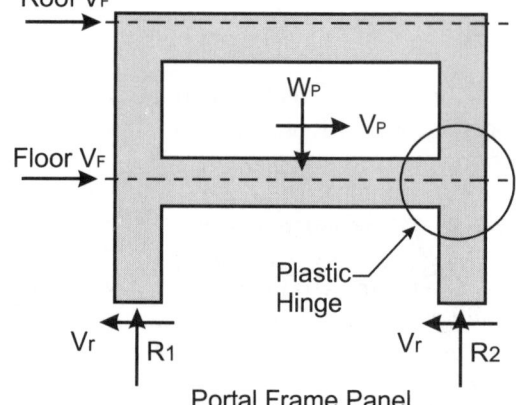

Portal Frame Panel

There may be several joints within a tilt-up panel frame, but often the flexural yielding occurs in only one or two of them. Clause 21.7.1.2 provides a test to determine where the provisions of 21.7.2 should apply by placing a threshold to the rotational demand at a joint of 0.02 radians. An upper limit of 0.04 radians is also given. This requires a displacement analysis of the entire building structure, and is beyond the scope of this Guide.

In lieu of this type of analysis, the designer has the option to use the provisions in Clause 21.8.2 for Conventional Construction, using $R_d = 1.5$ and $R_o = 1.3$. In either case, the reinforcement details should at least comply with the requirements of Clause 21.7.2.1, 21.7.2.2 and 21.7.2.3 for moment resisting frames.

Where the applied compressive stresses in the tilt-up panel components are less than $0.10\ f'_c$, reinforcement can be detailed in accordance with Clause 21.7.2.1 for beams rather than for columns. Buckling prevention ties are required around the longitudinal reinforcement in the joint regions and should comply with Clause 21.7.2.1.2. They should consist of closed hoops, 10M or larger, and the spacing must not exceed:

- d/4
- 8 times the longitudinal bar diameter
- 24 times the stirrup diameter
- 300 mm

Typical tie spacing would be:

Bar Size	Maximum Tie Spacing
20M	160 mm
25M	200 mm

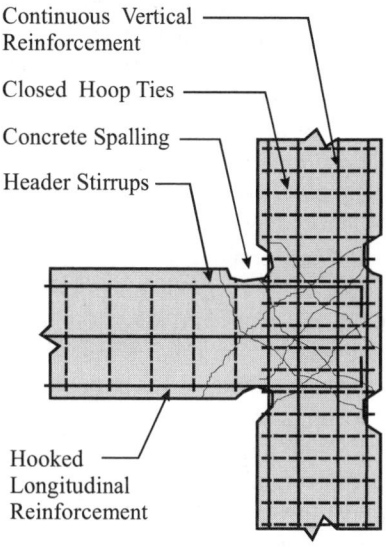

Buckling prevention ties are required for the longitudinal bars when they are highly stressed in compression due to in-plane flexural bending. This may only occur at the outer edges of the concrete cross section. Cross-ties for the intermediate bars are usually not required, since these are not generally subjected to

PLASTIC HINGE REGION

significant axial compression stresses. The spacing requirements for the hoop ties must extend a distance of 2d past the face of the joint. Beyond this, the spacing should not exceed d/2. The thickness of the panel cross section should not be less than 190 mm where closed 10M ties are used. When the axial stress on the panel cross section exceeds 0.10 f'_c, the detailing requirements for columns in Clause 21.7.2.2 should be met, including cross ties.

Longitudinal bars should be continuous through the joints in tilt-up frame panels. Vertical bars are typically detailed to run the full height of the panel. It is attractive to use larger size bars to avoid the tight spacing requirements for the buckling prevention ties. There are no specific requirements for maximum bar size in the provisions of Clause 21.8, *Conventional Construction*, but as a general rule, this should not exceed panel thickness divided by 10, as specified in Clause 21.6.4.4.

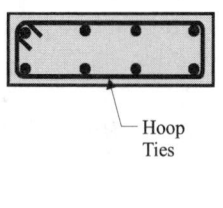

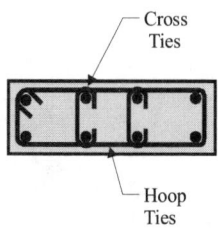

When the designer decides to use the provisions for Conventional Construction with R_d = 1.5 and R_o = 1.3, there should be a lower bound where the detailing rules for anti buckling ties are not required. A realistic approach would be to perform an elastic analysis of the panel wall elevation, based on R_dR_o = 1.0, to determine where flexural yielding might be expected to occur, and to design only those portions to meet the requirements of Clause 21.7.2.

The initial analysis should be carried out based on the prescribed seismic loads for Conventional Construction with R_d = 1.5 and R_o = 1.3. The forces obtained would then be increased by 1.5 x 1.3 = 1.95 (this is not always the same as starting with forces based on R_dR_o = 1.0). If the stresses in the longitudinal reinforcement under this magnitude of loading were less than the yield stress of the reinforcement ($\phi_s f_y$), then the requirements for buckling prevention hoop ties would not be necessary. The tendency in some design offices has been to take a somewhat conservative approach, where the ties are specified in all cases when it is *possible* to have compression yielding of the longitudinal reinforcement.

13

Tilt-up

Tilt-up wall panel frames will often have deep header sections such that the flexural yielding or plastic hinging would occur only in the vertical legs. Where the longitudinal reinforcement in the header is not expected to yield for seismic forces obtained as described in the previous paragraph, the tie spacing limitations of Clause 21.7.2.1.2 would not apply.

Closed hoop ties or stirrups should be provided in the legs and headers outside the plastic hinge regions to ensure adequate shear resistance. These should be designed in accordance with the requirements of Chapter 11 and as outlined earlier in this Design Guide based on $R_d R_o = 1.0$ forces.

The panel legs must also be checked to ensure that there will be sufficient post-seismic capacity to support the gravity loads imposed by the floor and roof structures. Where plastic hinging occurs in a joint, it is reasonable to expect that some of the concrete cross section will be damaged. The outer edge longitudinal bars and the surrounding concrete in a panel leg may no longer be effective for supporting gravity loads and out-of-plane wind loads. Where the leg cross section is sufficiently wide, the undamaged inner portions will be called upon to carry the loads. A minimum leg width to thickness ratio of 4.0 is therefore recommended, in order to help ensure that complete failure will not occur. A panel with a thickness of 190 mm should therefore have a minimum leg width of 760 mm. Narrower panel legs can be used if it can be shown that in-plane flexural yielding of the longitudinal reinforcement will not occur.

13.12 Connections For Tilt-Up Panels

Design requirements for connections to tilt-up panels generally follow traditional methods. Connections must be designed to resist forces equal to or greater than the maximum load imposed on the panel component. Ideally, connections in panels designed for seismic conditions should typically be stronger and more ductile than those for non-seismic forces.

The three main categories of connections for tilt-up panels are:

- Cast-in place concrete in-fill sections
- Welded embedded metal
- Drilled-in anchors

13.12.1 Cast-In-Place Concrete In-fill Sections

This type of connection involves casting concrete around reinforcing bars projecting from the panel in order to tie into another building component.

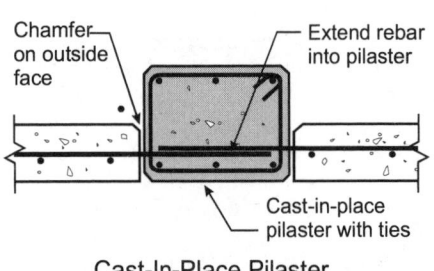

Cast-In-Place Pilaster

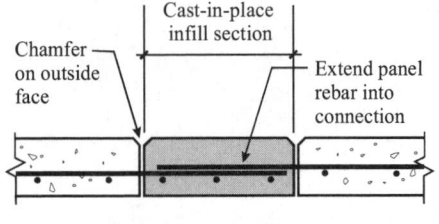

Cast-In-Place Panel Infill

These connections are often very strong and can be used to distribute loads over a greater length. Good ductility can be achieved if the overlapping bars are confined by closed ties. Cast-in-place connections are used infrequently because they are considerably more expensive than other types of connections. They may also cause problems such as panel cracking resulting from concrete shrinkage and excessive restraint.

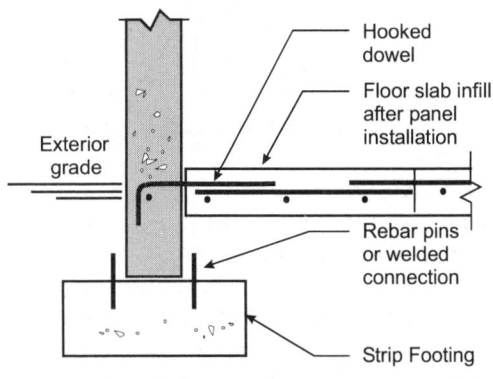

Panel on Strip Footing

13.12.2 Welded Embedded Metal

Welded embedded metal is the type of connection preferred by most designers and builders due to its relative cost advantage and construction flexibility in various applications. Strength and ductility can vary considerably, depending on the length of embedment and configuration of the anchor.

Steel plates with studs are suitable for shear and tension forces as long as they are located well away from the panel edges (300 mm or more).

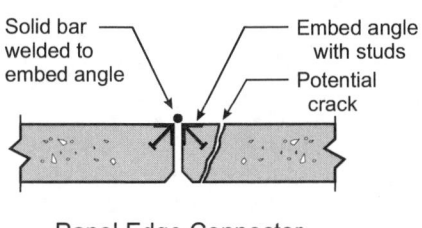

Panel Edge Connector
(not recommended)

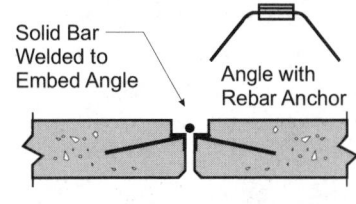

Panel Edge Connector
(for seismic shear transfer)

The lack of sufficient embedment makes these connectors non-ductile. Steel angles or plates with short studs located at the edge of the panel should be avoided entirely. Often concrete shrinkage in the panels after welding causes stress build-up may result in complete failure.

Where possible, embedded metal connections should have deformed bar anchors extending into the concrete panel. These are more expensive to fabricate and install but provide superior strength and performance, particularly for seismic loadings. In general, this type of connector can provide reasonable seismic ductility.

The adjacent figure contains five standard

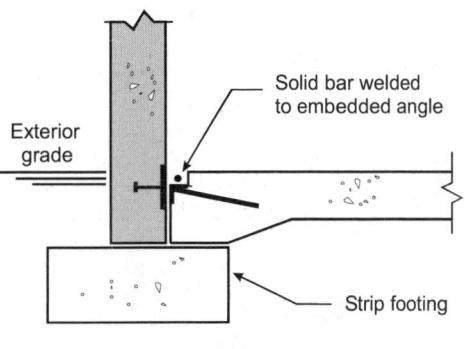

Panel on Strip Footing

connection types that have been used in tilt-up panels. These have been tested in static and cyclic loading (ref 6). Recommended load capacities are also indicated.

13

Tilt-up

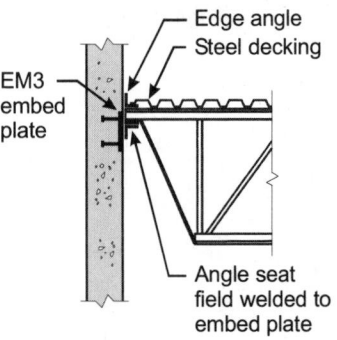

Steel Joist on Angle Seat

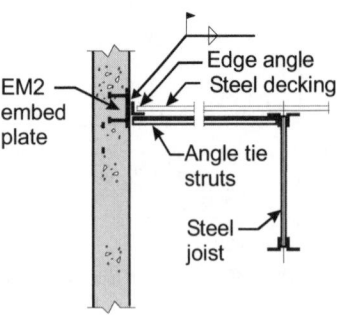

Edge Angle Connection

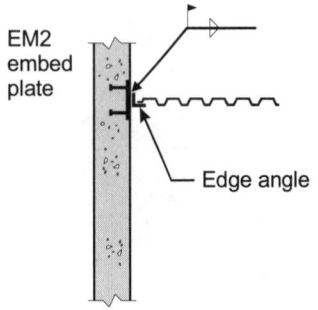

Shear Plate Connection

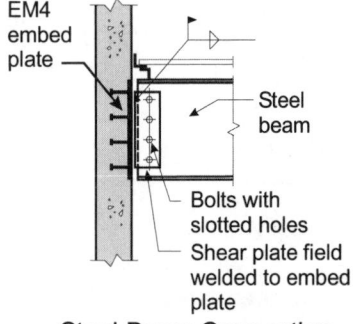

Steel Beam Connection

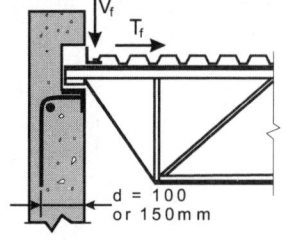

EM1 Joist Seat
L89 x 89 x 6 x 300mm
2 - 15M Gr 400 Rebar Anchors

	100mm	150mm
d =	100mm	150mm
Vr =	110 kN	110 kN
Tr =	45 kN	70 kN

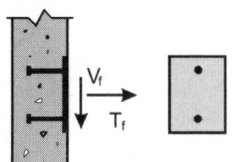

EM2 Shear Plate
PL 150 x 9.5 x 200
2 - 16mm studs

	100mm Studs	150mm Studs
Vr =	65 kN	65 kN
Tr =	50 kN	95 kN

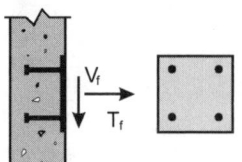

EM3 Shear Plate
PL 200 x 9.5 x 200
4 - 16mm studs

	100mm Studs	150mm Studs
Vr =	110 kN	130 kN
Tr =	65 kN	130 kN

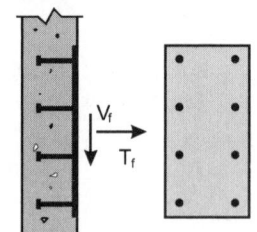

EM4 Shear Plate
PL 225 x 9.5 x 460
8 - 16mm Studs

	100mm Studs	150mm Studs
Vr =	170 kN	265 kN
Tr =	90 kN	200 kN

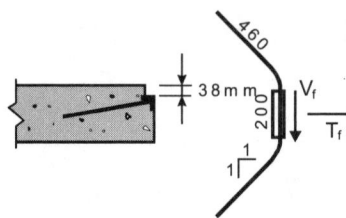

EM5 Edge Connector
L 38 x 38 x 6 x 200mm
20M Gr 400 Rebar Anchor

Vr = 125 kN, Tr = 100 kN

Standard Tilt-up Connectors

13.12.3 Drilled-In Anchors

Expansion bolts and adhesive anchors are used extensively in tilt-up construction. Their application should be restricted to supporting light loads or for repairs. There is very little ductility compared to cast-in-place or welded deformed bar anchors making them unsuitable where seismic forces or differential foundation movement is expected. Expansion anchors can also cause problems in thin panel sections particularly where edge distance is inadequate.

Powder driven fasteners or drive pins may be used for light architectural components or light gauge steel stud framing. Design loads should be restricted due to the limited reliability of these fasteners in concrete.

13.12.4 Connections for Seismic Forces

Tilt-up panel connections for seismic applications must be capable of resisting forces equal to or greater than that specified by the NBCC 2005 for the overall structural system. Ideally, the connection type would be assigned values of R_d and R_o based on testing. For example, the factored load capacity of the standard connections that were illustrated previously was based on a 0.6 reduction of the lowest test value for initial failure. A value of $R_o = 1.4$ would be a conservative, but appropriate assumption. If the design is based on the requirements for Conventional Construction, The value of R_o should be reduced to 1.3 to be consistent. The studded connections (EM2, EM3 and EM4) exhibited very little ductility during the testing program (ref 6) and should be assigned a value of $R_d = 1.0$ for the 100 mm (4" stud length). No testing was performed on the longer 150 mm (6") studs during the research program, but $R_d = 1.0$ is also recommended. The EM1 and EM5, on the other hand, had good ductile shear performance and could be assigned a minimum $R_d = 1.5$.

NBCC Clause 4.1.8.17(8) for connections of elements of structures requires minimum design forces to be based on:

$$V_p \quad = \quad 0.3\, F_a\, S_a(0.2)\, I_E\, S_p\, W_p$$

where

$$S_p \quad = \quad \frac{C_p\, A_r\, A_x}{R_p} \quad \text{where} \quad 0.7 \le S_p \le 4.0$$

C_p = Element risk factor, usually taken as 1.0 for ductile connections and 2.0 for non-ductile connections

A_r = Dynamic amplification factor that depends on the flexibility of the component being connected

     = 1.0 for rigid elements

     = 2.5 for flexible elements

A_x = Height factor = $1 + 2\,\dfrac{h_x}{h_n}$

R_p = Component response factor

     = 1.0 for non-ductile components or connections

     = 2.5 for ductile connections or materials

As an example, assume the following:

    Site location, Vancouver, Class D soils
    Out-of-plane connection between the roof and panel of a single storey building

    $S_a(0.2)=$ 0.94; F_a = 1.1

13

Tilt-up

$$C_p = 2.0 \qquad \text{(non-ductile connection)}$$

$$A_r = 2.5 \qquad \text{(flexible tilt-up panel)}$$

$$R_p = 1.0 \qquad \text{(non-ductile connection)}$$

$$h_x = 0.5\,h_n$$

$$A_x = 1.0 + 2\left(\frac{0.5}{1.0}\right) = 2.0$$

$$S_p = \frac{2.0 \times 2.5 \times 2.0}{1.0} = 10.0; \quad \therefore\ S_p = 4.0$$

$$V_p = 0.3 \times 1.1 \times .94 \times 1.0 \times 4.0\,W_p = 1.24\,W_p$$

Thus, the connection between the roof and the panel must be designed for a minimum out-of-plane design force of 1.24 times the tributary weight of the panel. Where ductile connections are used, this force can be reduced, but this is difficult to achieve in normal tilt-up construction.

13.13 Construction Requirements

13.13.1 Forming and Construction Tolerances

Chapter 23 does not provide specific requirements for tolerances in tilt-up construction. Instead, it refers to the CSA A23.4 standard for precast concrete with a precautionary note that adequate quality control procedures must be carried out. Otherwise, the tolerances are to comply with A23.1.

Quality control of panel forming and reinforcing steel placing for site cast tilt-up concrete panels is usually better than for standard cast-in-place concrete work, but cannot compare with the controlled conditions of a precast concrete plant. Tolerance requirements should therefore be somewhere in between.

The tilt-up industry in North America has developed tolerance guidelines that have been used succesfully over the past 30 years:

Length and Height:

Up to 3 m	+ 0 to – 10 mm
3 m to 6 m	+ 0 to – 12 mm
Over 6 m	+ 0 to – 15 mm

Straightness or Skewness:

Up to 3 m	± 10 mm
3 m to 6 m	± 15 mm
6 m to 12 m	± 20 mm

Thickness:

Overall   ± 5 mm

Clear concrete cover over reinforcement in tilt-up panels should be greater than that required by CSA A23.4 for plant cast precast concrete. In general, the following covers have been adequate for tilt-up panels above grade:

Main Reinforcing

Outside face of panel	25 mm
Inside face of panel	20 mm
Edge of panel	50 mm

Ties and Stirrups

| Inside or outside face | 20 mm |
| Edge of panel | 40 mm |

Some contractors have found that concrete covers of less than 20 mm on the inside can make it difficult to finish the panel surface. On the outside face, insufficient cover tends to result in "mirroring" of the bars through the finished concrete. Concrete cover may also have to be adjusted for fire rating requirements, or where reveal strips are installed on the outside face of the panel.

13.13.2 Concrete Requirements

Concrete used for tilt-up panels should provide adequate strength for both the in-place condition and for erection requirements. A minimum compressive strength of 25 MPa should be provided. Often, the concrete mix is proportioned for flexural strength requirements as defined by the modulus of rupture. This property is important for resisting flexural cracking, particularly during the lifting operation. Depending on what is specified, the actual compressive strength may be greater than 25 MPa. There has been a trend in recent years to use 28 to 30 MPa concrete for panels.

Entrained air for freeze/thaw resistance is not normally required where exposed surfaces are primarily vertical and protected with a paint or sealer. Air entrainment has a negative effect on the modulus of rupture and will increase the potential for cracking at the time of lifting. Local experience in the performance of non-air entrained concrete should be investigated.

In summary, the following concrete specifications are suggested:

28 Day Compressive Strength	30 MPa
28 Day Flexural Strength	4.5 MPa
Maximum Size Aggregate	20 mm
Exposure Class	F2 unless adequately sealed
Entrained Air	4–7% unless adequately sealed

13.13.3 Reinforcing Steel

Standard or weldable grade 400 MPa reinforcing steel should be specified for tilt-up panels. The main vertical bars should be 15M or 20M, with 10M bars used for horizontal distributed reinforcement or ties. Bars larger than 20M are not recommended for tilt-up panels with a thickness of 200 mm or less.

The following are the minimum requirements in Clause 14.1.8 for distributed reinforcement in walls:

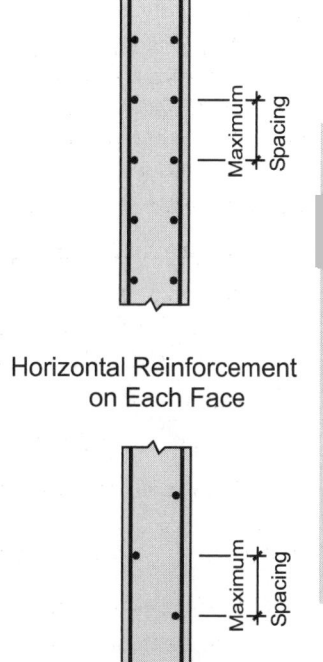

Horizontal Reinforcement
on Each Face

Maximum bar diameter	0.10 x wall thickness
Number of layers	1 layer for wall thickness not exceeding 210 mm
	2 layers for wall thickness of 160 mm or greater
Maximum spacing (see note)	3 times wall thickness or 500 mm
Minimum vertical reinforcement	.0015 A_g
Minimum horizontal reinforcement	.0020 A_g
Concentrated reinforcement	2 – 15M at perimeter
	1 – 15M bar in each layer around openings

Note: Where the reinforcement is placed in 2 layers, the horizontal distributed reinforcement can be on alternating faces and the spacing restrictions apply to the distance between alternate bars rather than to the bars in each individual layer. See adjacent diagram.

Horizontal Reinforcement
on Alternate Faces

13

Tilt-up

Clearances between bars should comply with the requirements of CSA A23.1. The requirements for walls are overly restrictive for tilt-up panels since these elements are formed and poured as flat, open-faced slabs. Closer bar spacing can usually be tolerated, particularly where the reinforcement is run the full height or width without lap splices.

13.14 Design For Lifting Stresses

It has been common practice for the panel lift analysis and pick up point locations to be carried out by a separate designer. This is often the supplier of embedded lift inserts or other specialist engineer. Although there is no direct conflict with this split in responsibility, it is important for the building designer to have some basic knowledge of the requirements for lifting and the potential limitations.

Panel lift design takes into account the following considerations:

- Bending stress should be kept low enough to avoid flexural cracking.
- The lift insert capacity should have a safety factor of at least 2.0 at the time of lift, including an allowance for adhesion and impact. Some Canadian jurisdictions require a safety factor of 2.5.
- The panel should tilt with about 10% of the weight at the bottom. It should be balanced to hang level when lifted off the casting bed.

A minimum concrete compressive strength of 17 MPa (2500 psi) is often specified for full lift insert capacity. Concrete flexural strengths of 2.9 MPa (420 psi) are sufficient to prevent panel cracking where computed bending stresses are less than 1.7 MPa (250 psi). Beyond this, reinforcing steel should be provided on the tension face to carry the entire load. Since the panel is often lifted before the full 28 day concrete strength is achieved, higher specified strengths are usually required. Many contractors will boost the specified concrete strength to ensure that there will be adequate strength for lifting in only a few days after pouring the panels.

Reinforcement in the middle of the panel section will only be effective after the concrete has cracked. It is also less efficient in resisting bending moments. Where two layers of reinforcement are specified for the panel design, it will often provide a net savings in the overall quantity of reinforcement since it is more efficient, and generally eliminates the need for additional reinforcement for lifting purposes. There has been a trend in recent years to go with 2 layers of reinforcement in almost all tilt-up panels. As a result, there has been a significant decrease in the panel cracking associated with lifting.

The following are a few simple tips for panel layout that will make panel lifting easier and more cost effective:

- Avoid large panels, and try to limit the maximum weight to about 30 Tonnes (66,000 lbs).
- Panel size and weight should be consistent. This will avoid multiple rigging changes.
- Keep panel widths to about 6.5m or less, particularly when the height is greater than 9m.
- Avoid spandrel panels, or panels with only one supporting leg. These will often require strongbacks for lifting, and can significantly increase erection time. These situations can usually be avoided by proper panel layout design.

13.15 Temporary Panel Bracing

The brace supplier usually provides design requirements for temporary bracing of tilt-up panels. It is recommended that this bracing comply with the guidelines outlined in the publication by the Tilt-up Concrete Association (ref. 8).

The building designer should be aware of some of the requirements for panel bracing, and make provisions in the building design to accommodate this. The following guidelines are suggested:

- Provide a minimum floor slab thickness of 140 mm (5½") for bracing. Bracing connections to the floor require this minimum requirement in order to develop the capacity of the connecting bolt.

- Additional floor slab thickenings may be required to provide sufficient weight for anchoring the braces for panel heights in excess of 10m above the floor slab. Floor slab reinforcement is also helpful for brace anchorage.

13.16 Design Examples

The purpose of these examples is to illustrate the CSA A23.3-04 requirements for design of tilt-up panels. Not all of the necessary checks are included in each example. Design engineers are encouraged to set up a spreadsheet analysis program that will routinely check the appropriate clauses of the code.

Material properties:

For the purposes of these examples the following material properties have been assumed:

ϕ_c = 0.65, ϕ_s = 0.85, ϕ_m = 0.75

f'_c = 30 MPa; E_c = $4500\sqrt{30}$ = 24,650 MPa

α_1 = .85 – .0015 x 30 = 0.805

β_1 = .97 – .0025 x 30 = 0.895

f_y = 400 MPa; E_s = 200,000 MPa

Example 13.1 - Plain Wall Panel

Panel properties:

ℓ = 7600 mm; t = 140 mm; Δ_0 = 25 mm

Self weight w_c = .140 x 24 = 3.36 kN/m^2

Check ℓ / t:

$\dfrac{7600}{140}$ = 54 < 65 ∴ OK for 2 layers of reinforcement

Assumed loading: Roof dead load = 1.0 kPa; snow load = 3.0 kPa

ecc = 140 / 2 = 70 mm; joist span = 10.9 m

Wind load w = 1.07 kPa

Strength Calculations:

Load case (4): 1.25**D** + 1.4**W** + 0.5**S**

P_{tf} = (1.25 x 1.0 + 0.5 x 3.0) 10.9 / 2 = 15.0 kN/m; P_{wf} = 1.25 x 3.36 x 7.6 / 2 = 16.0 kN/m

Axial load at mid-height: P_f = 15.0 + 16.0 = 31.0 kN/m; w_f = 1.4 x 1.07 = 1.5 kN/m^2

Check axial load limit: $\dfrac{P_f}{A_g}$ = $\dfrac{31.0}{.140 \times 1000}$ = 0.22 MPa < .09 x .65 x 30 = 1.75 MPa   OK

Assume reinforcing on each face (EF):

A_s = 15M @ 400 EF or 500 mm^2/m EF; d = 100 mm; b = 1000 mm

A_{se} = $\dfrac{.85 \times 500 \times 400 + 31.0 \times 1000}{.85 \times 400}$ = 591 mm^2/m a_e = $\dfrac{591 \times .85 \times 400}{.805 \times .65 \times 30 \times 1000}$ = 12.8 mm

Resisting Moment $M_r = \dfrac{.85 \times 591 \times 400\,(100 - 12.8\,/\,2)}{10^6} = 18.8$ kN-m/m

Bending stiffness (based on $A_s = 500$ mm^2):

$a = \dfrac{500 \times .85 \times 400}{.805 \times .65 \times 30 \times 1000} = 10.8$ mm; $c = \dfrac{10.8}{.895} = 12.1$ mm

$I_{cr} = \dfrac{b\,c^3}{3} + \dfrac{E_s\,A_s\,(d - c)^2}{E_c} = \dfrac{1000 \times 12.1^3}{3} + \dfrac{200\,000 \times 500\,(100 - 12.1)^2}{24\,650} = 31.9 \times 10^6$ mm^4/m

$K_{bf} = \dfrac{48 \times 24\,650 \times 31.9 \times 10^6}{5 \times 7600^2 \times 1000} = 130.8$ kN-m/m

Moment magnifier:

$\delta_b = \dfrac{1}{1 - \dfrac{P_f}{\phi_m\,K_{bf}}} = \dfrac{1}{1 - \dfrac{31.0}{.75 \times 130.8}} = 1.46$

Primary Bending Moment $M_b = 1.5 \times 7.6^2\,/\,8 + 15 \times .07\,/\,2 + 31.0 \times .025 = 12.1$ kN-m/m

Total Moment $M_f = 12.1 \times 1.46 = 17.7$ kN-m/m $<$ 18.8 kN-m/m   OK

Total factored deflection $\Delta_f = \dfrac{M_f}{\phi_m K_{bf}} = \dfrac{17.7 \times 1000}{0.75 \times 130.8} = 180$ mm

Load case (3): 1.25**D** + 1.5**S** + 0.4**W**

P_{tf} = $(1.25 \times 1.0 + 1.5 \times 3.0)\,10.9\,/\,2 = 31.3$ kN/m; $P_{wf} = 1.25 \times 3.36 \times 7.6\,/\,2 = 16.0$ kN/m
P_f = $31.3 + 16.0 = 47.3$ kN/m; $w_f = 0.4 \times 1.07 = 0.43$ kN/m^2
A_s = 500 mm^2/m EF; $A_{se} = 639$ mm^2/m; $M_r = 20.2$ kN-m/m
M_b = $0.43 \times 7.6^2\,/\,8 + 31.3 \times .07\,/\,2 + 47.3 \times .025 = 5.38$ kN-m/m
K_{bf} = 130.8 kN-m/m; $\delta_b = 1.93$; $M_f = 5.38 \times 1.93 = 10.4$ kN-m/m $<$ 20.2   OK

Deflections at service loads:

Load case: 1.0**D** + 1.0**W** + 0.5**S**   ($I_w = 0.75$, $I_s = 0.9$)

w_c = 3.36 kN/m^2; $P_{ws} = 3.36 \times 7.6\,/\,2 = 12.8$ kN/m
P_{ts} = $(1.0 + 0.5 \times 0.9 \times 3.0)\,10.9\,/\,2 = 12.8$ kN/m;   ecc = 70 mm
P_s = $12.8 + 12.8 = 25.6$ kN/m; $w_s = 0.75 \times 1.07 = 0.80$ kN/m^2
I_g = $1000 \times 140^3\,/\,12 = 229 \times 10^6$ mm^4/m

Cracking moment:

$M_{cr} = \dfrac{f_r\,I_g}{y_t} = \dfrac{0.6\,\sqrt{30} \times 229}{140\,/\,2} = 10.75$ kN-m/m

$M_{bs} = \dfrac{0.80 \times 7.6^2}{8} + \dfrac{12.8 \times .070}{2} + 25.6 \times .025 = 6.86$ kN-m/m

Initially assume $\Delta_s = \dfrac{\ell}{100} = \dfrac{7600}{100} = 76$ mm

M_s = $6.86 + 25.6 \times .076 = 8.81$ kN-m/m $<$ M_{cr}
$\therefore I_e$ = $I_g = 229 \times 10^6$ mm^4/m

$K_{bs} = \dfrac{48\,E_c\,I_e}{5\,\ell^2} = \dfrac{48 \times 24\,650 \times 229 \times 10^6}{5 \times 7600^2 \times 1000} = 938$ kN-m/m

$$\delta_{bs} = \frac{1}{1 - \dfrac{P_s}{K_{bs}}} = \frac{1}{1 - \dfrac{25.6}{938}} = 1.03$$

$M_s = 6.86 \times 1.03 = 7.06 < M_{cr} = 10.75$ kN-m/m $\qquad$ OK

$\Delta_s = \dfrac{M_s}{K_{bs}} = \dfrac{7.06 \times 1000}{938} = 7.5$ mm < 76 mm $\qquad$ OK

Panel design summary: $\qquad$ (Load case (4) controls the design)
Vertical reinforcing: $\qquad$ 15M @ 400 EF $\qquad$ (each face)
Horizontal reinforcing: $\qquad$ 10M @ 350 AF $\qquad$ (alternating faces)

Reinforcement weight per m^2 $= \left(\dfrac{2 \times 200}{400} + \dfrac{100}{350} \right) 7.85$ kg $= 10.1$ kg/m^2

Compare to a design with reinforcing in the center of the panel section:

Maximum $\dfrac{\ell}{t} = 50$ for 1 layer of reinforcement

Minimum t $= \dfrac{7600}{50} = 152$ mm $\rightarrow$ assume t $= 160$ mm $\qquad$ (formed with 2x6 plus 1x2)

<u>Load case (4): 1.25**D** + 1.4**W** + 0.5**S**</u>

Self weight $\qquad$ $w_c = .160 \times 24 = 3.84$ kN/m^2; $\qquad$ $P_{wf} = 1.25 \times 3.84 \times 7.6 / 2 = 18.2$ kN/m
$P_{tf} = (1.25 \times 1.0 + 0.5 \times 3.0)\, 10.9 / 2 = 15.0$ kN/m; $\qquad$ ecc $= 160 / 2 = 80$ mm
Axial load at mid height: $\qquad$ $P_f = 15.0 + 18.2 = 33.2$ kN/m: $\qquad$ $w_f = 1.4 \times 1.07 = 1.5$ kN/m^2

Assume reinforcing in center of section:
$A_s = $ 15M @ 250 $= 800$ mm^2/m $\qquad$ d $= 160 / 2 = 80$ mm; $\qquad$ b $= 1000$ mm

$A_{se} = \dfrac{.85 \times 800 \times 400 + 33.2 \times 1000}{.85 \times 400} = 898$ mm^2/m

$a_e = \dfrac{898 \times .85 \times 400}{.805 \times .65 \times 30 \times 1000} = 19.44$ mm

$M_r = .85 \times 898 \times 400\,(80 - 19.44 / 2) / 10^6 = 21.5$ kN-m/m

Bending stiffness (based on $A_s = 800$ mm^2):

$a = \dfrac{800 \times .85 \times 400}{.805 \times .65 \times 30 \times 1000} = 17.33$ mm; $\qquad$ $c = \dfrac{17.33}{.895} = 19.36$ mm

$I_{cr} = \dfrac{b\,c^3}{3} + \dfrac{E_s A_s (d - c)^2}{E_c} = \dfrac{1000 \times 19.36^3}{3} + \dfrac{200\,000 \times 800\,(80 - 19.36)^2}{24\,650} = 26.3 \times 10^6$ mm^4/m

$K_{bf} = \dfrac{48 \times 24\,650 \times 26.3 \times 10^6}{5 \times 7600^2 \times 1000} = 107.7$ kN-m/m

Moment magnifier: $\qquad$ $\delta_b = \dfrac{1}{1 - \dfrac{33.2}{.75 \times 107.7}} = 1.70$

$M_b = 1.5 \times 7.6^2 / 8 + 15 \times .08 / 2 + 33.2 \times .025 = 12.3$ kN-m/m
$M_f = 12.3 \times 1.70 = 20.9$ kN-m/m < 21.5 kN-m/m $\qquad$ OK

Total factored load deflection: $\qquad$ $\Delta_f = \dfrac{M_f}{\phi_m K_{bf}} = \dfrac{20.9 \times 1000}{0.75 \times 107.7} = 259$ mm

13

Tilt-up

Deflections at service loads

Load case   (1.0**D** + 1.0**W** + 0.5**S**)   ($I_w = 0.75$, $I_s = 0.9$)

w_c = 3.84 kN/m²; P_{ws} = 3.84 x 7.6 / 2 = 14.6 kN/m

P_{ts} = (1.0 + 0.5 x 0.9 x 3.0) 10.9 / 2 = 12.8 kN/m;   ecc = 80 mm

P_s = 12.8 + 14.6 = 27.4 kN/m; w_s = 0.75 x 1.07 = 0.80 kN/m²

I_g = 1000 x 160³ / 12 = 341 x 10⁶ mm⁴/m

Cracking moment: $M_{cr} = \dfrac{f_r I_g}{y_t} = \dfrac{0.6 \sqrt{30} \times 341}{160 / 2}$ = 14.0 kN-m/m

$M_{bs} = \dfrac{0.80 \times 7.6^2}{8} + \dfrac{12.8 \times .080}{2} + 27.4 \times .025$ = 6.97 kN-m/m

Initially assume $\Delta_s = \dfrac{\ell}{100} = \dfrac{7600}{100}$ = 76 mm

M_s = 6.97 + 27.4 x .076 = 9.05 < 14.0 kN-m/m; $\therefore I_e = I_g$ = 341 x 10⁶ mm⁴ /m

$K_{bs} = \dfrac{48\, E_c\, I_e}{5 \ell^2} = \dfrac{48 \times 24\,650 \times 341 \times 10^6}{5 \times 7600^2 \times 1000}$ = 1397 kN-m/m

$\delta_{bs} = \dfrac{1}{1 - \dfrac{P_s}{K_{bs}}} = \dfrac{1}{1 - \dfrac{27.4}{1397}}$ = 1.02

M_s = 6.97 x 1.02 = 7.11 < M_{cr} = 14.0 kN-m/m   OK

Panel design summary   (Load case (4) controls)
Vertical reinforcing: 15M @ 250 centered
Horizontal reinforcing: 10M @ 350

Reinforcement weight per m² = $\left(\dfrac{200}{250} + \dfrac{100}{350} \right)$ 7.85 kg = 8.52 kg/m²

$\therefore$ A thicker panel is required for 1 layer of reinforcement, but the total weight of reinforcement is about 15% less.

Example 13.2 – Panel Continuous over Support

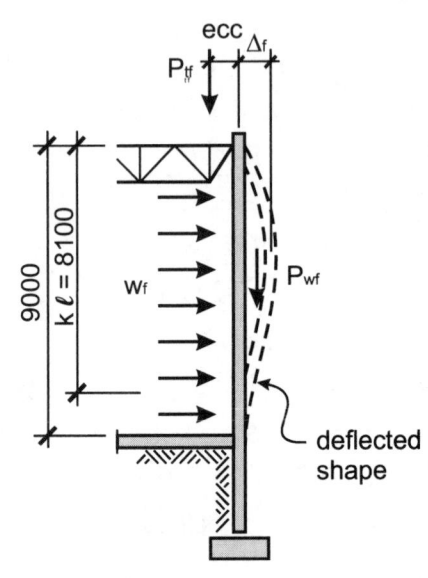

Assumed loading:
Roof dead load = 1.0 kPa;   snow load = 3.0 kPa
ecc = 140 / 2 = 70 mm;   joist span = 18 m
Wind load w = 1.07 kPa
Panel properties:
ℓ = 9000 mm, t = 140 mm, Δ_0 = 25 mm
Self weight w_c = .140 x 24 = 3.36 kN/m²
Check ℓ /t:

$\dfrac{9000}{140}$ = 64.2 < 65 $\therefore$ OK for 2 layers of reinforcement

Effective height   k ℓ = 0.9 x 9000 = 8100 mm

Load case (4): 1.25**D** + 1.4**W** + 0.5**S**

P_{tf} = (1.25 x 1.0 + 0.5 x 3.0) 18 / 2 = 24.75 kN/m

deflected shape

P_{wf} = 1.25 x 3.36 x 8.1 / 2 = 17.0 kN/m

P_f = 24.75 + 17.0 = 41.75 kN/m w_f = 1.4 x 1.07 = 1.5 kN/m^2

Assume reinforcing on each face (EF):

A_s = 15M @ 300 EF   or   667 mm^2/m EF;   d = 100 mm;   b = 1000 mm

A_{se} = $\dfrac{.85 \times 667 \times 400 + 41.75 \times 1000}{.85 \times 400}$ = 790 mm^2/m; M_r = 24.6 kN-m/m

M_b = 1.5 x 8.1^2 / 8 + 24.75 x .07 / 2 + 41.75 x .025 = 14.21 kN-m/m

I_{cr} = 39.5 x 10^6 mm^4/m; K_{bf} = 142.3 kN-m/m; δ_b = 1.64

M_f = 14.21 x 1.64 = 23.3 kN-m/m < 24.6 kN-m/m   OK

Load case (3): 1.25**D** + 1.5**S** + 0.4**W**

P_{tf} = (1.25 x 1.0 + 1.5 x 3.0) 18 / 2 = 51.75 kN/m

P_{wf} = 1.25 x 3.36 x 8.1 / 2 = 17.0 kN/m

P_f = 51.75 + 17.0 = 68.75 kN/m; w_f = 0.4 x 1.07 = .43 kN/m^2

A_s = 15M @ 300 EF   or   667 mm^2/m EF; A_{se} = 869 mm^2/m; M_r = 26.8 kN-m/m

M_b = 0.43 x 8.1^2 / 8 + 51.75 x .07 / 2 + 68.75 x .025 = 7.06 kN-m/m

I_{cr} = 39.5 x 10^6 mm^4; K_{bf} = 142.3 kN-m/m; δ_b = 2.81

M_f = 7.06 x 2.81 = 19.84 kN-m/m < 26.8   OK

Panel design summary   (Load case (4) controls)
Vertical reinforcing: 15M @ 300 EF
Horizontal reinforcing: 10M @ 350

Reinforcement weight per m^2 = $\left(\dfrac{200}{300} + \dfrac{100}{350} \right)$ x 7.85 kg = 7.48 kg/m^2

Example 13.3 – Panel with Openings

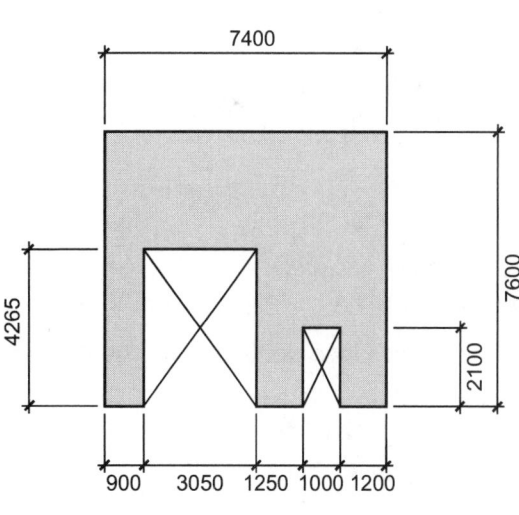

Panel properties:

ℓ = 7600 mm,   t = 160 mm, Δ_0 = 25 mm

Self weight w_c = .160 x 24 = 3.84 kN/m^2

Reinforcement on each face (EF), d = 120 mm

Assumed loading:

Roof dead load = 1.0 kPa; snow load = 3.0 kPa

ecc = 160 / 2 = 80 mm; joist span = 10.9 m

wind load w = 1.07 kPa

Assume load case (4): 1.25**D** + 1.4**W** + 0.5**S**

Left leg:

b = 900 mm

Tributary panel width = $900 + \dfrac{3050}{2}$ = 2425 mm

P_{tf} = 2.425 (1.25 x 1.0 + 0.5 x 3.0) 10.9 / 2 = 36.3 kN

P_{wf} = 2.425 (1.25 x 3.84) 7.6 / 2 = 44.2 kN

P_f = 36.3 + 44.2 = 80.5 kN; w_f = 2.425 (1.4 x 1.07) = 3.63 kN/m

A_s = 5-15M = 1000 mm^2 EF

A_{se} = $\dfrac{.85 \times 1000 \times 400 + 80.5 \times 1000}{.85 \times 400}$ = 1237 mm²; M_r = 44.2 kN-m

M_b = 3.63 x 7.6² / 8 + 36.3 x .08 / 2 + 80.5 x .025 = 29.7 kN-m

I_{cr} = 76.17 x 10⁶ mm⁴; K_{bf} = 312 kN-m/m; δ_b = 1.53

M_f = 29.7 x 1.53 = 45.4 kN-m/m ≈ 44.2 kN-m   OK

Middle leg:

b   = 1250 mm;   Tributary panel width = $1250 + \dfrac{(3050 + 1000)}{2}$ = 3275 mm

P_{tf} = 3.275 (1.25 x 1.0 + 0.5 x 3.0) 10.9 / 2 = 49.1 kN

P_{wf} = 3.275 (1.25 x 3.84) 7.6 / 2 = 59.7 kN

P_f = 49.1 + 59.7 = 108.8 kN w_f = 3.275 (1.4 x 1.07) = 4.91 kN/m

A_s = 7-15M = 1400 mm² EF;

A_{se} = $\dfrac{.85 \times 1400 \times 400 + 108.8 \times 1000}{.85 \times 400}$ = 1720 mm²; M_r = 61.45 kN-m

M_b = 4.91 x 7.6² / 8 + 49.1 x .08 / 2 + 108.8 x .025 = 40.1 kN-m

K_{bf} = 435.5 kN-m/m; δ_b = 1.50

M_f = 40.1x 1.50 = 60.2 kN-m/m < 61.45 kN-m   OK

Check for maximum reinforcement:

$\dfrac{A_s}{bd}$ ≤ $\dfrac{\alpha_1 \beta_1 \phi c\, f'_c}{\phi s\, f_y} \left(\dfrac{700}{700 + f_y} \right)$ = 0.0263

max A_s = 0.0263 x 120 x 1250 = 3945 > 1400 mm²   OK

Right leg:

b   = 1200 mm;   Tributary panel width = $1200 + \dfrac{1000}{2}$ = 1700 mm

P_{tf} = 1.700 (1.25 x 1.0 + 0.5 x 3.0) 10.9 / 2 = 25.5 kN

P_{wf} = 1.700 (1.25 x 3.84) 7.6 / 2 = 31.0 kN

P_f = 25.5 + 31.0 = 56.5 kN; w_f = 1.700 (1.4 x 1.07) = 2.55 kN/m

A_s = 4-15M = 800 mm² EF; A_{se} = $\dfrac{.85 \times 800 \times 400 + 56.5 \times 1000}{.85 \times 400}$ = 966 mm²; M_r = 36.6 kN-m

M_b = 2.55 x 7.6² / 8 + 25.5 x .08 / 2 + 56.5 x .025 = 20.8 kN-m

K_{bf} = 293.9 kN-m/m; δ_b = 1.35

M_f = 20.8 x 1.35 = 28.1 kN-m/m < 36.6 kN-m   OK

Check service load deflection on the middle leg:

Tributary width = 3275 mm;

Leg width b = 1250 mm

A_s = 7-15M EF = 1400 mm²

w   = 0.75 x 1.07 = 0.8 kN/m²;

w_c = 3.84 kN/m²

Assume load case: 1.0**D** + 1.0**W** + 0.5**S**

P_{ts} = 3.275 (1.0 + 0.5 x 0.9 x 3.0) 10.9 / 2 = 41.9 kN

P_{ws} = 3.275 (3.84 x 7.6 / 2) = 47.8 kN

P_s = 41.9 + 47.8 = 89.7 kN

I_g = 1250 x 160³ / 12 = 427 x 10⁶ mm⁴

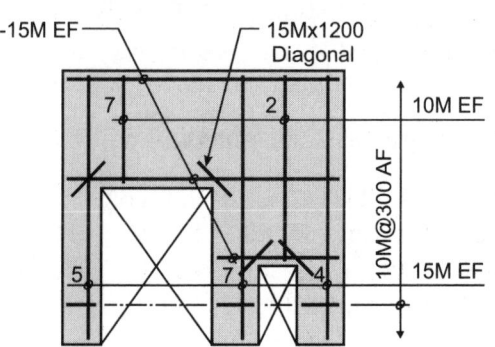

Panel Reinforcement

$$M_{cr} = \frac{f_r I_g}{y_t} = \frac{0.6\sqrt{30} \times 427}{160/2} = 17.5 \text{ kN-m}$$

$$M_{bs} = 3.275\left(\frac{0.80 \times 7.6^2}{8}\right) + \frac{41.9 \times .080}{2} + 89.7 \times .025 = 22.8 > M_{cr} = 17.5 \text{ kN-m}$$

$\therefore \quad I_{cr} < I_e < I_g; \qquad$ determine I_c by trial

$A_s = 1400 \text{ mm}^2;$

Using a triangular concrete stress distribution:

$$n = \frac{E_s}{E_c} = 8.11; \qquad\qquad kd = \frac{-n A_s + \sqrt{(n A_s)^2 + 2 b n A_s d}}{b}$$

$$kd = \frac{-8.11 \times 1400 + \sqrt{(8.11 \times 1400)^2 + 2 \times 1250 \times 8.11 \times 1400 \times 120}}{1250} = 38.5 \text{ mm}$$

$$I_{cr} = \frac{b(kd)^3}{3} + \frac{E_s A_s (kd-c)^2}{E_c} = \frac{1250 \times 38.5^3}{3} + \frac{200\,000 \times 1400 (120 - 38.5)^2}{24\,650}$$

$$= 99.2 \times 10^6 \text{ mm}^4$$

Initially assume $\Delta_s = \dfrac{\ell}{100} = \dfrac{7600}{100} = 76 \text{ mm};$ $M_s = M_{bs} + P_s \Delta_s = 22.8 + 89.7 \times .076 = 29.6 \text{ kN-m}$

$$I_e = I_{cr} + (I_g - I_{cr})\left(\frac{M_{cr}}{M_s}\right)^3 = 99.2 + (427 - 99.2)\left(\frac{17.5}{29.6}\right)^3 = 167 \times 10^6 \text{ mm}^4$$

$$K_{bs} = \frac{48 \times 24\,650 \times 167 \times 10^6}{5 \times 7600^2 \times 1000} = 684 \text{ kN-m/m}; \qquad \delta_b = \frac{1}{1 - \dfrac{P_s}{K_{bs}}} = \frac{1}{1 - \dfrac{89.7}{684}} = 1.15$$

$M_s = 22.8 \times 1.15 = 26.2 < 29.6 \text{ kN-m} \qquad$ OK

$\Delta_s = \dfrac{M_s}{K_{bs}} = \dfrac{26.2 \times 1000}{684} = 38 \text{ mm} < \Delta_{max} = 76 \text{ mm} \quad$ OK $(\therefore$ no need for further iterations)

Tilt-up Panel Shear Walls

The following examples illustrate the design of simple tilt-up concrete shear walls subjected to in-plane seismic forces. They represent the end wall of a 66.4 m x 27.4 m x 7.6 m high single storey building located in Langley B.C. The roof construction is assumed to be structural framing with a steel deck diaphragm. The seismic analysis of the overall building is not part of this example. The specified seismic force is 0.777 W before R_d or R_o reductions are applied. The shear force from the roof diaphragm to the top of the wall is 1904 kN. The panels can be designed for $R_d = 1.5$ and $R_o = 1.3$ as "Conventional Construction". Specific components within the panel system have to be designed for reduced R-values depending on their ductility.

Example 13.4   Shear Wall with Solid Panels

Given:

Panel thickness	t	=	140 mm		
Concrete	f'_c	=	30 MPa;	unit weight	$\gamma = 24 \text{ kN}/\text{m}^3$
Tributary roof weight		=	3 kN / m	(roof dead load only)	
Maximum hold down weight at corner		=	100 kN		

13

Tilt-up

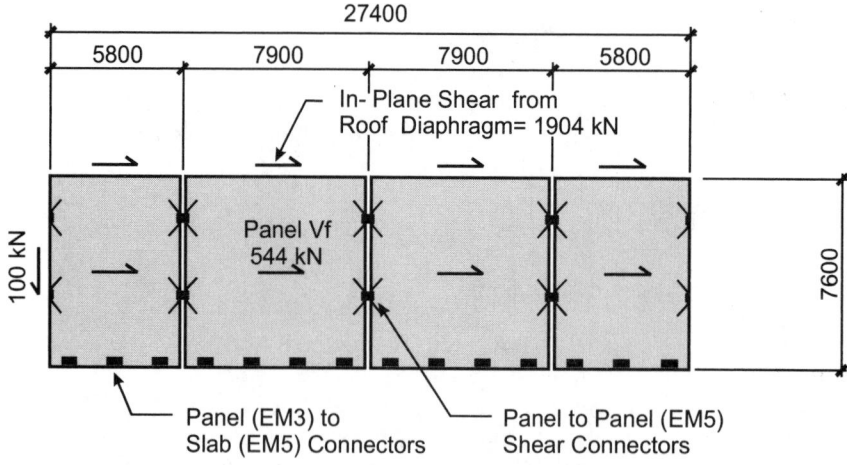

Roof weight   =   17 +   24 +   24 +   17 =   82 kN
Panel weight = 148 + 202 + 202 + 148 = 700 kN
                                              Total   782 kN

Panel seismic   115 + 157 + 157 + 115 = 544 kN

Base shear: ($R_d R_o = 1.0$)

Roof diaphragm V_f =   1904 kN
Panel seismic shear V_f =   .777 x 700 =   544
                                   Total   =   2448 kN

Check maximum concrete shear: ($R_d R_o = 1.0$)
V_f ≤ $0.25 \, \phi_c \, f'_c \, t \, d_v$ $d_v = 0.8 \times 27.4 = 21.92$ m
V_f =   2448 < 0.25 x 0.65 x 30 x 140 x 21.92 = 14, 960 > 2448 kN   OK
Panel shear resistance: ($R_d R_o = 1.0$)
v_c = $\phi_c \lambda \beta \sqrt{f'_c}$ = 0.65 x 1.0 x .18 $\sqrt{30}$ = 0.64 MPa
V_c = $v_c \, b_w \, d_v$ = 0.64 x 140 x 21.92 = 1964 kN
V_s = $\dfrac{\phi_s \, A_v \, f_y \, d_v \cot \theta}{s} = \dfrac{.486 \, A_v \, d_v}{s}$

Distributed reinforcement A_v = 10M @ 350; $\rho = \dfrac{100}{350 \times 140}$ = .00204 > .002   OK

V_s = $\dfrac{.486 \times 100 \times 21920}{350}$ = 3044 kN
Total V_r = 1964 + 3044 = 5008 kN > 2448 kN   OK
Average V_r = 5008 / 27.4 = 183 kN/m

Base connections:
Assume welded connections with studded embedments   ($R_d = 1.0$, $R_o = 1.3$)
EM3 V_r = 110 kN   in panel ← controls
EM5 V_r = 125 kN   in floor slab
Req'd V_f = $\dfrac{2448}{1.0 \times 1.3}$ = 1883 kN
Less friction =   0.5 x 782 = 391 kN;   net V_f = 1492 kN

No. req'd $= \dfrac{1492}{110} = 13.6 \rightarrow$ use 14 - EM3 / EM5 connectors

Alternate: 15M dowels ($R_d = 1.5$, $R_o = 1.3$)

$V_r = \phi_c \, \mu \, A_v \, f_y = \dfrac{0.65 \times 0.6 \times 200 \times 400}{1000} = 31$ kN, each dowel

Req'd $V_f = \dfrac{2448}{1.5 \times 1.3} - 391 = 864$ kN

No. req'd $= \dfrac{864}{31} = 27.9 \rightarrow 28$ - 15M dowels @ 1000 mm

Panel overturning: ($R_d = 1.5$, $R_o = 1.3$)

Roof $V_f = \dfrac{1904}{1.5 \times 1.3} = 976$ kN; Panel $V_f = \dfrac{544}{1.5 \times 1.3} = 279$ kN

Overturning moment: $M_{of} = 976 \times 7.6 + 279 \times 7.6 / 2 = 8480$ kN-m

Resisting moments:

Panel $M_r = \dfrac{2 \times 148 \times 5.8}{2} + \dfrac{2 \times 202 \times 7.9}{2} = 2454$ kN-m

Roof $M_r = \dfrac{2 \times 17 \times 5.8}{2} + \dfrac{2 \times 24 \times 7.9}{2} = 288$

End Conn. $= 100 \times 5.8 = \underline{580}$

$\qquad\qquad\qquad\qquad$ Total $= 3322 < 8480$ kN-m

Difference $= 8480 - 3322 = 5158$ kN-m

Try 2- EM5 edge connections per panel, $V_r = 125$ kN each

Required connection resistance $= \dfrac{5158}{2\,(7.9 + 7.9 + 5.8)} = 119.5$ kN < 125 kN $\qquad$ OK

$\qquad\qquad\qquad\qquad\qquad$ or $\quad$ 239 kN each panel

Resolution of forces: ($R_d = 1.5$, $R_o = 1.3$)

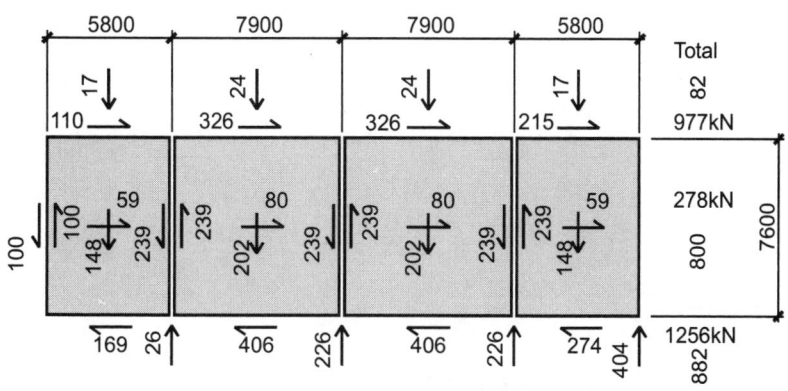

Panel $M_r = 1059 + 2780 + 2780 + 1865 = 8484$ kN-m

Maximum shear force in the panels $= 404 / 7.6 = 53 < 183$ kN/m

Maximum foundation load $= 404$ kN, based on $R_d = 1.5$ and $R_o = 1.3$. Foundation loads indicated may not be point loads, depending on the type of foundations selected. The distribution of roof shears forces to the top of the panel is controlled by the overturning capacity and are not necessarily in proportion to the panel width. A drag strut, such as a steel angle is needed to provide the redistribution of shear force.

Example 13.5   Shear Wall with Frame Panels

Given:

Panel thickness	t	=	240 mm
Concrete	f'_c =		30 MPa
Unit weight	γ	=	24 kN/m^3
Tributary roof weight		=	3 kN/m
Maximum hold down weight at corner		=	100 kN

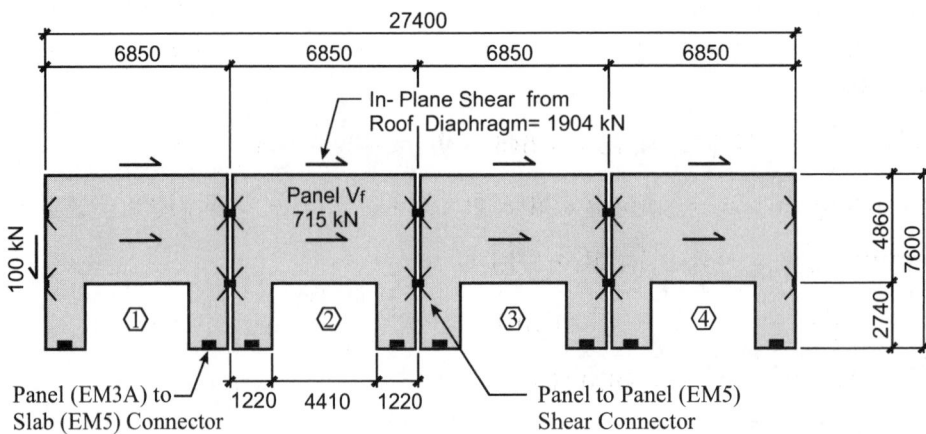

Roof weight = 3 x 6.85 = 21 kN on each panel

Panel weight = 24 (6.85 x 7.6 – 4.41 x 2.74) .240 = 230 kN each

Panel C of G = $\dfrac{24 (6.85 \times 7.6^2 / 2 - 4.41 \times 2.74^2 / 2).240}{230}$ = 4.54 m (from bottom)

Base shear: ($R_d R_o = 1.0$)

Roof diaphragm V_f = 1904 kN

Panel shear V_f = .777 x 4 x 230 = 715 kN

Total = 2620 kN

Check concrete shear in legs:

V_f = 2620 / 8 = 328 kN, each leg

h = 1220 mm d = 1220 – 75 = 1145 mm d_v = 0.9 x 1145 = 1030 mm

Check $h / t = \dfrac{1220}{240}$ = 5.1 > 4.0   OK

Max V_r = 0.25 x 0.65 x 30 x 240 x 1.030 = 1205 > 328 kN   OK

Panel leg shear resistance:

V_c = 0.64 x 240 x 1.030 = 158 kN

A_v = 10M ties @ 300   (maximum spacing) $V_s = \dfrac{.486 \times 200 \times 1030}{300}$ = 334 kN

Tot. V_f = 158 + 334 = 492 kN > 328 kN   OK

Base connections:

Assume welded connections with studded embedments   ($R_d = 1.0$, $R_o = 1.3$)

V_f = $\dfrac{2620}{1.0 \times 1.3}$ = 2015 kN

8 - EM3A connections V_r = 130 kN V_r = 8 x 130 = 1040 kN

Check concrete bearing where slab (25 MPa concrete, 200 mm thick) is locked into the panels:

V_r = 0.85 ϕ_c f'_c A_g = 0.85 x 0.65 x 25 x 240 x 200 / 1000 = 663 kN

Friction V_r = 0.5 (21 + 230) 4 = 502 kN

Total V_r = 1040 + 663 + 502 = 2205 < 2015 kN   OK

In-plane leg bending: (R_d =1.5, R_o = 1.3)

V_f = $\dfrac{2620}{8(1.5 \times 1.3)}$ = 168 kN, each leg

M_f = 168 x 2.74 = 460 kN-m

h = 1220 mm,   d = 1145 mm,   t = 240 mm

A_s = 3 – 25M = 1500 mm^2

M_r = $\dfrac{0.85 \times 400 \times 1500}{10^6}$ (1145 – 75) = 545 > 460 kN-m   OK

Tie spacing in hinge region = 8d_b = 8 x 25 = 200 mm $\therefore$ use 10M ties @ 200

Panel overturning: (R_d = 1.5 R_o = 1.3)

Roof V_f = $\dfrac{1904}{1.5 \times 1.3}$ = 976 kN   Panel V_f = $\dfrac{715}{1.5 \times 1.3}$ = 367 kN

M_{of} = 976 x 7.6 + 367 x 4.54 = 9084 kN-m

Resisting moments:

Panel M_r = $\dfrac{4 \times 230 \times 6.85}{2}$ = 3151 kN-m;

Roof M_r = $\dfrac{4 \times 21 \times 6.85}{2}$ = 288 kN-m

End Conn. = 100 x 6.85 = 685

                    Total = 4124 < 9084 kN-m

Difference = 9084 – 4124 = 4960 kN-m

Try 2- EM5 Connections per panel   Vr = 125 kN each   (R_d = 1.5, R_o = 1.3)

Required connection force = $\dfrac{4960}{2 \times 3 \times 6.85}$ = 121 kN < 125 kN   OK

Resolution of forces: (R_d = 1.5 R_o = 1.3)

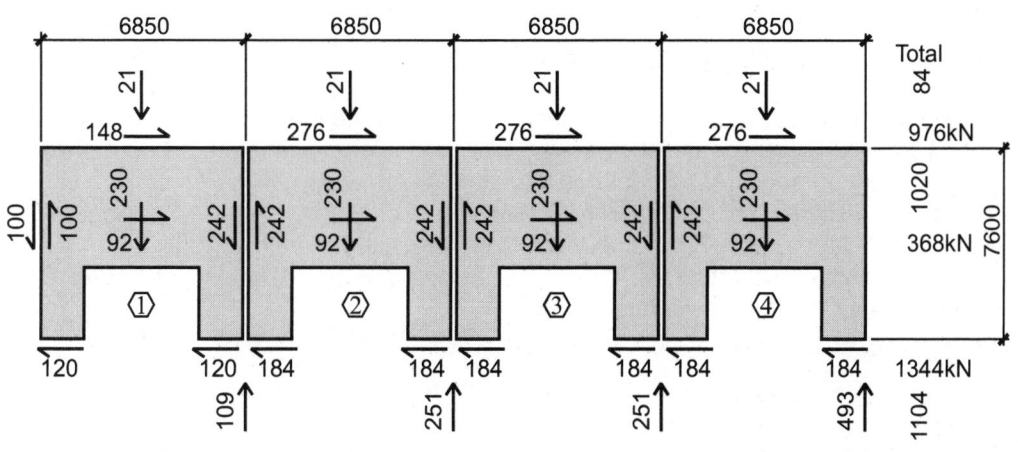

Section through panel leg (10M ties @ 200, 3-25M each end, 3-20M EF, 1220, 240)

13

Tilt-up

Check beam header in panel #3 for bending and shear:

From overturning analysis at $R_d = 1.5$, $R_o = 1.3$:

$\max V_f = 242 + 21 / 2 + 230 / 2 = 367.5$ kN

$M_f = 367.5 \times 3.425 + 10.5 \times 1.738 + 115 \times 1.53$
$\qquad - 138 \times 7.6 - 46 \times 4.54 = 195$ kN-m

$h = 4860$ mm $d = 4860 - 75 = 4785$ mm

Assume $A_s = 2 - 150M = 400$ mm^2

$M_r = \dfrac{0.85 \times 400 \times 400}{10^6}(4785 - 75) = 641 > 195$ kN-m

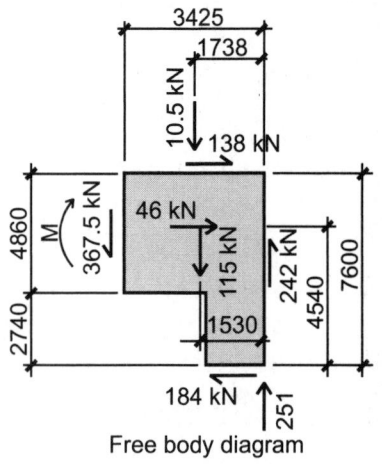

Free body diagram

Check for potential yielding of longitudinal reinforcement:

Multiply moment by $R_d = 1.5$, $R_o = 1.3$:

$M_f = 195 \times 1.5 \times 1.3 = 380$ kN-m < 641

$\therefore$ reinforcement will not yield and anti-buckling ties not required in header

use 10M @ 400 EW; $A_s = 500$ mm^2/m; $\rho = .0021 > .002$

Check shear in header, multiply by $R_d = 1.5$, $R_o = 1.3$:

$V_f = 367.5 \times 1.5 \times 1.3 = 716$ kN

$d_v = 0.9 \times 4785 = 4300$ mm

$V_c = \dfrac{0.64 \times 240 \times 4300}{1000} = 661$ kN

$V_s = \dfrac{.486 \times 200 \times 4300}{400} = 1045$ kN

$V_r = 661 + 1045 = 1706$ kN > 716 kN   OK

References

1.   Recommended Tilt-up Wall Panel Design, Structural Engineers Association of Southern California, 1979

2.   Test Report on Slender Walls, Southern California Chapter, American Concrete Association and Structural Engineers Association of Southern California, 1982.

3.   Approximate Methods for Analysis of Tilt-up Concrete Wall Panels, G. Weiler, ACI International, November, 1982.

4.   Spencer, R.A., Earthquake Resistant Connections for Low Rise Concrete Buildings, U.S./Japan Seminar on Precast Concrete Construction in Seismic Zones, October 1986, pp 61-81

5.   Weiler, G.J., Connections for Tilt-up Construction, Concrete International, June 1986.

6.   Kevin Lemieux, Robert Sexsmith, Gerry Weiler, Behavior of Embedded Steel Connectors in Concrete Tilt-up Panels, ACI Structural Journal, July-August 1998.

7.   Michael Dew, Robert Sexsmith, Gerry Weiler, Effect of Hinge Zone Tie Spacing on Ductility of Concrete Tilt-up Frame Panels, ACI Structural Journal, November, 2001.

8.   Tilt-up Concrete Association, Guideline for Temporary Wind Bracing of Tilt-up Concrete Panels During Construction, January 2005.